INSTRUCTOR'S SOLUTIONS MANUAL
TO ACCOMPANY

HOLT CALCULUS
WITH ANALYTIC GEOMETRY

ROBERT ELLIS
University of Maryland
at College Park

DENNY GULICK
University of Maryland
at College Park

Holt, Rinehart and Winston, Inc.
Harcourt Brace & Company
Austin • New York • Orlando • Chicago • Atlanta
San Francisco • Boston • Dallas • Toronto • London

Preface

The Instructor's Resource and Solutions Manual contains complete solutions to all exercises in Chapters 1–12 of *Holt Calculus with Analytic Geometry.* Our aim has been to provide all the details necessary for full understanding of the solutions. In each solution we have endeavored to include all important steps, so that instructors and students can easily follow the line of reasoning. Where possible, solutions are patterned after the examples in the corresponding text section.

The solutions to the exercises have been carefully checked. We would be grateful to have any residual errors in either the Instructor's Solutions Manual or the textbook brought to our attention.

Finally, we wish to give special thanks to Professor Dennis Kletzing, of Stetson University, who typeset (using TEX) the solutions manual with great care and accuracy.

Robert Ellis
Denny Gulick

Printed in the United States of America

Ellis and Gulick: Instructor's Solutions Manual to accompany *Holt Calculus with Analytic Geometry,* by Robert Ellis and Denny Gulick

ISBN 0-03-006916-5

Contents

Chapter 1

Functions

1.1 The Real Numbers

1. Notice that $4 \cdot 16 = 64 > 63 = 9 \cdot 7$. Multiplying by the positive number $1/(9 \cdot 16)$, we have $(4 \cdot 16)/(9 \cdot 16) > (9 \cdot 7)/(9 \cdot 16)$ or $\frac{4}{9} > \frac{7}{16}$. Therefore, $a > b$.

2. Notice that $7 \cdot (0.142857) = 0.999999 < 1$. Multiplying by the *negative* number $-\frac{1}{7}$, we have that $-7 \cdot (0.142857)/7 > -\frac{1}{7}$ or $-0.142857 > -\frac{1}{7}$. Therefore $a < b$.

3. Since $\pi^2 > (3.14)^2 = 9.8596$, we have $a > b$.

4. Since $(3.2)^2 = 10.24$, $a > b$.

5. $(1.41)^2 = 1.9881 < 2$, so $\sqrt{2} > 1.41$.

6. $(3.3)^2 = 10.89 < 11$, so $\sqrt{11} > 3.3$.

7. Closed, bounded: x -4 5

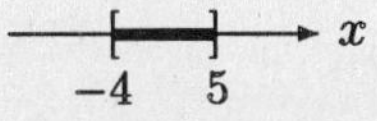

8. Open, bounded: x -2 -1

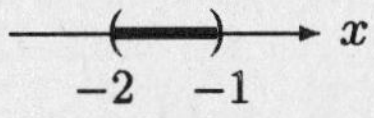

9. Open, unbounded: x 3

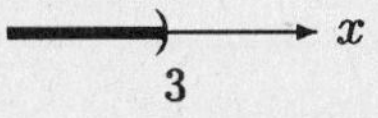

10. Half-open, bounded: x $\frac{3}{2}$ $\frac{5}{2}$

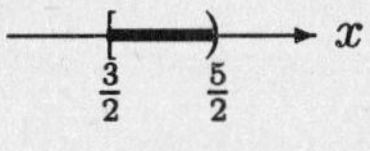

11. Closed, unbounded: x 0

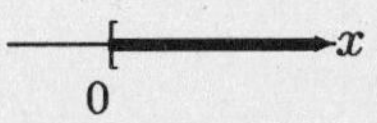

12. Open, bounded x 5 7

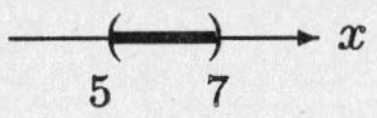

13. Closed, unbounded: x -1

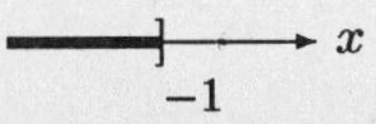

14. Closed, bounded: 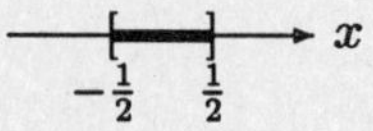

15. $(-3, 4)$

16. $(-\infty, 3)$

17. $(1, \infty)$

18. $(-\infty, \infty)$

19. If $-6x - 2 > 5$, then $-6x > 7$, so $x < -\frac{7}{6}$. Thus the solution is $(-\infty, -\frac{7}{6})$.

20. If $4 - 3x \geq 7$, then $-3x \geq 3$, so $x \leq -1$. Thus the solution is $(-\infty, -1]$.

21. If $-1 \leq 2x - 3 < 4$, then $2 \leq 2x < 7$, so $1 \leq x < \frac{7}{2}$. Thus the solution is $[1, \frac{7}{2})$.

22. If $-0.1 < 3x + 4 < 0.1$, then $-4.1 < 3x < -3.9$, so $-4.1/3 < x < -1.3$. Thus the solution is $(-4.1/3, -1.3)$.

23. From the diagram we see that the solution is the union of $(-\infty, -\frac{1}{2}]$ and $[1, \infty)$.

$x - 1$	−	−	−	−	−	−	−	0	+	+	+
$x + \frac{1}{2}$	−	−	0	+	+	+	+	+	+	+	+
$(x-1)(x+\frac{1}{2})$	+	+	0	−	−	−	−	0	+	+	+

24. From the diagram we see that the solution is the union of $(-\infty, 1]$ and $[2, 3]$.

$x - 1$	−	−	0	+	+	+	+	+	+	+	+
$x - 2$	−	−	−	−	−	0	+	+	+	+	+
$x - 3$	−	−	−	−	−	−	−	−	0	+	+
$(x-1)(x-2)(x-3)$	−	−	0	+	+	0	−	−	0	+	+

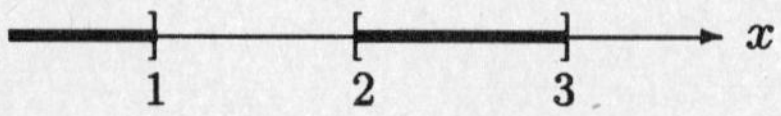

25. From the diagram we see that the solution is the union of $(-\infty, -\frac{1}{3})$ and $(0, \frac{2}{3})$.

x	−	−	−	−	0	+	+	+	+	+	+
$x - \frac{2}{3}$	−	−	−	−	−	−	−	−	0	+	+
$x + \frac{1}{3}$	−	−	0	+	+	+	+	+	+	+	+
$x(x-\frac{2}{3})(x+\frac{1}{3})$	−	−	0	+	0	−	−	−	0	+	+

26. From the diagram we see that the solution is the union of $(-2, 0)$ and $(1, \infty)$.

x	$- - - - - - 0 + + + +$
$x-1$	$- - - - - - - - 0 + +$
$x+2$	$- - 0 + + + + + + + +$
$\dfrac{x}{(x-1)(x+2)}$	$- - \quad + + + 0 - \quad + +$

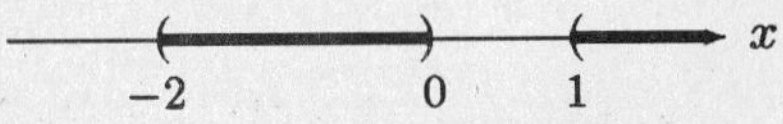

$-2 \quad 0 \quad 1 \quad x$

27. From the diagram we see that the solution is the union of $(-\infty, -3)$ and $(-1, \infty)$.

$(2x-1)^2$	$+ + + + + + + + + 0 +$
$x+1$	$- - - - - - 0 + + + +$
$x+3$	$- - 0 + + + + + + + +$
$\dfrac{(2x-1)^2}{(x+1)(x+3)}$	$+ + \quad - - - \quad + + 0 +$

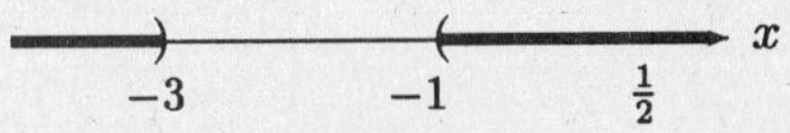

$-3 \quad -1 \quad \frac{1}{2} \quad x$

28. From the diagram we see that the solution is the union of $(-\infty, -\frac{1}{4}]$ and $[\frac{3}{2}, 2)$.

$2x-3$	$- - - - - - - 0 + + +$
$4x+1$	$- 0 + + + + + + + + +$
$x-2$	$- - - - - - - - - 0 +$
$\dfrac{(2x-3)(4x+1)}{x-2}$	$- 0 + + + + + 0 - \quad +$

$-\frac{1}{4} \quad \frac{3}{2} \quad 2 \quad x$

29. The given inequality is equivalent to $2x^2(2x-3) \leq 0$. From the diagram we see that the solution is $(-\infty, \frac{3}{2}]$.

x^2	$+ + 0 + + + + + + + +$
$2x-3$	$- - - - - - - 0 + + +$
$2x^2(2x-3)$	$- - 0 - - - - 0 + + +$

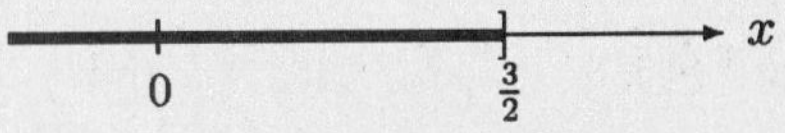

$0 \quad \frac{3}{2} \quad x$

30. The given inequality is equivalent to $(3x+1)(x-1) \geq 0$. From the diagram we see that the solution is the union of $(-\infty, -\frac{1}{3}]$ and $[1, \infty)$.

$3x+1$	$-\ -\ 0\ +\ +\ +\ +\ +\ +\ +\ +$
$x-1$	$-\ -\ -\ -\ -\ -\ -\ 0\ +\ +\ +$
$(3x+1)(x-1)$	$+\ +\ 0\ -\ -\ -\ -\ 0\ +\ +\ +$

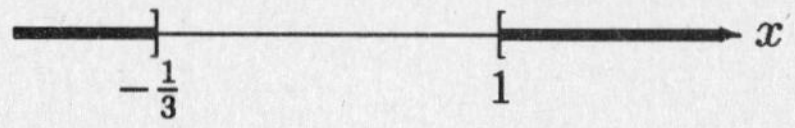

$-\frac{1}{3}$ $\quad$ 1 $\quad$ x

31. The given inequality is equivalent to $(8x^3-1)/x^2 > 0$. From the diagram we see that the solution is $(\frac{1}{2}, \infty)$.

$8x^3-1$	$-\ -\ -\ -\ -\ -\ -\ 0\ +\ +\ +$
x^2	$+\ +\ 0\ +\ +\ +\ +\ +\ +\ +\ +$
$\dfrac{8x^3-1}{x^2}$	$-\ -\quad -\ -\ -\ -\ 0\ +\ +\ +$

0 $\quad$ $\frac{1}{2}$ $\quad$ x

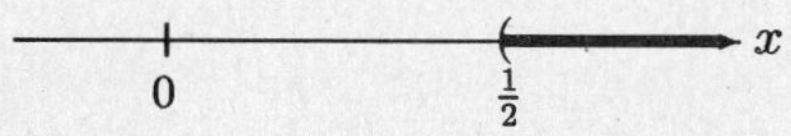

32. The given inequality is equivalent to $(8x^3+1)/x^2 < 0$. From the diagram we see that the solution is $(-\infty, -\frac{1}{2})$.

$8x^3+1$	$-\ -\ 0\ +\ +\ +\ +\ +\ +\ +\ +$
x^2	$+\ +\ +\ +\ +\ +\ +\ 0\ +\ +\ +$
$\dfrac{8x^3+1}{x^2}$	$-\ -\ 0\ +\ +\ +\ +\quad +\ +\ +$

$-\frac{1}{2}$ $\quad$ 0 $\quad$ x

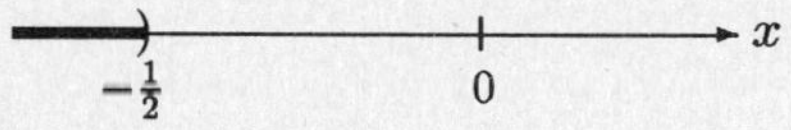

33. The given inequality is equivalent to

$$\frac{4x(x+\sqrt{6})(x-\sqrt{6})}{(x+2)(x-2)} < 0.$$

From the diagram we see that the solution is the union of $(-\infty, -\sqrt{6})$, $(-2, 0)$, and $(2, \sqrt{6})$.

x	$-\ -\ -\ -\ -\ 0\ +\ +\ +\ +\ +$
$x+\sqrt{6}$	$-\ 0\ +\ +\ +\ +\ +\ +\ +\ +\ +$
$x-\sqrt{6}$	$-\ -\ -\ -\ -\ -\ -\ -\ -\ 0\ +$
$x+2$	$-\ -\ -\ 0\ +\ +\ +\ +\ +\ +\ +$
$x-2$	$-\ -\ -\ -\ -\ -\ -\ 0\ +\ +\ +$
$\dfrac{4x(x+\sqrt{6})(x-\sqrt{6})}{(x+2)(x-2)}$	$-\ 0\ +\quad -\ 0\ +\quad -\ 0\ +$

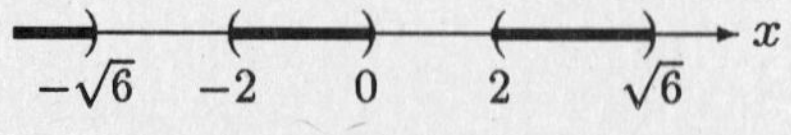

$-\sqrt{6}$ $\quad$ -2 $\quad$ 0 $\quad$ 2 $\quad$ $\sqrt{6}$ $\quad$ x

34. Since $(x^2+1)^3 > 0$ for all x, the given inequality is equivalent to $2x(x+\sqrt{3})(x-\sqrt{3}) \geq 0$. From the diagram we see that the solution is the union of $[-\sqrt{3}, 0]$ and $[\sqrt{3}, \infty)$.

x	$- - - - - 0 + + + +$
$x+\sqrt{3}$	$- - 0 + + + + + + + +$
$x-\sqrt{3}$	$- - - - - - - - - 0 + +$
$2x(x+\sqrt{3})(x+\sqrt{3})$	$- - 0 + + 0 - - 0 + +$

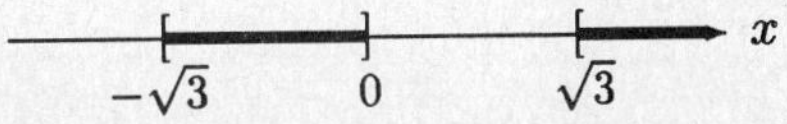

$-\sqrt{3}$ $\quad 0 \quad$ $\sqrt{3}$ $\quad x$

35. The given inequality is equivalent to

$$\frac{(t+2)(t-1)}{(t+1)^3(t-1)^3} \geq 0 \quad \text{or} \quad \frac{t+2}{(t+1)^3(t-1)^2} \geq 0.$$

From the diagram we see that the solution is the union of $(-\infty, -2]$, $(-1, 1)$, and $(1, \infty)$.

$t+2$	$- - 0 + + + + + + + +$
$(t+1)^3$	$- - - - 0 + + + + + +$
$(t-1)^2$	$+ + + + + + + + 0 + +$
$\dfrac{t+2}{(t+1)^3(t-1)^2}$	$+ + 0 - \quad + + + \quad + +$

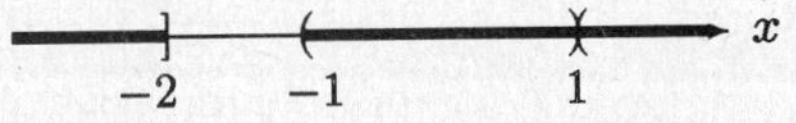

-2 $\quad -1$ $\quad 1$ $\quad x$

36. The given inequality is equivalent to

$$\frac{(t+1)(t-3)}{(t-5)(t-3)} > 0,$$

that is, $(t+1)/(t-5) > 0$ and $t \neq 3$. From the diagram we see that the solution is the union of $(-\infty, -1)$ and $(5, \infty)$.

$t+1$	$- - 0 + + + + + + + +$
$t-5$	$- - - - - - - - - 0 + +$
$\dfrac{(t+1)(t-3)}{(t-5)(t-3)}$	$+ + 0 - - - \quad - \quad + +$

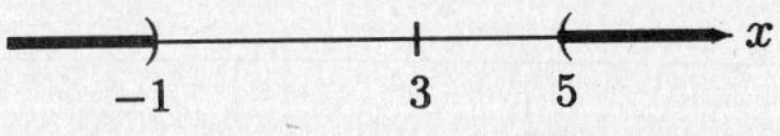

-1 $\quad 3$ $\quad 5$ $\quad x$

37. Observe that $\sqrt{9-6x}$ is defined only for $x \leq \frac{9}{6} = \frac{3}{2}$ and that $\sqrt{9-6x} > 0$ for $x < \frac{3}{2}$. Thus the given inequality is equivalent to the pair of inequalities $x < \frac{3}{2}$ and $2 - x > 0$ (that is, $x < 2$). Thus the solution is $(-\infty, \frac{3}{2})$.

38. Observe that $(1-x^2)^{1/2}$ is defined only for $-1 \leq x \leq 1$ and that $(1-x^2)^{1/2} > 0$ for $-1 < x < 1$. Moreover, $2x^2 - 1 = 2(x+\sqrt{2}/2)(x-\sqrt{2}/2)$. Thus the given inequality is equivalent to the pair of

inequalities $-1 < x < 1$ and $2(x+\sqrt{2}/2)(x-\sqrt{2}/2) < 0$ (that is, $-\sqrt{2}/2 < x < \sqrt{2}/2$). Thus the solution is $(-\sqrt{2}/2, \sqrt{2}/2)$.

39. The given inequality is equivalent to

$$\frac{1}{x+1} - \frac{3}{2} > 0 \quad \text{or} \quad \frac{-3(x+\frac{1}{3})}{2(x+1)} > 0.$$

From the diagram we see that the solution is $(-1, -\frac{1}{3})$.

$x+\frac{1}{3}$	− − − − − − − − − 0 + +
$x+1$	− − 0 + + + + + + + +
$\dfrac{-3(x+\frac{1}{3})}{2(x+1)}$	− − + + + + + 0 − −

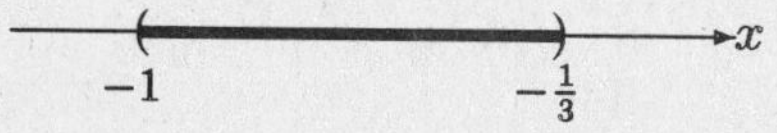

-1 $\quad -\frac{1}{3}$ $\quad x$

40. The given inequality is equivalent to

$$\frac{1}{3-x} + 2 < 0, \quad \text{or} \quad \frac{-2(x-\frac{7}{2})}{3-x} < 0.$$

From the diagram we see that the solution is $(3, \frac{7}{2})$.

$x-\frac{7}{2}$	− − − − − − − − − 0 + +
$3-x$	+ + 0 − − − − − − − −
$\dfrac{-2(x-\frac{7}{2})}{3-x}$	+ + − − − − − 0 + +

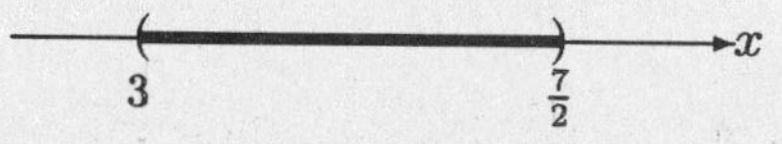

3 $\quad \frac{7}{2}$ $\quad x$

41. The given inequality is equivalent to

$$\frac{x+1}{x-1} - \frac{1}{2} \le 0, \quad \text{or} \quad \frac{x+3}{2(x-1)} \le 0.$$

From the diagram we see that the solution is $[-3, 1)$.

$x+3$	− − 0 + + + + + + + +
$x-1$	− − − − − − − − − 0 + +
$\dfrac{x+3}{2(x-1)}$	+ + 0 − − − − − − + +

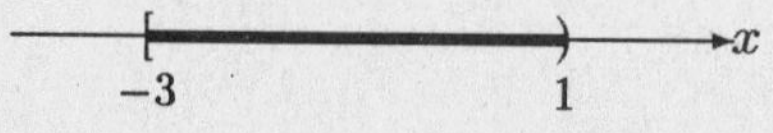

-3 $\quad 1$ $\quad x$

42. The given inequality is equivalent to

$$\frac{2-5x}{3-4x}+2\geq 0 \quad\text{or}\quad \frac{-13x+8}{3-4x}\geq 0 \quad\text{or}\quad \frac{13(x-8/13)}{4(x-3/4)}\geq 0.$$

From the diagram we see that the solution is the union of $(-\infty, \frac{8}{13}]$ and $(\frac{3}{4}, \infty)$.

$x-\frac{8}{13}$	$- \; - \; 0 \; + \; + \; + \; + \; + \; + \; + \; +$
$x-\frac{3}{4}$	$- \; - \; - \; - \; - \; - \; - \; - \; - \; 0 \; + \; +$
$\dfrac{13\left(x-\frac{8}{13}\right)}{4\left(x-\frac{3}{4}\right)}$	$+ \; + \; 0 \; - \; - \; - \; - \; - \quad + \; +$

$\frac{8}{13}$ $\quad$ $\frac{3}{4}$ $\quad x$

43. $-|-3|=-3$

44. $\left|-\sqrt{2}\right|^2=(\sqrt{2})^2=2$

45. $|-5|+|5|=5+5=10$

46. $|-5|-|5|=5-5=0$

47. $|x|=1$ if $x=1$ or $-x=1$; the solution is -1, 1.

48. $|x|=\pi$ if $x=\pi$ or $-x=\pi$; the solution is $-\pi$, π.

49. $|x-1|=2$ if $x-1=2$ (so that $x=3$), or $-(x-1)=2$ (so that $-x+1=2$, or $x=-1$); the solution is -1, 3.

50. $|2x-\frac{1}{2}|=\frac{1}{2}$ if $2x-\frac{1}{2}=\frac{1}{2}$ (so that $2x=1$, or $x=\frac{1}{2}$), or $-(2x-\frac{1}{2})=\frac{1}{2}$ (so that $-2x=0$, or $x=0$); the solution is 0, $\frac{1}{2}$.

51. $|6x+5|=0$ if $6x+5=0$, or $x=-\frac{5}{6}$; the solution is $-\frac{5}{6}$.

52. $|3-4x|=2$ if $3-4x=2$ (so that $-4x=-1$, or $x=\frac{1}{4}$), or $-(3-4x)=2$ (so that $4x=5$, or $x=\frac{5}{4}$); the solution is $\frac{1}{4}$, $\frac{5}{4}$.

53. If $|x|=|x|^2$, then either $|x|=0$ or we may divide by $|x|$ to obtain $1=|x|$ (so that $x=-1$ or $x=1$). The solution is -1, 0, 1.

54. If $|x|=|1-x|$, then either $x=1-x$ or $-x=1-x$. If $x=1-x$, then $2x=1$, or $x=\frac{1}{2}$. If $-x=1-x$, then $0=1$, which is impossible. The solution is $\frac{1}{2}$.

55. If $|x+1|^2+3|x+1|-4=0$, then $(|x+1|+4)(|x+1|-1)=0$. Since $|x+1|+4\neq 0$ it follows that $|x+1|-1=0$, or $|x+1|=1$. Thus either $x+1=1$ (so that $x=0$), or $-(x+1)=1$ (so that $-x=2$, or $x=-2$). The solution is 0, -2.

56. Let $u = |x-2|$. Then $|x-2|^2 - |x-2| = 6$ becomes $u^2 - u = 6$, or $u^2 - u - 6 = 0$, so that $(u-3)(u+2) = 0$, and thus $u = -2$ or $u = 3$. Since $u = |x-2| \geq 0$, it follows that $u = 3$, so $3 = u = |x-2|$. Therefore either $x - 2 = 3$ (so that $x = 5$), or $-(x-2) = 3$ (so that $x = -1$). The solution is -1, 5.

57. If $|x+4| = |x-4|$, then either $x + 4 = x - 4$ (so that $4 = -4$, which is impossible), or $x + 4 = -(x-4)$ (so that $2x = 0$, or $x = 0$). The solution is 0.

58. If $|x-1| = |2x+1|$, then either $x - 1 = 2x + 1$ (so that $x = -2$), or $x - 1 = -(2x+1)$ (so that $3x = 0$, or $x = 0$). The solution is -2, 0.

59. If $|x-2| < 1$, then $-1 < x - 2 < 1$, or $1 < x < 3$. The solution is $(1, 3)$.

60. If $|x-4| < 0.1$, then $-0.1 < x - 4 < 0.1$, or $3.9 < x < 4.1$. The solution is $(3.9, 4.1)$.

61. If $|x+1| < 0.01$, then $-0.01 < x + 1 < 0.01$, or $-1.01 < x < -0.99$. The solution is $(-1.01, -0.99)$.

62. If $|x + \frac{1}{2}| \leq 2$, then $-2 \leq x + \frac{1}{2} \leq 2$, or $-\frac{5}{2} \leq x \leq \frac{3}{2}$. The solution is $[-\frac{5}{2}, \frac{3}{2}]$.

63. If $|x+3| \geq 3$, then $x + 3 \geq 3$ (so that $x \geq 0$), or $-(x+3) \geq 3$ (so that $x \leq -6$). The solution is the union of $(-\infty, -6]$ and $[0, \infty)$.

64. If $|x - 0.3| > 1.5$, then $x - 0.3 > 1.5$ (so that $x > 1.8$) or $-(x - 0.3) > 1.5$ (so that $-x > 1.2$, or $x < -1.2$). The solution is the union of $(-\infty, -1.2)$ and $(1.8, \infty)$.

65. If $|2x+1| \geq 1$, then either $2x + 1 \geq 1$ (so that $x \geq 0$), or $-(2x+1) \geq 1$, (so that $2x \leq -2$, or $x \leq -1$). The solution is the union of $(-\infty, -1]$ and $[0, \infty)$.

66. If $|3x-5| \leq 2$, then $-2 \leq 3x - 5 \leq 2$, so $3 \leq 3x \leq 7$, or $1 \leq x \leq \frac{7}{3}$. The solution is $[1, \frac{7}{3}]$.

67. If $|2x - \frac{1}{3}| > \frac{2}{3}$, then either $2x - \frac{1}{3} > \frac{2}{3}$ (so that $2x > 1$, or $x > \frac{1}{2}$), or $-(2x - \frac{1}{3}) > \frac{2}{3}$ (so that $-2x > \frac{1}{3}$, or $x < -\frac{1}{6}$). The solution is the union of $(-\infty, -\frac{1}{6})$ and $(\frac{1}{2}, \infty)$.

68. If $0 < |x-1| < 0.5$, then $0 < |x-1|$ (so that $x \neq 1$) and $|x-1| < 0.5$ (so that $1 - 0.5 < x < 1 + 0.5$, or $0.5 < x < 1.5$). The solution is the union of $(0.5, 1)$ and $(1, 1.5)$.

69. Since $|4 - 2x| \geq 0 > -1$ for all x, the given inequality is equivalent to $|4 - 2x| < 1$, so that $-1 < 4 - 2x < 1$, or $-5 < -2x < -3$, or $\frac{5}{2} > x > \frac{3}{2}$. The solution is $(\frac{3}{2}, \frac{5}{2})$.

70. If $|x - a| \leq d$, then $-d \leq x - a \leq d$, so $a - d \leq x \leq a + d$. The solution is $[a - d, a + d]$.

71. $\dfrac{69^{800}}{59^{800}} = \left(\dfrac{69}{59}\right)^{800} \approx 2.498407507 \times 10^{54}$

72. $\dfrac{221^{907}}{221^{897}} = 221^{907-897} = 221^{10} \approx 2.779218787 \times 10^{23}$

73. $\dfrac{(0.123)^{9000}}{(0.125)^{9000}} = \left(\dfrac{0.123}{0.125}\right)^{9000} \approx 9.034120564 \times 10^{-64}$

74. a. $\dfrac{1}{\sqrt{25{,}000}-\sqrt{24{,}998}} = \dfrac{1}{\sqrt{25{,}000}-\sqrt{24{,}998}}\,\dfrac{\sqrt{25{,}000}+\sqrt{24{,}998}}{\sqrt{25{,}000}+\sqrt{24{,}998}}$

$$= \frac{\sqrt{25{,}000}+\sqrt{24{,}998}}{25{,}000-24{,}998} = \frac{1}{2}(\sqrt{25{,}000}+\sqrt{24{,}998})$$

b. Probably the latter, since it involves no division by small numbers.

75. We desire all x such that $|x-12|+|x-13|>4$. If $x \geq 13$, then the inequality becomes $x-12+x-13>4$, that is, $2x>4+25=29$, so $x>14.5$. If $x \leq 12$, then the inequality becomes $-(x-12)-(x-13)>4$, that is, $-2x>4-25=-21$, so $x<10.5$. Finally, if $12<x<13$, then $|x-12| \leq 1$ and $|x-13| \leq 1$, so $|x-12|+|x-13|<4$. Consequently the solution is the union of $(-\infty, 10.5)$ and $(14.5, \infty)$.

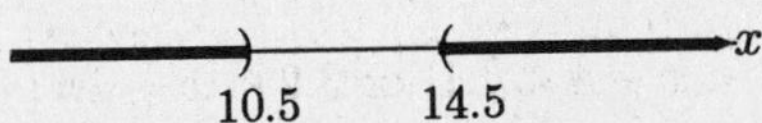

76. We desire all x such that $|x-2|<2|x-3|$. If $x \geq 3$, then the inequality becomes $x-2<2(x-3)=2x-6$, that is, $4<x$. If $x \leq 2$, then the inequality becomes $-(x-2)<-2(x-3)$, that is, $-x+2<-2x+6$, so that $x<4$. Finally, if $2<x<3$, then the inequality becomes $x-2<-2(x-3)=-2x+6$, that is, $3x<8$, or $x<\frac{8}{3}$. Thus the solution is the union of $(4,\infty)$, $(-\infty, 2]$ and $(2, \frac{8}{3})$, which is the union of $(-\infty, \frac{8}{3})$ and $(4, \infty)$.

77. Yes, because if $x>5$, then $x^2>25$.

78. Yes, because if $x<0$, then $x^3<0$, and if $0 \leq x \leq 5$, then $0 \leq x^3 \leq 125$.

79. No, because if $0<x\leq 1$, then $1/x \geq 1 \geq x$.

80. a. If $x<0$, then we have $x<0<x^2$, so $x<x^2$. If $x>1$, then $x^2=x\cdot x>x\cdot 1=x$.

b. If $0<x<1$, then $x^2=x\cdot x<x\cdot 1=x$.

81. a. If $a \geq 0$ and $b \geq 0$ (or $a \leq 0$ and $b \leq 0$), then $|ab|=ab=|a|\,|b|$. If $a\geq 0$ and $b \leq 0$ (or $a \leq 0$ and $b \geq 0$), then $|ab|=-(ab)=|a|\,|b|$. In either case, $|ab|=|a|\,|b|$.

b. If $b \geq 0$, then $b=|b| \geq -|b|$. If $b<0$, then $-b=|b|>-|b|$, so $b=-|b|<|b|$. In either case, $-|b| \leq b \leq |b|$.

c. $|a-b|=|(-1)(b-a)|=|-1|\,|b-a|=|b-a|$.

82. a. By (9), $|b|+|c| \geq |b+c|$, so $|c| \geq |b+c|-|b|$. If $c=a-b$, then $|a-b|=|c| \geq |b+(a-b)|-|b|=|a|-|b|$.

b. Interchanging the roles of a and b in (a), we have $|b-a| \geq |b|-|a|$. From (6), $|b-a|=|a-b|$. Thus $|a-b| \geq |b|-|a|$.

c. Since $\big||a|-|b|\big|=|a|-|b|$ or $\big||a|-|b|\big|=-(|a|-|b|)=|b|-|a|$, we have from (a) and (b) that $|a-b| \geq \big||a|-|b|\big|$.

83. $(|a|+|b|)^2=|a|^2+2|a|\,|b|+|b|^2=a^2+2|ab|+b^2 \geq a^2+2ab+b^2=(a+b)^2=|a+b|^2$, with equality holding if and only if $|ab|=ab$. But $|ab|=ab$ if and only if $ab \geq 0$. Thus $(|a|+|b|)^2=|a+b|^2$, and hence $|a|+|b|=|a+b|$, if and only if $ab \geq 0$.

84. If $a < b$, then $a+a < a+b < b+b$, so $a < (a+b)/2 < b$. Also $(a+b)/2$ is the midpoint of the interval $[a, b]$.

85. If $0 < a < b$, then $0 < (\sqrt{b/2}-\sqrt{a/2})^2 = (b/2-2\sqrt{ab/4}+a/2) = [(a+b)/2-\sqrt{ab}]$, so $\sqrt{ab} < (a+b)/2$. Also $a = \sqrt{a^2} < \sqrt{ab}$.

86. If $1/h = \frac{1}{2}(1/a + 1/b) = \frac{1}{2}[(a+b)/ab]$, then $h = 2ab/(a+b)$. By Exercise 84, $a < (a+b)/2 < b$, so $1/b < 2/(a+b) < 1/a$, and thus $a = ab \cdot 1/b < 2ab/(a+b) = h < ab \cdot 1/a = b$.

87. If $0 < a < b$, then $a = \sqrt{aa} < \sqrt{ab}$, so $-2a > -2\sqrt{ab}$, and thus $(\sqrt{b}-\sqrt{a})^2 = b - 2\sqrt{ab} + a < b - 2a + a = b - a$. Consequently $\sqrt{b} - \sqrt{a} < \sqrt{b-a}$.

88. Assume $\sqrt{2} = p/q$, where p and q are integers such that at most one of them is divisible by 2. Then $2 = p^2/q^2$, or $p^2 = 2q^2$. Thus 2 divides p^2, so 2 divides p—say $p = 2a$. Then $2q^2 = p^2 = 4a^2$, so we have $q^2 = 2a^2$. Thus 2 divides q^2 and hence q. Therefore 2 divides p and q, contradicting our assumption. Consequently $\sqrt{2}$ is irrational.

89. Assume $\sqrt{3} = p/q$, where p and q are integers such that at most one of them is divisible by 3. Then $3 = p^2/q^2$, or $p^2 = 3q^2$. Thus 3 divides p^2, so 3 divides p—say $p = 3a$. Then $3q^2 = p^2 = 9a^2$, so we have $q^2 = 3a^2$. Thus 3 divides q^2 and hence q. Therefore 3 divides both p and q, contradicting our assumption. Consequently $\sqrt{3}$ is irrational.

90. a. Since the area equals xy, the desired inequality is $xy < 10$.

    b. Since the perimeter equals $2x + 2y$, the desired inequality is $2x + 2y \geq 47$.

91. Let a and b be adjacent sides of the rectangle. Then $P = 2(a+b)$. By Exercise 85, $\sqrt{ab} \leq (a+b)/2$, so $ab \leq [(a+b)/2]^2 = (P/4)^2$. But ab is the area of the rectangle, whereas $(P/4)^2$ is the area of a square with perimeter P.

92. The radius of the circle is $P/(2\pi)$, so the area A_C of the circle is given by $A_C = \pi[(P/2\pi)]^2 = P^2/(4\pi)$. But the area A_S of the square is given by $A_S = (P/4)^2 = P^2/16$. Since $4\pi < 16$, we have $A_S < A_C$.

93. If A_R is the area of a rectangle of perimeter P, and A_S the area of a square of perimeter P, then by Exercise 91, $A_R \leq A_S$. If A_C is the area of a circle of circumference (perimeter) P, then by Exercise 92, $A_S < A_C$. Thus $A_R < A_C$.

1.2 Points and Lines in the Plane

1. 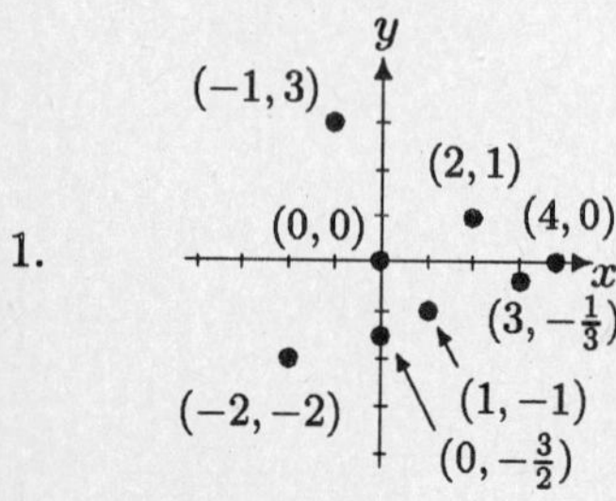

2. a. $(-a, b)$ is in the first quadrant on the line $y = b$ and has the same distance from the x axis as (a, b).

   b. $(a, -b)$ is in the third quadrant on the line $x = a$ and has the same distance from the y axis as (a, b).

   c. $(-a, -b)$ is in the fourth quadrant on the line through the origin and (a, b) and has the same distance from $(0, 0)$ as (a, b)

3. Distance $= \sqrt{(-2-3)^2 + (0-0)^2} = 5$

4. Distance $= \sqrt{(3-0)^2 + (4-0)^2} = \sqrt{25} = 5$

5. Distance $= \sqrt{(6-2)^2 + (-3-1)^2} = \sqrt{32} = 4\sqrt{2}$

6. Distance $= \sqrt{(-2-(-1))^2 + (2-(-3))^2} = \sqrt{26}$

7. Distance $= \sqrt{(-3-6)^2 + (-4-5)^2} = \sqrt{162} = 9\sqrt{2}$

8. Distance $= \sqrt{(3\sqrt{6} - \sqrt{6})^2 + (-\sqrt{3} - \sqrt{3})^2} = \sqrt{36} = 6$

9. Distance $= \sqrt{(\sqrt{3} - \sqrt{2})^2 + (2-1)^2} = \sqrt{6 - 2\sqrt{6}}$

10. Distance $= \sqrt{(b-a)^2 + (a-b)^2} = \sqrt{2(b-a)^2} = \sqrt{2}\,|b-a|$

11. Distance $= \sqrt{(b-a)^2 + (b-a)^2} = \sqrt{2(b-a)^2} = \sqrt{2}\,|b-a|$

12. Distance $= \sqrt{[(c+e)-(a+e)]^2 + [(d+e)-(b+e)]^2} = \sqrt{(c-a)^2 + (d-b)^2}$

13. By (3), $y - (-1) = 3(x-2)$,
    or $y = 3x - 7$.

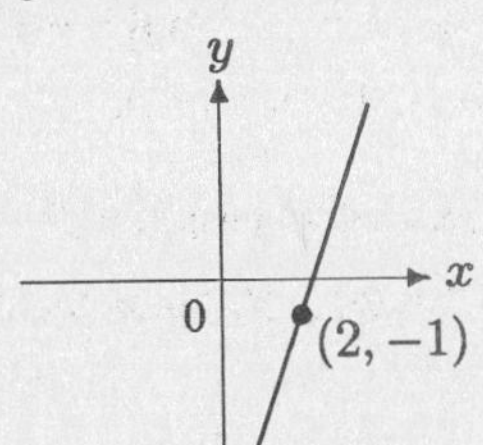

14. By (3), $y - (-2) = 1(x - (-3))$,
    or $y = x + 1$

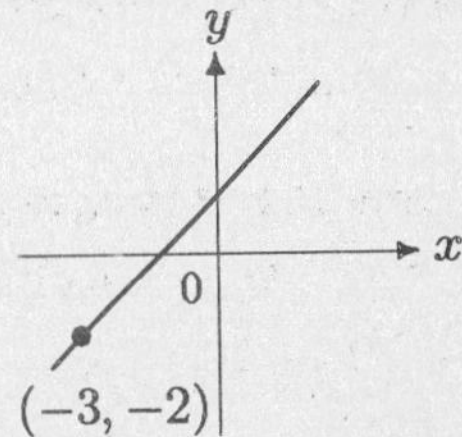

15. By (3), $y - \frac{1}{2} = -1(x - \frac{1}{2})$, or $y = -x + 1$.

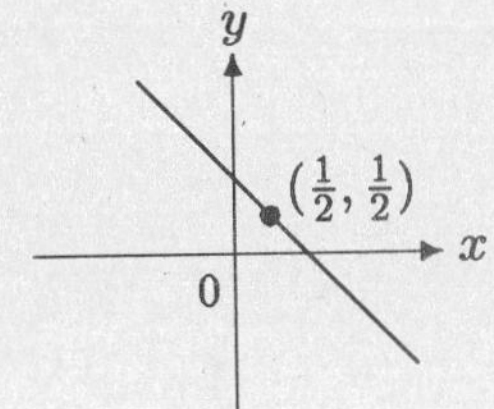

16. By (3), $y - \pi = 0(x - 0)$, or $y = \pi$

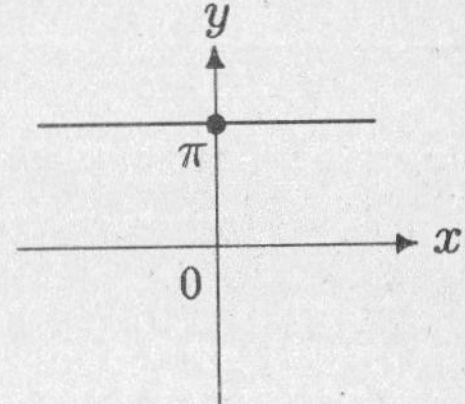

17. By (4), $y = (-1)x + 0$, or $y = -x$.

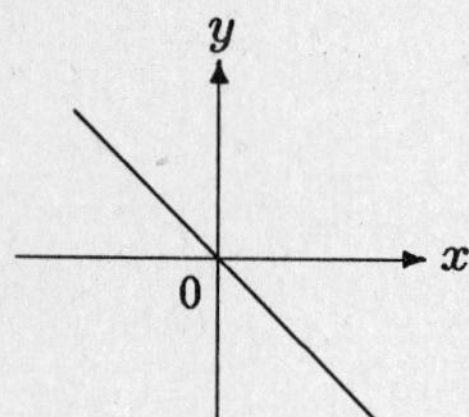

18. By (4), $y = \frac{1}{2}x - 1$.

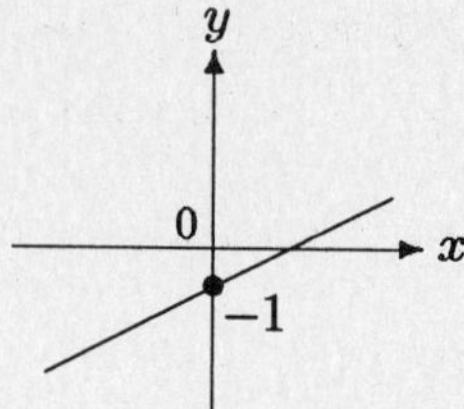

19. By (4), $y = 3x - 3$.

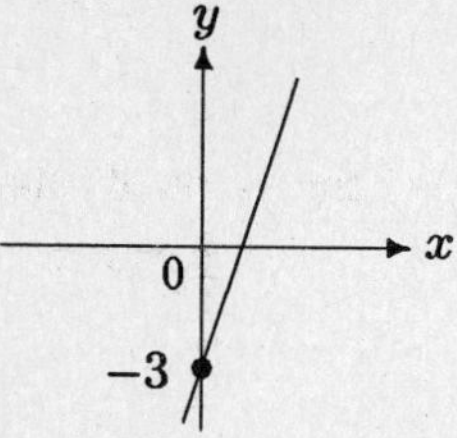

20. By (4), $y = -2x + \frac{5}{2}$.

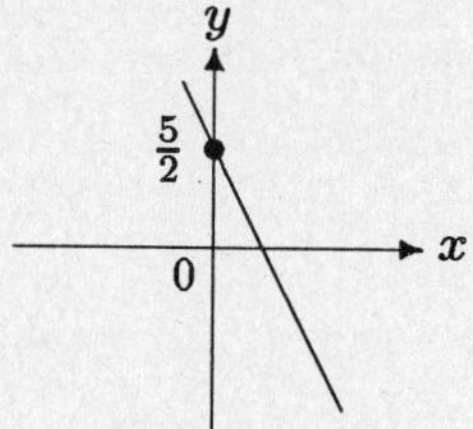

21. By (4), $m = -1$ and $b = 0$.

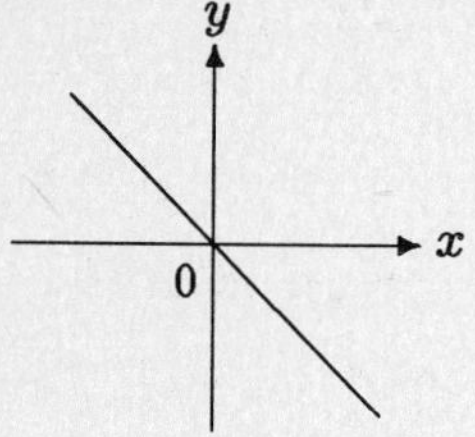

22. By (4), $m = 2$ and $b = -3$.

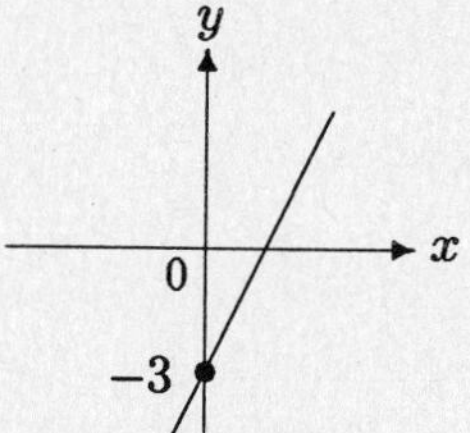

23. The slope-intercept equation of the line is $y = 2x + 7$. By (4), $m = 2$ and $b = 7$.

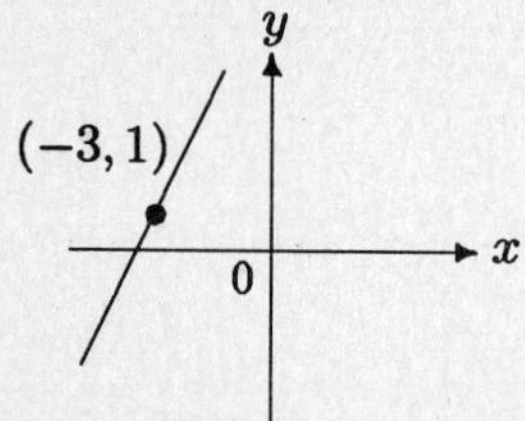

24. The slope-intercept equation of the line is $y = 2x - 4$. By (4), $m = 2$ and $b = -4$.

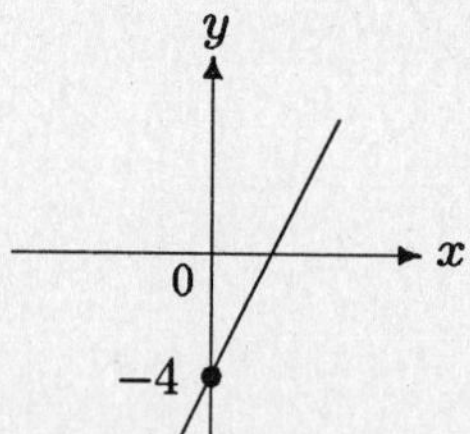

25. The slope-intercept equation of the line is $y = -2x + 4$. By (4), $m = -2$ and $b = 4$.

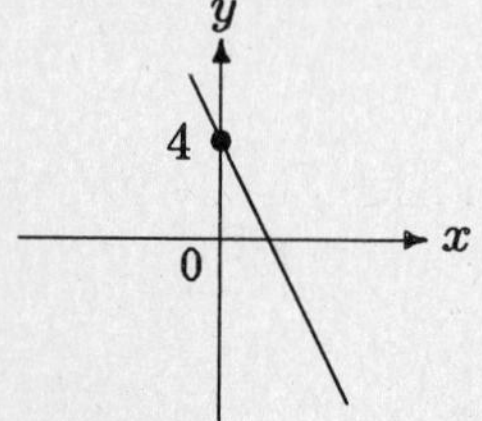

26. The slope-intercept equation of the line is $y = \frac{1}{2}x + 3$. By (4), $m = \frac{1}{2}$ and $b = 3$.

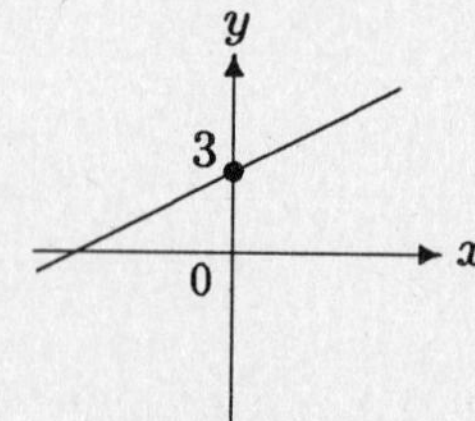

27. $m_1 = 2$; $m_2 = -\frac{1}{2}$. Since $m_1 m_2 = -1$, the lines are perpendicular. If (x, y) is the point of intersection, then $y = 2x + 3$ and $y = -\frac{1}{2}x - 1$, so that $2x + 3 = -\frac{1}{2}x - 1$, or $\frac{5}{2}x = -4$, or $x = -\frac{8}{5}$. Then $y = 2(-\frac{8}{5}) + 3 = -\frac{1}{5}$. The point of intersection is $(-\frac{8}{5}, -\frac{1}{5})$.

28. $m_1 = -2$; $m_2 = -2$. Since $m_1 = m_2$, the lines are parallel.

29. $m_1 = 1$; $m_2 = 1$. Since $m_1 = m_2$, the lines are parallel.

30. $m_1 = -1$; $m_2 = 1$. Since $m_1 m_2 = -1$, the lines are perpendicular. If (x, y) is the point of intersection, then $y = -x - 1$ and $y = x$, so that $-x - 1 = x$, or $-2x = 1$, or $x = -\frac{1}{2}$. Then $y = -\frac{1}{2}$ also. The point of intersection is $(-\frac{1}{2}, -\frac{1}{2})$.

31. $m_1 = -\frac{2}{3}$; $m_2 = \frac{3}{2}$. Since $m_1 m_2 = -1$, the lines are perpendicular. If (x, y) is the point of intersection, then $y = -\frac{2}{3}x - \frac{1}{3}$ and $y = \frac{3}{2}x - \frac{5}{2}$, so $-\frac{2}{3}x - \frac{1}{3} = \frac{3}{2}x - \frac{5}{2}$, or $-\frac{13}{6}x = -\frac{13}{6}$, or $x = 1$. Then $y = -\frac{2}{3}(1) - \frac{1}{3} = -1$. The point of intersection is $(1, -1)$.

32. $m_1 = -\frac{2}{3}$; $m_2 = -\frac{3}{2}$. Since $m_1 \neq m_2$ and $m_1 m_2 \neq -1$, the lines are neither parallel nor perpendicular. If (x, y) is the point of intersection, then $y = -\frac{2}{3}x - \frac{1}{3}$ and $y = -\frac{3}{2}x + 1$, so that $-\frac{2}{3}x - \frac{1}{3} = -\frac{3}{2}x + 1$, or $\frac{5}{6}x = \frac{4}{3}$, or $x = \frac{8}{5}$. Then $y = -\frac{2}{3}(\frac{8}{5}) - \frac{1}{3} = -\frac{21}{15} = -\frac{7}{5}$. The point of intersection is $(\frac{8}{5}, -\frac{7}{5})$.

33. Both lines are vertical. Thus the lines are parallel.

34. The line $x = -1$ is vertical and the line $y = 4$ is horizontal. Thus the lines are perpendicular. If (x, y) is the point of intersection, then $x = -1$ and $y = 4$, so the point of intersection is $(-1, 4)$.

35. $m_1 = -2$; $m_2 = -2$. Since $m_1 = m_2$, the lines are parallel.

36. $m_1 = \frac{1}{2}$; $m_2 = 2$. Since $m_1 \neq m_2$ and $m_1 m_2 \neq -1$, the lines are neither parallel nor perpendicular. If (x, y) is the point of intersection, then $y = \frac{1}{2}x - 4$ and $y = 2x + 8$, so that $\frac{1}{2}x - 4 = 2x + 8$, or $\frac{3}{2}x = -12$, or $x = -8$. Then $y = \frac{1}{2}(-8) - 4 = -8$. The point of intersection is $(-8, -8)$.

37. The slope of l is 3; the desired line has the same slope. From the point-slope equation, we get $y - (-1) = 3(x - 2)$, or $y = 3x - 7$.

38. The slope of l is $-\frac{1}{2}$; the desired line has the same slope. From the point-slope equation, we get $y - 0 = -\frac{1}{2}(x - (-1))$, or $y = -\frac{1}{2}x - \frac{1}{2}$.

39. The slope of l is -1; the desired line has the same slope. From the point-slope equation, we get $y - 0 = -1(x - 0)$, or $y = -x$.

40. The slope of l is $-\frac{2}{3}$; the desired line has the same slope. From the point-slope equation, we get $y - (-3) = -\frac{2}{3}(x - (-1))$, or $y = -\frac{2}{3}x - \frac{11}{3}$.

41. The slope of l is $\frac{2}{3}$; the desired line has the same slope. From the point-slope equation, we get $y - 1 = \frac{2}{3}(x - 2)$, or $y = \frac{2}{3}x - \frac{1}{3}$.

42. The slope of l is $\frac{5}{2}$; the desired line has the same slope. From the point-slope equation, we get $y - 3 = \frac{5}{2}(x - 3)$, or $y = \frac{5}{2}x - \frac{9}{2}$.

43. The slope of l is 2; from Theorem 1.3, the desired line has slope $-\frac{1}{2}$. By (3), an equation is $y - (-3) = -\frac{1}{2}(x - (-1))$, or $y = -\frac{1}{2}x - \frac{7}{2}$.

44. The slope of l is $-\frac{1}{3}$; from Theorem 1.3, the desired line has slope 3. By (3), an equation is $y - 0 = 3(x - 0)$, or $y = 3x$.

45. The slope of l is $-\frac{2}{3}$; from Theorem 1.3, the desired line has slope $\frac{3}{2}$. By (3), an equation is $y - 3 = \frac{3}{2}(x - 2)$, or $y = \frac{3}{2}x$.

46. The slope of l is 3; from Theorem 1.3, the desired line has slope $-\frac{1}{3}$. By (3), an equation is $y - 3 = -\frac{1}{3}(x - 1)$, or $y = -\frac{1}{3}x + \frac{10}{3}$.

47. The slope of l is 2; from Theorem 1.3, the desired line has slope $-\frac{1}{2}$. By (3), an equation is $y - (-5) = -\frac{1}{2}(x - 4)$, or $y = -\frac{1}{2}x - 3$.

48. The slope of l is $-\frac{3}{5}$; from Theorem 1.3, the desired line has slope $\frac{5}{3}$. By (3), an equation is $y - \frac{1}{2} = \frac{5}{3}(x - (-1))$, or $y = \frac{5}{3}x + \frac{13}{6}$.

49. By (1), the slope m is given by $m = (y_2 - y_1)/(x_2 - x_1)$. By (3), a point-slope equation of l is given by

$$y - y_1 = \frac{y_2 - y_1}{x_2 - x_1}(x - x_1).$$

50. By Exercise 49 with $(x_1, y_1) = (3, 4)$, the line is given by

$$y - 4 = \frac{3 - 4}{1 - 3}(x - 3), \quad \text{or equivalently,} \quad y - 4 = \frac{1}{2}(x - 3).$$

51. By Exercise 49 with $(x_1, y_1) = (-2, 4)$, the line is given by

$$y - 4 = \frac{3 - 4}{-1 - (-2)}(x - (-2)), \quad \text{or equivalently,} \quad y - 4 = -(x + 2).$$

52. By Exercise 49 with $(x_1, y_1) = (-\frac{3}{2}, -\frac{1}{2})$, the line is given by

$$y - 2 = \frac{2 - (-\frac{1}{2})}{\frac{1}{2} - (-\frac{3}{2})}\left(x - \frac{1}{2}\right), \quad \text{or equivalently,} \quad y - 2 = \frac{5}{4}\left(x - \frac{1}{2}\right).$$

53.

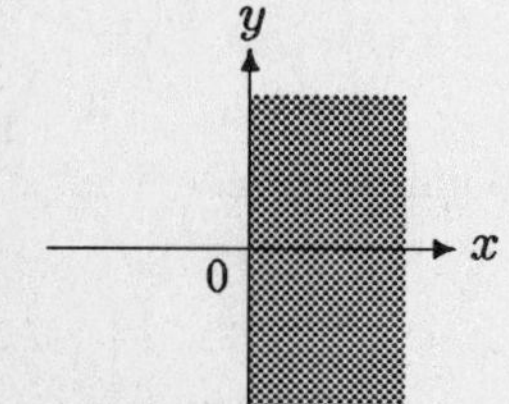

54.

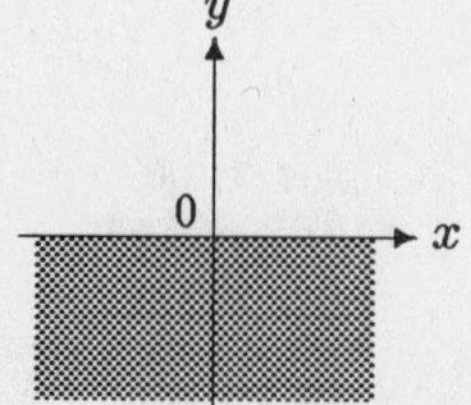

55.

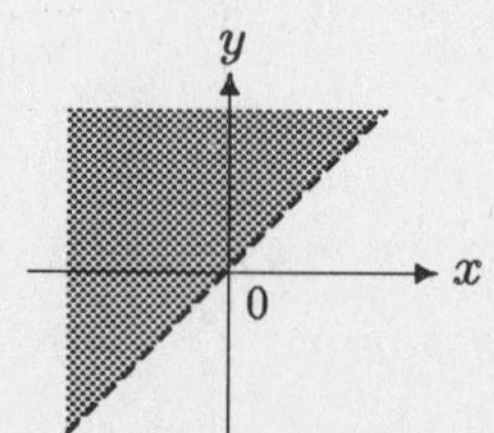

56.

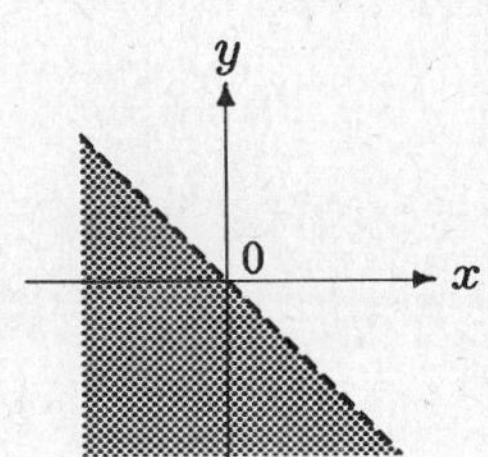

57.

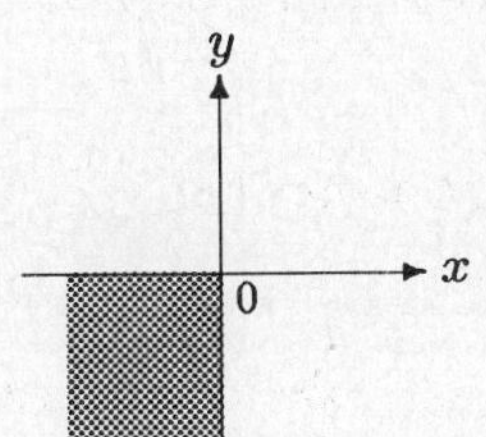

58.

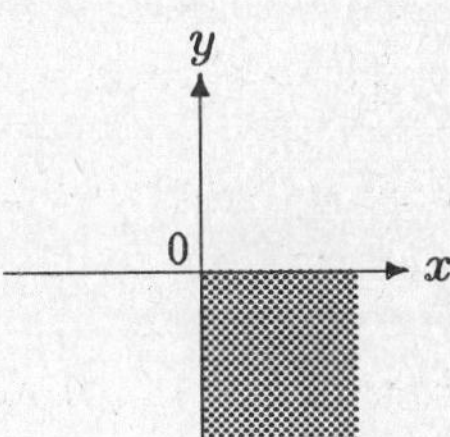

59.

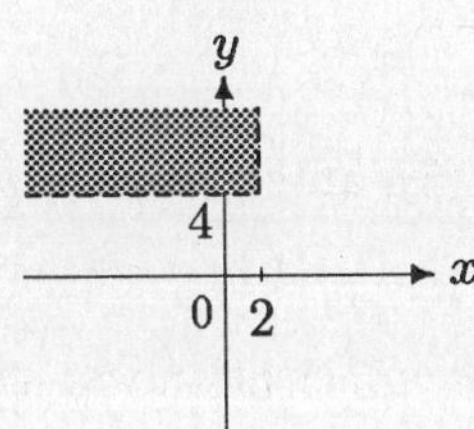

60.

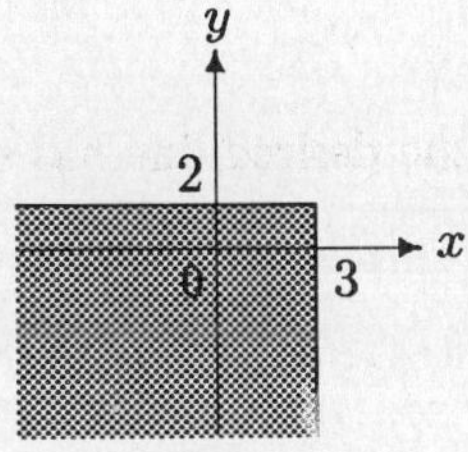

61.

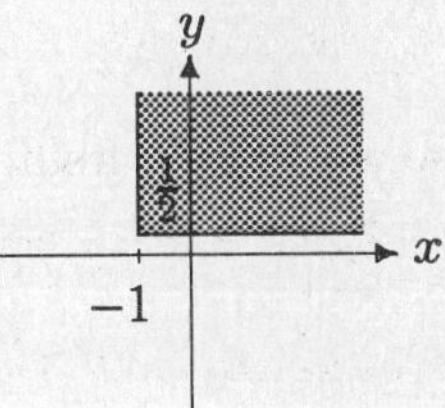

62.

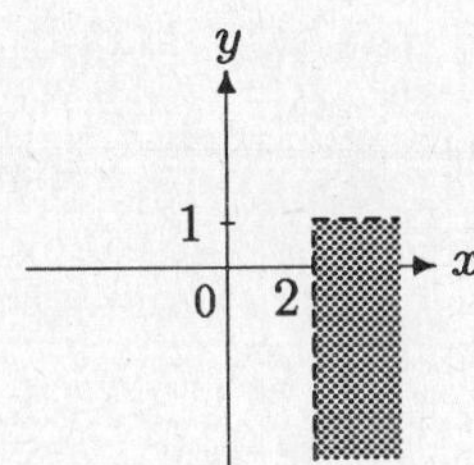

63. a. The requirement $(x, y) = (x, -y)$ is satisfied only when $y = -y$, or $y = 0$. Thus the region is the x axis.

b. The requirement $(x, y) = (-x, y)$ is satisfied only when $x = -x$, or $x = 0$. Thus the region is the y axis.

64. By the figure we deduce that the other two vertices are $(2, 1)$ and $(7, 5)$.

65. By the figure we deduce that the other vertices of the square are $(-3, 7)$, $(-7, 7)$, and $(-7, 3)$.

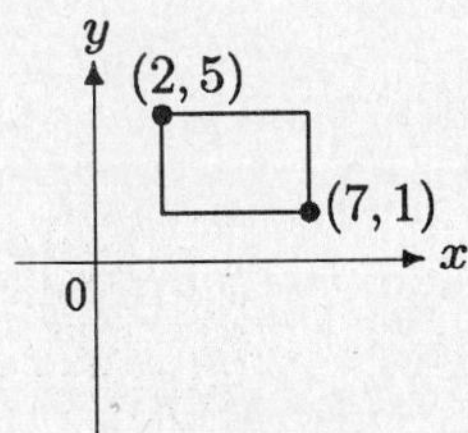

Exercise 64

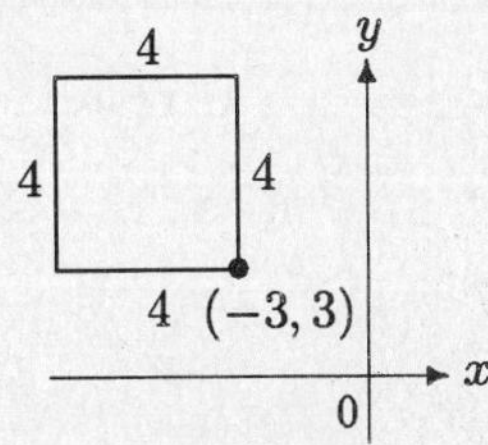

Exercise 65

66. The distance between (a, b) and $(2, 1)$ must equal the distance between (a, b) and $(-3, -2)$, so we solve the equation $\sqrt{(a-2)^2 + (b-1)^2} = \sqrt{(a+3)^2 + (b+2)^2}$ for b in terms of a:

$$\begin{aligned} (a-2)^2 + (b-1)^2 &= (a+3)^2 + (b+2)^2 \\ a^2 - 4a + 4 + b^2 - 2b + 1 &= a^2 + 6a + 9 + b^2 + 4b + 4 \\ -6b &= 10a + 8 \\ b &= -\frac{5}{3}a - \frac{4}{3} \end{aligned}$$

An equation of the line is $y = -\frac{5}{3}x - \frac{4}{3}$.

67. Let d_1, d_2, and d_3 be the lengths of the three sides. Then

$$\begin{aligned} d_1 &= \sqrt{\left(\sqrt{3} - 1 - (-1)\right)^2 + (3-2)^2} = 2 \\ d_2 &= \sqrt{\left(-1 - (\sqrt{3} - 1)\right)^2 + (4-3)^2} = 2 \\ d_3 &= \sqrt{\left(-1 - (-1)\right)^2 + (4-2)^2} = 2 \end{aligned}$$

Thus the triangle is equilateral.

68. The midpoints are $(a/2, 0)$, $(a, b/2)$, $(a/2, b)$, $(0, b/2)$. The lengths of l_1, l_2, l_3, l_4 are $\sqrt{(a/2)^2 + (b/2)^2}$.

69. Using the figure, we find that the midpoints are $(a/2, 0)$, $((a+b)/2, c/2)$, and $(b/2, c/2)$. The sum of the squares of the lengths of the sides is $a^2 + [(b-a)^2 + c^2] + (b^2 + c^2) = 2a^2 + 2b^2 + 2c^2 - 2ab$. The sum of the squares of the lengths of the medians is

$$\left[\left(b - \frac{a}{2}\right)^2 + c^2\right] + \left[\left(\frac{a+b}{2}\right)^2 + \left(\frac{c}{2}\right)^2\right] + \left[\left(\frac{b}{2} - a\right)^2 + \left(\frac{c}{2}\right)^2\right]$$

$$= b^2 - ab + \frac{a^2}{4} + c^2 + \frac{a^2}{4} + \frac{ab}{2} + \frac{b^2}{4} + \frac{c^2}{4} + \frac{b^2}{4} - ab + a^2 + \frac{c^2}{4} = \frac{3}{4}(2a^2 + 2b^2 + 2c^2 - 2ab).$$

70. Using the figure, we find that the sum of the squares of the lengths of the sides is $a^2 + [(a+b-a)^2 + c^2] + [(a+b-b)^2 + (c-c)^2] + (b^2 + c^2) = 2(a^2 + b^2 + c^2)$. The sum of the squares of the lengths of the diagonals is $[(a+b)^2 + c^2] + [(a-b)^2 + c^2] = 2(a^2 + b^2 + c^2)$.

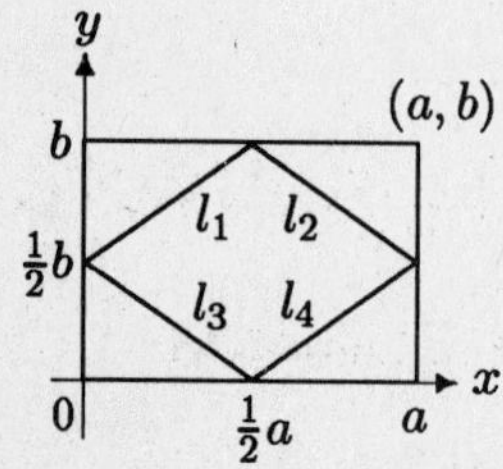

Exercise 68

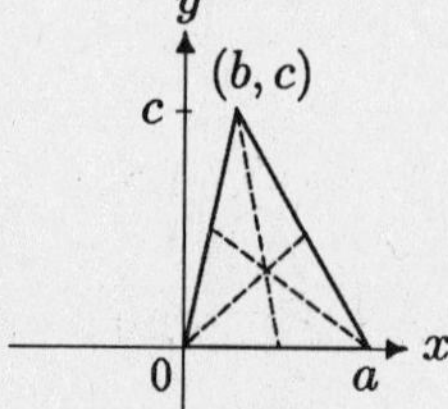

Exercise 69

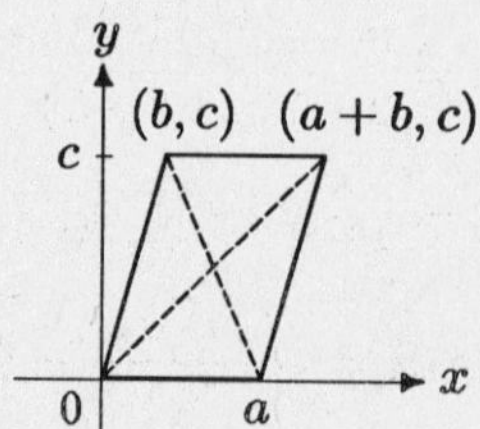

Exercise 70

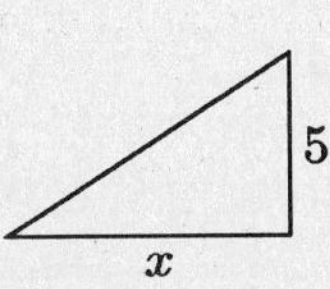

Exercise 71

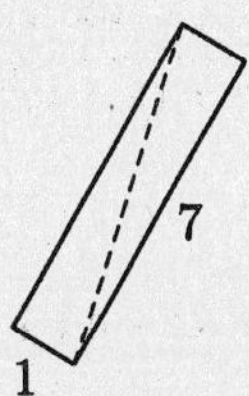

Exercise 72

71. Let x denote the distance between the base of the ramp and the wall. By hypothesis, $5/x = 0.28$, so that $x = 5/0.28 \approx 17.85714286$. Therefore the distance is approximately 17.9 feet.

72. The minimum vertical clearance equals the length of the diagonal of the rectangle in the figure. By the Pythagorean Theorem, that length is $\sqrt{7^2 + 1^2} = \sqrt{50} \approx 7.071067812$. Therefore the minimum vertical distance is approximately 7 feet 1 inch.

1.3 Functions

1. $f(\sqrt{5}) = \sqrt{3}$; $f(\pi) = \sqrt{3}$

2. $f(1) = 2 \cdot 1^2 - 3 = -1$; $f(-2) = 2(-2)^2 - 3 = 5$

3. $f(0) = 1 - 0 + 0^3 = 1$; $f(-1) = 1 - (-1) + (-1)^3 = 1$

4. $f(2) = \frac{1}{2}$; $f(\frac{1}{2}) = \frac{1}{1/2} = 2$

5. $g(\sqrt{2}) = \dfrac{1}{2(\sqrt{2})^2} = \dfrac{1}{4}$

6. $g(4) = \sqrt{4} = 2$; $g(\frac{1}{25}) = \sqrt{\frac{1}{25}} = \frac{1}{5}$

7. $g(27) = \sqrt[3]{27} = 3$; $g(-\frac{1}{8}) = \sqrt[3]{-\frac{1}{8}} = -\frac{1}{2}$

8. $g(6) = |2 - 6| = 4$

9. $f(2) = \dfrac{2-1}{2^2+4} = \dfrac{1}{8}$

10. $f(-1) = \dfrac{3(-1)^2 - 4(-1) - 1}{2(-1)^2 + 5(-1) - 3} = \dfrac{3+4-1}{2-5-3} = \dfrac{6}{-6} = -1$

11. $f(3.2) = \frac{-2}{169}(3.2)^2 + \frac{4}{13}(3.2) + 3 \approx 3.863431953$; $f(25.5) = \frac{-2}{169}(25.5)^2 + \frac{4}{13}(25.5) + 3 \approx 3.150887574$

12. $f(10{,}000) = \sqrt{\dfrac{192{,}000}{10{,}000}} - 6 \approx 3.633180425$; $f(21{,}729) = \sqrt{\dfrac{192{,}000}{21{,}729}} - 6 \approx 1.68407768$

13. $g(0.5) = \dfrac{100.24(0.5)^6}{(0.24)(0.5)^6 - 1} \approx -1.572145546$; $g(-7.31) = \dfrac{100.24(-7.31)^6}{(0.24)(-7.31)^6 - 1} \approx 417.6780725$

14. $g(3) = 4.5(3)^{1/2} - 3^{3/2} \approx 2.598076211$; $g(1.64) = 4.5(1.64)^{1/2} - (1.64)^{3/2} \approx 3.662587064$

15. All real numbers

16. All real numbers

17. $[-2, 8]$

18. $(-\infty, 4)$

19. $[-2, \infty)$

20. $(-\infty, \frac{2}{3}]$

21. Since $x(x-1) \geq 0$ for $x \leq 0$ and for $x \geq 1$, the domain is the union of $(-\infty, 0]$ and $[1, \infty)$.

22. Since $4 - 9t^2 \geq 0$ if $t^2 \leq \frac{4}{9}$, or equivalently, $-\frac{2}{3} \leq t \leq \frac{2}{3}$, the domain is $[-\frac{2}{3}, \frac{2}{3}]$

23. Since $3 - 1/t^2 \geq 0$ if $3 \geq 1/t^2$, or equivalently, $t^2 \geq \frac{1}{3}$, so that $|t| \geq 1/\sqrt{3} = \sqrt{3}/3$, the domain is the union of $(-\infty, -\sqrt{3}/3]$ and $[\sqrt{3}/3, \infty)$.

24. Since $\sqrt{t+5} > 0$ if $t > -5$, the domain is $(-5, \infty)$.

25. Since the cube root function is defined for all real numbers, the domain is all real numbers.

26. Since $x - 6 \geq 0$ if $x \geq 6$, the domain is $[6, \infty)$.

27. Since $x - 1 = 0$ if $x = 1$, the domain is all real numbers except 1.

28. Since $x - 3 = 0$ if $x = 3$, the domain is all real numbers except 3.

29. Since $w^2 - 16 = 0$ if $w = -4$ or 4, the domain is all real numbers except -4 and 4.

30. Since $w^2 - w - 6 = 0$ if $w = -2$ or 3, the domain is all real numbers except -2 and 3.

31. Since $x^2 + 4 > 0$ for all x, the domain is all real numbers.

32. Since $x + 1 = 0$ or $x - 1 = 0$ if $x = -1$ or $x = 1$, the domain is all real numbers except -1 and 1.

33. Union of $[-4, -1]$ and $(0, 6)$

34. Union of $(-\infty, 2]$ and $(\sqrt{5}, \infty)$

35. x is in the domain if $1 - \sqrt{9 - x^2} \geq 0$ (so that $1 \geq \sqrt{9 - x^2}$, or $1 \geq 9 - x^2$, or $x^2 \geq 8$) and $9 - x^2 \geq 0$ (so that $x^2 \leq 9$). Thus $8 \leq x^2 \leq 9$, so the domain is the union of $[-3, -2\sqrt{2}]$ and $[2\sqrt{2}, 3]$.

36. x is in the domain if $4 - \sqrt{1 + 9x^2} \geq 0$ (so that $4 \geq \sqrt{1 + 9x^2}$, or $16 \geq 1 + 9x^2$, or $x^2 \leq \frac{15}{9}$) and $1 + 9x^2 \geq 0$ (which is true for all x). The domain is $[-\frac{1}{3}\sqrt{15}, \frac{1}{3}\sqrt{15}]$.

37. The set consisting of the number -1.

38. All real numbers

39. If $x < 4$, then $f(x) = 3x - 2 < 3 \cdot 4 - 2 = 10$. Thus the range is $(\infty, 10)$.

40. The domain is $[-1, 1]$. For $-1 \leq x \leq 1$, we have $0 \leq x^2 \leq 1$, so that $0 \leq 1 - x^2 \leq 1$. Thus the range is $[0, 1]$.

41. y is in the range of f if there is an x such that $y = \dfrac{1}{x-1}$. This is equivalent to $x - 1 = \dfrac{1}{y}$, or $x = \dfrac{1}{y} + 1$. This equation has a solution x unless $y = 0$. Thus the range consists of all real numbers except 0.

42. y is in the range of f if there is an x such that $y = \dfrac{x^2-1}{x^2+1}$. This is equivalent to $(x^2+1)y = x^2 - 1$, or $x^2y + y = x^2 - 1$, or $x^2 = \dfrac{y+1}{1-y}$. This equation has a solution x if $\dfrac{y+1}{y-1} \geq 0$, which occurs if $-1 \leq y < 1$. Consequently the range is $[-1, 1)$.

43. a. A function is described.
    b. A function is not described because two values are assigned to the number -2.
    c. f is not a function because f assigns two values to every positive number.
    d. f is not a function because f assigns two values to every number.
    e. g is a function.
    f. g is a function.
    g. g is a function. (Note that $g(2) = 9$.)
    h. g is not a function because $g(1) = 2 - 3 = -1$ from the first line of the formula, whereas $g(1) = 3 - 3 = 0$ from the second line of the formula.
    i. f is a function.
    j. f is not a function because it assigns two values to numbers such as $\sqrt{2}$: $(\sqrt{2})^2 = 2$, which is rational, so that $f(\sqrt{2}) = 2$; but $\sqrt{2}$ is irrational, so $f(\sqrt{2}) = \sqrt{2}$.

44. a. They are not the same, because the domain of f is $(-\infty, \infty)$, whereas the domain of g is $(-1, 1)$.
    b. They are the same, because $\sqrt{x}$ is defined if and only if $x \geq 0$.
    c. They are the same, because $\sqrt{x^2} = |x|$ for all x.
    d. They are not the same, because f is not defined for $x = -2$, 0, 2, whereas g is.
    e. They are not the same, because f is not defined for $x = 1$, whereas g is.
    f. They are not the same because $\dfrac{x^2 - 5x + 6}{x+2} = \dfrac{(x-2)(x-3)}{x+2} \neq x - 3$ unless $x = 3$.

45. $f_1 = f_5$ and $f_2 = f_3$.

46. a. Since $x^2 + 1 \geq 0$ for all x, the domain of f is $(-\infty, \infty)$. Since $1 + \sqrt{x^2+1} \neq 0$ for all x, the domain of g is $(-\infty, \infty)$.

b. For any x,

$$f(x) = (\sqrt{x^2+1}-1)\frac{1+\sqrt{x^2+1}}{1+\sqrt{x^2+1}} = \frac{(x^2+1)-1}{1+\sqrt{x^2+1}} = \frac{x^2}{1+\sqrt{x^2+1}} = g(x).$$

Since f, g have the same domain and the same rule, $f = g$.

47. a. x is in the domain of f if and only if $x^2 - 1 \geq 0$, or $x^2 \geq 1$, so the domain of f is the union of $(-\infty, -1]$ and $[1, \infty)$. x is in the domain of g if and only if $x^2 - 1 \geq 0$ and $x + \sqrt{x^2-1} \neq 0$. The first condition requires x to be in $(-\infty, -1]$ or $[1, \infty)$. Since under this condition, $0 \leq x^2 - 1 < x^2$, we have $\sqrt{x^2-1} < |x|$. Therefore $\sqrt{x^2-1} \neq -x$, so $x + \sqrt{x^2-1} \neq x + (-x) = 0$. Thus the domain of f and the domain of g are equal to the union of $(-\infty, -1]$ and $[1, \infty)$.

b. For all x in the domain of f,

$$f(x) = (x - \sqrt{x^2-1})\frac{x+\sqrt{x^2-1}}{x+\sqrt{x^2-1}} = \frac{x^2-(x^2-1)}{x+\sqrt{x^2-1}} = \frac{1}{x+\sqrt{x^2-1}} = g(x).$$

Since f and g have the same domain and assign the same value to each x in that domain, $f = g$.

48. $f(x) = x^2 - 2x + \sqrt{2}$ for $x > -1$

49. $f(x) = \frac{1}{2}x^2\sqrt[3]{x/5}$ for $x \geq 0$

50. By hypothesis, $V = 60$. Since $V = s^2 l$, we have $60 = s^2 l$, so that $l = 60/s^2$. By the Pythagorean Theorem, the height of the triangle is $\sqrt{x^2 - (x/2)^2} = \sqrt{3}\,x/2$.

51. Let x denote the length of a side. Thus

$$A(x) = \frac{1}{2}x\left(\frac{\sqrt{3}}{2}x\right) = \frac{\sqrt{3}}{4}x^2 \quad \text{for } x \geq 0.$$

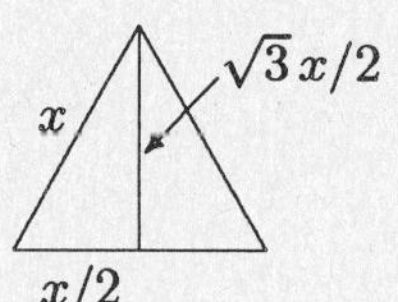

52. a. By (3) with $t = 2$, we have $h(2) = -16(2^2) - 144(2) + 832 = 480$. Thus the height after 2 seconds is 480 feet.

b. By (3) with $t = 3$, we have $h(3) = -16(3^2) - 144(3) + 832 = 256$. Thus the height after 3 seconds is 256 feet.

c. By (3) with $t = 3.9$, we have $h(3.9) = -16(3.9)^2 - 144(3.9) + 832 = 27.04$. Thus the height after 3.9 seconds is 27.04 feet.

53. a. If the initial height is 832 feet, then by the conversion table the height in meters is approximately $832/3.28 \approx 254$. Similarly, the initial speed of 144 feet per second corresponds to $144/3.28 \approx 43.9$ meters. Therefore the height of the ball in Example 1 is given (approximately) by $h(t) = -4.9t^2 - 43.9t + 254$.

b. Using the result of part (a), we find that $h(4) = -4.9(16) - 43.9(4) + 253.6 = -.4$. Thus the ball hits the ground in approximately 4 seconds (as before).

54. Until the ball hits the ground, the height is given by $h(t) = -4.9t^2 + h_0$. Since $h(2.5) = 0$, we have $0 = -4.9(2.5)^2 + h_0$, so that $h_0 = 30.625$ (meters).

55. From Exercise 54, $h(t) = -4.9t^2 + v_0 t + 30.625$ and $h(2) = 0$. Thus $-4.9(2)^2 + v_0(2) + 30.625 = 0$, so that $v_0 = \frac{1}{2}[(4.9)(4) - 30.625] = -5.5125$. Thus the ball was thrown downward at 5.5125 meters per second.

56. a. By (2), $h(t) = -16t^2 + 1350$.

b. Since $h(0) = 1350$ and $h(3) = -16(3^2) + 1350 = 1206$, the wrench travels $1350 - 1206 = 144$ feet during the first three seconds.

c. We need to find t such that $h(t) = 0$, or equivalently, $-16t^2 + 1350 = 0$. This occurs if $t = \sqrt{1350/16} \approx 9.185586535$. Thus it takes approximately 9.2 seconds for the wrench to hit the ground.

57. a. By (1), $h(t) = -4.9t^2 - 5t + 30$, so that $h(\frac{1}{2}) = -4.9(\frac{1}{2})^2 - 5(\frac{1}{2}) + 30 = 26.275$ and $h(1) = -4.9(1)^2 - 5(1) + 30 = 20.1$. Thus after $\frac{1}{2}$ second and after 1 second the ball is 26.275 meters and 20.1 meters, respectively, above the ground.

b. We need to find t such that $10 = h(t) = -4.9t^2 - 5t + 30$, or equivalently, $4.9t^2 + 5t - 20 = 0$. By the quadratic formula,

$$t = \frac{-5 \pm \sqrt{25 - 4(4.9)(-20)}}{2(4.9)}.$$

Since $t \geq 0$, we find that $t \approx 1.573528353$. Therefore it takes approximately 1.6 seconds for the ball to reach the window.

58. a. From the figure, we see that $V = \pi r^2 L + \frac{4}{3}\pi r^3$. Since $V = 100$ by hypothesis, $100 = \pi r^2 L + \frac{4}{3}\pi r^3$. Thus

$$L = \frac{100 - 4\pi r^3/3}{\pi r^2} = \frac{300 - 4\pi r^3}{3\pi r^2}.$$

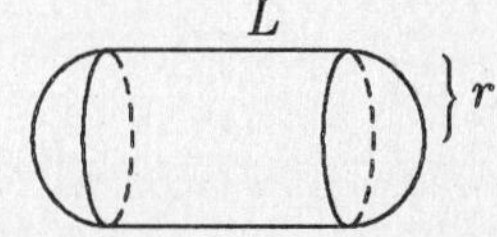

b. If $r = 2$, then

$$L = \frac{300 - 4\pi(2)^3}{3\pi(2)^2} \approx 5.291080488.$$

To the nearest centimeter, $L = 5.29$ meters.

c. If $r = 1$, then

$$L = \frac{300 - 4\pi}{3\pi} \approx 30.49765529$$

so that $L \approx 30.50$ meters. The length would have to be increased (approximately) by

$$30.49765529 - 5.291080488 = 25.20657480.$$

To the nearest centimeter the length would need to be increased by 25.21 meters.

59. a. If $T = 2\pi\sqrt{L/g}$, then $T^2 = 4\pi^2 L/g$, so that $L = gT^2/4\pi^2$.

b. Letting $g = 9.8$ and $L = 21.8$ in the formula for T, we have

$$T = 2\pi\sqrt{\frac{21.8}{9.8}} \approx 9.371197208.$$

Thus the period is approximately 9.4 seconds.

60. Each day the company receives 500,000 cents and spends 200,000 cents. If x denotes the number of working days, and P the profit, then

$$P(x) = 500{,}000x - 200{,}000x = 300{,}000x \quad \text{for } x \geq 0.$$

61. If t represents time in hours starting at noon and D distance in miles, then

$$D(t) = \begin{cases} 400t & \text{for } 0 \leq t < 2 \\ |400t - 800(t-2)| = |1600 - 400t| & \text{for } 2 \leq t \leq 5 \end{cases}$$

62. After t hours the distances of the two cars from the starting point are $40t$ and $50t$ miles, respectively. By the Pythagorean Theorem, the distance $D(t)$ between the two cars t hours after departure is given by $D(t) = \sqrt{(40t)^2 + (50t)^2} = 10t\sqrt{41}$ (miles).

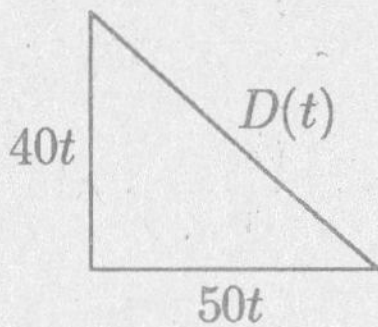

63. a. $R(0) = \dfrac{0}{c+0} = 0$ and $R(2) = \dfrac{2}{c+2d}$.

$R(0) = 0$ indicates no response in the absence of the drug.

b. Since $R(x)(c + dx) = x$, or equivalently, $cR(x) + dxR(x) = x$, we have $x - dxR(x) = cR(x)$, so that $x = cR(x)/[1 - dR(x)]$.

1.4 Graphs

1.

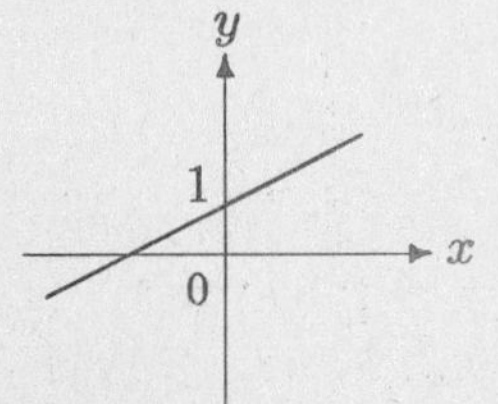

2.

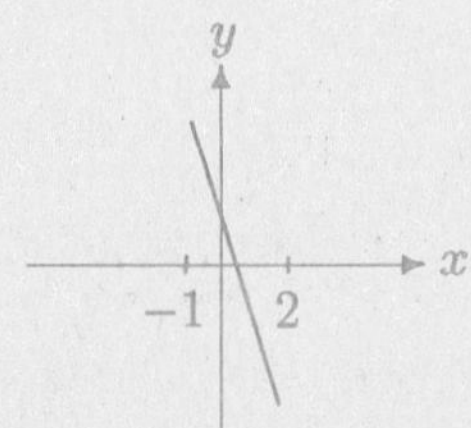

3.

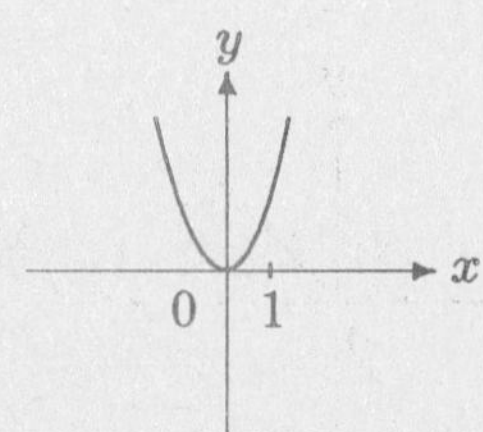

4.

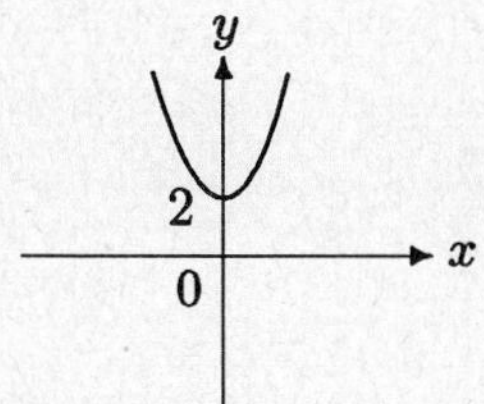

5.

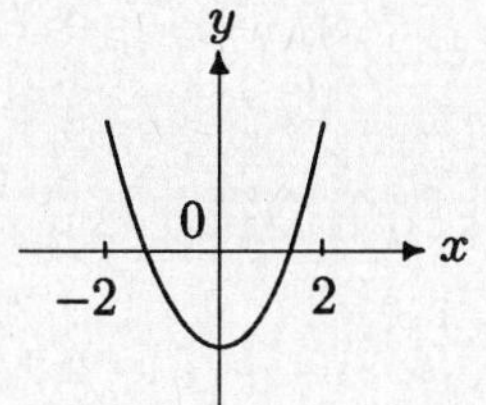

6.

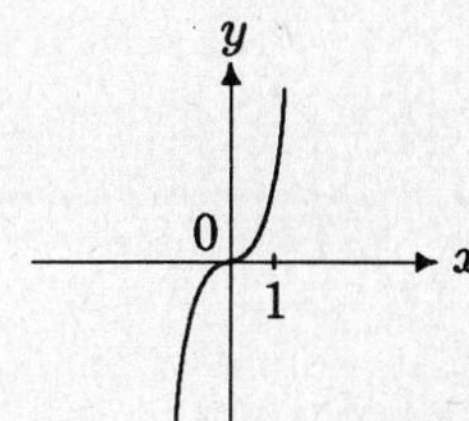

7.

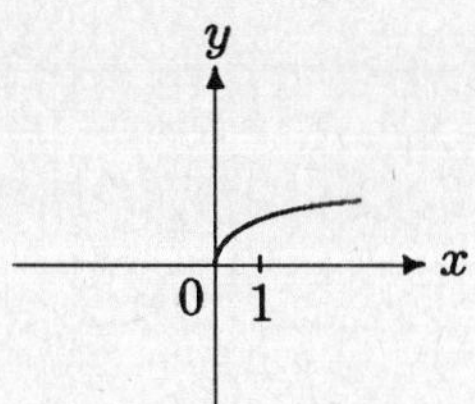

8.

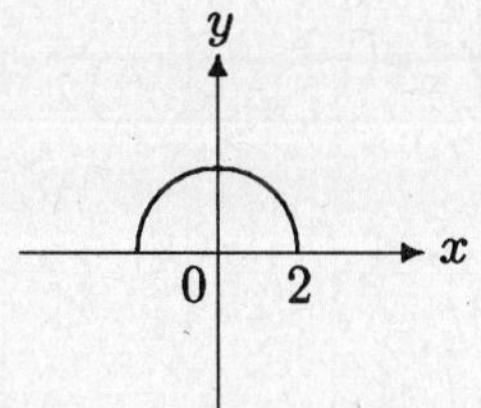

9.

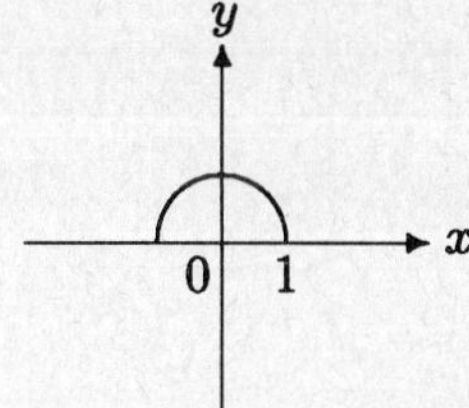

10.

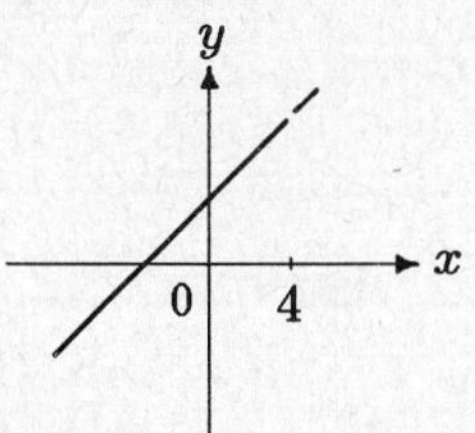

11.

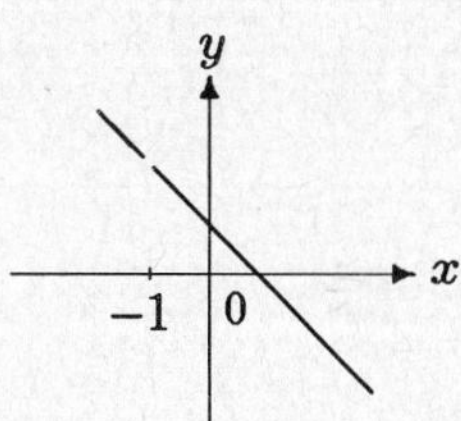

12.

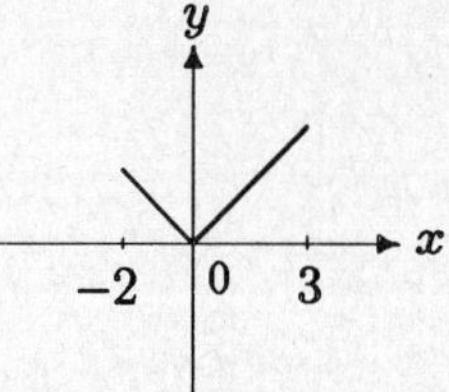

13.

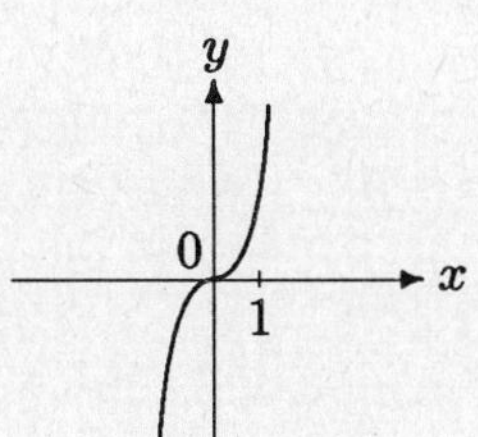

14.

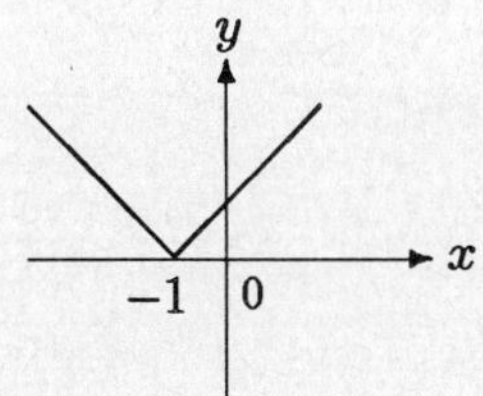

15.

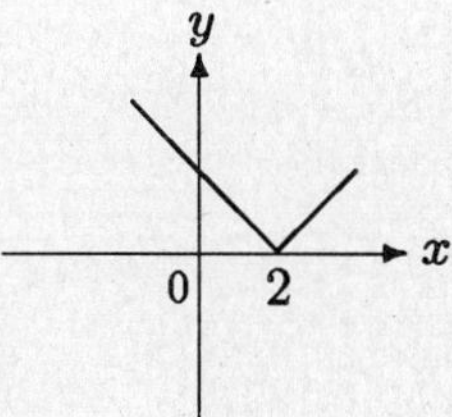

16.

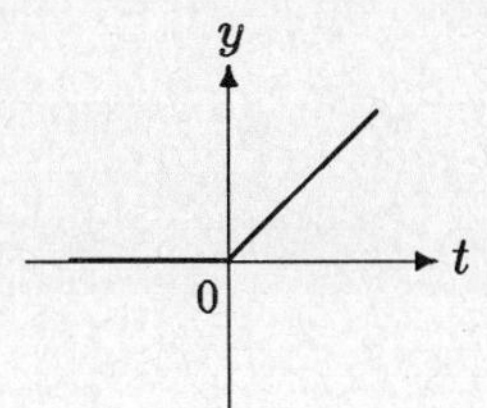

17.

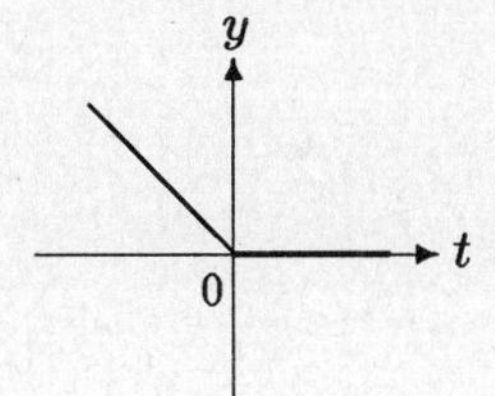

18.

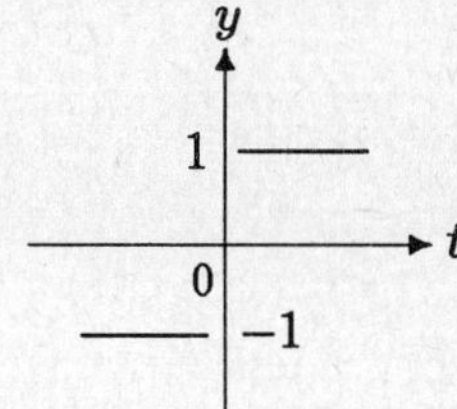

19.

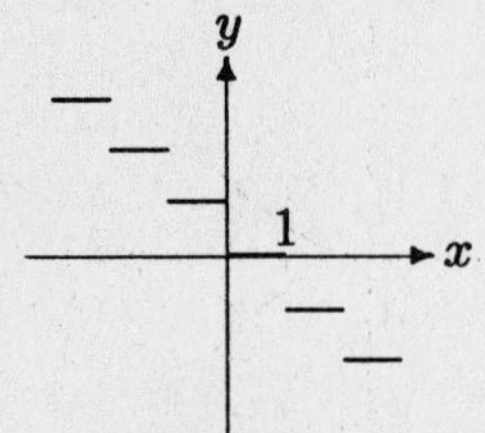

20.

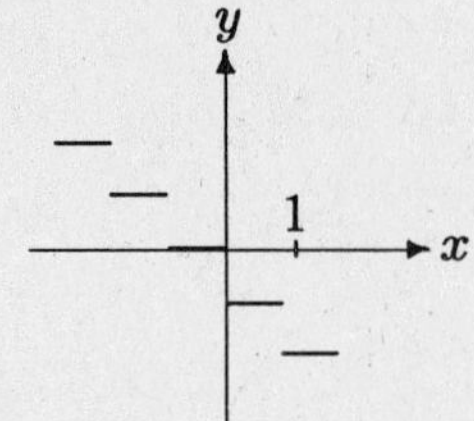

21.

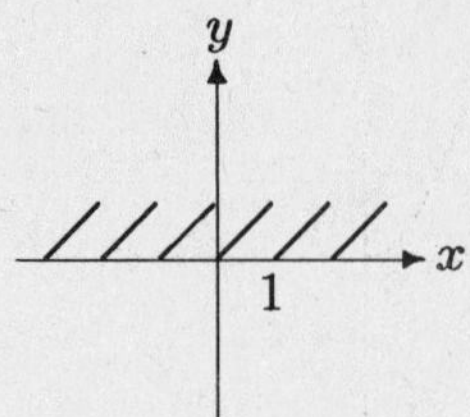

22.

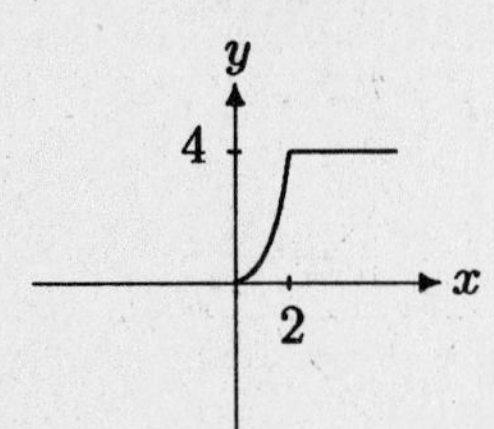

23.

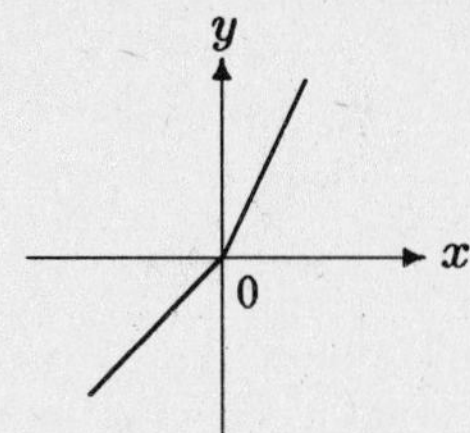

24.

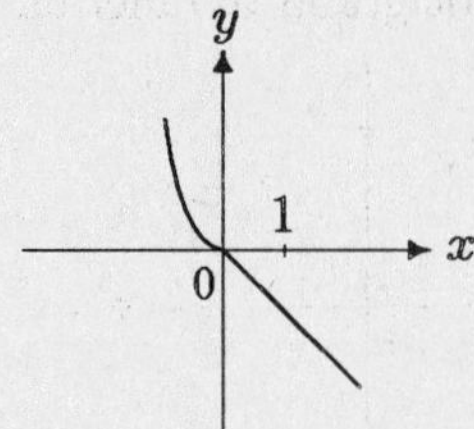

25.

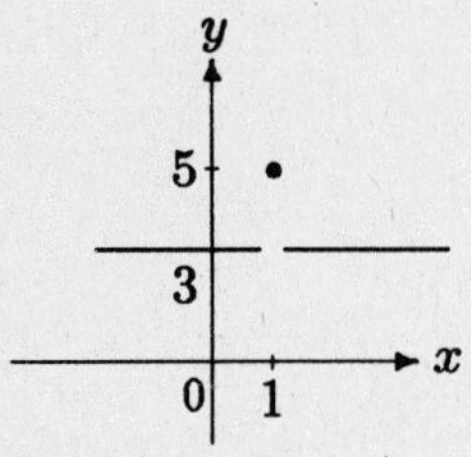

26.

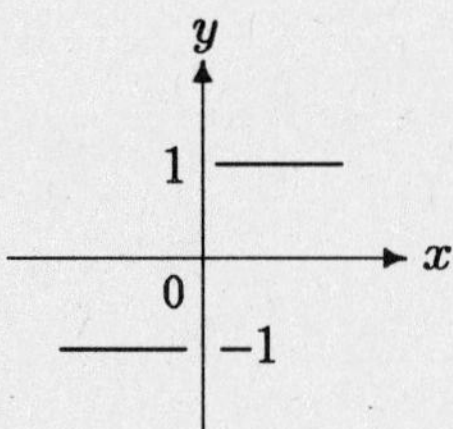

27.

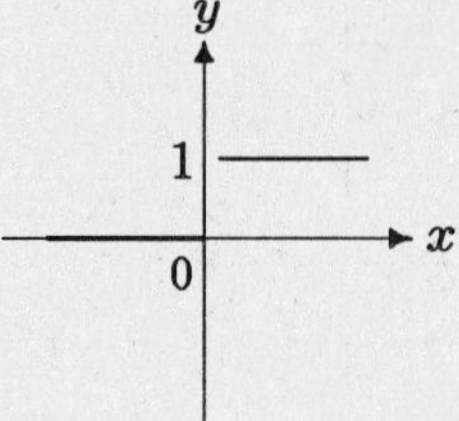

34. not graph of function

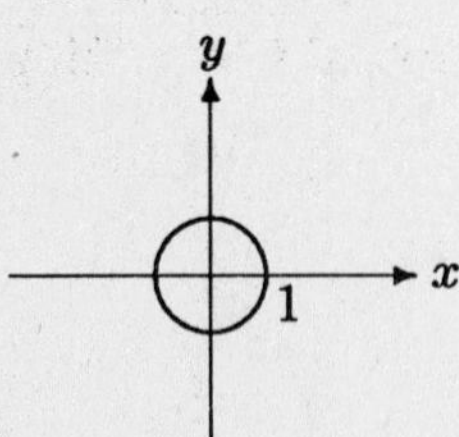

35. not graph of function

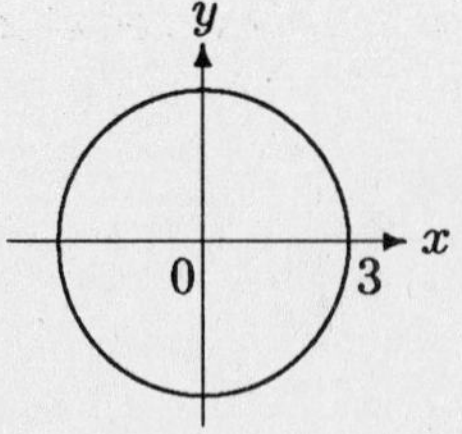

36. not graph of function

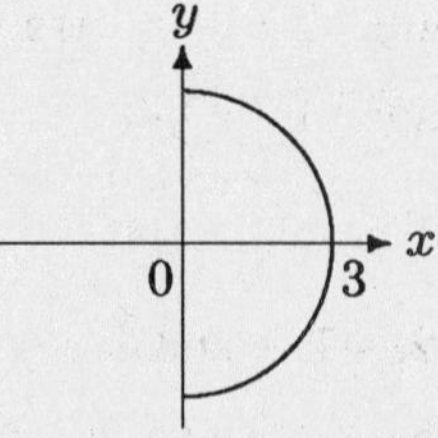

37. graph of function

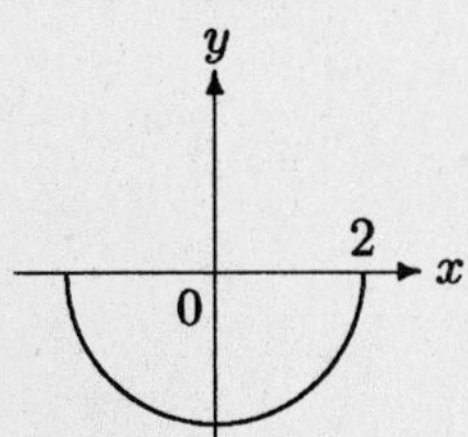

38. graph of function

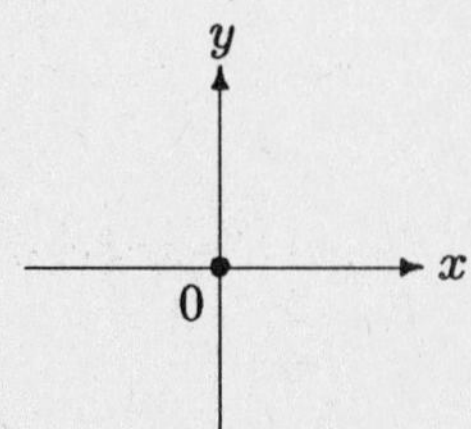

39. not graph of function

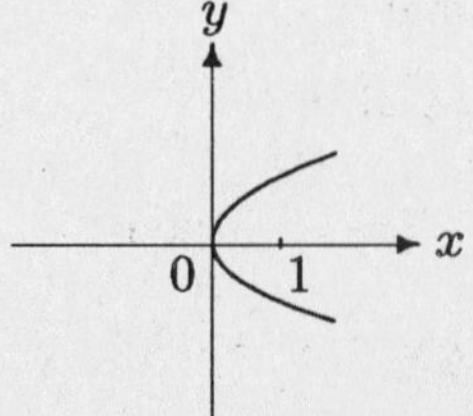

40. graph of function

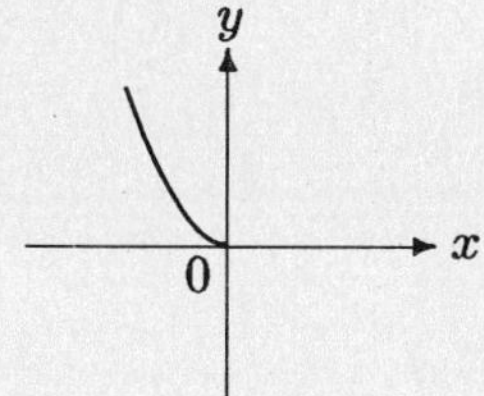

41. not graph of function

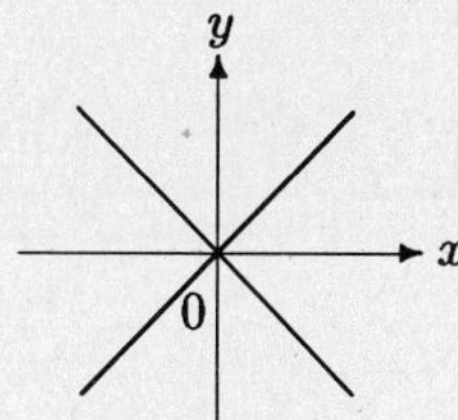

42. not graph of function

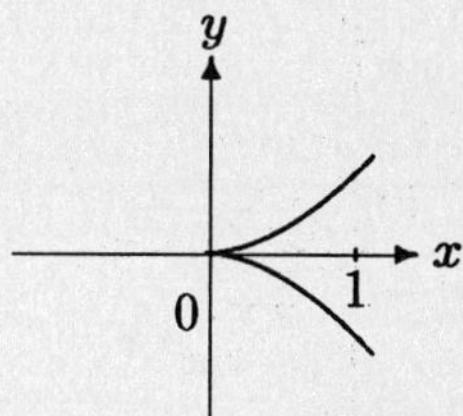

43. graph consists of the two axes; not graph of function

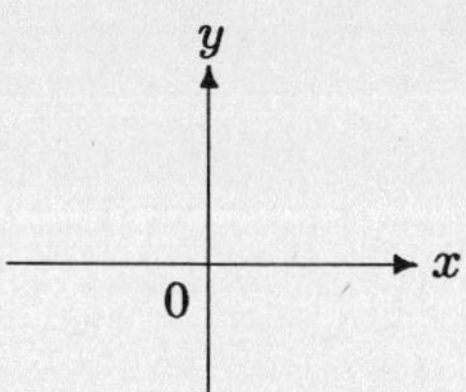

44. not graph of function

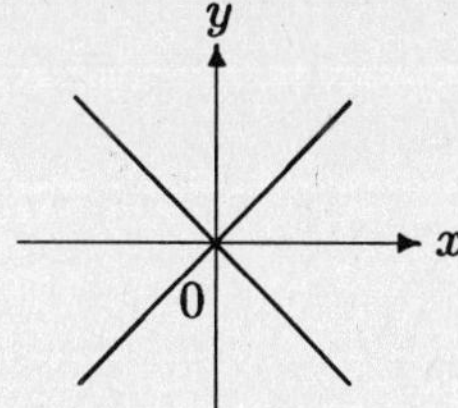

45. not graph of function

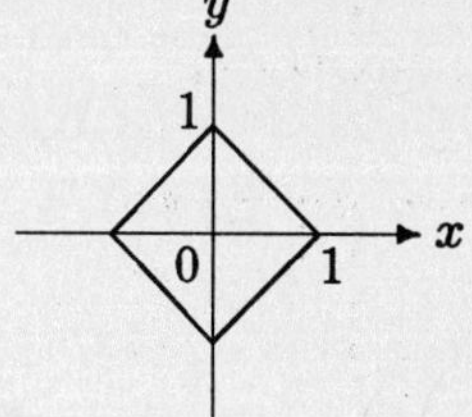

46. not graph of function

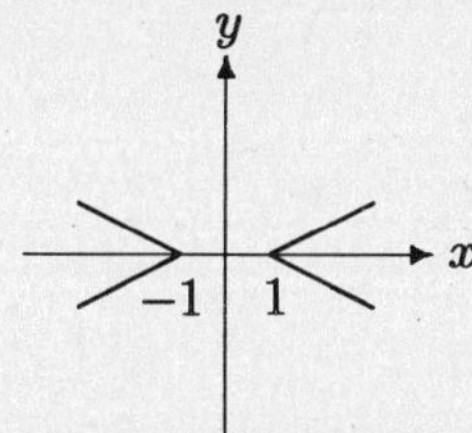

47. c. If $c > 0$, then the graph of $y = f(x + c)$ is obtained from the graph of f by shifting to the left c units. If $c < 0$, then the graph of $y = f(x + c)$ is obtained from the graph of f by shifting to the right $|c|$ units.

48. a, d, e, h

49. a. $-2, -1, 1$ and 3

    b. The union of $[-4, -2)$, $(-1, 1)$ and $(3, 4]$

    c. The union of $(-2, -1)$ and $(1, 3)$

    d. None

    e. $[-4, 4]$

50. Yes. If $f(x) = c$, then the horizontal line $y = c$ is the graph of f.

51. $p = 2$, $q = 1$, $r = -2$

52. $p = 3$, $q = 1$, $r = 2$

53. f is a possible revenue function, g a cost function, and h a profit function.

54. h, since at large production levels many CD's would be unsold. Thus revenue would not keep pace with cost, and the profit would plummet.

55.

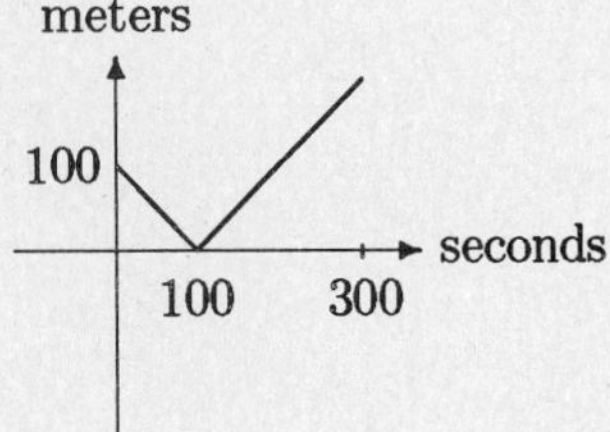

56. a. h_0 appears to be approximately 98.

b. Since the ball lands in the sand, it does not bounce.

c.

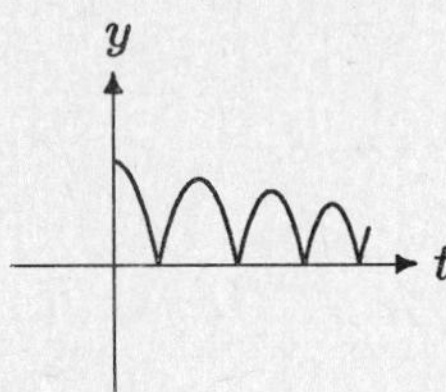

57. a.

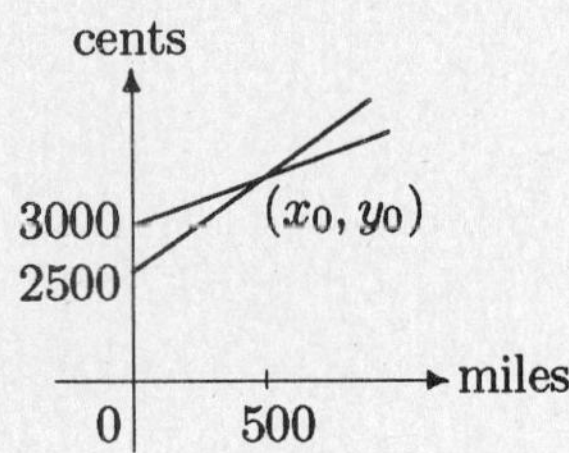

b. If $P = (x_0, y_0)$ is the intersection, then if you expect to travel fewer than x_0 miles, you should rent from Econ Agency; otherwise rent from Budge Agency.

58. a. The slope is given by $\dfrac{f(a) - f(0)}{a - 0} = \dfrac{f(a)}{a}$.

b. Since $f(2)/2 \approx 2/2 = 1$ and $f(5)/5 \approx 3/5$, it follows that $f(2)/2$ is the larger.

59.

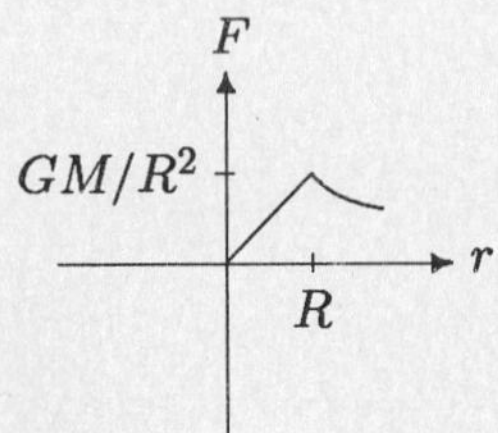

60. Notice that $P(x) = 29$ for $0 < x \le 1$, $P(x) = 29 + 23 \cdot 1$ for $1 < x \le 2$, $P(x) = 29 + 23 \cdot 2$ for $2 < x \le 3$, etc. Notice that $[-x] = -1$ for $0 < x \le 1$, $[-x] = -2$ for $1 < x \le 2$, $[-x] = -3$ for $2 < x \le 3$, etc. Thus $P(x) = 6 - 23\,[-x]$.

1.5 Aids to Graphing

			Symmetry		
	y intercepts	x intercepts	x axis	y axis	origin
1.	$-\sqrt{\frac{2}{3}}, \sqrt{\frac{2}{3}}$	-2	yes	no	no
2.	$-2\sqrt{3}, 2\sqrt{3}$	$-\sqrt{3}, \sqrt{3}$	yes	yes	yes
3.	none	$-1, 1$	yes	yes	yes
4.	$-1, 0, 1$	0	no	yes	no
5.	0	0	no	yes	no
6.	$\sqrt[3]{-\frac{4}{3}}$	$-\sqrt{2}, \sqrt{2}$	no	yes	no
7.	none	none	yes	yes	yes
8.	all reals	0	yes	no	no
9.	none	$-1, 1$	no	no	yes
10.	0	0	no	no	yes
11.	0	$[0, 1)$	no	no	no
12.	$-8, -2$	$-2, 8$	no	no	no
13.	3	$-3, 3$	no	yes	no
14.	0	0	yes	no	no
15.	1	1	no	no	no
16.	none	none	yes	yes	yes

17. y intercept: 0; x intercept: 0; symmetry with respect to origin

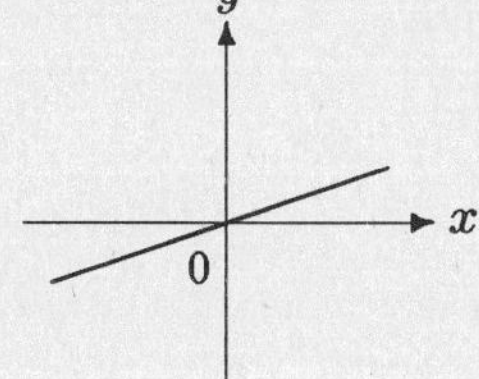

18. y intercept: 0; x intercept: 0; symmetry with respect to x axis

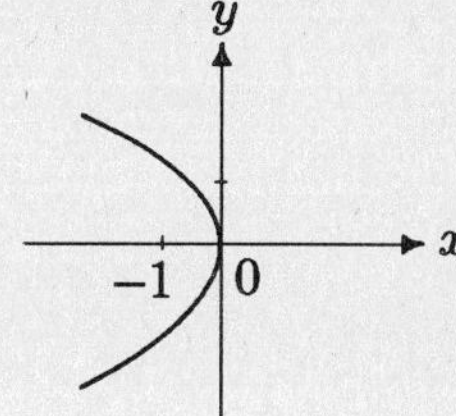

19. y intercept: -3; x intercepts: $-\sqrt{3}$, $\sqrt{3}$; symmetry with respect to y axis

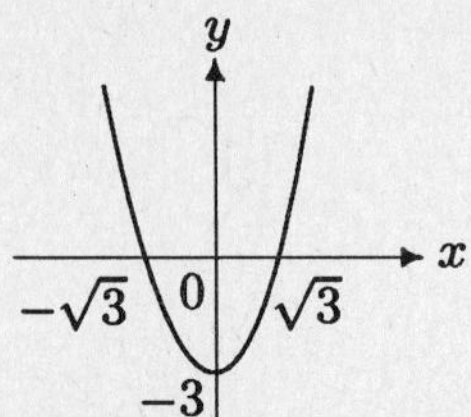

20. x intercepts: -2, 2; symmetry with respect to x axis, y axis, origin

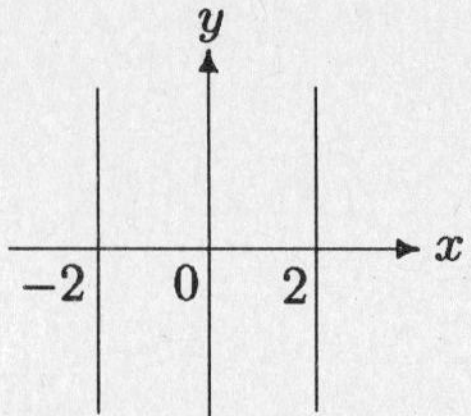

21. y intercepts: -1, 1; symmetry with respect to x axis, y axis, origin

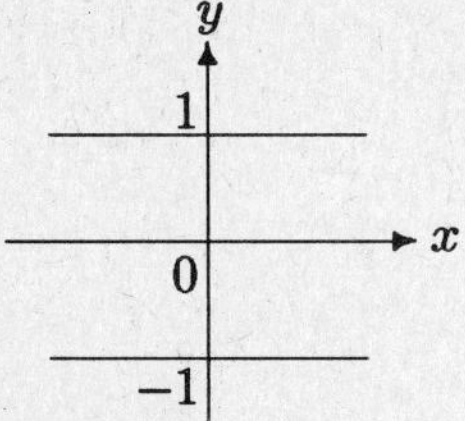

22. y intercepts: $-\frac{3}{2}$, $\frac{3}{2}$; x intercepts: $-\frac{3}{2}$, $\frac{3}{2}$; symmetry with respect to x axis, y axis, origin

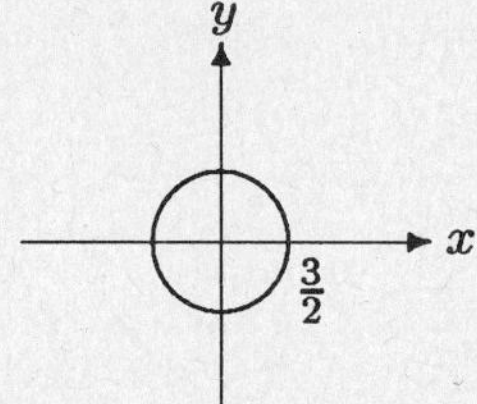

23. y intercepts: -2, 2; x intercept: 2; symmetry with respect to x axis

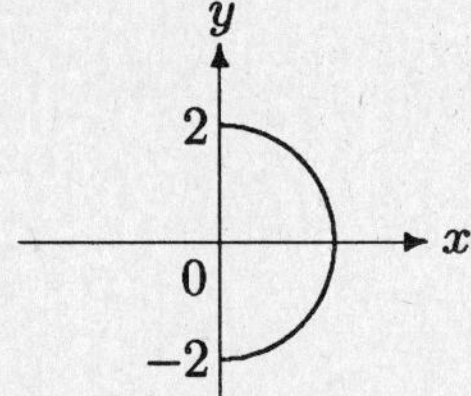

24. y intercept: 5; x intercepts: -5, 5; symmetry with respect to y axis

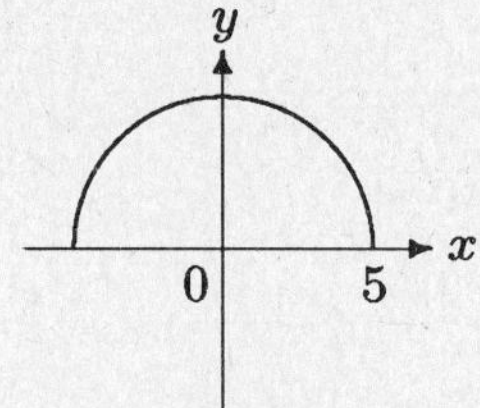

25. y intercept: 0; x intercept: 0; symmetry with respect to x axis, y axis, origin

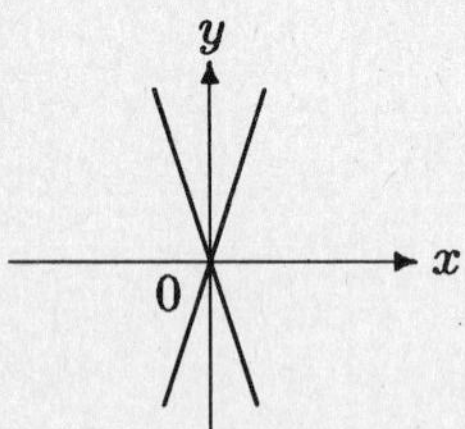

26. y intercepts: $-\frac{1}{2}$, $\frac{7}{2}$; x intercepts: -7, -1; not symmetric with respect to either axis or origin

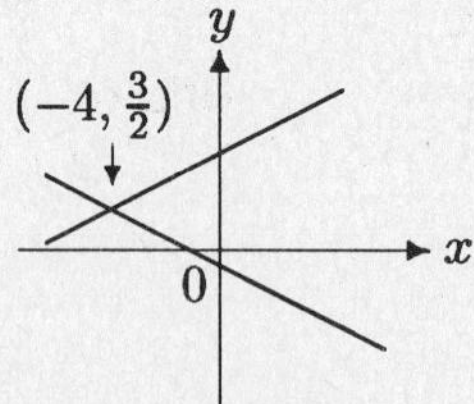

27. $(x-1)^2 + (y-3)^2 = 4$
Let $X = x - 1$, $Y = y - 3$. Then $X^2 + Y^2 = 4$.

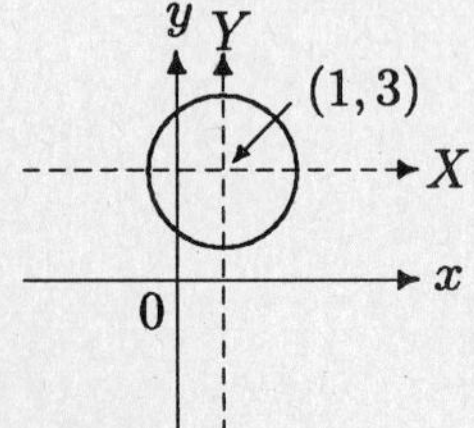

28. $(x+2)^2 + (y+4)^2 = \frac{1}{4}$
Let $X = x + 2$, $Y = y + 4$. Then $X^2 + Y^2 = \frac{1}{4}$.

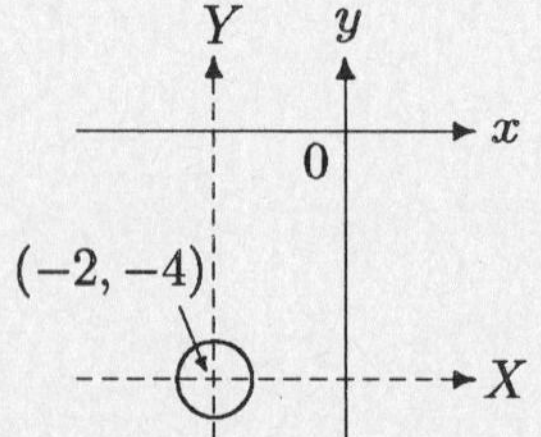

29. $x^2 - 2x + y^2 = 3$, so $(x-1)^2 + y^2 = 4$
Let $X = x - 1$, $Y = y$. Then $X^2 + Y^2 = 4$.

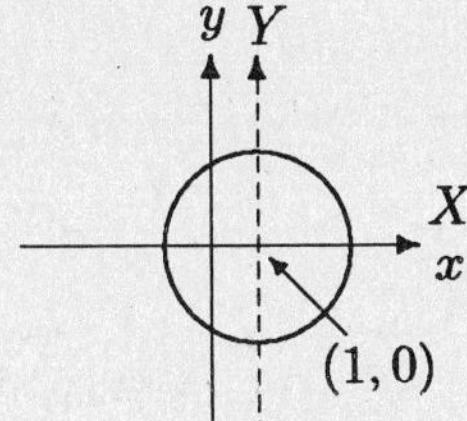

30. $x^2 + y^2 + 4y = -1$, so $x^2 + (y+2)^2 = 3$
Let $X = x$, $Y = y + 2$. Then $X^2 + Y^2 = 3$.

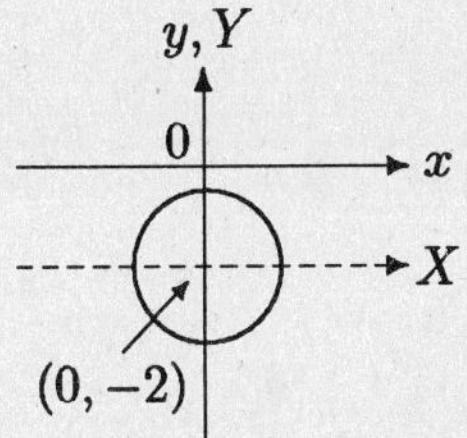

31. $x^2 + y - 3 = 0$, so $y - 3 = -x^2$
Let $X = x$, $Y = y - 3$. Then $Y = -X^2$.

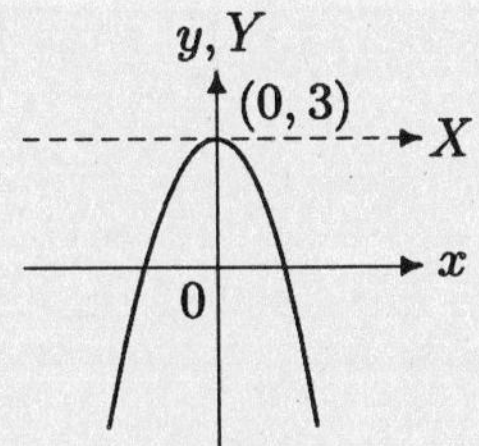

32. $x^2 - 4x + y = 5$, so $y - 9 = -(x-2)^2$
Let $X = x - 2$, $Y = y - 9$. Then $Y = -X^2$.

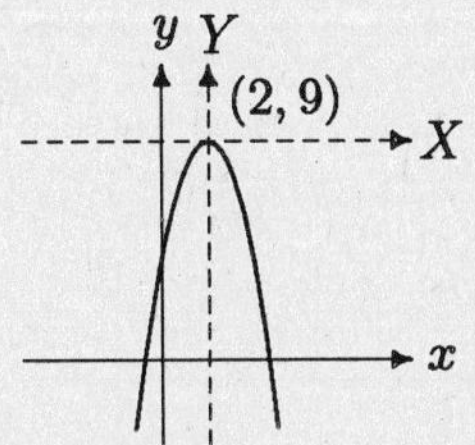

33. $x^2 + y^2 + 4x - 6y + 13 = 0$,
so $(x+2)^2 + (y-3)^2 = 0$
Let $X = x + 2$, $Y = y - 3$. Then $X^2 + Y^2 = 0$.

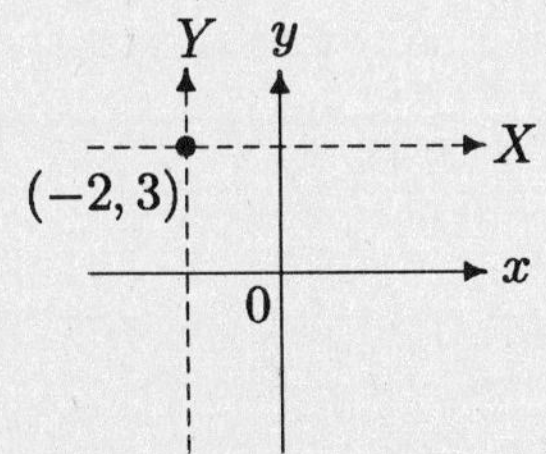

34. $x^2 - 6x + y^2 - y = -9$,
so $(x-3)^2 + (y - \frac{1}{2})^2 = \frac{1}{4}$
Let $X = x - 3$, $Y = y - \frac{1}{2}$. Then $X^2 + Y^2 = \frac{1}{4}$.

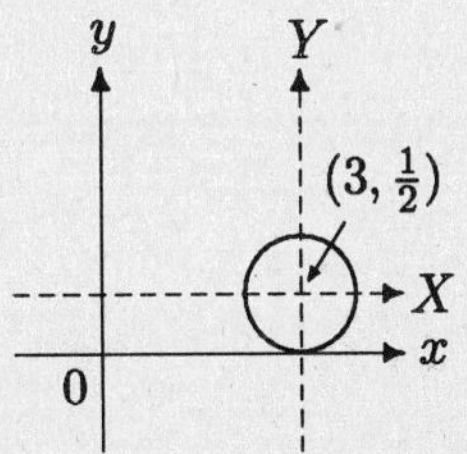

35. $y + 4 = \dfrac{1}{x+2}$
Let $X = x + 2$, $Y = y + 4$. Then $Y = 1/X$.

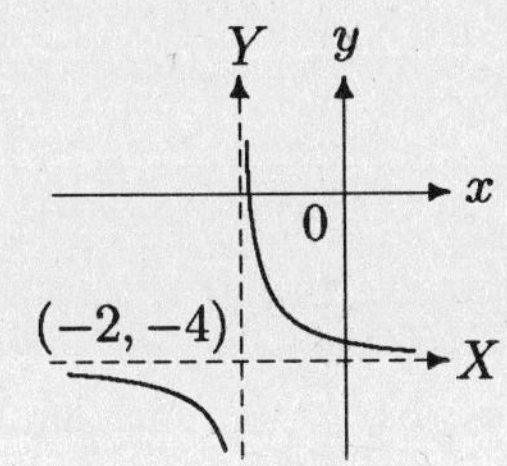

36. $y = |x - 4|$
Let $X = x - 4$, $Y = y$. Then $Y = |X|$.

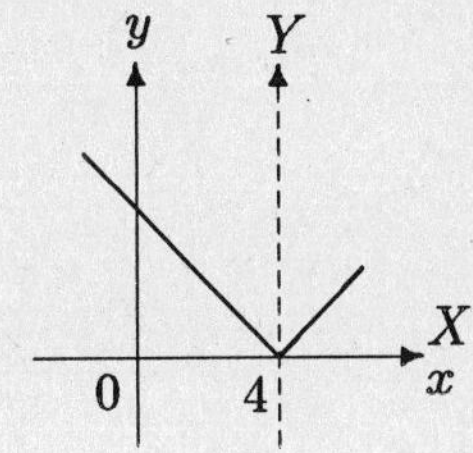

37. $x - 2 = |y - 2|$
Let $X = x - 2$, $Y = y - 2$. Then $X = |Y|$.

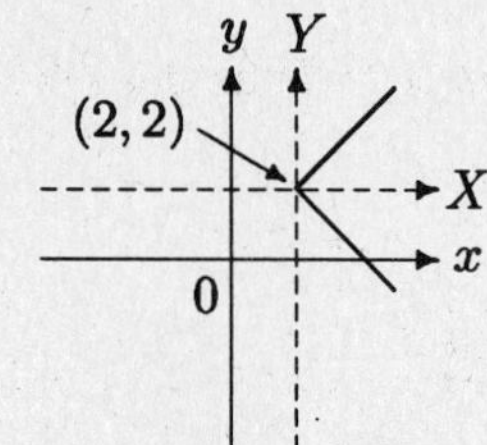

38. $y = \sqrt{x+3}$
Let $X = x + 3$, $Y = y$. Then $Y = \sqrt{X}$.

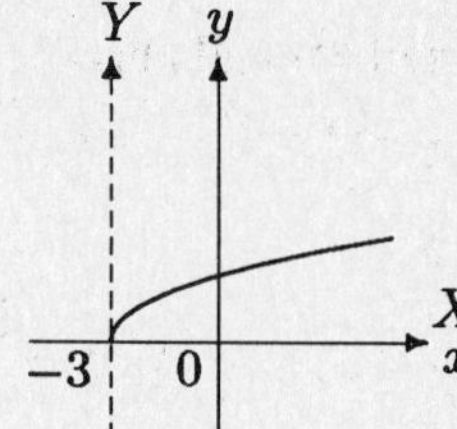

39. a. $f(-x) = -(-x) = x = -f(x)$, so f is odd.

b. $f(-x) = 5(-x)^2 - 3 = 5x^2 - 3 = f(x)$, so f is even.

c. $f(-x) = (-x)^3 + 1 = -x^3 + 1 \neq (x^3 + 1)$ or $-(x^3 + 1)$ if $x \neq 0$, so f is neither even nor odd.

d. $f(-x) = (-x-2)^2 = \left(-(x+2)\right)^2 = (x+2)^2 \neq (x-2)^2$ or $-(x-2)^2$ if $x \neq 0$, so f is neither even nor odd.

e. $f(-x) = \left((-x)^2 + 3\right)^3 = (x^2 + 3)^3 = f(x)$, so f is even.

f. $f(-x) = -x\left((-x)^2 + 1\right)^2 = -x(x^2 + 1)^2 = -f(x)$, so f is odd.

g. $\dfrac{-x}{(-x)^2 + 4} = -\dfrac{x}{x^2 + 4}$, so the function is odd.

h. $|-x| = |x|$, so the function is even.

i. $\dfrac{|-x|}{-x} = \dfrac{|x|}{-x} = -\dfrac{|x|}{x}$, so the function is odd.

40. $ax^2 + bx + c = 0$ if and only if $x^2 + \dfrac{b}{a}x + \dfrac{c}{a} = 0$, which occurs if and only if

$$x^2 + \frac{b}{a}x + \left(\frac{b}{2a}\right)^2 = \left(\frac{b}{2a}\right)^2 - \frac{c}{a}, \quad \text{or equivalently,} \quad \left(x + \frac{b}{2a}\right)^2 = \frac{b^2 - 4ac}{4a^2}.$$

Thus

$$x + \frac{b}{2a} = \pm\sqrt{\frac{b^2 - 4ac}{4a^2}}, \quad \text{so that} \quad x = -\frac{b}{2a} \pm \frac{1}{2a}\sqrt{b^2 - 4ac}.$$

This is equivalent to (1).

41. By Exercise 40 (or (1)), $x = \dfrac{-(-3) \pm \sqrt{(-3)^2 - 4(1)(1)}}{2(1)} = \dfrac{3 \pm \sqrt{5}}{2} = \dfrac{3}{2} + \dfrac{1}{2}\sqrt{5}$ or $\dfrac{3}{2} - \dfrac{1}{2}\sqrt{5}$.

42. By Exercise 40 (or (1)), $x = \dfrac{-2 \pm \sqrt{2^2 - 4(3)(-1)}}{2(3)} = \dfrac{-2 \pm \sqrt{16}}{6} = \dfrac{-2 \pm 4}{6} = -1$ or $\dfrac{1}{3}$.

43. Since $b^2 - 4ac = 7^2 - 4(2)(7) = -7$, g has no zero.

44. By Exercise 40 (or(1)), $t = \dfrac{-(-8) \pm \sqrt{(-8)^2 - 4(8)(2)}}{2(8)} = \dfrac{8 \pm \sqrt{0}}{16} = \dfrac{1}{2}$.

45. By (1), $x = \dfrac{-5.1 \pm \sqrt{(5.1)^2 - 4(-4.9)(1.2)}}{2(-4.9)} \approx -0.20$ or 1.24.

46. By (1), $x = \dfrac{-\pi \pm \sqrt{\pi^2 - 4(\sqrt{2})(1)}}{2\sqrt{2}} \approx -0.39$ or -1.84.

47. f has no real zeros if and only if the discriminant $b^2 - 4ac < 0$. But then $4ac > 0$. Thus the discriminant of g is $b^2 - 4a(-c) = b^2 + 4ac > 0$. Therefore g has two real zeros.

48. The zeros of f are

$$z_1 = \frac{-b - \sqrt{b^2 - 4ac}}{2a} \quad \text{and} \quad z_2 = \frac{-b + \sqrt{b^2 - 4ac}}{2a}.$$

Therefore

$$z_1 + z_2 = \frac{-b - \sqrt{b^2 - 4ac}}{2a} + \frac{-b + \sqrt{b^2 - 4ac}}{2a} = \frac{-b}{2a} + \frac{-b}{2a} = -\frac{b}{a}.$$

49. $(-1, 0)$ and $(1.54, 4.67)$

50. $(-1.32, 1.75)$

51. $(-1.21, \infty)$

52. $(-\infty, 0.567)$

53. a. The graph of g is 3 units to the left of the graph of f.

$$g(x) = f(x+3) = (x+3)^2$$

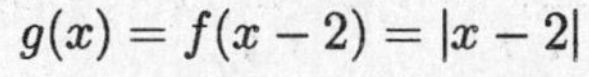

$$g(x) = f(x-2) = |x-2|$$

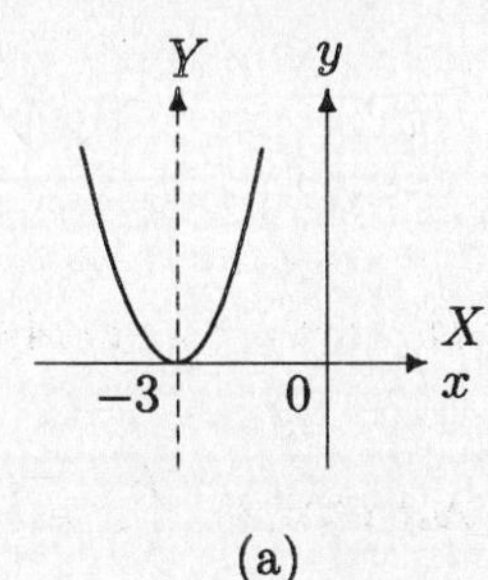

(a)

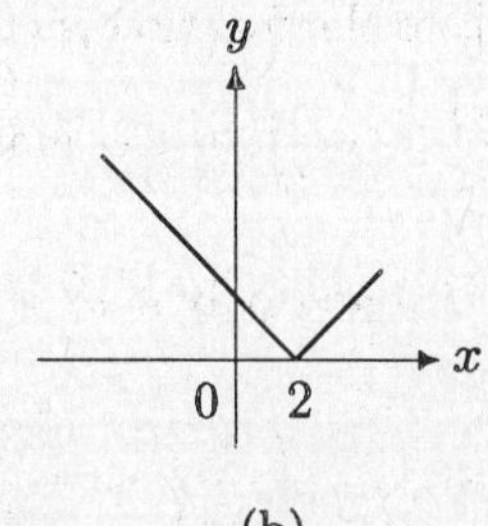

(b)

b. The graph of g is 2 units to the right of the graph of f.

54. The graph of g is 3 units below the graph of f.

55. The graph of g is d units above the graph of f if $d \geq 0$, and is $-d$ units below the graph of f if $d < 0$.

56. a. $f(-x) = |-x-1| + |-x+1| = |-(x+1)| + |-(x-1)| = |x+1| + |x-1| = f(x)$, so that f is symmetric with respect to the y axis. Since the graph of any nonzero function is not symmetric with respect to the x axis, and since f is clearly nonzero, it follows that the graph of f is not symmetric with respect to the x axis. It is also not symmetric with respect to the origin since $f(-1) = 2 = f(1)$ and hence $f(-1) \neq -f(1)$.

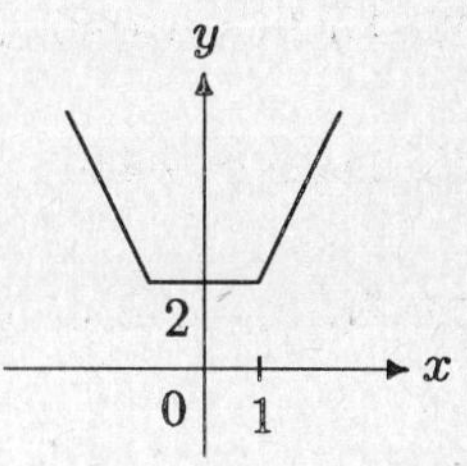

b. For $x < -1$, $f(x) = -(x-1) - (x+1) = -2x$.
For $-1 \leq x < 1$, $f(x) = -(x-1) + (x+1) = 2$.
For $x \geq 1$, $f(x) = (x-1) + (x+1) = 2x$.

57. Let (x, y) be on the graph. Since the graph is symmetric with respect to the x axis, $(x, -y)$ is on the graph. But then symmetry with respect to the y axis implies that $(-x, -y)$ is on the graph. Thus $(-x, -y)$ is on the graph whenever (x, y) is on the graph, so the graph is symmetric with respect to the origin. The converse is not true. For example, the graph of $xy = 1$ is symmetric with respect to the origin but not with respect to either axis.

58. Let (x, y) be on the graph. Since the graph is symmetric with respect to the origin, $(-x, -y)$ is on the graph. But then the symmetry with respect to the y axis implies that $(-(-x), -y) = (x, -y)$ is on the graph. Therefore, if (x, y) is on the graph, then $(x, -y)$ is on the graph, so the graph is symmetric with respect to the x axis.

59. Since $f(c - x) = f(c + x)$, the point $(c - x, y)$ is on the graph of f if and only if the point $(c + x, y)$ is on the graph of f. Thus the graph of f is symmetric with respect to the line $x = c$.

60. Let (x, y) be such a point. Then $\sqrt{(x-2)^2 + (y+3)^2} = 2\sqrt{(x+1)^2 + (y-0)^2}$. Squaring both sides, we have $(x-2)^2 + (y+3)^2 = 4[(x+1)^2 + y^2]$, or $3x^2 + 12x + 3y^2 - 6y = 9$, or $(x+2)^2 + (y-1)^2 = 8$. Thus such points form a circle with center $(-2, 1)$ and radius $\sqrt{8} = 2\sqrt{2}$.

61. The wave is moving to the right.

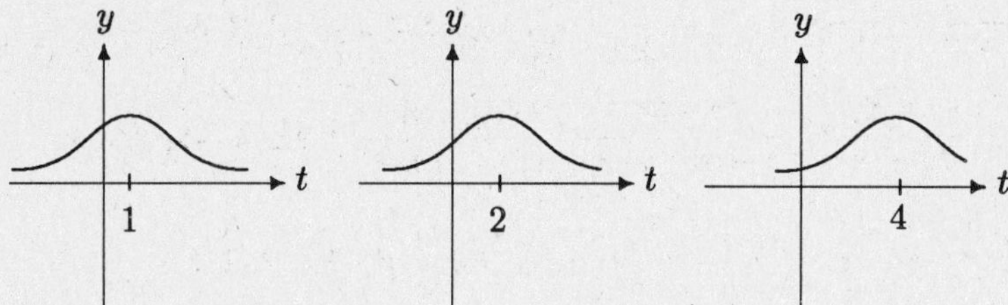

1.6 Combining Functions

1. $(f + g)(-1) = f(-1) + g(-1) = (-3) + (2) = -1$

2. $(f - g)(2) = f(2) - g(2) = 6 - (-1) = 7$

3. $(fg)(\frac{1}{2}) = f(\frac{1}{2})g(\frac{1}{2}) = (-3)(\frac{11}{4}) = -\frac{33}{4}$

4. $\left(\dfrac{f}{g}\right)(-3) = \dfrac{f(-3)}{g(-3)} = \dfrac{11}{(-6)} = -\dfrac{11}{6}$

5. $f(g(1)) = f(2) = 6$

6. $g(f(0)) = g(-4) = -13$

7. $\dfrac{f(x) - f(2)}{x - 2} = \dfrac{2x^2 + x - 10}{x - 2} = \dfrac{(x-2)(2x+5)}{x-2} = 2x + 5$

8. $\dfrac{g(a) - g(-1)}{a + 1} = \dfrac{3 - a^2 - 2}{a + 1} = \dfrac{1 - a^2}{1 + a} = 1 - a$

9. $(f+g)(16) = f(16) + g(16) = \dfrac{15}{257} + 2 = \dfrac{529}{257}$

10. $(f-g)(1) = f(1) - g(1) = 0 - 1 = -1$

11. $(fg)(9) = f(9)g(9) = \dfrac{8}{82}\sqrt{3} = \dfrac{4\sqrt{3}}{41}$

12. $\left(\dfrac{f}{g}\right)\left(\dfrac{1}{4}\right) = \dfrac{(-\frac{3}{4})/\frac{17}{16}}{1/\sqrt{2}} = -\dfrac{12}{17}\sqrt{2}$

13. $f(g(1)) = f(1) = 0$

14. $g(f(1)) = g(0) = 0$

15. $(f+g)(x) = \dfrac{2}{x-1} + x - 1 = \dfrac{x^2 - 2x + 3}{x-1}$ for $x \neq 1$

$(fg)(x) = \dfrac{2}{x-1}(x-1) = 2$ for $x \neq 1$

$\left(\dfrac{f}{g}\right)(x) = \dfrac{2}{(x-1)^2}$ for $x \neq 1$

16. $(f+g)(x) = \dfrac{x+2}{x-3} + \dfrac{x+3}{x^2-4} = \dfrac{x^3 + 3x^2 - 4x - 17}{x^3 - 3x^2 - 4x + 12}$ for $x \neq -2, 2, 3$

$(fg)(x) = \dfrac{x+2}{x-3} \cdot \dfrac{x+3}{x^2-4} = \dfrac{x+3}{(x-3)(x-2)} = \dfrac{x+3}{x^2 - 5x + 6}$ for $x \neq -2, 2, 3$

$\left(\dfrac{f}{g}\right)(x) = \dfrac{x+2}{x-3} \cdot \dfrac{x^2-4}{x+3} = \dfrac{x^3 + 2x^2 - 4x - 8}{x^2 - 9}$ for $x \neq -3, -2, 2, 3$

17. $(f+g)(t) = t^{3/4} + t^2 + 3$ for $t \geq 0$

$(fg)(t) = t^{3/4}(t^2 + 3) = t^{11/4} + 3t^{3/4}$ for $t \geq 0$

$\left(\dfrac{f}{g}\right)(t) = \dfrac{t^{3/4}}{t^2 + 3}$ for $t \geq 0$

18. $(f+g)(t) = \sqrt{1-t^2} + \sqrt{2+t-t^2}$ for $-1 \leq t \leq 1$

$(fg)(t) = \sqrt{1-t^2}\,\sqrt{2+t-t^2} = \sqrt{2 + t - 3t^2 - t^3 + t^4}$ for $-1 \leq t \leq 1$

$\left(\dfrac{f}{g}\right)(t) = \dfrac{\sqrt{1-t^2}}{\sqrt{2+t-t^2}} = \sqrt{\dfrac{1-t}{2-t}}$ for $-1 < t \leq 1$

19. $(g \circ f)(x) = g(f(x)) = g(1-x) = 2(1-x) + 5 = -2x + 7$ for all x

$(f \circ g)(x) = f(g(x)) = f(2x+5) = 1 - (2x+5) = -2x - 4$ for all x

20. $(g \circ f)(x) = g(f(x)) = g(x^2 + 2x + 3) = (x^2 + 2x + 3) - 1 = x^2 + 2x + 2$ for all x

$(f \circ g)(x) = f(g(x)) = f(x-1) = (x-1)^2 + 2(x-1) + 3 = x^2 + 2$ for all x

21. $(g \circ f)(x) = g(f(x)) = g(x^2) = \sqrt{x^2} = |x|$ for all x

    $(f \circ g)(x) = f(g(x)) = f(\sqrt{x}) = (\sqrt{x})^2 = x$ for $x \geq 0$

22. $(g \circ f)(x) = g(f(x)) = g(x^6) = (x^6)^{3/4} = |x|^{9/2}$ for all x (since $x^6 \geq 0$ for all x)

    $(f \circ g)(x) = f(g(x)) = f(x^{3/4}) = (x^{3/4})^6 = x^{9/2}$ for $x \geq 0$

23. $(g \circ f)(x) = g(f(x)) = g(\sqrt{x}) = (\sqrt{x})^2 - 5\sqrt{x} + 6 = x - 5\sqrt{x} + 6$ for $x \geq 0$

    $(f \circ g)(x) = f(g(x)) = f(x^2 - 5x + 6) = \sqrt{x^2 - 5x + 6}$ for $x \leq 2$ or $x \geq 3$

24. $(g \circ f)(x) = g(f(x)) = g\left(\frac{1}{x}\right) = \left(\frac{1}{x}\right)^2 - 3\left(\frac{1}{x}\right) - 10 = \frac{1}{x^2} - \frac{3}{x} - 10$ for $x \neq 0$

    $(f \circ g)(x) = f(g(x)) = f(x^2 - 3x - 10) = \frac{1}{x^2 - 3x - 10}$ for $x \neq -2, 5$

25. $(g \circ f)(x) = g(f(x)) = g\left(\frac{1}{x-1}\right) = \frac{1}{\frac{1}{x-1} + 1} = \frac{x-1}{x}$ for $x \neq 0, 1$

    $(f \circ g)(x) = f(g(x)) = f\left(\frac{1}{x+1}\right) = \frac{1}{\frac{1}{x+1} - 1} = -\frac{x+1}{x}$ for $x \neq -1, 0$

26. $(g \circ f)(x) = g(f(x)) = g(\sqrt{x^2+3}) = \sqrt{(\sqrt{x^2+3})^2 - 4} = \sqrt{x^2 - 1}$ for $x \leq -1$ or $1 \leq x$

    $(f \circ g)(x) = f(g(x)) = f(\sqrt{x^2-4}) = \sqrt{(\sqrt{x^2-4})^2 + 3} = \sqrt{x^2 - 1}$ for $x \leq -2$ or $x \geq 2$

27. Let $f(x) = x - 3$, $g(x) = \sqrt{x}$. Then $h(x) = g(x-3) = g(f(x)) = (g \circ f)(x)$.

28. Let $f(x) = 1 - x^2$, $g(x) = x^{3/2}$. Then $h(x) = g(1 - x^2) = g(f(x)) = (g \circ f)(x)$.

29. Let $f(x) = 3x^2 - 5\sqrt{x}$, $g(x) = x^{1/3}$. Then $h(x) = g(3x^2 - 5\sqrt{x}) = g(f(x)) = (g \circ f)(x)$.

30. Let $f(x) = x + (1/x)$, $g(x) = x^{5/2}$. Then $h(x) = g[x + (1/x)] = g(f(x)) = (g \circ f)(x)$.

31. Let $f(x) = x + 3$, $g(x) = 1/(x^2 + 1)$. Then $h(x) = g(x+3) = g(f(x)) = (g \circ f)(x)$. Alternatively, let $f(x) = (x+3)^2 + 1$ and $g(x) = 1/x$.

32. Let $f(x) = x^3 - 2x^2$, $g(x) = 1/x^5$. Then $h(x) = g(x^3 - 2x^2) = g(f(x)) = (g \circ f)(x)$.

33. Let $f(x) = \sqrt{x} - 1$, $g(x) = \sqrt{x}$. Then $h(x) = g(\sqrt{x} - 1) = g(f(x)) = (g \circ f)(x)$. Alternatively, let $f(x) = \sqrt{x}$ and $g(x) = \sqrt{x-1}$.

34. Let $f(x) = [x] - 1$, $g(x) = \sqrt{x}$. Then $h(x) = g([x] - 1) = g(f(x)) = (g \circ f)(x)$. Alternatively, let $f(x) = [x]$ and $g(x) = \sqrt{x-1}$.

35. $g(x) = -|x - 2|$

36. $g(x) = \dfrac{x+3}{x^2-4}$

37. If $0 \le x+3 \le 4$, then $-3 \le x \le 1$; the domain of g is $[-3, 1]$.

38. If $a \le x+c \le b$, then $a-c \le x \le b-c$; the domain of g is $[a-c, b-c]$.

39. f is red; g is green; $f+g$ is blue; fg is black.

40. The highest point on the graph of f is $(2,4)$, and the highest point on the graph of g is $(4,3)$. Thus $d=1$.

41. a. $h = f$ if $c = -1$

b. Since $2 = h(1) = g(1+c)$, and $g(.4) \approx 2$, c must satisfy the equation $1+c \approx .4$, so $c \approx -.6$.

42. a.

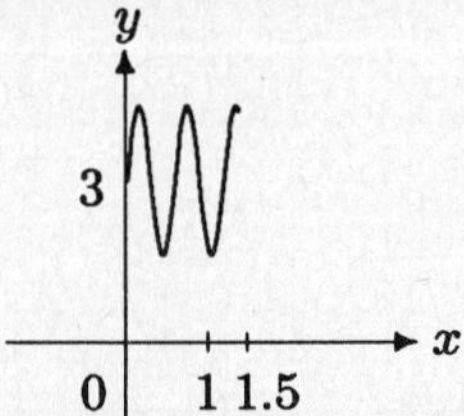

b.

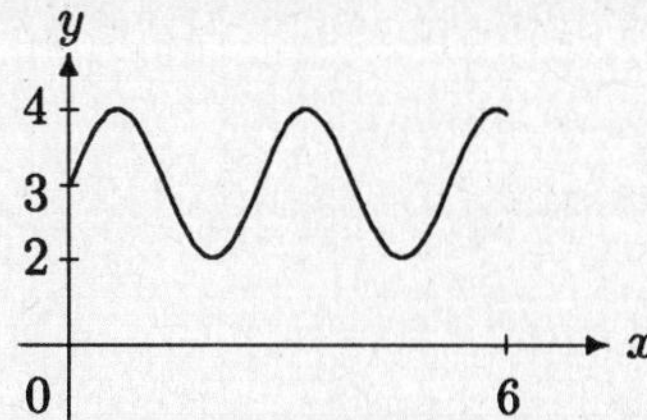

43. The graph of h is so short because $\sqrt{x+1}$ is defined for $x \ge -1$, and $\sqrt{2-x}$ is defined for $x \le 2$. Thus the domain of h is $[-1, 2]$.

44. All functions f such that $f(x) \ge 0$ for all x in the domain of f, that is, all functions with range contained in $[0, \infty)$

45. All functions

46. All functions f such that $f(x) \ne 0$ for all x in the domain of f.

47. Assume that $f(x) \ge 0$ for all x in the domain of f. Then let $g(x) = (f(x))^2 - 1$ for all such x. It follows that $(f(x))^2 = 1 + g(x)$ and thus $f(x) = \sqrt{1+g(x)}$. Thus all functions f such that $f(x) \ge 0$ for all x in either domain of f allow such a g.

48. If x is in the domain of both f and g, then since f and g are even, $-x$ is in the domains of f and g, and hence of $f+g$ and fg. For such x,

a. $(f+g)(-x) = f(-x) + g(-x) = f(x) + g(x) = (f+g)(x)$, so that $f+g$ is even.

b. $(fg)(-x) = f(-x)g(-x) = f(x)g(x) = (fg)(x)$, so that fg is even.

49. Since f is even and g is odd, $-x$ is in the domain of f and g and hence fg if x is. For such x, $(fg)(-x) = f(-x)g(-x) = f(x)(-g(x)) = -f(x)g(x) = -(fg)(x)$. Thus fg is odd.

50. $f(f(x)) = f\left(\dfrac{1}{x}\right) = \dfrac{1}{1/x} = x$ for $x \ne 0$

51. $f(f(x)) = f(a-x) = a-(a-x) = x$

52. $f\Big(f(f(x))\Big) = f\left(f\left(\frac{1}{1-x}\right)\right) = f\left(\frac{1}{1-1/(1-x)}\right) = f\left(\frac{1-x}{1-x-1}\right)$

$$= f\left(\frac{1-x}{-x}\right) = \frac{1}{1-[(1-x)/(-x)]} = \frac{-x}{-x-1+x} = x \quad \text{for } x \neq 0,\ 1$$

53. $g(x) = f(x+p) - f(x) = [a(x+p)+b] - (ax+b) = ap$

54. $f(x+y) = c(x+y) = cx + cy = f(x) + f(y)$

55. a. Since $g(-x) = \frac{1}{2}[f(-x) + f(x)] = g(x)$, g is an even function.

    b. Since $h(-x) = \frac{1}{2}[f(-x) - f(x)] = -\frac{1}{2}[f(x) - f(-x)] = -h(x)$, h is an odd function.

    c. $g(x) + h(x) = \frac{1}{2}[f(x) + f(-x)] + \frac{1}{2}[f(x) - f(-x)] = f(x)$

56. $T(x) = x$ for $\frac{1}{2} < x \le 1$ if $2(1-x) = x$, or $2 = 3x$. Thus $x = \frac{2}{3}$. We have $T(\frac{2}{3}) = \frac{2}{3}$. (Notice that if $0 < x \le \frac{1}{2}$, then $T(x) = 2x > x$, so $T(x) \neq x$.)

57. The nth iterate is close to 0.

58. The nth iterate is close to 0.6.

59. For large values of n, the nth iterate oscillates between numbers close to 0.80 and numbers close to 0.51.

60. For large values of n, the nth iterate oscillates between numbers close to .50, .87, .38, and .83.

61. For large values of n, the nth iterate oscillates between numbers close to .16, .50, and .96.

62. There is no apparent pattern or repetition.

63. $P(x) = R(x) - C(x) = 5x^2 - \frac{1}{10}x^4 - (4x^2 - 24x + 38) = -\frac{1}{10}x^4 + x^2 + 24x - 38$. Thus $P(1) = -\frac{1}{10} + 1 + 24 - 38 = -13.1$; $P(2) = -\frac{16}{10} + 4 + 48 - 38 = 12.4$. Since $P(1) = -13.1$, there is a loss when $x = 1$. Since $P(2) = 12.4$, there is a profit when $x = 2$.

64. $V\big(r(t)\big) = \frac{4}{3}\pi(3\sqrt{t})^3 = 36\pi t^{3/2}$ for $t \ge 0$

65. a. $V\big(r(s)\big) = \frac{4}{3}\pi\left(\frac{1}{2}\sqrt{\frac{s}{\pi}}\right)^3 = \frac{1}{6\sqrt{\pi}}s^{3/2}$ for $s \ge 0$

    b. $V\big(r(6)\big) = \frac{1}{6}\cdot 6\sqrt{\frac{6}{\pi}} = \sqrt{\frac{6}{\pi}}$

66. Since r is defined for $t \ge 0$, and F is defined for $r > 0$, $F\big(r(t)\big)$ is defined for $t \ge 0$. For such t,

$$F\big(r(t)\big) = \frac{k}{\left[4000\left(\dfrac{1+t}{1+t^2}\right)\right]^2} = \frac{k(1+t^2)^2}{16{,}000{,}000(1+t)^2}.$$

1.7 Trigonometric Functions

1. a. $210° = \left(\frac{\pi}{180} \cdot 210\right)$ radians $= \frac{7\pi}{6}$ radians

   b. $-405° = -\left(\frac{\pi}{180} \cdot 405\right)$ radians $= -\frac{9\pi}{4}$ radians

   c. $1° = \left(\frac{\pi}{180} \cdot 1\right)$ radian $= \frac{\pi}{180}$ radian

2. a. $\frac{\pi}{8}$ radians $= \left(\frac{180}{\pi} \cdot \frac{\pi}{8}\right)^{\circ} = 22.5°$

   b. $-\frac{3\pi}{10}$ radians $= -\left(\frac{180}{\pi} \cdot \frac{3\pi}{10}\right)^{\circ} = -54°$

   c. $\frac{13\pi}{6}$ radians $= \left(\frac{180}{\pi} \cdot \frac{13\pi}{6}\right)^{\circ} = 390°$

3. a. $\sin \frac{11\pi}{6} = \sin\left(-\frac{\pi}{6} + 2\pi\right) = \sin\left(-\frac{\pi}{6}\right) = -\sin \frac{\pi}{6} = -\frac{1}{2}$

   b. $\sin\left(-\frac{2\pi}{3}\right) = -\sin \frac{2\pi}{3} = -\frac{\sqrt{3}}{2}$

   c. $\cos \frac{5\pi}{4} = \cos\left(\pi + \frac{\pi}{4}\right) = -\cos \frac{\pi}{4} = -\frac{\sqrt{2}}{2}$

   d. $\cos\left(-\frac{7\pi}{6}\right) = \cos \frac{7\pi}{6} = \cos\left(\pi + \frac{\pi}{6}\right) = -\cos \frac{\pi}{6} = -\frac{\sqrt{3}}{2}$

   e. $\tan \frac{4\pi}{3} = \frac{\sin(4\pi/3)}{\cos(4\pi/3)} = \frac{\sin[\pi + (\pi/3)]}{\cos[\pi + (\pi/3)]} = \frac{-\sin(\pi/3)}{-\cos(\pi/3)} = \frac{-\sqrt{3}/2}{-1/2} = \sqrt{3}$

   f. $\tan\left(-\frac{\pi}{4}\right) = \frac{\sin(-\pi/4)}{\cos(-\pi/4)} = \frac{-\sin(\pi/4)}{\cos(\pi/4)} = \frac{-\sqrt{2}/2}{\sqrt{2}/2} = -1$

   g. $\cot \frac{\pi}{6} = \frac{\cos(\pi/6)}{\sin(\pi/6)} = \frac{\sqrt{3}/2}{1/2} = \sqrt{3}$

   h. $\cot\left(-\frac{17\pi}{3}\right) = \frac{\cos[-(17\pi)/3]}{\sin[-(17\pi)/3]} = \frac{\cos[-6\pi + (\pi/3)]}{\sin[-6\pi + (\pi/3)]} = \frac{\cos(\pi/3)}{\sin(\pi/3)} = \frac{1/2}{\sqrt{3}/2} = \frac{1}{\sqrt{3}} = \frac{\sqrt{3}}{3}$

   i. $\sec 3\pi = \frac{1}{\cos 3\pi} = \frac{1}{\cos(2\pi + \pi)} = \frac{1}{\cos \pi} = \frac{1}{-1} = -1$

   j. $\sec\left(-\frac{\pi}{3}\right) = \frac{1}{\cos(-\pi/3)} = \frac{1}{\cos(\pi/3)} = \frac{1}{1/2} = 2$

   k. $\csc \frac{\pi}{2} = \frac{1}{\sin(\pi/2)} = \frac{1}{1} = 1$

   l. $\csc[-(5\pi)/3] = \frac{1}{\sin[-(5\pi)/3]} = \frac{1}{\sin[-2\pi + (\pi/3)]} = \frac{1}{\sin(\pi/3)} = \frac{1}{\sqrt{3}/2} = \frac{2}{\sqrt{3}} = \frac{2\sqrt{3}}{3}$

4. a. all b. sine, cosecant c. tangent, cotangent d. cosine, secant e. none

5. $\tan x = \frac{\sin x}{\cos x} = -\frac{4}{3}$; $\cot x = \frac{1}{\tan x} = -\frac{3}{4}$; $\sec x = \frac{1}{\cos x} = -\frac{5}{3}$; $\csc x = \frac{1}{\sin x} = \frac{5}{4}$

6. $\sin x = \cos x \tan x = \dfrac{2\sqrt{2}}{3}$; $\cot x = \dfrac{1}{\tan x} = \dfrac{1}{2\sqrt{2}} = \dfrac{\sqrt{2}}{4}$; $\sec x = \dfrac{1}{\cos x} = 3$;
$\csc x = \dfrac{1}{\sin x} = \dfrac{3}{2\sqrt{2}} = \dfrac{3\sqrt{2}}{4}$

7. $7\pi/6$, $11\pi/6$

8. $\pi/3$, $4\pi/3$

9. $\sin x = \sin 2x = 2\sin x \cos x$, so $\sin x\,(2\cos x - 1) = 0$. But $\sin x = 0$ for $x = 0, \pi$; $2\cos x - 1 = 0$ if $\cos x = \frac{1}{2}$, which happens for $x = \pi/3, 5\pi/3$. Solutions: 0, $\pi/3$, π, $5\pi/3$.

10. $\cos x = \cos 2x = 2\cos^2 x - 1$ implies that $2\cos^2 x - \cos x - 1 = 0$, or $(2\cos x + 1)(\cos x - 1) = 0$. Now $2\cos x + 1 = 0$ if $\cos x = -\frac{1}{2}$, which happens for $x = 2\pi/3, 4\pi/3$; $\cos x - 1 = 0$ for $x = 0$. Solutions: 0, $2\pi/3$, $4\pi/3$.

11. The union of $[0, 7\pi/6)$ and $(11\pi/6, 2\pi)$

12. $[\pi/2, 3\pi/2]$

13. The union of $[\pi/4, \pi/2)$ and $[5\pi/4, 3\pi/2)$

14. The union of $[0, \pi/4]$ and $[5\pi/4, 2\pi)$

15. The union of $(0, \pi/4]$, $(\pi/2, 3\pi/4]$, $(\pi, 5\pi/4]$, and $(3\pi/2, 7\pi/4]$

16. a. From (12), $\sin x$ is odd.

    b. From (13), $\cos x$ is even.

    c. $\tan(-x) = \dfrac{\sin(-x)}{\cos(-x)} = \dfrac{-\sin x}{\cos x} = -\tan x$, so $\tan x$ is odd.

    d. Since $\cot x = \dfrac{1}{\tan x}$, $\cot x$ is odd by (c).

    e. $\sec(-x) = \dfrac{1}{\cos(-x)} = \dfrac{1}{\cos x} = \sec x$, so $\sec x$ is even.

    f. $\csc(-x) = \dfrac{1}{\sin(-x)} = \dfrac{1}{-\sin x} = -\csc x$, so $\csc x$ is odd.

17. $\cos(\pi - x) = \cos\pi\,\cos x + \sin\pi\,\sin x = -\cos x$; y intercept: -1; x intercepts: $\pi/2 + n\pi$ for any integer n; symmetric with respect to the y axis; an even function.

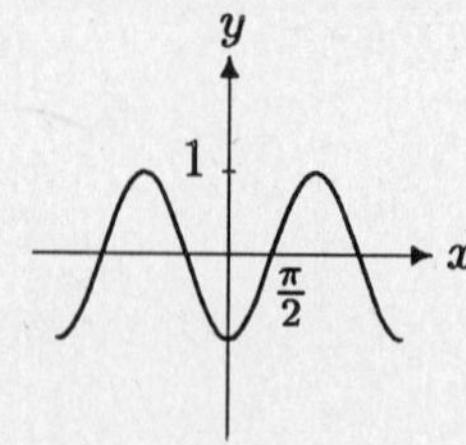

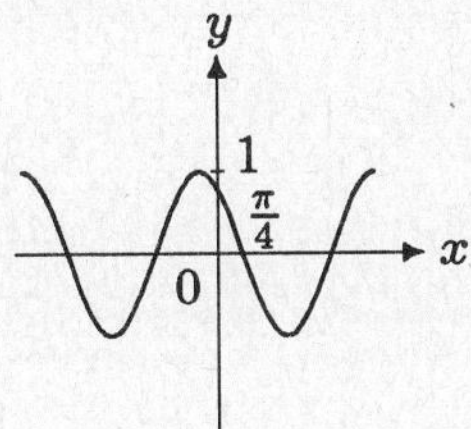

Exercise 18

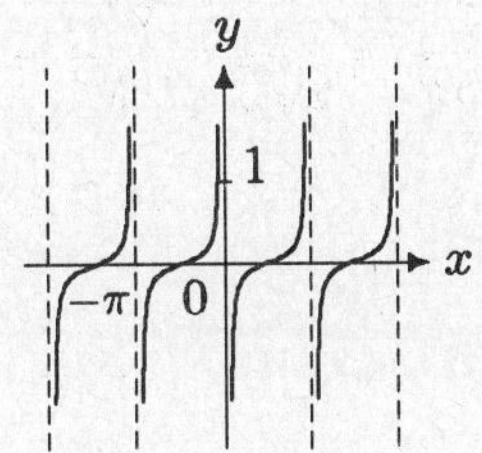

Exercise 19

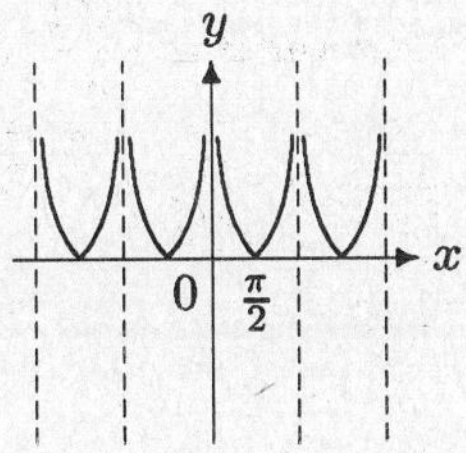

Exercise 20

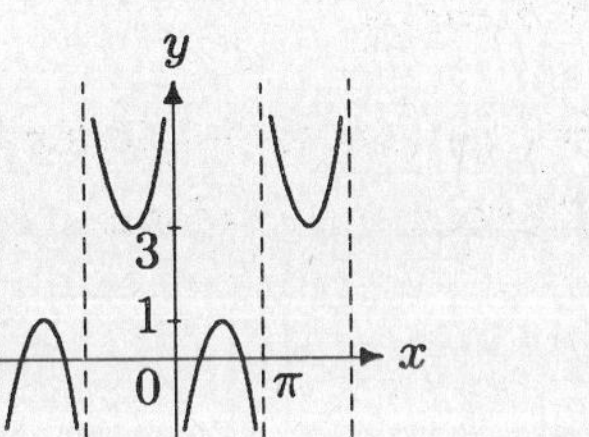

Exercise 22

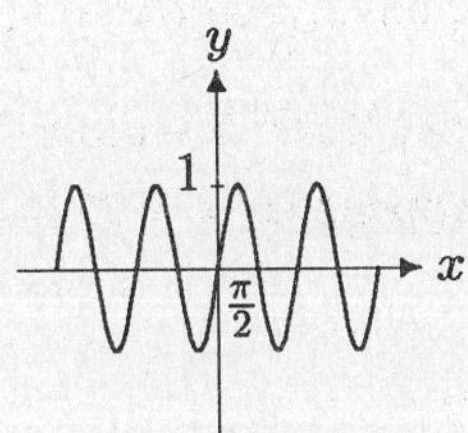

Exercise 23

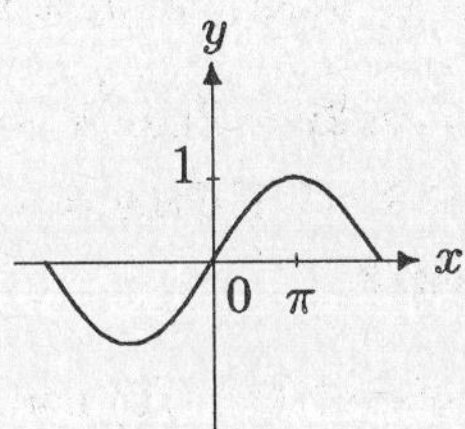

Exercise 24

18. y intercept: $\sqrt{2}/2$; x intercepts: $\pi/4 + n\pi$ for any integer n; not symmetric with respect to either axis or origin. (Let $X = x - (\pi/4)$, $Y = y$; equation becomes $Y = \sin(-X) = -\sin X$.)

19. y intercepts: none; x intercepts: $\pi/2 + n\pi$ for any integer n; symmetric with respect to origin; an odd function. (Let $X = x + \pi/2$, $Y = y$; equation becomes $Y = \tan X$.)

20. y intercepts: none; x intercepts: $\pi/2 + n\pi$ for any integer n; symmetric with respect to y axis; an even function.

21. y intercept: 1; x intercepts: none; symmetric with respect to y axis; an even function; $\sec(2\pi - x) = \sec(-x) = \sec x$; see Figure 1.70(c).

22. y intercepts: none; x intercepts: $\pi/6+2n\pi$ for any integer n, $5\pi/6+2n\pi$ for any integer n; no symmetry. (Let $X = x$, $Y = y - 2$; equation becomes $Y = -\csc X$.)

23. y intercept: 0; x intercepts: $n\pi/2$ for any integer n; symmetric about origin; an odd function.

24. y intercept: 0; x intercepts: $2n\pi$ for any integer n; symmetric with respect to origin; odd function. (Note: $\cos[(x-\pi)/2] = \cos(x/2 - \pi/2) = \sin(x/2)$.)

25. $\sin\frac{7\pi}{12} = \sin\left(\frac{\pi}{3} + \frac{\pi}{4}\right) = \sin\frac{\pi}{3}\cos\frac{\pi}{4} + \cos\frac{\pi}{3}\sin\frac{\pi}{4} = \frac{\sqrt{3}}{2}\cdot\frac{\sqrt{2}}{2} + \frac{1}{2}\cdot\frac{\sqrt{2}}{2} = \frac{\sqrt{2}}{4}(\sqrt{3}+1)$

26. $\cos\frac{5\pi}{12} = \cos\left(\frac{\pi}{4} + \frac{\pi}{6}\right) = \cos\frac{\pi}{4}\cos\frac{\pi}{6} - \sin\frac{\pi}{4}\sin\frac{\pi}{6} = \frac{\sqrt{2}}{2}\cdot\frac{\sqrt{3}}{2} - \frac{\sqrt{2}}{2}\cdot\frac{1}{2} = \frac{\sqrt{2}}{4}(\sqrt{3}-1)$

27. $2\sin^2 x + \sin x - 1 = 0$ if and only if $(2\sin x - 1)(\sin x + 1) = 0$, so the solution consists of all x for which $\sin x = \frac{1}{2}$ or $\sin x = -1$. Solution: $\pi/6 + 2n\pi$, $5\pi/6 + 2n\pi$, $3\pi/2 + 2n\pi$ for any integer n.

28. $4\cos^2 x - 4\sqrt{3}\cos x + 3 = 0$ if and only if $(2\cos x - \sqrt{3})^2 = 0$, so the solution consists of all x for which $\cos x = \sqrt{3}/2$. Solution: $\pi/6 + 2n\pi$ and $-\pi/6 + 2n\pi$ for any integer n.

29. If $\cos x \neq 0$, then

$$\frac{\sin^2 x + \cos^2 x}{\cos^2 x} = \frac{1}{\cos^2 x} \quad \text{or} \quad \left(\frac{\sin x}{\cos x}\right)^2 + 1 = \left(\frac{1}{\cos x}\right)^2.$$

Thus $1 + \tan^2 x = \sec^2 x$ whenever $\tan x$ and $\sec x$ are defined.

30. If $\sin x \neq 0$, then

$$\frac{\sin^2 x + \cos^2 x}{\sin^2 x} = \frac{1}{\sin^2 x} \quad \text{or} \quad 1 + \left(\frac{\cos x}{\sin x}\right)^2 = \left(\frac{1}{\sin x}\right)^2.$$

Thus $1 + \cot^2 x = \csc^2 x$ whenever $\cot x$ and $\csc x$ are defined.

31. a. By (10), $\sin(\pi - x) = \sin\pi \cos x - \cos\pi \sin x = \sin x$.

 b. By (10), $\sin[(3\pi/2) - x] = \sin(3\pi/2)\cos x - \cos(3\pi/2)\sin x = -\cos x$.

 c. By (11), $\cos(\pi - x) = \cos\pi \cos x + \sin\pi \sin x = -\cos x$.

 d. By (11), $\cos[(3\pi/2) - x] = \cos(3\pi/2)\cos x + \sin(3\pi/2)\sin x = -\sin x$.

32. a. From (9) we have $\cos^2 x = 1 - \sin^2 x$. If $0 \le x \le \pi/2$ or $3\pi/2 \le x \le 2\pi$ (so $\cos x \ge 0$), then $\cos x = \sqrt{1 - \sin^2 x}$. If $\pi/2 \le x \le 3\pi/2$ (so $\cos x \le 0$), then $\cos x = -\sqrt{1 - \sin^2 x}$.

 b. From (9) we have $\sin^2 x = 1 - \cos^2 x$. If $0 \le x \le \pi$ (so $\sin x \ge 0$), then $\sin x = \sqrt{1 - \cos^2 x}$. If $\pi \le x \le 2\pi$ (so $\sin x \le 0$), then $\sin x = -\sqrt{1 - \cos^2 x}$.

33. $m_1 = 4$, $m_2 = \dfrac{-2}{3}$; $\tan\theta = \dfrac{m_2 - m_1}{1 + m_1 m_2} = \dfrac{(-2/3) - 4}{1 + (-2/3)(4)} = \dfrac{14}{5}$.

34. $m_1 = 3$, $m_2 = \dfrac{11}{4}$; $\tan\theta = \dfrac{(11/4) - 3}{1 + (11/4)(3)} = -\dfrac{1}{37}$.

35. a. π b. $2\pi/3$ c. π d. π

36. Since $\beta = \dfrac{\pi}{2} - \alpha$, $\sin\alpha = \cos\left(\dfrac{\pi}{2} - \alpha\right)$ and $\cos\alpha = \sin\left(\dfrac{\pi}{2} - \alpha\right)$, we have

$$\begin{aligned}\cos 2\alpha + \cos 2\beta &= (\cos^2\alpha - \sin^2\alpha) + \left[\cos^2\left(\frac{\pi}{2} - \alpha\right) - \sin^2\left(\frac{\pi}{2} - \alpha\right)\right] \\ &= (\cos^2\alpha - \sin^2\alpha) + (\sin^2\alpha - \cos^2\alpha) = 0.\end{aligned}$$

37. Since $\beta = \dfrac{\pi}{2} - \alpha$, we have

$$\cos(\alpha - \beta) = \cos\left[\alpha - \left(\frac{\pi}{2} - \alpha\right)\right] = \cos\left(2\alpha - \frac{\pi}{2}\right) = \cos\left(\frac{\pi}{2} - 2\alpha\right) = \sin 2\alpha.$$

38. Let $r = m/n$, where m and n are integers with $n > 0$. Then

$$f(x + 2n\pi) = \sin(x + 2n\pi) + \sin\left[\frac{m}{n}(x + 2n\pi)\right] = \sin x + \sin\left(\frac{m}{n}x + 2m\pi\right) = \sin x + \sin\left(\frac{m}{n}x\right) = f(x).$$

39. In each case, the iterates approach a number approximately 0.739, so we conjecture that the same is true for any real number a.

40. The rim of the wheel travels 5280 feet, so if θ is the number of radians through which the wheel turns, then by (1), $5280 = 1 \cdot \theta$. Thus the number of revolutions through which the wheel turns is $5280/(2\pi) = 2640/\pi \approx 840.338$.

41. Let d be the distance between the beacon and the illuminated point. Then $\sec\theta = d/2$, so $d = 2\sec\theta$.

42. If one side of the angle is a diameter and the chord has length x, then $\sin\theta = x/1 = x$. Since inscribed angles subtending equal arcs are equal, if θ is any other angle that subtends the same arc, it equals an angle one of whose sides is a diameter.

43. $\pi/4$; the angle grows larger and larger, and the field of vision eventually becomes blocked.

44. Using the notation in the diagram, we have $y = 6\cos\theta$ and $x = 6\sin\theta$, so the cross-sectional area, which is the sum of the area of the rectangle and the two triangles, equals $6y + 2(\frac{1}{2}xy) = 6y + xy = 36(\cos\theta)(1+\sin\theta)$. Thus the volume equals $1080(\cos\theta)(1+\sin\theta)$.

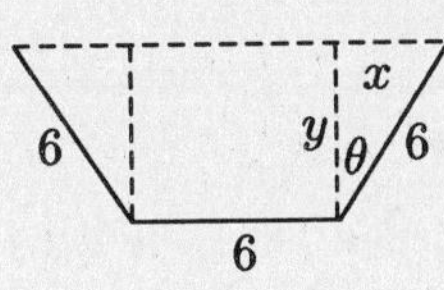

Exercise 44

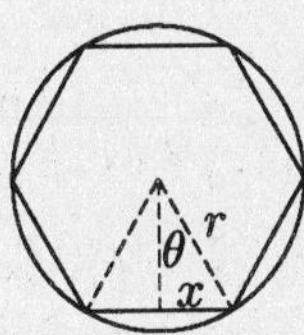

Exercise 45

45. a. Let θ be as in the figure, so that $\theta = \frac{1}{2}(2\pi/n) = \pi/n$. Next let x be half the length of one side of the polygon, as in the figure. Then $x = r\sin(\pi/n)$. Thus the perimeter of the n-sided polygon is given by $p_n(r) = 2nr\sin(\pi/n)$.

    b. From part (a), $2x = 2r\sin(\pi/n)$ or $r = 2x/[2\sin(\pi/n)]$. For the Pentagon, $2x = 921$ and $n = 5$, so $r = 921/[2\sin(\pi/5)] \approx 783.4$ (feet).

46. a. $F\left(\dfrac{\pi}{4}\right) = \dfrac{50\mu}{\mu\frac{1}{2}\sqrt{2} + \frac{1}{2}\sqrt{2}} = \dfrac{50\sqrt{2}\,\mu}{\mu+1}$ (pounds)

    b. $F\left(\dfrac{\pi}{3}\right) = \dfrac{50\mu}{\mu\frac{1}{2}\sqrt{3} + \frac{1}{2}} = \dfrac{100\mu}{\sqrt{3}\,\mu+1}$ (pounds)

    c. $F\left(\dfrac{\pi}{2}\right) = 50\mu/(\mu\cdot 1 + 0) = 50$; the sack is lifted, and the coefficient of friction plays no role.

47. b. Since $g < 0$ and since $\cos\theta$ is the largest for $\theta = 0$ and smallest for $\theta = \pi$, it follows that T is greatest when $\cos\theta$ is smallest, that is, for $\theta = \pi$. Analogously, T is smallest when $\cos\theta$ is largest, that is, for $\theta = 0$.

48. Since $A \geq 0$ and $-1 \leq \cos(\pi/26)t \leq 1$ for all t, we must have $-1 \leq b \leq 1$.

49. a. Since $\dfrac{2\pi}{5}t = 2\pi$ for $t = 5$, the period of R and hence of the cycle is 5 seconds.

b. By part (a), there are 12 cycles in a minute.

c.

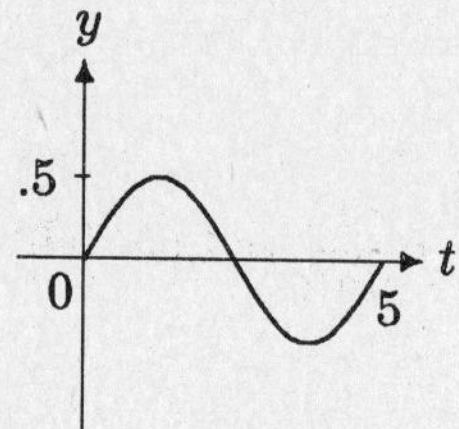

d. Positive values of R correspond to a flow into the lungs; negative values of R correspond to a flow out of the lungs.

e. When $t = 3$, $R = 0.5 \sin \dfrac{6\pi}{5} \approx -0.29$.

1.8 Exponential and Logarithmic Functions

1. By (8), $\ln e^3 = 3$.

2. By (8), $\ln \sqrt{e} = \ln e^{1/2} = \frac{1}{2}$.

3. By (8), $e^{\ln 3x} = 3x$.

4. By (8) and the Law of Exponents (*ii*), $e^{-4 \ln x} = (e^{\ln x})^{-4} = x^{-4}$.

5. By (8), $\ln(e^{\ln e}) = \ln e = 1$.

6. By (8), $\ln|\ln(1/e)| = \ln|\ln(e^{-1})| = \ln|-1| = \ln 1 = 0$.

7. By (7), $7^{\log_7 2x} = 2x$.

8. By (6), $\log_4 4^x = x$.

9. By (6), $\log_9 3 = \log_9 9^{1/2} = \frac{1}{2}$.

10. By (6), $\log_2 \frac{1}{4} = \log_2(2^{-2}) = -2$.

11. By (6) and the Law of Logarithms (*iv*), $\log_{\frac{1}{4}} 2^x = x \log_{\frac{1}{4}} 2 = x \log_{\frac{1}{4}} (\frac{1}{4})^{-1/2} = x(-\frac{1}{2}) = -\frac{1}{2}x$.

12. By Laws of Exponents (*i*) and (*ii*), as well as (8), $e^{x-2\ln x} = e^x e^{-2\ln x} = e^x (e^{\ln x})^{-2} = e^x(x^{-2}) = e^x/x^2$.

13. $e^{-1.24} \approx 0.2893842179$

14. $e^{-1.24 \times 10^{-4}} \approx 0.9998760077$

15. $2^{7/2} \approx 11.31370850$

16. $10^{-5/3} \approx 0.0215443469$

17. By (11), $\log_3 5 = \dfrac{\ln 5}{\ln 3} \approx 1.464973521$.

18. By (11), $\log_{\frac{1}{2}} \frac{1}{3} = \dfrac{\ln(1/3)}{\ln(1/2)} \approx 1.584962501.$

19. By (11), $\log_\pi e = \dfrac{\ln e}{\ln \pi} = \dfrac{1}{\ln \pi} \approx 0.8735685268.$

20. By (11) and Law of Logarithms (*iv*), $\log_{\sqrt{2}} \sqrt{\pi} = \dfrac{\ln \sqrt{\pi}}{\ln \sqrt{2}} = \dfrac{\ln \pi^{1/2}}{\ln 2^{1/2}} = \dfrac{\ln \pi}{\ln 2} \approx 1.651496129.$

21. $(x \ln x)^2 = x^2(\ln x)^2 \neq x^2 \ln(x^2)$ because $(\ln x)^2 \neq \ln(x^2)$.

22. $\dfrac{e^3}{e^{\sqrt{2}}e^{\sqrt{2}}} = \dfrac{e^3}{e^{\sqrt{2}+\sqrt{2}}} = \dfrac{e^3}{e^{2\sqrt{2}}} \neq \dfrac{e^3}{e^{\sqrt{2}\cdot\sqrt{2}}}$ because $e^{\sqrt{2}}e^{\sqrt{2}} \neq e^{\sqrt{2}\cdot\sqrt{2}}$.

23. $f(-x) = \dfrac{e^{-x}}{e^{-2x}+1} = \dfrac{e^{-x}}{e^{-2x}+1}\dfrac{e^{2x}}{e^{2x}} = \dfrac{e^x}{1+e^{2x}} = f(x)$, so that f is an even function.

24. $f(-x) = \ln(e^{-3x}+1) = \ln[e^{-3x}(1+e^{3x})] = \ln e^{-3x} + \ln(1+e^{3x}) = -3x + f(x)$. Thus if $x \neq 0$, then $f(-x) \neq f(x)$ and $f(-x) \neq -f(x)$, so that f is neither an even nor an odd function.

25. $f(x) = e^{2+x}$

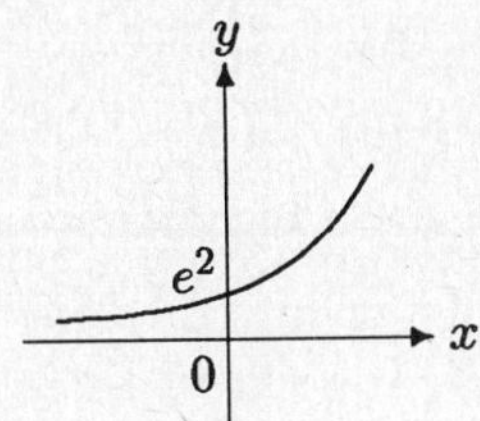

26. $f(x) = 2^{2-x}$

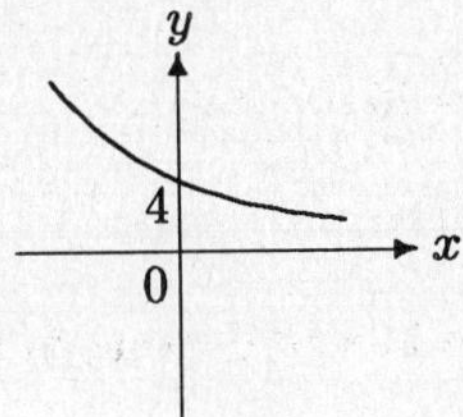

27. $f(x) = \ln(x+1)$

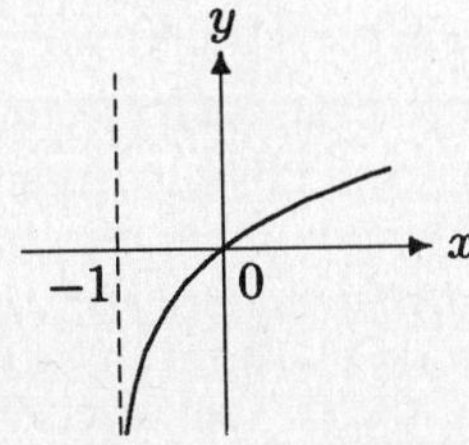

28. $f(x) = \ln(ex)$

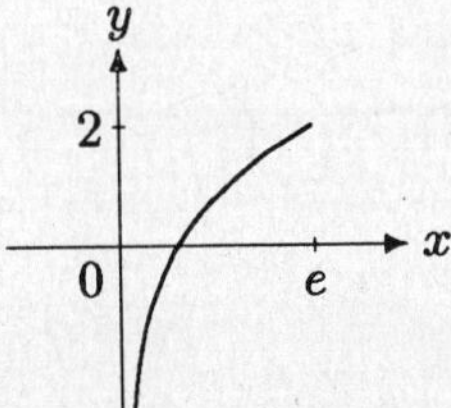

29. The graphs intersect at (x, y) if and only if $e^x = e^{1-x}$, so by (3), $x = 1 - x$ and thus $x = \frac{1}{2}$. Notice that $f(\frac{1}{2}) = e^{1/2} = g(\frac{1}{2})$. Thus the graphs intersect at $(\frac{1}{2}, e^{1/2})$.

30. The graphs intersect at (x, y) if and only if $e^x = e^{-x^2}$, so by (3), $x = -x^2$ and thus $x = 0$ or $x = -1$. Notice that $f(0) = e^0 = 1 = g(0)$ and $f(-1) = e^{-1} = g(-1)$. Thus the graphs intersect at $(0, 1)$ and $(-1, e^{-1})$.

31. The graphs intersect at (x, y) if and only if $e^{3x} = 3e^x$, so by (8) and the Law of Logarithms (*i*), $3x = \ln(e^{3x}) = \ln(3e^x) = \ln 3 + \ln e^x = \ln 3 + x$. Thus $x = \frac{1}{2}\ln 3$. Notice that $f(\frac{1}{2}\ln 3) = e^{3(\ln 3)/2} = (e^{\ln 3})^{3/2} = 3^{3/2} = g(\frac{1}{2}\ln 3)$. Thus the graphs intersect at $(\frac{1}{2}\ln 3, 3^{3/2})$.

32. The graphs intersect at (x, y) if and only if $5e^{-2x} = 3e^x$, or equivalently, $e^{3x} = \frac{5}{3}$, so that $3x = \ln\frac{5}{3}$ and thus $x = \frac{1}{3}\ln\frac{5}{3}$. Notice that $f(\frac{1}{3}\ln\frac{5}{3}) = 5e^{-(2/3)\ln(5/3)} = 5(\frac{5}{3})^{-2/3} = 5(\frac{5}{3})^{-1}(\frac{5}{3})^{1/3} = 3(\frac{5}{3})^{1/3} = g(\frac{1}{3}\ln\frac{5}{3})$. Thus the graphs intersect at $(\frac{1}{3}\ln\frac{5}{3}, 3(\frac{5}{3})^{1/3})$.

33. The graphs intersect at (x, y) if and only if $\log_3 x = \log_2 x$, so by (11),

$$\frac{\ln x}{\ln 3} = \frac{\ln x}{\ln 2}.$$

Since $\ln 3 \neq \ln 2$, this can occur only for $x = 1$. Notice that $f(1) = \log_3 1 = 0 = \log_2 1 = g(1)$. Thus the graphs intersect at $(1, 0)$.

34. The graphs intersect at (x, y) if and only if $3^x = 2^{(x^2)}$. By taking natural logarithms we find that $\ln 3^x = \ln 2^{(x^2)}$, or $x\ln 3 = x^2 \ln 2$. Thus $x = 0$ or $x = (\ln 3)/(\ln 2)$. Notice that $f(0) = 3^0 = 1 = 2^0 = g(0)$ and $f((\ln 3)/(\ln 2)) = 3^{(\ln 3)/(\ln 2)} = g((\ln 3)/(\ln 2))$. Thus the graphs intersect at $(0, 1)$ and $((\ln 3)/(\ln 2), 3^{(\ln 3)/(\ln 2)})$.

35. By the Law of Logarithms (i), $\ln x + \ln(3x - 1) = 0$ if $\ln[x(3x - 1)] = 0$, which by (5) is equivalent to $x(3x - 1) = 1$, or $3x^2 - x - 1 = 0$. By the quadratic formula,

$$x = \frac{-(-1) \pm \sqrt{(-1)^2 - 4(3)(-1)}}{2(3)} = \frac{1 \pm \sqrt{13}}{6}.$$

Since x must be positive, $x = (1 + \sqrt{13})/6$.

36. By the Law of Logarithms (i),

$$f(x) = \ln(x + \sqrt{x^2 - 9}) + \ln(x - \sqrt{x^2 - 9}) = \ln[(x + \sqrt{x^2 - 9})(x - \sqrt{x^2 - 9})] = \ln[x^2 - (x^2 - 9)] = \ln 9.$$

Thus the constant is $\ln 9$.

37. Since

$$x + \sqrt{x^2 - 1} = (x + \sqrt{x^2 - 1})\frac{x - \sqrt{x^2 - 1}}{x - \sqrt{x^2 - 1}} = \frac{x^2 - (x^2 - 1)}{x - \sqrt{x^2 - 1}} = \frac{1}{x - \sqrt{x^2 - 1}}$$

it follows by the Law of Logarithms (ii) that

$$\ln(x + \sqrt{x^2 - 1}) = \ln\frac{1}{x - \sqrt{x^2 - 1}} = -\ln(x - \sqrt{x^2 - 1}).$$

38. By (11),

$$\log_a x = \frac{\ln x}{\ln a} \quad \text{and} \quad \log_b x = \frac{\ln x}{\ln b}.$$

Thus $\log_a x = \log_b x$ if and only if

$$\frac{\ln x}{\ln a} = \frac{\ln x}{\ln b}.$$

Since $a \neq b$, it follows that $\ln a \neq \ln b$, so the preceding equation is equivalent to $\ln x = 0$, that is, $x = 1$. Consequently $\log_a x \neq \log_b x$ if $x \neq 1$.

39. By two applications of the Law of Exponents (i), $a^{b+c+d} = a^{b+(c+d)} = a^b a^{c+d} = a^b a^c a^d$.

40. By the Change of Base Formula,

$$\log_{1/a} x = \frac{\log_a x}{\log_a(1/a)} = \frac{\log_a x}{\log_a(a^{-1})} = \frac{\log_a x}{-\log_a a} = -\log_a x \quad \text{for } x > 0.$$

41. By the Law of Logarithms,

$$f(x) = \ln(4x) - \ln x^3 + \ln x^2 = \ln \frac{(4x)x^2}{x^3} = \ln 4.$$

This is the reason that the graph of f is a horizontal line.

42. Approximately 10.

43. a. $f(x+1) - f(x) = [a(x+1)+b] - (ax+b) = ax + a - ax = a$

b. $\dfrac{g(x+1)}{g(x)} = \dfrac{ba^{x+1}}{ba^x} = \dfrac{ba^x a}{ba^x} = a$

44. They do not; they become arbitrarily large.

45. Approximately 0.2591711018.

46. They do not; they become arbitrarily large.

47. Let x be the amplitude of the earthquake's largest wave 100 kilometers from the epicenter, and a the corresponding amplitude of a zero-level earthquake. By (13), $\log(x/a) = 2$, so $x/a = 10^2 = 100$. But $a = 0.001$. Therefore $x = 100a = 0.1$ (millimeters).

48. Let x denote the original amplitude. Since $\log(2x/a) = \log 2 + \log(x/a)$, it follows from (13) that if the amplitude of the maximal seismic wave is doubled, then the magnitude increases by $\log 2 \approx 0.301030$.

49. Let x_1 be the maximal amplitude of an earthquake of amplitude 8.5, and x_2 the maximal amplitude of an earthquake of amplitude 8.4. By (13), $8.5 = \log(x_1/a)$ and $8.4 = \log(x_2/a)$. Thus

$$\log \frac{x_2}{x_1} = \log \frac{x_2/a}{x_1/a} = \log \frac{x_2}{a} - \log \frac{x_1}{a} = 8.4 - 8.5 = -0.1.$$

Therefore $x_2/x_1 = 10^{-0.1} \approx 0.794328$.

50. By (13), $\log \dfrac{x}{a} = 8.9$, so $\dfrac{x}{a} = 10^{8.9} \approx 7.94328 \times 10^8$.

51. Since 90 kilotons releases $90(10^{20})$ ergs, let $E = 90(10^{20})$. Then

$$11.4 + 1.5M = \log E = \log[90(10^{20})] = \log 90 + 20.$$

Therefore $M = \frac{1}{1.5}(\log 90 + 8.6) \approx 7.036$. Consequently the magnitude would be approximately 7.

52. Let x_1 be the intensity of a whisper and x_2 the intensity of an ordinary conversation. Then $30 = 10\log(x_1/I_0)$ and $50 = 10\log(x_2/I_0)$, so

$$\log \frac{x_1}{x_2} = \log \frac{x_1/I_0}{x_2/I_0} = \log \frac{x_1}{I_0} - \log \frac{x_2}{I_0} = \frac{30}{10} - \frac{50}{10} = -2.$$

Therefore $x_2/x_1 = 10^{-2} = 1/100$.

53. a. $L(10^{-12}) = 10\log\frac{10^{-12}}{10^{-16}} = 10\log 10^4 = 10(4) = 40$; thus the threshold is at 40 decibels (approximately).

b. $L(10^{-11}) = 10\log\frac{10^{-11}}{10^{-16}} = 10\log 10^5 = 10(5) = 50$; thus leaves rustle at 50 decibels (approximately).

c. $L(10^{-2}) = 10\log\frac{10^{-2}}{10^{-16}} = 10\log 10^{14} = 10(14) = 140$; thus a power mower has 140 decibels (approximately).

d. $L(10) = 10\log\frac{10^{1}}{10^{-16}} = 10\log 10^{17} = 10(17) = 170$; thus a jackhammer has 170 decibels (approximately).

54. If $y = 1000x$, then

$$L(y) - L(x) = 10\log\frac{1000x}{I_0} - 10\log\frac{x}{I_0} = 10\log\frac{1000x/I_0}{x/I_0} = 10\log 1000 = 10(3) = 30.$$

Thus the difference in the noise levels is 30 decibels.

55. If $L(y) = L(x) + 100$, then $10\log(y/I_0) = 10\log(x/I_0) + 100$, so $\log(x/I_0) - \log(y/I_0) = -10$. Thus

$$\log\frac{x}{y} = \log\frac{x/I_0}{y/I_0} = \log\frac{x}{I_0} - \log\frac{y}{I_0} = -10$$

so that $x/y = 10^{-10}$. Therefore the ratio of the intensities is 10^{-10}.

56. If $L(y) = L(x) - 0.6$, then $10\log(y/I_0) = 10\log(x/I_0) - 0.6$, so $\log(x/I_0) - \log(y/I_0) = 0.06$. Thus

$$\log\frac{x}{y} = \log\frac{x/I_0}{y/I_0} = \log\frac{x}{I_0} - \log\frac{y}{I_0} = 0.06$$

so that $x/y = 10^{0.06}$. Therefore the ratio of the intensities is $10^{0.06} \approx 1.15$.

57. a. $p(0) \approx 29.92$ (inches of mercury)

b. $p(5) \approx (29.92)e^{(-0.2)(5)} \approx 11.00695288$ (inches of mercury)

c. $p(10) \approx (29.92)e^{(-0.2)(10)} \approx 4.049231674$ (inches of mercury)

58. a. For $p = 1$, $t = -\frac{\ln(1/100)}{0.000124} \approx 37138.46924$, or approximately 37,100 years old.

b. For $p = 60$, $t = -\frac{\ln(60/100)}{0.000124} \approx 4119.561482$, or approximately 4120 years old.

59. Let I_1 denote the intensity of the X-ray beam with wavelength 5×10^{-11}, and I_2 that of the X-ray beam with wavelength 10^{-10}. Then

$$I_{1,\text{exit}} = I_{1,\text{entry}}\, e^{-\sigma_1(.002)} \quad\text{and}\quad I_{2,\text{exit}} = I_{2,\text{entry}}\, e^{-\sigma_2(.002)}.$$

Since $I_{1,\text{entry}} = I_{2,\text{entry}}$ by hypothesis,

$$\frac{I_{1,\text{exit}}}{I_{2,\text{exit}}} = \frac{e^{-\sigma_1(.002)}}{e^{-\sigma_2(.002)}} = \frac{e^{-(5.4\times10^2)(.002)}}{e^{-(4.1\times10^3)(.002)}} = \frac{e^{-1.08}}{e^{-8.2}} \approx 1236.450433.$$

Thus the X-ray beam with wavelength 5×10^{-11} exits with approximately 1200 times the intensity of the other X-ray beam.

Chapter 1 Review

1. From the diagram we see that the solution is the union of $(-\infty, -\frac{3}{2})$ and $(4, \infty)$.

$2x+3$	$-\ -\ 0\ +\ +\ +\ +\ +\ +\ +\ +$
$(x-4)^3$	$-\ -\ -\ -\ -\ -\ -\ -\ -\ 0\ +\ +$
$\dfrac{2x+3}{(x-4)^3}$	$+\ +\ 0\ -\ -\ -\ -\ -\ \ \ +\ +$

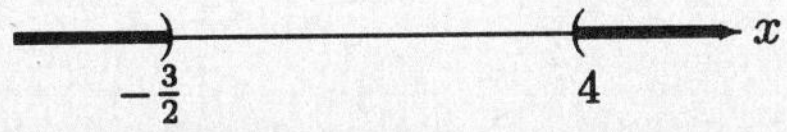

2. The given inequality is equivalent to

$$\frac{x(x-4)+(x+2)(x-1)}{(x-1)(x-4)} \le 0 \quad \text{or} \quad \frac{(2x+1)(x-2)}{(x-1)(x-4)} \le 0.$$

From the diagram we see that the solution is the union of $[-\frac{1}{2}, 1)$ and $[2, 4)$.

$2x+1$	$-\ 0\ +\ +\ +\ +\ +\ +\ +\ +\ +\ +$
$x-2$	$-\ -\ -\ -\ -\ -\ 0\ +\ +\ +\ +\ +$
$x-1$	$-\ -\ -\ -\ 0\ +\ +\ +\ +\ +\ +\ +$
$x-4$	$-\ -\ -\ -\ -\ -\ -\ -\ -\ -\ 0\ +$
$\dfrac{(2x+1)(x-2)}{(x-1)(x-4)}$	$+\ 0\ -\ -\ \ \ +\ 0\ -\ -\ -\ \ \ +$

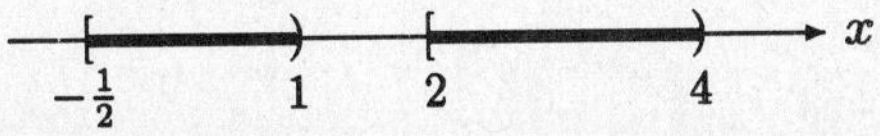

3. The given inequality is equivalent to

$$\frac{2}{3-x} - 4 \ge 0, \quad \text{or} \quad \frac{4(x-\frac{5}{2})}{3-x} \ge 0.$$

From the diagram we see that the solution is $[\frac{5}{2}, 3)$.

$x-\frac{5}{2}$	$-\ -\ 0\ +\ +\ +\ +\ +\ +\ +\ +$
$3-x$	$+\ +\ +\ +\ +\ +\ +\ +\ 0\ -\ -$
$\dfrac{4(x-\frac{5}{2})}{3-x}$	$-\ -\ 0\ +\ +\ +\ +\ +\ \ \ -\ -$

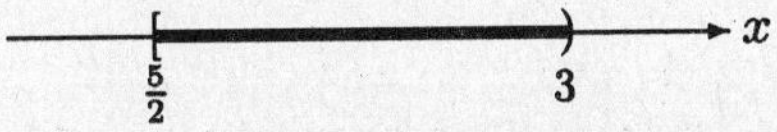

4. If $|x+1| = |2x-3|$, then either $x+1 = 2x-3$ (so that $x = 4$), or $x+1 = -(2x-3)$ (so that $3x = 2$, or $x = \frac{2}{3}$). The solution is $\frac{2}{3}$, 4.

5. If $|4-6x| < \frac{1}{2}$, then $-\frac{1}{2} < 4-6x < \frac{1}{2}$, or $-\frac{9}{2} < -6x < -\frac{7}{2}$, or $\frac{7}{12} < x < \frac{3}{4}$. The solution is $(\frac{7}{12}, \frac{3}{4})$.

6. If $|(x+1)/(x-1)| \leq 1$, then $-1 \leq (x+1)/(x-1) \leq 1$, which is equivalent to the two inequalities $-1 \leq (x+1)/(x-1)$ and $(x+1)/(x-1) \leq 1$. If $-1 \leq (x+1)/(x-1)$, then $0 \leq (x+1)/(x-1)+1$, or $0 \leq (x+1+x-1)/(x-1)$, or $0 \leq 2x/(x-1)$. This inequality is satisfied if $2x \geq 0$ and $x-1>0$ (so that $x \geq 0$ and $x > 1$), or $2x \leq 0$ and $x-1<0$ (so that $x \leq 0$ and $x < 1$). The first case yields $(1,\infty)$ and the second yields $(-\infty, 0]$. If $(x+1)/(x-1) \leq 1$, then $(x+1)/(x-1)-1 \leq 0$, or $[x+1-(x-1)]/(x-1) \leq 0$, or $2/(x-1) \leq 0$, or $x-1<0$, or $x<1$. Thus the solution in the second case is $(-\infty, 1)$. It follows that the solution of $|(x+1)/(x-1)| \leq 1$ is $(-\infty, 0]$.

7. a. For $a \geq 0$ we have $|a| = a$, so $(|a|+a)/2 = (a+a)/2 = a$.

   b. For $a < 0$ we have $|a| = -a$, so $(|a|+a)/2 = (-a+a)/2 = 0$.

8. $0 \leq (x-y)^2 = x^2 - 2xy + y^2$. Adding $2xy$ to both sides, we obtain $2xy \leq x^2 + y^2$.

9. The slope is $\dfrac{1-(-3)}{0-1} = -4$, so a point-slope equation is $y-1 = -4(x-0)$.

10. A point-slope equation is $y-2 = -\frac{1}{2}(x-(-2))$.

11. A slope-intercept equation is $y = -\frac{1}{3}x + 6$.

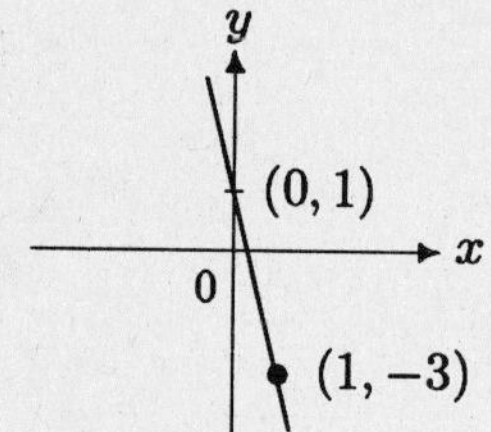

Exercise 9

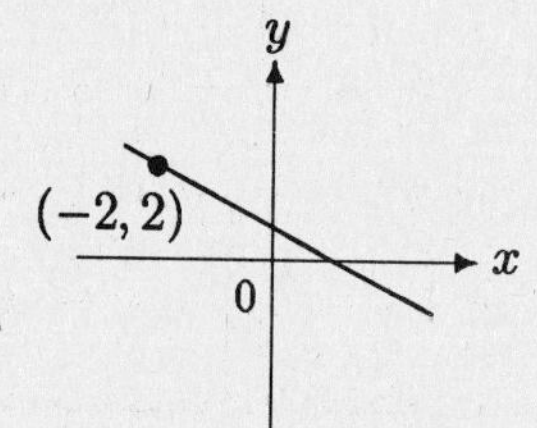

Exercise 10

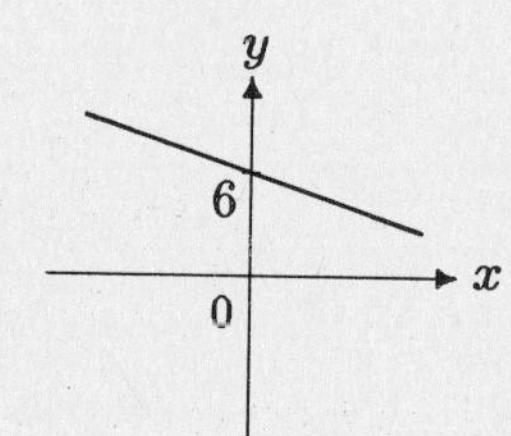

Exercise 11

12. Distance $= \sqrt{(-2-(-4))^2 + (\frac{1}{2}-(-1))^2} = \sqrt{2^2 + (\frac{3}{2})^2} = \sqrt{4+\frac{9}{4}} = \frac{1}{2}\sqrt{16+9} = \frac{5}{2}$

13. $m_1 = 2$; $m_2 = -\frac{1}{2}$. Since $m_1 m_2 = -1$, the lines are perpendicular.

14. The lines intersect at (x,y) such that $x+3y=4$ and $2x-3y=5$. This means that $x = 4-3y$, so $2(4-3y)-3y = 5$, and thus $8-9y=5$, so $y=\frac{1}{3}$. Then $x = 4-3(\frac{1}{3}) = 3$. The point of intersection is $(3, \frac{1}{3})$.

15. The slope of l is $-\frac{1}{2}$.

    a. The desired line has slope $-\frac{1}{2}$ also, so an equation is $y-(-2) = -\frac{1}{2}(x-1)$, or $y = -\frac{1}{2}x - \frac{3}{2}$.

    b. The desired line has slope 2, so an equation is $y-(-2) = 2(x-1)$, or $y = 2x-4$.

16. The first two lines are parallel with slope $-\frac{2}{3}$. The last two lines are parallel with slope $\frac{3}{2}$. Thus the first two lines are both perpendicular to the second two lines.

17. The first and fourth lines are parallel, with slope 1; the second and third lines are parallel, with slope -1. Thus the lines form a rectangle. The points of intersection are $(1,1)$, $(5,5)$, $(-3,5)$, and $(1,9)$. The lengths of the sides of the figure are

$$\sqrt{(5-1)^2+(5-1)^2} = \sqrt{(5-1)^2+(5-9)^2}$$

$$= \sqrt{(1-(-3))^2+(9-5)^2} = \sqrt{(-3-1)^2+(5-1)^2} = 4\sqrt{2}.$$

Since the sides all have the same length, the rectangle is a square.

18. Yes, because $(x^2)^2 = x^4$ and $x^2 \geq 0$, for all x.

19. Since $x(x^2+4x+3) = x(x+3)(x+1) = 0$ only if $x = -3$, -1 or 0, the domain is all numbers except -3, -1 and 0.

20. We must have $0 \leq t^3 - 4t = t(t+2)(t-2)$. From the diagram we see that the solution of this inequality is the union of $[-2,0]$ and $[2,\infty)$. Thus the domain is the union of $[-2,0]$ and $[2,\infty)$.

t	− − − − − − − 0 + + + + + +
$t+2$	− − − 0 + + + + + + + + + +
$t-2$	− − − − − − − − − − − 0 + +
$t(t+2)(t-2)$	− − − 0 + + + 0 − − − 0 + +

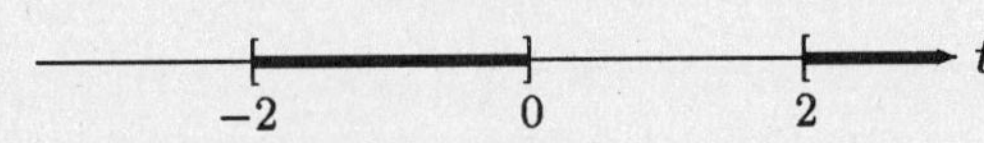

21. The domain consists of all x such that $e^x/(e^x-1) > 0$. Since $e^x > 0$ for all x, this means that $e^x - 1 > 0$, or $e^x > 1$, or $x > 0$. Thus the domain is $(0,\infty)$.

22. The domain of $\ln(1-x)$ is $(-\infty,1)$ and the domain of $\ln x$ is $(0,\infty)$. Thus the domain of f is $(0,1)$.

23.

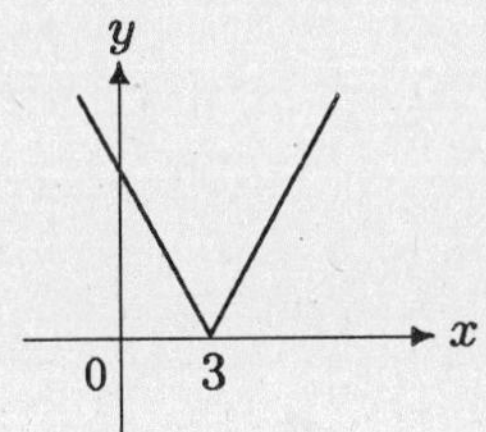

24.

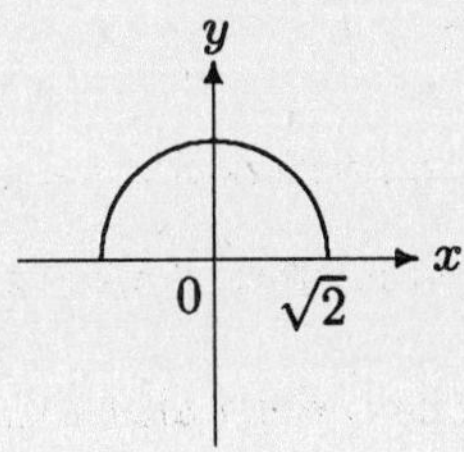

25.

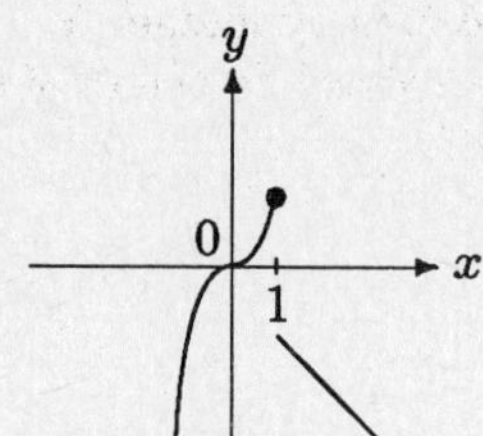

26.

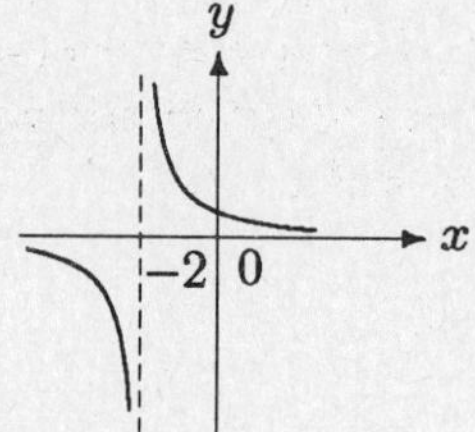

27. y intercept: 1; x intercept: 1;
not symmetric with respect to either axis or origin

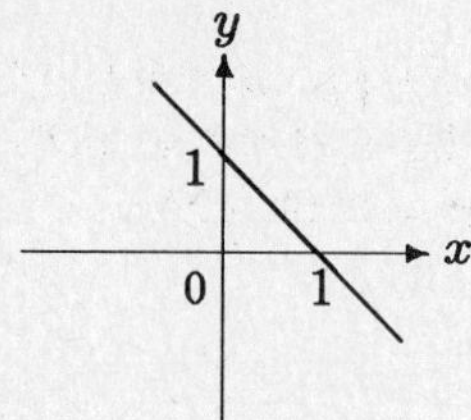

28. y intercepts: 1, -1;
x intercept: 1;
symmetric with respect to x axis

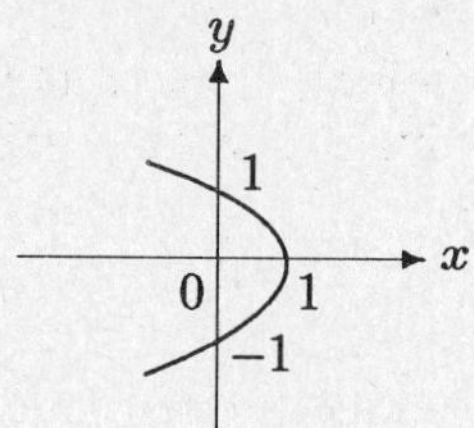

29. y intercepts: $-\sqrt{3}$, $\sqrt{3}$; x intercepts: $-\sqrt{3}$, $\sqrt{3}$;
symmetric with respect to the x axis, y axis and origin

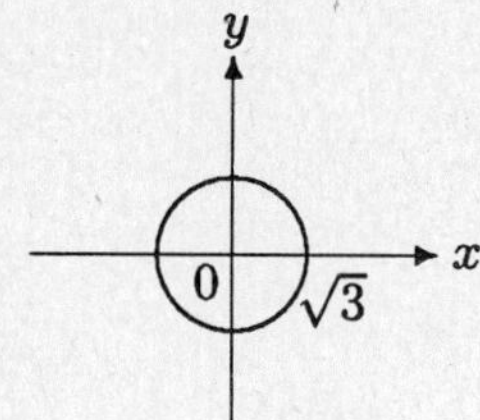

30. y intercept: 0; x intercepts: all points in the interval $[(2n+1)\pi, (2n+2)\pi]$ for every integer n

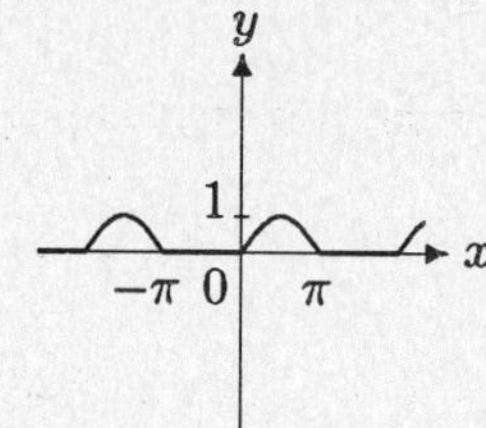

31. Notice that if $X = x$ and $Y = y - 1$, then $y = 1 - \sin x$ becomes $Y = -\sin X$.
y intercept: 1; x intercepts: $\pi/2 + 2n\pi$;
for any integer n; not symmetric with respect to either axis or origin.

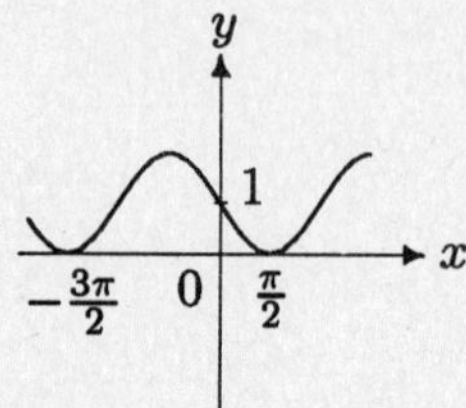

32. Since $\cos(-x) = \cos x$, we have $\cos|x| = \cos x$. Therefore the graph is the same as in Figure 1.68b. y intercept: 1; x intercepts: $\pi/2 + n\pi$ for any integer n; symmetric with respect to y the axis: an even function.

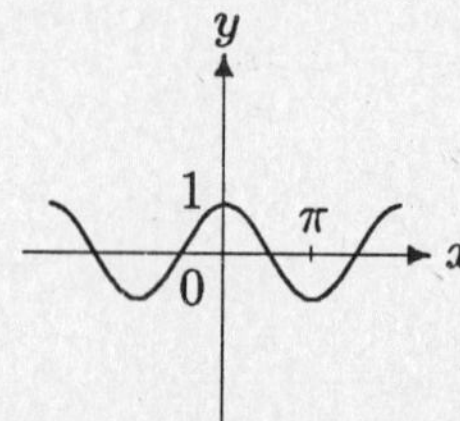

33. Notice that if $X = x - (\pi/4)$ and $Y = y$, then $y = \tan[x - (\pi/4)]$ becomes $Y = \tan X$. y intercept: -1; x intercepts: $\pi/4 + n\pi$ for any integer n; not symmetric with respect to either axis or origin.

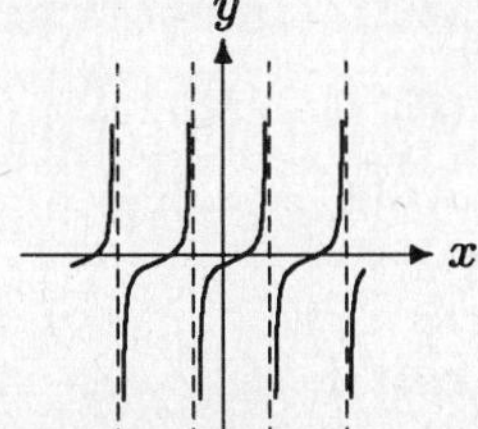

34. y intercepts: 0; x intercepts: $2n$ for any integer n; symmetric with respect to the origin: an odd function.

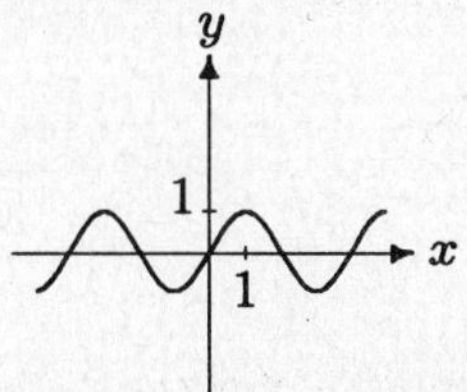

35. The domain is $(-1, 1)$; x and y intercepts: 0; symmetric with respect to the y axis: an even function.

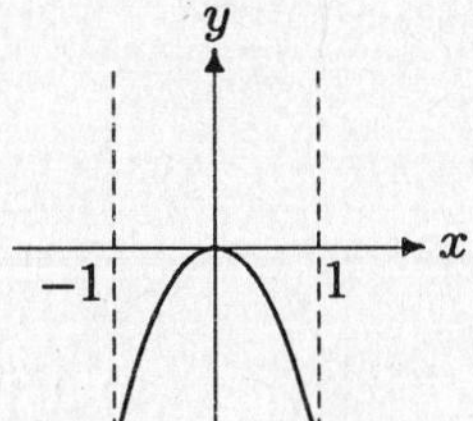

36. $f(x) = e^{x+3} = e^3e^x$; y intercept: e^3; no x intercept; not symmetric with respect to either axis or origin.

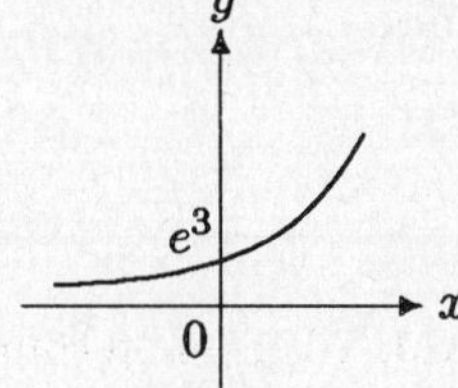

37. $f(-x) = (-x)^2 - \cos(-x) = x^2 - \cos x = f(x)$, so f is an even function.

38. $f(-x) = (-x)^2 + \sin(-x) = x^2 - \sin x$, so f is not an even or an odd function

39. $f(-x) = e^{-x} + e^{-(-x)} = e^{-x} + e^x = f(x)$, so f is an even function.

40. $f(-x) = e^{-x} - e^{-(-x)} = e^{-x} - e^x = -f(x)$, so f is an odd function.

41. $x^2 + 6x + y + 4 = 0$
$(x^2 + 6x + 9) + y + 4 = 9$
$(x + 3)^2 + (y - 5) = 0$
Let $X = x + 3$, $Y = y - 5$. The equation becomes $X^2 + Y = 0$, or $Y = -X^2$.

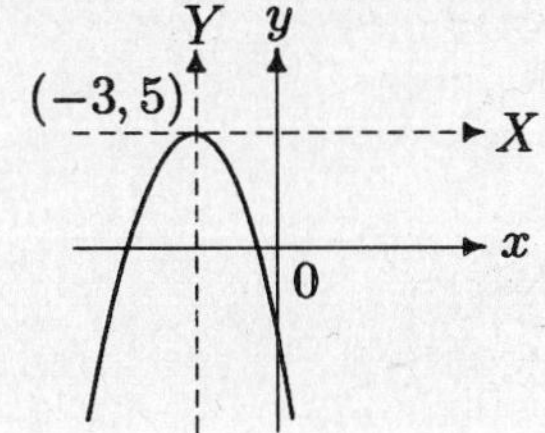

42. $x^2 - 4x + y^2 = 5$
$(x^2 - 4x + 4) + y^2 = 5 + 4$
$(x - 2)^2 + y^2 = 9$
Let $X = x - 2$, $Y = y$.
The equation becomes $X^2 + Y^2 = 9$.

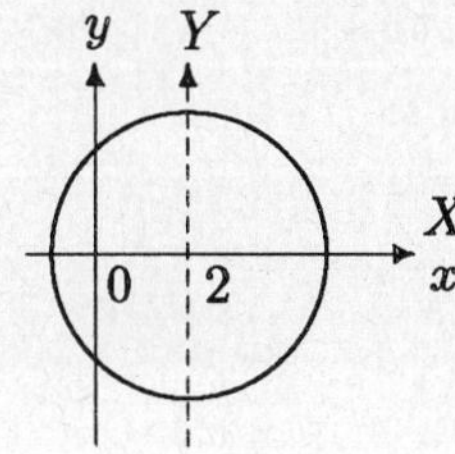

43. $x - 2 = 1/(y + 3)$
Let $X = x - 2$, $Y = y + 3$.
The equation becomes $X = 1/Y$.

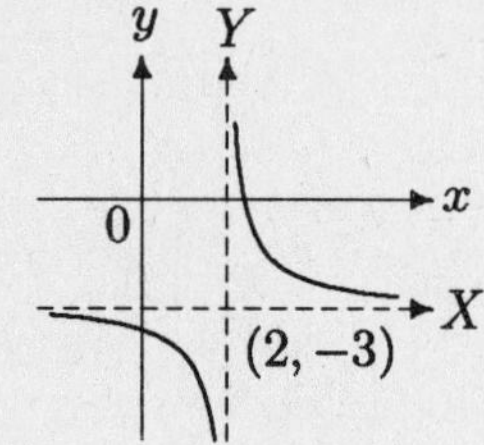

44. $x^2 - x + y^2 - 4y = \frac{19}{4}$
$(x^2 - x + \frac{1}{4}) + (y^2 - 4y + 4) = \frac{19}{4} + \frac{1}{4} + 4$
$(x - \frac{1}{2})^2 + (y - 2)^2 = 9$
Let $X = x - \frac{1}{2}$, $Y = y - 2$.
The equation becomes $X^2 + Y^2 = 9$.

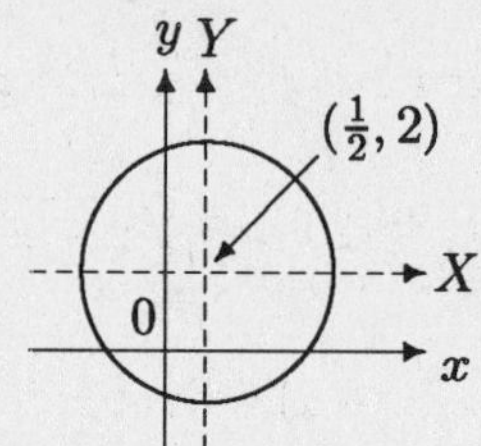

45. a. $$f(x) = \begin{cases} -(x-2)-(x-3) = -2x+5 & \text{for } x \le 2 \\ (x-2)-(x-3) = 1 & \text{for } 2 < x < 3 \\ (x-2)+(x-3) = 2x-5 & \text{for } x \ge 3 \end{cases}$$

$$g(x) = \begin{cases} -(x-2)+(x-3) = -1 & \text{for } x \le 2 \\ (x-2)+(x-3) = 2x-5 & \text{for } 2 < x < 3 \\ (x-2)-(x-3) = 1 & \text{for } x \ge 3 \end{cases}$$

b.

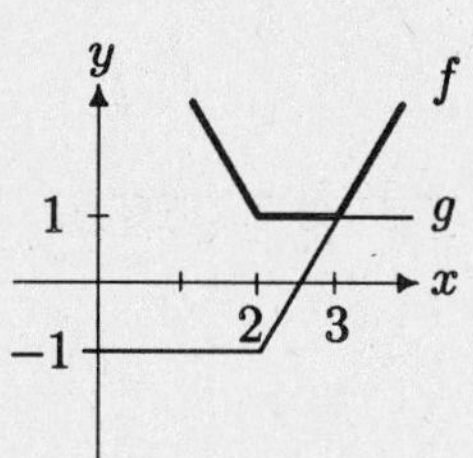

46. If $x \ge 0$, then $\sqrt{x^2} = x = |x|$. If $x < 0$, then $\sqrt{x^2} = \sqrt{(-x)^2} = -x = |x|$. Thus $|x| = \sqrt{x^2}$ for all x.

47. $$(f - g)(x) = \frac{x+2}{x^2-4x+3} - \frac{x+1}{x^2-2x-3} = \frac{x+2}{(x-1)(x-3)} - \frac{x+1}{(x-3)(x+1)}$$
$$= \frac{x+2}{(x-1)(x-3)} - \frac{1}{x-3} = \frac{(x+2)-(x-1)}{(x-1)(x-3)} = \frac{3}{(x-1)(x-3)} \quad \text{for } x \ne -1,\ 1, \text{ and } 3$$
$$\left(\frac{f}{g}\right) = \frac{(x+2)/(x^2-4x+3)}{(x+1)/(x^2-2x-3)} = \frac{(x+2)(x-3)(x+1)}{(x-1)(x-3)(x+1)} = \frac{x+2}{x-1} \quad \text{for } x \ne -1,\ 1, \text{ and } 3$$

48. The domain of $g \circ f$ consists of all x such that $x \ne 0$ and $[(x^2-1)/2x]+1 \ge 0$, that is, $(x^2+2x-1)/2x \ge 0$. This occurs if $x^2 + 2x - 1 \ge 0$ and $x > 0$ (so that $(x+1)^2 = x^2 + 2x + 1 \ge 2$ and $x > 0$, or $|x+1| \ge \sqrt{2}$ and $x > 0$, so $x \ge \sqrt{2} - 1$), or if $x^2 + 2x - 1 \le 0$ and $x < 0$ (so that $|x+1| \le \sqrt{2}$ and $x < 0$, so $-1 - \sqrt{2} \le x < 0$). The domain is thus the union of $[-1-\sqrt{2}, 0)$ and $[\sqrt{2}-1, \infty)$. Also $(g \circ f)(x) = g[(x^2-1)/2x] = \sqrt{(x^2-1)/2x + 1} = \sqrt{(x^2+2x-1)/2x}$. The domain of $f \circ g$ consists of all x such that $x + 1 \ge 0$ and $\sqrt{x+1} \ne 0$, that is, $(-1, \infty)$. Also
$$(f \circ g)(x) = f(\sqrt{x+1}) = \frac{(\sqrt{x+1})^2 - 1}{2\sqrt{x+1}} = \frac{x+1-1}{2\sqrt{x+1}} = \frac{x}{2\sqrt{x+1}}.$$

49. a. Domain of f: $[-1,\infty)$; domain of g: $[-2,\infty)$; domain of h: the union of $(-\infty,-2]$ and $[-1,\infty)$.

b. Domain of fg: $[-1,\infty)$. The domain of fg is smaller than the domain of h (although the rules of fg and h are the same).

50. If $0 \le x \le 1$, then $0 \le f(x) \le 1$, so x is in the domain of $f \circ f$. Now

$$f(f(x)) = f(\sqrt{1-x^2}) = \sqrt{1-(\sqrt{1-x^2})^2} = \sqrt{1-(1-x^2)} = \sqrt{x^2} = x.$$

51. If $x \ne 1$, then $x/(x-1) \ne 1$, so x is in the domain of $f \circ f$.

a. $f(f(x)) = \dfrac{x/(x-1)}{[x/(x-1)]-1} = \dfrac{x}{x-(x-1)} = x$

b. By part (a), $f\Big(f\big(f(f(x))\big)\Big) = f(f(x)) = x$ for $x \ne 1$.

52. If $x \ge 0$, then

$$g(\sqrt{x^2+1}) = \sqrt{x^2+1} + \sqrt{(\sqrt{x^2+1})^2-1} = \sqrt{x^2+1} + \sqrt{x^2+1-1} = \sqrt{x^2+1} + x = f(x).$$

If $x \ge 1$, then

$$f(\sqrt{x^2-1}) = \sqrt{x^2-1} + \sqrt{(\sqrt{x^2-1})^2+1} = \sqrt{x^2-1} + \sqrt{x^2-1+1} = \sqrt{x^2-1} + x = g(x).$$

53. The domain of f is $(-\infty,\infty)$ if $c = 0$ and $a \ne 0$, and in this case, $f(x) = -x-(b/a)$, so $f(f(x)) = -[-x-(b/a)] - b/a = x$. Next, the domain consists of all $x \ne a/c$ if $c \ne 0$. In this case, if $f(x) = a/c$, then $(ax+b)/(cx-a) = a/c$, so that $acx + bc = acx - a^2$, and hence $a^2 + bc = 0$. By hypothesis $a^2 + bc \ne 0$, so $f(x) \ne a/c$ for all x in the domain of f. Consequently the domain of $f \circ f$ is the domain of f. Finally,

$$f(f(x)) = f\left(\frac{ax+b}{cx-a}\right) = \frac{a[(ax+b)/(cx-a)]+b}{c[(ax+b)/(cx-a)]-a} = \frac{a^2x+ab+bcx-ab}{acx+bc-acx+a^2} = \frac{(a^2+bc)x}{a^2+bc} = x.$$

54. Let $f(x) = x^2+4$; let $g(x) = 1/\sqrt{x}$. Then $h(x) = g(x^2+4) = g\big(f(x)\big) = (g \circ f)(x)$.

55. $\cos x = \dfrac{\sin x}{\tan x} = \dfrac{-2/3}{-2\sqrt{5}/5} = \dfrac{\sqrt{5}}{3}$; $\cot x = \dfrac{1}{\tan x} = -\dfrac{5}{2\sqrt{5}} = -\dfrac{\sqrt{5}}{2}$; $\sec x = \dfrac{1}{\cos x} = \dfrac{3}{\sqrt{5}} = \dfrac{3\sqrt{5}}{5}$;

$\csc x = \dfrac{1}{\sin x} = -\dfrac{3}{2}$

56. $\cos x < -\frac{1}{2}$ for all numbers in the interval $(2\pi/3, 4\pi/3)$.

57. $|\sin x| = |\cos x|$ for $x = \pi/4$, $3\pi/4$, $5\pi/4$, and $7\pi/4$. By comparing values in the intervals $[0,\pi/4)$, $(\pi/4,3\pi/4)$, $(3\pi/4,5\pi/4)$, $(5\pi/4,7\pi/4)$, and $(7\pi/4,2\pi)$, we see that $|\sin x| \ge |\cos x|$ for x in the intervals $[\pi/4,3\pi/4]$ and $[5\pi/4,7\pi/4]$.

58. b. By (11) of Section 1.8, if $a \neq 1$, then

$$\log_{\sqrt{a}} \sqrt{x} = \frac{\ln \sqrt{x}}{\ln \sqrt{a}} = \frac{(\ln x)/2}{(\ln a)/2} = \frac{\ln x}{\ln a} = \log_a x.$$

59. a. $a \sin(x+b) = a \sin x \cos b + a \cos x \sin b = \sin x + \sqrt{3} \cos x$ if $a \cos b = 1$ and $a \sin b = \sqrt{3}$. Thus $\tan b = (a \sin b)/(a \cos b) = \sqrt{3}/1 = \sqrt{3}$, so $b = \pi/3 + n\pi$ for any integer n. If $b = \pi/3 + 2n\pi$, then $a = 1/(\cos b) = 1/[\cos(\pi/3)] = 1/\frac{1}{2} = 2$. If $b = 4\pi/3 + 2n\pi$, then $a = 1/(\cos b) = 1/[\cos(4\pi/3)] = 1/(-\frac{1}{2}) = -2$. Thus the solutions are $a = 2$, $b = \pi/3 + 2n\pi$ for any integer n, and $a = -2$, $b = 4\pi/3 + 2n\pi$ for any integer n.

b. $a \cos(x+b) = a \cos x \cos b - a \sin x \sin b = \sin x + \sqrt{3} \cos x$ if $a \cos b = \sqrt{3}$ and $-a \sin b = 1$. Thus $\tan b = (a \sin b)/(a \cos b) = -1/\sqrt{3}$, so $b = -\pi/6 + n\pi$ for any integer n. If $b = -\pi/6 + 2n\pi$, then

$$a = \frac{\sqrt{3}}{\cos b} = \frac{\sqrt{3}}{\cos(-\pi/6)} = \frac{\sqrt{3}}{\sqrt{3}/2} = 2.$$

If $b = 5\pi/6 + 2n\pi$, then $a = \sqrt{3}/(\cos b) = \sqrt{3}/\cos(5\pi/6) = \sqrt{3}/(-\sqrt{3}/2) = -2$. Thus the solutions are $a = 2$, $b = -\pi/6 + 2n\pi$ for any integer n, and $a = -2$, $b = 5\pi/6 + 2n\pi$ for any integer n.

60. $2 \sin x \geq \sin(2x) = 2 \sin x \cos x$ if and only if $2 \sin x - 2 \sin x \cos x \geq 0$, that is, $\sin x(1 - \cos x) \geq 0$. Now $1 - \cos x \geq 0$ for all x. Thus the inequality holds for x in $[0, 2\pi]$ if and only if $\sin x \geq 0$, that is, for x in $[0, \pi]$.

61. $2e^x \geq e^{2x}$ if and only if $2e^x - e^{2x} \geq 0$, that is, $e^x(2 - e^x) \geq 0$. Since $e^x > 0$ for all x, the inequality holds if and only if $2 - e^x \geq 0$, or equivalently, $e^x \leq 2$. Thus $x \leq \ln 2$. Therefore $2e^x \geq e^{2x}$ for x in $(-\infty, \ln 2]$.

62. $2 \ln x \geq \ln(2x)$ if and only if $2 \ln x \geq \ln(2x) = \ln 2 + \ln x$, so that $\ln x \geq \ln 2$, and thus $x \geq 2$. Therefore $2 \ln x \geq \ln(2x)$ for x in $[2, \infty)$.

63. a. red in (a) b. blue in (b) c. blue in (a) d. red in (b) e. green in (a) f. green in (b)

64. a.

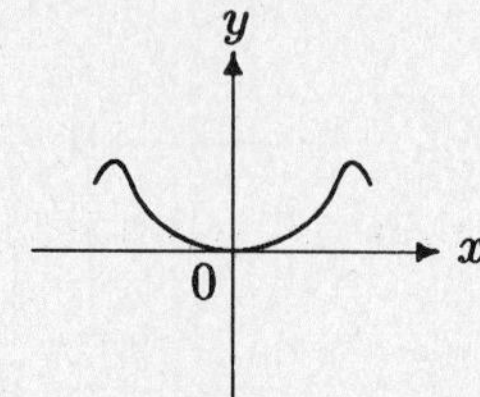

b.

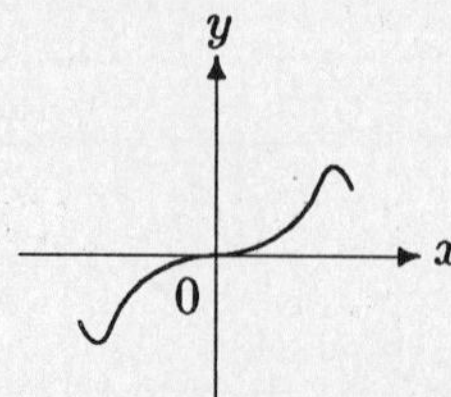

c. Same as (a).

d. Same as (b).

65. If $0 \leq x \leq \pi/3$, then $\frac{1}{2} \leq \cos x \leq 1$, and thus $1 \leq 1/(\cos x) \leq 2$. Since $\tan x = (\sin x)/(\cos x)$, it follows that for such x, $\sin x \leq (\sin x)/(\cos x) \leq 2 \sin x$, or equivalently, $\sin x \leq \tan x \leq 2 \sin x$.

66. By (9), $\dfrac{1}{1-\cos 10^{-10}} = \dfrac{1}{1-\cos 10^{-10}}\,\dfrac{1+\cos 10^{-10}}{1+\cos 10^{-10}} = \dfrac{1+\cos 10^{-10}}{1-\cos^2 10^{-10}} = \dfrac{1+\cos 10^{-10}}{\sin^2 10^{-10}} \approx 2\times 10^{20}$

67. Let P be the perimeter of the square and the equilateral triangle. Then each side of the square has length $\frac{1}{4}P$, so the area of the square is $\frac{1}{16}P^2$. Each side of the triangle has length $\frac{1}{3}P$, so by Exercise 51 of Section 1.3, the area of the triangle is $\frac{1}{4}\sqrt{3}\,(\frac{1}{3}P)^2 = (\sqrt{3}/36)P^2$. Since $\sqrt{3}/36 < \frac{1}{16}$, the square has the larger area. However, one can make the area of the rectangle with perimeter P as small as one wishes by making the length of one side of the rectangle small enough. Thus an equilateral triangle can have a larger area or smaller area than a rectangle with the same perimeter.

68. The area A is given by $A = \frac{1}{2}(4b) = 2b$. But $m = [0-(-4)]/(b-0) = 4/b$, so $b = 4/m$. Thus $A = 2(4/m) = 8/m$.

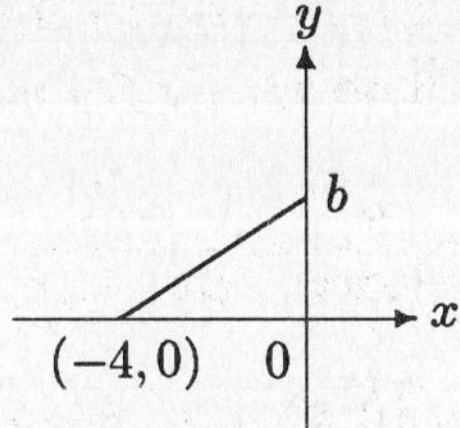

69. The fourth vertex could be $(1,3)(\text{opposite}(2,0))$, $(5,1)(\text{opposite}(0,1))$, or $(-1,-1)(\text{opposite}(3,2))$.

70. Let $h_1(t) = -4.9t^2 + v_0t + h_0$ and $h_2(t) = -4.9t^2 - v_0t + h_0$ denote the heights of the ball until it hits the ground in the two trials. Since the ball was thrown upward the first time, $v_0 > 0$. If the first time the ball hits the ground after t_1 seconds, then since $v_0 > 0$, we deduce from the quadratic formula that

$$t_1 = \frac{-v_0 - \sqrt{v_0^2 - 4(-4.9)h_0}}{-9.8} = \frac{v_0 + \sqrt{v_0^2 + 19.6h_0}}{9.8}.$$

If t_2 is the time it takes for the ball to hit the ground the second time, then since $t_2 > 0$,

$$t_2 = \frac{v_0 - \sqrt{v_0^2 - 4(-4.9)h_0}}{-9.8} = \frac{-v_0 + \sqrt{v_0^2 + 19.6h_0}}{9.8}.$$

By hypothesis, $t_1 - t_2 = 2$, so that

$$2 = t_1 - t_2 = \frac{v_0 + \sqrt{v_0^2 + 19.6h_0}}{9.8} - \frac{-v_0 + \sqrt{v_0^2 + 19.6h_0}}{9.8} = \frac{2v_0}{9.8}.$$

Thus $v_0 = 9.8$ (meters per second).

71. By the Pythagorean Theorem, $|AB| = \sqrt{24^2 + 18^2} = \sqrt{900} = 30$, so that if you pass through B, then you drive $30 + 14 + 16 = 60$ kilometers. Since

$$|AC| = \sqrt{24^2 + (18+14)^2} = \sqrt{1600} = 40$$

if you do not pass through B, then you drive $40 + 16 = 56$ kilometers. At a speed of 60 kilometers per hour, the trip through B takes 1 hour, whereas the trip that avoids B takes 56 minutes. Since your trip lasts 1 hour, you pass through B.

72.

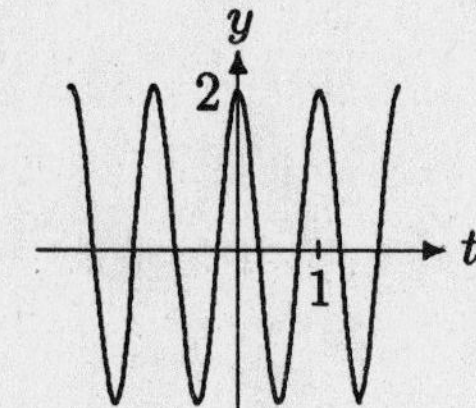

73. Using (1) in Section 1.7 and the notation in the diagram, we have $800 = 600\theta$, so $\theta = \frac{4}{3}$ radians. Thus $d = 600 \sin \frac{4}{3} \approx 583$ feet.

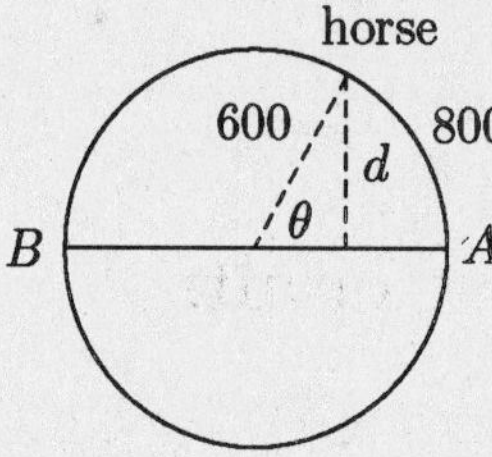

74. Let the distance between the motorist and the intersection be $60 + x$. Then $x = 40 \cot(\pi/6) = 40\sqrt{3}$, and thus the distance is $60 + 40\sqrt{3} \approx 129.3$ meters.

75. a. By hypothesis, $34{,}703 = P(0) = b$ and $44{,}485 = P(10) = 10a + 34{,}703$, so that $a = 978.2$. Thus the predicted population in the year 2000 is $P(30) = (978.2)(30) + 34{,}703 = 64{,}049$.

b. By hypothesis, $34{,}703 = P(0) = ae^0 = a$ and $44{,}485 = P(10) = 34{,}703e^{10b}$, so that $e^{10b} = \frac{44{,}485}{34{,}703}$. Thus $b = \frac{1}{10} \ln \frac{44{,}485}{34{,}703} \approx 0.0248325915$. Thus the predicted population in the year 2000 is $P(30) = 34{,}703e^{30(0.0248325915)} \approx 73{,}098$.

76. a. If $N = 1$, then $0 = \log 1 = 8.73 - 1.15M$, so that $M = 8.73/1.15 \approx 7.59130$.

b. Since $\log N = 8.73 - 1.15M$, we have $N = 10^{\log N} = 10^{8.73-1.15M} = 10^{8.73}10^{-1.15M}$. Taking $M = 7.5, 7.6, 7.7, 7.8, 7.9$, and 8.0 successively and adding the corresponding values of N, we find that the average number of earthquakes with magnitude between 7.45 and 8.05 is approximately

$$10^{8.73}[10^{-(1.15)(7.5)} + 10^{-(1.15)(7.6)} + 10^{-(1.15)(7.7)}$$

$$+10^{-(1.15)(7.8)} + 10^{-(1.15)(7.9)} + 10^{-(1.15)(8)}] \approx 4.35649.$$

Chapter 2

Limits and Continuity

2.1 Informal Discussion of Limits

1. 3 2. −3 3. 0 4. 1 5. $-\frac{1}{11}$ 6. $-\frac{1}{2}$ 7. $\frac{2}{5}$ 8. 1

9. $\lim_{x\to-2}\frac{x^2-4}{x+2}=\lim_{x\to-2}\frac{(x+2)(x-2)}{x+2}=\lim_{x\to-2}(x-2)=-4$

10. $\lim_{x\to1}\frac{x^2+4x-5}{x-1}=\lim_{x\to1}\frac{(x-1)(x+5)}{x-1}=\lim_{x\to1}(x+5)=6$

11. $\lim_{x\to-5}\frac{x^2+4x-5}{x+5}=\lim_{x\to-5}\frac{(x-1)(x+5)}{x+5}=\lim_{x\to-5}(x-1)=-6$

12. $\lim_{x\to\pi}\frac{x^2-2x+1}{(x-1)^2}=\lim_{x\to\pi}\frac{(x-1)^2}{(x-1)^2}=\lim_{x\to\pi}1=1$

13. $\lim_{x\to1}\frac{x^3-1}{x-1}=\lim_{x\to1}\frac{(x-1)(x^2+x+1)}{x-1}=\lim_{x\to1}(x^2+x+1)=3$

14. $\lim_{x\to-2}\frac{x^3+8}{x+2}=\lim_{x\to-2}\frac{(x+2)(x^2-2x+4)}{x+2}=\lim_{x\to-2}(x^2-2x+4)=12$

15. $\lim_{x\to0}3(\sin^2 x+\cos^2 x)=\lim_{x\to0}3=3$

16. $\lim_{x\to\pi}\frac{\sin 2x}{\sin x\,\cos x}=\lim_{x\to\pi}\frac{2\sin x\,\cos x}{\sin x\,\cos x}=\lim_{x\to\pi}2=2$

17. $\lim_{x\to-1}-\frac{|x|}{x}=\lim_{x\to-1}-\frac{-x}{x}=\lim_{x\to-1}1=1$

18. $\lim_{x\to-6}\frac{x^2}{|x|}=\lim_{x\to-6}\frac{x^2}{-x}=\lim_{x\to-6}(-x)=6$

19. 1.003346721, 1.000033335, 1.000000333, 1.003346721, 1.000033335, 1.000000333; $\lim_{x\to0}f(x)=1$

20. 1.986693308, 1.999866669, 1.999998667, 1.986693308, 1.999866669, 1.999998667; $\lim_{x\to0}f(x)=2$

21. 0.0499583472, 0.0049999583, 0.0005, −0.0499583472, −0.0049999583, −0.0005; $\lim_{x\to0}f(x)=0$

22. 0.4995834722, 0.499995833, 0.5, 0.4995834722, 0.499995833, 0.5; $\lim_{x\to 0} f(x) = \frac{1}{2}$

23. 0.6164048071, 0.6001600395, 0.6000016, 0.6164048071, 0.6001600395, 0.6000016;

$$\lim_{x\to 0} \frac{\sin 3x}{\sin 5x} = 0.6$$

24. 6.003000786, 6.000030012, 5.9999988, 6.003000785, 6.000030012, 5.9999988;

$$\lim_{x\to 0} \frac{x^3}{x - \sin x} = 6$$

25. 0.0500417084, 0.0050000417, 0.0004999999, −0.0500417084, −0.0050000417, −0.0004999999;

$$\lim_{x\to 0} (\csc x - \cot x) = 0$$

26. 0.953101798, 0.9950330853, 0.9995003331, 1.053605157, 1.005033585, 1.000500334;

$$\lim_{x\to 0} \frac{\ln(1+x)}{x} = 1$$

27. 3.498588076, 3.045453395, 3.004504503, 2.591817793, 2.955446645, 2.995504497;

$$\lim_{x\to 0} \frac{e^{3x} - 1}{x} = 3$$

28. (b) or (d)

29. 1.6

30. a. Approximately 1 b. Approximately 0

31. The limit equals 0.

32. The limit equals 1.

33. The limit does not exist.

34. The limit equals 0.

35. b. 1

36. x must be between 1.75 and 2.5. Thus x must be within 0.25 of 2.

37. $(f(2) - f(1))/(2 - 1)$ is larger.

38. a. −6 b. $-\frac{2}{3}$

39. $f(3) = 9$ and

$$\frac{f(x) - f(3)}{x - 3} = \frac{x^2 - 9}{x - 3} = \frac{(x+3)(x-3)}{x - 3} = x + 3.$$

The slope of the line tangent to the graph of f at $(3, 9)$ is

$$\lim_{x\to 3} \frac{f(x) - f(3)}{x - 3} = \lim_{x\to 3} (x + 3) = 6.$$

40. $f(-2) = 0$ and

$$\frac{f(x) - f(-2)}{x - (-2)} = \frac{(x^2 + 2x) - 0}{x + 2} = x.$$

The slope of the line tangent to the graph of f at $(-2, 0)$ is

$$\lim_{x \to -2} \frac{f(x) - f(-2)}{x - (-2)} = \lim_{x \to -2} x = -2.$$

41. $f(4) = 33$ and

$$\frac{f(x) - f(4)}{x - 4} = \frac{(2x^2 + 1) - 33}{x - 4} = \frac{2(x^2 - 16)}{x - 4} = \frac{2(x + 4)(x - 4)}{x - 4} = 2(x + 4).$$

The slope of the line tangent to the graph of f at $(4, 33)$ is

$$\lim_{x \to 4} \frac{f(x) - f(4)}{x - 4} = \lim_{x \to 4} 2(x + 4) = 16.$$

42. $f(-2) = -7$ and

$$\frac{f(x) - f(-2)}{x - (-2)} = \frac{(x^3 + 1) - (-7)}{x + 2} = \frac{x^3 + 8}{x + 2} = \frac{(x + 2)(x^2 - 2x + 4)}{x + 2} = x^2 - 2x + 4.$$

The slope of the line tangent to the graph of f at $(-2, -7)$ is

$$\lim_{x \to -2} \frac{f(x) - f(-2)}{x - (-2)} = \lim_{x \to -2} (x^2 - 2x + 4) = 12.$$

43. .5129329439, .5012541824, .5001250418, .4879016417, .4987541511, .4998750416; the slope is .5.

44. −0.142333359, −0.1360142209, −0.1354029734, −0.1287885498, −0.1346608568, −0.135267381; the slope is approximately −0.135.

45. 1.583844403, 1.570925532, 1.570797619, 1.583844403, 1.570925532, 1.570797619; the slope is approximately 1.57.

46. .8459869848, .8044192657, .8004401921, .7578558226, .7956191345, .7995601919; the slope is 0.8.

47. $v(\frac{1}{2}) = \lim_{t \to 1/2} \frac{f(t) - f(\frac{1}{2})}{t - \frac{1}{2}} = \lim_{t \to 1/2} \frac{t^2 - \frac{1}{4}}{t - \frac{1}{2}} = \lim_{t \to 1/2} \frac{(t - \frac{1}{2})(t + \frac{1}{2})}{t - \frac{1}{2}} = \lim_{t \to 1/2} (t + \frac{1}{2}) = 1$ (mile per minute)

48. average velocity $= \frac{f(t) - f(2)}{t - 2} = \frac{(2t^2 + 1) - 9}{t - 2} = \frac{2(t^2 - 4)}{t - 2} = \frac{2(t - 2)(t + 2)}{t - 2} = 2(t + 2);$

$v(t) = \lim_{t \to 2} 2(t + 2) = 8$ (miles per minute)

2.2 Definition of Limit

1. -5 2. $\sqrt{2}/3$ 3. $\frac{1}{2}$

4. π 5. $2(-1)+5=3$ 6. $-4(0)-\frac{1}{3}=-\frac{1}{3}$

7. $\left|\frac{3}{2}\right|=\frac{3}{2}$ 8. $|-0.1|=0.1$ 9. $\lim_{x\to 0} f(x)=\lim_{x\to 0} 2x=0$

10. $\lim_{x\to 0} f(x)=\lim_{x\to 0}(-\frac{3}{2}x+\frac{1}{4})=\frac{1}{4}$

11. Observe that $|(4x+7)-7|=4|x|$. For any $\varepsilon>0$, let $\delta=\frac{1}{4}\varepsilon$. If $0<|x-0|<\delta$, then $|(4x+7)-7|=4|x|=4|x-0|<4\delta=\varepsilon$. Therefore by Definition 2.1, $\lim_{x\to 0}(4x+7)=7$.

12. Observe that $|(-2x+5)-(-1)|=|-2x+6|=|-2(x-3)|=2|x-3|$. For any $\varepsilon>0$, let $\delta=\frac{1}{2}\varepsilon$. If $0<|x-3|<\delta$, then $|(-2x+5)-(-1)|=2|x-3|<2\delta=\varepsilon$. Therefore by Definition 2.1, $\lim_{x\to 3}(-2x+5)=-1$.

13. Observe that $|(x^2+5)-5|=|x^2|=|x|^2$. For any $\varepsilon>0$, let $\delta=\sqrt{\varepsilon}$. If $0<|x-0|<\delta$, then $|(x^2+5)-5|=|x|^2<\delta^2=\varepsilon$. Therefore by Definition 2.1, $\lim_{x\to 0}(x^2+5)=5$.

14. Observe that

$$\left|\frac{2x}{x^2+1}-1\right|=\left|\frac{2x-(x^2+1)}{x^2+1}\right|=\left|\frac{-(x-1)^2}{x^2+1}\right|=\frac{|(x-1)^2|}{x^2+1}\leq\frac{|x-1|^2}{1}.$$

For any $\varepsilon>0$, let $\delta=\sqrt{\varepsilon}$. If $0<|x-1|<\delta$, then

$$\left|\frac{2x}{x^2+1}-1\right|\leq|x-1|^2<\delta^2=\varepsilon.$$

Therefore by Definition 2.1, $\lim_{x\to 1}\frac{2x}{x^2+1}=1$.

15. $\lim_{x\to 3}\frac{f(x)-f(3)}{x-3}=\lim_{x\to 3}\frac{\pi-\pi}{x-3}=0$; l: $y-\pi=0(x-3)$, or $y=\pi$

16. $\lim_{x\to 8}\frac{f(x)-f(8)}{x-8}=\lim_{x\to 8}\frac{(-\frac{1}{2}x+2)-(-2)}{x-8}=\lim_{x\to 8}=-\frac{1}{2}$; l: $y-(-2)=-\frac{1}{2}(x-8)$, or $y=-\frac{1}{2}x+2$

17. $$\lim_{x\to 1/2}\frac{f(x)-f(\frac{1}{2})}{x-\frac{1}{2}}=\lim_{x\to 1/2}\frac{(4x^2+\frac{1}{2})-\frac{3}{2}}{x-\frac{1}{2}}=\lim_{x\to 1/2}\frac{4(x^2-\frac{1}{4})}{x-\frac{1}{2}}=\lim_{x\to 1/2}\frac{4(x-\frac{1}{2})(x+\frac{1}{2})}{x-\frac{1}{2}}$$
$$=\lim_{x\to 1/2}4(x+\tfrac{1}{2})=4;\quad l\text{: } y-\tfrac{3}{2}=4(x-\tfrac{1}{2}),\text{ or } y=4x-\tfrac{1}{2}$$

18. $$\lim_{x\to 2}\frac{f(x)-f(2)}{x-2}=\lim_{x\to 2}\frac{(-\frac{1}{2}x^2+3)-1}{x-2}=\lim_{x\to 2}\frac{-\frac{1}{2}x^2+2}{x-2}=\lim_{x\to 2}\frac{-\frac{1}{2}(x^2-4)}{x-2}$$
$$=\lim_{x\to 2}\frac{-\frac{1}{2}(x-2)(x+2)}{x-2}=\lim_{x\to 2}-\tfrac{1}{2}(x+2)=-2;$$
l: $y-1=-2(x-2)$, or $y=-2x+5$

19. $\lim_{x\to 1}\dfrac{f(x)-f(1)}{x-1}=\lim_{x\to 1}\dfrac{(x^2+3x)-4}{x-1}=\lim_{x\to 1}\dfrac{(x-1)(x+4)}{x-1}=\lim_{x\to 1}(x+4)=5;$
l: $y-4=5(x-1)$, or $y=5x-1$

20. $\lim_{x\to -1}\dfrac{f(x)-f(-1)}{x-(-1)}=\lim_{x\to -1}\dfrac{(-x^2+4x)-(-5)}{x+1}=\lim_{x\to -1}\dfrac{-(x^2-4x-5)}{x+1}$
$=\lim_{x\to -1}\dfrac{-(x+1)(x-5)}{x+1}=\lim_{x\to -1}-(x-5)=6$
l: $y-(-5)=6\big(x-(-1)\big)$, or $y=6x+1$

21. $v(2)=\lim_{t\to 2}\dfrac{f(t)-f(2)}{t-2}=\lim_{t\to 2}\dfrac{(2t+1)-5}{t-2}=\lim_{t\to 2}\dfrac{2(t-2)}{t-2}=\lim_{t\to 2}2=2$

22. $v(0)=\lim_{t\to 0}\dfrac{f(t)-f(0)}{t-0}=\lim_{t\to 0}\dfrac{(-3t+\frac{1}{5})-\frac{1}{5}}{t-0}=\lim_{t\to 0}(-3)=-3$

23. $v(4)=\lim_{t\to 4}\dfrac{f(t)-f(4)}{t-4}=\lim_{t\to 4}\dfrac{-16t^2-(-16)4^2}{t-4}=\lim_{t\to 4}\dfrac{-16(t^2-16)}{t-4}$
$=\lim_{t\to 4}\dfrac{-16(t-4)(t+4)}{t-4}=\lim_{t\to 4}-16(t+4)=-128$

24. $v(1)=\lim_{t\to 1}\dfrac{f(t)-f(1)}{t-1}=\lim_{t\to 1}\dfrac{(-16t^2+100)-84}{t-1}=\lim_{t\to 1}\dfrac{-16(t^2-1)}{t-1}$
$=\lim_{t\to 1}\dfrac{-16(t-1)(t+1)}{t-1}=\lim_{t\to 1}-16(t+1)=-32$

25. $v(2)=\lim_{t\to 2}\dfrac{f(t)-f(2)}{t-2}=\lim_{t\to 2}\dfrac{(-16t^2+8t+54)-6}{t-2}=\lim_{t\to 2}\dfrac{-16t^2+8t+48}{t-2}$
$=\lim_{t\to 2}\dfrac{-8(2t^2-t-6)}{t-2}=\lim_{t\to 2}\dfrac{-8(t-2)(2t+3)}{t-2}=\lim_{t\to 2}-8(2t+3)=-56$

26. The graphs in (b) and (c)

27. Yes. For f take any function of the form $f(x)=mx+b$, whose graph is a line. The tangent lines at $\big(-3,f(-3)\big)$ and $\big(2,f(2)\big)$ are the same line $y=mx+b$. Other solutions are possible.

28. There is no tangent line at $(0,0)$.

29. The line $y=0$ is tangent to the graph at $(0,0)$.

30. a. No. The limit does not exist.

    b. No

31. a. The slope of the line is approximately 2, so $\delta\approx\varepsilon/2=0.0005$.

    b. The slope of the line is approximately 5, so $\delta\approx\varepsilon/5\approx 0.0002$.

32. For any $\varepsilon>0$, let $\delta=\varepsilon$. If $0<|x-a|<\delta$, then $\big||x|-|a|\big|\le|x-a|<\delta=\varepsilon$. Thus $\lim_{x\to a}|x|=|a|$.

33. If $m = 0$, the result to be proved is $\lim_{x\to a} b = b$, which was proved in Example 1. If $m \neq 0$, then for any $\varepsilon > 0$, let $\delta = \varepsilon/|m|$. If $0 < |x-a| < \delta$, then $|(mx+b)-(ma+b)| = |mx-ma| = |m|\,|x-a| < |m|\delta = \varepsilon$. Therefore $\lim_{x\to a}(mx+b) = ma+b$.

34. a. We must find all positive numbers x such that $x^2+x < .11$, or $x^2+x-.11 < 0$. By the quadratic formula, $x^2+x-.11 = 0$ for $x = \frac{1}{2}(-1 \pm \sqrt{1^2-4(1)(-.11)}\,) = \frac{1}{2}(-1 \pm \sqrt{1.44}\,) = \frac{1}{2}(-1 \pm 1.2)$. Thus $x^2+x-.11 = 0$ for $x = -1.1$ and for $x = .1$. Thus a positive number x must be less than .1 in order that $x^2+x < .11$.

    b. We must find all positive numbers x such that $x^2+x < \varepsilon$, or $x^2+x-\varepsilon < 0$. By the quadratic formula, $x^2+x-\varepsilon = 0$ for $x = \frac{1}{2}(-1 \pm \sqrt{1+4\varepsilon})$. Since x must be positive, this means that $x = -\frac{1}{2}+\frac{1}{2}\sqrt{1+4\varepsilon}$. Thus a positive number x must be less than $-\frac{1}{2}+\frac{1}{2}\sqrt{1+4\varepsilon}$ in order that $x^2+x < \varepsilon$.

35. The statement $\lim_{x\to a}|f(x)-L| = 0$ means that for every $\varepsilon > 0$ there is a $\delta > 0$ such that if $0 < |x-a| < \delta$, then $\big||f(x)-L|-0\big| < \varepsilon$, or equivalently, if $0 < |x-a| < \delta$, then $|f(x)-L| < \varepsilon$. But this is the meaning of $\lim_{x\to a} f(x) = L$.

36. By Definition 2.1, $\lim_{x\to a} f(x) = L$ means that for every $\varepsilon > 0$ there is a $\delta > 0$ such that if $0 < |x-a| < \delta$, then $|f(x)-L| < \varepsilon$. By Definition 2.1, $\lim_{h\to 0} f(a+h) = L$ means that for every $\varepsilon > 0$ there is a $\delta > 0$ such that if $0 < |h-0| < \delta$, then $|f(a+h)-L| < \varepsilon$. If we let $h = x-a$ in the first statement, we obtain the second statement. If we let $x = a+h$ in the second statement we get the first statement. Thus the two are equivalent.

37. No. It does not require $f(x)$ to approach L as x approaches a, since ε could always be chosen to be greater than 1.

38. As in the solution of Example 4,

$$v(1) = \lim_{t\to 1}\frac{h(t)-h(1)}{t-1} = \lim_{t\to 1}\frac{(-4.9t^2+49)-(-4.9+49)}{t-1} = \lim_{t\to 1}\frac{-4.9t^2+4.9}{t-1}$$

$$= \lim_{t\to 1}\frac{-4.9(t+1)(t-1)}{t-1} = \lim_{t\to 1} -4.9(t+1) = \lim_{t\to 1}(-4.9t-4.9) = -4.9-4.9 = -9.8 \text{ (meters per second)}.$$

39. The iron balls hit the ground when $h(t) = 0$. By the solution of Example 4, $h(t) = -4.9t^2+49$. Thus $h(t) = 0$ when $t^2 = 10$, or $t = \sqrt{10} < 4$. Therefore the iron balls are not moving after 4 seconds, so the velocity is 0.

40. a. By (11), $h(t) = -4.9t^2-6t+49$. Therefore by (10),

$$v(2) = \lim_{t\to 2}\frac{h(t)-h(2)}{t-2} = \lim_{t\to 2}\frac{(-4.9t^2-6t+49)-(-4.9\cdot 2^2-6\cdot 2+49)}{t-2}$$

$$= \lim_{t\to 2}\frac{-4.9(t^2-2^2)-6(t-2)}{t-2} = \lim_{t\to 2}\frac{-4.9(t+2)(t-2)-6(t-2)}{t-2}$$

$$= \lim_{t\to 2}[-4.9(t+2)-6] = \lim_{t\to 2}(-4.9t-15.8) = (-4.9)2-15.8 = -25.6 \text{ (meters per second)}.$$

b. The speed of the iron balls after 2 seconds is $|v(2)| = |-25.6| = 25.6$ (meters per second).

41. a. By (11), $h(t) = -4.9t^2 + 4t + 20$. By (10),

$$v(1) = \lim_{t\to 1} \frac{h(t) - h(1)}{t-1} = \lim_{t\to 1} \frac{(-4.9t^2 + 4t + 20) - (-4.9 \cdot 1^2 + 4 \cdot 1 + 20)}{t-1}$$

$$= \lim_{t\to 1} \frac{-4.9(t^2 - 1) + 4(t-1)}{t-1} = \lim_{t\to 1} \frac{-4.9(t+1)(t-1) + 4(t-1)}{t-1}$$

$$= \lim_{t\to 1} [-4.9(t+1) + 4] = \lim_{t\to 1} (-4.9t - .9) = -4.9 - .9 = -5.8.$$

Therefore the speed of the stone after 1 second is $|v(1)| = 5.8$ meters per second.

b. By (11), $h(t) = -4.9t^2 + 4t + 20$. By (10),

$$v(2) = \lim_{t\to 2} \frac{h(t) - h(2)}{t-2} = \lim_{t\to 2} \frac{(-4.9t^2 + 4t + 20) - (-4.9 \cdot 2^2 + 4 \cdot 2 + 20)}{t-2}$$

$$= \lim_{t\to 2} \frac{-4.9(t^2 - 2^2) + 4(t-2)}{t-2} = \lim_{t\to 2} \frac{-4.9(t+2)(t-2) + 4(t-2)}{t-2}$$

$$= \lim_{t\to 2} [-4.9(t+2) + 4] = \lim_{t\to 2} (-4.9t - 5.8) = (-4.9)2 - 5.8 = -15.6.$$

Therefore the speed of the stone after 2 seconds is $|v(2)| = 15.6$ meters per second.

42. By (11), $h(t) = -4.9t^2 - 4t + 20$. By (10),

$$v(2) = \lim_{t\to 2} \frac{h(t) - h(2)}{t-2} = \lim_{t\to 2} \frac{(-4.9t^2 - 4t + 20) - (-4.9 \cdot 2^2 - 4 \cdot 2 + 20)}{t-2}$$

$$= \lim_{t\to 2} \frac{-4.9(t^2 - 2^2) - 4(t-2)}{t-2} = \lim_{t\to 2} \frac{-4.9(t+2)(t-2) - 4(t-2)}{t-2}$$

$$= \lim_{t\to 2} [-4.9(t+2) - 4] = \lim_{t\to 2} (-4.9t - 13.8) = -4.9 - 13.8 = -18.7.$$

Therefore the speed of the stone after 2 seconds is $|v(2)| = 18.7$ meters per second.

43. a. By (11) with $h_0 = 40$, $h(t) = -4.9t^2 + v_0 t + 40$. Since $v(1) = -9.8$, we have from (10) that

$$-9.8 = v(1) = \lim_{t\to 1} \frac{h(t) - h(1)}{t-1} = \lim_{t\to 1} \frac{(-4.9t^2 + v_0 t + 40) - (-4.9 + v_0 + 40)}{t-1}$$

$$= \lim_{t\to 1} \frac{-4.9(t^2 - 1) + v_0(t-1)}{t-1} = \lim_{t\to 1} \frac{-4.9(t+1)(t-1) + v_0(t-1)}{t-1}$$

$$= \lim_{t\to 1} [-4.9(t+1) + v_0] = \lim_{t\to 1} (-4.9t - 4.9 + v_0) = -4.9 - 4.9 + v_0 = -9.8 + v_0.$$

Thus $v_0 = 0$.

b. Yes. The answer would be the same because the initial height disappears by subtraction in $h(t) - h(1)$.

2.3 Limit Theorems and Continuity

1. By the Constant Multiple Rule and (8), $\lim_{x\to 16} -\frac{1}{2}\sqrt{x} = -\frac{1}{2}\lim_{x\to 16}\sqrt{x} = -\frac{1}{2}\sqrt{16} = -2$.

2. By (4), $\lim_{x\to -1}(-5x^2+2x-\frac{1}{2}) = -5(-1)^2+2(-1)-\frac{1}{2} = -\frac{15}{2}$.

3. By the Sum and Constant Multiple Rules, along with (8) of this section and (8) of Section 2.2, $\lim_{x\to 4}(3x^2-5\sqrt{x}-6|x|) = 3(4)^2-5\sqrt{4}-6|4| = 14$.

4. By the Sum and Constant Multiple Rules and (6),

$$\lim_{x\to 1/27}(9x+6x^{2/3}-2x^{1/3}+2) = 9\left(\frac{1}{27}\right)+6\left(\frac{1}{27}\right)^{2/3}-2\left(\frac{1}{27}\right)^{1/3}+2 = \frac{7}{3}.$$

5. By the Product Rule and (4),

$$\lim_{x\to\sqrt{2}}(x^2+5)(\sqrt{2}\,x+1) = \lim_{x\to\sqrt{2}}(x^2+5)\lim_{x\to\sqrt{2}}(\sqrt{2}\,x+1) = [(\sqrt{2})^2+5][\sqrt{2}\cdot\sqrt{2}+1] = 21.$$

6. By the Product Rule and (4),

$$\lim_{x\to -1}(x+1)\left(4x^3-9x+\frac{3}{4}\right) = \lim_{x\to -1}(x+1)\lim_{x\to -1}\left(4x^3-9x+\frac{3}{4}\right) = (-1+1)\left(4(1)^3-9(1)+\frac{3}{4}\right) = 0.$$

7. By the Product and Sum Rules and (7),

$$\lim_{y\to 64}(\sqrt[3]{y}+\sqrt{y})^2 = \left[\lim_{y\to 64}(\sqrt[3]{y}+\sqrt{y})\right]^2 = (\sqrt[3]{64}+\sqrt{64})^2 = 144.$$

8. By the Product and Difference Rules and (8),

$$\lim_{y\to 3}\sqrt{y}\,(y-1)^4 = \left(\lim_{y\to 3}\sqrt{y}\right)\left[\lim_{y\to 3}(y-1)\right]^4 = \sqrt{3}\,(3-1)^4 = 16\sqrt{3}.$$

9. By (5), $\lim_{y\to -2}\dfrac{4y-1}{5y+4} = \dfrac{4(-2)-1}{5(-2)+4} = \dfrac{3}{2}$.

10. By the Quotient and Sum Rules and (6),

$$\lim_{t\to 0}\frac{2t^{1/3}-4}{-3t^{1/3}+5} = \frac{\lim_{t\to 0}(2t^{1/3}-4)}{\lim_{t\to 0}(-3t^{1/3}+5)} = \frac{2(0)-4}{-3(0)+5} = -\frac{4}{5}.$$

11. By the Difference and Quotient Rules, along with (9) and (4),

$$\lim_{x\to 2}\frac{e^x-2}{\pi x} = \frac{\lim_{x\to 2}(e^x-2)}{\lim_{x\to 2}\pi x} = \frac{\lim_{x\to 2}e^x-\lim_{x\to 2}2}{(\pi)(2)} = \frac{e^2-2}{2\pi}.$$

12. By the Difference and Product Rules, along with (6) and (9),

$$\lim_{x\to 0}e^{-x}(x^2-5) = \lim_{x\to 0}\frac{x^2-5}{e^x} = \frac{\lim_{x\to 0}x^2-\lim_{x\to 0}5}{\lim_{x\to 0}e^x} = \frac{0-5}{e^0} = -5.$$

13. By the Constant Multiple, Sum, and Product Rules, along with (9) of this section and Example 1 of Section 2.2,

$$\lim_{x\to 1}(e^x+1)^2 = \lim_{x\to 1}(e^x e^x + 2e^x + 1) = \lim_{x\to 1}(e^x e^x) + 2\lim_{x\to 1} e^x + \lim_{x\to 1} 1$$
$$= \left(\lim_{x\to 1} e^x\right)\left(\lim_{x\to 1} e^x\right) + 2e^1 + 1 = e^1 e^1 + 2e + 1 = e^2 + 2e + 1.$$

14. By the Product Rule and (9),

$$\lim_{x\to 0} e^{2x} = \lim_{x\to 0}(e^x)^2 = \lim_{x\to 0}(e^x e^x) = \left(\lim_{x\to 0} e^x\right)\left(\lim_{x\to 0} e^x\right) = e^0 \cdot e^0 = 1\cdot 1 = 1.$$

15. By the Quotient Rule, along with (9) and (4),

$$\lim_{x\to e}\frac{\ln x}{x} = \frac{\lim_{x\to e}\ln x}{\lim_{x\to e} x} = \frac{\ln e}{e} = \frac{1}{e}.$$

16. By the Sum and Product Rules, along with (9) and (4),

$$\lim_{x\to 2}(\ln x + 2)(x^2 + x - 1) = \lim_{x\to 2}(\ln x + 2)\lim_{x\to 2}(x^2 + x - 1)$$
$$= \left(\lim_{x\to 2}\ln x + \lim_{x\to 2} 2\right)(2^2 + 2 - 1) = (\ln 2 + 2)5 = 10 + 5\ln 2.$$

17. $\displaystyle\lim_{x\to -1}\frac{x^2-1}{x+1} = \lim_{x\to -1}\frac{(x-1)(x+1)}{x+1} = \lim_{x\to -1}(x-1) = -1-1 = -2$

18. $\displaystyle\lim_{x\to 3}\frac{x^2-9}{x-3} = \lim_{x\to 3}\frac{(x-3)(x+3)}{x-3} = \lim_{x\to 3}(x+3) = 3+3 = 6$

19. $\displaystyle\lim_{x\to 1}\frac{x^3-1}{x-1} = \lim_{x\to 1}\frac{(x-1)(x^2+x+1)}{x-1} = \lim_{x\to 1}(x^2+x+1) = 1+1+1 = 3$

20. $\displaystyle\lim_{x\to 2}\frac{x^2-4}{x^3-8} = \lim_{x\to 2}\frac{(x-2)(x+2)}{(x-2)(x^2+2x+4)} = \lim_{x\to 2}\frac{x+2}{x^2+2x+4} = \lim_{x\to 2}\frac{2+2}{(2)^2+2(2)+4} = \frac{1}{3}$

21. $\displaystyle\lim_{x\to -2}\frac{x^4-16}{4-x^2} = -\lim_{x\to -2}\frac{x^4-16}{x^2-4} = -\lim_{x\to -2}\frac{(x^2-4)(x^2+4)}{x^2-4} = -\lim_{x\to -2}(x^2+4) = -((-2)^2+4) = -8$

22. $\displaystyle\lim_{x\to -4}\frac{x^2-16}{|x|-4} = \lim_{x\to -4}\frac{(|x|-4)(|x|+4)}{|x|-4} = \lim_{x\to -4}(|x|+4) = |-4|+4 = 8$

23. $\displaystyle\lim_{x\to 3}\frac{x^2-x-6}{x^3-3x^2+x-3} = \lim_{x\to 3}\frac{(x+2)(x-3)}{(x-3)(x^2+1)} = \lim_{x\to 3}\frac{x+2}{x^2+1} = \frac{3+2}{3^2+1} = \frac{1}{2}$

24. $\displaystyle\lim_{x\to 4}\frac{x^3+4x^2+x+4}{x^2+3x-4} = \lim_{x\to 4}\frac{(x+4)(x^2+1)}{(x+4)(x-1)} = \lim_{x\to 4}\frac{x^2+1}{x-1} = \frac{4^2+1}{4-1} = \frac{17}{3}$

25. $\displaystyle\lim_{x\to 100}\frac{x-100}{\sqrt{x}-10} = \lim_{x\to 100}\frac{(\sqrt{x}-10)(\sqrt{x}+10)}{\sqrt{x}-10} = \lim_{x\to 100}(\sqrt{x}+10) = \sqrt{100}+10 = 20$

26. $\displaystyle\lim_{x\to 1/16}\frac{x^{1/2}-\frac{1}{4}}{x^{1/4}-\frac{1}{2}} = \lim_{x\to 1/16}\frac{(x^{1/4}-\frac{1}{2})(x^{1/4}+\frac{1}{2})}{x^{1/4}-\frac{1}{2}} = \lim_{x\to 1/16}(x^{1/4}+\tfrac{1}{2}) = (\tfrac{1}{16})^{1/4}+\tfrac{1}{2} = 1$

27. $\lim_{y\to 1/27}\dfrac{y^{2/3}-\frac{1}{9}}{y^{1/3}-\frac{1}{3}} = \lim_{y\to 1/27}\dfrac{(y^{1/3}-\frac{1}{3})(y^{1/3}+\frac{1}{3})}{y^{1/3}-\frac{1}{3}} = \lim_{y\to 1/27}(y^{1/3}+\frac{1}{3}) = (\frac{1}{27})^{1/3}+\frac{1}{3} = \frac{2}{3}$

28. $\lim_{y\to 2}\dfrac{\sqrt{y}-\sqrt{2}}{y^2-2y} = \lim_{y\to 2}\dfrac{\sqrt{y}-\sqrt{2}}{y(y-2)} = \lim_{y\to 2}\dfrac{\sqrt{y}-\sqrt{2}}{y(\sqrt{y}-\sqrt{2})(\sqrt{y}+\sqrt{2})} = \lim_{y\to 2}\dfrac{1}{y(\sqrt{y}+\sqrt{2})}$

$= \dfrac{1}{2(\sqrt{2}+\sqrt{2})} = \dfrac{1}{4\sqrt{2}} = \dfrac{\sqrt{2}}{8}$

29. $\lim_{y\to 1/2}\dfrac{6y-3}{y(1-2y)} = -3\lim_{y\to 1/2}\dfrac{1-2y}{y(1-2y)} = -3\lim_{y\to 1/2}\dfrac{1}{y} = -3\left(\dfrac{1}{1/2}\right) = -6$

30. $\lim_{x\to 0} x\left(1-\dfrac{1}{x}\right) = \lim_{x\to 0}(x-1) = 0-1 = -1$

31. $\lim_{x\to -2}\left(\dfrac{x^2}{x+2}-\dfrac{4}{x+2}\right) = \lim_{x\to -2}\dfrac{x^2-4}{x+2} = \lim_{x\to -2}\dfrac{(x-2)(x+2)}{x+2} = \lim_{x\to -2}(x-2) = -2-2 = -4$

32. $\lim_{x\to 0}\dfrac{1+1/x}{2+1/x} = \lim_{x\to 0}\dfrac{x(1+1/x)}{x(2+1/x)} = \lim_{x\to 0}\dfrac{x+1}{2x+1} = 1$

33. $\lim_{x\to 0}\dfrac{e^{2x}-1}{e^x-1} = \lim_{x\to 0}\dfrac{(e^x)^2-1}{e^x-1} = \lim_{x\to 0}\dfrac{(e^x+1)(e^x-1)}{e^x-1} = \lim_{x\to 0}(e^x+1) = e^0+1 = 1+1 = 2$

34. $\lim_{x\to 0}\dfrac{e^{3x}-1}{e^x-1} = \lim_{x\to 0}\dfrac{(e^x)^3-1}{e^x-1} = \lim_{x\to 0}\dfrac{(e^x-1)\left((e^x)^2+e^x+1\right)}{e^x-1}$

$= \lim_{x\to 0}(e^xe^x+e^x+1) = e^0e^0+e^0+1 = 1\cdot 1+1+1 = 3$

35. $\lim_{x\to -1}\dfrac{f(x)-f(-1)}{x-(-1)} = \lim_{x\to -1}\dfrac{(x^2+4x+1)-(-2)}{x+1} = \lim_{x\to -1}\dfrac{x^2+4x+3}{x+1}$

$= \lim_{x\to -1}\dfrac{(x+1)(x+3)}{x+1} = \lim_{x\to -1}(x+3) = 2$

l: $y-(-2) = 2\left(x-(-1)\right)$, or $y+2 = 2(x+1)$

36. $\lim_{x\to 1}\dfrac{f(x)-f(1)}{x-1} = \lim_{x\to 1}\dfrac{(x^6-1)-0}{x-1} = \lim_{x\to 1}\dfrac{(x-1)(x^5+x^4+x^3+x^2+x+1)}{x-1}$

$= \lim_{x\to 1}(x^5+x^4+x^3+x^2+x+1) = 6$

l: $y-0 = 6(x-1)$, or $y = 6(x-1)$

37. $\lim_{x\to 2}\dfrac{f(x)-f(2)}{x-2} = \lim_{x\to 2}\dfrac{1/x-1/2}{x-2} = \lim_{x\to 2}\dfrac{(2-x)/(2x)}{x-2} = \lim_{x\to 2}-\dfrac{1}{2x} = -\dfrac{1}{4}$

l: $y-\frac{1}{2} = -\frac{1}{4}(x-2)$

38. $\lim_{x\to -1/2}\dfrac{f(x)-f(-\frac{1}{2})}{x-(-\frac{1}{2})} = \lim_{x\to -1/2}\dfrac{1/x-(-2)}{x+\frac{1}{2}} = \lim_{x\to -1/2}\dfrac{(1+2x)/x}{x+\frac{1}{2}} = \lim_{x\to -1/2}\dfrac{2}{x} = -4$

l: $y-(-2) = -4\left(x-(-\frac{1}{2})\right)$, or $y+2 = -4(x+\frac{1}{2})$

39. $\lim_{x\to-1} \dfrac{f(x)-f(-1)}{x-(-1)} = \lim_{x\to-1} \dfrac{1/(x+3)-1/2}{x+1} = \lim_{x\to-1} \dfrac{\dfrac{-1-x}{2(x+3)}}{x+1} = \lim_{x\to-1} \dfrac{-1}{2(x+3)} = -\dfrac{1}{4}$

l: $y - \frac{1}{2} = -\frac{1}{4}(x+1)$

40. $\lim_{x\to2/3} \dfrac{f(x)-f(\frac{2}{3})}{x-\frac{2}{3}} = \lim_{x\to2/3} \dfrac{1/x^2-9/4}{x-\frac{2}{3}} = \lim_{x\to2/3} \dfrac{\dfrac{4-9x^2}{4x^2}}{x-\frac{2}{3}} = \lim_{x\to2/3} \dfrac{\dfrac{(2-3x)(2+3x)}{4x^2}}{x-\frac{2}{3}}$

$$= \lim_{x\to2/3} \frac{-3(2+3x)}{4x^2} = \frac{-12}{\frac{16}{9}} = -\frac{27}{4}$$

l: $y - \frac{9}{4} = -\frac{27}{4}(x-\frac{2}{3})$

41. $\lim_{x\to16} \dfrac{f(x)-f(16)}{x-16} = \lim_{x\to16} \dfrac{\sqrt{x}-4}{x-16} = \lim_{x\to16} \dfrac{(\sqrt{x}-4)(\sqrt{x}+4)}{(x-16)(\sqrt{x}+4)} = \lim_{x\to16} \dfrac{x-16}{(x-16)(\sqrt{x}+4)}$

$$= \lim_{x\to16} \frac{1}{\sqrt{x}+4} = \frac{1}{8}$$

l: $y - 4 = \frac{1}{8}(x-16)$

42. $\lim_{x\to1} \dfrac{f(x)-f(1)}{x-1} = \lim_{x\to1} \dfrac{x^{1/4}-1}{x-1} = \lim_{x\to1} \dfrac{x^{1/4}-1}{(x^{1/4}-1)(x^{3/4}+x^{1/2}+x^{1/4}+1)}$

$$= \lim_{x\to1} \frac{1}{x^{3/4}+x^{1/2}+x^{1/4}+1} = \frac{1}{4}$$

l: $y - 1 = \frac{1}{4}(x-1)$

43. f is a polynomial function, so f is continuous at 2.

44. f is a polynomial function, so f is continuous at -1.

45. f is a rational function and 0 is in the domain of f, so f is continuous at 0.

46. f is a rational function and -1 is in the domain of f, so f is continuous at -1.

47. Since $\sqrt{x}$ is continuous at 4 and the polynomial x^2+4 is continuous at 4, Theorem 2.4 implies that the product, which is f, is continuous at 4.

48. Since $\sqrt{x}$ is continuous at 2, Theorem 2.4 implies that $4\sqrt{x}$ is continuous at 2. Since 2 is in the domain of the rational function $3x+1/x$, the numerator of f is continuous at 2. Since $\sqrt{x}$ is continuous at 2, Theorem 2.4 implies that the denominator $4\sqrt{x}$ of f is continuous at 2 also. Since $4\sqrt{2} \neq 0$, Theorem 2.4 implies that f is continuous at 2.

49. a. For f to be continuous at 3, we need $\lim_{x\to3} f(x) = f(3)$. We have

$$\lim_{x\to3} f(x) = \lim_{x\to3} \frac{x^2-9}{x-3} = \lim_{x\to3} \frac{(x+3)(x-3)}{x-3} = \lim_{x\to3}(x+3) = 3+3 = 6.$$

Thus if we define $f(3) = 6$, then f will be continuous at 3.

b. For f to be continuous at -2, we need $\lim_{x\to -2} f(x) = f(-2)$. We have

$$\lim_{x\to -2} f(x) = \lim_{x\to -2} \frac{x^2+5x+6}{x+2} = \lim_{x\to -2} \frac{(x+2)(x+3)}{x+2} = \lim_{x\to -2}(x+3) = -2+3 = 1.$$

Thus if we define $f(-2) = 1$, then f will be continuous at -2.

c. For f to be continuous at 1, we need $\lim_{x\to 1} f(x) = f(1)$. Since

$$\lim_{x\to 1}(x-1) = 0 \quad \text{and} \quad \lim_{x\to 1}(x^2+5x+4) = 1+5+4 = 10 \neq 0,$$

it follows that

$$\lim_{x\to 1} \frac{x^2+5x+4}{x-1}$$

does not exist. Therefore there is no way to define $f(1)$ so that f will be continuous at 1.

50. a. For f to be continuous at 3, we need $\lim_{x\to 3} f(x) = f(3)$. Since $f(x) = x$ for $x \neq 3$, we have $\lim_{x\to 3} f(x) = \lim_{x\to 3} x = 3$. Thus if we redefine $f(3)$ to be 3, then the resulting function will be continuous at 3.

b. For f to be continuous at 1, we need $\lim_{x\to 1} f(x) = f(1)$. Thus there must be a $\delta > 0$ such that if $0 < |x-1| < \delta$, then $|f(x) - f(1)| < \frac{1}{2}$. However, for x close to 1 and $x < 1$, $f(x) = 2x-3$, so $f(x)$ is close to $2\cdot 1 - 3 = -1$. By contrast, for x close to 1 and $x > 1$, we have $f(x) = 3x-2$, so $f(x)$ is close to $3\cdot 1 - 2 = 1$. Therefore there is no way of redefining $f(1)$ so that f is continuous at 1.

51. a. $\lim_{x\to 0} \dfrac{f(x)-f(0)}{x-0} = \lim_{x\to 0} \dfrac{x^2-0}{x-0} = \lim_{x\to 0} x = 0$; $\lim_{x\to 0} \dfrac{g(x)-g(0)}{x-0} = \lim_{x\to 0} \dfrac{x^3-0}{x-0} = \lim_{x\to 0} x^2 = 0.$

Since the tangent lines through $(0,0)$ have the same slope, they are the same.

b. $\lim_{x\to 0} \dfrac{f(x)-f(0)}{x-0} = \lim_{x\to 0} \dfrac{(x^2+1)-1}{x-0} = \lim_{x\to 0} x = 0;$

$\lim_{x\to 0} \dfrac{g(x)-g(0)}{x-0} = \lim_{x\to 0} \dfrac{(-x^2+1)-1}{x-0} = \lim_{x\to 0}(-x) = 0.$

Since the tangent lines through $(0,1)$ have the same slope, they are the same.

52. First we find the point where the line intersects the graph of f:

$$x^2 - 2x = 8x - 25 \implies x^2 - 10x + 25 = 0 \implies (x-5)^2 = 0, \text{ or } x = 5.$$

Since

$$\lim_{x\to 5} \frac{f(x)-f(5)}{x-5} = \lim_{x\to 5} \frac{(x^2-2x)-15}{x-5} = \lim_{x\to 5} \frac{(x-5)(x+3)}{x-5} = \lim_{x\to 5}(x+3) = 8$$

the tangent line at $(5,15)$ is $y - 15 = 8(x-5)$, or $y = 8x - 25$. The point of tangency is $(5,15)$.

53. a. $\lim_{x\to a} \dfrac{f(x)-f(a)}{x-a} = \lim_{x\to a} \dfrac{(1/x)-(1/a)}{x-a} = \lim_{x\to a} \dfrac{a-x}{ax(x-a)} = \lim_{x\to a} \dfrac{-1}{ax} = \dfrac{-1}{a^2}$

Thus an equation of the tangent line is $y - 1/a = (-1/a^2)(x-a)$, or $y = -(1/a^2)x + 2/a$.

b. The x intercept of the tangent line is $2a$, and the y intercept is $2/a$. Thus the area A of the triangle is $\frac{1}{2}(2a)(2/a) = 2$, so the area is independent of a.

54. Since $g(x) = f(x) - [f(x) - g(x)]$, and $\lim_{x\to -1} f(x)$ and $\lim_{x\to -1}[f(x) - g(x)]$ exist, it follows from the Difference Rule that $\lim_{x\to -1} g(x)$ exists and $\lim_{x\to -1} g(x) = \lim_{x\to -1} f(x) - \lim_{x\to -1}[f(x) - g(x)] = 4 - 6 = -2$.

55. Since $g(x) = (fg)(x)/f(x)$ (if $f(x) \neq 0$), and $\lim_{x\to\sqrt{2}}(fg)(x)$ and $\lim_{x\to\sqrt{2}} f(x)$ both exist, the Quotient Rule tells us that $\lim_{x\to\sqrt{2}} g(x)$ exists. Moreover,

$$\lim_{x\to\sqrt{2}} g(x) = \frac{\lim_{x\to\sqrt{2}}(fg)(x)}{\lim_{x\to\sqrt{2}} f(x)} = -\frac{\sqrt{2}}{3}.$$

56. $$\lim_{x\to a} \frac{Af(x) - Bg(x)}{f(x) - g(x)} = \frac{\lim_{x\to a}\big(Af(x) - Bg(x)\big)}{\lim_{x\to a}\big(f(x) - g(x)\big)} = \frac{A\lim_{x\to a} f(x) - B\lim_{x\to a} g(x)}{\lim_{x\to a} f(x) - \lim_{x\to a} g(x)}$$
$$= \frac{A^2 - B^2}{A - B} = \frac{(A-B)(A+B)}{A-B} = A + B$$

57. a. $2x^2 + x - 3 = (2x+3)(x-1)$, so that $2x^2 + x - 3 = 0$ for $x = -\frac{3}{2}$ and for $x = 1$. If follows that if $\lim_{x\to a} f(x)$ exists for all a, then the numerator, $x^2 + cx + 3$, must equal 0 for $x = -\frac{3}{2}$ and for $x = 1$. This implies that $(-\frac{3}{2})^2 - \frac{3}{2}c + 3 = 0$ and $1 + c + 3 = 0$. Since there is no number c satisfying both of the latter two equations, we conclude that there is no c such that $\lim_{x\to a} f(x)$ exists for all a.

b. Consider the zeros (roots) of the denominator, $2x^2 - 3x + c$. Since $(-3)^2 - 4(2)c = 9 - 8c$, it follows from the quadratic formula that the denominator has no zeros if $9 - 8c < 0$, that is, if $c > \frac{9}{8}$. Thus $\lim_{x\to a} f(x)$ exists for all a if $c > \frac{9}{8}$. If $c = \frac{9}{8}$, then

$$f(x) = \frac{x^2 + x - 6}{2x^2 - 3x + \frac{9}{8}} = \frac{(x+3)(x-2)}{2(x - \frac{3}{4})^2},$$

so that $\lim_{x\to 3/4} f(x)$ does not exist. If $c < \frac{9}{8}$, then the denominator has two roots r_1 and r_2. Since $2x^2 - 3x + c$ is not a scalar multiple of the numerator, $x^2 + x - 6$, the roots r_1 and r_2 must be different (as a pair) from the roots -3 and 2 of the numerator. Thus either $\lim_{x\to r_1} f(x)$ or $\lim_{x\to r_2} f(x)$ does not exist. We conclude that $\lim_{x\to a} f(x)$ exists for all x if and only if $c > \frac{9}{8}$.

58. $\lim_{x\to 0}[f(x) + g(x)] = \lim_{x\to 0}(1/x - 1/x) = \lim_{x\to 0} 0 = 0$, but by Example 3, $\lim_{x\to 0}(1/x)$ does not exist and $\lim_{x\to 0}(-1/x) = -\lim_{x\to 0}(1/x)$ does not exist.

59. $\lim_{x\to 0}[f(x)g(x)] = \lim_{x\to 0}(1/x)(x) = \lim_{x\to 0} 1 = 1$, but by Example 3, $\lim_{x\to 0}(1/x)$ does not exist.

60. If $\lim_{x\to a} g(x)$ did exist, then by the Sum Rule, $\lim_{x\to a}[f(x) + g(x)]$ would exist.

61. a. $\lim_{x\to 0} 1/(x^2 + x)$ does not exist, so we cannot use the Product Rule to conclude that

$$\lim_{x\to 0}\left[x\left(\frac{1}{x^2+x}\right)\right] = \left(\lim_{x\to 0} x\right)\left(\lim_{x\to 0}\frac{1}{x^2+x}\right).$$

b. $$\lim_{x\to 0}\left[x\left(\frac{1}{x^2+x}\right)\right] = \lim_{x\to 0}\frac{1}{x+1} = \frac{1}{\lim_{x\to 0}(x+1)} = 1$$

62. a. Since $f(x) \le g(x)$ for all $x \neq a$, we have $L \le M$.

b. Since $f(x) < g(x)$ for all $x \neq a$, we have $L \le M$. Notice that we cannot conclude that $L < M$. For example, if $f(x) = 0$ and $g(x) = x^2$, then $f(x) < g(x)$ for $x \neq 0$. Nevertheless $\lim_{x\to 0} f(x) = 0 = \lim_{x\to 0} f(x)$.

63. a. Suppose $\lim_{x\to a} f(x)/g(x)$ exists and equals L. Then by the Product Rule,

$$\lim_{x\to a} f(x) = \lim_{x\to a}\left[g(x)\frac{f(x)}{g(x)}\right] = \left(\lim_{x\to a} g(x)\right)\left(\lim_{x\to a}\frac{f(x)}{g(x)}\right) = 0 \cdot L = 0.$$

However, $\lim_{x\to a} f(x) = c \neq 0$ by hypothesis. Therefore $\lim_{x\to a} f(x)/g(x)$ does not exist.

b. $\dfrac{x^2+1}{x(x+2)} = \dfrac{f(x)}{g(x)}$, where $f(x) = x^2+1$ and $g(x) = x(x+2)$. Since $\lim_{x\to 0} f(x) = 0^2+1 \neq 0$ and $\lim_{x\to 0} g(x) = 0(0+2) = 0$, it follows from part (a) that $\lim_{x\to 0}\dfrac{x^2+1}{x(x+2)}$ does not exist.

64. The graphs of the functions in (b) and (f) are continuous at 2. For the function in (a), $\lim_{x\to 2} f(x)$ exists but does not equal $f(2)$. For the functions in (c), (d), and (e), $\lim_{x\to 2} f(x)$ does not exist.

65. Suppose a is rational, so that $f(a) = 0$. To show that f is not continuous at a, we will show that $\lim_{x\to a} f(x) = 0$ is not true. Suppose to the contrary that $\lim_{x\to a} f(x) = 0$. Then corresponding to $\varepsilon = 1$ in Definition 2.1 there would be a number $\delta > 0$ such that if $0 < |x-a| < \delta$, then $|f(x) - 0| < 1$. Since $f(x)$ can only be 0 or 1, this means that $f(x) = 0$ for $a - \delta < x < a + \delta$. But there is an irrational number x in the open interval $(a-\delta, a+\delta)$ and for that x, we have $f(x) = 1$, not $f(x) = 0$. Thus $\lim_{x\to a} f(x) = 0$ cannot be true, and hence f is not continuous at a. An analogous argument shows that $\lim_{x\to a} f(x) = 1 = f(a)$ cannot be true for any irrational number. Therefore f is not continuous at any real number.

66. To show that f is continuous at 0, we show that $\lim_{x\to 0} f(x) = f(0) = 0$. For any $\varepsilon > 0$, let $\delta = \varepsilon$. If $0 < |x - 0| < \delta$, then either $f(x) = 0$, in which case $|f(x) - 0| = 0 < \varepsilon$, or $f(x) = x$, in which case $|f(x) - 0| = |x - 0| < \delta = \varepsilon$. Thus if $0 < |x - 0| < \delta$, then $|f(x) - 0| < \varepsilon$. By Definition 2.1, $\lim_{x\to 0} f(x) = 0$, so f is continuous at 0. For $x \neq 0$, we have $g(x) = f(x)/x$, where g is the function in Exercise 65. If f were continuous at any $x \neq 0$, then it would follow from Theorem 2.4 that g must also be continuous at x. But g is not continuous at any real number. Therefore f is not continuous at any nonzero real number.

67. Since F is a polynomial, F is continuous at every number in $(\frac{1}{2}r_0, r_0)$.

68. Since v is a rational function whose denominator has no roots, v is continuous at every number in $(0,\infty)$. By Theorem 2.4, K is also continuous at every number in $(0,\infty)$.

2.4 The Squeezing Theorem and Substitution Rule

1. By (5), $\lim_{x\to\pi/3}(\sqrt{3}\sin x - 2x) = \sqrt{3}\sin\dfrac{\pi}{3} - 2\left(\dfrac{\pi}{3}\right) = \dfrac{3}{2} - \dfrac{2\pi}{3}$.

2. By (5), $\lim_{x\to 0} \dfrac{x^2-2}{\cos x} = \dfrac{0^2-2}{\cos 0} = -2.$

3. By (5), $\lim_{x\to -\pi/3} 3x^2\cos x = 3\left(-\frac{\pi}{3}\right)^2 \cos\left(-\frac{\pi}{3}\right) = \dfrac{\pi^2}{6}.$

4. By (5), $\lim_{x\to 0} \dfrac{1-\cos x}{1-x} = \dfrac{1-\cos 0}{1-0} = 0.$

5. By (9) of Section 2.3 and (5) of this section, $\lim_{x\to 0} e^x \cos x = e^0 \cos 0 = 1 \cdot 1 = 1.$

6. By (11) of Section 2.3 and (13) of this section, $\lim_{x\to e} \dfrac{\ln x}{e^{-x}} = \dfrac{\ln e}{e^{\lim_{x\to e}(-x)}} = \dfrac{1}{e^{-e}} = e^e.$

7. By (5), $\lim_{y\to 2\pi/3} \dfrac{\pi \sin y \cos y}{y} = \dfrac{\pi \sin 2\pi/3 \cos 2\pi/3}{2\pi/3} = -\dfrac{3\sqrt{3}}{8}.$

8. By (5) and Example 2, $\lim_{y\to 0} \dfrac{\pi \sin y \cos y}{y} = \pi \cdot 1 \cdot \cos 0 = \pi.$

9. Let $y = 3x^3$. Then $\lim_{x\to 3} y = \lim_{x\to 3} 3x^3 = 81$. By the Substitution Rule, $\lim_{x\to 3} \sqrt{3x^3} = \lim_{y\to 81} \sqrt{y} = \sqrt{81} = 9.$

10. Let $y = 9 - x^2$. Then $\lim_{x\to\sqrt{5}} y = \lim_{x\to\sqrt{5}} (9-x^2) = 4$. By the Substitution Rule, $\lim_{x\to\sqrt{5}} (9-x^2)^{-5/2} = \lim_{y\to 4} y^{-5/2} = 4^{-5/2} = \frac{1}{32}.$

11. Let $y = (\pi/2)\sin t$. Then $\lim_{t\to 3\pi/2} y = \lim_{t\to 3\pi/2} (\pi/2)\sin t = (\pi/2)\sin(3\pi/2) = -\pi/2$. By the Substitution Rule, $\lim_{t\to 3\pi/2} \sin[(\pi/2)\sin t] = \lim_{y\to -\pi/2} \sin y = \sin(-\pi/2) = -1.$

12. Let $y = \sin x$. Then $\lim_{x\to\pi/6} y = \lim_{x\to\pi/6} \sin x = \frac{1}{2}$. By the Substitution Rule, $\lim_{x\to\pi/6} e^{\sin x} = \lim_{y\to 1/2} e^y = e^{1/2}.$

13. Let $y = 6x^2 - 1$. Then $\lim_{x\to 1/2} y = \lim_{x\to 1/2}(6x^2-1) = \frac{1}{2}$. By the Substitution Rule, $\lim_{x\to 1/2} \ln(6x^2-1) = \lim_{y\to 1/2} \ln y = \ln \frac{1}{2}.$

14. Let $y = \ln x$. Then $\lim_{x\to e} y = \lim_{x\to e} \ln x = 1$. By the Substitution Rule,

$$\lim_{x\to e} \frac{\ln(\ln x)}{\ln x} = \lim_{y\to 1} \frac{\ln y}{y} = \frac{\lim_{y\to 1} \ln y}{\lim_{y\to 1} y} = \frac{\ln 1}{1} = 0.$$

15. Let $y = \dfrac{e^x - 1}{x}$. Then $\lim_{x\to 0} y = \lim_{x\to 0} \dfrac{e^x-1}{x} = 1$ by (8) of Section 2.1. By the Substitution Rule,

$$\lim_{x\to 0} \ln\left(\frac{e^x-1}{x}\right) = \lim_{y\to 1} \ln y = \ln 1 = 0.$$

16. Let $y = 2x$. Then $\lim_{x\to 0} y = \lim_{x\to 0} 2x = 0$. By the Substitution Rule and (8) of Section 2.1,

$$\lim_{x\to 0} \frac{e^{2x}-1}{x} = \lim_{y\to 0} \frac{e^y-1}{y/2} = 2\lim_{y\to 0} \frac{e^y-1}{y} = 2 \cdot 1 = 2.$$

17. By Example 3 and the Substitution Rule with $y = 3x$,

$$\lim_{x\to 0} \frac{\sin 3x}{5x} = \lim_{y\to 0} \frac{\sin y}{\frac{5}{3}y} = \frac{3}{5} \lim_{y\to 0} \frac{\sin y}{y} = \frac{3}{5}.$$

18. By Example 4 and the Substitution Rule with $y = 4x$,

$$\lim_{x\to 0} \frac{\cos 4x - 1}{x} = \lim_{y\to 0} \frac{\cos y - 1}{y/4} = 4 \lim_{y\to 0} \frac{\cos y - 1}{y} = 4 \cdot 0 = 0.$$

19. By Example 3 and the Substitution Rule with $y = x^{1/3}$,

$$\lim_{x\to 0} \frac{\sin x^{1/3}}{x^{1/3}} = \lim_{y\to 0} \frac{\sin y}{y} = 1.$$

20. By Example 4 and the Substitution Rule with $y = x^2$,

$$\lim_{x\to 0} \frac{\cos x^2 - 1}{x^2} = \lim_{y\to 0} \frac{\cos y - 1}{y} = 0.$$

21. Using Example 4 and (5), we have

$$\lim_{t\to 0} \frac{\cos^2 t - 1}{t} = \lim_{t\to 0} \frac{(\cos t - 1)(\cos t + 1)}{t} = \lim_{t\to 0} \frac{\cos t - 1}{t} \cdot \lim_{t\to 0}(\cos t + 1) = 0(1+1) = 0.$$

22. Using Example 4, we have

$$\lim_{t\to 0} \frac{\cos t - 1}{\sqrt[3]{t}} = \lim_{t\to 0} \left(\frac{\cos t - 1}{\sqrt[3]{t}} \cdot \frac{t^{2/3}}{t^{2/3}} \right) = \lim_{t\to 0} \frac{\cos t - 1}{t} \cdot \lim_{t\to 0} t^{2/3} = 0 \cdot 0 = 0.$$

23. Using Example 3 and (5), we have

$$\lim_{y\to 0} \frac{\tan y}{y} = \lim_{y\to 0} \left(\frac{\sin y}{y} \cdot \frac{1}{\cos y} \right) = \lim_{y\to 0} \frac{\sin y}{y} \cdot \lim_{y\to 0} \frac{1}{\cos y} = 1 \cdot \frac{1}{\cos 0} = 1.$$

24. Using Example 3 and (5), we have

$$\lim_{y\to 0} y \cot y = \lim_{y\to 0} \frac{\cos y}{(\sin y)/y} = \frac{\lim_{y\to 0} \cos y}{\lim_{y\to 0} [(\sin y)/y]} = \frac{\cos 0}{1} = 1.$$

25. Using Example 3, and the Substitution Rule with $y = 2x$, we have

$$\lim_{x\to 0} \frac{\sin x}{\sin 2x} = \lim_{x\to 0} \frac{(\sin x)/(2x)}{(\sin 2x)/(2x)} = \frac{1}{2} \frac{\lim_{x\to 0} [(\sin x)/x]}{\lim_{x\to 0} [(\sin 2x)/(2x)]} = \frac{1}{2} \frac{1}{\lim_{y\to 0} [(\sin y)/y]} = \frac{1}{2}.$$

26. Using (5), we have

$$\lim_{x\to 0} \frac{\sin^2 x}{1 - \cos x} = \lim_{x\to 0} \frac{1 - \cos^2 x}{1 - \cos x} = \lim_{x\to 0} \frac{(1 - \cos x)(1 + \cos x)}{1 - \cos x} = \lim_{x\to 0} (1 + \cos x) = 1 + \cos 0 = 2.$$

27. Using the comment following Example 2, we have

$$\lim_{x\to\pi}\frac{\tan^2 x}{1+\sec x}=\lim_{x\to\pi}\frac{\sec^2 x-1}{1+\sec x}=\lim_{x\to\pi}\frac{(\sec x+1)(\sec x-1)}{1+\sec x}=\lim_{x\to\pi}(\sec x-1)=\sec\pi-1=-2.$$

28. Using (5) and the Substitution Rule with $y=3x$, we have

$$\lim_{x\to0}\frac{1-\cos 3x}{\sin 3x}=\lim_{y\to0}\frac{1-\cos y}{\sin y}=\lim_{y\to0}\frac{(1-\cos y)(1+\cos y)}{(\sin y)(1+\cos y)}$$

$$=\lim_{y\to0}\frac{\sin^2 y}{(\sin y)(1+\cos y)}=\lim_{y\to0}\frac{\sin y}{1+\cos y}=\frac{0}{1+1}=0.$$

29. By (5),

$$\lim_{x\to0}\frac{2x-\cot x}{x+3\cot x}=\lim_{x\to0}\frac{2x-\dfrac{\cos x}{\sin x}}{x+3\dfrac{\cos x}{\sin x}}=\lim_{x\to0}\frac{2x\sin x-\cos x}{x\sin x+3\cos x}=\frac{2\cdot0\cdot\sin0-\cos0}{0\cdot\sin0-3\cos0}=\frac{-1}{-3}=\frac{1}{3}.$$

30. By (5),

$$\lim_{x\to0}\frac{\cos x-\sec x}{1-\sec x}=\lim_{x\to0}\frac{\cos x-\dfrac{1}{\cos x}}{1-\dfrac{1}{\cos x}}=\lim_{x\to0}\frac{\cos^2 x-1}{\cos x-1}$$

$$=\lim_{x\to0}\frac{(\cos x+1)(\cos x-1)}{\cos x-1}=\lim_{x\to0}(\cos x+1)=\cos0+1=1+1=2.$$

31. Since $-1\le\cos(1/x^2)\le1$, we have $-|x|\le x\cos(1/x^2)\le|x|$. Since $\lim_{x\to0}(-|x|)=0$ and $\lim_{x\to0}|x|=0$, it follows from the Squeezing Theorem that $\lim_{x\to0}x\cos(1/x^2)=0$.

32. Since $-1\le\sin(\tan(\pi x/2))\le1$, we have

$$-(x-1)^4\le(x-1)^4\sin\left(\tan\frac{\pi x}{2}\right)\le(x-1)^4.$$

Since $\lim_{x\to1}-(x-1)^4=0$ and $\lim_{x\to1}(x-1)^4=0$, it follows from the Squeezing Theorem that

$$\lim_{x\to1}(x-1)^4\sin\left(\tan\frac{\pi x}{2}\right)=0.$$

33. Since $-1\le\sin[1/(x-1)]\le1$ and $-1\le\cos x\le1$, we have

$$-1\le\sin\frac{1}{x-1}\cos x\le1\quad\text{and hence}\quad-|\ln x|\le(\ln x)\sin\frac{1}{x-1}\cos x\le|\ln x|.$$

By the Substitution Rule with $y=\ln x$, $\lim_{x\to1}|\ln x|=\lim_{y\to0}|y|=|0|=0$ and hence $\lim_{x\to1}-|\ln x|=-0=0$. It follows from the Squeezing Theorem that

$$\lim_{x\to1}(\ln x)\sin\frac{1}{x-1}\cos x=0.$$

34. Since $e^{1/(x-1)} > 0$, we have

$$0 < \frac{1}{1+e^{1/(x-1)}} < 1 \quad \text{and hence} \quad 0 < \frac{(\ln x)^2}{1+e^{1/(x-1)}} < (\ln x)^2.$$

Since $\lim_{x\to 1} 0 = 0$ and $\lim_{x\to 1}(\ln x)^2 = (\ln 1)^2 = 0^2 = 0$, it follows from the Squeezing Theorem that

$$\lim_{x\to 1} \frac{(\ln x)^2}{1+e^{1/(x-1)}} = 0.$$

35. Yes

36. Yes

37. Since e^x and $-x$ are continuous at every real number, so is the composite e^{-x} by Theorem 2.6. Since $\sin x$ is also continuous at every real number, it follows from Theorem 2.4 that the product $e^{-x} \sin x$ is continuous at every real number.

38. Observe that $\sqrt{x}$ is continuous at every positive real number, and that $1+e^x$ is continuous at every real number and $1+e^x > 0$ for all x. Therefore $\sqrt{1+e^x}$ is continuous at every real number by Theorem 2.6.

39. Since t^2 is continuous at every real number and the tangent function is continuous at every number in its domain, it follows from Theorem 2.6 that $\tan t^2$ is continuous at every number in its domain. Then Theorem 2.4 implies that f is continuous at every number in its domain.

40. Since the sine function and the function t^2 are continuous at every real number, so is the composite $\sin t^2$ by Theorem 2.6. Since $2+t^4$ is continuous at every real number and $2+t^4 > 0$ for all t, Theorem 2.4 implies that f is continuous at every real number.

41. Observe that $\cot x = (\cos x)/(\sin x)$. Since both $\sin x$ and $\cos x$ are continuous at every real number, Theorem 2.4 implies that $\cot x$ is continuous at every number in its domain.

42. Observe that $\sec x = 1/(\cos x)$. Since $\cos x$ is continuous at every real number, Theorem 2.4 implies that $\sec x$ is continuous at every number in its domain.

43. Observe that $\csc x = 1/(\sin x)$. Since $\sin x$ is continuous at every real number, Theorem 2.4 implies that $\csc x$ is continuous at every number in its domain.

44. a. Yes

b. Let a be any positive number, and write $\ln x = \ln(x/a) + \ln a$. Using the substitution $y = x/a$, we conclude from the limit in part (a) that

$$\lim_{x\to a} \ln x = \lim_{x\to a}\left(\ln\frac{x}{a} + \ln a\right) = \lim_{y\to 1}(\ln y + \ln a) = \lim_{y\to 1} \ln y + \ln a = 0 + \ln a = \ln a.$$

Since $\lim_{x\to a} \ln x = \ln a$ for every $a > 0$, the natural logarithm is continuous at every number in its domain and hence is a continuous function.

45. a. For f to be continuous at 0, we need $\lim_{x\to 0} f(x) = f(0)$. By Example 4 and the Substitution Rule with $y = 3x$, we have

$$\lim_{x\to 0} f(x) = \lim_{x\to 0} \frac{1-\cos 3x}{x} = \lim_{y\to 0} \frac{1-\cos y}{y/3} = 3 \lim_{y\to 0} \frac{1-\cos y}{y} = 3\cdot 0 = 0.$$

Therefore if $f(0)$ is defined to be 0, then f will be continuous at 0.

b. For f to be continuous at 0, we need $\lim_{x\to 0} f(x) = f(0)$. By (8) of Section 2.1 and the Substitution Rule with $y = -x$, we have

$$\lim_{x\to 0} f(x) = \lim_{x\to 0} \frac{e^{-x}-1}{x} = \lim_{y\to 0} \frac{e^y-1}{-y} = -\lim_{y\to 0} \frac{e^y-1}{y} = -1.$$

Therefore if $f(0)$ is defined to be -1, then f will be continuous at 0.

c. For f to be continuous at 0, we need $\lim_{x\to 0} f(x) = f(0)$. Since $f(1/(n\pi)) = \sin n\pi = 0$ for any integer n, and $f(1/(2n\pi + \pi/2)) = \sin(2n\pi + \pi/2) = 1$ for any integer n, and since $1/(n\pi)$ and $1/(2n\pi + \pi/2)$ can be made as close to 0 as we like by taking n large enough, it follows that $\lim_{x\to 0} f(x)$ does not exist. Therefore we cannot define $f(0)$ so that f will be continuous at 0.

46. Both $3x^2+4$ and $x+2$ are polynomial functions and thus are continuous at every real number. Therefore the composite $h(x) = g(x+2)$ is continuous at every real number and hence at -3 by Theorem 2.6.

47. Let $f(x) = x + b$. Then f is a polynomial and hence is continuous at every real number. Also $f(a-b) = a - b + b = a$ and $h(x) = g(x+b) = g(f(x))$. Since f is continuous at $a-b$ and g is continuous at $a = f(a-b)$, Theorem 2.6 implies that h is continuous at $a-b$.

48. By Example 4, $\lim_{x\to 0} \dfrac{f(x)-f(0)}{x-0} = \lim_{x\to 0} \dfrac{\cos x - 1}{x} = 0$; l: $y - 1 = 0(x-0)$, or $y = 1$.

49. Using Example 3 and the Substitution Rule with $y = 4x$, we have

$$\lim_{x\to 0} \frac{f(x)-f(0)}{x-0} = \lim_{x\to 0} \frac{\sin 4x - 0}{x} = \lim_{y\to 0} \frac{\sin y}{y/4} = 4 \lim_{y\to 0} \frac{\sin y}{y} = 4\cdot 1 = 4;$$

l: $y - 0 = 4(x-0) = 4x$, or $y = 4x$.

50. Using the Substitution Rule with $y = 4 - x^2$, we have

$$\lim_{x\to 1} \frac{f(x)-f(1)}{x-1} = \lim_{x\to 1} \frac{\sqrt{4-x^2}-\sqrt{3}}{x-1} = \lim_{x\to 1} \frac{(\sqrt{4-x^2}-\sqrt{3})(\sqrt{4-x^2}+\sqrt{3})}{(x-1)(\sqrt{4-x^2}+\sqrt{3})}$$

$$= \lim_{x\to 1} \frac{4-x^2-3}{(x-1)(\sqrt{4-x^2}+\sqrt{3})} = \lim_{x\to 1} \frac{1-x^2}{(x-1)(\sqrt{4-x^2}+\sqrt{3})} = \lim_{x\to 1} \frac{(1-x)(1+x)}{(x-1)(\sqrt{4-x^2}+\sqrt{3})}$$

$$= \lim_{x\to 1} -\frac{1+x}{\sqrt{4-x^2}+\sqrt{3}} = -\frac{\lim_{x\to 1}(1+x)}{\lim_{y\to 3}(\sqrt{y}+\sqrt{3})} = \frac{-2}{2\sqrt{3}} = -\frac{\sqrt{3}}{3};$$

l: $y - \sqrt{3} = -\dfrac{\sqrt{3}}{3}(x-1)$.

51. Using the Substitution Rule with $y = x + x^2$, we have

$$\lim_{x\to 1}\frac{f(x)-f(1)}{x-1} = \lim_{x\to 1}\frac{\sqrt{x+x^2}-\sqrt{2}}{x-1} = \lim_{x\to 1}\frac{(\sqrt{x+x^2}-\sqrt{2})(\sqrt{x+x^2}+\sqrt{2})}{(x-1)(\sqrt{x+x^2}+\sqrt{2})}$$

$$= \lim_{x\to 1}\frac{x+x^2-2}{(x-1)(\sqrt{x+x^2}+\sqrt{2})} = \lim_{x\to 1}\frac{x+2}{\sqrt{x+x^2}+\sqrt{2}} = \frac{\lim_{x\to 1}(x+2)}{\lim_{x\to 1}(\sqrt{x+x^2}+\sqrt{2})}$$

$$= \frac{\lim_{x\to 1}(x+2)}{\lim_{y\to 2}(\sqrt{y}+\sqrt{2})} = \frac{3}{2\sqrt{2}} = \frac{3\sqrt{2}}{4};$$

l: $y - \sqrt{2} = \dfrac{3\sqrt{2}}{4}(x-1)$

52. By (8) in Section 2.1,

$$\lim_{h\to 0}\frac{f(a+h)-f(a)}{h} = \lim_{h\to 0}\frac{e^{a+h}-e^a}{h} = \lim_{h\to 0}\frac{e^a e^h - e^a}{h} = e^a\lim_{h\to 0}\frac{e^h-1}{h} = e^a\cdot 1 = e^a.$$

Therefore the slope of the line tangent to the graph of f at (a, e^a) is e^a. An equation of the tangent line is $y - e^a = e^a(x-a)$.

53. By hypothesis, $-M|x-a| \le f(x) \le M|x-a|$ for $x \ne a$. Also $\lim_{x\to a} M|x-a| = 0$. By the Squeezing Theorem, $\lim_{x\to a} f(x) = 0$.

54. Suppose that $\lim_{x\to a} f(x) = L$. By the Substitution Rule with $y = a+h$, we have $\lim_{h\to 0} f(a+h) = \lim_{y\to a} f(y) = \lim_{x\to a} f(x) = L$. Now suppose $\lim_{h\to 0} f(a+h) = L$. By the Substitution Rule with $y = x-a$, we have

$$\lim_{x\to a} f(x) = \lim_{x\to a} f(a+(x-a)) = \lim_{y\to 0} f(a+y) = \lim_{h\to 0} f(a+h) = L.$$

55. a. Let $y = f(x)$. Then $\lim_{x\to a} y = \lim_{x\to a} f(x) = L$. By the Substitution Rule and Exercise 32 in Section 2.2, $\lim_{x\to a}|f(x)| = \lim_{y\to L}|y| = |L|$.

b. Suppose $\lim_{x\to a}|f(x)| = 0$, and let ε be any positive number. By Definition 2.1, there is a number $\delta > 0$ such that if $0 < |x-a| < \delta$, then $||f(x)| - 0| < \varepsilon$. Since $||f(x)|-0| = |f(x)| = |f(x)-0|$, it follows that if $0 < |x-a| < \delta$, then $|f(x)-0| < \varepsilon$. This implies that $\lim_{x\to a} f(x) = 0$.

c. Let $f(x) = -1$ for $x \le 0$ and $f(x) = 1$ for $x > 0$. Then $\lim_{x\to 0} f(x)$ does not exist. But $|f(x)| = 1$ for all x, so that $\lim_{x\to 0}|f(x)| = \lim_{x\to 0} 1 = 1$.

56. By hypothesis, if $x \ne a$, then $-M \le |g(x)| \le M$, so that

$$-M|f(x)| \le -|f(x)g(x)| \le f(x)g(x) \le |f(x)g(x)| \le M|f(x)|.$$

Since $\lim_{x\to a} f(x) = 0$ by hypothesis, it follows from Exercise 55(a) and the Constant Multiple Rule that $\lim_{x\to a} -M|f(x)| = \lim_{x\to a} M|f(x)| = 0$, so by the Squeezing Theorem, $\lim_{x\to a} f(x)g(x) = 0$.

57. $\dfrac{x\sin^2(1/x)}{1+\sin^2(1/x)} = f(x)g(x)$, where $f(x) = x$ and $g(x) = \dfrac{\sin^2(1/x)}{1+\sin^2(1/x)}$.
Since $\lim_{x\to 0} f(x) = \lim_{x\to 0} x = 0$ and $|g(x)| \le 1$ for all $x \ne 0$, it follows from Exercise 56 with $M = 1$ that

$$\lim_{x\to 0} \frac{x\sin^2(1/x)}{1+\sin^2(1/x)} = 0.$$

58. Let $y = [f(x)]^2$, and notice that $f(x) = \sqrt{[f(x)]^2}$ because $f(x) \ge 0$. Since $[f(x)]^2$ approaches L as x approaches a, it follows that y approaches L. Therefore by the Substitution Rule, $\lim_{x\to a} f(x) = \lim_{x\to a} \sqrt{[f(x)]^2} = \lim_{y\to L} \sqrt{y} = \sqrt{L}$.

59. Let $y = x^n$. Since x^n approaches 0 as x approaches 0, it follows that y approaches 0, so by the Substitution Rule, $\lim_{x\to 0} f(x^n) = \lim_{y\to 0} f(y) = L$.

60. Since $\lim_{x\to 0} \sin x = 0$, Exercise 59 implies that $\lim_{x\to 0} \sin x^n = 0$ for any $n > 0$.

61. a. $m_r = \dfrac{\sqrt{1-a^2}-0}{a-0} = \dfrac{\sqrt{1-a^2}}{a}$

b. $m_t = \dfrac{-1}{m_r} = \dfrac{-a}{\sqrt{1-a^2}}$

c. $m_x = \dfrac{\sqrt{1-x^2}-\sqrt{1-a^2}}{x-a}$

d.
$$\begin{aligned}\lim_{x\to a} m_x &= \lim_{x\to a} \frac{\sqrt{1-x^2}-\sqrt{1-a^2}}{x-a} = \lim_{x\to a} \frac{\sqrt{1-x^2}-\sqrt{1-a^2}}{x-a}\,\frac{\sqrt{1-x^2}+\sqrt{1-a^2}}{\sqrt{1-x^2}+\sqrt{1-a^2}} \\ &= \lim_{x\to a} \frac{(1-x^2)-(1-a^2)}{(x-a)(\sqrt{1-x^2}+\sqrt{1-a^2})} = \lim_{x\to a} \frac{-(x^2-a^2)}{(x-a)(\sqrt{1-x^2}+\sqrt{1-a^2})} \\ &= \lim_{x\to a} \frac{-(x+a)}{\sqrt{1-x^2}+\sqrt{1-a^2}} = \frac{-a}{\sqrt{1-a^2}}\end{aligned}$$

62. By the comment following Example 2, $\sin\theta$ and $\cot\theta$ are continuous at every number θ in $(0, \pi/2)$. Since $\sin\theta \ne 0$ for $0 < \theta < \pi/2$, it follows from Theorem 2.4 that S is continuous at every number θ in $(0, \pi/2)$.

63. Since $-cx$ and e^x are continuous at every real number, Theorem 2.6 implies that the composite e^{-cx} is continuous at every real number. The same is true of $-be^{-cx}$ by Theorem 2.4. Theorem 2.6 now implies that the composite $e^{-be^{-cx}}$ is continuous at every real number. Another application of Theorem 2.4 shows that $ae^{-be^{-cx}}$ is continuous at every real number.

64. Let $f(x) = \sqrt{1-x^2}$. The graph of f is the upper semicircle in Figure 2.37. By Exercise 61, $m_a = -a/\sqrt{1-a^2}$. Thus an equation of the tangent line at $(a, \sqrt{1-a^2})$ is $y - \sqrt{1-a^2} = (-a/\sqrt{1-a^2})(x-a)$. The tangent line passes through $(0, 5)$ if $5 - \sqrt{1-a^2} = (-a/\sqrt{1-a^2})(-a)$, or $5\sqrt{1-a^2} - (1-a^2) = a^2$, or $5\sqrt{1-a^2} = 1$, or $a^2 = \frac{24}{25}$. Thus the flea first sees the point of attachment when it arrives at the point $(2\sqrt{6}/5, 1/5)$.

2.5 One-Sided and Infinite Limits

1. $\lim_{x\to-2^+}(x^3+3x-5) = \lim_{x\to-2}(x^3+3x-5) = (-2)^3+3(-2)-5 = -19$

2. Let $y = x+\pi/6$. As x approaches $\pi/3$ from the left, $x+\pi/6$ approaches $\pi/2$ from the left, so that y approaches $\pi/2$ from the left. By the version of the Substitution Rule for one-sided limits, $\lim_{x\to\pi/3^-}\cos(x+\pi/6) = \lim_{y\to\pi/2^-}\cos y = \lim_{y\to\pi/2}\cos y = \cos(\pi/2) = 0$.

3. $\displaystyle\lim_{x\to2^-}\frac{x^2-4}{x-2} = \lim_{x\to2^-}\frac{(x-2)(x+2)}{x-2} = \lim_{x\to2^-}(x+2) = \lim_{x\to2}(x+2) = 4$

4. $\displaystyle\lim_{x\to2^+}\frac{x^2-4}{x-2} = \lim_{x\to2^+}\frac{(x-2)(x+2)}{x-2} = \lim_{x\to2^+}(x+2) = \lim_{x\to2}(x+2) = 4$

5. $\displaystyle\lim_{x\to1^+}\frac{x^2+3x-4}{x^2-1} = \lim_{x\to1^+}\frac{(x-1)(x+4)}{(x-1)(x+1)} = \lim_{x\to1^+}\frac{x+4}{x+1} = \lim_{x\to1}\frac{x+4}{x+1} = \frac{5}{2}$

6. $\displaystyle\lim_{x\to2^-}\frac{x^2-3x-10}{x^2-9} = \lim_{x\to-2}\frac{x^2-3x-10}{x^2-9} = 0$

7. Since $t-5>0$ for $t>5$, $\lim_{t\to5^+}|t-5|/(5-t) = \lim_{t\to5^+}(t-5)/(5-t) = \lim_{t\to5^+}(-1) = -1$.

8. Let $y = t+3$. As t approaches -3 from the right, $t+3$ approaches 0 from the right, so y approaches 0 from the right. By the version of the Substitution Rule for one-sided limits, $\lim_{t\to-3^+}\sqrt{t+3} = \lim_{y\to0^+}\sqrt{y} = 0$.

9. If $x<0$, then $x^3<0$. Thus $4/x^3<0$, so $\lim_{x\to0^-}(4/x^3) = -\infty$.

10. If $x>0$, then $x^3>0$. Thus $4/x^3>0$, so $\lim_{x\to0^+}(4/x^3) = \infty$.

11. For all x except $x=0$, we have $-1/x^2<0$. Thus $\lim_{x\to0^+}(-1/x^2) = \lim_{x\to0^-}(-1/x^2) = -\infty$. Therefore $\lim_{x\to0}(-1/x^2) = -\infty$.

12. If $x>0$, then $x^{1/4}>0$, so $2/x^{1/4}>0$. Therefore $\lim_{x\to0^+}(2/x^{1/4}) = \infty$.

13. If $y<-1$, then $y+1<0$, so $\pi/(y+1)<0$. Therefore $\lim_{y\to-1^-}[\pi/(y+1)] = -\infty$.

14. For all z except $z=3$, $2/(z-3)^2>0$. Thus $\lim_{z\to3^+}[2/(z-3)^2] = \lim_{z\to3^-}[2/(z-3)^2] = \infty$. Therefore $\lim_{z\to3}[2/(z-3)^2] = \infty$.

15. For $0<z<\pi/2$, $\tan z>0$. Since $\tan z = (\sin z)/(\cos z)$, $\lim_{z\to\pi/2}\cos z = 0$, and $\lim_{z\to\pi/2}\sin z = 1$, we have $\lim_{z\to\pi/2^-}\tan z = \infty$.

16. We have $\sec z = 1/\cos z$. Since $\cos z>0$ for $-\pi/2<z<0$ and $\lim_{z\to-\pi/2^+}\cos z = 0$, it follows that $\lim_{z\to\pi/2^+}\sec z = \infty$.

17. If $-1<x<1$, then $0<1-|x|<1$. Therefore the substitution $y = 1-|x|$ yields $\lim_{x\to1^-}\ln(1-|x|) = \lim_{y\to0^+}\ln y = -\infty$.

18. If $x > 1$, then $x-1>0$. Therefore the substitution $y = x-1$ yields $\lim_{x\to 1^+}\ln(x-1) = \lim_{y\to 0^+}\ln y = -\infty$. Since $\lim_{x\to 1^+}\ln(x^2+1) = \lim_{x\to 1}\ln(x^2+1) = \ln(1^2+1) = \ln 2 > 0$, we conclude that

$$\lim_{x\to 1^+}\frac{\ln(x-1)}{\ln(x^2+1)} = -\infty.$$

19. If $x > 0$, then $\sqrt{x} > 0$, so that $1 - e^{\sqrt{x}} < 0$. By the Substitution Rule with $y = \sqrt{x}$, $\lim_{x\to 0^+}(1-e^{\sqrt{x}}) = \lim_{y\to 0^+}(1-e^y) = 1 - e^0 = 0$. By the version of the Substitution Rule for one-sided limits with $y = 1 - e^{\sqrt{x}}$,

$$\lim_{x\to 0^+}\frac{1}{1-e^{\sqrt{x}}} = \lim_{y\to 0^-}\frac{1}{y} = -\infty.$$

20. For $-\pi/2 < x < 0$ and for $0 < x < \pi/2$ we have $\sec x - 1 > 0$ and $\lim_{x\to 0}(\sec x - 1) = 0$. If $y = \sec x - 1$, then by the version of the Substitution Rule for one-sided limits, $\lim_{x\to 0^-}\ln(\sec x - 1) = \lim_{y\to 0^+}\ln y = -\infty$.

21. If $x > 5$ then $x - 5 > 0$, so $\sqrt{x-5}$ is defined. By the version of the Substitution Rule for one-sided limits, $\lim_{x\to 5^+}\sqrt{x-5} = \lim_{y\to 0^+}\sqrt{y} = 0$. Thus $\lim_{x\to 5^+} 1/(x\sqrt{x-5}) = \infty$.

22. If $x > 1$ then $x^2 - x > 0$ and $\lim_{x\to 1^+}(x^2-x) = 0$. By the version of the Sum and Substitution Rules for one-sided limits,

$$\lim_{x\to 1^+}(\sqrt{x^2-x}+x) = \lim_{x\to 1^+}\sqrt{x^2-x} + \lim_{x\to 1^+} x = \left(\lim_{y\to 0^+}\sqrt{y}\right) + 1 = 0 + 1 = 1.$$

23. By the versions of the Product and Substitution Rules for one-sided limits, with $y = 2x$ and $z = \cos y$,

$$\lim_{x\to 0^+}\sqrt{x\cos 2x} = \lim_{x\to 0^+}\sqrt{x}\lim_{x\to 0^+}\sqrt{\cos 2x} = \lim_{x\to 0^+}\sqrt{x}\lim_{y\to 0^+}\sqrt{\cos y} = \lim_{x\to 0^+}\sqrt{x}\lim_{z\to 1^-}\sqrt{z} = 0\cdot 1 = 0.$$

24. If $-\pi/3 < x < 0$, then $-\pi < 3x < 0$, so $-\sin 3x > 0$. Thus $\lim_{x\to 0^-}\sqrt{-\sin 3x} = \lim_{y\to 0^+}\sqrt{y} = 0$. Therefore $\lim_{x\to 0^-}\sqrt{-x^2\sin 3x} = \lim_{x\to 0^-}\sqrt{x^2}\lim_{x\to 0^-}\sqrt{-\sin 3x} = 0\cdot 0 = 0$.

25. $\lim_{x\to 0}\sqrt{\dfrac{1}{x^2}} = \lim_{x\to 0}\dfrac{1}{\sqrt{x^2}} = \lim_{x\to 0}\dfrac{1}{|x|} = \infty$

26. Since $x/|x| = x/x = 1$ for $x > 0$, and $x/|x| = x/(-x) = -1$ for $x < 0$, we have

$$\lim_{x\to 0^+}\frac{x}{|x|} = \lim_{x\to 0^+} 1 = 1 \quad\text{and}\quad \lim_{x\to 0^-}\frac{x}{|x|} = \lim_{x\to 0^-}(-1) = -1.$$

Since the one-sided limits are not equal, the given limit does not exist.

27. If $x < -\frac{1}{2}$, then $x + \frac{1}{2} < 0$ and $4x - 7 < 0$. Thus $(4x-7)/(x+\frac{1}{2}) > 0$, so

$$\lim_{x\to -1/2^-}\frac{4x-7}{x+\frac{1}{2}} = \lim_{x\to -1/2^-}(4x-7)\cdot\frac{1}{x+\frac{1}{2}} = \infty.$$

28. $\lim_{x\to -1^+}\dfrac{x^2+5x+4}{x+1} = \lim_{x\to -1^+}\dfrac{(x+1)(x+4)}{x+1} = \lim_{x\to -1^+}(x+4) = \lim_{x\to -1}(x+4) = 3$

29. If $0 < x < 2$, then $x+1>0$ and $x^2-4<0$, so $(x+1)/[2(x^2-4)]<0$, and thus

$$\lim_{x\to 2^-} \frac{x+1}{2(x^2-4)} = \lim_{x\to 2^-} \left[\frac{x+1}{2}\cdot\frac{1}{x^2-4}\right] = -\infty.$$

30. For $x \neq 1$, we have

$$\frac{x^2-3x+2}{x^2-2x+1} = \frac{(x-1)(x-2)}{(x-1)^2} = \frac{x-2}{x-1}.$$

If $1 < x < 2$, then $x-2<0$ and $x-1>0$, so $(x-2)/(x-1)<0$, and thus

$$\lim_{x\to 1^+} \frac{x^2-3x+2}{x^2-2x+1} = \lim_{x\to 1^+} \left[(x-2)\cdot\frac{1}{x-1}\right] = -\infty.$$

31. If $y<3$, then $3-y>0$ and $\lim_{y\to 3^-}\sqrt{3-y}=0$. Thus $\lim_{y\to 3^-}(-1/\sqrt{3-y}) = -\infty$.

32. If $y<-5$, then $-y-5>0$ and $\lim_{y\to -5^-}\sqrt{-y-5}=0$. Thus $\lim_{y\to -5^-}(1/\sqrt{-y-5}) = \infty$.

33. If $-1<y<1$, then $1+y>0$ and $1-y>0$, so

$$\frac{\sqrt{1-y^2}}{y-1} = \frac{\sqrt{1+y}\,\sqrt{1-y}}{-(1-y)} = \frac{-\sqrt{1+y}}{\sqrt{1-y}} < 0.$$

Thus

$$\lim_{y\to 1^-} \frac{\sqrt{1-y^2}}{y-1} = \lim_{y\to 1^-} \left[(-\sqrt{1+y})\cdot\frac{1}{\sqrt{1-y}}\right] = -\infty.$$

34. If $-3<y<3$, then $3+y>0$ and $3-y>0$, so

$$\frac{\sqrt{9-y^2}}{y+3} = \frac{\sqrt{3-y}\cdot\sqrt{3+y}}{3+y} = \frac{\sqrt{3-y}}{\sqrt{3+y}} > 0.$$

Thus

$$\lim_{y\to -3^+} \frac{\sqrt{9-y^2}}{y+3} = \lim_{y\to -3^+} \left[\sqrt{3-y}\cdot\frac{1}{\sqrt{3+y}}\right] = \infty.$$

35. For $y<0$, $\sqrt{y}$ is undefined. Therefore $\lim_{y\to 0^-}[(5+\sqrt{1+y^2})/\sqrt{y}]$ does not exist.

36. If $0<t<\pi$ and $t\neq \pi/2$, then $\cos^2 t>0$ and $\lim_{t\to\pi/2}\cos^2 t = 0$. Thus $\lim_{t\to\pi/2}\sec^2 t = \lim_{t\to\pi/2}(1/\cos^2 t) = \infty$.

37. $$\lim_{t\to 0}\frac{1-\cos t}{t^2} = \lim_{t\to 0}\left[\frac{1-\cos t}{t^2}\cdot\frac{1+\cos t}{1+\cos t}\right] = \lim_{t\to 0}\left[\frac{\sin^2 t}{t^2}\cdot\frac{1}{1+\cos t}\right]$$

$$= \lim_{t\to 0}\frac{\sin t}{t}\,\lim_{t\to 0}\frac{\sin t}{t}\,\lim_{t\to 0}\frac{1}{1+\cos t} = 1\cdot 1\cdot\frac{1}{2} = \frac{1}{2}$$

38. We have

$$\frac{\sqrt{1+x}-\sqrt{1-x}}{x} = \frac{\sqrt{1+x}-\sqrt{1-x}}{x}\cdot\frac{\sqrt{1+x}+\sqrt{1-x}}{\sqrt{1+x}+\sqrt{1-x}} = \frac{2}{\sqrt{1+x}+\sqrt{1-x}}.$$

Thus

$$\lim_{x\to 0^-}\frac{\sqrt{1+x}-\sqrt{1-x}}{x} = \lim_{x\to 0^-}\frac{2}{\sqrt{1+x}+\sqrt{1-x}} = \frac{2}{1+1} = 1.$$

39. For $x \neq 3, -3$, we have

$$\frac{1}{x-3} - \frac{6}{x^2-9} = \frac{x+3}{(x-3)(x+3)} - \frac{6}{(x-3)(x+3)} = \frac{x-3}{(x-3)(x+3)} = \frac{1}{x+3}.$$

Thus

$$\lim_{x\to 3^-}\left(\frac{1}{x-3} - \frac{6}{x^2-9}\right) = \lim_{x\to 3^-}\frac{1}{x+3} = \frac{1}{6}.$$

40. For $x \neq 3, -3$, we have

$$\frac{1}{x-3} - \frac{3}{x^2-9} = \frac{x+3}{(x-3)(x+3)} - \frac{3}{(x-3)(x+3)} = \frac{x}{(x-3)(x+3)} = \frac{x}{x+3}\cdot\frac{1}{x-3}.$$

Now $\lim_{x\to 3^-}[x/(x+3)] = \frac{3}{6} = \frac{1}{2}$, and if $x < 3$, then $x - 3 < 0$. Therefore

$$\lim_{x\to 3^-}\left(\frac{1}{x-3} - \frac{3}{x^2-9}\right) = \lim_{x\to 3^-}\left[\frac{x}{x+3}\cdot\frac{1}{x-3}\right] = -\infty.$$

41. Since $\lim_{h\to 0^+}(1-\sqrt{h}) = 1$, we have $\lim_{h\to 0^+}(1/h - 1/\sqrt{h}) = \lim_{h\to 0^+}(1/h)(1-\sqrt{h}) = \infty$.

42. $\lim_{x\to 0^+} e^{2+\ln x} = \lim_{x\to 0^+} e^2 e^{\ln x} = \lim_{x\to 0^+} e^2 x = e^2 \lim_{x\to 0^+} x = e^2 \cdot 0 = 0$.

43. If $x > 0$, then $e^x > 1$, or $e^x - 1 > 0$. If $y = e^x - 1$, then by the version of the Substitution Rule for one-sided limits, $\lim_{x\to 0^+}\sqrt{e^x - 1} = \lim_{y\to 0^+}\sqrt{y} = 0$.

44. If $x < 0$, then $e^x < 1$, so $e^x - 1 < 0$, which implies that $\sqrt{e^x - 1}$ is not defined for $x < 0$. Therefore $\lim_{x\to 0^-}\sqrt{e^x - 1}$ does not exist.

45. If $0 < x < 1$, then $\ln x < 0$, which implies that $\ln(\ln x)$ is not defined for $0 < x < 1$. Therefore $\lim_{x\to 1^-}\ln(\ln x)$ does not exist.

46. If $x > 1$, then $\ln x > 0$. If $y = \ln x$, then by the version of the Substitution Rule for one-sided limits, $\lim_{x\to 1^+}\ln(\ln x) = \lim_{y\to 0^+}\ln y = -\infty$.

47. If $0 < x < 1$, then $\sin x > 0$ and $\ln(1-x) < 0$, so that $(\sin x)\ln(1-x) < 0$. Also $\lim_{x\to 0^+}(\sin x)\ln(1-x) = (\sin 0)\ln 1 = 0 \cdot 0 = 0$. Therefore $\lim_{x\to 0^+} 1/[(\sin x)\ln(1-x)] = -\infty$.

48. $\lim_{x\to 0^-} f(x) = \lim_{x\to 0^-}(2x-4) = \lim_{x\to 0}(2x-4) = -4$;

$\lim_{x\to 0^+} f(x) = \lim_{x\to 0^+} -(x+2)^2 = \lim_{x\to 0} -(x+2)^2 = -4$.

Therefore $\lim_{x\to 0} f(x) = -4$.

49. $\lim_{x\to -2^-} f(x) = \lim_{x\to -2^-}(-1+4x) = -9$; $\lim_{x\to -2^+} f(x) = \lim_{x\to -2^+}(-9) = -9$.

Thus $\lim_{x\to -2} f(x) = -9$.

50. $\lim_{x\to -1^-} f(x) = \lim_{x\to -1^-}(2x+1)/(3x-1) = \frac{1}{4}$; $\lim_{x\to -1^+} f(x) = \lim_{x\to -1^+} 1/(x-1)^2 = \frac{1}{4}$.
Thus $\lim_{x\to -1} f(x) = \frac{1}{4}$.

51. $\lim_{x\to -4^+}[1/(x+4)] = \infty$, so $x = -4$ is a vertical asymptote.

52. $\lim_{x\to 3^+}(x+2)/(x-3) = \infty$, so $x = 3$ is a vertical asymptote.

53. $\lim_{x\to 2^+}(x^2-1)/(x^2-4) = \infty = \lim_{x\to 2^-}(x^2-1)/(x^2-4)$, so $x = 2$ and $x = -2$ are vertical asymptotes.

54. $\lim_{x\to 1^+} f(x) = \infty = \lim_{x\to 1^-} f(x)$, so $x = 1$ and $x = -1$ are vertical asymptotes. (Notice that

$$\lim_{x\to 0} f(x) = \lim_{x\to 0}\left[\frac{\sin x}{x}\cdot\frac{1}{x^2-1}\right] = \lim_{x\to 0}\frac{\sin x}{x}\lim_{x\to 0}\frac{1}{x^2-1} = (1)(-1) = -1$$

so $x = 0$ is *not* a vertical asymptote.)

55. $\lim_{x\to 4^-} f(x) = \infty = \lim_{x\to -4^+} f(x)$, so $x = 4$ and $x = -4$ are vertical asymptotes. Since $x^2 + 1 > 0$ for all x, there are no other vertical asymptotes.

56. $\lim_{x\to -1^-} f(x) = \infty = \lim_{x\to -2^+} f(x) = \lim_{x\to -3^-} f(x)$, so $x = -1$, $x = -2$, and $x = -3$ are vertical asymptotes.

57. If $x \neq -2, 3$, then

$$\frac{x^2-4x-12}{x^2-x-6} = \frac{(x+2)(x-6)}{(x+2)(x-3)} = \frac{x-6}{x-3}.$$

Thus $\lim_{x\to 3^-} f(x) = \lim_{x\to 3^-}(x-6)/(x-3) = \infty$, so $x = 3$ is a vertical asymptote.

58. If $x \neq 2$, then

$$\frac{x^2-5x+6}{x^3-8} = \frac{(x-2)(x-3)}{(x-2)(x^2+2x+4)} = \frac{x-3}{x^2+2x+4}.$$

Since $x^2 + 2x + 4 = (x+1)^2 + 3 > 0$, there are no vertical asymptotes.

59. If $x \neq -5, -2, 0$, then

$$\frac{x^2+2x-15}{x^3+7x^2+10x} = \frac{(x-3)(x+5)}{x(x+2)(x+5)} = \frac{x-3}{x(x+2)}.$$

Thus $\lim_{x\to 0^-} f(x) = \infty = \lim_{x\to -2^+} f(x)$, so $x = -2$ and $x = 0$ are vertical asymptotes.

60. $\lim_{x\to 1}(x+1)/|x-1| = \infty$, so $x = 1$ is a vertical asymptote.

61. $\dfrac{x+1/x}{x^4+1} = \dfrac{x^2+1}{x(x^4+1)}$, so $\lim\limits_{x\to 0^+} f(x) = \infty$, and thus $x = 0$ is a vertical asymptote.

62. $\lim_{x\to 1^+}\sqrt{x/(x-1)} = \infty$, so $x = 1$ is a vertical asymptote.

63. $\lim_{x\to 0}(\sin x)/x = 1$, so there are no vertical asymptotes.

64. $\lim_{x\to 0^+}(\cos x)/x = \infty$, so $x = 0$ is a vertical asymptote.

65. $\lim_{x\to(\pi/2+n\pi)^-}\tan x = \infty$ for any integer n, so $x = \pi/2 + n\pi$ is a vertical asymptote for any integer n.

66. $\lim_{x\to 2n\pi^+}\csc x = \infty = \lim_{x\to(\pi+2n\pi)^-}\csc x$ for any integer n, so $x = n\pi$ is a vertical asymptote for any integer n.

67. $\lim_{x\to 0}\dfrac{f(x)-f(0)}{x-0}=\lim_{x\to 0}\dfrac{x^{1/5}-0}{x-0}=\lim_{x\to 0}\dfrac{1}{x^{4/5}}=\infty$

Thus there is a vertical tangent line l at $(0,0)$; l: $x=0$.

68. $\lim_{x\to -1}\dfrac{f(x)-f(-1)}{x-(-1)}=\lim_{x\to -1}\dfrac{(x+1)^{1/3}-0}{x+1}=\lim_{x\to -1}\dfrac{1}{(x+1)^{2/3}}=\infty$

Thus there is a vertical tangent line l at $(-1,0)$; l: $x=-1$.

69. $\lim_{x\to 0}\dfrac{f(x)-f(0)}{x-0}=\lim_{x\to 0}\dfrac{(1-5x^{3/5})-1}{x-0}=\lim_{x\to 0}\dfrac{-5}{x^{2/5}}=-\infty$

Thus there is a vertical tangent line l at $(0,1)$; l: $x=0$.

70. Two-sided limit: (a); right-hand limit: (a), (e), (f); left-hand limit: (a), (b), (f); none: (c), (d)

71. As x approaches 2 from the right, $x-2$ approaches 0 from the right. Thus f is continuous from the right at 2. Note that if $x<2$, then $x-2<0$, so $\sqrt{x-2}$ is not defined for $x<2$ and hence f is not continuous from the left at 2.

72. As x approaches 0, x^2+1 approaches 1, so that $\lim_{x\to 0}\ln(x^2+1)=\ln 1=0$. Thus f is continuous at 0.

73. As x approaches 0 from the left, $1-e^x$ approaches 0 from the right. Thus $\sqrt{1-e^x}$ is continuous from the left at 0. Note that if $x>0$, then $1-e^x<0$, so $\sqrt{1-e^x}$ is not defined for $x>0$, and hence f is not continuous from the right at 0.

74. As x approaches $\pi/2$ from the right, $x-\pi/2$ approaches 0 from the right. Thus $\sqrt{x-\pi/2}$ and hence $\tan\sqrt{x-\pi/2}$ are continuous from the right at $\pi/2$. If $0<x<\pi/2$, then $x-\pi/2<0$, so $\sqrt{x-\pi/2}$ and hence $\tan\sqrt{x-\pi/2}$ are not defined. Thus f is not continuous from the left at $\pi/2$.

75. Notice that $e^{4-4}=e^0=1$, and

$$\frac{|x-4|}{x-4}=\begin{cases}1 & \text{if } x>4\\ -1 & \text{if } x<4.\end{cases}$$

Thus f is continuous from the right but is not continuous from the left at 4. Since $f(x)=-1$ for $x<4$, it follows that f is continuous at 0.

76. Since $\lim_{x\to 0^-}f(x)=-1$, $\lim_{x\to 0^+}f(x)=1$ and $f(0)=0$, it follows that f is continuous from neither the right nor the left at 0.

77. Since $f(t)=t^2\sqrt{t^2-t^4}=t^2\sqrt{t^2(1-t^2)}$, the domain is $[-1,1]$. Next,

$$\lim_{t\to 0}t^2\sqrt{t^2-t^4}=\left(\lim_{t\to 0}t^2\right)\left(\lim_{t\to 0}\sqrt{t^2-t^4}\right)=0\cdot 0=0=f(0).$$

Thus f is continuous at 0. As t approaches 1 from the left, $t^2-t^4=t^2(1-t^2)$ approaches 0 from the right, so $\lim_{t\to 1^-}t^2\sqrt{t^2-t^4}=(\lim_{t\to 1^-}t^2)(\lim_{t\to 1^-}\sqrt{t^2-t^4})=1\cdot 0=0=f(1)$. Thus f is continuous from the left at 1. If $t>1$, then $t^2-t^4<0$, so $\sqrt{t^2-t^4}$ and hence $t^2\sqrt{t^2-t^4}$ are not defined. Thus f is not continuous from the right at 1.

78. The domain of f consists of all $t \geq -2$ such that $\sqrt{t+2} \geq t$, that is, $t+2 \geq t^2$, or $t^2 - t - 2 \leq 0$, or $(t-2)(t+1) \leq 0$, so that $-1 \leq t \leq 2$. Thus $\lim_{t\to 2^-} f(t)$ makes sense. Moreover, $\lim_{t\to 2^-} f(t) = 0 = f(2)$, so f is continuous from the left at 2. Since $f(t)$ is not defined for $t > 2$, f is not continuous from the right at 2.

79. a. $\lim_{x\to 1^-} f(x) = \lim_{x\to 1^-}(2x-3) = \lim_{x\to 1}(2x-3) = -1$;

$\lim_{x\to 1^+} f(x) = \lim_{x\to 1^+}(3x-4) = \lim_{x\to 1}(3x-4) = -1$.

Since the two one-sided limits are equal, $\lim_{x\to 1} f(x) = -1$. Thus if we redefine $f(1)$ to be -1, then the resulting function will be continuous.

b. $\lim_{x\to -1^-} f(x) = \lim_{x\to -1^-}(x^2+1) = \lim_{x\to -1}(x^2+1) = 2$;

$\lim_{x\to -1^+} f(x) = \lim_{x\to -1^+}(6x^3-8) = \lim_{x\to -1}(6x^3-8) = -14$.

Since the two one-sided limits are not equal, $\lim_{x\to -1} f(x)$ does not exist. Therefore it is impossible to redefine $f(-1)$ to make f continuous at -1.

80. a. $\displaystyle\lim_{x\to 0^+} \frac{4x+|x|}{5x-3|x|} = \lim_{x\to 0} \frac{4x+x}{5x-3x} = \lim_{x\to 0} \frac{5x}{2x} = \lim_{x\to 0} \frac{5}{2} = \frac{5}{2}$

b. $\displaystyle\lim_{x\to 0^-} \frac{4x+|x|}{5x-3|x|} = \lim_{x\to 0} \frac{4x-x}{5x-3(-x)} = \lim_{x\to 0} \frac{3x}{8x} = \lim_{x\to 0} \frac{3}{8} = \frac{3}{8}$

c. Since the two one-sided limits in (a) and (b) are not equal, $\lim_{x\to 0} f(x)$ does not exist.

81. Let n be an arbitrary integer. If $n-1 < x < n$, then $[x] = n-1$, so that $\lim_{x\to n^-}[x] = \lim_{x\to n^-}(n-1) = n-1$. If $n < x < n+1$, then $[x] = n$, so that $\lim_{x\to n^+}[x] = \lim_{x\to n^+} n = n$.

82. For example, if $f(x) = 1/(x-a)^2$ and $g(x) = f(x) - 2$, then $\lim_{x\to a} f(x) = \infty = \lim_{x\to a} g(x)$. But $f(x) - g(x) = 2$, so $\lim_{x\to a}[f(x) - g(x)] = 2$.

83. $\displaystyle\lim_{x\to 0} \frac{f(x)-f(0)}{x-0} = \lim_{x\to 0} \frac{x^{1/n}-0}{x-0} = \lim_{x\to 0} \frac{1}{x^{1-1/n}} = \lim_{x\to 0} \frac{1}{x^{(n-1)/n}} = \infty$ since $n-1$ is even.

Thus there is a vertical tangent line at $(0,0)$.

84. a. By (11) of Section 2.2, until the rock hits the bottom of the well its height is given by $h(t) = -4.9t^2$. It hits the bottom when $h(t) = -49$, that is, $-4.9t^2 = -49$, or $t = \sqrt{10}$. Since

$$\lim_{t\to\sqrt{10}^-} \frac{h(t)-h(\sqrt{10})}{t-\sqrt{10}} = \lim_{t\to\sqrt{10}^-} \frac{-4.9t^2-(-49)}{t-\sqrt{10}} = \lim_{t\to\sqrt{10}^-} \left[-4.9\frac{(t+\sqrt{10})(t-\sqrt{10})}{t-\sqrt{10}}\right]$$

$$= \lim_{t\to\sqrt{10}^-} \left[-4.9(t+\sqrt{10})\right] = -4.9(2\sqrt{10}) = -9.8\sqrt{10},$$

the rock hits the bottom with velocity $-9.8\sqrt{10}$ meters per second.

b. Since $h(t) = -49$ for $t > \sqrt{10}$, the velocity of the rock is 0 for $t > \sqrt{10}$.

85. a. Let $t = 0$ correspond to the time a water droplet reaches the top of the falls. By (11) of Section 2.2 the height of a descending water droplet is given by $h(t) = -4.9t^2 - 2t + 40$. A water droplet reaches bottom at the positive time t_0 for which $h(t_0) = 0$, or $-4.9t_0^2 - 2t_0 + 40 = 0$. By the quadratic formula,

$$t_0 = \frac{2 - \sqrt{(-2)^2 - 4(-4.9)(40)}}{2(-4.9)} = \frac{-2 + \sqrt{788}}{9.8} \approx 2.7\,\text{(seconds)}.$$

The velocity at time t_0 is

$$v(t_0) = \lim_{t \to t_0^-} \frac{h(t) - h(t_0)}{t - t_0} = \lim_{t \to t_0^-} \frac{(-4.9t^2 - 2t + 40) - (-4.9t_0^2 - 2t_0 + 40)}{t - t_0}$$

$$= \lim_{t \to t_0} \frac{-4.9(t^2 - t_0^2) - 2(t - t_0)}{t - t_0} = \lim_{t \to t_0} [-4.9(t + t_0) - 2]$$

$$= -9.8t_0 - 2 = -\sqrt{788} = -2\sqrt{197}\,\text{(meters per second)}.$$

b. Since the final velocity is $-2\sqrt{197}$ by part (a), we will find the time t_1 at which $v(t_1)$ is half the terminal velocity, that is,

$$\frac{1}{2}(-2\sqrt{197}) = -\sqrt{197}.$$

As in the solution of part (a),

$$v(t_1) = \lim_{t \to t_1} \frac{h(t) - h(t_1)}{t - t_1} = \lim_{t \to t_1} \frac{-4.9(t^2 - t_1^2) - 2(t - t_1)}{t - t_1}$$

$$= \lim_{t \to t_1} [-4.9(t + t_1) - 2] = -9.8t_1 - 2.$$

Thus $-9.8t_1 - 2 = -\sqrt{197}$, so

$$t_1 = \frac{\sqrt{197} - 2}{9.8} \approx 1.2\,\text{(seconds)}.$$

By calculator we find that $h_{1/2} = h(t_1) \approx 30.2$ (meters).

86. a. By (11) in Section 2.2 with $v_0 = 0$ and $h_0 = 2$, the position of the ball is given by $h(t) = -4.9t^2 + 2$ until the ball hits the floor. The ball hits the floor at the time $t_0 > 0$ for which $h(t_0) = 0$, or $-4.9t_0^2 + 2 = 0$, or $t_0 = \sqrt{\frac{2}{4.9}}$. The velocity of the ball as it hits the ground is

$$v(t_0) = \lim_{t \to t_0^-} \frac{h(t) - h(t_0)}{t - t_0} = \lim_{t \to t_0^-} \frac{(-4.9t^2 + 2) - (-4.9t_0^2 + 2)}{t - t_0} = \lim_{t \to t_0^-} \frac{-4.9(t^2 - t_0^2)}{t - t_0}$$

$$= \lim_{t \to t_0^-} -4.9(t + t_0) = -9.8t_0 = -9.8\sqrt{\frac{2}{4.9}} = -9.8\sqrt{\frac{4}{9.8}} = -2\sqrt{9.8}\,\text{(meters per second)}$$

which is approximately -6.3 meters per second.

b. We proceed as in part (a) with $t = 0$ corresponding to the time when the ball reaches its maximum height of 1.8 meters after the first bounce. At that time the ball is neither rising nor falling, so $v_0 = 0$. By (11) of Section 2.2 the height between the first and second bounces is given by $h(t) = -4.9t^2 + 1.8$. The first bounce occurred at the negative time t_0 for which $h(t_0) = 0$, that is, $-4.9t_0^2 + 1.8 = 0$, or $t_0 = -\sqrt{\frac{1.8}{4.9}}$. The velocity of the ball as it bounces off the floor is

$$v(t_0) = \lim_{t\to t_0^+} \frac{h(t) - h(t_0)}{t - t_0} = \lim_{t\to t_0^+} \frac{(-4.9t^2 + 1.8) - (-4.9t_0^2 + 1.8)}{t - t_0}$$

$$= \lim_{t\to t_0^+} \frac{-4.9(t^2 - t_0^2)}{t - t_0} = \lim_{t\to t_0^+} -4.9(t + t_0) = -9.8t_0 = 9.8\sqrt{\frac{1.8}{4.9}} = 9.8\sqrt{\frac{3.6}{9.8}} = \sqrt{3.6}\,\sqrt{9.8}$$

which is approximately 5.9 meters per second.

c. Observe that $\sqrt{3.6}\,\sqrt{9.8} < 2\sqrt{9.8}$. Thus the speed of the ball after it bounces is less than the speed of the ball as it hit the floor. The physical reason is that some of the kinetic energy of the ball was converted to heat during the collision with the floor.

87. $\lim_{x\to 0^-} E(x) = \lim_{x\to 0^-} c\left[\frac{x}{-x} - \frac{x}{(x^2 + r^2)^{1/2}}\right] = \lim_{x\to 0} c\left[-1 - \frac{x}{(x^2 + r^2)^{1/2}}\right] = -c;$

$\lim_{x\to 0^+} E(x) = \lim_{x\to 0^+} c\left[\frac{x}{x} - \frac{x}{(x^2 + r^2)^{1/2}}\right] = \lim_{x\to 0} c\left[1 - \frac{x}{(x^2 + r^2)^{1/2}}\right] = c$

Since $c > 0$ by hypothesis, the two one-sided limits are not equal, so that $\lim_{x\to 0} E(x)$ does not exist.

2.6 Continuity on Intervals and the Intermediate Value Theorem

1. f is a polynomial, so f is continuous on $(-\infty, \infty)$.

2. f is a rational function whose denominator is never 0, so f is continuous on $(-\infty, \infty)$.

3. Since $\sin x$ and x are both continuous on $(-\infty, \infty)$ and $x \neq 0$ on $(-\infty, 0)$ and $(0, \infty)$, Theorem 2.4 implies that f is continuous on $(\infty, 0)$ and $(0, \infty)$.

4. Since $\sin x$ and x are both continuous on $(-\infty, \infty)$, and since $x \neq 0$ on $(-\infty, 0)$ and $(0, \infty)$, Theorem 2.4 implies that f is continuous on $(-\infty, 0)$ and $(0, \infty)$. Since $\lim_{x\to 0} f(x) = \lim_{x\to 0}(\sin x)/x = 1 = f(0)$, f is also continuous at 0. Therefore f is continuous on $(-\infty, \infty)$.

5. Since $x + 3$ is continuous on $(-\infty, \infty)$, the square root function is continuous on $[0, \infty)$, and $x + 3 \geq 0$ for x in $[-3, \infty)$, Theorem 2.6 implies that f is continuous on $[-3, \infty)$.

6. Since $x^2 - x^4$ is continuous on $(-\infty, \infty)$, the square root function is continuous on $[0, \infty)$, and $x^2 - x^4 \geq 0$ for x in $[-1, 1]$, Theorem 2.6 implies that f is continuous on $[-1, 1]$.

7. Since $x^2 - x^4$ is continuous on $(-\infty, \infty)$, the square root function is continuous on $[0, \infty)$, and $x^2 - x^4 > 0$ for x in $(0, 1)$, Theorem 2.6 implies that $\sqrt{x^2 - x^4}$ is continuous on $(0, 1)$. Finally, the constant function 1 is continuous on $(-\infty, \infty)$. Therefore Theorem 2.4 implies that f is continuous on $(0, 1)$.

8. Observe that $16x^4 - x^2 = x^2(16x^2 - 1) \geq 0$ for x in $(-\infty, -\frac{1}{4}]$ and for x in $[\frac{1}{4}, \infty)$. Since $16x^4 - x^2$ is continuous on $(-\infty, \infty)$ and the square root function is continuous on $[0, \infty)$, it follows from Theorem 2.10 that f is continuous on $(-\infty, -\frac{1}{4}]$ and on $[\frac{1}{4}, \infty)$.

9. Observe that $1 - x \geq 0$ and $3x - 2 > 0$ for $\frac{2}{3} < x \leq 1$, so that $(1-x)/(3x-2) \geq 0$ for $\frac{2}{3} < x \leq 1$. Since $(1-x)/(3x-2)$, being a rational function, is continuous on $(\frac{2}{3}, 1]$, and since the square root function is continuous on $[0, \infty)$, it follows from Theorem 2.6 that f is continuous on $(\frac{2}{3}, 1]$.

10. Being polynomials, $x - 1$ and $2 - x$ are continuous on $(-\infty, \infty)$. Also, $x - 1 \geq 0$ for x in $[1, \infty)$, while $2 - x \geq 0$ for x in $(-\infty, 2]$. Since the square root function is continuous on $[0, \infty)$, Theorem 2.6 implies that $\sqrt{x-1}$ is continuous for x in $[1, \infty)$ and $\sqrt{2-x}$ is continuous for x in $(-\infty, 2]$, so that both $\sqrt{x-1}$ and $\sqrt{2-x}$ are continuous on $[1, 2]$. Finally, since $\sqrt{2-x} \neq 0$ for $x < 2$, Theorem 2.4 implies f is continuous on $[1, 2)$.

11. This follows from (7) in Section 2.4. Alternatively, one could apply Theorem 2.4 to the quotient of the continuous functions $\sin x$ and $\cos x$, noting that $\cos x \neq 0$ for x in $(-\pi/2, \pi/2)$.

12. As a rational function whose denominator is never zero, $1/(x^2+1)$ is continuous on $(-\infty, \infty)$. For all x, $-\pi/2 < 0 < 1/(x^2+1) \leq 1 < \pi/2$. By Exercise 11, the tangent function is continuous on $(-\pi/2, \pi/2)$, so Theorem 2.6 implies that f is continuous on $(-\infty, \infty)$.

13. Since $1/x$ is continuous on $(0, \infty)$, $\cot x = (\cos x)/(\sin x)$ is continuous on $(0, \pi)$, and $0 < 1/x < \pi$ for x in $(1/\pi, \infty)$, Theorem 2.6 implies that f is continuous on $(1/\pi, \infty)$.

14. Since $\sqrt{x}$ is continuous on $[0, \infty)$ and $\sec x$ is continuous on $(-\pi/2, \pi/2)$, and since $-\pi/2 < \sqrt{x} < \pi/2$ for x in $[0, \pi^2/4)$, Theorem 2.6 implies that f is continuous on $[0, \pi^2/4)$.

15. Since e^t is continuous on $(-\infty, \infty)$, with $e^t > 0$ for all t, and since the square root function is continuous on $[0, \infty)$, Theorem 2.6 implies that $\sqrt{e^t}$ is continuous on $(-\infty, \infty)$.

16. Since the natural logarithm function is continuous on $(0, \infty)$ with $\ln t > 0$ for $t > 1$, it follows from Theorem 2.6 that $\ln(\ln t)$ is continuous on $(1, \infty)$.

17. Since e^t is continuous on $(-\infty, \infty)$ and $1 - e^t > 0$ for $t < 0$, and since the natural logarithm function is continuous on $(0, \infty)$, it follows from Theorem 2.6 that $\ln(1 - e^t)$ is continuous on $(-\infty, 0)$.

18. Since the natural logarithm function is continuous on $(0, \infty)$ and since $3 - t > 0$ and $t - 1 > 0$ for $1 < t < 2$, it follows from Theorem 2.6 that $\ln(3-t)$ and $\ln(t-1)$ are continuous on $(1, 2)$. Since $\ln(t-1) \neq 0$ for $1 < t < 2$, Theorem 2.4 now implies that $\ln(3-t)/\ln(t-1)$ is continuous on $(1, 2)$ also.

19. Let $f(x) = x^4 - x - 1$. Then f is continuous. Since $f(-1) = 1$ and $f(1) = -1$, the Intermediate Value Theorem implies that there is a c in $[-1, 1]$ such that $f(c) = 0$, that is, $c^4 - c - 1 = 0$.

20. Let $f(x) = x^3 - x - 5$. Then f is continuous. Since $f(0) = -5$ and $f(2) = 1$, the Intermediate Value Theorem implies that there is a c in $[0, 2]$ such that $f(c) = 0$, that is, $c^3 - c - 5 = 0$.

21. Let $f(x) = x^2 + 1/x$. Then f is continuous. Since $f(-2) = \frac{7}{2}$ and $f(-\frac{1}{2}) = -\frac{7}{4}$, the Intermediate Value Theorem implies that there is a c in $[-2, -\frac{1}{2}]$ such that $f(c) = 1$, that is, $c^2 + (1/c) = 1$.

22. Let $f(x) = x^2 + (1/2x)$. Then f is continuous. Since $f(\frac{1}{4}) = \frac{33}{16}$ and $f(1) = \frac{3}{2}$, the Intermediate Value Theorem implies that there is a c in $[\frac{1}{4}, 1]$ such that $f(c) = 2$, that is, $c^2 + 1/(2c) = 2$.

23. Let $f(x) = x^3 + x^2 + x - 2$. Then f is continuous. Since $f(-1) = -3$ and $f(1) = 1$, the Intermediate Value Theorem implies that there is a c in $[-1, 1]$ such that $f(c) = 0$, that is, $c^3 + c^2 + c - 2 = 0$.

24. Let $f(x) = x^{7/3} + x^{5/3} - 1$. Then f is continuous. Since $f(-1) = -3$ and $f(1) = 1$, the Intermediate Value Theorem implies that there is a c in $[-1, 1]$ such that $f(c) = 0$, that is, $c^{7/3} + c^{5/3} - 1 = 0$.

25. Let $f(x) = \cos x - x$. Then f is continuous. Since $f(0) = 1$ and $f(\pi/2) = -\pi/2$, the Intermediate Value Theorem implies that there is a c in $[0, \pi/2]$ such that $f(c) = 0$, that is, $\cos c = c$.

26. Let $f(x) = \sin x + x - 1$. Then f is continuous. Since $f(0) = -1$ and $f(\pi/6) = \frac{1}{2} + (\pi/6) - 1 > -\frac{1}{2} + \frac{3}{6} = 0$, the Intermediate Value Theorem implies that there is a c in $[0, \pi/6]$ such that $f(c) = 0$, that is, $\sin c = 1 - c$.

27. Let $f(x) = e^{-x} - x$. Then f is continuous. Since $f(0) = 1$ and $f(1) = e^{-1} - 1 < 0$, the Intermediate Value Theorem implies that there is a c in $(0, 1)$ such that $e^{-c} - c = 0$, that is, $e^{-c} = c$.

28. Let $f(x) = x \ln x - 1$. Then f is continuous. Since $f(1) = -1$ and $f(e) = e - 1 > 0$, the Intermediate Value Theorem implies that there is a c in $(1, e)$ such that $c \ln c - 1 = 0$, that is, $c \ln c = 1$.

29. Let $f(x) = (2 - x)^2(40 - 8x)$. Then $f(x) = 8(2 - x)^2(5 - x) = 0$ if $x = 2$ or 5.

Interval	c	$f(c)$	Sign of $f(x)$ on interval
$(-\infty, 2)$	0	160	+
$(2, 5)$	3	16	+
$(5, \infty)$	6	-128	$-$

Therefore $(2 - x)^2(40 - 8x) > 0$ on the union of $(-\infty, 2)$ and $(2, 5)$.

30. Let $f(x) = (x + 1)(x - 2)(2x - \frac{1}{4})$. Then $f(x) = 2(x + 1)(x - 2)(x - \frac{1}{8}) = 0$ if $x = -1$, $\frac{1}{8}$, or 2.

Interval	c	$f(c)$	Sign of $f(x)$ on interval
$(-\infty, -1)$	-2	-17	$-$
$(-1, \frac{1}{8})$	0	$\frac{1}{2}$	+
$(\frac{1}{8}, 2)$	1	$-\frac{7}{2}$	$-$
$(2, \infty)$	3	23	+

Therefore $(x + 1)(x - 2)(2x - \frac{1}{4}) \geq 0$ on the union of $[-1, \frac{1}{8}]$ and $[2, \infty)$.

31. Let $f(x) = (x^4 + x)(x + 3)$. Then $f(x) = x(x^3 + 1)(x + 3) = 0$ if $x = -3$, -1, or 0.

Interval	c	$f(c)$	Sign of $f(x)$ on interval
$(-\infty, -3)$	-4	-252	$-$
$(-3, -1)$	-2	14	$+$
$(-1, 0)$	$-\frac{1}{2}$	$-\frac{35}{32}$	$-$
$(0, \infty)$	1	8	$+$

Therefore $(x^4 + x)(x + 3) \leq 0$ on the union of $(-\infty, -3]$ and $[-1, 0]$.

32. Let $f(x) = x(x - 4)/[2(x - 2)^2]$. Then $2(x - 2)^2 = 0$ if $x = 2$, so the domain of f is the union of $(-\infty, 2)$ and $(2, \infty)$. Next, $f(x) = 0$ if $x = 0$ or 4.

Interval	c	$f(c)$	Sign of $f(x)$ on interval
$(-\infty, 0)$	-1	$\frac{5}{18}$	$+$
$(0, 2)$	1	$-\frac{3}{2}$	$-$
$(2, 4)$	3	$-\frac{3}{2}$	$-$
$(4, \infty)$	5	$\frac{5}{18}$	$+$

Therefore $x(x - 4)/[2(x - 2)^2] < 0$ on the union of $(0, 2)$ and $(2, 4)$.

33. Let $f(x) = (x - 1)(x - 3)/[(2x + 1)(2x - 1)]$. Then $(2x + 1)(2x - 1) = 0$ if $x = -\frac{1}{2}$ or $\frac{1}{2}$, so the domain of f is the union of $(-\infty, -\frac{1}{2})$, $(-\frac{1}{2}, \frac{1}{2})$, and $(\frac{1}{2}, \infty)$. Next, $f(x) = 0$ if $x = 1$ or 3.

Interval	c	$f(c)$	Sign of $f(x)$ on interval
$(-\infty, -\frac{1}{2})$	-1	$\frac{8}{3}$	$+$
$(-\frac{1}{2}, \frac{1}{2})$	0	-3	$-$
$(\frac{1}{2}, 1)$	$\frac{3}{4}$	$\frac{9}{20}$	$+$
$(1, 3)$	2	$-\frac{1}{15}$	$-$
$(3, \infty)$	4	$\frac{1}{21}$	$+$

Therefore $(x - 1)(x - 3)/[(2x + 1)(2x - 1)] \geq 0$ on the union of $(-\infty, -\frac{1}{2})$, $(\frac{1}{2}, 1]$ and $[3, \infty)$.

34. Let $f(x) = (6x^2 - 2)/(x^2 - 1)^3$. Then $(x^2 - 1)^3 = (x - 1)^3(x + 1)^3 = 0$ if $x = -1$ or 1, so the domain of f is the union of $(-\infty, -1)$, $(-1, 1)$ and $(1, \infty)$. Next, $f(x) = 0$ if $x = -1/\sqrt{3}$ or $1/\sqrt{3}$. Since f is an even function we will first discuss the values of $f(x)$ on $(-\infty, 0)$ and then use the symmetry to deduce the values of $f(x)$ on $(-\infty, \infty)$.

Interval	c	$f(c)$	Sign of $f(x)$ on interval
$(-\infty, -1)$	-2	$\frac{22}{27}$	$+$
$(-1, -1/\sqrt{3})$	$-\frac{2}{3}$	$-\frac{486}{125}$	$-$
$(-1/\sqrt{3}, 0)$	$-\frac{1}{2}$	$\frac{32}{27}$	$+$

Using the symmetry, we conclude that $(6x^2-2)/(x^2-1)^3 > 0$ on the union of $(-\infty, -1)$, $(-1/\sqrt{3}, 1/\sqrt{3})$ and $(1, \infty)$.

35. Let $f(x) = -2(x-1)(x^2+2x+4)/(27-x^3)$. Then $27 - x^3 = 0$ if $x = 3$, so the domain of f is the union of $(-\infty, 3)$ and $(3, \infty)$. Next, since $x^2+2x+4 = (x+1)^2+3 > 0$ for all x, $f(x) = 0$ if $x = 1$.

Interval	c	$f(c)$	Sign of $f(x)$ on interval
$(-\infty, 1)$	0	$\frac{8}{27}$	$+$
$(1, 3)$	2	$-\frac{24}{19}$	$-$
$(3, \infty)$	4	$\frac{168}{37}$	$+$

Therefore $\dfrac{-2(x-1)(x^2+2x+4)}{27-x^3} < 0$ on $(1, 3)$.

36. Let $f(x) = 3x(x^3-2)/(x^3+1)^3$. Then $(x^3+1)^3 = 0$ if $x = -1$, so the domain of f is the union of $(-\infty, -1)$ and $(-1, \infty)$. Next, $3x(x^3-2) = 0$ if $x = 0$ or $\sqrt[3]{2}$.

Interval	c	$f(c)$	Sign of $f(x)$ on interval
$(-\infty, -1)$	-2	$-\frac{60}{343}$	$-$
$(-1, 0)$	$-\frac{1}{2}$	$\frac{1632}{343}$	$+$
$(0, \sqrt[3]{2})$	1	$-\frac{3}{8}$	$-$
$(\sqrt[3]{2}, \infty)$	2	$\frac{4}{81}$	$+$

Therefore $3x(x^3-2)/(x^3+1)^3 \le 0$ on the union of $(-\infty, -1)$ and $[0, \sqrt[3]{2}]$.

37. Since $f(1) < 0$ and $f(2) > 0$, we let $a = 1$ and $b = 2$, and assemble the following table:

Interval	Length	Midpoint c	$f(c)$
$[1, 2]$	1	$\frac{3}{2}$	$\frac{1}{4}$
$[1, \frac{3}{2}]$	$\frac{1}{2}$	$\frac{5}{4}$	$-\frac{7}{16}$
$[\frac{5}{4}, \frac{3}{2}]$	$\frac{1}{4}$	$\frac{11}{8}$	$-\frac{7}{64}$
$[\frac{11}{8}, \frac{3}{2}]$	$\frac{1}{8}$		

Since the length of $[\frac{11}{8}, \frac{3}{2}]$ is $\frac{1}{8}$, and neither $\frac{11}{8}$ nor $\frac{3}{2}$ is a zero of f, the midpoint $\frac{23}{16}$ of $[\frac{11}{8}, \frac{3}{2}]$ is less than $\frac{1}{16}$ from a zero of f.

38. Since $f(2) < 0$ and $f(3) > 0$, we let $a = 2$ and $b = 3$, and assemble the following table:

Interval	Length	Midpoint c	$f(c)$
$[2,3]$	1	$\frac{5}{2}$	$-\frac{3}{4}$
$[\frac{5}{2},3]$	$\frac{1}{2}$	$\frac{11}{4}$	$\frac{9}{16}$
$[\frac{5}{2},\frac{11}{4}]$	$\frac{1}{4}$	$\frac{21}{8}$	$-\frac{7}{64}$
$[\frac{21}{8},\frac{11}{4}]$	$\frac{1}{8}$		

Since the length of $[\frac{21}{8},\frac{11}{4}]$ is $\frac{1}{8}$, and neither $\frac{21}{8}$ nor $\frac{11}{4}$ is a zero of f, the midpoint $\frac{43}{16}$ of $[\frac{21}{8},\frac{11}{4}]$ is less than $\frac{1}{16}$ from a zero of f.

39. Since $f(1) < 0$ and $f(2) > 0$, we let $a = 1$ and $b = 2$, and assemble the following table:

Interval	Length	Midpoint c	$f(c)$
$[1,2]$	1	$\frac{3}{2}$	$\frac{3}{8}$
$[1,\frac{3}{2}]$	$\frac{1}{2}$	$\frac{5}{4}$	$-\frac{67}{64}$
$[\frac{5}{4},\frac{3}{2}]$	$\frac{1}{4}$	$\frac{11}{8}$	$-\frac{205}{512}$
$[\frac{11}{8},\frac{3}{2}]$	$\frac{1}{8}$		

Since the length of $[\frac{11}{8},\frac{3}{2}]$ is $\frac{1}{8}$,and neither $\frac{11}{8}$ nor $\frac{3}{2}$ is a zero of f, the midpoint $\frac{23}{16}$ of $[\frac{11}{8},\frac{3}{2}]$ is less than $\frac{1}{16}$ from a zero of f.

40. Since $f(1) < 0$ and $f(2) > 0$, we let $a = 1$ and $b = 2$, and assemble the following table:

Interval	Length	Midpoint c	$f(c)$
$[1,2]$	1	$\frac{3}{2}$	$\frac{15}{8}$
$[1,\frac{3}{2}]$	$\frac{1}{2}$	$\frac{5}{4}$	$\frac{13}{64}$
$[1,\frac{5}{4}]$	$\frac{1}{4}$	$\frac{9}{8}$	$-\frac{231}{512}$
$[\frac{9}{8},\frac{5}{4}]$	$\frac{1}{8}$		

Since the length of $[\frac{9}{8},\frac{5}{4}]$ is $\frac{1}{8}$, and neither $\frac{9}{8}$ nor $\frac{5}{4}$ is a zero of f, the midpoint $\frac{19}{16}$ of $[\frac{9}{8},\frac{5}{4}]$ is less than $\frac{1}{16}$ from a zero of f.

41. Let $f(x) = x^2 - 5$, so that $\sqrt{5}$ is the zero of f. Since $f(2) < 0$ and $f(3) > 0$, the zero lies in $(2,3)$. We let $a = 2$ and $b = 3$, and assemble the following table:

Interval	Length	Midpoint c	$f(c)$
$[2,3]$	1	$\frac{5}{2}$	$\frac{5}{4}$
$[2,\frac{5}{2}]$	$\frac{1}{2}$	$\frac{9}{4}$	$\frac{1}{16}$
$[2,\frac{9}{4}]$	$\frac{1}{4}$	$\frac{17}{8}$	$-\frac{31}{64}$
$[\frac{17}{8},\frac{9}{4}]$	$\frac{1}{8}$		

Since the length of $[\frac{17}{8}, \frac{9}{4}]$ is $\frac{1}{8}$, and neither $\frac{17}{8}$ nor $\frac{9}{4}$ is a zero of f, the midpoint $\frac{35}{16}$ of $[\frac{17}{8}, \frac{9}{4}]$ is less than $\frac{1}{16}$ from $\sqrt{5}$.

42. Let $f = x^2 - 12$, so that $\sqrt{12}$ is the zero of f. Since $f(3) < 0$ and $f(4) > 0$, the zero lies in $(3, 4)$. We let $a = 3$ and $b = 4$, and assemble the following table:

Interval	Length	Midpoint c	$f(c)$
$[3, 4]$	1	$\frac{7}{2}$	$\frac{1}{4}$
$[3, \frac{7}{2}]$	$\frac{1}{2}$	$\frac{13}{4}$	$-\frac{23}{16}$
$[\frac{13}{4}, \frac{7}{2}]$	$\frac{1}{4}$	$\frac{27}{8}$	$-\frac{39}{64}$
$[\frac{27}{8}, \frac{7}{2}]$	$\frac{1}{8}$		

Since the length of $[\frac{27}{8}, \frac{7}{2}]$ is $\frac{1}{8}$, and neither $\frac{27}{8}$ nor $\frac{7}{2}$ is a zero of f, the midpoint $\frac{55}{16}$ of $[\frac{27}{8}, \frac{7}{2}]$ is less than $\frac{1}{16}$ from $\sqrt{12}$.

43. Let $f(x) = x^2 - 0.7$, so that $\sqrt{0.7}$ is the zero of f. Since $f(0) < 0$ and $f(1) > 0$, the zero lies in $(0, 1)$. We let $a = 0$ and $b = 1$, and assemble the following table:

Interval	Length	Midpoint c	$f(c)$
$[0, 1]$	1	$\frac{1}{2}$	$-\frac{9}{20}$
$[\frac{1}{2}, 1]$	$\frac{1}{2}$	$\frac{3}{4}$	$-\frac{11}{80}$
$[\frac{3}{4}, 1]$	$\frac{1}{4}$	$\frac{7}{8}$	$\frac{21}{320}$
$[\frac{3}{4}, \frac{7}{8}]$	$\frac{1}{8}$		

Since the length of $[\frac{3}{4}, \frac{7}{8}]$ is $\frac{1}{8}$, and neither $\frac{3}{4}$ nor $\frac{7}{8}$ is a zero of f, the midpoint $\frac{13}{16}$ of $[\frac{3}{4}, \frac{7}{8}]$ is less than $\frac{1}{16}$ from $\sqrt{0.7}$.

44. Let $f(x) = x^3 - 10$, so that $\sqrt[3]{10}$ is the zero of f. Since $f(2) < 0$ and $f(3) > 0$, the zero lies in $(2, 3)$. We let $a = 2$ and $b = 3$, and assemble the following table:

Interval	Length	Midpoint c	$f(c)$
$[2, 3]$	1	$\frac{5}{2}$	$\frac{45}{8}$
$[2, \frac{5}{2}]$	$\frac{1}{2}$	$\frac{9}{4}$	$\frac{89}{64}$
$[2, \frac{9}{4}]$	$\frac{1}{4}$	$\frac{17}{8}$	$-\frac{207}{512}$
$[\frac{17}{8}, \frac{9}{4}]$	$\frac{1}{8}$		

Since the length of $[\frac{17}{8}, \frac{9}{4}]$ is $\frac{1}{8}$, and neither $\frac{17}{8}$ nor $\frac{9}{4}$ is a zero of f, the midpoint $\frac{35}{16}$ of $[\frac{17}{8}, \frac{9}{4}]$ is less than $\frac{1}{16}$ from $\sqrt[3]{10}$.

45. .738...

46. 1.16...

47. .567...

48. 3.14...

49. Let p be any number, and let $f(x) = x^3$. If $p = 0$ and $c = 0$, then $c^3 = p$. If $p > 0$, then $f(0) = 0$, whereas $f(p+1) = (p+1)^3 \geq p+1 > p > 0$. The Intermediate Value Theorem implies that there exists a number c in $[0, p+1]$ such that $c^3 = f(c) = p$. If $p < 0$, then $f(0) = 0$ and $f(p-1) = (p-1)^3 < p-1 < p < 0$. The Intermediate Value Theorem implies that there is a number c in $[p-1, 0]$ such that $c^3 = f(c) = p$. In any case, c is the desired cube root of p.

50. Let p be any real number, and recall that $\tan 0 = 0$. If $p = 0$ and $c = 0$, then $\tan c = p$. If $p > 0$, then since $\lim_{x \to \pi/2^-} \tan x = \infty$, there is a number M in $(0, \pi/2)$ such that if $M < x < \pi/2$ then $\tan x > p$. By the Intermediate Value Theorem there is a c in $[0, (M + \pi/2)/2]$ such that $\tan c = p$. If $p < 0$, then $-p > 0$, so there is a c such that $\tan c = -p$. Consequently $\tan(-c) = -\tan c = -(-p) = p$.

51. Let $A(0) = \pi x^2$. Notice that A is continuous, with $A(0) = 0$ and $A(10) = 100\pi > 300$. By the Intermediate Value Theorem there is a c in $[0, 10]$ such that $A(c) = 200$.

52. Let $V(x) = 10\pi x^2$. Notice that V is continuous, with $V(0) = 0$ and $V(1) = 10\pi > 30$. By the Intermediate Value Theorem there is a c in $[0, 1]$ such that $V(c) = 25$.

53. a. From the diagram, the radius R of the cylinder satisfies

$$R^2 = r^2 - \left(\frac{h}{2}\right)^2 = r^2 - \frac{1}{4}h^2.$$

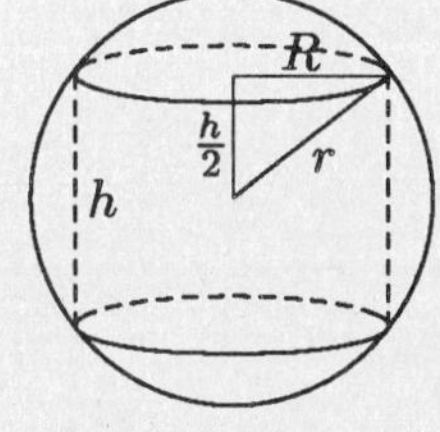

Therefore the volume $V(h)$ is given by

$$V(h) = \pi R^2 h = \pi \left(r^2 - \frac{1}{4}h^2\right) h = \pi r^2 h - \frac{\pi}{4}h^3.$$

Since the height of the cylinder cannot exceed the diameter $2r$ of the sphere, the domain of V is $[0, 2r]$.

b. Since V is a polynomial function, it is continuous on $[0, 2r]$.

54. Since $-1.25 \times 10^{-4}x$ and e^x are continuous on $(-\infty, \infty)$, so is $e^{-1.25 \times 10^{-4}x}$ by Theorem 2.6. Therefore p is continuous on $[0, \infty)$.

55. Since 2θ and the sine function are continuous on $(-\infty, \infty)$, so is $\sin 2\theta$ by Theorem 2.6. Therefore $(v_0^2/g) \sin 2\theta$ is continuous on $(-\infty, \infty)$ by Theorem 2.4. It follows that R is continuous on $[0, \pi/2]$.

56. Since the polynomial $x^2 + a^2$ is continuous and positive on $(-\infty, \infty)$ and since $x^{3/2}$ is continuous on $(0, \infty)$, it follows from Theorem 2.6 that $(x^2 + a^2)^{3/2}$ is continuous on $(-\infty, \infty)$. Since Qx is also continuous and $(x^2 + a^2)^{3/2} \neq 0$ for any x, it follows from Theorem 2.4 that E is continuous on $(-\infty, \infty)$.

57. Since G, M, and R are constants, the function GMr/R^3 is a polynomial in r and the function GM/r^2 is a rational function in r. Therefore F is continuous on $(0, R)$ and on (R, ∞). To investigate continuity at R, we examine the one-sided limits of F at R:

$$\lim_{r\to R^-} F(r) = \lim_{r\to R^-} \frac{GMr}{R^3} = \lim_{r\to R} \frac{GMr}{R^3} = \frac{GMR}{R^3} = \frac{GM}{R^2};$$

$$\lim_{r\to R^+} F(r) = \lim_{r\to R^+} \frac{GM}{r^2} = \lim_{r\to R} \frac{GM}{r^2} = \frac{GM}{R^2}.$$

Since the two one-sided limits are equal, we have $\lim_{r\to R} F(r) = GM/R^2 = F(R)$. Therefore F is continuous at R. Thus F is continuous on $(0, \infty)$.

Chapter 2 Review

1. By (5) of Section 2.3, $\lim_{x\to 2} \frac{-4x+3}{x^2-1} = \frac{-4(2)+3}{2^2-1} = -\frac{5}{3}$.

2. By (5) of Section 2.3,

$$\lim_{x\to 1/2} \frac{2x-1}{8x^2-4x} = \lim_{x\to 1/2} \frac{2x-1}{4x(2x-1)} = \lim_{x\to 1/2} \frac{1}{4x} = \frac{1}{4(1/2)} = \frac{1}{2}.$$

3. By the Product Rule, $\lim_{x\to 1} x\sqrt{x+3} = (\lim_{x\to 1} x)(\lim_{x\to 1} \sqrt{x+3}) = \lim_{x\to 1} \sqrt{x+3}$. Let $y = x+3$, so that y approaches 4 as x approaches 1. By the Substitution Rule, $\lim_{x\to 1} \sqrt{x+3} = \lim_{y\to 4} \sqrt{y} = \sqrt{4} = 2$. Thus $\lim_{x\to 1} x\sqrt{x+3} = \lim_{x\to 1} \sqrt{x+3} = 2$.

4. $\lim_{x\to 4} \frac{\sqrt{x}-2}{4-x} = \lim_{x\to 4} \frac{-(2-\sqrt{x})}{(2-\sqrt{x})(2+\sqrt{x})} = \lim_{x\to 4} \frac{-1}{2+\sqrt{x}} = \frac{-1}{2+\sqrt{4}} = -\frac{1}{4}$

5. Let $y = x + 3\pi/4$. Since y approaches π as x approaches $\pi/4$, the Substitution Rule implies that $\lim_{x\to\pi/4} \sec^3(x+3\pi/4) = \lim_{y\to\pi} \sec^3 y = \sec^3 \pi = (-1)^3 = -1$.

6. By the Product Rule,

$$\lim_{x\to 0} \frac{\tan^2 x}{x} = \lim_{x\to 0} \left[\frac{\sin x}{x} \cdot \sin x \cdot \frac{1}{\cos^2 x}\right] = \left(\lim_{x\to 0} \frac{\sin x}{x}\right)\left(\lim_{x\to 0} \sin x\right)\left(\lim_{x\to 0} \frac{1}{\cos^2 x}\right) = (1)(0)(1^2) = 0.$$

7. Let $y = 6v$. Since y approaches 0 as v approaches 0, it follows from the Substitution Rule, the Constant Multiple Rule, and Example 2 of Section 2.4 that

$$\lim_{v\to 0} \frac{5\sin 6v}{4v} = \lim_{y\to 0} \frac{5\sin y}{4(y/6)} = \frac{15}{2} \lim_{y\to 0} \frac{\sin y}{y} = \frac{15}{2}.$$

8. By the Constant Multiple and Product Rules and Example 2 of Section 2.4,

$$\lim_{v\to 0} \frac{\sin^6 v}{6v^6} = \frac{1}{6} \lim_{v\to 0} \frac{\sin^6 v}{v^6} = \frac{1}{6}\left(\lim_{v\to 0} \frac{\sin v}{v}\right)^6 = \frac{1}{6}(1)^6 = \frac{1}{6}.$$

9. Using (9) of Section 2.3, along with the Quotient, Sum, and Difference Rules, we have

$$\lim_{x\to 0}\frac{1-e^x}{1+e^x}=\frac{1-e^0}{1+e^0}=\frac{1-1}{1+1}=0.$$

10. Let $y=(5-x^2)^2$. Since y approaches $[5-(-2)^2]^2=1$ as x approaches -2, the Substitution Rule implies that $\lim_{x\to-2}\ln[(5-x^2)^2]=\lim_{y\to 1}\ln y=\ln 1=0$.

11. If $x\neq -10$, then $(x+10)^2>0$ and $\lim_{x\to-10}(x+10)^2=0$. Thus

$$\lim_{x\to-10}\frac{4x}{(x+10)^2}=-\infty.$$

12. If $x>0$, then $2x-8\sqrt{x}+8=2(\sqrt{x}-2)^2$, so

$$\lim_{x\to 4}\frac{2x-8\sqrt{x}+8}{\sqrt{x}-2}=\lim_{x\to 4}\frac{2(\sqrt{x}-2)^2}{\sqrt{x}-2}=\lim_{x\to 4}2(\sqrt{x}-2)=2(\sqrt{4}-2)=0.$$

13. If $x<0$, then $-x>0$, so $\sqrt{-x}>0$ and thus $9+\sqrt{-x}>9$, so $\sqrt{9+\sqrt{-x}}>0$. Using the Substitution Rule twice, we find that

$$\lim_{x\to 0^-}\sqrt{9+\sqrt{-x}}=\lim_{y\to 0^+}\sqrt{9+y}=\lim_{z\to 9^+}\sqrt{z}=\sqrt{9}=3.$$

14. $\displaystyle\lim_{x\to 5}\frac{x^2-2x-15}{x^2-x-20}=\lim_{x\to 5}\frac{(x-5)(x+3)}{(x-5)(x+4)}=\lim_{x\to 5}\frac{x+3}{x+4}=\frac{8}{9}$

15. First notice that

$$\begin{aligned}\frac{\sqrt{2+3w}-\sqrt{2-3w}}{w}&=\frac{\sqrt{2+3w}-\sqrt{2-3w}}{w}\,\frac{\sqrt{2+3w}+\sqrt{2-3w}}{\sqrt{2+3w}+\sqrt{2-3w}}\\&=\frac{(2+3w)-(2-3w)}{w(\sqrt{2+3w}+\sqrt{2-3w})}=\frac{6}{\sqrt{2+3w}+\sqrt{2-3w}}.\end{aligned}$$

By the Substitution Rule, $\lim_{w\to 0}\sqrt{2+3w}=\lim_{y\to 2}\sqrt{y}=\sqrt{2}$ and $\lim_{w\to 0}\sqrt{2-3w}=\lim_{y\to 2}\sqrt{y}=\sqrt{2}$, so it follows that

$$\lim_{w\to 0}\frac{\sqrt{2+3w}-\sqrt{2-3w}}{w}=\lim_{w\to 0}\frac{6}{\sqrt{2+3w}+\sqrt{2-3w}}=\frac{6}{\sqrt{2}+\sqrt{2}}=\frac{3}{2}\sqrt{2}.$$

16. If $0<w<\pi^2/9$, then $\cos\sqrt{w}>\frac{1}{2}$ and $\sin w>0$. Since $\lim_{w\to 0}\sin w=0$ it follows that

$$\lim_{w\to 0^+}\frac{\cos\sqrt{w}}{\sin w}=\infty.$$

17. Let $f(x)=\cos(1/w)$. If $w=1/2n\pi$ for any positive integer n, then $0<w<1/n$ and $f(w)=1$. If $w=1/(2n\pi+\pi)$ for any positive integer n, then $0<w<1/n$ and $f(w)=-1$. Thus $\lim_{w\to 0^+}f(w)$ does not exist.

18. If $x > 0$, then

$$\frac{\sin x}{\sqrt{x}} = \frac{\sqrt{x}}{\sqrt{x}} \cdot \frac{\sin x}{\sqrt{x}} = \sqrt{x}\,\frac{\sin x}{x}.$$

Thus

$$\lim_{x \to 0^+} \frac{\sin x}{\sqrt{x}} = \lim_{x \to 0^+} \left(\sqrt{x} \cdot \frac{\sin x}{x}\right) = \left(\lim_{x \to 0^+} \sqrt{x}\right)\left(\lim_{x \to 0^+} \frac{\sin x}{x}\right) = 0 \cdot 1 = 0.$$

19. Since $\lim_{x \to 0^+} e^x = e^0 = 1$ and $\lim_{x \to 0^+} \ln x = -\infty$, it follows that $\lim_{x \to 0^+} e^x / \ln x = 0$.

20. If $x > 1$, then $\ln x > 0$, $e^x > 0$, and $\lim_{x \to 1^+} \ln x = \ln 1 = 0$. Since $\lim_{x \to 1^+} e^x = e^1 \neq 0$, it follows that $\lim_{x \to 1^+} e^x / \ln x = \infty$.

21. Since $\lim_{x \to 4^+} (3 - 2|x|)/(x - 4) = -\infty$, $x = 4$ is a vertical asymptote.

22. Since

$$\lim_{x \to -2/3^+} \frac{(x+3)^2}{4 - 9x^2} = \infty = \lim_{x \to 2/3^-} \frac{(x+3)^2}{4 - 9x^2}$$

$x = -\frac{2}{3}$ and $x = \frac{2}{3}$ are vertical asymptotes.

23. We have

$$\frac{x^2 + 3x - 4}{x^2 - 5x - 14} = \frac{(x+4)(x-1)}{(x-7)(x+2)}.$$

Since $\lim_{x \to 7^+} f(x) = \infty = \lim_{x \to -2^+} f(x)$, $x = -2$ and $x = 7$ are vertical asymptotes.

24. Since

$$\lim_{x \to -2} f(x) = \lim_{x \to -2} \frac{(x+2)(x-1)}{x+2} = \lim_{x \to -2} (x - 1) = -3$$

f has no vertical asymptotes.

25. Since

$$\lim_{x \to -2^+} f(x) = \lim_{x \to -2^+} \frac{(x-2)^2}{(x-2)(x+2)} = \lim_{x \to -2^+} \frac{x-2}{x+2} = -\infty$$

$x = -2$ is a vertical asymptote. (Since $\lim_{x \to 2} f(x) = \lim_{x \to 2} (x-2)/(x+2) = 0$, $x = 2$ is *not* a vertical asymptote.)

26. Since

$$\lim_{x \to 0^+} \frac{\tan x}{x} = \lim_{x \to 0^+} \left(\frac{\sin x}{x} \cdot \frac{1}{\cos x}\right) = \left(\lim_{x \to 0^+} \frac{\sin x}{x}\right)\left(\lim_{x \to 0^+} \frac{1}{\cos x}\right) = 1 \cdot 1 = 1$$

$x = 0$ is not a vertical asymptote. Since $\lim_{x \to (n\pi + \pi/2)^-} \tan x = \infty$ for any integer n, it follows that $\lim_{x \to (n\pi + \pi/2)^-} \tan x / x = \infty$, so $x = n\pi + \pi/2$ is a vertical asymptote, for any integer n.

27. Notice that $-1/x > 0$ for $x < 0$. Thus $\lim_{x \to 0^-} (-1/x) = \infty$ and hence $\lim_{x \to 0^-} e^{-1/x} = \infty$. Therefore $x = 0$ is a vertical asymptote.

28. $x^2 - 2x - 3 = (x-3)(x+1)$, so that $x^2 - 2x - 3 > 0$ for $x < -1$ and for $x > 3$. Since $x^2 - 2x - 3 = 0$ for $x = -1$ and for $x = 3$, it follows that $\lim_{x \to -1^-} \ln(x^2 - 2x - 3) = -\infty$ and $\lim_{x \to 3^+} \ln(x^2 - 2x - 3) = -\infty$. Therefore $x = -1$ and $x = 3$ are vertical asymptotes.

29. Since $\lim_{x \to 0^+} \ln x = -\infty$ and $\lim_{x \to 0^+} e^x = 1$, it follows that $\lim_{x \to 0^+} (\ln x)/e^x = -\infty$. Therefore $x = 0$ is a vertical asymptote.

30. Observe that $e^x - 1 = 0$ only for $x = 0$. Since

$$\lim_{x \to 0} \frac{x}{e^x - 1} = \lim_{x \to 0} \frac{1}{\dfrac{e^x - 1}{x}} = \frac{1}{1} = 1$$

by (8) in Section 2.1, f has no vertical asymptotes.

31. $f(x)$ is defined for all x in $(-\infty, -\sqrt{13}]$ and for all x in $[\sqrt{13}, \infty)$. Thus f is continuous from the left at $-\sqrt{13}$.

32. If $x \geq 0$ then x is in the domain of f if we have $\sqrt{x+3} - 2x \geq 0$, that is, if $\sqrt{x+3} \geq 2x$, or equivalently, if $x + 3 \geq 4x^2$, or $4x^2 - x - 3 = 4(x-1)(x + \frac{3}{4}) \leq 0$, or $0 \leq x \leq 1$. Thus if $x \geq 0$, then x is in the domain of f if $0 \leq x \leq 1$. Using the Substitution Rule with $y = x + 3$, we find that $\lim_{x \to 1^-} (\sqrt{x+3} - 2x) = \lim_{x \to 1^-} \sqrt{x+3} - \lim_{x \to 1^-} 2x = \lim_{y \to 4} \sqrt{y} - \lim_{x \to 1} 2x = \sqrt{4} - 2(1) = 0$. Using the Substitution Rule again, we have $\lim_{x \to 1^-} f(x) = \lim_{x \to 1^-} \sqrt{\sqrt{x+3} - 2x} = \lim_{y \to 0^+} \sqrt{y} = 0 = f(1)$. Thus f is continuous from the left at 1.

33. Since $\lim_{x \to 2^+} f(x) = \lim_{x \to 2^+} (3x + 4) = 10 = f(2)$ but $\lim_{x \to 2^-} f(x) = \lim_{x \to 2^-} (3x - 4) = 2 \neq f(2)$, f is continuous from the right at 2 but is not continuous at 2.

34. Since $\lim_{x \to 1^-} f(x) = \lim_{x \to 1^-} \sqrt{2 - x} = 1 = f(1)$ and $\lim_{x \to 1^+} f(x) = \lim_{x \to 1^+} (2x^2 - x) = 1 = f(1)$, f is continuous at 1.

35. Since f is a rational function whose denominator is not zero for x in the interval $(2, \infty)$, f is continuous on $(2, \infty)$.

36. Since $5 - 2x \geq 0$ for x in the interval $(-\infty, \frac{5}{2}]$ and is continuous on that interval, and since the square root function is continuous on the interval $[0, \infty)$, Theorem 2.6 implies that f is continuous on $(-\infty, \frac{5}{2}]$.

37. If x is in $[\sqrt{2}/3, 4)$, then $3x - \sqrt{2} \geq 0$ and $4 - x > 0$. Thus for such x, $(3x - \sqrt{2})/(4 - x)$ is nonnegative, so on $[\sqrt{2}/3, 4)$, the rational function $(3x - \sqrt{2})/(4 - x)$ is continuous. Since the square root function is continuous for x in $[0, \infty)$, Theorem 2.6 implies that f is continuous on $[\sqrt{2}/3, 4)$.

38. For every real number x, $0 < 1/(1 + x^2) \leq 1$. Since $1/(1 + x^2)$ is a rational function whose denominator is never zero, it is continuous for all real numbers. Next, the secant function is continuous on $(0, 1]$. Thus Theorem 2.6 implies that f is continuous on $(-\infty, \infty)$.

39. Since x^2 and e^x are continuous on $(-\infty, \infty)$, Theorem 2.6 implies that $e^{(x^2)}$ is continuous on $(-\infty, \infty)$. Since $e^{(x^2)} > 0$ for all x and since the square root function is continuous on $(0, \infty)$, it follows from Theorem 2.6 that f is continuous on $(-\infty, \infty)$.

40. Since e^x is continuous on $(-\infty, \infty)$, so is $1 - e^x$. Since the natural logarithm function is continuous on $(0, \infty)$ and since $1 - e^x > 0$ for $x < 0$, it follows that f is continuous on $(-\infty, 0)$.

41. Since $\lim_{x\to 2} f(x) = \lim_{x\to 2}[(x+8)(x-2)]/(x-2) = \lim_{x\to 2}(x+8) = 10$, we can define $f(2) = 10$ to make f continuous at 2.

42. a. 1, 2, 3, 4; b. 0, 1, 2, 3, 4; c. 3, 4; d. 1, 3; e. 2, 3; f. 3

43. a. Since $\lim_{x\to 0^+} f(x)$ exists and is positive, and since $\lim_{x\to 0^+} g(x) = \infty$, it follows that $\lim_{x\to 0^+} f(x)/g(x) = 0$.

b. Since $\lim_{x\to a} f(x) = f(a) = g(a) = \lim_{x\to a} g(x) \neq 0$, it follows that $\lim_{x\to a} f(x)/g(x) = f(a)/g(a) = 1$.

c. Since $g(x) > 0$ for $x < b$, $\lim_{x\to b^-} g(x) = 0$, and $\lim_{x\to b^-} f(x) = f(b) > 0$, it follows that $\lim_{x\to b^-} f(x)/g(x) = \infty$.

d. Since $g(x) < 0$ for $x > b$, $\lim_{x\to b^+} g(x) = 0$, and $\lim_{x\to b^+} f(x) = f(b) > 0$, it follows that $\lim_{x\to b^+} f(x)/g(x) = -\infty$.

44. a. It is 5. b. It does not exist. c. It does not exist. d. It does not exist.

e. It is 0. f. It is ∞.

45. Let $f(x) = (2x-3)(4-x)/(1+x)^2$. Then $(1+x)^2 = 0$ if $x = -1$, so the domain of f is the union of $(-\infty, -1)$ and $(-1, \infty)$. Next, $(2x-3)(4-x) = 0$ if $x = \frac{3}{2}$ or 4.

Interval	c	$f(c)$	Sign of $f(x)$ on interval
$(--\infty, -1)$	-2	-42	$-$
$(-1, \frac{3}{2})$	0	-12	$-$
$(\frac{3}{2}, 4)$	2	$\frac{2}{9}$	$+$
$(4, \infty)$	5	$-\frac{7}{36}$	$-$

Therefore $(2x-3)(4-x)/(1+x)^2 < 0$ on the union of $(-\infty, -1)$, $(-1, \frac{3}{2})$ and $(4, \infty)$.

46. Let $f(x) = (x+4)/[(x^2-4)(1+x^2)]$. Then $(x^2-4)(1+x^2) = 0$ if $x = -2$ or 2, so the domain of f is the union of $(-\infty, -2)$, $(-2, 2)$ and $(2, \infty)$. Next, $x + 4 = 0$ if $x = -4$.

Interval	c	$f(c)$	Sign of $f(x)$ on interval
$(-\infty, -4)$	-5	$-\frac{1}{546}$	$-$
$(-4, -2)$	-3	$\frac{1}{50}$	$+$
$(-2, 2)$	0	-1	$-$
$(2, \infty)$	3	$\frac{7}{50}$	$+$

Therefore $(x+4)/[(x^2-4)(1+x^2)] \geq 0$ on the union of $[-4, -2)$ and $(2, \infty)$.

47. Let $f(x) = x^3 + 3x - 3$. Since f is continuous on $[-1, 1]$, $f(-1) < 0$ and $f(1) > 0$, the Intermediate Value Theorem implies that there is a c in $[-1, 1]$ such that $f(c) = 0$, that is, a solution of the given equation. For the bisection method we let $a = -1$ and $b = 1$, and assemble the following table:

Interval	Length	Midpoint c	$f(c)$
$[-1,1]$	2	0	-3
$[0,1]$	1	$\frac{1}{2}$	$-\frac{11}{8}$
$[\frac{1}{2},1]$	$\frac{1}{2}$	$\frac{3}{4}$	$-\frac{21}{64}$
$[\frac{3}{4},1]$	$\frac{1}{4}$	$\frac{7}{8}$	$\frac{151}{512}$
$[\frac{3}{4},\frac{7}{8}]$	$\frac{1}{8}$		

Since the length of $[\frac{3}{4},\frac{7}{8}]$ is $\frac{1}{8}$, and neither $\frac{3}{4}$ nor $\frac{7}{8}$ is a zero of f, the midpoint $\frac{13}{16}$ of $[\frac{3}{4},\frac{7}{8}]$ is less than $\frac{1}{16}$ from a zero of f, and hence from a solution of the equation $x^3+3x-3=0$.

48. Let $f(x)=\sqrt{x}+1-x^2$. Since f is continuous on $[1,2]$, $f(1)>0$ and $f(2)<0$, the Intermediate Value Theorem implies that there is a c in $[1,2]$ such that $f(c)=0$, that is, a solution of the given equation. For the bisection method we let $a=1$ and $b=2$, and assemble the following table:

Interval	Length	Midpoint c	$f(c)$
$[1,2]$	1	$\frac{3}{2}$	$\sqrt{\frac{3}{2}}+1-\frac{9}{4}\approx -.0253$
$[1,\frac{3}{2}]$	$\frac{1}{2}$	$\frac{5}{4}$	$\sqrt{\frac{5}{4}}+1-\frac{25}{16}\approx .556$
$[\frac{5}{4},\frac{3}{2}]$	$\frac{1}{4}$	$\frac{11}{8}$	$\sqrt{\frac{11}{8}}+1-\frac{121}{64}\approx .282$
$[\frac{11}{8},\frac{3}{2}]$	$\frac{1}{8}$		

Since the length of $[\frac{11}{8},\frac{3}{2}]$ is $\frac{1}{8}$, and neither $\frac{11}{8}$ nor $\frac{3}{2}$ is a zero of f, the midpoint $\frac{23}{16}$ of $[\frac{11}{8},\frac{3}{2}]$ is less than $\frac{1}{16}$ from a zero of f, and hence from a solution of the equation $\sqrt{x}+1=x^2$.

49. Let $f(x)=x+\sin x-\cos x$. Then the zeros of f are the solutions of the given equation. By plotting f and zooming in, we find that the only solution of the equation is approximately .456.

50. Let $f(x)=e^{-x^2/2}-0.3x$. Then the zeros of f are the solutions of the given equation. By plotting f and zooming in, we find that the only solution of the equation is approximately 1.34.

51. $\displaystyle\lim_{x\to 0}\frac{e^{-ax}-e^{-bx}}{x}=\lim_{x\to 0}\frac{(e^{-ax}-1)-(e^{-bx}-1)}{x}=\lim_{x\to 0}\frac{e^{-ax}-1}{x}-\lim_{x\to 0}\frac{e^{-bx}-1}{x}$,

provided each of these limits exists. Let $y=-ax$. Then by the Substitution Rule, and (8) of Section 2.1,

$$\lim_{x\to 0}\frac{e^{-ax}-1}{x}=\lim_{y\to 0}\frac{e^y-1}{y/(-a)}=-a\lim_{y\to 0}\frac{e^y-1}{y}=(-a)1=-a.$$

Similarly

$$\lim_{x\to 0}\frac{e^{-bx}-1}{x}=-b.$$

Consequently

$$\lim_{x\to 0}\frac{e^{-ax}-e^{-bx}}{x}=(-a)-(-b)=b-a.$$

52. Let p be any number in $[-1, 1]$. Since $\sin(-\pi/2) = -1$ and $\sin(\pi/2) = 1$, the Intermediate Value Theorem implies that there is a c in $[-1, 1]$ such that $\sin c = p$.

53. It does not include the phrase "provided the limits of the two functions both exist."

54. a. Let $y = -x$. Then y approaches a as x approaches $-a$. If $\lim_{x\to a} f(x) = L$, then the Substitution Rule implies that $\lim_{x\to -a} f(-x) = \lim_{y\to a} f(y) = \lim_{x\to a} f(x) = L$.

b. Suppose that f is even and continuous at a. Then $f(x) = f(-x)$ and $\lim_{x\to a} f(x) = f(a)$, so that by part (a), $\lim_{x\to -a} f(x) = \lim_{x\to -a} f(-x) = \lim_{x\to a} f(x) = f(a) = f(-a)$, which implies that f is continuous at $-a$. Now suppose that f is odd and continuous at a. Then $f(x) = -f(-x)$ and $\lim_{x\to a} f(x) = f(a)$, so that by part (a), $\lim_{x\to -a} f(x) = \lim_{x\to -a}[-f(-x)] = -\lim_{x\to -a} f(-x) = -\lim_{x\to a} f(x) = -f(a) = f(-a)$, which implies that f is continuous at $-a$.

55. a. Since the absolute value function is continuous, the result follows from Theorem 2.6 since $|f|$ is a composite of f and the absolute value function.

b. $|f(x)| = 1$ for all x, so $|f|$ is continuous at 2. Since $\lim_{x\to 2^+} f(x) = 1 \neq f(2)$, f is not continuous at 2.

56. a. Let $\varepsilon > 0$. Since $\lim_{x\to a} f(x) = \infty$, there exists a $\delta > 0$ such that if $0 < |x - a| < \delta$, then $|f(x)| > 1/\varepsilon$ and hence $|1/f(x)| < \varepsilon$. Thus $\lim_{x\to a} 1/f(x) = 0$.

b. Let $f(x) = 1/x$. Then $1/f(x) = x$ for $x \neq 0$. Thus $\lim_{x\to 0} 1/f(x) = 0$. But $\lim_{x\to 0^+} f(x) = \lim_{x\to 0^+}(1/x) = \infty$ and $\lim_{x\to 0^-} f(x) = \lim_{x\to 0^-}(1/x) = -\infty$, so that $\lim_{x\to 0} f(x)$ does not exist. Thus the converse of part (a) is not true.

57. a. $m_1 = \lim\limits_{x\to 0} \dfrac{f(x) - f(0)}{x - 0} = \lim\limits_{x\to 0} \dfrac{2\sin x - 0}{x - 0} = 2$

$m_2 = \lim\limits_{x\to 1} \dfrac{g(x) - g(0)}{x - 1} = \lim\limits_{x\to 1} \dfrac{(-1/x^2) - (-1)}{x - 1} = \lim\limits_{x\to 1} \dfrac{x^2 - 1}{x^2(x-1)} = \lim\limits_{x\to 1} \dfrac{x+1}{x^2} = 2$

Since $m_1 = m_2$, the tangent lines are parallel.

b. $m_1 = \lim\limits_{x\to -1} \dfrac{f(x) - f(-1)}{x - (-1)} = \lim\limits_{x\to -1} \dfrac{x^3 - (-1)}{x + 1} = \lim\limits_{x\to -1} (x^2 - x + 1) = 3$

$m_2 = \lim\limits_{x\to 4} \dfrac{g(x) - g(4)}{x - 4} = \lim\limits_{x\to 4} \dfrac{(3/8)x^2 - 6}{x - 4} = \lim\limits_{x\to 4} (3/8)(x + 4) = 3$

Since $m_1 = m_2$, the tangent lines are parallel.

c. $m_1 = \lim\limits_{x\to -4} \dfrac{f(x) - f(-4)}{x - (-4)} = \lim\limits_{x\to -4} \dfrac{(x^2 + 5x + 1) - (-3)}{x + 4} = \lim\limits_{x\to -4} \dfrac{x^2 + 5x + 4}{x + 4} = \lim\limits_{x\to -4} (x + 1) = -3$

$m_2 = \lim\limits_{x\to 3} \dfrac{g(x) - g(3)}{x - 3} = \lim\limits_{x\to 3} \dfrac{(-3x - 7) - (-16)}{x - 3} = \lim\limits_{x\to 3} \dfrac{-3x + 9}{x - 3} = -3$

Since $m_1 = m_2$, the tangent lines are parallel.

58. a. $m_1 = \lim\limits_{x\to 0} \dfrac{f(x) - f(0)}{x - 0} = \lim\limits_{x\to 0} \dfrac{\sin x - 0}{x - 0} = 1$

$m_2 = \lim\limits_{x\to 1} \dfrac{g(x) - g(1)}{x - 1} = \lim\limits_{x\to 1} \dfrac{(1/x) - 1}{x - 1} = \lim\limits_{x\to 1} \dfrac{1 - x}{x(x-1)} = \lim\limits_{x\to 1} \left(\dfrac{-1}{x}\right) = -1$

Since $m_1 m_2 = -1$, the tangent lines are perpendicular.

b. $m_1 = \lim_{x\to 0} \frac{f(x)-f(0)}{x-0} = \lim_{x\to 0} \frac{(\frac{1}{2})\sin x - 0}{x-0} = \frac{1}{2}\lim_{x\to 0}\frac{\sin x}{x} = \frac{1}{2}$

$m_2 = \lim_{x\to 1} \frac{g(x)-g(1)}{x-1} = \lim_{x\to 1} \frac{(1/x^2)-1}{x-1} = \lim_{x\to 1} \frac{1-x^2}{x^2(x-1)} = \lim_{x\to 1} \frac{-(x+1)}{x^2} = -2$

Since $m_1 m_2 = -1$, the tangent lines are perpendicular.

c. $m_1 = \lim_{x\to 6} \frac{f(x)-f(6)}{x-6} = \lim_{x\to 6} \frac{(x-10)-(-4)}{x-6} = 1$

$m_2 = \lim_{x\to -5} \frac{g(x)-g(-5)}{x-(-5)} = \lim_{x\to -5} \frac{(-x+3)-8}{x+5} = -1$

Since $m_1 m_2 = -1$, the tangent lines are perpendicular.

59. First we find the point of intersection of the line and the graph of f:

$$\begin{aligned} \sqrt{x} &= \frac{x+4}{4} \\ 4\sqrt{x} &= x+4 \\ 16x &= x^2+8x+16 \\ x^2-8x+16 &= 0 \\ (x-4)^2 &= 0, \text{ or } x = 4 \end{aligned}$$

Since

$$\lim_{x\to 4} \frac{f(x)-f(4)}{x-4} = \lim_{x\to 4} \frac{\sqrt{x}-2}{x-4} = \lim_{x\to 4} \frac{1}{\sqrt{x}+2} = \frac{1}{4}$$

the tangent line at $(4, 2)$ is $y - 2 = \frac{1}{4}(x-4)$, or $4y = x+4$. The point of tangency is $(4, 2)$.

60. Let the origin be at the bottom of the well. Then by (11) of Section 2.2 with $v_0 = 0$, the position of the thimble after t seconds is given by $h(t) = -4.9t^2 + 15$. Thus

$$v(1.5) = \lim_{t\to 1.5} \frac{h(t)-h(1.5)}{t-1.5} = \lim_{t\to 1.5} \frac{(-4.9t^2+15)-(-4.9(1.5)^2+15)}{t-1.5} = \lim_{t\to 1.5} \frac{-4.9(t^2-1.5^2)}{t-1.5}$$

$$= \lim_{t\to 1.5} \frac{-4.9(t+1.5)(t-1.5)}{t-1.5} = \lim_{t\to 1.5} -4.9(t+1.5) = (-4.9)(3) = -14.7 \text{ (meters per second)}.$$

The speed at that moment is $|-14.7| = 14.7$ (meters per second).

61. a. By (11) of Section 2.2, the height of the drip above the basin is given by $h(t) = -4.9t^2 + h_0$, where h_0 is the height of the faucet above the basin. Since $h(\frac{1}{4}) = 0$, we have $-4.9(\frac{1}{4})^2 + h_0 = 0$, so that $h_0 = \frac{4.9}{16} = .30625$ meters. Thus the faucet is approximately .3 meters (or approximately 1 foot) high.

b. As the drip hits the basin, its velocity is

$$\lim_{t\to 1/4^-} \frac{h(t)-h(1/4)}{t-1/4} = \lim_{t\to 1/4^-} \frac{(-4.9t^2+h_0)-0}{t-1/4} = \lim_{t\to 1/4} \frac{-4.9t^2+4.9/16}{t-1/4}$$

$$= \lim_{t\to 1/4} \frac{-4.9(t+1/4)(t-1/4)}{t-1/4} = \lim_{t\to 1/4} [-4.9(t+1/4)] = -4.9(1/4+1/4) = -2.45.$$

Thus the drip hits the basin with a speed of $|-2.45| = 2.45$ meters per second.

Chapter 3

Derivatives

3.1 The Derivative

1. $f'(4) = \lim_{x \to 4} \frac{f(x) - f(4)}{x - 4} = \lim_{x \to 4} \frac{5 - 5}{x - 4} = \lim_{x \to 4} 0 = 0$

2. $f'(0) = \lim_{x \to 0} \frac{f(x) - f(0)}{x - 0} = \lim_{x \to 0} \frac{(-4x + 7) - 7}{x} = \lim_{x \to 0} (-4) = -4$

3. $f'(1) = \lim_{x \to 1} \frac{f(x) - f(1)}{x - 1} = \lim_{x \to 1} \frac{(2x + 3) - 5}{x - 1} = \lim_{x \to 1} \frac{2x - 2}{x - 1} = \lim_{x \to 1} 2 = 2$

4. $f'(-1) = \lim_{x \to -1} \frac{f(x) - f(-1)}{x - (-1)} = \lim_{x \to -1} \frac{(x^2 - 2) - (-1)}{x + 1} = \lim_{x \to -1} \frac{(x - 1)(x + 1)}{x + 1} = \lim_{x \to -1} (x - 1) = -2$

5. $f'(0) = \lim_{x \to 0} \frac{f(x) - f(0)}{x - 0} = \lim_{x \to 0} \frac{x^3 - 0}{x} = \lim_{x \to 0} x^2 = 0$

6. $f'(-2) = \lim_{x \to -2} \frac{f(x) - f(-2)}{x - (-2)} = \lim_{x \to -2} \frac{(1/x) - (-1/2)}{x + 2} = \lim_{x \to -2} \frac{x + 2}{2x(x + 2)} = \lim_{x \to -2} \frac{1}{2x} = -\frac{1}{4}$

7. $f'(1) = \lim_{x \to 1} \frac{f(x) - f(1)}{x - 1} = \lim_{x \to 1} \frac{(2x - 3/x) - (-1)}{x - 1} = \lim_{x \to 1} \frac{2x^2 + x - 3}{x(x - 1)}$

   $= \lim_{x \to 1} \frac{(2x + 3)(x - 1)}{x(x - 1)} = \lim_{x \to 1} \frac{2x + 3}{x} = 5$

8. $f'(-1) = \lim_{x \to -1} \frac{f(x) - f(-1)}{x - (-1)} = \lim_{x \to -1} \frac{(4x^2 + 1/x^2) - 5}{x + 1} = \lim_{x \to -1} \frac{4x^4 - 5x^2 + 1}{x^2(x + 1)}$

   $= \lim_{x \to -1} \frac{(4x^2 - 1)(x + 1)(x - 1)}{x^2(x + 1)} = \lim_{x \to -1} \frac{(4x^2 - 1)(x - 1)}{x^2} = -6$

9. $f'(4) = \lim_{x \to 4} \frac{f(x) - f(4)}{x - 4} = \lim_{x \to 4} \frac{(1/\sqrt{x} - (1/2)}{x - 4} = \lim_{x \to 4} \frac{2 - \sqrt{x}}{2\sqrt{x}(\sqrt{x} - 2)(\sqrt{x} + 2)}$

   $= \lim_{x \to 4} \frac{-1}{2\sqrt{x}(\sqrt{x} + 2)} = -\frac{1}{16}$

10. For x near $-\sqrt{2}$, $f(x) = -x$. Thus

$$f'(-\sqrt{2}) = \lim_{x\to-\sqrt{2}} \frac{f(x)-f(-\sqrt{2})}{x-(-\sqrt{2})} = \lim_{x\to-\sqrt{2}} \frac{-x-\sqrt{2}}{x+\sqrt{2}} = \lim_{x\to-\sqrt{2}}(-1) = -1.$$

11. $\displaystyle\lim_{x\to2^-} \frac{f(x)-f(2)}{x-2} = \lim_{x\to2^-} \frac{x^2-4}{x-2} = \lim_{x\to2^-} \frac{(x-2)(x+2)}{x-2} = \lim_{x\to2^-}(x+2) = 4;$

$\displaystyle\lim_{x\to2^+} \frac{f(x)-f(2)}{x-2} = \lim_{x\to2^+} \frac{(4x-4)-4}{x-2} = \lim_{x\to2^+} 4 = 4.$ Thus $\displaystyle f'(2) = \lim_{x\to2} \frac{f(x)-f(2)}{x-2} = 4.$

12. $\displaystyle\lim_{x\to1/16^-} \frac{f(x)-f(\frac{1}{16})}{x-\frac{1}{16}} = \lim_{x\to1/16^-} \frac{\sqrt{x}-\frac{1}{4}}{x-\frac{1}{16}} = \lim_{x\to1/16^-} \frac{\sqrt{x}-\frac{1}{4}}{(\sqrt{x}-\frac{1}{4})(\sqrt{x}+\frac{1}{4})} = \lim_{x\to1/16^-} \frac{1}{\sqrt{x}+\frac{1}{4}} = 2;$

$\displaystyle\lim_{x\to1/16^+} \frac{f(x)-f(\frac{1}{16})}{x-\frac{1}{16}} = \lim_{x\to1/16^+} \frac{(2x+\frac{1}{8})-\frac{1}{4}}{x-\frac{1}{16}} = \lim_{x\to1/16^+} \frac{2(x-\frac{1}{16})}{x-\frac{1}{16}} = \lim_{x\to1/16^+} 2 = 2.$

Thus $\displaystyle f'(\tfrac{1}{16}) = \lim_{x\to1/16} \frac{f(x)-f(\frac{1}{16})}{x-\frac{1}{16}} = 2.$

13. $\displaystyle f'(x) = \lim_{t\to x} \frac{f(t)-f(x)}{t-x} = \lim_{t\to x} \frac{-\pi-(-\pi)}{t-x} = \lim_{t\to x} 0 = 0$

14. $\displaystyle f'(x) = \lim_{t\to x} \frac{f(t)-f(x)}{t-x} = \lim_{t\to x} \frac{(3t-7)-(3x-7)}{t-x} = \lim_{t\to x} \frac{3(t-x)}{t-x} = \lim_{t\to x} 3 = 3$

15. $\displaystyle f'(x) = \lim_{t\to x} \frac{f(t)-f(x)}{t-x} = \lim_{t\to x} \frac{-5t^2-(-5x^2)}{t-x} = \lim_{t\to x} \frac{-5(t-x)(t+x)}{t-x}$

$\displaystyle = \lim_{t\to x} -5(t+x) = -5(2x) = -10x$

16. $\displaystyle f'(x) = \lim_{t\to x} \frac{f(t)-f(x)}{t-x} = \lim_{t\to x} \frac{(-5t^2+t)-(-5x^2+x)}{t-x} = \lim_{t\to x} \frac{-5(t-x)(t+x)+(t-x)}{t-x}$

$\displaystyle = \lim_{t\to x}[-5(t+x)+1] = -5(2x)+1 = -10x+1$

17. $\displaystyle g'(x) = \lim_{t\to x} \frac{g(t)-g(x)}{t-x} = \lim_{t\to x} \frac{t^3-x^3}{t-x} = \lim_{t\to x} \frac{(t-x)(t^2+tx+t^2)}{t-x}$

$\displaystyle = \lim_{t\to x}(t^2+tx+x^2) = (x^2+x^2+x^2) = 3x^2$

18. $\displaystyle g'(x) = \lim_{t\to x} \frac{g(t)-g(x)}{t-x} = \lim_{t\to x} \frac{(1/t)-(1/x)}{t-x} = \lim_{t\to x} \frac{x-t}{tx(t-x)} = \lim_{t\to x} \frac{-1}{tx} = -\frac{1}{x^2}$

19. $\displaystyle k'(x) = \lim_{t\to x} \frac{k(t)-k(x)}{t-x} = \lim_{t\to x} \frac{[(1/t^2)-\sqrt{7}]-[(1/x^2)-\sqrt{7}]}{t-x} = \lim_{t\to x} \frac{x^2-t^2}{t^2x^2(t-x)}$

$\displaystyle = \lim_{t\to x} \frac{(x-t)(x+t)}{t^2x^2(t-x)} = \lim_{t\to x} \frac{-(t+x)}{t^2x^2} = \frac{-2x}{x^4} = -\frac{2}{x^3}$

20. $k'(x) = \lim_{t \to x} \dfrac{k(t) - k(x)}{t - x} = \lim_{t \to x} \dfrac{t^{1/3} - x^{1/3}}{(t^{1/3} - x^{1/3})(t^{2/3} + t^{1/3}x^{1/3} + x^{2/3})}$

$= \lim_{t \to x} \dfrac{1}{t^{2/3} + t^{1/3}x^{1/3} + x^{2/3}} = \dfrac{1}{3x^{2/3}}$

21. $\dfrac{dy}{dx} = \lim_{t \to x} \dfrac{\frac{7}{3} - \frac{7}{3}}{t - x} = \lim_{t \to x} 0 = 0$

22. $\dfrac{dy}{dx} = \lim_{t \to x} \dfrac{[1 - \frac{1}{2}t] - [1 - \frac{1}{2}x]}{t - x} = \lim_{t \to x} \dfrac{-\frac{1}{2}(t - x)}{t - x} = \lim_{t \to x}(-\frac{1}{2}) = -\frac{1}{2}$

23. $\dfrac{dy}{dx} = \lim_{t \to x} \dfrac{(3t^2 + 1) - (3x^2 + 1)}{t - x} = \lim_{t \to x} \dfrac{3(t - x)(t + x)}{t - x} = \lim_{t \to x} 3(t + x) = 3(2x) = 6x$

24. $\dfrac{dy}{dx} = \lim_{t \to x} \dfrac{(1/t^3) - (1/x^3)}{t - x} = \lim_{t \to x} \dfrac{x^3 - t^3}{t^3x^3(t - x)} = \lim_{t \to x} \dfrac{(x - t)(x^2 + tx + t^2)}{t^3x^3(t - x)}$

$= \lim_{t \to x} \dfrac{-(x^2 + tx + t^2)}{t^3x^3} = -\dfrac{3x^2}{x^6} = -\dfrac{3}{x^4}$

25. $\left.\dfrac{dy}{dx}\right|_{x=2} = \lim_{x \to 2} \dfrac{0.25 - 0.25}{x - 2} = \lim_{x \to 2} 0 = 0$

26. $\left.\dfrac{dy}{dx}\right|_{x=2} = \lim_{x \to 2} \dfrac{(-5x + 9) - (-1)}{x - 2} = \lim_{x \to 2} \dfrac{-5(x - 2)}{x - 2} = \lim_{x \to 2}(-5) = -5$

27. $\left.\dfrac{dy}{dx}\right|_{x=2} = \lim_{x \to 2} \dfrac{(x^2 - 3) - 1}{x - 2} = \lim_{x \to 2} \dfrac{(x - 2)(x + 2)}{x - 2} = \lim_{x \to 2}(x + 2) = 4$

28. $\left.\dfrac{dy}{dx}\right|_{x=2} = \lim_{x \to 2} \dfrac{-(1/x) - (-1/2)}{x - 2} = \lim_{x \to 2} \dfrac{-2 + x}{2x(x - 2)} = \lim_{x \to 2} \dfrac{1}{2x} = \dfrac{1}{4}$

29. $\lim_{x \to 0} \dfrac{f(x) - f(0)}{x - 0} = \lim_{x \to 0} \dfrac{x^{1/3} - 0}{x - 0} = \lim_{x \to 0} \dfrac{1}{x^{2/3}} = \infty$; no derivative at 0.

30. $\lim_{x \to 0} \dfrac{f(x) - f(0)}{x - 0} = \lim_{x \to 0} \dfrac{x^{7/3} - 0}{x - 0} = \lim_{x \to 0} x^{4/3} = 0$; $f'(0) = 0$.

31. $\lim_{x \to 0^-} \dfrac{f(x) - f(0)}{x - 0} = \lim_{x \to 0^-} \dfrac{(-x - x) - 0}{x - 0} = \lim_{x \to 0^-} (-2) = -2$;

$\lim_{x \to 0^+} \dfrac{f(x) - f(0)}{x - 0} = \lim_{x \to 0^+} \dfrac{(x - x) - 0}{x - 0} = \lim_{x \to 0^+} 0 = 0$; no derivative at 0.

32. $\lim_{x \to 3^-} \dfrac{g(x) - g(3)}{x - 3} = \lim_{x \to 3^-} \dfrac{-(x - 3) - 0}{x - 3} = \lim_{x \to 3^-} (-1) = -1$;

$\lim_{x \to 3^+} \dfrac{g(x) - g(3)}{x - 3} = \lim_{x \to 3^+} \dfrac{(x - 3) - 0}{x - 3} = \lim_{x \to 3^+} 1 = 1$; no derivative at 3.

33. $\lim_{x \to 3} \dfrac{g(x) - g(3)}{x - 3} = \lim_{x \to 3} \dfrac{(x + 3) - 6}{x - 3} = \lim_{x \to 3} 1 = 1$; $g'(3) = 1$.

34. g is not defined at 0, so has no derivative at 0.

35. $\lim_{x\to 0^-} \dfrac{k(x)-k(0)}{x-0} = \lim_{x\to 0^-} \dfrac{(-x^2+4x)-(-1)}{x-0} = \lim_{x\to 0^-}\left(-x+4+\dfrac{1}{x}\right) = -\infty$; no derivative at 0.

36. $\lim_{x\to 0^-} \dfrac{k(x)-k(0)}{x-0} = \lim_{x\to 0^-} \dfrac{3x^2+4x-0}{x-0} = \lim_{x\to 0^-}(3x+4) = 4;$

$\lim_{x\to 0^+} \dfrac{k(x)-k(0)}{x-0} = \lim_{x\to 0^+} \dfrac{x^2+4x-0}{x-0} = \lim_{x\to 0^+}(x+4) = 4;\ k'(0) = 4.$

37. $f'(-2) = 2(-2) = -4$ from Example 4. Thus l: $y-4 = -4(x-(-2))$, or $y = -4x-4$.

38. $f'(-3) = \lim_{x\to -3} \dfrac{f(x)-f(-3)}{x-(-3)} = \lim_{x\to -3} \dfrac{(1/x)-(-1/3)}{x+3} = \lim_{x\to -3} \dfrac{3+x}{3x(x+3)} = \lim_{x\to -3} \dfrac{1}{3x} = -\dfrac{1}{9}.$

Thus l: $y-(-\frac{1}{3}) = -\frac{1}{9}(x-(-3))$, or $y = -\frac{1}{9}x - \frac{2}{3}$.

39. $f'(4) = \frac{1}{2}\cdot 4^{-1/2} = \frac{1}{4}$ from Example 5. Thus l: $y-2 = \frac{1}{4}(x-4)$, or $y = \frac{1}{4}x+1$.

40. $f'(0) = \lim_{x\to 0} \dfrac{\sin x - \sin 0}{x-0} = \lim_{x\to 0} \dfrac{\sin x}{x} = 1$. Thus l: $y-0 = 1(x-0)$, or $y = x$.

41. It appears that $f'(0) \approx -2$, $f'(1) \approx -1.5$, $f'(2) \approx -.5$ and $f'(3) \approx .7$.

42. The average rate of change of f on $[1,3]$ is larger, since the graph is steeper on that interval.

43. f is decreasing on $[-10, 2]$ and is increasing on $[2, 10]$.

44. f is increasing on $[-10,-1]$ and on $[1, 10]$, and is decreasing on $[-1, 1]$.

45. f is decreasing on $[-10,-1]$ and on $[0, 2]$, and is increasing on $[-1, 0]$ and on $[2, 10]$.

46. f is increasing on $[-10, 10]$.

47. f is increasing on $[-10, 10]$.

48. The domain of f is the union of $(-\infty,-1)$ and $(0,\infty)$. For values of x in the domain of f and in the interval $[-10, 10]$ we find that f is decreasing on $[-10,-1)$ and is increasing on $(0, 10]$.

49. $m_2 = \dfrac{f(2.1)-f(2)}{0.1} = \dfrac{(2.1)^2-4}{0.1} = \dfrac{0.41}{0.1} = 4.1;$

$f'(2) = \lim_{x\to 2} \dfrac{f(x)-f(2)}{x-2} = \lim_{x\to 2} \dfrac{x^2-4}{x-2} = \lim_{x\to 2} \dfrac{(x-2)(x+2)}{x-2} = \lim_{x\to 2}(x+2) = 4;$

$|f'(2) - m_2| = |4-4.1| = 0.1$

50. $m_{-1} = \dfrac{f(-0.9)-f(-1)}{0.1} = \dfrac{\frac{1}{3}(-0.9)^3 - \frac{1}{3}(-1)}{0.1} = \dfrac{0.271}{0.3} \approx 0.9033333333$

$f'(-1) = \lim_{x\to -1} \dfrac{f(x)-f(-1)}{x-(-1)} = \lim_{x\to -1} \dfrac{\frac{1}{3}x^3 - \frac{1}{3}(-1)}{x+1} = \lim_{x\to -1} \dfrac{(x+1)(x^2-x+1)}{3(x+1)}$

$= \lim_{x\to -1} \dfrac{1}{3}(x^2-x+1) = 1$

$|f'(-1) - m_{-1}| \approx |1 - 0.9033333333| = 0.0966666667$

51. It appears that $f'(x) = x$.

52. It appears that $f'(x) = \cos x$.

53. It appears that $f'(x) = -\sin x$.

54. It appears that $f'(x) = e^x$.

55. $f'(-2) \approx \dfrac{1.9536874 - 2.0457932}{-2.006579 - (-1.993421)} \approx 6.9999848$ (Thus we conjecture that $f'(-2) = 7$.)

56. $f'(3) \approx \dfrac{.40310467 - .42108723}{3.0016447 - 2.9983553} \approx -5.466820697$

57. $f'(\frac{1}{2}) \approx \dfrac{1.6514352 - 1.6460118}{.50164474 - .49835526} \approx 1.648710434$

58. $f'(1.3) \approx \dfrac{.26280698 - .26217447}{1.3005757 - 1.2997533} \approx .7691026265$

59. a. $f(x) = x^4$, $a = 2$;

$$f'(2) = \lim_{x\to 2} \frac{x^4 - 16}{x - 2} = \lim_{x\to 2} \frac{(x-2)(x+2)(x^2+4)}{x-2} = \lim_{x\to 2}(x+2)(x^2+4) = 32$$

b. $x^3 + 2x^2 + 4x + 8 = \dfrac{(x^3 + 2x^2 + 4x + 8)(x-2)}{x-2} = \dfrac{x^4 - 16}{x-2}$; $f(x) = x^4$, $a = 2$; $f'(2) = 32$

60. a. $-f'(a)$ b. $f'(a)$

61. By the Substitution Rule, with $x = a - h$, we find that

$$\lim_{h\to 0} \frac{f(a-h) - f(a)}{h} = -\lim_{h\to 0} \frac{f(a-h) - f(a)}{-h} = -\lim_{x\to a} \frac{f(x) - f(a)}{x - a} = -f'(a).$$

62. $$\lim_{h\to 0} \frac{f(a+h) - f(a-h)}{h} = \lim_{h\to 0} \frac{f(a+h) - f(a) + f(a) - f(a-h)}{h}$$

$$= \lim_{h\to 0} \left[\frac{f(a+h) - f(a)}{h} - \frac{f(a-h) - f(a)}{h}\right]$$

$$= \lim_{h\to 0} \frac{f(a+h) - f(a)}{h} - \lim_{h\to 0} \frac{f(a-h) - f(a)}{h}$$

$$= f'(a) - \lim_{h\to 0} \frac{f(a-h) - f(a)}{h} = f'(a) - (-f'(a)) = 2f'(a)$$

where the next to the last equality comes from Exercise 61.

63. a. Since $f(-a) = f(a)$, we use the solution of Exercise 61 to deduce that

$$f'(-a) = \lim_{h\to 0} \frac{f(-a+h) - f(-a)}{h} = \lim_{h\to 0} \frac{f(a-h) - f(a)}{h} = -f'(a) = -2.$$

b. Since $f(-a) = -f(a)$, we use the solution of Exercise 61 to deduce that

$$f'(-a) = \lim_{h\to 0} \frac{f(-a+h) - f(-a)}{h} = \lim_{h\to 0} \frac{-f(a-h) + f(a)}{h} = -\lim_{h\to 0} \frac{f(a-h) - f(a)}{h} = f'(a) = 2.$$

64. a. Since $f(x) = g(x)$ for all x in an open interval containing a, we have

$$\lim_{x\to a} \frac{g(x) - g(a)}{x - a} = \lim_{x\to a} \frac{f(x) - f(a)}{x - a} = f'(a).$$

Therefore $g'(a) = f'(a)$.

b. Let $f(x) = x$. Then for $x > 0$ we have $f(x) = g(x)$, so that by part (a),

$$g'(x) = f'(x) = \lim_{t\to x} \frac{f(t) - f(x)}{t - x} = \lim_{t\to x} \frac{t - x}{t - x} = 1.$$

Next, let $h(x) = -x$. Then for $x < 0$ we have $h(x) = g(x)$, so that by part (a),

$$g'(x) = h'(x) = \lim_{t\to x} \frac{h(t) - h(x)}{t - x} = \lim_{t\to x} \frac{-t - (-x)}{t - x} = -1.$$

65. No. Let $f(x) = 1$ and $g(x) = x$ for all x. Then $f(1) = 1 = g(1)$, but $f'(1) = 0$ and $g'(1) = 1$.

66. The slope of the tangent line is 8, so $f'(5) = 8$.

67. $\lim_{x\to a} g(x) = \lim_{x\to a} \dfrac{f(x) - f(a)}{x - a} = f'(a) = g(a)$. Thus g is continuous at a.

68. Since the graph oscillates wildly in an interval about 0, there could not be any tangent line. Thus $f'(0)$ cannot exist.

69. Although $|f(x)|$ is small when x is near 0, the graph oscillates with slopes ranging from -1 to 1 on any interval about 0. Thus there could not be any tangent line. Consequently $f'(0)$ cannot exist.

70. a. $f'(r) = \lim_{x\to r} \dfrac{f(x) - f(r)}{x - r} = \lim_{x\to r} \dfrac{x^2 - r^2}{x - r} = \lim_{x\to r} \dfrac{(x - r)(x + r)}{x - r} = \lim_{x\to r} (x + r) = 2r;$

the line tangent at (r, r^2) has equation $\dfrac{y - r^2}{x - r} = 2r$, or $y = 2rx - r^2$.

b. The points (p, q) that lie on a line tangent have the property that $q^2 \le p$, because every tangent lies below the graph of f.

71. b. $f'(0) = \lim_{x\to 0} \dfrac{f(x) - f(0)}{x - 0} = \lim_{x\to 0} \dfrac{\frac{1}{2}x + 10x^2 \sin(1/x) - 0}{x} = \lim_{x\to 0} \left(\frac{1}{2} + 10x \sin(1/x)\right)$

Since $-|x| \le 10x \sin(1/x) \le |x|$ for all x, and since $\lim_{x\to 0}(-|x|) = 0 = \lim_{x\to 0} |x|$, the Squeezing Theorem implies that $\lim_{x\to 0}(\frac{1}{2} + 10x \sin(1/x)) = \frac{1}{2} + \lim_{x\to 0} 10x \sin(1/x) = \frac{1}{2} + 0 = \frac{1}{2}$. Therefore $f'(0) = \frac{1}{2}$.

72. The velocity if given by

$$v(1/2) = \lim_{t\to 1/2} \frac{f(t) - f(1/2)}{t - 1/2} = \lim_{t\to 1/2} \frac{2t^2 - 2(1/2)^2}{t - 1/2}$$

$$= \lim_{t\to 1/2} \frac{2(t^2 - (1/2)^2)}{t - 1/2} = \lim_{t\to 1/2} \frac{2(t + 1/2)(t - 1/2)}{t - 1/2} = \lim_{t\to 1/2} 2(t + 1/2) = 2.$$

73. $m_C(40) = \lim_{x\to 40} \dfrac{C(x)-C(40)}{x-40} = \lim_{x\to 40} \dfrac{[400x-(0.1)x^2]-[400\cdot 40-(0.1)40^2]}{x-40}$

$= \lim_{x\to 40} \dfrac{400(x-40)-(0.1)(x^2-40^2)}{x-40} = \lim_{x\to 40}[400-(0.1)(x+40)]$

$= 400 - 8 = 392$ (dollars per barrel)

74. $m_C(50) = C'(50) = \lim_{x\to 50} \dfrac{C(x)-C(50)}{x-50} = \lim_{x\to 50} \dfrac{(10{,}000+3/x)-(10{,}000+\frac{3}{50})}{x-50}$

$= \lim_{x\to 50} \dfrac{3(50-x)}{50x(x-50)} = \lim_{x\to 50} \dfrac{-3}{50x} = -\dfrac{3}{2500}$

75. $m_R(16) = R'(16) = \lim_{x\to 16} \dfrac{R(x)-R(16)}{x-16} = \lim_{x\to 16} \dfrac{450x^{1/2}-450\cdot 16^{1/2}}{x-16}$

$= \lim_{x\to 16} \left[\dfrac{450(x^{1/2}-16^{1/2})}{x-16}\cdot\dfrac{x^{1/2}+16^{1/2}}{x^{1/2}+16^{1/2}}\right] = \lim_{x\to 16} \dfrac{450(x-16)}{(x-16)(x^{1/2}+16^{1/2})}$

$= \lim_{x\to 16} \dfrac{450}{x^{1/2}+16^{1/2}} = \dfrac{450}{16^{1/2}+16^{1/2}} = \dfrac{225}{4}$ (dollars per barrel)

76. a. $m_C(1) = \lim_{x\to 1} \dfrac{C(x)-C(1)}{x-1} = \lim_{x\to 1} \dfrac{(3+12x-2x^2)-(3+12-2)}{x-1}$

$= \lim_{x\to 1} \left[\dfrac{12(x-1)}{x-1} - \dfrac{2(x^2-1)}{x-1}\right] = \lim_{x\to 1}[12-2(x+1)]$

$= 8$ (thousand dollars per thousand gallons)

b. $m_C(a) = \lim_{x\to a} \dfrac{C(x)-C(a)}{x-a} = \lim_{x\to a} \dfrac{(3+12x-2x^2)-(3+12a-2a^2)}{x-a}$

$= \lim_{x\to a} \left[\dfrac{12(x-a)}{x-a} - \dfrac{2(x^2-a^2)}{x-a}\right] = \lim_{x\to a}[12-2(x+a)] = 12-4a$

For $m_C(a) = \frac{1}{2}C(1)$, we must have $12-4a = \frac{1}{2}(13)$, or $a = \frac{11}{8}$.

77. Since the cost of each thousand gallons has been increased by $\frac{1}{2}$ thousand dollars, the cost is given by

$$C(x) = \frac{1}{2}x + (3+12x-2x^2) = 3 + \frac{25x}{2} - 2x^2 \quad \text{for } 0 \le x \le 3.$$

Thus

$$m_C(1) = \lim_{x\to 1} \frac{C(x)-C(1)}{x-1} = \lim_{x\to 1} \frac{(3+\frac{25}{2}x-2x^2)-(3+\frac{25}{2}-2)}{x-1}$$

$$= \lim_{x\to 1} \frac{\frac{25}{2}(x-1)-2(x^2-1)}{x-1} = \lim_{x\to 1}\left[\frac{25}{2}-2(x+1)\right] = \frac{17}{2}.$$

Thus the marginal cost is increased by $\frac{1}{2}$ thousand dollars per thousand gallons.

78. Since the cost has been increased by 1 thousand dollars, the cost function is given by

$$C(x) = 1 + (3 + 12x - 2x^2) = 4 + 12x - 2x^2 \quad \text{for } 0 \le x \le 3.$$

Thus

$$m_C(1) = \lim_{x\to 1} \frac{C(x) - C(1)}{x - 1} = \lim_{x\to 1} \frac{(4 + 12x - 2x^2) - (4 + 12 - 2)}{x - 1}$$

$$= \lim_{x\to 1} \left[\frac{12(x-1) - 2(x^2-1)}{x-1}\right] = \lim_{x\to 1}[12 - 2(x+1)] = 8.$$

Thus the marginal cost has remained the same.

79. We set up a coordinate system so that the port is at the origin, the positive x and y axes point east and north, respectively, and the units represent nautical miles. By assumption, after t hours the northbound ship is at $(0, 15t)$ and the other ship is at $(-20t, 0)$. If $D(t)$ represents the distance between the ships t hours after they leave port, then

$$D(t) = \sqrt{(-20t - 0)^2 + (0 - 15t)^2} = \sqrt{400t^2 + 225t^2} = 25t.$$

Thus

$$D'(t_0) = \lim_{t\to t_0} \frac{D(t) - D(t_0)}{t - t_0} = \lim_{t\to t_0} \frac{25t - 25t_0}{t - t_0} = 25$$

so the distance is increasing at the constant rate of 25 knots.

80. We set up a coordinate system with the airport at the origin, the positive x and y axes pointing east and north, respectively, and the units representing miles. By hypothesis, t hours after noon the Cessna is at $(200t, 0)$. At that time the jet is $400t$ units from the origin along the line $y = -\sqrt{3}\,x$ (see figure), so that $400t = \sqrt{x^2 + (-\sqrt{3}\,x)^2} = x\sqrt{1+3} = 2x$, and thus $x = 200t$ and $y = -200\sqrt{3}\,t$, so the jet is at $(200t, -200\sqrt{3}\,t)$. If $D(t)$ represents the distance between the planes t hours after noon, then

$$D(t) = \sqrt{(200t - 200t)^2 + (-200\sqrt{3}\,t - 0)^2} = 200\sqrt{3}\,t.$$

Thus

$$D'(t_0) = \lim_{t\to t_0} \frac{D(t) - D(t_0)}{t - t_0} = \lim_{t\to t_0} \frac{200\sqrt{3}\,t - 200\sqrt{3}\,t_0}{t - t_0} = 200\sqrt{3}$$

so the distance between the planes increases at $200\sqrt{3}$ miles an hour.

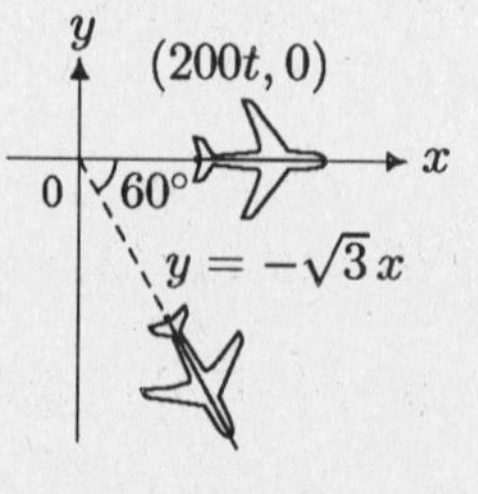

y
(200t, 0)
x
0
60°
$y = -\sqrt{3}\,x$

81. a. By hypothesis, after t minutes one boat is at $(2t, 0)$. The other boat is $2t$ units from the origin on the line $y = \sqrt{3}\,x$, so

$$2t = \sqrt{x^2 + y^2} = \sqrt{x^2 + 3x^2} = 2x;$$

thus $x = t$, so $y = \sqrt{3}\,t$, and the second boat is at $(t, \sqrt{3}\,t)$. The distance $D(t)$ between the boats t minutes after starting is given by

$$D(t) = \sqrt{(t - 2t)^2 + (\sqrt{3}\,t - 0)^2} = \sqrt{t^2 + 3t^2} = 2t.$$

Then $D'(t) = 2$, so the rate of the increase is 2 meters per minute.

b. Let the speed of the boats be b meters per minute. After t minutes one boat is at $(bt, 0)$. The other boat is bt units from the origin on the line $y = \sqrt{3}\,x$, and is traveling at b meters per minute. Thus

$$bt = \sqrt{x^2 + (\sqrt{3}\,x)^2} = 2x,$$

so that $x = bt/2$ and $y = \sqrt{3}\,bt/2$. Thus the second boat is at $(bt/2, \sqrt{3}\,bt/2)$. The distance $D(t)$ between the boats is given by

$$D(t) = \sqrt{(bt/2 - bt)^2 + (\sqrt{3}\,bt/2)^2} = bt\sqrt{\frac{1}{4} + \frac{3}{4}} = bt.$$

Since $D'(t) = b$, and since $D'(t) = 3$ by hypothesis, it follows that $b = 3$. Consequently the speed of the boats is 3 meters per minute.

82. From the graph, the slope appears to be approximately $\dfrac{-7.88 - (-7.90)}{.7 - .90} = -0.1$.

3.2 Differentiable Functions

1. By Example 1, $f'(x) = 0$ for all x, so $f'(1) = 0$.

2. By Example 1, $f'(x) = 0$ for all x, so $f'(-3) = 0$.

3. By (1), $f'(x) = 2x$ for all x, so $f'(3/2) = 3$ and $f'(0) = 0$.

4. By (1), $f'(x) = 3x^2$, so $f'(-1/4) = 3/16$.

5. By (1), $f'(x) = 4x^3$, so $f'(\sqrt[3]{2}) = 4(\sqrt[3]{2})^3 = 4 \cdot 2 = 8$.

6. By (1), $f'(x) = 5x^4$, so $f'(-2) = 5(-2)^4 = 5 \cdot 16 = 80$.

7. By (1), $f'(x) = 10x^9$, so $f'(1) = 10$.

8. By (3), $f'(t) = \cos t$, so $f'(\pi/4) = \sqrt{2}/2$ and $f'(\pi/3) = 1/2$.

9. By (4), $f'(t) = -\sin t$, so $f'(0) = 0$ and $f'(-\pi/3) = \sqrt{3}/2$.

10. By (6), $f'(t) = e^t$, so $f'(1) = e^1 = e$ and $f'(\ln 3) = e^{\ln 3} = 3$.

11. $f'(x) = \lim_{t\to x} \dfrac{f(t)-f(x)}{t-x} = \lim_{t\to x} \dfrac{(-2t-1)-(-2x-1)}{t-x} = \lim_{t\to x}(-2) = -2$

12. $f'(x) = \lim_{t\to x} \dfrac{f(t)-f(x)}{t-x} = \lim_{t\to x} \dfrac{(1-t^2)-(1-x^2)}{x-t} = \lim_{x\to t} \dfrac{-(t^2-x^2)}{t-x} = \lim_{t\to x} -(x+t) = -2x$

13. $f'(x) = \lim_{t\to x} \dfrac{f(t)-f(x)}{t-x} = \lim_{t\to x} \dfrac{t^5-x^5}{t-x} = \lim_{t\to x} \dfrac{(t-x)(t^4+t^3x+t^2x^2+tx^3+x^4)}{t-x} = 5x^4$

14. $f'(x) = \lim_{t\to x} \dfrac{f(t)-f(x)}{t-x} = \lim_{t\to x} \dfrac{t^6-x^6}{t-x} = \lim_{t\to x} \dfrac{(t-x)(t^5+t^4x+t^3x^2+t^2x^3+tx^4+x^5)}{t-x} = 6x^5$

15. $f'(x) = \lim_{t\to x} \dfrac{f(t)-f(x)}{t-x} = \lim_{t\to x} \dfrac{\dfrac{t}{t+1} - \dfrac{x}{x+1}}{t-x} = \lim_{t\to x} \dfrac{t-x}{(t+1)(x+1)(t-x)}$

$= \lim_{t\to x} \dfrac{1}{(t+1)(x+1)} = \dfrac{1}{(x+1)^2}$

16. $f'(x) = \lim_{t\to x} \dfrac{f(t)-f(x)}{t-x} = \lim_{t\to x} \dfrac{\dfrac{2t-1}{t+3} - \dfrac{2x-1}{x+3}}{t-x} = \lim_{t\to x} \dfrac{7t-7x}{(t+3)(x+3)(t-x)}$

$= \lim_{t\to x} \dfrac{7}{(t+3)(x+3)} = \dfrac{7}{(x+3)^2}$

17. $f'(x) = \lim_{t\to x} \dfrac{f(t)-f(x)}{t-x} = \lim_{t\to x} \dfrac{[(t^2-1)/(t^2+1)] - [(x^2-1)/(x^2+1)]}{t-x}$

$= \lim_{t\to x} \dfrac{(t^2-1)(x^2+1)-(x^2-1)(t^2+1)}{(t^2+1)(x^2+1)(t-x)} = \lim_{t\to x} \dfrac{2(t-x)(t+x)}{(t^2+1)(x^2+1)(t-x)}$

$= \lim_{t\to x} \dfrac{2(t+x)}{(t^2+1)(x^2+1)} = \dfrac{4x}{(x^2+1)^2}$

18. $\dfrac{dy}{dx} = \lim_{h\to 0} \dfrac{5\sin(x+h)-5\sin x}{h} = 5\lim_{h\to 0} \dfrac{\sin(x+h)-\sin x}{h} = 5\cos x$ by the discussion preceding (3).

19. $\dfrac{dy}{dx} = \lim_{h\to 0} \dfrac{-3\cos(x+h)-(-3\cos x)}{h} = -3\lim_{h\to 0} \dfrac{\cos(x+h)-\cos x}{h}$

$= (-3)(-\sin x) = 3\sin x$ by the discussion preceding (4).

20. $\dfrac{dy}{dx} = \lim_{h\to 0} \dfrac{(\cos(x+h)-\sin(x+h))-(\cos x - \sin x)}{h}$

$= \lim_{h\to 0} \dfrac{\cos(x+h)-\cos x}{h} - \lim_{h\to 0} \dfrac{\sin(x+h)-\sin x}{h}$

$= -\sin x - \cos x$ by the discussion preceding (3) and (4).

21. If $x \neq 0$, then

$$\frac{dy}{dx} = \lim_{t\to x} \frac{t^{2/3}-x^{2/3}}{t-x} = \lim_{t\to x} \frac{(t^{1/3}-x^{1/3})(t^{1/3}+x^{1/3})}{(t^{1/3}-x^{1/3})(t^{2/3}+t^{1/3}x^{1/3}+x^{2/3})}$$

$$= \lim_{t\to x} \frac{t^{1/3}+x^{1/3}}{t^{2/3}+t^{1/3}x^{1/3}+x^{2/3}} = \frac{2x^{1/3}}{3x^{2/3}} = \frac{2}{3x^{1/3}} = \frac{2}{3}x^{-1/3}.$$

22. If $x > 0$, then

$$\frac{dy}{dx} = \lim_{t\to x} \frac{t^{3/2}-x^{3/2}}{t-x} = \lim_{t\to x} \frac{(t^{1/2}-x^{1/2})(t+t^{1/2}x^{1/2}+x)}{(t^{1/2}-x^{1/2})(t^{1/2}+x^{1/2})}$$

$$= \lim_{t\to x} \frac{t+t^{1/2}x^{1/2}+x}{t^{1/2}+x^{1/2}} = \frac{3x}{2x^{1/2}} = \frac{3}{2}x^{1/2}.$$

23. If $x > 1$, then

$$\frac{dy}{dx} = \lim_{t\to x} \frac{\sqrt{t-1}-\sqrt{x-1}}{t-x} = \lim_{t\to x} \frac{\sqrt{t-1}-\sqrt{x-1}}{t-x} \cdot \frac{\sqrt{t-1}+\sqrt{x-1}}{\sqrt{t-1}+\sqrt{x-1}}$$

$$= \lim_{t\to x} \frac{(t-1)-(x-1)}{(t-x)(\sqrt{t-1}+\sqrt{x-1})} = \lim_{t\to x} \frac{1}{\sqrt{t-1}+\sqrt{x-1}} = \frac{1}{2\sqrt{x-1}}.$$

24. $$\frac{dy}{dx} = \lim_{h\to 0} \frac{\sin 2(x+h)-\sin 2x}{h} = \lim_{h\to 0} \frac{\sin(2x+2h)-\sin 2x}{h}$$

$$= \lim_{k\to 0} \frac{\sin(2x+k)-\sin 2x}{k/2} = 2\lim_{k\to 0} \frac{\sin(2x+k)-\sin 2x}{k}$$

by the Substitution Rule with $k = 2h$. From the discussion preceding (3), substituting $2x$ for x and k for h, we conclude that

$$\frac{dy}{dx} = 2\lim_{k\to 0} \frac{\sin(2x+k)-\sin 2x}{k} = 2\cos 2x.$$

25. $$f'(x) = \lim_{h\to 0} \frac{f(x+h)-f(x)}{h} = \lim_{h\to 0} \frac{e^{2(x+h)}-e^{2x}}{h} = \lim_{h\to 0} \frac{e^{2x}e^{2h}-e^{2x}}{h} = e^{2x}\lim_{h\to 0} \frac{e^{2h}-1}{h}$$

Let $y = 2h$. Then

$$\lim_{h\to 0} \frac{e^{2h}-1}{h} = 2\lim_{y\to 0} \frac{e^{y}-1}{y} = 2$$

by the Substitution Rule. Therefore $f'(x) = e^{2x}(2) = 2e^{2x}$.

26. $$f'(x) = \lim_{h\to 0} \frac{f(x+h)-f(x)}{h} = \lim_{h\to 0} \frac{e^{3(x+h)}-e^{3x}}{h} = \lim_{h\to 0} \frac{e^{3x}(e^{3h}-1)}{h} = e^{3x}\lim_{h\to 0} \frac{e^{3h}-1}{h}$$

Let $y = 3h$. Then

$$\lim_{h\to 0} \frac{e^{3h}-1}{h} = 3\lim_{y\to 0} \frac{e^{y}-1}{y} = 3$$

by the Substitution Rule. Therefore $f'(x) = e^{3x}(3) = 3e^{3x}$.

27. For all x,

$$\lim_{t\to x} \frac{f(t)-f(x)}{t-x} = \lim_{t\to x} \frac{(t^2+t)-(x^2+x)}{t-x} = \lim_{t\to x} \frac{(t^2-x^2)+(t-x)}{t-x}$$

$$= \lim_{t\to x} \frac{(t-x)(t+x)+(t-x)}{t-x} = \lim_{t\to x}(t+x+1) = 2x+1.$$

Thus f is differentiable on $(-\infty, \infty)$.

28. For $x > 0$,

$$\lim_{t\to x}\frac{f(t)-f(x)}{t-x}=\lim_{t\to x}\frac{(2t^3-\sqrt{t})-(2x^3-\sqrt{x})}{t-x}=\lim_{t\to x}\frac{(2t^3-2x^3)-(\sqrt{t}-\sqrt{x})}{t-x}$$

$$=\lim_{t\to x}\left[\frac{2(t-x)(t^2+tx+x^2)}{t-x}-\frac{\sqrt{t}-\sqrt{x}}{(\sqrt{t}-\sqrt{x})(\sqrt{t}+\sqrt{x})}\right]$$

$$=\lim_{t\to x}\left[2(t^2+tx+x^2)-\frac{1}{\sqrt{t}+\sqrt{x}}\right]=6x^2-\frac{1}{2\sqrt{x}}.$$

Thus f is differentiable on $(0,\infty)$.

29. For $x > 4$,

$$\lim_{t\to x}\frac{f(t)-f(x)}{t-x}=\lim_{t\to x}\frac{[1/(4-t)]-[1/(4-x)]}{t-x}$$

$$=\lim_{t\to x}\frac{(4-x)-(4-t)}{(4-t)(4-x)(t-x)}=\lim_{t\to x}\frac{1}{(4-t)(4-x)}=\frac{1}{(4-x)^2}.$$

Therefore f is differentiable on $(4,\infty)$.

30. For $x < -2$,

$$\lim_{t\to x}\frac{f(t)-f(x)}{t-x}=\lim_{t\to x}\frac{[1/(4-t^2)]-[1/(4-x^2)]}{t-x}=\lim_{t\to x}\frac{(4-x^2)-(4-t^2)}{(4-t^2)(4-x^2)(t-x)}$$

$$=\lim_{t\to x}\frac{t^2-x^2}{(4-t^2)(4-x^2)(t-x)}=\lim_{t\to x}\frac{t+x}{(4-t^2)(4-x^2)}=\frac{2x}{(4-x^2)^2}.$$

Therefore f is differentiable on $(-\infty,-2)$.

31. For $x \ge 1$, $f(x)=x-1$, and for $x>1$,

$$\lim_{t\to x}\frac{f(t)-f(x)}{t-x}=\lim_{t\to x}\frac{(t-1)-(x-1)}{t-x}=\lim_{t\to x}1=1.$$

Therefore f is differentiable on $(1,\infty)$. Also,

$$\lim_{t\to 1^+}\frac{f(t)-f(1)}{t-1}=\lim_{t\to 1^+}\frac{t-1-0}{t-1}=1.$$

Thus f is differentiable on $[1,\infty)$.

32. For $x \le -\frac{2}{3}$, $f(x)=-(2+3x)$, and for $x<-\frac{2}{3}$,

$$\lim_{t\to x}\frac{f(t)-f(x)}{t-x}=\lim_{t\to x}\frac{-(2+3t)+(2+3x)}{t-x}=\lim_{t\to x}\frac{-3(t-x)}{t-x}=-3.$$

Thus f is differentiable on $(-\infty,-\frac{2}{3})$. Also,

$$\lim_{t\to -2/3^-}\frac{f(t)-f(-2/3)}{t-(-2/3)}=\lim_{t\to -2/3^-}\frac{-(2+3t)-0}{t+(2/3)}=\lim_{t\to -2/3^-}(-3)=-3.$$

Therefore f is differentiable on $(-\infty,-\frac{2}{3}]$.

33. a. $f'(x) = \lim_{t\to x} \dfrac{-2t^2 + 2x^2}{t - x} = \lim_{t\to x}[-2(t + x)] = -4x$

Since $f'(a) = 12$, we have $-4a = 12$, so $a = -3$.

b. $f'(x) = \lim_{t\to x} \dfrac{(3t + t^2) - (3x + x^2)}{t - x} = \lim_{t\to x}[3 + (t + x)] = 3 + 2x$

Since $f'(a) = 13$, we have $3 + 2a = 13$, so $a = 5$.

c. $f'(x) = \lim_{t\to x} \dfrac{(1/t) - (1/x)}{t - x} = \lim_{t\to x} \dfrac{-(t - x)}{tx(t - x)} = \lim_{t\to x} \dfrac{-1}{tx} = -\dfrac{1}{x^2}$

Since $f'(a) = -\frac{1}{9}$, we have $-1/a^2 = -\frac{1}{9}$. Thus $a = 3$ or $a = -3$.

d. $f'(x) = \cos x$ by (3). Since $f'(a) = \sqrt{3}/2$, we have $\cos a = \sqrt{3}/2$. Thus $a = -\pi/6 + 2n\pi$ or $a = \pi/6 + 2n\pi$, where n is any integer.

35. The graphs are not virtually coincident because $((x + .1)^{1/2} - x^{1/2})/0.1$ is continuous on $[0, 1]$ and $\frac{1}{2}x^{-1/2}$ is not.

36. If f is decreasing on an open interval I, and if x is in I, then $z - x$ and $f(x) - f(z)$ have opposite signs for any z in I with $z \neq x$. Therefore

$$\frac{f(z) - f(x)}{z - x} < 0 \quad \text{for all } z \text{ in } I.$$

Since $f'(x)$ exists by hypothesis,

$$f'(x) = \lim_{z\to x} \frac{f(z) - f(x)}{z - x} \leq 0.$$

37. Since $f'(x) > 0$ for $x > 1$, the graph of f is in Figure 3.13(b).

38. From Figure 3.14(a) we see that $f'(x) = 0$ for three values of x. Thus the only possible graph of f' in Figure 3.14(b) is the one colored green.

39. Since f is decreasing on $(-\infty, \frac{1}{2}]$ and increasing on $[\frac{1}{2}, \infty)$, we have $f'(x) < 0$ for $x < \frac{1}{2}$ and $f'(x) > 0$ for $x > \frac{1}{2}$. Thus $h = f'$. Similarly, $k = g'$.

40. a. By (1), $f'(x) = 2x$, so that $f'(-1) = -2$. Thus the slope of the tangent line at $(-1, 1)$ is -2, so that the slope of the normal line at $(-1, 1)$ is $\frac{1}{2}$. An equation of the normal line is $y - 1 = \frac{1}{2}(x + 1)$.

b. $f'(-1) = \lim_{x\to -1} \dfrac{f(x) - f(-1)}{x - (-1)} = \lim_{x\to -1} \dfrac{(2x - 3) - (-5)}{x + 1} = \lim_{x\to -1} \dfrac{2(x + 1)}{x + 1} = \lim_{x\to -1} 2 = 2$

Thus the slope of the tangent line at $(-1, -5)$ is 2, so that the slope of the normal line is $-\frac{1}{2}$. An equation of the normal line is $y - (-5) = -\frac{1}{2}(x - (-1))$ or $y + 5 = -\frac{1}{2}(x + 1)$.

c. By (3), $f'(x) = \cos x$, so that $f'(0) = 1$. Thus the slope of the tangent line at $(0, 0)$ is 1, so that the slope of the normal line is -1. An equation of the normal line is $y - 0 = -1(x - 0)$, or $y = -x$.

41. By (1), $f'(x) = 2x$, so the slope of the line tangent at (a, a^2) is $2a$. If $a = 0$, the tangent line is $y = 0$, so the normal line is vertical and hence intersects the graph of f only at $(0, 0)$. If $a \neq 0$, the normal line at (a, a^2) has slope $-1/(2a)$ and hence has equation $y - a^2 = [-1/(2a)](x - a)$, or

$y = -x/(2a) + a^2 + \frac{1}{2}$. To find the points at which this line intersects the graph of f, we solve the equation $x^2 = -x/(2a) + a^2 + \frac{1}{2}$, or $x^2 + x/(2a) - a^2 - \frac{1}{2} = 0$, or $(x-a)[x+a+1/(2a)] = 0$. If $a \neq 0$, the normal line at (a, a^2) intersects the graph of f at two points: (a, a^2) and $(-a - 1/(2a), [a + 1/(2a)]^2)$.

42. $v(t) = f'(t) = \lim_{h\to 0} \dfrac{f(t+h) - f(t)}{h} = \lim_{h\to 0} \dfrac{-3\sin(t+h) - (-3\sin t)}{h}$

$$= -3 \lim_{h\to 0} \frac{\sin(t+h) - \sin t}{h} = -3\cos t$$

by the discussion preceding (3). In particular, $v(\pi/6) = -3\cos(\pi/6) = -\frac{3}{2}\sqrt{3}$.

43. a. $W'(r) = \lim_{t\to r} \dfrac{W(t) - W(r)}{t - r} = \lim_{t\to r} \dfrac{\dfrac{GMm}{t^2} - \dfrac{GMm}{r^2}}{t - r} = GMm \lim_{t\to r} \dfrac{r^2 - t^2}{(t-r)t^2r^2}$

$$= -GMm \lim_{t\to r} \frac{(t-r)(t+r)}{(t-r)t^2r^2} = -GMm \lim_{t\to r} \frac{t+r}{t^2r^2} = -\frac{2GMm}{r^3}$$

b. Since G, M, m, and $r > 0$, it follows that $W'(r) < 0$.

c. As the astronaut recedes from earth, the astronaut's weight decreases.

44. a. We have

$$\lim_{r\to R^-} \frac{F(r) - F(R)}{r - R} = \lim_{r\to R^-} \frac{\dfrac{GMr}{R^3} - \dfrac{GM}{R^2}}{r - R} = \frac{GM}{R^3} \lim_{r\to R^-} \frac{r - R}{r - R} = \frac{GM}{R^3}$$

and

$$\lim_{r\to R^+} \frac{F(r) - F(R)}{r - R} = \lim_{r\to R^+} \frac{\dfrac{GM}{r^2} - \dfrac{GM}{R^2}}{r - R} = GM \lim_{r\to R^+} \frac{R^2 - r^2}{r^2R^2(r - R)}$$

$$= GM \lim_{r\to R^+} \frac{(R-r)(R+r)}{r^2R^2(r-R)} = -GM \lim_{r\to R^+} \frac{R+r}{r^2R^2} = -\frac{2GM}{R^3}.$$

Thus F is not differentiable at R, and hence F is not differentiable on $(0, \infty)$.

b. We have

$$\lim_{r\to b^-} \frac{f(r) - f(b)}{r - b} = \lim_{r\to b^-} \frac{\dfrac{ar}{b} - \dfrac{c}{b^2}}{r - b} = \frac{1}{b^2} \lim_{r\to b^-} \frac{abr - c}{r - b}.$$

Notice that this limit only exists if $c = ab^2$, for then we would have

$$\frac{1}{b^2} \lim_{r\to b^-} \frac{abr - c}{r - b} = \frac{1}{b^2} \lim_{r\to b^-} \frac{abr - ab^2}{r - b} = \frac{a}{b} \lim_{r\to b^-} \frac{r - b}{r - b} = \frac{a}{b}.$$

Thus if $f'(b)$ exists, then $f'(b) = a/b > 0$. Next we see that

$$\lim_{r\to b^+} \frac{f(r) - f(b)}{r - b} = \lim_{r\to b^+} \frac{\dfrac{c}{r^2} - \dfrac{c}{b^2}}{r - b} = c \lim_{r\to b^+} \frac{b^2 - r^2}{r^2b^2(r - b)}$$

$$= c \lim_{r\to b^+} \frac{(b-r)(b+r)}{r^2b^2(r-b)} = -c \lim_{r\to b^+} \frac{b+r}{r^2b^2} = -\frac{2c}{b^3}.$$

Since c is positive by hypothesis, if $f'(b)$ exists, then $f'(b) = -2c/b^3 < 0$. Consequently $f'(b)$ cannot exist, so f cannot be differentiable on $(0, \infty)$.

45. a. $\lim_{x\to 1^-} \dfrac{R(x)-R(1)}{x-1} = \lim_{x\to 1^-} \dfrac{4x-4}{x-1} = \lim_{x\to 1^-} 4 = 4;$

$\lim_{x\to 1^+} \dfrac{R(x)-R(1)}{x-1} = \lim_{x\to 1^+} \dfrac{(6x-x^2-1)-4}{x-1} = \lim_{x\to 1^+} \dfrac{-x^2+6x-5}{x-1} = \lim_{x\to 1^+}(-x+5) = 4.$

Thus $m_R(1) = \lim_{x\to 1} \dfrac{R(x)-R(1)}{x-1} = 4.$

b. If $0 < x < 1$, then

$$R'(x) = \lim_{t\to x} \frac{R(t)-R(x)}{t-x} = \lim_{t\to x} \frac{4t-4x}{t-x} = \lim_{t\to x} 4 = 4.$$

If $1 < x < 3$, then

$$R'(x) = \lim_{t\to x} \frac{R(t)-R(x)}{t-x} = \lim_{t\to x} \frac{(6t-t^2-1)-(6x-x^2-1)}{t-x}$$

$$= \lim_{t\to x}\left[\frac{6(t-x)}{t-x} - \frac{t^2-x^2}{t-x}\right] = \lim_{t\to x}[6-(t+x)] = 6-2x.$$

Thus R is differentiable on $(0,1)$ and $(1,3)$. By (a), R is also differentiable at 1, so that R is differentiable on $(0,3)$. Since

$$\lim_{t\to 0^+} \frac{R(t)-R(0)}{t-0} = \lim_{t\to 0^+} \frac{4t-0}{t-0} = 4$$

and

$$\lim_{t\to 3^-} \frac{R(t)-R(3)}{t-3} = \lim_{t\to 3^-} \frac{(6t-t^2-1)-8}{t-3} = \lim_{t\to 3^-}(-t+3) = 0$$

R is differentiable on $[0,3]$.

46. If $0 < x < 6$, then $R'(x) = \lim_{t\to x}(1432t - 1432x)/(t-x) = 1432$, so R is differentiable on $(0,6)$. If $x > 6$, then $R'(x) = \lim_{t\to x}(8592-8592)/(t-x) = 0$, so R is differentiable on $(6,\infty)$. Since

$$\lim_{x\to 6^-} \frac{R(x)-R(6)}{x-6} = \lim_{x\to 6^-} \frac{1432x-8592}{x-6} = \lim_{x\to 6^-} 1432 = 1432$$

and

$$\lim_{x\to 6^+} \frac{R(x)-R(6)}{x-6} = \lim_{x\to 6^+} \frac{8592-8592}{x-6} = 0$$

R is not differentiable at 6.

47. The circumference of a circle of radius r is given by $C(r) = 2\pi r$. Thus

$$C'(r) = \lim_{t\to r} \frac{2\pi t - 2\pi r}{t-r} = \lim_{t\to r} 2\pi = 2\pi$$

for $r > 0$, so the rate of change is constant.

48. The area of a circle of radius r is given by $A(r) = \pi r^2$ for $r > 0$. Thus

$$A'(r) = \lim_{t\to r} \frac{A(t)-A(r)}{t-r} = \lim_{t\to r} \frac{\pi t^2 - \pi r^2}{t-r} = \lim_{t\to r} \pi(t+r) = 2\pi r$$

(which is the circumference of the circle).

49. Let $A(x)$ be the area of a square with side of length x. Then $A(x) = x^2$, so

$$A'(x) = \lim_{t\to x} \frac{A(t) - A(x)}{t - x} = \lim_{t\to x} \frac{t^2 - x^2}{t - x} = \lim_{t\to x}(t + x) = 2x \quad \text{for } x > 0.$$

50. a. The altitude of the triangle with side of length x is $(\sqrt{3}/2)x$, so the area of the triangle is given by $A(x) = \frac{1}{2}[(\sqrt{3}/2)x](x) = (\sqrt{3}/4)x^2$. Then

$$A'(x) = \lim_{t\to x} \frac{(\sqrt{3}/4)t^2 - (\sqrt{3}/4)x^2}{t - x} = \lim_{t\to x} \frac{\sqrt{3}}{4}(t + x) = \frac{\sqrt{3}}{2}x \quad \text{for } x > 0.$$

b. If $A'(x) = A(x)$ and $x > 0$, then $(\sqrt{3}/2)x = (\sqrt{3}/4)x^2$, or $2x = x^2$, so that $x = 2$.

51. a. The volume of a sphere of radius r is given by $V(r) = \frac{4}{3}\pi r^3$. Thus

$$V'(r) = \lim_{t\to r} \frac{\frac{4}{3}\pi t^3 - \frac{4}{3}\pi r^3}{t - r} = \lim_{t\to r} \tfrac{4}{3}\pi(t^2 + tr + r^2) = 4\pi r^2, \quad \text{for } r > 0.$$

b. The rate of change equals the surface area.

52. a. 7 minutes

b. 2 minutes (from 5 to 7 minutes after leaving home)

c. From 0 to 5 minutes after leaving home.

53. a. $A'(t) = -0.028A(t)$

b. $A'(1) = -0.028A(1) = -0.028(3) = -0.084$

3.3 Derivatives of Combinations of Functions

1. $f'(x) = -12x^2$

2. $f'(x) = 5x^4 - 8x^7$

3. $f'(x) = 16x^3 + 9x^2 + 4x + 1$

4. $f'(t) = -35t^{-6}$

5. $f'(t) = \dfrac{36}{t^{10}}$

6. $f'(t) = -6t - \dfrac{18}{t^7}$

7. $g'(x) = 2(x + 5) + (2x - 3) \cdot 1 = 4x + 7$

8. $g'(x) = (1 - 4x)(x - 2x^2) + (x - 2x^2)(1 - 4x) = 2(x - 2x^2)(1 - 4x)$

9. $g'(x) = \left(-\dfrac{1}{x^2}\right)\left(2 - \dfrac{1}{x}\right) + \left(1 + \dfrac{1}{x}\right)\left(\dfrac{1}{x^2}\right) = -\dfrac{1}{x^2} + \dfrac{2}{x^3}$

10. $g'(x) = \left(1 + \frac{1}{x^2}\right)\left(x^2 - \frac{1}{x^2}\right) + \left(x - \frac{1}{x}\right)\left(2x + \frac{2}{x^3}\right) = 3x^2 - 1 + \frac{1}{x^2} - \frac{3}{x^4}$

11. $g'(x) = 12x^{-4} - 2\sin x$

12. $g'(x) = 3\cos x - 5\sin x$

13. $f'(z) = -6z^2 + 4\sec z\, \tan z$

14. $f'(z) = -11z^{-12} + \pi \sec^2 z$

15. $f'(z) = 2z\sin z + z^2 \cos z$

16. $f'(x) = \cos x\, \cos x + \sin x\,(-\sin x) = \cos^2 x - \sin^2 x = \cos 2x$

17. $f(x) = \sin x\, \sin x$, so $f'(x) = \cos x\, \sin x + \sin x\, \cos x = 2\sin x\, \cos x = \sin 2x$

18. $f'(x) = 2(x - \tan x) + (2x+1)(1 - \sec^2 x)$

19. $f'(x) = \dfrac{2(4x-1) - (2x+3)4}{(4x-1)^2} = -\dfrac{14}{(4x-1)^2}$

20. $f'(x) = \dfrac{(-2x)(x^2+9) - (-x^2+3)(2x)}{(x^2+9)^2} = -\dfrac{24x}{(x^2+9)^2}$

21. $f'(t) = \dfrac{1(t^2+4t+4) - (t+2)(2t+4)}{(t^2+4t+4)^2} = -\dfrac{1}{t^2+4t+4}$

22. Since

$$f(t) = \frac{t^2 - 5t + 4}{t^2 + t - 20} = \frac{(t-4)(t-1)}{(t-4)(t+5)} = \frac{t-1}{t+5}$$

it follows that

$$f'(t) = \frac{1(t+5) - 1(t-1)}{(t+5)^2} = \frac{6}{(t+5)^2}.$$

23. $f'(t) = \dfrac{(2t+5)(t^2+t-20) - (t^2+5t+4)(2t+1)}{(t^2+t-20)^2} = \dfrac{-4(t^2+12t+26)}{(t^2+t-20)^2}$

24. $f'(t) = \dfrac{-2\sin t - (-2t)\cos t}{(\sin t)^2} = \dfrac{-2\sin t + 2t\cos t}{\sin^2 t}$

25. $f'(x) = \dfrac{(-\sin x)\sin x - \cos x\, \cos x}{(\sin x)^2} = \dfrac{-1}{\sin^2 x} = -\csc^2 x$

26. $f(x) = \dfrac{1}{\sin x}$; $f'(x) = \dfrac{-\cos x}{\sin^2 x} = -\csc x\, \cot x$ by (6)

27. $f'(y) = \dfrac{1}{2\sqrt{y}}\sec y + \sqrt{y}\, \sec y\, \tan y$

28. Using the result of Exercise 26, we have

$$g'(y) = \frac{(-\csc y\, \cot y)y^2 - (\csc y)2y}{y^4} = \frac{-\csc y}{y^3}(y\cot y + 2).$$

29. $f'(x) = e^x + \dfrac{e^x}{(e^x)^2} = e^x + \dfrac{1}{e^x}$

30. $f'(x) = e^x \sin x + e^x \cos x$

31. $f'(t) = \dfrac{2e^t - 2te^t}{(e^t)^2} = \dfrac{2-2t}{e^t}$

32. $f'(t) = \dfrac{e^t(1+e^t) - e^t e^t}{(1+e^t)^2} = \dfrac{e^t}{(1+e^t)^2}$

33. $\dfrac{dy}{dx} = 3(2x^2 - 5x) + (3x+1)(4x-5) = 18x^2 - 26x - 5$

34. $\dfrac{dy}{dx} = 1 - \dfrac{1}{x^2}$

35. $\dfrac{dy}{dx} = 2x - \dfrac{2}{x^3}$

36. $\dfrac{dy}{dx} = \dfrac{(2x+1)(x^2-x+1) - (x^2+x+1)(2x-1)}{(x^2-x+1)^2} = \dfrac{-2x^2+2}{(x^2-x+1)^2}$

37. $\dfrac{dy}{dx} = \dfrac{3x^2(x^4+1) - (x^3-1)(4x^3)}{(x^4+1)^2} = \dfrac{-x^6+4x^3+3x^2}{(x^4+1)^2}$

38. $\dfrac{dy}{dx} = 4\sec x + 4x \sec x \tan x$

39. $\dfrac{dy}{dx} = (-\csc x \cot x)\sec x + \csc x(\sec x \tan x) = -\csc^2 x + \sec^2 x$

40. $\dfrac{dy}{dx} = \dfrac{(2x + (1/2\sqrt{x}))(\sin x \cos x) - (x^2+\sqrt{x})(\cos^2 x - \sin^2 x)}{\sin^2 x \cos^2 x}$

41. $\dfrac{dy}{dx} = \dfrac{(\sin x + x\cos x)(x^2+1) - (x \sin x)(2x)}{(x^2+1)^2} = \dfrac{(x^3+x)\cos x + (1-x^2)\sin x}{(x^2+1)^2}$

42. $\dfrac{dy}{dx} = e^x(1-\cos x) + e^x \sin x = e^x(1 - \cos x + \sin x)$

43. $\dfrac{dy}{dx} = \dfrac{(2\sin x + 2x\cos x)e^x - (2x \sin x)e^x}{(e^x)^2} = \dfrac{2\sin x + 2x\cos x - 2x\sin x}{e^x}$

44. a. $y = 2\sin x \cos x$; $dy/dx = 2(\cos^2 x - \sin^2 x) = 2\cos 2x$

b. $y = -\sin x$; $dy/dx = -\cos x$

c. $y = \frac{1}{2}\cos x + \frac{1}{2}$; $dy/dx = -\frac{1}{2}\sin x$

45. $f'(x) = 63/x^{10}$; $f'(1) = 63$

46. $f'(x) = (3-\cos x)(x^2+\cos x) + (3x - \sin x)(2x - \sin x)$; $f'(0) = 2$

47. $f'(x) = (1/\pi)(6x-4)$; $f'(-2) = -16/\pi$

48. $f'(x) = \dfrac{4x(x^2+1) - (2x^2-1)(2x)}{(x^2+1)^2} = \dfrac{6x}{(x^2+1)^2}$; $f'(\sqrt{3}) = \dfrac{6\sqrt{3}}{16} = \dfrac{3\sqrt{3}}{8}$

49. $f'(x) = e^x + xe^x$; $f'(1) = e^1 + 1(e^1) = 2e$

50. $f'(x) = \dfrac{(\sec x \tan x)x^2 - (\sec x)(2x)}{x^4} = \dfrac{x \sec x \tan x - 2\sec x}{x^3}$; $f'(\pi) = \dfrac{0 - 2(-1)}{\pi^3} = \dfrac{2}{\pi^3}$

51. $f'(x) = 2x - 3$, so $f'(2) = 4 - 3 = 1$. Thus l: $y - (-6) = 1(x - 2)$, or $y = x - 8$.

52. $f'(x) = \dfrac{1(x-1) - (x+1)1}{(x-1)^2} = \dfrac{-2}{(x-1)^2}$, so $f'(3) = -\frac{1}{2}$. Thus l: $y - 2 = -\frac{1}{2}(x - 3)$, or $y = -\frac{1}{2} + \frac{7}{2}$.

53. $f'(x) = \cos x - (-\sin x) = \cos x + \sin x$, so $f'(\pi/2) = 1$. Thus l: $y - 1 = 1(x - (\pi/2))$, or $y = x + 1 - (\pi/2)$.

54. $f'(x) = 2e^x$, so $f'(0) = 2e^0 = 2$. Thus l: $y - 2 = 2(x - 0)$, or $y = 2x + 2$.

55. $f'(x) = 6x^2 - 18x + 12 = 6(x^2 - 3x + 2) = 6(x - 1)(x - 2)$, and the tangent is horizontal if $f'(x) = 0$. Now $f'(x) = 0$ for $x = 1$ and $x = 2$. If $x = 1$ then $f(x) = 6$, and if $x = 2$ then $f(x) = 5$. Thus the points on the graph of f at which the tangent line is horizontal are $(1, 6)$ and $(2, 5)$.

56. The slope of a tangent line is a number, not a function. The slope of the line tangent at $(1, 2)$ is $f'(1) = 6(1) - 2 = 4$. Thus the tangent line has equation $y - 2 = 4(x - 1)$.

57. Since $f(x) = ax^2 + bx + c$, we have $f'(x) = 2ax + b$. By hypothesis, $f'(1) = 4$ and $f'(-1) = -8$. This means that $2a + b = 4$ and $-2a + b = -8$. Thus $b = 4 - 2a$, so substituting for b in $-2a + b = -8$ yields $-2a + (4 - 2a) = -8$, so $-4a = -12$ and thus $a = 3$. Then $b = 4 - 2(3) = -2$. Finally, $f(1) = 2$, so $2 = f(1) = a + b + c = 3 - 2 + c$, and thus $c = 1$.

58. Suppose $f(x) = ax^2 + bx + c$. By hypothesis, $f(0) = 1$, so $c = 1$; similarly, $f(1) = 2$, so $2 = a + b + c = a + b + 1$, and thus $a + b = 1$. Next $f'(x) = 2ax + b$. If $y = x + 1$ is tangent to the graph of f at $(0, 1)$, then $1 = f'(0) = 2a \cdot 0 + b$, so $b = 1$. Thus $1 = a + b = a + 1$, so $a = 0$. Finally, suppose $y = 3x - 1$ is tangent to the graph of f at $(1, 2)$. Then $3 = f'(1) = 2a(1) + b = b$. But since $b = 1$, this is a contradiction. Consequently f cannot be a polynomial of degree two or less.

59. b. Let g denote the desired polynomial. Then

$$g(x) = 1 - \frac{x^2}{2!} + \frac{x^4}{4!} - \frac{x^6}{6!} + \frac{x^8}{8!} - \frac{x^{10}}{10!} + \frac{x^{12}}{12!} - \frac{x^{14}}{14!}.$$

60. Let g be as in the solution of Exercise 59(b). Since g approximates $\cos x$ and $\dfrac{d}{dx}\cos x = -\sin x$, we let

$$h(x) = -g'(x) = x - \frac{x^3}{3!} + \frac{x^5}{5!} - \frac{x^7}{7!} + \frac{x^9}{9!} - \frac{x^{11}}{11!} + \frac{x^{13}}{13!}.$$

61. $(f + g)(x) = |x| - |x| = 0$, so $(f + g)'(x) = 0$ for all x. By Example 3 in Section 3.1, $f'(x)$ exists only for $x \neq 0$, and the Constant Multiple Rule therefore implies that $g'(x)$ also exists only for $x \neq 0$.

62. Since $g(x) = (f + g)(x) - f(x)$ for all x in the domain of $f + g$, and since $(f + g)'(a)$ and $f'(a)$ exist, it follows from the Difference Rule that $g'(a)$ exists.

63. Since $f(x) = [(fg)(x)]/g(x)$ for all x in the domain of fg for which $g(x) \neq 0$, and since $(fg)'(a)$ and $g'(a)$ exist with $g(a) \neq 0$, it follows from Theorem 3.7 that $f'(a)$ exists.

64. a. Since $f'(a)$ and $g'(a)$ exist, Theorem 3.4 implies that $(f+g)'(a)$ exists and $(f+g)'(a) = f'(a) + g'(a)$. Since $(f+g)'(a)$ and $h'(a)$ exist, Theorem 3.7 implies that $(f+g+h)'(a)$ exists and $(f+g+h)'(a) = (f+g)'(a) + h'(a) = f'(a) + g'(a) + h'(a)$.

b. Since $f'(a)$ and $g'(a)$ exist, Theorem 3.6 implies that $(fg)'(a)$ exists and $(fg)'(a) = f'(a)g(a) + f(a)g'(a)$. Since $(fg)'(a)$ and $h'(a)$ exist, Theorem 3.6 implies that $[(fg)h]'(a)$ exists and

$$(fgh)'(a) = [(fg)h]'(a) = (fg)'(a)h(a) + (fg)(a)h'(a)$$

$$= [f'(a)g(a) + f(a)g'(a)]h(a) + f(a)g(a)h'(a) = f'(a)g(a)h(a) + f(a)g'(a)h(a) + f(a)g(a)h'(a).$$

65. $$\frac{f(x)g(x) - f(a)g(a)}{x-a} = \frac{f(x)g(x) - f(a)g(x) + f(a)g(x) - f(a)g(a)}{x-a}$$

$$= \frac{f(x)-f(a)}{x-a}g(x) + f(a)\frac{g(x)-g(a)}{x-a} = \frac{f(x)-f(a)}{x-a}g(x)$$

because $f(a) = 0$ by hypothesis. Since $f'(a)$ exists and g is continuous at a, the above calculation implies that

$$(fg)'(a) = \lim_{x\to a}\frac{f(x)g(x) - f(a)g(a)}{x-a} = \lim_{x\to a}\left[\frac{f(x)-f(a)}{x-a}g(x)\right]$$

$$= \lim_{x\to a}\frac{f(x)-f(a)}{x-a}\lim_{x\to a}g(x) = f'(a)g(a).$$

66. a. By Theorem 3.6, $h'(a) = (fg)'(a) = f'(a)g(a) + f(a)g'(a)$. Dividing by $h(a)$, which equals $f(a)g(a)$, we find that

$$\frac{h'(a)}{h(a)} = \frac{f'(a)g(a)}{f(a)g(a)} + \frac{f(a)g'(a)}{f(a)g(a)} = \frac{f'(a)}{f(a)} + \frac{g'(a)}{g(a)}.$$

b. By Theorem 3.7,

$$k'(a) = \left(\frac{f}{g}\right)'(a) = \frac{f'(a)g(a) - f(a)g'(a)}{[g(a)]^2}.$$

Since $k(a) = \dfrac{f(a)}{g(a)}$, we have $\dfrac{1}{k(a)} = \dfrac{g(a)}{f(a)}$, so that

$$\frac{k'(a)}{k(a)} = \frac{f'(a)g(a) - f(a)g'(a)}{[g(a)]^2}\cdot\frac{g(a)}{f(a)} = \frac{f'(a)g(a) - f(a)g'(a)}{g(a)f(a)} = \frac{f'(a)}{f(a)} - \frac{g'(a)}{g(a)}.$$

67. By (6) we have $(1/g)'(a) = [-g'(a)]/[g(a)]^2$. Thus

$$\left(\frac{f}{g}\right)'(a) = \left(f\frac{1}{g}\right)'(a) = f'(a)\frac{1}{g(a)} + f(a)\left\{\frac{-g'(a)}{[g(a)]^2}\right\} = \frac{f'(a)g(a) - f(a)g'(a)}{[g(a)]^2}.$$

68. Let

$$v_1(t) = \text{velocity of the first ball at time } t$$
$$v_2(t) = \text{velocity of the second ball at time } t.$$

Then by hypothesis, $v_1(t) = -9.8t + 10$ and $v_2(t) = -9.8t - 10$. Then

$$v_1(t) - v_2(t) = (-9.8t + 10) - (-9.8t - 10) = 20.$$

Therefore the difference is 20 meters per second.

69. The height of the ball at any time t before the ball hits the ground is given by $h(t) = -16t^2 + 128t + 8$. Thus $h(t) = 8$ if $-16t^2 + 128t = 0$. But $-16t^2 + 128t = -16(t - 8)$, so the ball returns to the 8-foot level after 8 seconds. Since $v(t) = h'(t) = -32t + 128$, we conclude that $v(8) = -32(8) + 128 = -128$ (feet per second).

70. a. The height of the lowest point of the chandelier is given by $h(t) = -16t^2 + 30$ until the chandelier hits something. It would hit your head when $h(t) = 6$, that is, $-16t^2 + 30 = 6$, or $16t^2 = 24$, or $t = \sqrt{1.5}$. Thus you have $\sqrt{1.5} \approx 1.225$ seconds to get out of the way.

b. Since $v(t) = h'(t) = -32t$, it follows from part (a) that the chandelier would hit your head with velocity $v(\sqrt{1.5}) = -32\sqrt{1.5}$. Thus the chandelier will be moving at the rate of $32\sqrt{1.5} \approx 39.19$ feet per second when it hits your head.

c. If you were only 5 feet tall, the chandelier would hit your head when $h(t) = 5$, that is, $-16t^2 + 30 = 5$, or $16t^2 = 25$, or $t = \frac{5}{4} = 1.25$. Since $v(1.25) = -32(1.25) = -40$, the speed would be $40 - 32\sqrt{1.5} \approx 40 - 39.19 = 0.81$ feet per second greater.

71. a. Let $f(x) = ax^2 + bx + c$, so that $f'(x) = 2ax + b$. From Figure 3.18(a), $f(1) = 0$, so $a + b + c = 0$. Also, $f(-1) = 0$, so $a - b + c = 0$. Since $a + b + c = 0$ and $a - b + c = 0$, it follows that $b = 0$ and that $a = -c$. Next, $f'(-1) = -1$, so that $-1 = -2a + b = -2a$. Thus $a = \frac{1}{2}$ and hence $c = -\frac{1}{2}$. Consequently there is a unique polynomial of degree 2, namely $f(x) = \frac{1}{2}x^2 - \frac{1}{2}$, that has the desired properties.

b. Let $f(x) = ax^2 + bx + c$, so that $f'(x) = 2ax + b$. From Figure 3.18(b), $f(-1) = 0$, so $a - b + c = 0$. Also $f(0) = -1$, so $c = -1$. Thus $a - b = 1$. Next $f'(0) = 0$, so $2a \cdot 0 + b = 0$, and thus $b = 0$. Therefore $a = 1 + b = 1$. Finally, $f'(-1) = -1$, so that $-1 = 2a(-1) + b = 2(1)(-1) + 0 = -2$. This is a contradiction. Therefore there is no polynomial of degree 2 with the desired properties.

72. Since $-\frac{2}{169}x^2 + \frac{4}{13}x + 3$ is a polynomial, it is differentiable on $(-\infty, \infty)$. Thus h is differentiable on $[0, 26]$; $h'(x) = -\frac{4}{169}x + \frac{4}{13}$.

73. Since $\mu > 0$, we have $\mu \sin x + \cos x > 0$ for $0 \le x \le \pi/2$. Since the sine and cosine functions are differentiable on $(-\infty, \infty)$, so is the function $\mu \sin x + \cos x$. By the Quotient Rule, the function $50\mu/(\mu \sin x + \cos x)$ is differentiable at every point in $[0, \pi/2]$. Thus F is differentiable on $[0, \pi/2]$; $F'(x) = [-50\mu(\mu \cos x - \sin x)]/(\mu \sin x + \cos x)^2$.

74. The polynomial $a + bx$ is differentiable on $(-\infty, \infty)$ and is 0 only for $x = -a/b$, which is negative. By the Quotient Rule, R is differentiable on $(-a/b, \infty)$, and since $-a/b < 0$, R is differentiable on $[0, 1]$. Moreover,

$$R'(x) = \frac{(a+bx) - (x)(b)}{(a+bx)^2} = \frac{a}{(a+bx)^2} \quad \text{for } x > 0.$$

75. $f'(x) = \dfrac{100nkx^{n-1}(1+kx^n) - (100kx^n)(nkx^{n-1})}{(1+kx^n)^2} = \dfrac{100nkx^{n-1}}{(1+kx^n)^2}$ for $x > 0$.

76. $P(x) = R(x) - C(x) = (15x^{1/2} - x^{3/2}) - (3x^{1/2} + 4) = 12x^{1/2} - x^{3/2} - 4$

a. $m_P(x) = P'(x) = 6x^{-1/2} - \frac{3}{2}x^{1/2}$, so that $m_P(1) = 6 - \frac{3}{2} = \frac{9}{2}$.

b. $m_P(4) = 6(4^{-1/2}) - \frac{3}{2}(4^{1/2}) = \frac{6}{2} - (\frac{3}{2})(2) = 0$

77. $P(x) = R(x) - C(x) = \sqrt{x} - \dfrac{x+3}{\sqrt{x}+1} = \dfrac{x + \sqrt{x} - (x+3)}{\sqrt{x}+1} = \dfrac{\sqrt{x}-3}{\sqrt{x}+1}$ for $1 \le x \le 15$.

Thus $P(x) = 0$ if $\sqrt{x} - 3 = 0$, that is, if $x = 9$. Since the function $(\sqrt{x}-3)/(\sqrt{x}+1)$ is differentiable on $(0, \infty)$, it follows that P is differentiable on $[1, 15]$, and

$$m_P(x) = P'(x) = \frac{[1/(2\sqrt{x})](\sqrt{x}+1) - (\sqrt{x}-3)[1/(2\sqrt{x})]}{(\sqrt{x}+1)^2}$$

$$= \frac{(\sqrt{x}+1) - (\sqrt{x}-3)}{2\sqrt{x}(\sqrt{x}+1)^2} = \frac{2}{\sqrt{x}(\sqrt{x}+1)^2} \neq 0 \quad \text{for } 1 \le x \le 15.$$

Therefore for no value of x is the marginal profit equal to 0.

3.4 The Chain Rule

1. $f'(x) = \frac{9}{4}x^{5/4}$

2. $f'(x) = \frac{2}{3}x^{-1/3} - 7(-\frac{1}{3})x^{-4/3} = \frac{2}{3}x^{-1/3} + \frac{7}{3}x^{-4/3}$

3. $f'(x) = \frac{3}{2}(1-3x)^{1/2}(-3) = -\frac{9}{2}(1-3x)^{1/2}$

4. $f'(x) = 400(4-3x^2)^{399}(-6x) = -2400x(4-3x^2)^{399}$

5. $f'(x) = \sqrt{2-7x^2} + x\dfrac{1}{2\sqrt{2-7x^2}}(-14x) = \dfrac{2-14x^2}{\sqrt{2-7x^2}}$

6. $f'(x) = \dfrac{1}{2\sqrt{4x-\sqrt{x}}}\left(4 - \dfrac{1}{2\sqrt{x}}\right)$

7. $f'(t) = (\cos 5t)(5) = 5\cos 5t$

8. $f'(t) = 3(-\sin \pi t^2)(2\pi t) = -6\pi t \sin \pi t^2$

9. $f'(t) = 4\sin^3 t\, \cos t + 4\cos^3 t\,(-\sin t) = 4\sin^3 t\, \cos t - 4\cos^3 t\, \sin t$

10. $g'(x) = 6\tan^5 x\, \sec^2 x$

11. $g'(x) = \frac{1}{3}(1 - \sin x)^{-2/3}(-\cos x) = (-\frac{1}{3}\cos x)(1 - \sin x)^{-2/3}$

12. $g'(x) = -\frac{1}{3}(\tan x - \cot x)^{-4/3}(\sec^2 x - (-\csc^2 x)) = -\frac{1}{3}(\tan x - \cot x)^{-4/3}(\sec^2 x + \csc^2 x)$

13. $f'(x) = [-\sin(\sin x)]\cos x$

14. $f'(x) = [\sec^2(\csc x)](-\csc x\, \cot x) = -[\sec^2 x\,(\csc x)]\csc x\, \cot x$

15. $f'(x) = 3\left(\frac{x-1}{x+1}\right)^2\left(\frac{(x+1)-(x-1)}{(x+1)^2}\right) = \frac{6(x-1)^2}{(x+1)^4}$

16. $f'(x) = \frac{\frac{1}{2}(x^2-1)^{-1/2}(2x)(x) - \sqrt{x^2-1}}{x^2} = \frac{x^2-(x^2-1)}{x^2\sqrt{x^2-1}} = \frac{1}{x^2\sqrt{x^2-1}}$

17. $f'(x) = \frac{-1}{(x\sqrt{5-2x})^2}\left[\sqrt{5-2x} + x\frac{-2}{2\sqrt{5-2x}}\right] = -\frac{1}{x^2(5-2x)}\left[\frac{(5-2x)-x}{\sqrt{5-2x}}\right] = \frac{3x-5}{x^2(5-2x)^{3/2}}$

18. $f'(x) = \frac{2(x^2+1)(2x)(x^4+1)^4 - (x^2+1)^2 4(x^4+1)^3(4x^3)}{(x^4+1)^8}$

$= \frac{4x(x^2+1)(x^4+1)^3[(x^4+1)-(x^2+1)4x^2]}{(x^4+1)^8} = \frac{4x(x^2+1)(-3x^4-4x^2+1)}{(x^4+1)^5}$

19. $f'(x) = \cos\frac{1}{x} + x\left(-\sin\frac{1}{x}\right)\left(-\frac{1}{x^2}\right) = \cos\frac{1}{x} + \frac{1}{x}\sin\frac{1}{x}$

20. $f'(x) = 2x\sec\frac{1}{x^3} + x^2\left(\sec\frac{1}{x^3}\tan\frac{1}{x^3}\right)\left(-\frac{3}{x^4}\right) = \sec\frac{1}{x^3}\left(2x - \frac{3}{x^2}\tan\frac{1}{x^3}\right)$

21. $g'(z) = \frac{1}{2}[2z - (2z)^{1/3}]^{-1/2}[2 - \frac{1}{3}(2z)^{-2/3}(2)] = [2z - (2z)^{1/3}]^{-1/2}[1 - \frac{1}{3}(2z)^{-2/3}]$

22. $g'(z) = -2[z^7 + (z^2-1)^5]^{-3}[7z^6 + 5(z^2-1)^4(2z)] = -2[z^7 + (z^2-1)^5]^{-3}[7z^6 + 10z(z^2-1)^4]$

23. $g'(z) = [2\cos(3z^6)][-\sin(3z^6)][18z^5] = -36z^5\cos(3z^6)\sin(3z^6)$

24. $g'(z) = \frac{1}{2}(1+\sin^2 z)^{-1/2}(2\sin z\cos z) = (1+\sin^2 z)^{-1/2}(\sin z\cos z)$

25. $f'(x) = [-\sin(1+\tan 2x)](\sec^2 2x)(2) = -2[\sin(1+\tan 2x)]\sec^2 2x$

26. $f'(x) = [2\cot(2\sqrt{3x+1})][-\csc^2(2\sqrt{3x+1})]\frac{2}{2\sqrt{3x+1}}(3) = \frac{-6\cot(2\sqrt{3x+1})\csc^2(2\sqrt{3x+1})}{\sqrt{3x+1}}$

27. By (4), $f'(x) = 5x^4e^{(x^5)}$.

28. By (4), $f'(x) = -\frac{1}{2\sqrt{x}}e^{-\sqrt{x}}$.

29. By (4), $f'(t) = (\sec^2(e^{3t}))(3e^{3t}) = 3e^{3t}(\sec^2(e^{3t}))$.

30. By (4), $f'(t) = -e^{-t}\sin at + e^{-t}(\cos at)a = e^{-t}(-\sin at + a\cos at)$.

31. By (7), $g'(t) = \frac{1}{t^2+1}(2t) = \frac{2t}{t^2+1}$.

32. By (7), $g'(t) = \frac{1}{\ln t}\frac{1}{t} = \frac{1}{t\ln t}$.

33. By (7), $g'(t) = (2\ln t)\frac{1}{t} = \frac{2\ln t}{t}$.

34. By (7), $g'(t) = \frac{1}{\sin e^t}(\cos e^t)e^t = \frac{e^t \cos e^t}{\sin e^t}$.

35. By (3), $f'(x) = (\ln 3)(3^{5x-7})(5) = 5(\ln 3)3^{5x-7}$.

36. By (3), $f'(x) = \frac{6(1+6^x) - (6x)(\ln 6)6^x}{(1+6^x)^2}$.

37. By (11) of Section 1.8, $\log_3(x^2+4) = \frac{\ln(x^2+4)}{\ln 3}$. With (8) of this present section, this implies that

$$f'(x) = \frac{1}{\ln 3}\frac{1}{x^2+4}(2x) = \frac{2x}{(\ln 3)(x^2+4)}.$$

38. By (11) of Section 1.8, $x\log_2 x = \frac{1}{\ln 2}x\ln x$. With (8) of the present section this implies that

$$f'(x) = \frac{1}{\ln 2}\left[\ln x + x\left(\frac{1}{x}\right)\right] = \frac{1}{\ln 2}(\ln x + 1) = \log_2 x + \frac{1}{\ln 2}.$$

39. $\frac{dy}{dx} = 3(-\frac{2}{3})x^{-5/3} = -2x^{-5/3}$

40. $\frac{dy}{dx} = -6\left(2x + \frac{1}{x}\right)^{-7}\left(2 - \frac{1}{x^2}\right)$

41. $\frac{dy}{dx} = -\sqrt{1+3x^2} - x \cdot \frac{1}{2}(1+3x^2)^{-1/2}(6x) = -\frac{1+6x^2}{\sqrt{1+3x^2}}$

42. $\frac{dy}{dx} = \frac{-1}{[(x^8+1)^{12}+1]^2}[12(x^8+1)^{11} \cdot 8x^7] = -\frac{96x^7(x^8+1)^{11}}{[(x^8+1)^{12}+1]^2}$

43. $\frac{dy}{dx} = \frac{2}{3}\left(\frac{1}{x\sin x}\right)^{-1/3}\left[\frac{-1}{(x\sin x)^2}\right][\sin x + x\cos x] = -\frac{2}{3}\frac{\sin x + x\cos x}{(x\sin x)^{5/3}}$

44. $\frac{dy}{dx} = \cos(\sqrt{2x+1})\frac{2}{2\sqrt{2x+1}} = \frac{\cos(\sqrt{2x+1})}{\sqrt{2x+1}}$

45. $\frac{dy}{dx} = [3\tan^2(\frac{1}{2}x)][\sec^2(\frac{1}{2}x)](\frac{1}{2}) = \frac{3}{2}\tan^2(\frac{1}{2}x)\sec^2(\frac{1}{2}x)$

46. $\frac{dy}{dx} = [-\csc(1-3x)^2\cot(1-3x)^2][2(1-3x)(-3)] = 6(1-3x)\csc(1-3x)^2\cot(1-3x)^2$

47. $\frac{dy}{dx} = e^{\cos x}(-\sin x) = -(\sin x)e^{\cos x}$

48. $\frac{dy}{dx} = e^{-1/x}\left(\frac{1}{x^2}\right) = \frac{1}{x^2}e^{-1/x}$

49. By (3), $\dfrac{dy}{dx} = (\ln a)(a^x)\cos bx - a^x(\sin bx)(b) = a^x[(\ln a)(\cos bx) - b\sin bx]$.

50. By (3), $\dfrac{dy}{dx} = (\ln a)(a^x)(\ln x) + a^x\dfrac{1}{x} = (\ln a)a^x(\ln x) + \dfrac{1}{x}a^x$.

51. $\dfrac{d}{dx}(y^5) = 5y^4\dfrac{dy}{dx}$

52. $\dfrac{d}{dx}(y^{-2/3}) = -\dfrac{2}{3}y^{-5/3}\dfrac{dy}{dx}$

53. $\dfrac{d}{dx}\left(\dfrac{2}{y}\right) = \dfrac{-2}{y^2}\dfrac{dy}{dx}$

54. $\dfrac{d}{dx}(\cos y^2) = (-\sin y^2)(2y)\dfrac{dy}{dx} = (-2y\sin y^2)\dfrac{dy}{dx}$

55. $\dfrac{d}{dx}(\sin\sqrt{y}) = (\cos\sqrt{y})\dfrac{1}{2\sqrt{y}}\dfrac{dy}{dx} = \left(\dfrac{1}{2\sqrt{y}}\cos\sqrt{y}\right)\dfrac{dy}{dx}$

56. $$\begin{aligned}\frac{d}{dx}(\sec\sqrt{y^2-1}) &= (\sec\sqrt{y^2-1}\tan\sqrt{y^2-1})\left(\frac{1}{2\sqrt{y^2-1}}\right)(2y)\frac{dy}{dx}\\ &= (\sec\sqrt{y^2-1}\tan\sqrt{y^2-1})\frac{y}{\sqrt{y^2-1}}\frac{dy}{dx}\end{aligned}$$

57. $\dfrac{d}{dx}(x^3y^2) = 3x^2y^2 + x^3\left(2y\dfrac{dy}{dx}\right) = 3x^2y^2 + 2x^3y\dfrac{dy}{dx}$

58. $$\begin{aligned}\frac{d}{dx}\left[\frac{1}{x^2-xy+y^3}\right] &= \frac{-1}{(x^2-xy+y^3)^2}\left[2x - \left(y + x\frac{dy}{dx}\right) + 3y^2\frac{dy}{dx}\right]\\ &= \frac{-2x + y + x(dy/dx) - 3y^2(dy/dx)}{(x^2-xy+y^3)^2}\end{aligned}$$

59. $\dfrac{d}{dx}(\sqrt{x^2+y^2}) = \dfrac{1}{2\sqrt{x^2+y^2}}\left[2x + 2y\dfrac{dy}{dx}\right] = \dfrac{x + y(dy/dx)}{\sqrt{x^2+y^2}}$

60. $\dfrac{d}{dx}\cos x^5y^3 = -(\sin x^5y^3)\left(5x^4y^3 + x^5\,3\,y^2\dfrac{dy}{dx}\right) = -x^4y^2\left(5y + 3x\dfrac{dy}{dx}\right)\sin x^5y^3$

61. $f'(x) = \dfrac{1}{x+\sqrt{x^2-1}}\left[1 + \dfrac{1}{2\sqrt{x^2-1}}(2x)\right] = \dfrac{\sqrt{x^2-1}+x}{(x+\sqrt{x^2-1})\sqrt{x^2-1}} = \dfrac{1}{\sqrt{x^2-1}}$

62. $f(x) = \ln(x+\sqrt{x^2-1}) - \ln(x-\sqrt{x^2-1})$, so $f'(x) = \dfrac{d}{dx}\ln(x+\sqrt{x^2-1}) - \dfrac{d}{dx}\ln(x-\sqrt{x^2-1})$. By Exercise 61,

$$\frac{d}{dx}\ln(x+\sqrt{x^2-1}) = \frac{1}{\sqrt{x^2-1}}.$$

Similarly,

$$\frac{d}{dx}\ln(x-\sqrt{x^2-1}) = \frac{1}{x-\sqrt{x^2-1}}\left[1 - \frac{1}{2\sqrt{x^2-1}}(2x)\right] = \frac{\sqrt{x^2-1}-x}{(x-\sqrt{x^2-1})\sqrt{x^2-1}} = \frac{-1}{\sqrt{x^2-1}}.$$

Thus

$$f'(x) = \frac{1}{\sqrt{x^2-1}} - \left(\frac{-1}{\sqrt{x^2-1}}\right) = \frac{2}{\sqrt{x^2-1}}.$$

63. $f'(x) = -2(x+1)^{-3}(1)$, so $f'(0) = -2$. Thus l: $y - 1 = -2(x - 0)$, or $y = -2x + 1$.

64. $f'(x) = \frac{2}{3}(1 + x^{1/3})^{-1/3}(\frac{1}{3}x^{-2/3})$, so $f'(-8) = -\frac{1}{18}$. Thus l: $y - 1 = -\frac{1}{18}(x - (-8))$, or $y = -\frac{1}{18}x + \frac{5}{9}$.

65. $f'(x) = (-2)(-\sin 3x)(3) = 6\sin 3x$, so $f'(\pi/3) = 6\sin\pi = 0$. Thus l: $y = 2$.

66. $f'(x) = (\cos\sqrt{x})[1/(2\sqrt{x})]$, so $f'(\pi^2) = (\cos\pi)/2\pi = -1/(2\pi)$. Thus l: $y - 0 = -(1/2\pi)(x - \pi^2)$, or $y = -x/(2\pi) + \pi/2$.

67. $f'(x) = 2e^{-3x}(-3) = -6e^{-3x}$, so $f'(0) = -6e^{-3(0)} = -6$. Thus l: $y - 2 = -6(x - 0)$, or $y = -6x + 2$.

68. $f'(x) = \dfrac{1}{\sin x}(\cos x) = \cot x$, so $f'(\pi/6) = \cot\pi/6 = \sqrt{3}$. Thus l: $y + \ln 2 = \sqrt{3}(x - \pi/6)$, or $y = \sqrt{3}x - \ln 2 - \pi\sqrt{3}/6$.

69. Yes, because $(\ln(x + 0.1) - \ln x)/(0.1)$ should be approximately $(d/dx)(\ln x)$, which is $1/x$ for $x > 0$.

70. $(g \circ f)'(-3) = g'(f(-3))f'(-3) = g'(2)f'(-3) = (\sqrt{2})4 = 4\sqrt{2}$

$(f \circ g)'(0) = f'(g(0))g'(0) = f'(-3)g'(0) = 4(-7) = -28$

$(g \circ f)'(0) = g'(f(0))f'(0) = g'(1)f'(0) = 13 \cdot 2 = 26$

$(f \circ g)'(2) = f'(g(2))g'(2) = f'(0)g'(2) = 2(\sqrt{2}) = 2\sqrt{2}$

$(g \circ f)'(2) = g'(f(2))f'(2) = g'(-3)f'(2) = 11 \cdot 2 = 22$

71. a. $s'(x) = \left[\cos\left(\frac{\pi}{180}x\right)\right]\frac{\pi}{180} = \frac{\pi}{180}c(x)$; $c'(x) = \left[-\sin\left(\frac{\pi}{180}x\right)\right]\frac{\pi}{180} = -\frac{\pi}{180}s(x)$

72. a. $\dfrac{d}{dx}E(cx) = [E'(cx)]c = cE(cx)$

b. Since $g(x) = \dfrac{E(cx)}{e^{cx}}$, (a) implies that

$$g'(x) = \frac{[cE(cx)]e^{cx} - [E(cx)]ce^{cx}}{(e^{cx})^2} = 0.$$

73. a. If $g(x) = -x$, then $(f \circ g)(x) = f(-x)$. By the Chain Rule, $(f \circ g)'(x) = f'(g(x))g'(x) = [f'(-x)](-1) = -f'(-x)$. If f is even, then $f(x) = f(-x)$, so $(f \circ g)(x) = f(x)$, and thus $f'(x) = (f \circ g)'(x) = -f'(-x)$. Therefore f' is an odd function.

b. If $g(x) = -x$, then $(f \circ g)(x) = f(-x)$. As in part (a), $(f \circ g)'(x) = -f'(-x)$. If f is odd, then $f(x) = -f(-x) = -(f \circ g)(x)$, so $f'(x) = -(f \circ g)'(x) = f'(-x)$. Therefore f' is an even function.

74. $f'(t) = a(-\sin 2\pi\omega t)(2\pi\omega) = -2\pi\omega a \sin 2\pi\omega t$

75. Since the cosine function and the polynomial $\pi t/24$ are differentiable on $(-\infty, \infty)$, $\cos(\pi t/24)$ and hence F are differentiable on $[0, 24]$. Also

$$F'(t) = \frac{336{,}000}{\pi}\left(\sin\frac{\pi t}{24}\right)\left(\frac{\pi}{24}\right) = 14{,}000 \sin\frac{\pi t}{24}.$$

76. a. If $v_0 = 30$ and $g = 9.8$, then $R(\theta) = (30^2/9.8)\sin 2\theta = (900/9.8)\sin 2\theta$. Thus

$$R'(\theta) = \frac{900}{9.8}(\cos 2\theta)2 = \frac{1800}{9.8}\cos 2\theta.$$

Therefore $R'(\pi/4) = (1800/9.8)\cos(\pi/2) = 0$.

b. $R'(\theta) > 0$ if $\cos 2\theta > 0$, which occurs for those values of θ in $[0, \pi/2]$ for which $0 < \theta < \pi/4$.

77. a. $\dfrac{dE}{dv} = 100(.4)\left(1 - \dfrac{v}{V}\right)^{-0.6}\left(\dfrac{-1}{V}\right) = \dfrac{-40}{V}\left(1 - \dfrac{v}{V}\right)^{-0.6}$

b. $\dfrac{dE}{dV} = 100(.4)\left(1 - \dfrac{v}{V}\right)^{-0.6}\left(\dfrac{v}{V^2}\right) = \dfrac{40v}{V^2}\left(1 - \dfrac{v}{V}\right)^{-0.6}$

78. a. By the Chain Rule,

$$(F \circ r)'(t) = F'(r(t))r'(t) = -\frac{2k}{r^3}(48 - 32t) = \frac{32k(2t-3)}{(64 + 48t - 16t^2)^3}.$$

b. By part (a), $(F \circ r)'(1) = \dfrac{32k(2\cdot 1 - 3)}{[64 + 48\cdot 1 - 16(1)^2]^3} = \dfrac{-32k}{(96)^3}$;

by part (a), $(F \circ r)'(2) = \dfrac{32k(2\cdot 2 - 3)}{[64 + 48\cdot 2 - 16(2)^2]^3} = \dfrac{32k}{(96)^3}$;

thus $(F \circ r)'(1) = -(F \circ r)'(2)$.

79. a. $v'(r) = \dfrac{1}{2}\left(\dfrac{192{,}000}{r} + v_0^2 - 48\right)^{-1/2}\left(\dfrac{-192{,}000}{r^2}\right) = -\dfrac{96{,}000}{r^2}\left(\dfrac{192{,}000}{r} + v_0^2 - 48\right)^{-1/2}$

b. If $v_0 = 8$, then

$$v'(24{,}000) = -\frac{96{,}000}{(24{,}000)^2}\left(\frac{192{,}000}{24{,}000} + 16\right)^{-1/2} = -\frac{\sqrt{6}}{72{,}000} \text{ (miles per second per mile).}$$

80. Since $W'(t) = krt^{r-1}$, we have $\dfrac{W'(t)}{W(t)} = \dfrac{krt^{r-1}}{kt^r} = \dfrac{r}{t}$ for $t > 0$.

81. $\dfrac{dV}{dt} = \dfrac{dV}{dr}\dfrac{dr}{dt} = [\frac{4}{3}\pi(3r^2)](10) = 40\pi r^2$.

82. $\dfrac{dV}{dS} = \dfrac{dV}{dr}\dfrac{dr}{dS} = (4\pi r^2)\left[\dfrac{1}{2}\left(\dfrac{S}{4\pi}\right)^{-1/2}\dfrac{1}{4\pi}\right] = r^2\sqrt{\dfrac{\pi}{S}} = \dfrac{1}{4}\sqrt{\dfrac{S}{\pi}}$

83. $\dfrac{dA}{dh} = \dfrac{dA}{dx}\dfrac{dx}{dh} = \left(\dfrac{\sqrt{3}}{2}x\right)\left(\dfrac{2\sqrt{3}}{3}\right) = x = \frac{2}{3}\sqrt{3}\,h$, so that $\left.\dfrac{dA}{dh}\right|_{h=\sqrt{3}} = \dfrac{2\sqrt{3}}{3}(\sqrt{3}) = 2$

84. Let h be the height and V the volume of the cider after t seconds. Then $h = \frac{1}{3}t$ and $V = 2^2\pi h = 4\pi h$. By the Chain Rule, $dV/dt = (dV/dh)/(dh/dt) = 4\pi \cdot \frac{1}{3} = \frac{4}{3}\pi$, which is constant.

85. Since $D'(x) = \frac{1}{2}(3-2x)^{-1/2}(-2) = -(3-2x)^{-1/2}$, we have $D'(x) < 0$ for $0 < x < \frac{3}{2}$.

86. a. Since

$$D'(x) = 1000 \cdot \frac{1}{3}\left(\frac{6}{x-16}\right)^{-2/3}\left(\frac{-6}{(x-16)^2}\right) = -\frac{1000}{3}\frac{6^{1/3}}{(x-16)^{4/3}}$$

for $17 < x < 37$, we have

$$D'(22) = -\frac{1000}{3}\frac{6^{1/3}}{6^{4/3}} = -\frac{500}{9}.$$

b. From the formula in (a) we conclude that $D'(x) < 0$ for all x in $(17, 37)$.

3.5 Higher Derivatives

1. $f'(x) = 5$; $f''(x) = 0$

2. $f'(x) = 3x^2 + 3$; $f''(x) = 6x$

3. $f'(x) = -60x^4 + 2x^3 - \frac{1}{2}(1-x)^{-1/2}(-1) = -60x^4 + 2x^3 + \frac{1}{2}(1-x)^{-1/2}$

$f''(x) = -240x^3 + 6x^2 + \frac{1}{2}(-\frac{1}{2})(1-x)^{-3/2}(-1) = -240x^3 + 6x^2 + \frac{1}{4}(1-x)^{-3/2}$

4. $f'(x) = \dfrac{(x-1)-(x+1)}{(x-1)^2} = -2(x-1)^{-2}$; $f''(x) = (-2)(-2)(x-1)^{-3} = 4(x-1)^{-3}$

5. $f'(x) = 2(-2)(1-4x)^{-3}(-4) = 16(1-4x)^{-3}$; $f''(x) = 16(-3)(1-4x)^{-4}(-4) = 192(1-4x)^{-4}$

6. $f'(x) = (-\frac{1}{2})x^{-3/2}$; $f''(x) = (-\frac{1}{2})(-\frac{3}{2})x^{-5/2} = \frac{3}{4}x^{-5/2}$

7. $f'(x) = a(-n)x^{-n-1}$; $f''(x) = (-an)(-n-1)x^{-n-2} = an(n+1)x^{-n-2}$

8. $f'(x) = 4x + \dfrac{4000}{x^2}$; $f''(x) = 4 - \dfrac{8000}{x^3}$

9. $f'(x) = \dfrac{-3x^2}{(x^3-1)^2}$

$$f''(x) = \frac{-6x(x^3-1)^2 + 3x^2(2)(x^3-1)(3x^2)}{(x^3-1)^4} = \frac{6x(x^3-1)(-x^3+1+3x^3)}{(x^3-1)^4} = \frac{6x(2x^3+1)}{(x^3-1)^3}$$

10. $f'(x) = \dfrac{2x\sqrt{1-x^2} - x^2(\frac{1}{2})(1-x^2)^{-1/2}(-2x)}{1-x^2} = \dfrac{2x-x^3}{(1-x^2)^{3/2}}$

$$f''(x) = (2-3x^2)(1-x^2)^{-3/2} + (2x-x^3)(-\tfrac{3}{2})(1-x^2)^{-5/2}(-2x)$$
$$= (1-x^2)^{-5/2}(2-5x^2+3x^4+6x^2-3x^4) = (1-x^2)^{-5/2}(2+x^2)$$

11. $f'(x) = \dfrac{5}{2}\pi x^{3/2} + \dfrac{(-\sin x)x - \cos x}{x^2} = \dfrac{5}{2}\pi x^{3/2} - \dfrac{\sin x}{x} - \dfrac{\cos x}{x^2}$

$$f''(x) = \frac{5}{2}\pi\left(\frac{3}{2}\right)x^{1/2} - \frac{x\cos x - \sin x}{x^2} - \frac{-x^2\sin x - 2x\cos x}{x^4} = \frac{15}{4}\pi x^{1/2} - \frac{\cos x}{x} + \frac{2\sin x}{x^2} + \frac{2\cos x}{x^3}$$

12. $f'(x) = \sec^3 x$; $f''(x) = 2\sec x\,(\sec x\,\tan x) = 2\sec^2 x\,\tan x$

13. $f'(x) = \sec x\,\tan x$; $f''(x) = (\sec x\,\tan x)\tan x + \sec x\,(\sec^2 x) = \sec x\,\tan^2 x + \sec^3 x$

14. $f'(x) = 3(x^2 + \sin x)^2(2x + \cos x)$

$$\begin{aligned} f''(x) &= 6(x^2 + \sin x)(2x + \cos x)^2 + 3(x^2 + \sin x)^2(2 - \sin x) \\ &= 3(x^2 + \sin x)[2(2x + \cos x)^2 + (x^2 + \sin x)(2 - \sin x)] \end{aligned}$$

15. $f'(x) = \cot(-4x) + x\big(-\csc^2(-4x)\big)(-4) = \cot(-4x) + 4x\csc^2(-4x)$

$$\begin{aligned} f''(x) &= -\csc^2(-4x)(-4) + 4\csc^2(-4x) + 4x[2\csc(-4x)\big(-\csc(-4x)\big)\cot(-4x)(-4)] \\ &= 8\csc^2(-4x) + 32x\csc^2(-4x)\cot(-4x) \end{aligned}$$

16. $f'(x) = \frac{1}{2}(1 + \sin x)^{-1/2}(\cos x)$

$$\begin{aligned} f''(x) &= \tfrac{1}{2}(-\tfrac{1}{2})(1 + \sin x)^{-3/2}(\cos x)^2 + \tfrac{1}{2}(1 + \sin x)^{-1/2}(-\sin x) \\ &= -\tfrac{1}{4}(1 + \sin x)^{-3/2}\cos^2 x - \tfrac{1}{2}(1 + \sin x)^{-1/2}\sin x \end{aligned}$$

17. $f'(x) = \tan^3 2x + x[3(\tan^2 2x)(\sec^2 2x)(2)] = \tan^3 2x + 6x\tan^2 2x\,\sec^2 2x$

$$\begin{aligned} f''(x) &= 3[\tan^2 2x\,\sec^2 2x](2) + 6\tan^2(2x)\,\sec^2 2x + 6x[(2\tan 2x\,\sec^4 2x)(2) \\ &\quad +(\tan^2 2x)2(\sec^2 2x\,\tan 2x)(2)] \\ &= 12\tan^2 2x\,\sec^2 2x + 24x(\tan 2x\,\sec^4 2x + \tan^3 2x\,\sec^2 2x) \end{aligned}$$

18. $f'(x) = \frac{1}{2}(1 + \sqrt{x})^{-1/2}(\frac{1}{2}x^{-1/2}) = \frac{1}{4}(1 + \sqrt{x})^{-1/2}x^{-1/2} = \frac{1}{4}(x + x^{3/2})^{-1/2}$

$f''(x) = \frac{1}{4}(-\frac{1}{2})(x + x^{3/2})^{-3/2}(1 + \frac{3}{2}x^{1/2}) = -\frac{1}{8}(x + x^{3/2})^{-3/2}(1 + \frac{3}{2}x^{1/2})$

19. $f'(x) = -\dfrac{1}{x^2}e^{1/x}$; $f''(x) = \dfrac{2}{x^3}e^{1/x} + \dfrac{1}{x^4}e^{1/x}$

20. $f'(x) = (\cos x)e^{\sin x}$; $f''(x) = (-\sin x)e^{\sin x} + (\cos^2 x)e^{\sin x}$

21. $f'(x) = \dfrac{2x}{1 + x^2}$; $f''(x) = \dfrac{2(1 + x^2) - 2x(2x)}{(1 + x^2)^2} = \dfrac{2 - 2x^2}{(1 + x^2)^2}$

22. $f'(x) = \dfrac{(1/x)\cdot x - (\ln x)\cdot 1}{x^2} = \dfrac{1 - \ln x}{x^2}$; $f''(x) = \dfrac{(-1/x)x^2 - (1 - \ln x)(2x)}{x^4} = \dfrac{-3 + 2\ln x}{x^3}$

23. $\dfrac{dy}{dx} = \dfrac{3}{2}x^{1/2}$; $\dfrac{d^2y}{dx^2} = \dfrac{3}{4}x^{-1/2}$

24. $\dfrac{dy}{dx} = -\dfrac{8}{9}x - 42x^5$; $\dfrac{d^2y}{dx^2} = -\dfrac{8}{9} - 210x^4$

25. $\dfrac{dy}{dx} = 3(x^4 - \tan x)^2(4x^3 - \sec^2 x)$

$$\frac{d^2y}{dx^2} = 3[2(x^4 - \tan x)(4x^3 - \sec^2 x)^2 + (x^4 - \tan x)^2 \cdot (12x^2 - 2\sec^2 x \tan x)]$$

26. $\dfrac{dy}{dx} = \dfrac{3}{2}(1 - x^2)^{1/2}(-2x) = -3x(1 - x^2)^{1/2}$

$$\frac{d^2y}{dx^2} = -3(1 - x^2)^{1/2} - 3x\left(\frac{1}{2}\right)(1 - x^2)^{-1/2}(-2x) = -3(1 - x^2)^{1/2} + 3x^2(1 - x^2)^{-1/2}$$

27. $\dfrac{dy}{dx} = 2ax + b;\ \dfrac{d^2y}{dx^2} = 2a$

28. $\dfrac{dy}{dx} = \dfrac{1}{2}(1 + x^4)^{-1/2}(4x^3) = 2x^3(1 + x^4)^{-1/2}$

$$\frac{d^2y}{dx^2} = 6x^2(1 + x^4)^{-1/2} + 2x^3\left(-\frac{1}{2}\right)(1 + x^4)^{-3/2}(4x^3) = 6x^2(1 + x^4)^{-1/2} - 4x^6(1 + x^4)^{-3/2}$$

29. $\dfrac{dy}{dx} = \dfrac{-1}{(3 - x)^2}(-1) = \dfrac{1}{(3 - x)^2};\ \dfrac{d^2y}{dx^2} = (-2)\dfrac{1}{(3 - x)^3}(-1) = \dfrac{2}{(3 - x)^3}$

30. $\dfrac{dy}{dx} = \dfrac{(x^2 - 1) - x(2x)}{(x^2 - 1)^2} = \dfrac{-1 - x^2}{(x^2 - 1)^2}$

$$\frac{d^2y}{dx^2} = \frac{-2x(x^2 - 1)^2 + (1 + x^2)(2)(x^2 - 1)(2x)}{(x^2 - 1)^4} = \frac{2x(x^2 + 3)}{(x^2 - 1)^3}$$

31. $\dfrac{dy}{dx} = -\csc x \cot x;\ \dfrac{d^2y}{dx^2} = -(-\csc x \cot x)\cot x - \csc x\,(-\csc^2 x) = \csc x \cot^2 x + \csc^3 x$

32. $\dfrac{dy}{dx} = \dfrac{(1 + \cos x)(x + 2) - (x + \sin x)}{(x + 2)^2} = \dfrac{1 + \cos x}{x + 2} - \dfrac{x + \sin x}{(x + 2)^2}$

$$\frac{d^2y}{dx^2} = \frac{(-\sin x)(x + 2) - (1 + \cos x)}{(x + 2)^2} - \frac{(1 + \cos x)(x + 2)^2 - (x + \sin x)2(x + 2)}{(x + 2)^4}$$

$$= \frac{-\sin x}{x + 2} - \frac{2(1 + \cos x)}{(x + 2)^2} + \frac{2(x + \sin x)}{(x + 2)^3}$$

33. $\dfrac{dy}{dx} = \cos x - \sin x;\ \dfrac{d^2y}{dx^2} = -\sin x - \cos x$

34. $y = \left\{\begin{matrix} -1/x^2 & \text{for } x < 0 \\ 1/x^2 & \text{for } x > 0 \end{matrix}\right\};\ \dfrac{dy}{dx} = \left\{\begin{matrix} 2/x^3 & \text{for } x < 0 \\ -2/x^3 & \text{for } x > 0 \end{matrix}\right\};\ \dfrac{d^2y}{dx^2} = \left\{\begin{matrix} -6/x^4 & \text{for } x < 0 \\ 6/x^4 & \text{for } x > 0 \end{matrix}\right\}$

35. $\dfrac{dy}{dx} = e^x \sin x + e^x \cos x;\ \dfrac{d^2y}{dx^2} = (e^x \sin x + e^x \cos x) + (e^x \cos x - e^x \sin x) = 2e^x \cos x$

36. $\dfrac{dy}{dx} = e^{(e^x)}e^x = e^x e^{(e^x)};\ \dfrac{d^2y}{dx^2} = e^x e^{(e^x)} + e^x(e^x e^{(e^x)}) = (e^x + e^{2x})e^{(e^x)}$

37. $\dfrac{dy}{dx} = 2x \ln x + x^2\left(\dfrac{1}{x}\right) = 2x \ln x + x;\ \dfrac{d^2y}{dx^2} = 2\ln x + 2x\left(\dfrac{1}{x}\right) + 1 = 2\ln x + 3$

38. $\dfrac{dy}{dx}=\dfrac{1}{e^{2x}-1}(2e^{2x})=\dfrac{2e^{2x}}{e^{2x}-1};\ \dfrac{d^2y}{dx^2}=\dfrac{4e^{2x}(e^{2x}-1)-2e^{2x}(2e^{2x})}{(e^{2x}-1)^2}=\dfrac{-4e^{2x}}{(e^{2x}-1)^2}$

39. $f'(x)=-8x;\ f''(x)=-8;\ f^{(3)}(x)=0$

40. $f'(x)=8x^7-24x^5+12x^3-4x;\ f''(x)=56x^6-120x^4+36x^2-4;\ f^{(3)}(x)=336x^5-480x^3+72x$

41. $f'(x)=2x\cos x^2;\ f''(x)=2\cos x^2-4x^2\sin x^2$

$f^{(3)}(x)=-4x\sin x^2-8x\sin x^2-8x^3\cos x^2=-12x\sin x^2-8x^3\cos x^2$

42. $f'(x)=\cos x-x\sin x;\ f''(x)=-\sin x-\sin x-x\cos x=-2\sin x-x\cos x$

$f^{(3)}(x)=-2\cos x-\cos x+x\sin x=-3\cos x+x\sin x$

43. $f'(x)=-1/x^2;\ f''(x)=2/x^3;\ f^{(3)}(x)=-6/x^4$

44. $f'(x)=\frac{1}{3}(-\frac{1}{2})x^{-3/2}=-\frac{1}{6}x^{-3/2};\ f''(x)=(-\frac{1}{6})(-\frac{3}{2})x^{-5/2}=\frac{1}{4}x^{-5/2}$

$f^{(3)}(x)=\frac{1}{4}(-\frac{5}{2})x^{-7/2}=-\frac{5}{8}x^{-7/2}$

45. $f'(x)=\dfrac{3(4x+5)-(3x)(4)}{(4x+5)^2}=\dfrac{15}{(4x+5)^2};\ f''(x)=\dfrac{15(-2)(4)}{(4x+5)^3}=\dfrac{-120}{(4x+5)^3}$

$f^{(3)}(x)=\dfrac{(-120)(-3)(4)}{(4x+5)^4}=\dfrac{1440}{(4x+5)^4}$

46. $f(x)=\left\{\begin{matrix}-x^3 & \text{for } x<0\\ x^3 & \text{for } x\ge 0\end{matrix}\right\};\ f'(0)=\lim\limits_{x\to 0}\dfrac{x^2|x|-0}{x-0}=\lim\limits_{x\to 0}x|x|=0$

$f'(x)=\left\{\begin{matrix}-3x^2 & \text{for } x<0\\ 0 & \text{for } x=0\\ 3x^2 & \text{for } x>0\end{matrix}\right\}=3x|x|;\ f''(0)=\lim\limits_{x\to 0}\dfrac{3x|x|-0}{x-0}=\lim\limits_{x\to 0}3|x|=0$

$f''(x)=\left\{\begin{matrix}-6x & \text{for } x<0\\ 0 & \text{for } x=0\\ 6x & \text{for } x>0\end{matrix}\right\}=6|x|;\ f^{(3)}(0)=\lim\limits_{x\to 0}\dfrac{6|x|-0}{x-0}$ does not exist.

$f^{(3)}(x)=\left\{\begin{matrix}-6 & \text{for } x<0\\ 6 & \text{for } x>0\end{matrix}\right\}$

47. $f'(x)=1/x;\ f''(x)=-1/x^2;\ f^{(3)}(x)=2/x^3$

48. $f'(x)=2xe^{(x^2)};\ f''(x)=2e^{(x^2)}+4x^2e^{(x^2)};\ f^{(3)}(x)=4xe^{(x^2)}+8xe^{(x^2)}+8x^3e^{(x^2)}=12e^{(x^2)}+8x^3e^{(x^2)}$

49. $\dfrac{dy}{dx}=6x;\ \dfrac{d^2y}{dx^2}=6;\ \dfrac{d^3y}{dx^3}=0$

50. $\dfrac{dy}{dx} = \dfrac{7}{2}x^{5/2} - 5x^{3/2}$; $\dfrac{d^2y}{dx^2} = \dfrac{35}{4}x^{3/2} - \dfrac{15}{2}x^{1/2}$; $\dfrac{d^3y}{dx^3} = \dfrac{105}{8}x^{1/2} - \dfrac{15}{4}x^{-1/2}$

51. $\dfrac{dy}{dx} = -\dfrac{3}{70}x^{-5/2}$; $\dfrac{d^2y}{dx^2} = \dfrac{3}{28}x^{-7/2}$; $\dfrac{d^3y}{dx^3} = -\dfrac{3}{8}x^{-9/2}$

52. $\dfrac{dy}{dx} = -\csc x \cot x$; $\dfrac{d^2y}{dx^2} = -(-\csc x \cot x)\cot x - \csc x\,(-\csc^2 x) = \csc x \cot^2 x + \csc^3 x$

$$\begin{aligned}\frac{d^3y}{dx^3} &= (-\csc x \cot x)\cot^2 x + \csc x\,[2\cot x\,(-\csc^2 x)] + 3\csc^2 x\,(-\csc x \cot x)\\ &= -\csc x \cot^3 x - 5\csc^3 x \cot x\end{aligned}$$

53. $\dfrac{dy}{dx} = 2x\sin\dfrac{1}{x} + x^2\left(\cos\dfrac{1}{x}\right)\left(\dfrac{-1}{x^2}\right) = 2x\sin\dfrac{1}{x} - \cos\dfrac{1}{x}$

$$\frac{d^2y}{dx^2} = 2\sin\frac{1}{x} + 2x\left(\cos\frac{1}{x}\right)\left(\frac{-1}{x^2}\right) + \left(\sin\frac{1}{x}\right)\left(\frac{-1}{x^2}\right) = 2\sin\frac{1}{x} - \frac{2}{x}\cos\frac{1}{x} - \frac{1}{x^2}\sin\frac{1}{x}$$

$$\frac{d^3y}{dx^3} = 2\left(\cos\frac{1}{x}\right)\left(\frac{-1}{x^2}\right) + \frac{2}{x^2}\cos\frac{1}{x} + \frac{2}{x}\left(\sin\frac{1}{x}\right)\left(\frac{-1}{x^2}\right) + \frac{2}{x^3}\sin\frac{1}{x} - \frac{1}{x^2}\left(\cos\frac{1}{x}\right)\left(\frac{-1}{x^2}\right) = \frac{1}{x^4}\cos\frac{1}{x}$$

54. $\dfrac{dy}{dx} = \dfrac{4}{(1-x)^3}$; $\dfrac{d^2y}{dx^2} = \dfrac{12}{(1-x)^4}$; $\dfrac{d^3y}{dx^3} = \dfrac{48}{(1-x)^5}$

55. $\dfrac{dy}{dx} = 3ax^2 + 2bx + c$; $\dfrac{d^2y}{dx^2} = 6ax + 2b$; $\dfrac{d^3y}{dx^3} = 6a$

56. $\dfrac{dy}{dx} = 4ax^3 + 3bx^2 + 2cx + d$; $\dfrac{d^2y}{dx^2} = 12ax^2 + 6bx + 2c$; $\dfrac{d^3y}{dx^3} = 24ax + 6b$

57. $f'(x) = 24x^7 + \frac{9}{2}x^5 - 3x^{-1/4} - 2x^{-2}$

$f''(x) = 168x^6 + \frac{45}{2}x^4 + \frac{3}{4}x^{-5/4} + 4x^{-3}$

$f^{(3)}(x) = 1008x^5 + 90x^3 - \frac{15}{16}x^{-9/4} - 12x^{-4}$

$f^{(4)}(x) = 5040x^4 + 270x^2 + \frac{135}{64}x^{-13/4} + 48x^{-5}$

58. $f'(x) = \cos x + \sin x$; $f''(x) = -\sin x + \cos x$; $f^{(3)}(x) = -\cos x - \sin x$; $f^{(4)}(x) = \sin x - \cos x$

59. $f'(x) = \pi\cos\pi x$; $f''(x) = -\pi^2\sin\pi x$; $f^{(3)}(x) = -\pi^3\cos\pi x$; $f^{(4)}(x) = \pi^4\sin\pi x$

60. $f'(x) = 4ax^3 + 3bx^2 + 2cx + d$; $f''(x) = 12ax^2 + 6bx + 2c$; $f^{(3)}(x) = 24ax + 6b$; $f^{(4)}(x) = 24a$

61. $f'(x) = -\sqrt{2}\,e^{-\sqrt{2}x}$; $f''(x) = (-\sqrt{2})^2e^{-\sqrt{2}x} = 2e^{-\sqrt{2}x}$;

$f^{(3)}(x) = -2\sqrt{2}\,e^{-\sqrt{2}x}$; $f^{(4)}(x) = (-\sqrt{2})(-2\sqrt{2}\,e^{-\sqrt{2}x}) = 4e^{-\sqrt{2}x}$

62. $f'(x) = \ln x + 1$; $f''(x) = 1/x$; $f^{(3)}(x) = -1/x^2$; $f^{(4)}(x) = 2/x^3$

63. $v(t) = f'(t) = -32t + 3$; $a(t) = v'(t) = f''(t) = -32$

64. $v(t) = f'(t) = -32t - \frac{1}{2}$; $a(t) = v'(t) = f''(t) = -32$

65. $v(t) = f'(t) = 2\cos t + 3\sin t$; $a(t) = v'(t) = f''(t) = -2\sin t + 3\cos t$

66. $v(t) = f'(t) = 2/t^3$; $a(t) = v'(t) = f''(t) = -6/t^4$

67. Let $f(x) = c_n x^n + c_{n-1}x^{n-1} + \cdots + c_1 x + c_0$, where $c_n \neq 0$. Then $f'(x) = nc_n x^{n-1} + (n-1)c_{n-1}x^{n-2} + \cdots + c_1$. Thus f' is a polynomial of degree $n-1$. In the same way we find that f'' is a polynomial of degree $n-2$. Continuing, we see that $f^{(n)}$ is a polynomial of degree 0, that is $f^{(n)}$ is a constant function. Thus $f^{(n+1)} = 0$, and consequently $f^{(n+2)} = 0$ also.

68. a. $v(t) = 2t - \dfrac{50t}{(t^2+1)^2}$;

$$a(t) = 2 - \frac{50(t^2+1)^2 - 50t(t^2+1)(4t)}{(t^2+1)^4} = 2 - \frac{50(t^2+1) - 200t^2}{(t^2+1)^3} = 2 - \frac{50 - 150t^2}{(t^2+1)^3}$$

b. The object can change direction only for $t > 0$ such that $v(t) = 0$, which occurs if $2t - 50t/(t^2+1)^2 = 0$, that is, $(t^2+1)^2 = 25$, or $t^2 + 1 = 5$, or $t = 2$. Since $v(1) < 0$ and $v(3) > 0$, it follows that the object changes direction when $t = 2$.

c. The velocity is negative for $t > 0$ if $v(t) < 0$, or $2t - 50t/(t^2+1)^2 < 0$, or $(t^2+1)^2 < 25$, or $t^2 + 1 < 5$, or $0 < t < 2$.

69. $f'(x) = e^x = f(x)$, so $f^{(n)}(x) = e^x$ for any $n \geq 1$.

70. $f'(x) = 3e^x = 3f(x)$, so $f^{(n)}(x) = 3^n e^x$ for any $n \geq 1$.

71. $f'(x) = e^{-x} - xe^{-x} = e^{-x} - f(x)$; $f''(x) = -e^{-x} - e^{-x} + xe^{-x} = -2e^{-x} + xe^{-x} = -2e^{-x} + f(x)$

$f^{(3)}(x) = 2e^{-x} + e^{-x} - xe^{-x} = 3e^{-x} - f(x)$;

in general, $f^{(n)}(x) = (-1)^n(xe^{-x} - ne^{-x}) = (-1)^n e^{-x}(x-n)$ for any $n \geq 1$.

72. $f'(x) = -1/x^2$; $f''(x) = 2!/x^3$; $f^{(3)}(x) = -(3!)/x^4$; in general, $f^{(n)}(x) = (-1)^n n!/x^{n+1}$ for any $n \geq 1$.

73. $f'(x) = -\dfrac{1}{(1-x)^2}(-1) = \dfrac{1}{(1-x)^2}$; $f''(x) = \dfrac{2!}{(1-x)^3}$; $f^{(3)}(x) = \dfrac{3!}{(1-x)^4}$;

in general, $f^{(n)}(x) = \dfrac{n!}{(1-x)^{n+1}}$ for any $n \geq 1$.

74. $f'(x) = 1/x$; $f''(x) = -1/x^2$; $f^{(3)}(x) = 2!/x^3$;

in general, $f^{(n)}(x) = (-1)^{n-1}(n-1)!/x^n$ for any integer $n \geq 1$.

75. a. $f'(x) = \cos x$; $f''(x) = -\sin x$; $f^{(3)}(x) = -\cos x$; $f^{(4)}(x) = \sin x = f(x)$. Thus $f^{(4n)}(x) = \sin x$; $f^{(4n+1)}(x) = \cos x$; $f^{(4n+2)}(x) = -\sin x$; $f^{(4n+3)}(x) = -\cos x$. This is equivalent to $f^{(2n)}(x) = (-1)^n \sin x$ and $f^{(2n+1)}(x) = (-1)^n \cos x$.

b. $f'(x) = -\sin x$; $f''(x) = -\cos x$; $f^{(3)}(x) = \sin x$; $f^{(4)}(x) = \cos x = f(x)$. Thus $f^{(4n)}(x) = \cos x$; $f^{(4n+1)}(x) = -\sin x$; $f^{(4n+2)}(x) = -\cos x$; $f^{(4n+3)}(x) = \sin x$. This is equivalent to $f^{(2n)}(x) = (-1)^n \cos x$ and $f^{(2n+1)}(x) = (-1)^{n+1} \sin x$.

76. a. $f'(x) = \sin x + x\cos x$; $f''(x) = \cos x + \cos x - x\sin x = 2\cos x - x\sin x$; $f^{(3)}(x) = -2\sin x - \sin x - x\cos x = -3\sin x - x\cos x$; $f^{(4)}(x) = -3\cos x - \cos x + x\sin x = -4\cos x + x\sin x$. In general, for any positive integer n, $f^{(2n)}(x) = (-1)^{n-1}[2n\cos x - x\sin x]$ and $f^{(2n+1)}(x) = (-1)^n[(2n+1)\sin x + x\cos x]$.

b. Proceeding as in part (a), we obtain $f'(x) = \cos x - x\sin x$; $f''(x) = -2\sin x - x\cos x$; $f^{(3)}(x) = -3\cos x + x\sin x$; $f^{(4)}(x) = 4\sin x + x\cos x$. In general, for any positive integer n, $f^{(2n)}(x) = (-1)^n(2n\sin x + x\cos x)$ and $f^{(2n+1)}(x) = (-1)^n[(2n+1)\cos x - x\sin x]$.

77. Let $g(x) = 1/x$ and $h(x) = 1/(x+1)$. Then

$$g'(x) = -\frac{1}{x^2}, \qquad g''(x) = \frac{(-2)(-1)}{x^3}, \qquad g^{(3)}(x) = \frac{(-3)(-2)(-1)}{x^4}$$

and in general,

$$g^{(n)}(x) = \frac{(-1)^n n!}{x^{n+1}}.$$

Similarly,

$$h^{(n)}(x) = \frac{(-1)^n n!}{(x+1)^{n+1}}.$$

Since $f(x) = g(x) - h(x)$, it follows that

$$f^{(n)}(x) = g^{(n)}(x) - h^{(n)}(x) = \frac{(-1)^n n!}{x^{n+1}} - \frac{(-1)^n n!}{(x+1)^{n+1}} = (-1)^n n!\left[\frac{1}{x^{n+1}} - \frac{1}{(x+1)^{n+1}}\right].$$

78. a. $f''(x) = 2xf(x) + x^2f'(x) = 2xf(x) + x^2(x^2f(x)) = 2xf(x) + x^4f(x) = (2x + x^4)f(x)$

b. $f''(3) = (2\cdot 3 + 3^4)f(3) = (6+81)\pi = 87\pi$

79. $f(x) = x^3 + ax^2 + bx + c$; $f'(x) = 3x^2 + 2ax + b$; $f''(x) = 6x + 2a$; $f^{(3)}(x) = 6$. We are to find a, b and c so that $f(0) = f'(1) = f''(2) = f^{(3)}(3) = 6$. Thus $6 = f(0) = c$. Next, $6 = f'(1) = 3(1) + 2a(1) + b = 3 + 2a + b$. In addition, $6 = f''(2) = 6(2) + 2a = 12 + 2a$, so $a = -3$. Therefore $b = 6 - 3 - 2a = 3 - 2(-3) = 9$. It follows that $f(x) = x^3 - 3x^2 + 9x + 6$. You can check that $f(0) = f'(1) = f''(2) = f^{(3)}(3)$.

80. $h'(x) = f'(x)g(x) + f(x)g'(x)$;

$$h''(x) = f''(x)g(x) + f'(x)g'(x) + f'(x)g'(x) + f(x)g''(x) = f''(x)g(x) + 2f'(x)g'(x) + f(x)g''(x)$$

81. $h'(x) = g'(f(x))f'(x)$; $h''(x) = g''(f(x))\left(f'(x)\right)^2 + g'(f(x))f''(x)$

82. Angular velocity $= f'(t) = -2\pi\omega a\sin 2\pi\omega t$; angular acceleration $= f''(t) = -4\pi^2\omega^2 a\cos 2\pi\omega t$.

83. $f'(x) = ae^{(-be^{-cx})}(-be^{-cx})(-c) = abce^{-cx}e^{(-be^{-cx})}$;

$$f''(x) = -abc^2e^{-cx}e^{(-be^{-cx})} + ab^2c^2e^{-2cx}e^{(-be^{-cx})} = abc^2e^{-cx}e^{(-be^{-cx})}(-1 + be^{-cx})$$

84. $\dfrac{ds}{dt} = kae^{kt} - bke^{-kt}$; $\dfrac{d^2s}{dt^2} = k^2ae^{kt} + bk^2e^{-kt} = k^2(ae^{kt} + be^{-kt}) = k^2s$, so acceleration is k^2 times the distance traveled.

85. a. Let $f(x) = ax^2 + bx + c$, so $f'(x) = 2ax + b$. If $f(0) = 0$, then $c = 0$. If $f'(0) = 1$, then $b = 1$. If $f(-1) = 0$, then $0 = a(-1)^2 + b(-1) + c = a - 1$, so $a = 1$. Thus $f(x) = x^2 + x$ does the job.

b. Suppose g is such a polynomial. Since the highways are linear, it would follow that $g''(-1) = 0$ and $g''(0) = 0$, but $g''(x) \neq 0$ for some x in $(-1, 0)$. Therefore g'' must be divisible by $x(x+1)$ and hence g must have at least degree 4. (Since g must satisfy the six conditions $g(-1) = 0$, $g(0) = -1$, $g'(-1) = -1$, $g'(0) = 0$, $g''(-1) = 0$, and $g''(0) = 2$, it turns out that no polynomial of degree 4 (having only 5 coefficients) satisfies all six conditions. However, the polynomial $-3x^5 - 8x^4 - 6x^3 - 1$ of degree five does satisfy all six conditions. Thus, in fact, the minimal degree is 5.)

86. a. $f'(x) = \dfrac{a^2bke^{-kax}}{(1+be^{-kax})^2}$;

$$f''(x) = \frac{-a^3bk^2e^{-kax}(1+be^{-kax})^2 - a^2bke^{-kax}[2(1+be^{-kax})(-abke^{-kax})]}{(1+be^{-kax})^4}$$

$$= \frac{a^3bk^2e^{-kax}(-1+be^{-kax})}{(1+be^{-kax})^3}$$

b. Since a, b, and k are positive constants, $f''(c) = 0$ if $-1 + be^{-kac} = 0$, that is, $b = e^{kac}$, so $kac = \ln b$. Thus $c = (\ln b)/ka$.

c. $f((\ln b)/ka) = \dfrac{a}{1 + be^{-ka((\ln b)/ka)}} = \dfrac{a}{1+be^{-\ln b}} = \dfrac{a}{1+1} = \dfrac{a}{2}$

87. $a = \dfrac{dv}{dt} = \dfrac{dv}{dx}\dfrac{dx}{dt} = \dfrac{dv}{dx}v = \left(\dfrac{x}{30} - \dfrac{11}{10}\right)\left(\dfrac{x^2}{60} - \dfrac{11x}{10} + 25\right)$

If $x = -1$, then

$$a = \left(\frac{-1}{30} - \frac{11}{10}\right)\left(\frac{1}{60} + \frac{11}{10} + 25\right) = -29.60 \text{ (feet per second per second).}$$

3.6 Implicit Differentiation

1. $6y\dfrac{dy}{dx} = 8x^3$; $\dfrac{dy}{dx} = \dfrac{4x^3}{3y}$

2. $2y\dfrac{dy}{dx} = \dfrac{3x^2(2-x) - x^3(-1)}{(2-x)^2} = \dfrac{6x^2 - 2x^3}{(2-x)^2}$; $\dfrac{dy}{dx} = \dfrac{3x^2 - x^3}{y(2-x)^2}$

3. $2y\dfrac{dy}{dx} + \dfrac{dy}{dx} = \dfrac{(1-x) - (1+x)(-1)}{(1-x)^2} = \dfrac{2}{(1-x)^2}$; $\dfrac{dy}{dx} = \dfrac{2}{(2y+1)(1-x)^2}$

4. $2x = \dfrac{2y(dy/dx)(y^2-1) - y^2(2y(dy/dx))}{(y^2-1)^2} = \dfrac{-2y(dy/dx)}{(y^2-1)^2}$; $\dfrac{dy}{dx} = -\dfrac{x}{y}(y^2-1)^2$

5. $\sec y \tan y \dfrac{dy}{dx} - \sec^2 x = 0$; $\dfrac{dy}{dx} = \dfrac{\sec^2 x}{\sec y \tan y}$

6. $\dfrac{1}{2}x^{-1/2} - \dfrac{1}{2}y^{-3/2}\dfrac{dy}{dx} = 0$; $\dfrac{dy}{dx} = \dfrac{\sqrt{y^3}}{\sqrt{x}}$

7. $\dfrac{(\cos y)(dy/dx)(y^2+1)-(\sin y)2y(dy/dx)}{(y^2+1)^2}=3;\ \dfrac{dy}{dx}=\dfrac{3(y^2+1)^2}{(y^2+1)\cos y-2\sin y}$

8. $1=\dfrac{\left(-\frac{1}{2}y^{-1/2}(dy/dx)\right)(1+y^{1/2})-(1-y^{1/2})\left(\frac{1}{2}y^{-1/2}(dy/dx)\right)}{(1+y^{1/2})^2};\ \dfrac{dy}{dx}=-\sqrt{y}\,(1+\sqrt{y})^2$

9. $2x+\left(2xy^2+2x^2y\dfrac{dy}{dx}\right)+3y^2\dfrac{dy}{dx}=0;\ \dfrac{dy}{dx}=\dfrac{-2x-2xy^2}{2x^2y+3y^2}$

10. $2x=\dfrac{(1-2y(dy/dx))(x+y)-(x-y^2)(1+dy/dx)}{(x+y)^2}=\dfrac{(y+y^2)-(x+2xy+y^2)(dy/dx)}{(x+y)^2}$

$\dfrac{dy}{dx}=\dfrac{y+y^2-2x(x+y)^2}{x+2xy+y^2}$

11. $2x+2y\dfrac{dy}{dx}=\dfrac{(2y(dy/dx))x^2-y^2(2x)}{x^4}=\dfrac{2y}{x^2}\dfrac{dy}{dx}-\dfrac{2y^2}{x^3};\ \dfrac{dy}{dx}=\dfrac{x+(y^2/x^3)}{(y/x^2)-y}=\dfrac{x^4+y^2}{xy-x^3y}$

12. $\dfrac{1}{2}(1+xy)^{-1/2}\left(y+x\dfrac{dy}{dx}\right)=\dfrac{y-x(dy/dx)}{y^2}+\dfrac{x(dy/dx)-y}{x^2}=\dfrac{1}{y}-\dfrac{x}{y^2}\dfrac{dy}{dx}+\dfrac{1}{x}\dfrac{dy}{dx}-\dfrac{y}{x^2}$

$\dfrac{dy}{dx}=\dfrac{(y/2)(1+xy)^{-1/2}-(1/y)+(y/x^2)}{(1/x)-(x/y^2)-(x/2)(1+xy)^{-1/2}}$

13. $\dfrac{1}{2}(xy)^{1/2}\left(y+x\dfrac{dy}{dx}\right)+\dfrac{1}{2}(x+2y)^{-1/2}\left(1+2\dfrac{dy}{dx}\right)=0;\ \dfrac{dy}{dx}=\dfrac{-y(xy)^{-1/2}-(x+2y)^{-1/2}}{x(xy)^{-1/2}+2(x+2y)^{-1/2}}$

14. $2\left(y+x\dfrac{dy}{dx}\right)=\dfrac{3}{2}(x^2+y^3)^{1/2}\left(2x+3y^2\dfrac{dy}{dx}\right);\ \dfrac{dy}{dx}=\dfrac{3x(x^2+y^3)^{1/2}-2y}{2x-\frac{9}{2}y^2(x^2+y^3)^{1/2}}$

15. $x^2+y^2=(x^2+y^2)^{1/2}+2x;\ 2x+2y\dfrac{dy}{dx}=\dfrac{x+y(dy/dx)}{(x^2+y^2)^{1/2}}+2;$

$2y\dfrac{dy}{dx}-\dfrac{y}{(x^2+y^2)^{1/2}}\dfrac{dy}{dx}=\dfrac{x}{(x^2+y^2)^{1/2}}-2x+2;$

$\dfrac{dy}{dx}=\dfrac{x/(x^2+y^2)^{1/2}-2x+2}{2y-y/(x^2+y^2)^{1/2}}=\dfrac{x+2(1-x)(x^2+y^2)^{1/2}}{2y(x^2+y^2)^{1/2}-y}$

16. $x^2+y^2=(x^2+y^2)^{1/2}-x;\ 2x+2y\dfrac{dy}{dx}=\dfrac{x+y(dy/dx)}{(x^2+y^2)^{1/2}}-1;$

$2y\dfrac{dy}{dx}-\dfrac{y}{(x^2+y^2)^{1/2}}\dfrac{dy}{dx}=\dfrac{x}{(x^2+y^2)^{1/2}}-2x-1;$

$\dfrac{dy}{dx}=\dfrac{x/(x^2+y^2)^{1/2}-2x-1}{2y-y/(x^2+y^2)^{1/2}}=\dfrac{x-(2x+1)(x^2+y^2)^{1/2}}{2y(x^2+y^2)^{1/2}-y}$

17. $e^y+xe^y\dfrac{dy}{dx}=\dfrac{dy}{dx}+2x;\ \dfrac{dy}{dx}=\dfrac{2x-e^y}{xe^y-1}$

18. $e^{xy}\left(y+x\dfrac{dy}{dx}\right)=2+\dfrac{dy}{dx}$, so $xe^{xy}\dfrac{dy}{dx}-\dfrac{dy}{dx}=2-ye^{xy};\ \dfrac{dy}{dx}=\dfrac{2-ye^{xy}}{xe^{xy}-1}$

19. $\dfrac{dy}{dx}+\dfrac{1}{2\sqrt{y}}\dfrac{dy}{dx}(\ln x)+\dfrac{\sqrt{y}}{x}=2x+2y\dfrac{dy}{dx};\ \dfrac{dy}{dx}=\dfrac{2x-\sqrt{y}/x}{1+(\ln x)/(2\sqrt{y})-2y}$

20. $\dfrac{1}{x-y}\left(1-\dfrac{dy}{dx}\right)=y+x\dfrac{dy}{dx}$, so $x\dfrac{dy}{dx}+\dfrac{1}{x-y}\dfrac{dy}{dx}=\dfrac{1}{x-y}-y$; $\dfrac{dy}{dx}=\dfrac{1/(x-y)-y}{x+1/(x-y)}=\dfrac{1-xy+y^2}{x^2-xy+1}$

21. $2x+2y\dfrac{dy}{dx}=\dfrac{dy}{dx}$; $\dfrac{dy}{dx}=\dfrac{2x}{1-2y}$. At $(0,1)$, $\dfrac{dy}{dx}=\dfrac{0}{1-2}=0$.

22. $2x-2y\dfrac{dy}{dx}=0$; $\dfrac{dy}{dx}=\dfrac{x}{y}$. At $(\sqrt{3},\sqrt{2})$, $\dfrac{dy}{dx}=\dfrac{\sqrt{3}}{\sqrt{2}}=\dfrac{\sqrt{6}}{2}$.

23. $y+x\dfrac{dy}{dx}=0$; $\dfrac{dy}{dx}=-\dfrac{y}{x}$. At $(-2,-1)$, $\dfrac{dy}{dx}=\dfrac{-(-1)}{-2}=-\dfrac{1}{2}$.

24. $4x^3+\left(y^3+3xy^2\dfrac{dy}{dx}\right)=0$; $\dfrac{dy}{dx}=-\dfrac{4x^3+y^3}{3xy^2}$. At $(-1,1)$, $\dfrac{dy}{dx}=-\dfrac{4(-1)+1}{3(-1)(1)}=-1$.

25. $3x^2+2\left(y+x\dfrac{dy}{dx}\right)=0$; $\dfrac{dy}{dx}=-\dfrac{3x^2+2y}{2x}$. At $(1,2)$, $\dfrac{dy}{dx}=\dfrac{3+2\cdot 2}{-2}=-\dfrac{7}{2}$.

26. $2x+3\left(y+x\dfrac{dy}{dx}\right)+4y\dfrac{dy}{dx}=0$; $(2x+3y)+(3x+4y)\dfrac{dy}{dx}=0$, so $\dfrac{dy}{dx}=-\dfrac{2x+3y}{3x+4y}$.

At $(-1,-1)$, $\dfrac{dy}{dx}=\dfrac{-2-3}{-(-3-4)}=-\dfrac{5}{7}$.

27. $2x+\dfrac{y-x(dy/dx)}{y^2}=0$; $\dfrac{dy}{dx}=\dfrac{2x+(1/y)}{x/y^2}=\dfrac{2xy^2+y}{x}$. At $(1,-\frac{1}{3})$, $\dfrac{dy}{dx}=\dfrac{2(1)(-\frac{1}{3})^2+(-\frac{1}{3})}{1}=-\dfrac{1}{9}$.

28. $\dfrac{(x+2y)-x\big(1+2(dy/dx)\big)}{(x+2y)^2}=-\dfrac{dy}{dx}$; $\dfrac{2y}{(x+2y)^2}=\left(\dfrac{2x}{(x+2y)^2}-1\right)\dfrac{dy}{dx}$,

or $\dfrac{dy}{dx}=\dfrac{2y}{(x+2y)^2}\cdot\dfrac{(x+2y)^2}{2x-(x+2y)^2}=\dfrac{2y}{2x-(x+2y)^2}$. At $(1,0)$, $\dfrac{dy}{dx}=0$.

29. $\dfrac{1}{2\sqrt{x}}(\sqrt{y}+2)+(\sqrt{x}+1)\left(\dfrac{1}{2\sqrt{y}}\dfrac{dy}{dx}\right)=0$; $\dfrac{dy}{dx}=\dfrac{\sqrt{y}+2}{2\sqrt{x}}\cdot\dfrac{-2\sqrt{y}}{\sqrt{x}+1}=-\dfrac{y+2\sqrt{y}}{x+\sqrt{x}}$.

At $(1,4)$, $\dfrac{dy}{dx}=-\dfrac{4+2\cdot 2}{1+1}=-4$.

30. $5(2x+y)^4\left(2+\dfrac{dy}{dx}\right)=\dfrac{1}{x^2}$; $\dfrac{dy}{dx}=\dfrac{1}{5x^2(2x+y)^4}-2$. At $(-1,4)$, $\dfrac{dy}{dx}=\dfrac{1}{5(-2+4)^4}-2=-\dfrac{159}{80}$.

31. $\cos x=-(\sin y)\dfrac{dy}{dx}$; $\dfrac{dy}{dx}=-\dfrac{\cos x}{\sin y}$. At $\left(\dfrac{\pi}{6},\dfrac{\pi}{3}\right)$, $\dfrac{dy}{dx}=-\dfrac{\cos(\pi/6)}{\sin(\pi/3)}=-\dfrac{\sqrt{3}/2}{\sqrt{3}/2}=-1$.

32. $2y\dfrac{dy}{dx}\sin 2x+y^2(\cos 2x)(2)=-2\dfrac{dy}{dx}$, so $2(y\sin 2x+1)\dfrac{dy}{dx}=-2y^2\cos 2x$, or $\dfrac{dy}{dx}=-\dfrac{y^2\cos 2x}{y\sin 2x+1}$.

At $(\pi/4,-2)$, $\dfrac{dy}{dx}=0$.

33. $2e^{x^2y}\left(2xy+x^2\dfrac{dy}{dx}\right)=1$, so $4xye^{x^2y}+2x^2e^{x^2y}\dfrac{dy}{dx}=1$; $\dfrac{dy}{dx}=\dfrac{1-4xye^{x^2y}}{2x^2e^{x^2y}}$.

At $(2,0)$, $\dfrac{dy}{dx}=\dfrac{1-4(2)(0)e^0}{2(2^2)e^0}=\dfrac{1}{8}$.

34. $\dfrac{1}{x^2-3y}\left(2x-3\,\dfrac{dy}{dx}\right)=1-\dfrac{dy}{dx}$, so $\dfrac{dy}{dx}-\dfrac{3}{x^2-3y}\,\dfrac{dy}{dx}=1-\dfrac{2x}{x^2-3y}$;

$\dfrac{dy}{dx}=\dfrac{1-2x/(x^2-3y)}{1-3/(x^2-3y)}=\dfrac{x^2-3y-2x}{x^2-3y-3}$. At $(2,1)$, $\dfrac{dy}{dx}=\dfrac{4-3-4}{4-3-3}=\dfrac{3}{2}$.

35. $y^2+2xy\,\dfrac{dy}{dx}=0$; $\dfrac{dy}{dx}=-\dfrac{y}{2x}$. At $(2,-3)$, $\dfrac{dy}{dx}=-\dfrac{(-3)}{2(2)}=\dfrac{3}{4}$.

Thus l: $y-(-3)=\frac{3}{4}(x-2)$, or $y=\frac{3}{4}x-\frac{9}{2}$.

36. $2x+2y\,\dfrac{dy}{dx}=3\,\dfrac{dy}{dx}$; $(2y-3)\dfrac{dy}{dx}=-2x$, or $\dfrac{dy}{dx}=\dfrac{-2x}{2y-3}$. At $(-\sqrt{2},2)$, $\dfrac{dy}{dx}=\dfrac{-2(-\sqrt{2})}{2(2)-3}=2\sqrt{2}$.

Thus l: $y-2=2\sqrt{2}\,(x-(-\sqrt{2}))$, or $y=2\sqrt{2}\,x+6$.

37. $\cos(x+y)\left(1+\dfrac{dy}{dx}\right)=2$; $\dfrac{dy}{dx}=\dfrac{2}{\cos(x+y)}-1$. At $(0,\pi)$, $\dfrac{dy}{dx}=\dfrac{2}{\cos(0+\pi)}-1=-2-1=-3$.

Thus l: $y-\pi=-3(x-0)$, or $y=-3x+\pi$.

38. $2y\,\dfrac{dy}{dx}=\dfrac{3x^2(2-x)-x^3(-1)}{(2-x)^2}$; $\dfrac{dy}{dx}=\dfrac{6x^2-2x^3}{2y(2-x)^2}=\dfrac{3x^2-x^3}{y(2-x)^2}$. At $(1,1)$, $\dfrac{dy}{dx}=\dfrac{3-1}{1(2-1)^2}=2$.

Thus l: $y-1=2(x-1)$, or $y=2x-1$.

39. $2x-4y^3\,\dfrac{dy}{dx}=0$; $\dfrac{dy}{dx}=\dfrac{x}{2y^3}$;

$$\frac{d^2y}{dx^2}=\frac{2y^3-x\big(6y^2(dy/dx)\big)}{(2y^3)^2}=\frac{2y^3-6xy^2[x/(2y^3)]}{4y^6}=\frac{2y^3-(3x^2/y)}{4y^6}=\frac{2y^4-3x^2}{4y^7}$$

40. $2y^2+2x\left(2y\dfrac{dy}{dx}\right)=0$; $\dfrac{dy}{dx}=\dfrac{-2y^2}{4xy}=\dfrac{-y}{2x}$;

$$\frac{d^2y}{dx^2}=\frac{-(dy/dx)(2x)-(-y)(2)}{4x^2}=\frac{-[-y/(2x)](2x)+2y}{4x^2}=\frac{3y}{4x^2}$$

41. $2x\sin 2y+2x^2(\cos 2y)\,\dfrac{dy}{dx}=0$; $\dfrac{dy}{dx}=-\dfrac{2x\sin 2y}{2x^2\cos 2y}=-\dfrac{\tan 2y}{x}$

$$\frac{d^2y}{dx^2}=-\frac{(\sec^2 2y)(2(dy/dx))x-\tan 2y}{x^2}=-\frac{(\sec^2 2y)2(-(\tan 2y)/x)x-\tan 2y}{x^2}=\frac{\tan 2y\,(2\sec^2 2y+1)}{x^2}$$

42. $\tan y+(x\sec^2 y)\,\dfrac{dy}{dx}=\dfrac{dy}{dx}$; $\dfrac{dy}{dx}=\dfrac{\tan y}{1-x\sec^2 y}$;

$$\frac{d^2y}{dx^2}=\frac{\left(\sec^2 y\,\dfrac{dy}{dx}\right)(1-x\sec^2 y)-\tan y\left(-\sec^2 y-2x\sec y\,\sec y\,\tan y\,\dfrac{dy}{dx}\right)}{(1-x\sec^2 y)^2}$$

$$=\frac{\sec^2 y\left(\dfrac{\tan y}{1-x\sec^2 y}\right)(1-x\sec^2 y)+\tan y\left(\sec^2 y+2x\sec^2 y\,\tan y\,\dfrac{\tan y}{1-x\sec^2 y}\right)}{(1-x\sec^2 y)^2}$$

$$=\frac{2\sec^2 y\,\tan y\,(1-x\sec^2 y)+2x\sec^2 y\,\tan^3 y}{(1-x\sec^2 y)^3}$$

43. $2y\dfrac{dy}{dt} - 2x\dfrac{dx}{dt} = 0$, so $\dfrac{dy}{dt} = \dfrac{2x(dx/dt)}{2y} = \dfrac{x}{y}\dfrac{dx}{dt}$

44. $2x\dfrac{dx}{dt} + 3y^2\dfrac{dy}{dt} = \dfrac{dx}{dt}$, so $3y^2\dfrac{dy}{dt} = (1-2x)\dfrac{dx}{dt}$, and thus $\dfrac{dy}{dt} = \dfrac{1-2x}{3y^2}\dfrac{dx}{dt}$

45. $\dfrac{dx}{dt}\sin y + x\cos y\dfrac{dy}{dt} = 0$, so $\dfrac{dy}{dt} = -\dfrac{\sin y}{x\cos y}\dfrac{dx}{dt} = -\dfrac{\tan y}{x}\dfrac{dx}{dt}$

46. $\left(4x^3\dfrac{dx}{dt}\right)y^2 + x^4\left(2y\dfrac{dy}{dt}\right) = \dfrac{dy}{dt}$, so $(1-2x^4y)\dfrac{dy}{dt} = 4x^3y^2\dfrac{dx}{dt}$, and thus $\dfrac{dy}{dt} = \dfrac{4x^3y^2}{1-2x^4y}\dfrac{dx}{dt}$.

47. $\dfrac{dy}{dt} = -\sin(xy^2)\left[\dfrac{dx}{dt}y^2 + 2xy\dfrac{dy}{dt}\right]$, so $\dfrac{dy}{dt} = -\dfrac{y^2\sin(xy^2)(dx/dt)}{1+2xy\sin(xy^2)}$

48. $\dfrac{dy}{dt} + \dfrac{1}{x}\dfrac{dx}{dt} + e^y\dfrac{dy}{dt} = 0$, so $\dfrac{dy}{dt} = \left(-\dfrac{1}{x}\dfrac{dx}{dt}\right)\dfrac{1}{1+e^y} = \dfrac{-1}{x+xe^y}\dfrac{dx}{dt}$

49. a. $5y^4\dfrac{dy}{dx} + \dfrac{dy}{dx} + 1 = 0$; $\dfrac{dy}{dx} = \dfrac{-1}{5y^4+1}$

b. $5y^4\dfrac{dy}{dx} + 3y^2\dfrac{dy}{dx} + 3x^2 + \dfrac{dy}{dx} = 0$; $\dfrac{dy}{dx} = \dfrac{-3x^2}{5y^4+3y^2+1}$

c. $5 = 3y^2\dfrac{dy}{dx} + \cos y\dfrac{dy}{dx} + \dfrac{dy}{dx}$; $\dfrac{dy}{dx} = \dfrac{5}{3y^2+\cos y+1}$

50. a. $3y^2\dfrac{dy}{dx} = 2x$; $\dfrac{dy}{dx} = \dfrac{2x}{3y^2}$. Also $y = x^{2/3}$; $\dfrac{dy}{dx} = \dfrac{2}{3}x^{-1/3} = \dfrac{2x}{3x^{4/3}} = \dfrac{2x}{3y^2}$.

b. $\dfrac{-8}{y^2}\dfrac{dy}{dx} = 2x$; $\dfrac{dy}{dx} = \dfrac{-xy^2}{4}$. Also $y = \dfrac{8}{x^2+4}$; $\dfrac{dy}{dx} = \dfrac{-16x}{(x^2+4)^2} = \dfrac{-x}{4}\left(\dfrac{8}{x^2+4}\right)^2 = \dfrac{-xy^2}{4}$.

c. $3y^2\dfrac{dy}{dx} = \dfrac{2x(x^2-1)-x^2(2x)}{(x^2-1)^2} = \dfrac{-2x}{(x^2-1)^2}$; $\dfrac{dy}{dx} = \dfrac{-2x}{3y^2(x^2-1)^2}$.

Also $y = \left(\dfrac{x^2}{x^2-1}\right)^{1/3}$;

$$\frac{dy}{dx} = \frac{1}{3}\left(\frac{x^2}{x^2-1}\right)^{-2/3}\left[\frac{2x(x^2-1)-x^2(2x)}{(x^2-1)^2}\right] = \frac{1}{3}y^{-2}\left[\frac{-2x}{(x^2-1)^2}\right] = \frac{-2x}{3y^2(x^2-1)^2}.$$

51. Using implicit differentiation, we find that

$$3x^2 + 3y^2\frac{dy}{dx} = 2y + 2x\frac{dy}{dx}.$$

Now $dy/dx = -1$ provided that $3x^2 - 3y^2 = 2y - 2x$, which occurs if $x = 1 = y$. Since $(1,1)$ is on the folium, we conclude that $Q = (1,1)$.

52. $3x^2 + 3y^2\dfrac{dy}{dx} = 3y + 3x\dfrac{dy}{dx}$; $\dfrac{dy}{dx} = \dfrac{x^2-y}{x-y^2}$, and at $(\frac{3}{2},\frac{3}{2})$, $\dfrac{dy}{dx} = \dfrac{\frac{9}{4}-\frac{3}{2}}{\frac{3}{2}-\frac{9}{4}} = -1$.

Tangent line: $y - \frac{3}{2} = -1(x - \frac{3}{2})$, or $y = -x + 3$. Normal line: $y - \frac{3}{2} = x - \frac{3}{2}$, or $y = x$. The normal line passes through the origin.

53. $\frac{2}{3}x^{-1/3}+\frac{2}{3}y^{-1/3}\frac{dy}{dx}=0$; $\frac{dy}{dx}=-\left(\frac{y}{x}\right)^{1/3}$, and at $(2\sqrt{2},2\sqrt{2})$, $\frac{dy}{dx}=-1$. Thus l: $y-2\sqrt{2}=-1(x-2\sqrt{2})$, or $y=-x+4\sqrt{2}$. The x intercept is $4\sqrt{2}$, and the y intercept is $4\sqrt{2}$, so the area of the triangle is $\frac{1}{2}(4\sqrt{2})(4\sqrt{2})=16$.

54. a. By implicit differentiation we obtain $\frac{2}{3}x^{-1/3}+\frac{2}{3}y^{-1/3}(dy/dx)=0$, so $dy/dx=-y^{1/3}/x^{1/3}$. For the tangent in the first quadrant we have $dy/dx=-1$ (see Figure 3.25). This means that $-1=-y^{1/3}/x^{1/3}$, so $x=y$. Thus $x^{2/3}+x^{2/3}=4$, so $x^{2/3}=2$ and thus $x=2^{3/2}=2\sqrt{2}$. Therefore the point of tangency in the first quadrant is $(2\sqrt{2},2\sqrt{2})$, and the corresponding tangent line is $y-2\sqrt{2}=-1(x-2\sqrt{2})$, or $y=-x+4\sqrt{2}$. By symmetry the remaining tangent lines are given by $y=x+4\sqrt{2}$, $y=x-4\sqrt{2}$, and $y=-x-4\sqrt{2}$.

b. The sides of the square have length 8, so $A=8^2=64$.

55. Let (p,q) be on the graph of $\sqrt{x}+\sqrt{y}=\sqrt{c}$. At (p,q), we have

$$\frac{1}{2\sqrt{p}}+\frac{1}{2\sqrt{q}}\frac{dy}{dx}=0, \quad \text{so} \quad \frac{dy}{dx}=-\frac{\sqrt{q}}{\sqrt{p}}.$$

Thus the line tangent at (p,q) is given by $y-q=-(\sqrt{q}/\sqrt{p})(x-p)$. Setting $x=0$, we find that the y intercept b is given by

$$b=q-\frac{\sqrt{q}}{\sqrt{p}}(-p)=q+\sqrt{pq}.$$

Setting $y=0$, we find that the x intercept satisfies

$$-q=-\frac{\sqrt{q}}{\sqrt{p}}(a-p), \quad \text{so that} \quad a=p+\sqrt{pq}.$$

Therefore

$$a+b=(p+\sqrt{pq})+(q+\sqrt{pq})=p+2\sqrt{pq}+q=(\sqrt{p}+\sqrt{q})^2=c.$$

56. The curves intersect at (x,y) such that $x^2+y^2=(x-1)^2+y^2$, or $x^2=(x-1)^2=x^2-2x+1$, or $x=\frac{1}{2}$. Thus $y^2=1-x^2=1-\frac{1}{4}=\frac{3}{4}$, so that points of intersection are $(\frac{1}{2},\sqrt{3}/2)$ and $(\frac{1}{2},-\sqrt{3}/2)$. To obtain dy/dx, we proceed as follows:

$$x^2+y^2=1 \qquad\qquad (x-1)^2+y^2=1$$

$$2x+2y\frac{dy}{dx}=0 \qquad\qquad 2(x-1)+2y\frac{dy}{dx}=0$$

$$\frac{dy}{dx}=\frac{-x}{y} \qquad\qquad \frac{dy}{dx}=\frac{1-x}{y}$$

At $(\frac{1}{2},\sqrt{3}/2)$ the slopes are $m_1=-\frac{1}{2}/(\sqrt{3}/2)=-1/\sqrt{3}$ and $m_2=\frac{1}{2}/(\sqrt{3}/2)=1/\sqrt{3}$. Thus

$$\tan\theta=\frac{(1/\sqrt{3})-(-1/\sqrt{3})}{1+(-1/\sqrt{3})(1/\sqrt{3})}=\sqrt{3}$$

so $\theta = \pi/3$. At $(\frac{1}{2}, -\sqrt{3}/2)$ the slopes are $m_1 = -\frac{1}{2}/(-\sqrt{3}/2) = 1/\sqrt{3}$ and $m_2 = \frac{1}{2}/(-\sqrt{3}/2) = -1/\sqrt{3}$. Thus

$$\tan\theta = \frac{-1/\sqrt{3} - 1/\sqrt{3}}{1 + (1/\sqrt{3})(-1/\sqrt{3})} = -\sqrt{3}$$

so $\theta = \frac{2}{3}\pi$.

57. The circle has the form $x^2 + (y-b)^2 = 1$. At the points at which the curves touch, the slopes of the tangents are equal. Differentiating the equations with respect to x, we obtain

$$2x + 2(y-b)\frac{dy}{dx} = 0 \qquad \frac{dy}{dx} = 4x$$

$$\frac{dy}{dx} = \frac{x}{b-y}$$

Thus x and y must also satisfy $4x = x/(b-y)$, or $y - b = -\frac{1}{4}$. Substituting this value in $x^2 + (y-b)^2 = 1$, we find that $x = \pm\sqrt{15}/4$. Then $y = 2x^2$ becomes $y = \frac{15}{8}$. The points are $(\sqrt{15}/4, \frac{15}{8})$ and $(-\sqrt{15}/4, \frac{15}{8})$.

58. Differentiating implicitly, we obtain $2(x^2+y^2)(2x + 2y(dy/dx)) = 2x - 2y(dy/dx)$. If $dy/dx = 0$, then $(x^2+y^2)(2x) = x$, that is, $(2x^2+2y^2-1)x = 0$. Since $x \neq 0$ by hypothesis, it follows that $2x^2+2y^2-1 = 0$, or $y^2 = \frac{1}{2} - x^2$. Substituting for y^2 in the original equation, we obtain $(x^2 + \frac{1}{2} - x^2)^2 = x^2 - (\frac{1}{2} - x^2)$, so that $\frac{1}{4} = 2x^2 - \frac{1}{2}$, or $x = \pm\sqrt{\frac{3}{8}} = \pm\sqrt{6}/4$. Then $y^2 = \frac{1}{2} - x^2 = \frac{1}{2} - \frac{3}{8} = \frac{1}{8}$. Thus the points at which the tangent lines are horizontal are $(\sqrt{6}/4, \sqrt{2}/4)$, $(\sqrt{6}/4, -\sqrt{2}/4)$, $(-\sqrt{6}/4, \sqrt{2}/4)$, and $(-\sqrt{6}/4, -\sqrt{2}/4)$.

3.7 Related Rates

1. As in (2), $dV/dt = 4\pi r^2(dr/dt)$, and we are to determine dV/dt at the instant t_0 when $r = 4$. Since $dr/dt = -\frac{1}{2}$ by hypothesis, we have

$$\left.\frac{dV}{dt}\right|_{t=t_0} = 4\pi r^2 \left.\frac{dr}{dt}\right|_{t=t_0} = 4\pi(4^2)(-\tfrac{1}{2}) = -32\pi.$$

Thus the volume decreases at the rate of 32π cubic centimeters per minute when $t = t_0$.

2. As in (2), $dV/dt = 4\pi r^2(dr/dt)$, and we are to determine dV/dt at the instant t_0 when $r = 2$. Since $dr/dt = -1$ by hypothesis, we have

$$\left.\frac{dV}{dt}\right|_{t=t_0} = 4\pi r^2 \left.\frac{dr}{dt}\right|_{t=t_0} = 4\pi(2^2)(-1) = -16\pi.$$

Thus the volume decreases at the rate of 16π cubic inches per hour when $t = t_0$.

3. Here

$$4\pi r^2\frac{dr}{dt} = \frac{dV}{dt} = -\frac{2}{V} = -\frac{2}{4\pi r^3/3} = -\frac{3}{2\pi r^3}$$

and we are to determine dr/dt at the instant t_0 when $r = \frac{1}{2}$. We have

$$\left.\frac{dr}{dt}\right|_{t=t_0} = -\frac{3}{(2\pi r^3)4\pi r^2} = -\frac{3}{8\pi^2 r^5} = -\frac{3}{8\pi^2(1/32)} = -\frac{12}{\pi^2}.$$

Thus the radius decreases at the rate of $12/\pi^2$ inches per hour.

4. As in (2), $dV/dt = 4\pi r^2(dr/dt)$, and we are to determine dr/dt at the instant t_0 when $r = 6$. Since $dV/dt = 3$ by hypothesis, we have

$$3 = \left.\frac{dV}{dt}\right|_{t=t_0} = 4\pi r^2 \left.\frac{dr}{dt}\right|_{t=t_0} = 4\pi 6^2 \left.\frac{dr}{dt}\right|_{t=t_0}, \quad \text{so} \quad \left.\frac{dr}{dt}\right|_{t=t_0} = \frac{3}{4\pi 6^2} = \frac{1}{48\pi}.$$

Thus the radius increases at the rate of $1/(48\pi)$ centimeters per minute when $t = t_0$.

5. Here $4\pi r^2(dr/dt) = dV/dt = (d/dt)(4\sqrt{t}) = 2/\sqrt{t}$ for $t > 0$, and we are to determine dr/dt when $t = 64$. Since $V = 4\sqrt{64} = 32$ for $t = 64$, we have $32 = V = \frac{4}{3}\pi r^3$ at that instant, so $r^3 = 96/(4\pi) = 24/\pi$ and thus $r = (24/\pi)^{1/3}$ when $t = 64$. Then

$$\left.\frac{dr}{dt}\right|_{t=64} = \frac{2}{\sqrt{t}}\frac{1}{4\pi r^2} = \frac{2}{\sqrt{64}}\frac{1}{4\pi(24/\pi)^{2/3}} = \frac{1}{64\pi^{1/3}3^{2/3}}.$$

Thus after 64 seconds the radius increases at the rate of $1/(64\pi^{1/3}3^{2/3})$ centimeters per second.

6. As in (2), $dV/dt = 4\pi r^2(dr/dt)$, and we are to determine dr/dt at the instant t_0 when $r = 8$. Since $dV/dt = -2$ by hypothesis, we have

$$-2 = \left.\frac{dV}{dt}\right|_{t=t_0} = 4\pi r^2 \left.\frac{dr}{dt}\right|_{t=t_0} = 4\pi(8)^2 \left.\frac{dr}{dt}\right|_{t=t_0}, \quad \text{so} \quad \left.\frac{dr}{dt}\right|_{t=t_0} = \frac{-2}{4\pi 8^2} = \frac{-1}{128\pi}.$$

Thus the radius shrinks at the rate of $1/(128\pi)$ centimeters per minute when $t = t_0$.

7. Let A denote the area and r the radius of the circular pool. Then $A = \pi r^2$ and $dA/dt = 2\pi r(drdt)$, and we are to determine dr/dt at the instant t_0 when $r = 10$. Since $dA/dt = 3$ by hypothesis, we have

$$3 = \left.\frac{dA}{dt}\right|_{t=t_0} = 2\pi r \left.\frac{dr}{dt}\right|_{t=t_0} = 2\pi(10) \left.\frac{dr}{dt}\right|_{t=t_0}, \quad \text{so} \quad \left.\frac{dr}{dt}\right|_{t=t_0} = \frac{3}{2\pi(10)} = \frac{3}{20\pi}.$$

Thus the radius increases at the rate of $3/(20\pi)$ centimeters per minute when $t = t_0$.

8. Differentiating $x^2 + y^2 = 9$ implicitly with respect to t, we obtain $2x(dx/dt) + 2y(dy/dt) = 0$. We are to determine dy/dt at the instant t_0 when $x = -\sqrt{3}$ and $y = \sqrt{6}$. Since $dx/dt = 20$ by hypothesis, this yields

$$2(-\sqrt{3})(20) + 2(\sqrt{6}) \left.\frac{dy}{dt}\right|_{t=t_0} = 0, \quad \text{so that} \quad \left.\frac{dy}{dt}\right|_{t=t_0} = \frac{2(\sqrt{3})20}{2\sqrt{6}} = 10\sqrt{2}.$$

Thus the y coordinate grows at the rate of $10\sqrt{2}$ units per second when $t = t_0$.

9. Let x be the distance from the bottom of the ladder to the wall and y the distance from the ground to the top of the ladder. Then $x^2+y^2 = 13^2$, so $2x(dx/dt)+2y(dy/dt) = 0$. We are to find dx/dt at the instant t_0 when $x = 3$. Because $x^2+y^2 = 13^2$, it follows that if $x = 3$, then $y^2 = 13^2 - x^2 = 13^2 - 3^2 = 160$, so $y = \sqrt{160} = 4\sqrt{10}$. Since $dy/dt = 1$ by hypothesis, for $t = t_0$ the equation $2x(dx/dt) + 2y(dy/dt) = 0$ becomes

$$2(3)\left.\frac{dx}{dt}\right|_{t=t_0} + 2(4\sqrt{10}) = 0, \quad \text{so that} \quad \left.\frac{dx}{dt}\right|_{t=t_0} = -\frac{8\sqrt{10}}{6} = -\frac{4}{3}\sqrt{10}.$$

Thus the base of the ladder approaches the wall at the rate of $\frac{4}{3}\sqrt{10}$ feet per second when $t = t_0$.

10. Let x be the distance from the bottom of the ladder to the wall, and y the distance from the ground to the top of the ladder. Then $x^2 + y^2 = 15^2$, so $2x(dx/dt) + 2y(dy/dt) = 0$. We are to find dy/dt at the instant t_0 when $x = 5$, which means that $y^2 = 15^2 - x^2 = 15^2 - 5^2 = 200$. Since $dx/dt = -\frac{1}{2}x$ by hypothesis, we obtain

$$\frac{dy}{dt} = -\frac{x}{y}\frac{dx}{dt} = -\frac{x}{y}\left(-\frac{1}{2}x\right) = \frac{1}{2}\frac{x^2}{y}, \quad \text{so that} \quad \left.\frac{dy}{dt}\right|_{t=t_0} = \left.\frac{1}{2}\frac{x^2}{y}\right|_{t=t_0} = \frac{1}{2}\cdot\frac{25}{\sqrt{200}} = \frac{5}{8}\sqrt{2}.$$

Thus the top of the ladder is rising at $\frac{5}{8}\sqrt{2}$ feet per second when $t = t_0$.

11. Let x be the distance from the bottom of the board to the wall and y the distance from the ground to the top of the board, so $x^2 + y^2 = 5^2$, and thus $2x(dx/dt) + 2y(dy/dt) = 0$.

   a. We are to find dx/dt at the instant t_0 when $x = 4$ and $dy/dt = -2$. If $x = 4$, then $y^2 = 5^2 - x^2 = 5^2 - 4^2 = 9$, so $y = 3$. We obtain

$$2(4)\left.\frac{dx}{dt}\right|_{t=t_0} + 2(3)(-2) = 0, \quad \text{so} \quad \left.\frac{dx}{dt}\right|_{t=t_0} = \frac{-2(3)(-2)}{2(4)} = \frac{3}{2}.$$

   Thus the bottom end slides at the rate of 3/2 feet per second when $t = t_0$.

   b. Let A denote the area of the region, so $A = \frac{1}{2}xy$, and $dA/dt = \frac{1}{2}(dx/dt)y + \frac{1}{2}x(dy/dt)$. We are to find dA/dt at the instant t_0 when $x = 4$, $y = 3$, $dx/dt = \frac{3}{2}$, and $dy/dt = -2$. We obtain

$$\left.\frac{dA}{dt}\right|_{t=t_0} = \frac{1}{2}\left(\frac{3}{2}\right)3 + \frac{1}{2}(4)(-2) = -\frac{7}{4}.$$

   Thus the area shrinks at the rate of $\frac{7}{4}$ square feet per second when $t = t_0$.

12. From (8) we have $dh/dt = [9/(\pi h^2)](dV/dt)$, and we are to find dh/dt at the instant t_0 when $h = 2$. Since $dV/dt = \frac{3}{2}$ by hypothesis, we obtain

$$\left.\frac{dh}{dt}\right|_{t=t_0} = \frac{9}{\pi(2)^2}\left(\frac{3}{2}\right) = \frac{27}{8\pi}.$$

Thus the water level rises at the rate of $27/(8\pi)$ inches per second when $t = t_0$.

13. Let x be the depth of the water, y the width of the top of the water, and V the volume at any time. Then $V = \frac{1}{2}xy(12) = 6xy$, and we are to find dx/dt at the instant t_0 when $x = \frac{1}{2}$. From the figure, $y/2 = x\tan(\pi/6) = (\sqrt{3}/3)x$, so that $y = (2\sqrt{3}/3)x$ and thus $V = 6x(2\sqrt{3}/3)x = 4\sqrt{3}\,x^2$. Then $dV/dt = 8\sqrt{3}\,x(dx/dt)$. Since $dV/dt = 3$ by hypothesis, we obtain

$$3 = 8\sqrt{3}\left(\frac{1}{2}\right)\left.\frac{dx}{dt}\right|_{t=t_0}, \quad \text{so that} \quad \left.\frac{dx}{dt}\right|_{t=t_0} = \frac{3}{8\sqrt{3}\left(\frac{1}{2}\right)} = \frac{\sqrt{3}}{4}.$$

Thus the water level rises at the rate of $\sqrt{3}/4$ feet per minute when $t = t_0$.

14. Since $x = \tan\theta$ and $d\theta/dt = 10\pi$, the Chain Rule implies that

$$\frac{dx}{dt} = (\sec^2\theta)\left(\frac{d\theta}{dt}\right) = 10\pi\sec^2\theta.$$

At any time t_0 at which the spotlight shines on the sand 2 miles from the lighthouse, $\sec\theta = 2$, so that $(dx/dt)\big|_{t=t_0} = 40\pi$ (miles per minute).

15. Since $pV = c$, we have $(dp/dt)V + p(dV/dt) = 0$. We are to find dp/dt at the instant t_0 when $p = 100$ and $V = 20$. Since $dV/dt = -10$ by hypothesis, we obtain

$$\left(\left.\frac{dp}{dt}\right|_{t=t_0}\right)20 + 100(-10) = 0, \quad \text{so that} \quad \left.\frac{dp}{dt}\right|_{t=t_0} = 50.$$

Thus the pressure increases at the rate of 50 pounds per square centimeter per second when $t = t_0$.

16. We are to find dp/dt at the instant t_0 when $V = 30$ and $p = 3 \times 10^6$. Now

$$\frac{dp}{dt}V^{1.4} + p(1.4V^{0.4})\frac{dV}{dt} = 0,$$

and by hypothesis, $dV/dt = -2$. We obtain

$$\left.\frac{dp}{dt}\right|_{t=t_0} = \frac{-3\times 10^6[1.4(30^{0.4})2]}{30^{1.4}} = -2.8\times 10^5 \text{ dynes per square centimeter per second.}$$

17. We are to find dx/dt at the moment t_0 when the nucleus is at $(2c, c\sqrt{3})$, that is, $x = 2c$ and $y = c\sqrt{3}$. Now $2x(dx/dt) - 2y(dy/dt) = 0$, and by hypothesis, $dy/dt = 2$. Therefore

$$\left.\frac{dx}{dt}\right|_{t=t_0} = \frac{y}{x}\frac{dy}{dt} = \frac{c\sqrt{3}}{2c}(2) = \sqrt{3}.$$

18. We are to find dv_{esc}/dt at the instant t_0 when $r = 45{,}000$ and $dr/dt = -3\times 10^{-6}$. Now

$$\frac{dv_{\text{esc}}}{dt} = \frac{1}{2\sqrt{2GM/r}}\left(-\frac{2GM}{r^2}\frac{dr}{dt}\right) = \frac{-\sqrt{GM}}{r\sqrt{2r}}\frac{dr}{dt}$$

so that

$$\left.\frac{dv_{\text{esc}}}{dt}\right|_{t=t_0} = \frac{-\sqrt{(6.67\times 10^{-11})(4\times 10^{30})}}{(4.5\times 10^3)\sqrt{9\times 10^3}}(-3\times 10^{-6}) \approx 0.115.$$

Thus the escape velocity is increasing at approximately 0.115 kilometers per second at that time.

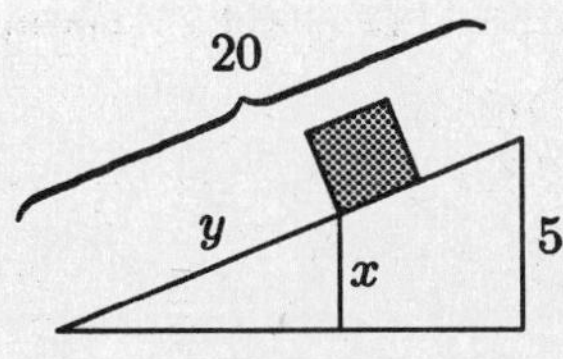

Exercise 19

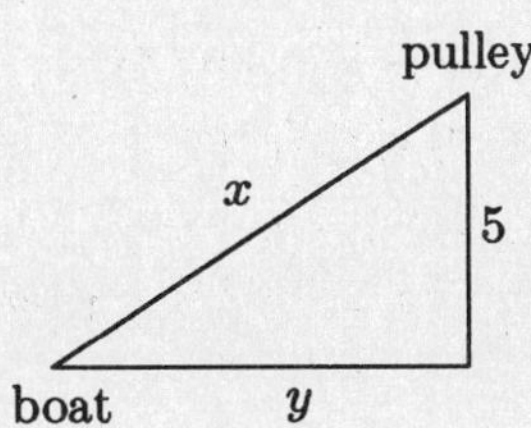

Exercises 20 & 21

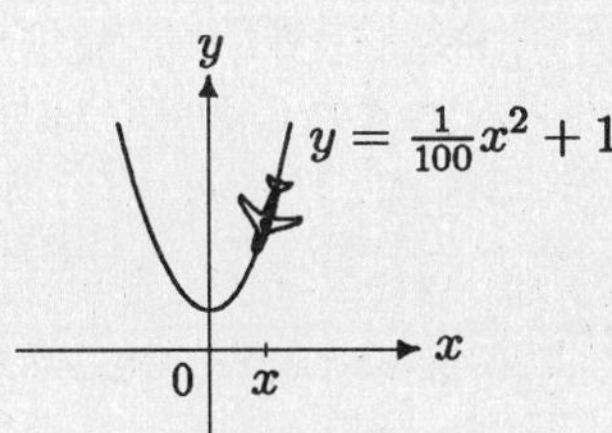

Exercise 23

19. Let x be the height of the bottom end of the box, and y the distance the bottom end has traveled at any time (see the figure on the next page). Then by similar triangles, $x/5 = y/20$, so that $x = \frac{1}{4}y$. We are to find dx/dt. Since $dy/dt = 3$ by hypothesis, we obtain $dx/dt = \frac{1}{4}(dy/dt) = \frac{1}{4}(3) = \frac{3}{4}$. Thus the bottom of the box rises at the rate of $\frac{3}{4}$ foot per second.

20. Let x be the distance along the rope from the bow to the pulley and y the distance from the bow to the dock at any given time. Then from the figure, $x^2 = y^2 + 5^2$, so $2x(dx/dt) = 2y(dy/dt)$. We are to find dy/dt at the instant t_0 when $x = 13$. If $x = 13$, then $y^2 = x^2 - 5^2 = 13^2 - 5^2 = 144$, so $y = 12$. Since $dx/dt = -2$ by hypothesis, we obtain

$$2(13)(-2) = 2(12)\left.\frac{dy}{dt}\right|_{t=t_0}, \quad \text{so} \quad \left.\frac{dy}{dt}\right|_{t=t_0} = -\frac{13}{6}.$$

Thus the boat docks at the rate of $\frac{13}{6}$ feet per second when $t = t_0$.

21. Let x be the distance along the pulley and y the distance from the bow to the dock at any given time. Then from the figure, $x^2 = y^2 + 5^2$, so that $2x(dx/dt) = 2y(dy/dt)$. We are to find dx/dt at the instant t_0 when $y = 12$. If $y = 12$, then $x^2 = y^2 + 5^2 = 12^2 + 5^2 = 169$, so $x = 13$. Since $dy/dt = -2$ by hypothesis, we obtain

$$2(13)\left.\frac{dx}{dt}\right|_{t=t_0} = 2(12)(-2), \quad \text{so} \quad \left.\frac{dx}{dt}\right|_{t=t_0} = -\frac{24}{13}.$$

Thus the rope is pulled in at the rate of $24/13$ feet per second when $t = t_0$.

22. As in Exercise 20, $2x(dx/dt) = 2y(dy/dt)$. We are to find dx/dt at the instant t_0 when $y = 8$. If $y = 8$, then $x^2 = y^2 + 5^2 = 8^2 + 5^2 = 89$, so $x = \sqrt{89}$. Since $dy/dt = -y^{1/3}$ by hypothesis, we obtain

$$2\sqrt{89}\left.\frac{dx}{dt}\right|_{t=t_0} = 2(8)(-8^{1/3}), \quad \text{so that} \quad \left.\frac{dx}{dt}\right|_{t=t_0} = \frac{-16}{\sqrt{89}} = -\frac{16}{89}\sqrt{89}.$$

Thus the length of rope is shrinking at the rate of $16\sqrt{89}/89$ feet per second when $t = t_0$.

23. Assume that $x > 0$, as in the figure. By hypothesis, $y = \frac{1}{100}x^2 + 1$, so that $dy/dt = \frac{1}{50}x(dx/dt)$. We are to find dx/dt at the instant t_0 when $y = 2501$. If $y = 2501$, then $\frac{1}{100}x^2 = y - 1 = 2501 - 1 = 2500$, so $x = 500$. Since $dy/dt = -100$ by hypothesis, we obtain

$$-100 = \frac{1}{50}(500)\left.\frac{dx}{dt}\right|_{t=t_0}, \quad \text{so that} \quad \left.\frac{dx}{dt}\right|_{t=t_0} = -10.$$

Thus the shadow moves at the rate of 10 feet per second when $t = t_0$.

24. By hypothesis, $y = 5001 - 2500\sqrt{4-x}$, so $dy/dt = 1250(4-x)^{-1/2}(dx/dt)$.

a. We are to find dy/dt at the instant t_0 when $x = 3$. Since $dx/dt = -10$ by hypothesis, we obtain

$$\left.\frac{dy}{dt}\right|_{t=t_0} = 1250(4-x)^{-1/2}\frac{dx}{dt} = 1250(4-3)^{-1/2}(-10) = -12{,}500.$$

Thus the hare moves at the rate of 12,500 feet per minute when $t = t_0$.

b. When the tortoise crosses the finish line, $x = 0$ and $y = 5001 - 2500\sqrt{4-x} = 5001 - 2500\sqrt{4-0} = 5001 - 5000 = 1$, so the tortoise wins by 1 foot.

25. Let x be the distance between the runner and third base. Then $\tan\theta = x/90$, so that $(\sec^2\theta)(d\theta/dt) = \frac{1}{90}(dx/dt)$. We are to find $d\theta/dt$ at the instant t_0 when $x = 30$. Since the runner is approaching third base at the rate of 24 feet per second, we have $dx/dt = -24$. Moreover, if $x = 30$, then $\tan\theta = \frac{30}{90} = \frac{1}{3}$, and thus $\sec^2\theta = 1 + \tan^2\theta = 1 + (\frac{1}{3})^2 = \frac{10}{9}$. Therefore

$$\left.\frac{d\theta}{dt}\right|_{t=t_0} = \frac{1}{90\sec^2\theta}\left.\frac{dx}{dt}\right|_{t=t_0} = \frac{1}{90(\frac{10}{9})}(-24) = -\frac{6}{25}.$$

Consequently the angle θ is changing at the rate of $\frac{6}{25}$ radians per second when the runner is 30 feet from third base.

26. Let x be the distance between the sports car and the intersection, and y the distance between the police car and sports car. Then $y^2 = x^2 + (\frac{1}{4})^2$, so $2y(dy/dt) = 2x(dx/dt)$. We are to find dy/dt at the instant t_0 when $x = \frac{1}{8}$. If $x = \frac{1}{8}$, then $y^2 = (\frac{1}{8})^2 + (\frac{1}{4})^2 = \frac{5}{64}$, so that $y = \frac{1}{8}\sqrt{5}$. Since $dx/dt = -40$ by hypothesis, we obtain

$$2\left(\frac{1}{8}\sqrt{5}\right)\left.\frac{dy}{dt}\right|_{t=t_0} = 2\left(\frac{1}{8}\right)(-40), \quad \text{and thus} \quad \left.\frac{dy}{dt}\right|_{t=t_0} = -8\sqrt{5}.$$

Thus the distance between the cars shrinks $8\sqrt{5}$ miles per hour when $t = t_0$.

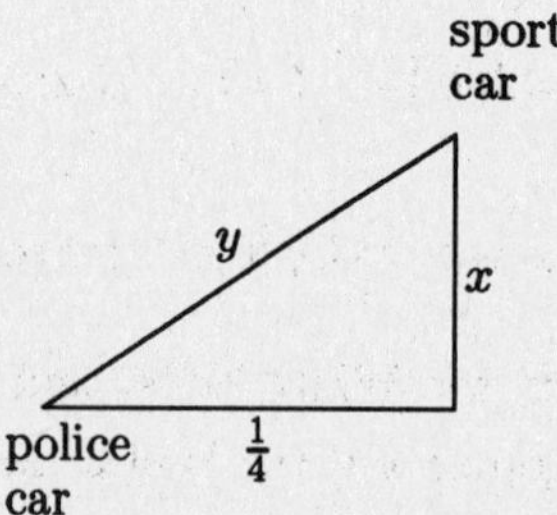

27. Let x be the distance between the sports car and the intersection, and y the distance between the police car and sports car (see the figure in Exercise 26). Then $y^2 = x^2 + (\frac{1}{4})^2$, so $2y(dy/dt) = 2x(dx/dt)$. We are to find x under the condition that $dx/dt = -50$ and $dy/dt = -30$. This yields $2y(-30) = 2x(-50)$, so that $y = \frac{5}{3}x$. Since $x^2 = y^2 - (\frac{1}{4})^2$, we substitute $y = \frac{5}{3}x$ to obtain $x^2 = (\frac{5}{3}x)^2 - (\frac{1}{4})^2$. Thus $x^2 = \frac{25}{9}x^2 - \frac{1}{16}$, so that $\frac{16}{9}x^2 = \frac{1}{16}$, or $x^2 = \frac{9}{16^2}$. Therefore $x = \frac{3}{16}$. Consequently the sports car would be $\frac{3}{16}$ mile from the intersection.

Exercise 28

Exercise 30

28. Let x be the distance between the person and the building, and y the length of the shadow. By the figure, $6/(100-x) = y/100$, so that $y = 600/(100-x)$.

   a. We are to find dy/dt at the instant t_0 when $x = 50$. Since $dx/dt = -5$ by hypothesis, we obtain

$$\left.\frac{dy}{dt}\right|_{t=t_0} = \frac{600}{(100-x)^2}\left.\frac{dx}{dt}\right|_{t=t_0} = \frac{600}{50^2}(-5) = -\frac{6}{5}.$$

   Thus the top of the shadow moves down the building at the rate of $\frac{6}{5}$ feet per second when $t = t_0$.

   b. If we substitute $x = 25$ in part (a), we obtain

$$\left.\frac{dy}{dt}\right|_{t=t_0} = \frac{600}{(100-x)^2}\left.\frac{dx}{dt}\right|_{t=t_0} = \frac{600}{75^2}(-5) = -\frac{8}{15}.$$

   Thus the top of the shadow moves down the building at the rate of $\frac{8}{15}$ feet per second when $t = t_0$.

29. Let x be the length of string let out, and y the ground distance from the holder to a position directly below the kite. Then $x^2 = y^2 + 100^2$, so that $2x(dx/dt) = 2y(dy/dt)$. We are to find dx/dt at the instant t_0 when $x = 200$. If $x = 200$, then $y^2 = x^2 - 100^2 = 200^2 - 100^2 = 30{,}000$, so $y = 100\sqrt{3}$. Since $dy/dt = 10$ by hypothesis, we have

$$2(200)\left.\frac{dx}{dt}\right|_{t=t_0} = 2(100\sqrt{3})(10), \quad \text{so that} \quad \left.\frac{dx}{dt}\right|_{t=t_0} = 5\sqrt{3}.$$

Thus the string must be let out at the rate of $5\sqrt{3}$ feet per second when $t = t_0$.

30. Let x be the ground distance between the White House and the point directly under the helicopter, and y the distance between the helicopter and the White House. Then $y^2 = \frac{1}{4} + x^2$, so $2y(dy/dt) = 2x(dx/dt)$. We are to find dy/dt when $t = 1$. If $t = 1$, then $x = 2$ and thus $y^2 = x^2 + (\frac{1}{2})^2 = 2^2 + (\frac{1}{2})^2 = \frac{17}{4}$, so $y = \frac{1}{2}\sqrt{17}$. Since $dx/dt = 2$, we obtain

$$2\left(\frac{1}{2}\sqrt{17}\right)\left.\frac{dy}{dt}\right|_{t=1} = 2(2)(2), \quad \text{so that} \quad \left.\frac{dy}{dt}\right|_{t=1} = \frac{8}{17}\sqrt{17}.$$

Thus the distance between helicopter and White House changes at the rate of $8\sqrt{17}/17$ kilometers per minute when $t = 1$.

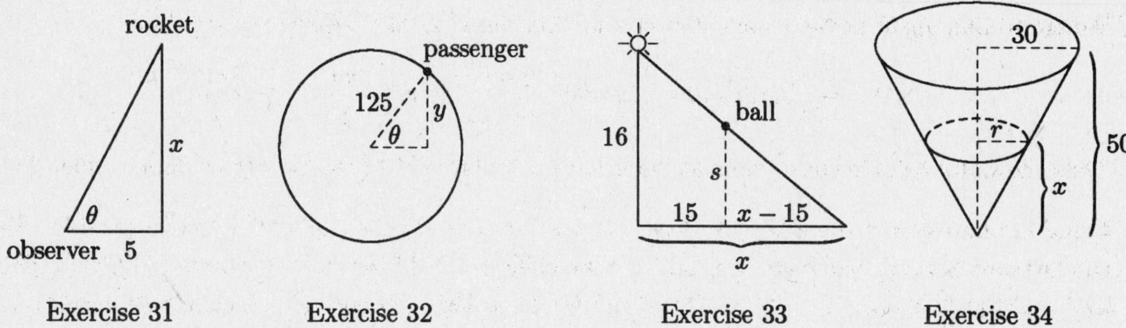

Exercise 31 Exercise 32 Exercise 33 Exercise 34

31. Let x be the altitude of the rocket, and θ the angle of elevation (see the figure). Then $\tan\theta = x/5$, and we are to find $d\theta/dt$ at the instant t_0 when $x = 2$. Now $(\sec^2\theta)(d\theta/dt) = \frac{1}{5}(dx/dt)$, and if $x = 2$, then $\sec\theta = \sqrt{x^2+5^2}/5 = \sqrt{2^2+5^2}/5 = \sqrt{29}/5$, so that $\sec^2\theta = \frac{29}{25}$. Since at that instant $dx/dt = 300$, we obtain

$$\frac{29}{25}\left.\frac{d\theta}{dt}\right|_{t=t_0} = \frac{1}{5}(300), \quad \text{so that} \quad \left.\frac{d\theta}{dt}\right|_{t=t_0} = \frac{1500}{29}.$$

Thus the angle of elevation increases at the rate of of $\frac{1500}{29}$ radians per hour when $t = t_0$.

32. Using the notation in the figure and the fact that the passenger is rising, we have $d\theta/dt = 2$ and $y = 125\sin\theta$, so that $dy/dt = (125\cos\theta)(d\theta/dt) = 250\cos\theta$. At any instant at which the passenger is 75 feet higher than the center and is rising we have

$$\cos\theta = \frac{\sqrt{125^2 - 75^2}}{125} = \frac{100}{125} = \frac{4}{5}, \quad \text{so} \quad \frac{dy}{dt} = 250\left(\frac{4}{5}\right) = 200.$$

Thus the passenger is rising at the rate of 200 feet per minute at such an instant.

33. Let x be the distance from the shadow to the point directly beneath the light, and s the distance from the ball to the ground. We are to find dx/dt at the instant t_0 when $s = 5$. Notice that $s/(x-15) = 16/x$, or $s = 16(1 - (15/x))$, so that $ds/dt = (240/x^2)(dx/dt)$. But $s = 16 - 16t^2$, so that $ds/dt = -32t$. Thus $-32t = ds/dt = (240/x^2)/(dx/dt)$, or $dx/dt = -2tx^2/15$. If $s = 5$, then $5 = 16(1 - (15/x))$, so that $x = \frac{240}{11}$. Also if $s = 5$, then $5 = 16 - 16t^2$, so that $t = \sqrt{11}/4$. Thus if $s = 5$, then

$$\left.\frac{dx}{dt}\right|_{t=t_0} = \frac{-2}{15}\left(\frac{\sqrt{11}}{4}\right)\left(\frac{240}{11}\right)^2 = \frac{-1920\sqrt{11}}{121}$$

so that the shadow moves at the rate of $(1920\sqrt{11})/121$ feet per second when $t = t_0$.

34. Let V be the volume of water in the conical tank when the height of the water is x and the radius at the top of the water is r. Then $V = \frac{1}{3}\pi r^2 x$, and by the figure, $r/x = \frac{30}{50} = \frac{3}{5}$, so that $r = \frac{3}{5}x$ and thus $V = \frac{1}{3}\pi(\frac{3}{5}x)^2 x = (3\pi/25)x^3$. Let W be the volume of water in the rectangular tank when the height of water is y. Then $W = 400y$. Since the total amount of water is constant, there is a number C so that $V + W = C$. Thus

$$0 = \frac{dV}{dt} + \frac{dW}{dt} = 3\left(\frac{3\pi}{25}x^2\right)\frac{dx}{dt} + 400\frac{dy}{dt}.$$

We are to find dy/dt at the instant t_0 when $x = 10$. Since $dx/dt = -(50 - x)$, we obtain

$$0 = \frac{-9\pi}{25}(10)^2(50-10) + 400\left.\frac{dy}{dt}\right|_{t=t_0}, \quad \text{so} \quad \left.\frac{dy}{dt}\right|_{t=t_0} = \frac{18\pi}{5}.$$

Thus the water level in the rectangular tank rises at the rate of $18\pi/5$ inches per minute when $t = t_0$.

35. Using the notation in the figure, we have $x = 3000\tan\theta$, so that $dx/dt = 3000(\sec^2\theta)(d\theta/dt)$. When the distance between the helicopter and the searchlight is 5000 feet, we have $\sec\theta = \frac{5000}{3000} = \frac{5}{3}$. Since $dx/dt = 100$, it follows that $100 = 3000(\frac{5}{3})^2(d\theta/dt)$, so that $d\theta/dt = \frac{3}{250}$ (radians per second) when the distance between the helicopter and the searchlight is 5000 feet.

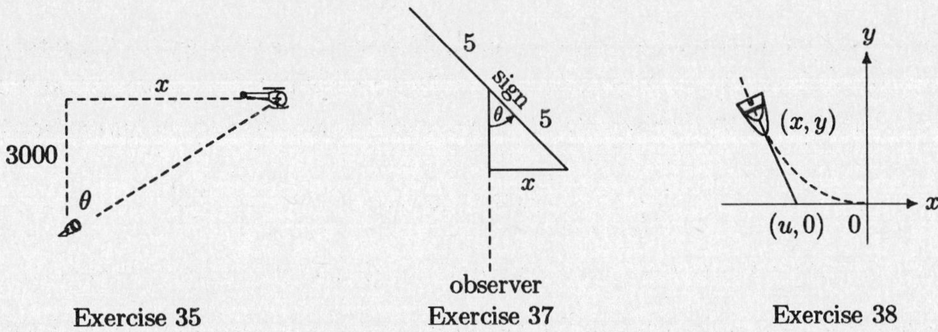

Exercise 35 Exercise 37 Exercise 38

36. By Figure 3.40, $\tan\theta = 20/x$, so that $(\sec^2\theta)(d\theta/dt) = -(20/x^2)/(dx/dt)$. Notice that the distance between the car and deer is $\sqrt{400 + x^2}$, so $\sec^2\theta = (400 + x^2)/x^2$. By hypothesis, $dx/dt = -v$ (since x is shrinking). Thus

$$\frac{d\theta}{dt} = -\frac{20}{x^2}\frac{1}{\sec^2\theta}\frac{dx}{dt} = -\frac{20}{x^2}\frac{x^2}{400+x^2}(-v) = \frac{20v}{400+x^2}.$$

37. Let x be one half the width of the sign as seen by the observer, and θ the angle shown in the figure. We are to find dx/dt at the instant t_0 when $x = 3$ and $dx/dt > 0$. Since the sign makes 10 revolutions per minute and appears to grow when $t = t_0$, we have $d\theta/dt = 20\pi$. Notice that $x = 5\sin\theta$, so that $dx/dt = (5\cos\theta)(d\theta/dt)$. If $x = 3$, then $\cos\theta = \frac{4}{5}$. Therefore

$$\left.\frac{dx}{dt}\right|_{t=t_0} = (5\cos\theta)\left.\frac{d\theta}{dt}\right|_{t=t_0} = 5\left(\frac{4}{5}\right)(20\pi) = 80\pi.$$

Thus half the width changes at the rate of 80π feet per minute, and the total width changes at the rate of 160π feet per minute when $t = t_0$.

38. Let $(u, 0)$ be the point on the shore illuminated when the boat is at (x, y). We are to find du/dt at the instant t_0 when $x = -2$. Since the tangent line at (x, y) has slope dy/dx and passes through (x, y) and $(u, 0)$, we have $(y - 0)/(x - u) = dy/dx$. Since $y = -\frac{1}{2}x^3$, we know that $dy/dx = -\frac{3}{2}x^2$, so $(y-0)/(x-u) = -\frac{3}{2}x^2$, so $y = \frac{3}{2}x^2(u - x)$. Since $y = -\frac{1}{2}x^3$, it follows that $-\frac{1}{2}x^3 = \frac{3}{2}x^2(u-x) = \frac{3}{2}x^2u - \frac{3}{2}x^3$, so that $x^3 = \frac{3}{2}x^2u$, and since $x \neq 0$, we find that $u = \frac{2}{3}x$. Thus $du/dt = \frac{2}{3}(dx/dt)$. Since $dx/dt = -x$ by hypothesis, we obtain $(du/dt)|_{t=t_0} = \frac{2}{3}(-(-2)) = \frac{4}{3}$. Therefore the illuminated spot moves at the rate of $\frac{4}{3}$ units per unit time when $t = t_0$.

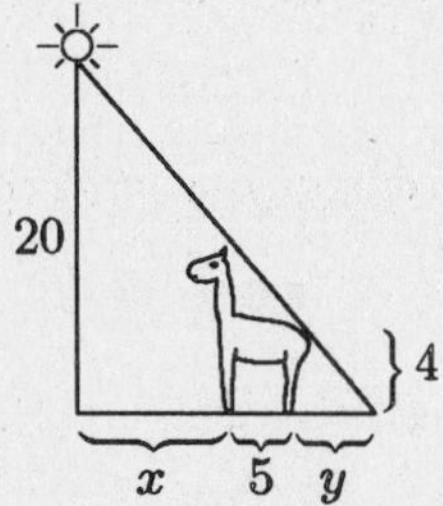

Light ray over deer's rump

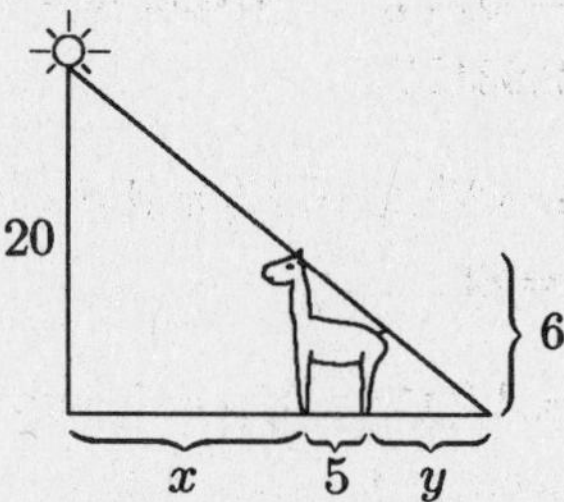

Light ray over deer's head

39. Let x be the distance from the base of the street light to forelegs of the deer, and let y be the distance from the rear legs of the deer to the tip of the shadow. We want y as a function of x.

Notice that if the deer is close to the base of the light, the tip is formed by a ray just passing over the deer's rump. Since the rump is 4 feet high and the deer is 5 feet long, by using similar triangles we have

$$\frac{y}{4} = \frac{x+y+5}{20}, \quad \text{or} \quad y = \frac{x+5}{4}.$$

Thus for "small" x, $dy/dt = \frac{1}{4}(dx/dt) = -\frac{3}{4}$ (feet per second).

Now if the deer is far from the base of the light, the tip of the shadow is formed by light just passing over the deer's head. Since the head is 6 feet high and the deer is 5 feet long, by using similar triangles we have

$$\frac{y+5}{6} = \frac{x+y+5}{20}, \quad \text{or} \quad y = \frac{3}{7}x - 5.$$

Thus for "large" x, $dy/dt = \frac{3}{7}(dx/dt) = -9/7$ (feet per second).

We now determine the boundary between "x small" and "x large". That boundary occurs when the same ray of light just passes over the head and just passes over the rump. At that point $(x+5)/4 = y = \frac{3}{7}x - 5$. Solving for x, we find the boundary at $x = 35$ (feet). For (a) we conclude that when the deer is 48 feet from the street light, x is "large", so the shadow is decreasing at $\frac{9}{7}$ feet per second. For (b) we conclude that when the deer is 24 feet from the street light, x is "small", so the shadow is decreasing at $\frac{3}{4}$ feet per second.

3.8 Approximations

Exercises 1–14 can be solved with either (2) or (7). We will use (2).

1. Let $f(x) = \sqrt{x}$, $a = 100$, and $h = 1$. Then $f'(x) = \frac{1}{2}x^{-1/2}$, $f'(100) = \frac{1}{20}$, and $\sqrt{101} \approx f(100) + f'(100)h = 10 + \frac{1}{20}(1) = 10.05$.

2. Let $f(x) = \sqrt{x}$, $a = 100$, and $h = -0.5$. Then $f'(x) = \frac{1}{2}x^{-1/2}$, $f'(100) = \frac{1}{20}$, and $\sqrt{99.5} \approx f(100) + f'(100)h = 10 + (\frac{1}{20})(-0.5) = 9.975$.

3. Let $f(x) = \sqrt[3]{x}$, $a = 27$, and $h = 2$. Then $f'(x) = \frac{1}{3}x^{-2/3}$, $f'(27) = \frac{1}{27}$, and $\sqrt[3]{29} \approx f(27) + f'(27)h = 3 + \frac{1}{27}(2) \approx 3.074074074$.

4. Let $f(x) = \sqrt[4]{x}$, $a = 16$, and $h = 1$. Then $f'(x) = \frac{1}{4}x^{-3/4}$, $f'(16) = \frac{1}{32}$, and $\sqrt[4]{17} \approx f(16) + f'(16)h = 2 + \frac{1}{32} = 2.03125$.

5. Let $f(x) = x^{4/3}$, $a = 27$, and $h = 1$. Then $f'(x) = \frac{4}{3}x^{1/3}$, $f'(27) = 4$, and $(28)^{4/3} \approx f(27) + f'(27)h = 81 + 4(1) = 85$.

6. Let $f(x) = 1/(1+x^2)$, $a = 1$, and $h = 0.0175$. Then

$$f'(x) = \frac{-2x}{(1+x^2)^2}, \quad f'(1) = -\frac{1}{2}$$

and

$$\frac{1}{1+(1.0175)^2} \approx f(1) + f'(1)h = \frac{1}{2} + \left(\frac{-1}{2}\right)(0.0175) = .49125.$$

7. Let $f(x) = \cos x$, $a = \pi/6$, and $h = -\pi/78$. Then

$$f'(x) = -\sin x, \quad f'(x)\left(\frac{\pi}{6}\right) = \frac{-1}{2}$$

and

$$\cos\left(\frac{2\pi}{13}\right) \approx f\left(\frac{\pi}{6}\right) + f'\left(\frac{\pi}{6}\right)h = \frac{\sqrt{3}}{2} + \left(\frac{-1}{2}\right)\left(\frac{-\pi}{78}\right) = \frac{\sqrt{3}}{2} + \frac{\pi}{156} \approx .8861638182.$$

8. Let $f(x) = \cot x$, $a = \pi/3$, and $h = -\pi/36$. Then

$$f'(x) = -\csc^2 x, \quad f'\left(\frac{\pi}{3}\right) = -\left(\frac{2\sqrt{3}}{3}\right)^2 = \frac{-4}{3}$$

and

$$\cot\left(\frac{11}{36}\pi\right) \approx f\left(\frac{\pi}{3}\right) + f'\left(\frac{\pi}{3}\right)h = \frac{\sqrt{3}}{3} + \left(\frac{-4}{3}\right)\left(\frac{-\pi}{36}\right) = \frac{\sqrt{3}}{3} + \frac{\pi}{27} \approx .6937055527.$$

9. Let $f(x) = \sec x$, $a = \pi/4$, and $h = -\pi/68$. Then $f'(x) = \sec x \tan x$, $f'(\pi/4) = \sqrt{2}$, and $\sec(4\pi/17) \approx f(\pi/4) + f'(\pi/4)h = \sqrt{2} + \sqrt{2}(-\pi/68) \approx 1.348877049$.

10. Let $f(x) = \tan x$, $a = \pi$, and $h = -\pi/100$. Then $f'(x) = \sec^2 x$, $f'(\pi) = 1$, and $\tan(99\pi/100) \approx f(\pi) + f'(\pi)h = 0 + (1)(-\pi/100) = -\pi/100 \approx 0.3141592654$.

11. Let $f(x) = e^x$, $a = 0$, and $h = 0.1$. Then $f'(x) = e^x$, $f'(0) = e^0 = 1$, and $e^{0.1} \approx f(0) + f'(0)h = 1 + 1(0.1) = 1.1$.

12. Let $f(x) = e^x$, $a = 0$, and $h = -0.124$. Then $f'(x) = e^x$, $f'(0) = e^0 = 1$, and $e^{-0.124} \approx f(0) + f'(0)h = 1 + 1(-0.124) = 0.876$.

13. Let $f(x) = \ln x$, $a = 1$, and $h = 0.1$. Then $f'(x) = 1/x$, $f'(1) = 1$, and $\ln 1.1 \approx f(1) + f'(1)h = 0 + 1(0.1) = 0.1$.

14. Let $f(x) = \ln x$, $a = 1$, and $h = -0.05$. Then $f'(x) = 1/x$, $f'(1) = 1$, and $\ln 0.95 \approx f(1) + f'(1)h = 0 + 1(-0.05) = -0.05$.

15. $df = f'(4)h = \left(\frac{1}{2\sqrt{4}}\right)(.2) = .05$

16. $df = f'(64)h = \frac{1}{3}(64)^{-2/3}(-0.1) = \frac{-1}{480} \approx -.0020833333$

17. $df = f'(2)h = \frac{1}{2}(1+2^3)^{-1/2}(12)(.01) = .02$

18. $df = f'(2)h = \frac{1}{2}(1+2^3)^{-1/2}(12)(-.001) = -.002$

19. $df = 15x^2\,dx$

20. $df = 2x\cos x^2\,dx$

21. $df = -\sin x\cos(\cos x)\,dx$

22. $du = \left[\sqrt{x-1} + \frac{1}{2}\frac{x}{\sqrt{x-1}}\right]dx = \frac{3x-2}{2\sqrt{x-1}}\,dx$

23. $du = 2x^3(1+x^4)^{-1/2}\,dx$

24. $du = \frac{2x(x^3-4)-(x^2+3)(3x^2)}{(x^3-4)^2}\,dx = \frac{-x^4-9x^2-8x}{(x^3-4)^2}\,dx$

25. a. By (9) and Theorem 3.4,

$$d(u+v) = \frac{d}{dx}(u+v)\,dx = \left(\frac{du}{dx}+\frac{dv}{dx}\right)dx = \left(\frac{du}{dx}\right)dx + \left(\frac{dv}{dx}\right)dx = du + dv.$$

b. By (9) and Theorem 3.5, $d(cu) = \frac{d}{dx}(cu)\,dx = c\left(\frac{du}{dx}\right)dx = c\,du.$

c. By (9) and Theorem 3.6,

$$d(uv) = \frac{d}{dx}(uv)\,dx = \left(\frac{du}{dx}v + u\frac{dv}{dx}\right)dx = v\left(\frac{du}{dx}\right)dx + u\left(\frac{dv}{dx}\right)dx = v\,du + u\,dv.$$

d. By (9) and Theorem 3.7,

$$d\left(\frac{u}{v}\right) = \left(\frac{d}{dx}\left(\frac{u}{v}\right)\right)dx = \left[\frac{v\left(\frac{du}{dx}\right) - u\left(\frac{dv}{dx}\right)}{v^2}\right]dx = \frac{v\left(\frac{du}{dx}\right)dx - u\left(\frac{dv}{dx}\right)dx}{v^2} = \frac{v\,du - u\,dv}{v^2}.$$

26. Let $f(x) = \cos x$, $a = \pi/6$, and $h = 2\pi/13 - \pi/6 = -\pi/78$. Then $f'(x) = -\sin x$ and $f''(x) = -\cos x$. Next, $|f''(x)| = |-\cos x| \le 1$ for $-\pi/78 \le x \le 0$, so we can let $M = 1$. Therefore by (3),

$$\text{error} \le \frac{1}{2}(1)\left(-\frac{\pi}{78}\right)^2 = \frac{\pi^2}{12{,}168}.$$

Consequently $\pi^2/12{,}168$ is an upper bound for the error.

27. Let $f(x) = \sqrt{x}$, $a = 100$, and $h = 101 - 100 = 1$. Then $f'(x) = \frac{1}{2}x^{-1/2}$ and $f''(x) = -\frac{1}{4}x^{-3/2}$. Next, $|f''(x)| = \left|-\frac{1}{4}x^{-3/2}\right| \le \frac{1}{4}(100)^{-3/2} = \frac{1}{4000}$ for $100 \le x \le 101$, so that we can let $M = \frac{1}{4000}$. Therefore by (3),
$$\text{error} \le \frac{1}{2}\left(\frac{1}{4000}\right)1^2 = \frac{1}{8000}.$$
Consequently $1/8000$ is an upper bound for the error.

28. Let $f(x) = \sqrt[3]{x}$, $a = 27$, and $h = 28 - 27 = 1$. Then $f'(x) = \frac{1}{3}x^{-2/3}$ and $f''(x) = -\frac{2}{9}x^{-5/3}$. Next, $|f''(x)| = \left|-\frac{2}{9}x^{-5/3}\right| \le \frac{2}{9}(27)^{-5/3} = \frac{2}{2187}$ for $27 \le x \le 28$, so we can let $M = \frac{2}{2187}$. Therefore by (3),
$$\text{error} \le \frac{1}{2}\left(\frac{2}{2187}\right)1^2 = \frac{1}{2187}.$$
Consequently $1/2187$ is an upper bound for the error.

29. Let $f(x) = x^3 - 3x - 1$, so that $f'(x) = 3x^2 - 3$. Letting the initial value of c be 2, we obtain 1.879385242 for the desired approximate solution.

30. Let $f(x) = x^3 + x - 1$, so that $f'(x) = 3x^2 + 1$. Letting the initial value of c be 0, we obtain 0.6823278038 for the desired approximate solution.

31. Let $f(x) = x^3 - 2x - 5$, so that $f'(x) = 3x^2 - 2$. Letting the initial value of c be 2, we obtain 2.094551482 for the desired approximate solution.

32. Let $f(x) = 2x^3 - 5x - 3$, so that $f'(x) = 6x^2 - 5$. Letting the initial value of c be 2, we obtain 1.822875656 for the desired approximate solution.

33. Let $f(x) = 2x^3 - 5x - 3$, so that $f'(x) = 6x^2 - 5$. Letting the initial value of c be -0.5, we obtain -0.8228756555 for the desired approximate solution.

34. Let $f(x) = x^2 + 4x^6 - 2$, so that $f'(x) = 2x + 24x^5$. Letting the initial value of c be 0.4, we obtain 0.8303001566 for the desired approximate solution.

35. Let $f(x) = \tan x - x$, so that $f'(x) = \sec^2 x - 1$. Letting the initial value of c be 4.5, we obtain 4.493409458 for the desired approximate solution.

36. Let $f(x) = x^4 + \sin x$, so that $f'(x) = 4x^3 + \cos x$. Letting the initial value of c be -1, we obtain -0.9496166887 for the desired approximate solution.

37. Let $f(x) = e^{-x} - x$, so that $f'(x) = -e^{-x} - 1$. Letting the initial value of c be 0, we obtain 0.5671432904 for the desired approximate solution.

38. Let $f(x) = \ln x - x + 3$, so that $f'(x) = 1/x - 1$. Letting the initial value of c be 5, we obtain 4.505241496 for the desired approximate solution.

39. Let $f(x) = x^2 - 15$, so that $f'(x) = 2x$. Using the Newton-Raphson method with initial value 4 for c, we find that $\sqrt{15} \approx 3.872983346$.

40. Let $f(x) = x^2 - 0.2$, so that $f'(x) = 2x$. Using the Newton-Raphson method with initial value 0.5 for c, we find that $\sqrt{0.2} \approx 0.4472135955$.

41. Let $f(x) = x^3 - 9$, so that $f'(x) = 3x^2$. Using the Newton-Raphson method with initial value 2 for c, we find that $\sqrt[3]{9} \approx 2.080083823$.

42. Let $f(x) = x^4 - 13$, so that $f'(x) = 4x^3$. Using the Newton-Raphson method with initial value 2 for c, we find that $\sqrt[4]{13} \approx 1.898828922$.

43. Notice that $f'(x) = 4x^3 + 4x - 1$. Letting the initial value of c be first -0.5 and then 0.5, we obtain $-.1823735451$ and $.6001766211$, respectively, for the approximate zeros of f.

44. Notice that $f'(x) = 4x^3 + 6x^2 - 1$. Letting the initial value of c be first -1.8 and then 0.5, we obtain -1.866760399 and $.8667603992$, respectively, for the approximate zeros of f.

45. By (11), $c_{n+1} = c_n - 0 = c_n$. Thus $f(c_{n+1}) = f(c_n) = 0$ and $f'(c_{n+1}) = f'(c_n) \neq 0$, so by using (11) again with n replaced by $n+1$, we find that $c_{n+2} = c_{n+1} = c_n$. In general, $c_m = c_n$ for $m \geq n$.

46. Equation (11) can be used only when c_n is in the domain of both f and f' and when $f'(c_n) \neq 0$. If $f(x) = \sqrt{x} - \frac{1}{2}$, the domain of f is $[0, \infty)$, and the domain of f' is $(0, \infty)$. Thus for all $c_n > 0$, (11) becomes

$$c_{n+1} = c_n - \frac{\sqrt{c_n} - 1/2}{1/(2\sqrt{c_n})} = \sqrt{c_n} - c_n.$$

   a. If $c_1 = 1$, then $c_2 = 0$, which is not in the domain of f', so the process terminates.

   b. If $c_1 = 4$, then $c_2 = -2$, which is not in the domain of f or f', so the process terminates.

47. Notice that $f'(x) = 4x^3 + 2x + 8$. Letting the initial value of c be -1, we obtain 0.1230777986 for an approximate zero of f. However, 0.1230777986 lies outside the interval $[-2, 0]$, and hence is not the desired zero.

48. If the initial value of c is $1/\sqrt{5}$, then successive values of c oscillate, $-1/\sqrt{5}$, $1/\sqrt{5}$, $-1/\sqrt{5}$, $1/\sqrt{5}$, and so on. (Actually, f has no zeros in $(0, 1)$.)

49. Notice that $f'(x) = \frac{1}{3}x^{-2/3}$, so that (11) becomes

$$c_{n+1} = c_n - \frac{f(c_n)}{f'(c_n)} = c_n - \frac{c_n^{1/3}}{c_n^{-2/3}/3} = c_n - 3c_n = -2c_n.$$

Thus if the initial value of c is any nonzero number, then the iterates double in distance from the origin.

50. Notice that $f'(x) = (x-1)^6 + 6x(x-1)^5 = (x-1)^5(7x-1)$.

   a. Since $f'(1) = 0$, the process stops.

   b. Eventually the iterates approach $-.2554228711$, which is an approximate zero of the function f.

   c. As in (b), eventually the iterates approach $-.2554228711$.

d. Since $f'(\frac{1}{7}) = 0$, the process stops. However, a calculator or computer can run the method because it uses an approximate value for $\frac{1}{7}$.

51. The two-point equation of the line through $(c_{n-1}, f(c_{n-1}))$ and $(c_n, f(c_n))$ is

$$\frac{y - f(c_n)}{x - c_n} = \frac{f(c_n) - f(c_{n-1})}{c_n - c_{n-1}}.$$

To obtain the x intercept we let $y = 0$, obtaining

$$x - c_n = -f(c_n)\left[\frac{c_n - c_{n-1}}{f(c_n) - f(c_{n-1})}\right],$$

or equivalently,

$$x = c_n - \frac{[f(c_n)](c_n - c_{n-1})}{f(c_n) - f(c_{n-1})}.$$

Thus c_{n+1} is the x intercept.

52. Let $c_1 = 1$ and $c_2 = 2$. Then the method yields 1.904160859 as an approximate zero of f.

53. Let $c_1 = 1$ and $c_2 = 1.2$. Then the method yields 1.230959417 as an approximate zero of f.

54. Using the Difference and Quotient Rules for differentiation, we find that

$$g'(x) = 1 - \frac{f'(x)f'(x) - f(x)f''(x)}{[f'(x)]^2} = \frac{[f'(x)]^2 - [f'(x)]^2 + f(x)f''(x)}{[f'(x)]^2} = \frac{f(x)f''(x)}{[f'(x)]^2}.$$

55. a. Let $f(x) = x^{4/3}$, $a = 8$, and $h = 1$. Then $f'(x) = \frac{4}{3}x^{1/3}$ and $f''(x) = \frac{4}{9}x^{-2/3}$, so that $f'(8) = \frac{4}{3}(8)^{1/3} = \frac{8}{3}$ and $f''(8) = \frac{4}{9}(8)^{-2/3} = \frac{1}{9}$. Therefore

$$9^{4/3} \approx f(8) + f'(8)(1) + \frac{1}{2}f''(8)(1)^2 = 16 + \frac{8}{3} + \frac{1}{18} = \frac{337}{18} \approx 18.72222222.$$

b. Let $f(x) = \tan x$, $a = \pi/4$, and $h = 2\pi/9 - \pi/4 = -\pi/36$. Then $f'(x) = \sec^2 x$ and $f''(x) = 2\sec^2 x \tan x$, so that $f'(\pi/4) = \sec^2(\pi/4) = 2$ and $f''(\pi/4) = 2(2)(1) = 4$. Therefore

$$\tan\left(\frac{2}{9}\pi\right) \approx f\left(\frac{\pi}{4}\right) + f'\left(\frac{\pi}{4}\right)\left(-\frac{\pi}{36}\right) + \frac{1}{2}f''\left(\frac{\pi}{4}\right)\left(-\frac{\pi}{36}\right)^2 = 1 - \frac{\pi}{18} + 2\frac{\pi^2}{(36)^2} \approx .8406979458.$$

56. The volume of a hemispherical dome of radius r is given by $V(r) = \frac{2}{3}\pi r^3$. Since $V'(r) = 2\pi r^2$, we use (2) to determine that the volume of paint necessary is

$$V\left(20 + \frac{1}{1200}\right) - V(20) \approx V'(20)\frac{1}{1200} = 2\pi(20)^2\frac{1}{1200} = \frac{2}{3}\pi \approx 2.094395102 \text{ (cubic feet)}.$$

57. The volume of a ball of radius r is given by $V(r) = \frac{4}{3}\pi r^3$. Since $V'(r) = 4\pi r^2$, we use (2) to determine that the volume of the material in the ball is $V(5.137) - V(5) \approx V'(5)(.137) = 4\pi 5^2(.137) \approx 43.04$ (cubic inches).

58. a. Let $f(v) = 1/\sqrt{1 - (v^2/c^2)}$. Then $f(c/2) = 1/\sqrt{1 - (1/4)} = (2\sqrt{3})/3 \approx 1.154700538$.

b. Let $f(x) = 1/\sqrt{1-x}$, $a = 0$, and $h = v^2/c^2 = 1/(3600)^2$. Then $f'(x) = \frac{1}{2}(1-x)^{-3/2}$, $f'(0) = \frac{1}{2}$, and

$$\frac{1}{\sqrt{1-(v^2/c^2)}} = f\left(\frac{v^2}{c^2}\right) = f\left(\frac{1}{(3600)^2}\right) \approx f(0) + f'(0)h = 1 + \frac{1}{2}\frac{1}{(3600)^2} \approx 1.00000004.$$

59. Let $p(V) = 22.414/V$, $V_0 = 20$, and $h = 0.35$. Then $p'(V) = -22.414/V^2$ and $p'(20) = -22.414/400$. By (2),

$$p(20.35) - p(20) \approx p'(20)h = -\frac{22.414}{400}(0.35) \approx -.01961.$$

Therefore the pressure decreases approximately .01961 atmosphere.

60. a. By hypothesis, $P(0) = 500$; by Figure 3.51, $P'(0) = 5$. Letting $a = 0$ and $h = 1$ in (2), we have $P(1) \approx P(0) + P'(0)h = 500 + 5(1) = 505$.

b. From (a) we find that $P(1) = 505$, and from Figure 3.51, $P'(1) = 5$. Letting $a = 1$ and $h = 1$ in (2), we have $P(2) \approx P(1) + P'(1)h = 505 + 5(1) = 510$.

c. By using our data and Figure 3.51, we obtain in succession

$$\begin{aligned} P(3) &\approx P(2) + P'(2)h = 510 + 10(1) = 520 \\ P(4) &\approx P(3) + P'(3)h = 520 + 20(1) = 540 \\ P(5) &\approx P(4) + P'(4)h = 540 + 30(1) = 570 \\ P(6) &\approx P(5) + P'(5)h = 570 + 0(1) = 570 \\ P(7) &\approx P(6) + P'(6)h = 570 - 10(1) = 560 \end{aligned}$$

61. Let $f(x) = 3x^3 + 12x^2 + 10x - 6$, so that $f'(x) = 9x^2 + 24x + 10$. Letting the initial value of c be 0, we obtain .3946556506 (inches) as the desired approximation for the value of x that maximizes the volume.

Chapter 3 Review

1. $f'(x) = -12x^2 - \dfrac{4}{x^3}$

2. $f'(x) = \frac{1}{2}x^{-1/2}(x^2-3)^{4/7} + \sqrt{x}\left(\frac{4}{7}\right)(x^2-3)^{-3/7}(2x) = \frac{1}{2}x^{-1/2}(x^2-3)^{4/7} + \frac{8}{7}x^{3/2}(x^2-3)^{-3/7}$

3. $g'(x) = \dfrac{(2x-1)^2 - x[2(2x-1)(2)]}{(2x-1)^4} = -\dfrac{2x+1}{(2x-1)^3}$

4. $g'(x) = -\frac{3}{2}(4-x^2)^{-5/2}(-2x) = \dfrac{3x}{(4-x^2)^{5/2}}$

5. $f'(t) = (-\sin t)\sin 2t + (\cos t)(2\cos 2t) = -\sin t\, \sin 2t + 2\cos t\, \cos 2t$

6. $f'(t) = 2t\sin\dfrac{1}{t} + t^2\left(\cos\dfrac{1}{t}\right)\left(-\dfrac{1}{t^2}\right) = 2t\sin\dfrac{1}{t} - \cos\dfrac{1}{t}$

7. $f'(t) = 5\tan t + 5t\sec^2 t + 9\sec 3t\, \tan 3t$

8. $f'(t) = \sec^2(\sin t^2)(\cos t^2)(2t) = 2t\sec^2(\sin t^2)\cos t^2$

9. $f'(t) = 2e^{2t}\ln(3+e^t) + e^{2t}\dfrac{1}{3+e^t}e^t = 2e^{2t}\ln(3+e^t) + \dfrac{e^{3t}}{3+e^t}$

10. $f'(t) = \dfrac{(1/t)(1-e^t) - (\ln t)(-e^t)}{(1-e^t)^2} = \dfrac{1-e^t+(t\ln t)e^t}{t(1-e^t)^2}$

11. $\dfrac{dy}{dx} = 12x^2 - \sqrt{3} - \dfrac{2}{5x^2}$

12. $\dfrac{dy}{dx} = 2x\tan^2 x + x^2(2\tan x\sec^2 x) = 2x\tan^2 x + 2x^2\tan x\sec^2 x$

13. $\dfrac{dy}{dx} = \dfrac{\cos x(1-\sec x) - \sin x(-\sec x\tan x)}{(1-\sec x)^2} = \dfrac{\cos x - 1 + \tan^2 x}{(1-\sec x)^2}$

14. $\dfrac{dy}{dx} = \frac{5}{9}(3x-5)^{-4/9}(3) = \frac{5}{3}(3x-5)^{-4/9}$

15. $\dfrac{dy}{dx} = 3x^2\sqrt{x^2-4} + x^3[\frac{1}{2}(x^2-4)^{-1/2}(2x)] = 3x^2\sqrt{x^2-4} + x^4/\sqrt{x^2-4}$

16. $\dfrac{dy}{dx} = \dfrac{(2x-1)(x^2+x+1) - (x^2-x+1)(2x+1)}{(x^2+x+1)^2} = \dfrac{2x^2-2}{(x^2+x+1)^2}$

17. $\dfrac{dy}{dx} = e^x + xe^x + 5e^{-x}$

18. $\dfrac{dy}{dx} = \dfrac{(1/x)(1-\ln x) - (1+\ln x)(-1/x)}{(1-\ln x)^2} = \dfrac{2}{x(1-\ln x)^2}$

19. $f'(x) = 9x^2 - 4x$, so $f'(1) = 5$. Thus l: $y - 5 = 5(x-1)$, or $y = 5x$.

20. $f'(x) = \dfrac{2(5x+2) - 5(2x-1)}{(5x+2)^2} = \dfrac{9}{(5x+2)^2}$, so $f'(0) = \frac{9}{4}$. Thus l: $y - (-\frac{1}{2}) = \frac{9}{4}(x-0)$, or $y = \frac{9}{4}x - \frac{1}{2}$.

21. $f'(x) = \cos\sqrt{2}\,x - x(\sqrt{2}\sin\sqrt{2}\,x)$, so $f'(0) = 1$. Thus l: $y - 0 = 1(x-0)$, or $y = x$.

22. $f'(x) = \cos x + 6\sin 2x$, so $f'(\pi/6) = \frac{1}{2}\sqrt{3} + 6(\frac{1}{2}\sqrt{3}) = \frac{7}{2}\sqrt{3}$.
Thus l: $y - (-1) = \frac{7}{2}\sqrt{3}\,(x - \pi/6)$, or $y = \frac{7}{2}\sqrt{3}\,x - \frac{7}{12}\sqrt{3}\,\pi - 1$.

23. $f'(x) = \sqrt{x-1} + x\dfrac{1}{2\sqrt{x-1}}$, so $f'(5) = 2 + \frac{5}{4} = \frac{13}{4}$. Thus l: $y - 10 = \frac{13}{4}(x-5)$, or $y = \frac{13}{4}x - \frac{25}{4}$.

24. $f'(x) = \dfrac{1}{2\sqrt{1+3e^x}}3e^x = \dfrac{3e^x}{2\sqrt{1+3e^x}}$, so $f'(0) = \dfrac{3}{2\sqrt{1+3}} = \dfrac{3}{4}$. Thus l: $y-2 = \frac{3}{4}(x-0)$, or $y = \frac{3}{4}x+2$.

25. $\displaystyle\lim_{x\to 0^-}\frac{f(x)-f(0)}{x-0} = \lim_{x\to 0^-}\frac{2\sin x - 0}{x} = 2\lim_{x\to 0^-}\frac{\sin x}{x} = 2;$
$\displaystyle\lim_{x\to 0^+}\frac{f(x)-f(0)}{x-0} = \lim_{x\to 0^+}\frac{3x^2+2x-0}{x} = \lim_{x\to 0^+}(3x+2) = 2.$
Therefore $f'(0) = 2$. Thus l: $y - 0 = 2(x-0)$, or $y = 2x$.

26. Since $|x \sin(1/x)| \leq |x|$ for all x,

$$f'(0) = \lim_{x\to 0} \frac{f(x) - f(0)}{x - 0} = \lim_{x\to 0} \frac{x^2 \sin(1/x) - 0}{x} = \lim_{x\to 0} x \sin\frac{1}{x} = 0$$

by the Squeezing Theorem. Thus l: $y - 0 = 0(x - 0)$, or $y = 0$.

27. $f'(x) = 3x^{11} - 36x^5$; $f''(x) = 33x^{10} - 180x^4$

28. $f'(x) = \sin(3 - x)$, $f''(x) = -\cos(3 - x)$

29. $f'(t) = 3t(t^2 + 9)^{1/2}$; $f''(t) = 3(t^2 + 9)^{1/2} + 3t^2(t^2 + 9)^{-1/2}$

30. $f'(t) = \dfrac{2(2t - 1) - (2t + 1)2}{(2t - 1)^2} = -\dfrac{4}{(2t - 1)^2}$; $f''(t) = \dfrac{16}{(2t - 1)^3}$

31. $f'(x) = 2x + \ln x + 1$; $f''(x) = 2 + 1/x$

32. $f'(x) = \sin x + x \cos x$; $f''(x) = \cos x + (\cos x - x \sin x) = 2 \cos x - x \sin x$

33. $9y^2 \dfrac{dy}{dx} - \left(8xy + 4x^2 \dfrac{dy}{dx}\right) + \left(y + x\dfrac{dy}{dx}\right) = 0$; $\dfrac{dy}{dx} = \dfrac{8xy - y}{9y^2 - 4x^2 + x}$

34. $2x + 2y\dfrac{dy}{dx} = \dfrac{2xy^2 - 2x^2y(dy/dx)}{y^4}$; $\dfrac{dy}{dx} = \dfrac{2xy^2 - 2xy^4}{2y^5 + 2x^2y} = \dfrac{xy - xy^3}{y^4 + x^2}$

35. $\dfrac{dy}{dx}(\sqrt{x} + 1) + y\left(\dfrac{1}{2\sqrt{x}}\right) = 1$; $\dfrac{dy}{dx} = \dfrac{2\sqrt{x} - y}{2\sqrt{x}\,(\sqrt{x} + 1)}$

36. $e^y + xe^y\dfrac{dy}{dx} + \dfrac{dy}{dx}e^x + ye^x = 0$; $\dfrac{dy}{dx} = \dfrac{-e^y - ye^x}{xe^y + e^x}$

37. $3y^2\dfrac{dy}{dx} + \cos(xy^2)\left[y^2 + 2xy\dfrac{dy}{dx}\right] = 0$; $\dfrac{dy}{dx} = \dfrac{-y^2 \cos xy^2}{3y^2 + 2xy \cos xy^2} = -\dfrac{y \cos xy^2}{3y + 2x \cos xy^2}$

38. $\tan x^2y + x \sec^2(x^2y)\left[2xy + x^2\dfrac{dy}{dx}\right] = 2y\dfrac{dy}{dx}$; $\dfrac{dy}{dx} = \dfrac{\tan x^2y + 2x^2y \sec^2 x^2y}{2y - x^3 \sec^2 x^2y}$

39. $6x^2 - (4 \cos 4y)\dfrac{dy}{dx} = 2xy + x^2\dfrac{dy}{dx}$; $\dfrac{dy}{dx} = \dfrac{6x^2 - 2xy}{x^2 + 4 \cos 4y}$. At $(1, 0)$, $\dfrac{dy}{dx} = \dfrac{6}{1 + 4} = \dfrac{6}{5}$.

40. $2x - \left(y^2 + 2xy\dfrac{dy}{dx}\right) + 3y^2\dfrac{dy}{dx} = 0$; $\dfrac{dy}{dx} = \dfrac{y^2 - 2x}{3y^2 - 2xy}$. At $(-1, 2)$, $\dfrac{dy}{dx} = \dfrac{4 + 2}{12 + 4} = \dfrac{3}{8}$.

41. $\dfrac{dx}{dt}y + x\dfrac{dy}{dt} = 0$, so $\dfrac{dy}{dt} = -\dfrac{y}{x}\dfrac{dx}{dt}$

42. $\dfrac{dy}{dt} = \cos(xy^2)\left[\dfrac{dx}{dt}y^2 + 2xy\dfrac{dy}{dt}\right]$, so $\dfrac{dy}{dt} = \dfrac{y^2 \cos xy^2}{1 - 2xy \cos xy^2}\dfrac{dx}{dt}$

43. $df = (2x \cos x - x^2 \sin x)\, dx$

44. $df = \dfrac{x[\frac{2}{3}(3x - 1)^{-1/3}3] - (3x - 1)^{2/3}}{x^2}\, dx = \dfrac{2x - (3x - 1)}{x^2(3x - 1)^{1/3}}\, dx = \dfrac{1 - x}{x^2(3x - 1)^{1/3}}\, dx$

45. $df = 5(x - e^x)^4(1 - e^x)\,dx$

46. $df = \dfrac{[(\sec^2 x^2)2x]x - \tan x^2}{x^2}\,dx = \dfrac{2x^2 \sec^2 x^2 - \tan x^2}{x^2}\,dx$

47. Let $f(x) = 1 + \sqrt{x}$. Then $df = f'(x)\,dx = (1/2\sqrt{x})\,dx$, so if $x = 9$ and $dx = 1$, then $f(9) = 4$ and $df = \frac{1}{6}$. Thus $1 + \sqrt{10} = f(10) \approx f(9) + df = 4 + \frac{1}{6} = \frac{25}{6}$.

48. Let $f(x) = \sec x$. Then $df = f'(x)\,dx = \sec x \tan x\,dx$, so if $x = \pi/4$ and $dx = \frac{1}{100}\pi$, then

$$f\left(\frac{\pi}{4}\right) = \sec\frac{\pi}{4} = \sqrt{2} \quad \text{and} \quad df = \left(\sec\frac{\pi}{4}\tan\frac{\pi}{4}\right)\left(\frac{1}{100}\pi\right) = \frac{\sqrt{2}}{100}\pi.$$

Thus $\sec 0.26\pi = f(0.26\pi) \approx f(\pi/4) + df = \sqrt{2} + (\sqrt{2}/100)\pi = \sqrt{2}\,(1 + \pi/100)$.

49. Notice that $f'(x) = 2x - 4\sin x$ and $f''(x) = 2 - 4\cos x$. Letting the initial value of c be 2, we obtain 1.895494267 as an approximate solution of $f'(x) = 0$. Since f' is an odd function, -1.895494267 is also an approximate solution. Finally, 0 is a solution.

50. Notice that $f'(x) = e^x - 8x$ and $f''(x) = e^x - 8$. Letting the initial value of c be 0, we obtain .1444213531 as an approximate solution of $f'(x) = 0$. Letting the initial value of c be 3, we also obtain 3.261685685 as a second approximate solution.

51. Notice that $f'(x) = \ln x - 1/x$ and $f''(x) = 1/x + 1/x^2$. Letting the initial value of c be 1, we obtain 1.763222834 as an approximate solution of $f'(x) = 0$.

52. To find the point of intersection, we solve the equation $x^2 + 2x - 3 = x^2 - \frac{9}{4}x + \frac{5}{4}$. We obtain $\frac{17}{4}x = \frac{17}{4}$, or $x = 1$. Since $f'(x) = 2x + 2$ and $g'(x) = 2x - \frac{9}{4}$, $f'(1)g'(1) = 4(-1/4) = -1$. Thus the tangent lines at the point of intersection are perpendicular.

53. To find the point of intersection, we solve the equation

$$x^2 + 1 = x^2 - \cos\left(\frac{\pi}{x^2+1}\right), \quad \text{or} \quad \cos\left(\frac{\pi}{x^2+1}\right) = -1$$

so that $\pi/(x^2+1) = \pi + 2n\pi$ for some integer n. Since $0 < \pi/(x^2+1) \le \pi$, the only solution is $x = 0$. Since

$$f'(x) = 2x \quad \text{and} \quad g'(x) = 2x - \frac{2\pi x}{(x^2+1)^2}\sin\left(\frac{\pi}{x^2+1}\right)$$

we have $f'(0) = 0 = g'(0)$. Thus the tangent lines at the point of intersection are identical.

54. $f'(3) = \lim_{x\to 3} \dfrac{f(x) - f(3)}{x - 3} = \lim_{x\to 3} \dfrac{(x^2 + 3x) - 18}{x - 3} = \lim_{x\to 3} \dfrac{(x-3)(x+6)}{x-3} = \lim_{x\to 3}(x+6) = 9$

55. $\lim_{x\to a} \dfrac{f(x) - f(a)}{x^{1/2} - a^{1/2}} = \lim_{x\to a}\left[\dfrac{f(x) - f(a)}{x^{1/2} - a^{1/2}}\,\dfrac{x^{1/2} + a^{1/2}}{x^{1/2} + a^{1/2}}\right] = \lim_{x\to a}\dfrac{f(x) - f(a)}{x - a}\cdot\lim_{x\to a}(x^{1/2} + a^{1/2}) = 2a^{1/2}f'(a)$

56. a. Let c be an arbitrary number. Since $cx(2-x)$ is a polynomial, f is continuous at all $x < 0$; since $\sin x$ is continuous, f is continuous at all $x > 0$. Finally,

$$\lim_{x\to 0^-} f(x) = \lim_{x\to 0^-} cx(2-x) = 0 \quad \text{and} \quad \lim_{x\to 0^+} f(x) = \lim_{x\to 0^+} \sin x = 0 = f(0).$$

Thus f is continuous at 0. Consequently f is continuous for every value of c.

b. Notice that

$$\frac{f(x)-f(0)}{x-0}=\begin{cases}\dfrac{cx(2-x)-0}{x-0}=c(2-x) & \text{if } x<0\\[2mm] \dfrac{\sin x-0}{x-0}=\dfrac{\sin x}{x} & \text{if } x>0.\end{cases}$$

Since $\lim_{x\to0^-} c(2-x)=2c$ and $\lim_{x\to0^+}(\sin x)/x=1$, it follows that $f'(0)$ exists if and only if $2c=1$, that is, if $c=\frac{1}{2}$.

57. $g'(x)=f'(x^2)(2x)$, so that $g'(0)=[f'(0)](0)=0$.

58. $\dfrac{dy}{dx}=a\cos x-b\sin x$; $\dfrac{d^2y}{dx^2}=-a\sin x-b\cos x=-y$. Thus $\dfrac{d^2y}{dx^2}+y=0$.

59. Since $dy/dx=-1/x^2$, the tangent line at $(a,1/a)$ is

$$y-\frac{1}{a}=\frac{-1}{a^2}(x-a),\quad\text{or}\quad y=\frac{-1}{a^2}x+\frac{2}{a}.$$

To find the tangent line that passes through $(4,0)$, we substitute $x=4$, $y=0$ in the equation of the tangent line: $0=(-1/a^2)(4)+(2/a)=(-4+2a)/a^2$. Thus $a=2$, so the particular tangent line is $y=(-1/4)x+1$. The x and y intercepts of this tangent line are 4 and 1, respectively. The area of the triangle is $\frac{1}{2}(4)(1)=2$.

60. a. $\dfrac{dV}{dr}=\dfrac{2\pi}{3}rh$

b. $\dfrac{dV}{dh}=\dfrac{\pi}{3}r^2$

c. Differentiating the equation $V=\pi r^2h/3$ implicitly with respect to V, we obtain

$$1=\frac{\pi}{3}r^2\frac{dh}{dV},\quad\text{so that}\quad\frac{dh}{dV}=\frac{3}{\pi r^2}.$$

61. Let h denote the height (or depth) of the water. If water is flowing in at a constant rate, then h is increasing but at an ever slower rate. Thus the rate of change of h, which is h', is decreasing, and therefore the graph in Figure 3.53(c) is reasonable and the graph in Figure 3.53(a) is unreasonable. Since the rate of change never becomes 0, neither of the graphs in Figures 3.53 (b) and (d) could be the graph of the rate of change.

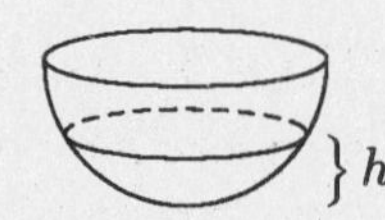

62. Let r be the radius of the surface of the water, h the height of the water and V the volume at any given time. Then $V=\frac{1}{3}\pi r^2h$, and we are to find dV/dt at the instant t_0 when $h=3$. From the figure, $r/h=\frac{2}{6}$, so that $r=\frac{1}{3}h$, and thus $V=\frac{1}{3}\pi(\frac{1}{3}h)^2h=\frac{1}{27}\pi h^3$. Then $dV/dt=\frac{1}{9}\pi h^2(dh/dt)$. Since $dh/dt=1$ by hypothesis, we find that $(dV/dt)\big|_{t=t_0}=\frac{1}{9}\pi 3^2(1)=\pi$ (cubic inches per second).

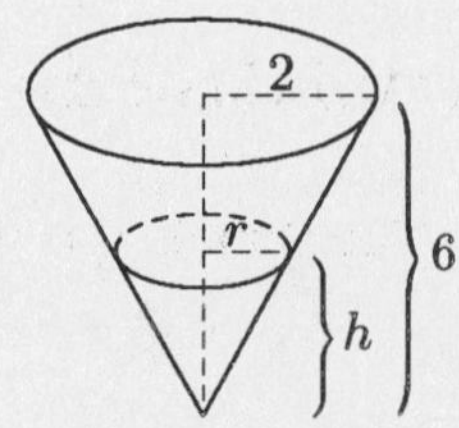

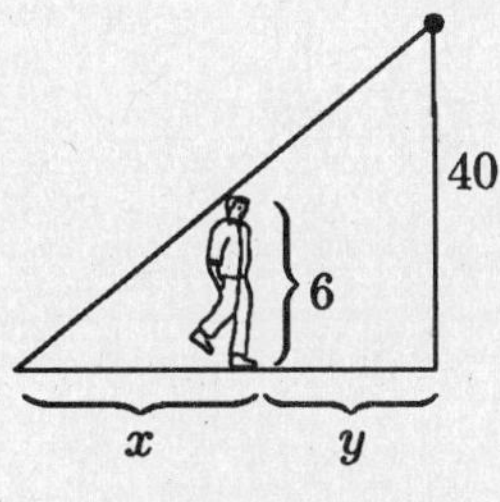

Exercise 63

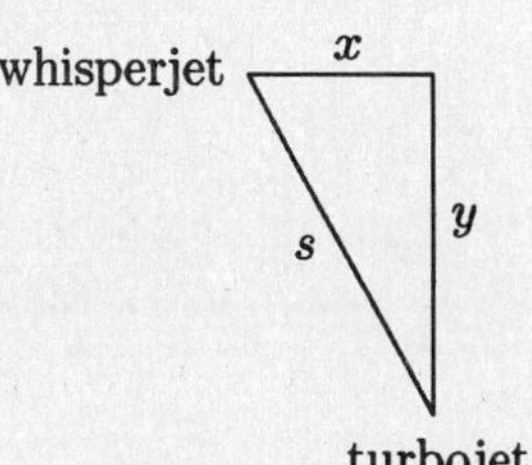

Exercise 64

63. Let x be the length of the shadow and y the distance from the person to the tower. By the figure, $(x+y)/40 = x/6$, so that $6x + 6y = 40x$ and thus $x = \frac{3}{17}y$. We are to show that dx/dt is constant and negative. Now $dx/dt = \frac{3}{17}(dy/dt)$, and since $dy/dt = -150$ by hypothesis, we obtain $dx/dt = \frac{3}{17}(-150) = -\frac{450}{17}$, a negative constant.

64. Let x be the distance from the whisperjet to St. Louis, y the distance from the turbojet to St.Louis, and s the distance between the two jets. Then $s^2 = x^2 + y^2$, and we are to find ds/dt at the instant t_0 when $s = 300$ and $x = 100$. Now $2s(ds/dt) = 2x(dx/dt) + 2y(dy/dt)$, and $dx/dt = -500$ and $dy/dt = -600$ by hypothesis. Also, at t_0 when $s = 300$ and $x = 100$, we have $y = \sqrt{s^2 - x^2} = \sqrt{300^2 - 100^2} = 200\sqrt{2}$. Thus

$$2(300)\left.\frac{ds}{dt}\right|_{t=t_0} = 2(100)(-500) + 2(200\sqrt{2})(-600)$$

so

$$\left.\frac{ds}{dt}\right|_{t=t_0} = -\frac{500 + 1200\sqrt{2}}{3} \approx -732.352 \text{ (miles per hour)}.$$

65. $m_C(x) = C'(x) = 3 + 1/\sqrt{x}$ and $m_R(x) = R'(x) = 5/\sqrt{x}$, so we need to determine the value of x for which $0 \le x \le 2$ and $3 + 1/\sqrt{x} = 5/\sqrt{x}$, or equivalently, $3 = 4\sqrt{x}$. Therefore $\sqrt{x} = \frac{4}{3}$, so $x = \frac{16}{9}$. Consequently if $a = \frac{16}{9}$, then $m_C(a) = m_R(a)$.

66. The volume of a box with side length x is given by $V(x) = x^3$. Thus the volume of sand that can be poured into the box is $V(3 - \frac{1}{12})$. Since $V'(x) = 3x^2$, we have $V'(3) = 27$. Thus $V(3 - \frac{1}{12}) \approx V(3) + V'(3)(-\frac{1}{2}) = 27 + 27(-\frac{1}{12}) = 24.75$ (cubic feet).

Cumulative Review(Chapters 1–2)

1. The given inequality is equivalent to

$$\frac{x(x+\sqrt{3})(x-\sqrt{3})}{(1-x)^3} > 0.$$

From the diagram we see that the solution is the union of $(-\sqrt{3}, 0)$ and $(1, \sqrt{3})$.

x	− − − − − − 0 + + + + + +
$x+\sqrt{3}$	− 0 + + + + + + + + + + +
$x-\sqrt{3}$	− − − − − − − − − − − 0 +
$(1-x)^3$	+ + + + + + + + 0 − − − −
$\dfrac{x(x+\sqrt{3})(x-\sqrt{3})}{(1-x)^3}$	− 0 + + + + 0 − + + 0 −

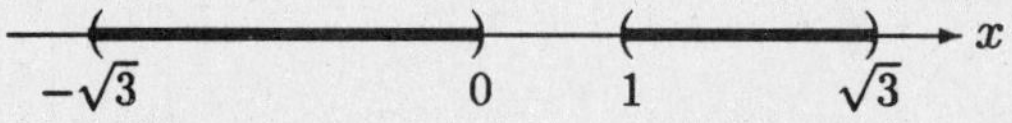

$-\sqrt{3}$ 0 1 $\sqrt{3}$ x

2. The given inequality is equivalent to

$$\frac{6(t-1/2)^2+1/2}{t(t-1)} \le 0.$$

From the diagram we see that the solution is the interval $(0,1)$.

t	− − − 0 + + + + + + +
$t-1$	− − − − − − − 0 + + +
$\dfrac{6t^2-6t+2}{t(t-1)}$	+ + + − − − + + +

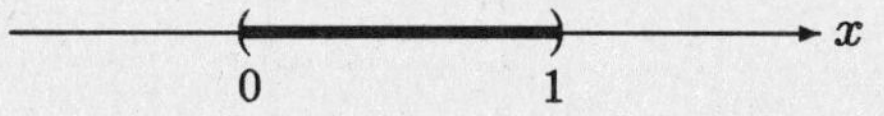

0 1 x

3. The given inequality is equivalent to $3-2 < 1/|x| < 3+2$, or $\frac{1}{5} < |x| < 1$. Thus the solution is the union of $(-1,-\frac{1}{5})$ and $(\frac{1}{5},1)$.

4. The given inequality is equivalent to $\sin x \le \frac{1}{2}$ for x in $[0,2\pi)$. Thus the solution is the union of $[0,\pi/6]$ and $[5\pi/6, 2\pi)$.

5. Since $f(x) = 6x^2-x-2 = (2x+1)(3x-2)$, the inequality $f(x) > 0$ is equivalent to $(2x+1)(3x-2) > 0$. From the diagram we see that the solution is the union of $(-\infty,-\frac{1}{2})$ and $(\frac{2}{3},\infty)$.

$2x+1$	− − − 0 + + + + + + + +
$3x-2$	− − − − − − − − 0 + + +
$(2x+1)(3x-2)$	+ + + 0 − − − − 0 + + +

$-\frac{1}{2}$ $\frac{2}{3}$ x

6. $(1+\sin x+\cos x)^2 - 2(1+\sin x+\cos x) = (1+\sin^2 x+\cos^2 x+2\sin x+2\cos x+2\sin x\cos x) - (2+2\sin x+2\cos x) = 2\sin x\cos x = \sin 2x$.

7. The domain consists of all x for which $x^2-1\ge 0$ (hence $x\le -1$ or $x\ge 1$) and $\sqrt{x^2-1}-x\ge 0$. But if $x\ge 1$, then the fact that $x^2-1<x^2$ implies that $\sqrt{x^2-1}<x$ (so $\sqrt{x^2-1}-x<0$); if $x\le -1$, then $-x\ge 0$, so $\sqrt{x^2-1}-x\ge 0$. Thus the domain is $(-\infty,-1]$.

8. a. The domain of f consists of all real numbers except 1, and the domain of g consists of all real numbers except 4. Thus the domain of $f \circ g$ consists of all real numbers except 4 such that $1/(4-x) \neq 1$ (so $x \neq 3$). Therefore the domain of $f \circ g$ consists of all real numbers except 3 and 4.

   b. $(f \circ g)(x) = f(g(x)) = f\left(\dfrac{1}{4-x}\right) = \dfrac{[1/(4-x)]^2}{[1/(4-x)]-1} = \dfrac{1}{(4-x)-(4-x)^2} = \dfrac{1}{-12+7x-x^2}$

9. $\displaystyle\lim_{x\to 2}\frac{x^2-3x+2}{x^2-5x+6} = \lim_{x\to 2}\frac{(x-1)(x-2)}{(x-2)(x-3)} = \lim_{x\to 2}\frac{x-1}{x-3} = -1.$

10. $$\lim_{x\to 0}\frac{\sqrt{1+xe^x}-\sqrt{1-xe^x}}{x} = \lim_{x\to 0}\left[\frac{\sqrt{1+xe^x}-\sqrt{1-xe^x}}{x}\,\frac{\sqrt{1+xe^x}+\sqrt{1-xe^x}}{\sqrt{1+xe^x}+\sqrt{1-xe^x}}\right]$$
$$= \lim_{x\to 0}\frac{(1+xe^x)-(1-xe^x)}{x(\sqrt{1+xe^x}+\sqrt{1-xe^x})} = \lim_{x\to 0}\frac{2xe^x}{x(\sqrt{1+xe^x}+\sqrt{1-xe^x})}$$
$$= \lim_{x\to 0}\frac{2e^x}{\sqrt{1+xe^x}+\sqrt{1-xe^x}} = \frac{2}{1+1} = 1$$

11. Since $|x^2| = x^2$, we have
$$\lim_{x\to 0}\frac{|x^3|-x^2}{x^3+x^2} = \lim_{x\to 0}\frac{|x|x^2-x^2}{x^3+x^2} = \lim_{x\to 0}\frac{|x|-1}{x+1} = \frac{0-1}{0+1} = -1.$$

12. $$\lim_{x\to 0^+}\frac{\sqrt{1+x^2}-\sqrt{1-x^2}}{x^3} = \lim_{x\to 0^+}\frac{\sqrt{1+x^2}-\sqrt{1-x^2}}{x^3}\,\frac{\sqrt{1+x^2}+\sqrt{1-x^2}}{\sqrt{1+x^2}+\sqrt{1-x^2}}$$
$$= \lim_{x\to 0^+}\frac{(1+x^2)-(1-x^2)}{x^3(\sqrt{1+x^2}+\sqrt{1-x^2})} = \lim_{x\to 0^+}\frac{2}{x(\sqrt{1+x^2}+\sqrt{1-x^2})} = \infty$$

13. $$\lim_{x\to 2}\frac{f(x)-f(2)}{x-2} = \lim_{x\to 2}\frac{\sqrt{2x^2-4}-2}{x-2} = \lim_{x\to 2}\frac{\sqrt{2x^2-4}-2}{x-2}\,\frac{\sqrt{2x^2-4}+2}{\sqrt{2x^2-4}+2}$$
$$= \lim_{x\to 2}\frac{2x^2-4-4}{(x-2)(\sqrt{2x^2-4}+2)} = \lim_{x\to 2}\frac{2(x-2)(x+2)}{(x-2)(\sqrt{2x^2-4}+2)}$$
$$= \lim_{x\to 2}\frac{2(x+2)}{\sqrt{2x^2-4}+2} = 2$$

14. $\displaystyle\lim_{x\to -1^-} f(x) = \lim_{x\to -1^-}(x+1) = 0;\ \lim_{x\to -1^+} f(x) = \lim_{x\to -1^+}(x+1)^2 = 0$

    Thus $\lim_{x\to -1} f(x) = 0 = f(-1)$, so f is continuous at -1.

15. 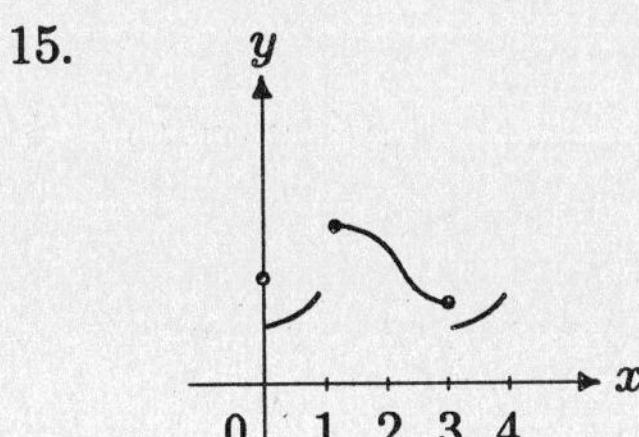

16. Let $f(x) = x^4 - 15$, so that $\sqrt[4]{15}$ is the zero of f. Since $f(1) < 0$ and $f(2) > 0$, a zero lies in $(1, 2)$. We begin by letting $a = 1$ and $b = 2$. Using the algorithm for the bisection method, we assemble the following table:

Interval	Length	Midpoint c	$f(c)$
$[1, 2]$	1	$\frac{3}{2}$	$-\frac{159}{16}$
$[\frac{3}{2}, 2]$	$\frac{1}{2}$	$\frac{7}{4}$	$-\frac{1439}{256}$
$[\frac{7}{4}, 2]$	$\frac{1}{4}$	$\frac{15}{8}$	$-\frac{10,815}{4096}$
$[\frac{15}{8}, 2]$	$\frac{1}{8}$		

Since the length of $[\frac{15}{8}, 2]$ is $\frac{1}{8}$, and neither $\frac{15}{8}$ nor 2 is a zero of f, the midpoint $\frac{31}{16}$ of $[\frac{15}{8}, 2]$ is less than $\frac{1}{16}$ from a zero of f.

17. $f(\sqrt{a}) = \frac{1}{2}\left(\sqrt{a} + \frac{a}{\sqrt{a}}\right) = \frac{1}{2}(\sqrt{a} + \sqrt{a}) = \sqrt{a}.$

Chapter 4

Applications of the Derivative

4.1 Maximum and Minimum Values

1. $f'(x) = 2x + 4 = 2(x + 2)$, so $f'(x) = 0$ for $x = -2$. Critical number: -2.

2. $f'(x) = 12x^2 - 12x - 9 = 3(2x + 1)(2x - 3)$, so $f'(x) = 0$ for $x = -\frac{1}{2}$ or $x = \frac{3}{2}$. Critical numbers: $-\frac{1}{2}$, $\frac{3}{2}$.

3. $f'(x) = 12x^3 + 12x^2 - 24x = 12x(x + 2)(x - 1)$, so $f'(x) = 0$ for $x = -2$, 0, or 1. Critical numbers: -2, 0, 1.

4. $f'(x) = 5x^4 - 15x^2 + 10 = 5(x^2 - 1)(x^2 - 2)$, so $f'(x) = 0$ for $x = \pm 1$ or $x = \pm\sqrt{2}$. Critical numbers: $-\sqrt{2}$, -1, 1, $\sqrt{2}$.

5. $g'(x) = 1 - (1/x^2) = (x^2 - 1)/x^2$, so $g'(x) = 0$ for $x = \pm 1$. Critical numbers: -1, 1.

6. $g'(x) = 1 + (8/x^3)$, so $g'(x) = 0$ if $8/x^3 = -1$, and thus $x = -2$. Critical number: -2.

7. $k'(t) = \dfrac{\sqrt{t^2+1} - (t^2/\sqrt{t^2+1})}{t^2+1} = \dfrac{1}{(t^2+1)^{3/2}}$, so $k'(t)$ is never 0 and exists for all t. No critical numbers.

8. $k'(t) = 2 - \frac{2}{3}t^{-1/3} = (2/\sqrt[3]{t})(\sqrt[3]{t} - \frac{1}{3})$, so $k'(t) = 0$ for $t = \frac{1}{27}$ and k' does not exist at 0. Critical numbers: 0, $\frac{1}{27}$.

9. $f'(x) = \cos x$, so $f'(x) = 0$ for $x = (\pi/2) + n\pi$ for any integer n. Critical numbers: $(\pi/2) + n\pi$ for any integer n.

10. $f'(x) = (-\sin\sqrt{x})/2\sqrt{x}$, so $f'(x) = 0$ for $x = n^2\pi^2$ for any positive integer n, and f' does not exist at 0. Critical numbers: $n^2\pi^2$ for any nonnegative integer n.

11. $f'(x) = 1 + \cos x$, so $f'(x) = 0$ for $x = \pi + 2n\pi = (2n + 1)\pi$ for any integer n. Critical numbers: $(2n + 1)\pi$ for any integer n.

12. $f'(x) = \sec^2 x$ for all x in the domain of f, and $f'(x)$ is never zero. No critical numbers.

13. $f'(z) = 1$ for $z > 2$, $f'(z) = -1$ for $z < 2$, and $f'(2)$ does not exist. Critical number: 2.

14. $f(z) = \begin{Bmatrix} z^2 + 3z & \text{for } z \geq -3 \\ -z^2 - 3z & \text{for } z < -3 \end{Bmatrix}$ so $f'(z) = \begin{Bmatrix} 2z + 3 & \text{for } z > -3 \\ -2z - 3 & \text{for } z < -3 \end{Bmatrix}$

and f' is not defined at -3. Moreover, $f'(z) = 0$ for $z = -\frac{3}{2}$. Critical numbers: -3, $-\frac{3}{2}$.

15. $f'(x) = 2xe^x + x^2e^x = x(2+x)e^x$, so $f'(x) = 0$ for $x = -2$ or $x = 0$. Critical numbers: -2, 0.

16. $f'(x) = \dfrac{e^x}{e^x - 1}$, so $f'(x)$ is never 0. No critical numbers.

17. $f'(x) = \ln x + x(1/x) = 1 + \ln x$, so $f'(x) = 0$ for $x = 1/e$. Critical number: $1/e$.

18. $f'(x) = \dfrac{2 - e^{-x}}{2x + e^{-x}}$, so $f'(x) = 0$ if $e^{-x} = 2$, or $x = -\ln 2$. Critical number: $-\ln 2$.

19. Since $f'(x) = 2x - 1$, the only critical number in $(0, 2)$ is $\frac{1}{2}$. Thus the extreme values of f on $[0, 2]$ can occur only at 0, $\frac{1}{2}$, or 2. Since $f(0) = 0$, $f(\frac{1}{2}) = -\frac{1}{4}$ and $f(2) = 2$, the minimum value of f on $[0, 2]$ is $f(\frac{1}{2})$, which equals $-\frac{1}{4}$, and the maximum value is $f(2)$, which equals 2.

20. Since $g'(x) = -1/x^2$ is never zero and is defined for all x in $(0, 3]$, there are no critical numbers. Thus g can have an extreme value on $(0, 3]$ only at the endpoint 3. Now observe that for $0 < x \leq 3$, we have $g(x) = 1/x \geq \frac{1}{3} = g(3)$, so that the minimum value of g on $(0, 3]$ is $g(3)$, which is $\frac{1}{3}$. Since $\lim_{x \to 0^+} 1/x = \infty$, there is no maximum value on $(0, 3]$.

21. Since $f'(t) = 1/(2t^2)$ is never zero and is defined for every positive number t, there are no critical numbers. Because f can have an extreme value on $(0, \infty)$ only at a critical number or at an endpoint in the interval, and because neither exists, f has neither maximum nor minimum values.

22. Since $f'(t) = 2t + 4/t^2 > 0$ for $1 < t < 3$, there are no critical numbers of f in $(1, 3)$. Thus f can have an extreme value on $[1, 3)$ only at the endpoint 1. Observe that for $1 \leq t < 3$, $f(t) = t^2 - (4/t) \geq t^2 - 4 \geq 1 - 4 = -3 = f(1)$, so the minimum value of f on $[1, 3)$ is $f(1)$, which equals -3, and there is no maximum value.

23. Since $k'(z) = z/\sqrt{1 + z^2}$, the only critical number of k in $(-2, 3)$ is 0. Thus the extreme values of k on $[-2, 3]$ can occur only at -2, 0, or 3. Since $k(-2) = \sqrt{5}$, $k(0) = 1$ and $k(3) = \sqrt{10}$, the minimum value of k on $[-2, 3]$ is $k(0)$, which equals 1, and the maximum value is $k(3)$, which equals $\sqrt{10}$.

24. Since $k'(z) = \frac{1}{2}(1 + z)^{-1/2}$, there are no critical numbers of k in $(3, 8)$. Thus k can have an extreme value on $(3, 8]$ only at the endpoint 8. Observe that for $3 < z \leq 8$, we have $k(z) = \sqrt{1 + z} \leq \sqrt{1 + 8} = 3 = k(8)$, so that the maximum value of k on $(3, 8]$ is $k(8)$, which equals 3, and there is no minimum value.

25. Since $f'(x) = 1/(2\sqrt{x})$ for $x > 0$ and $f'(x) = -1/(2\sqrt{-x})$ for $x < 0$ and $f'(0)$ does not exist, the only critical number of f in $(-1, 2)$ is 0. Thus the only possible extreme value of f on $(-1, 2)$ can occur at 0. Observe that for $-1 < x < 2$ we have $f(x) = \sqrt{|x|} \geq 0 = f(0)$, so that the minimum value of f on $(-1, 2)$ is $f(0)$, which equals 0, and there is no maximum value.

26. Since $f'(x) = \frac{2}{3}x^{-1/3}$ for $x \neq 0$ and $f'(0)$ does not exist, the only critical number of f in $(-8, 8)$ is 0. Thus the extreme values of f on $[-8, 8]$ can occur only at -8, 0, or 8. Since $f(-8) = 4$, $f(0) = 0$ and $f(8) = 4$, the minimum value of f on $[-8, 8]$ is $f(0)$, which equals 0, and the maximum value is $f(-8)$ or $f(8)$, both of which equal 4.

27. Since $f'(x) = -\frac{1}{3}x^{-2/3}\cos\sqrt[3]{x}$ for $x \neq 0$ and $f'(0)$ does not exist, the only critical number of f in $(-\pi^3/27, \pi^3/8)$ is 0. Thus the extreme values of f on $[-\pi^3/27, \pi^3/8]$ can occur at $-\pi^3/27$, 0, or $\pi^3/8$. Since $f(-\pi^3/27) = -\sin(-\pi/3) = \frac{1}{2}\sqrt{3}$, $f(0) = 0$, and $f(\pi^3/8) = -\sin(\pi/2) = -1$, the minimum value of f on $[-\pi^3/27, \pi^3/8]$ is $f(\pi^3/8)$, which equals -1, and the maximum value is $f(-\pi^3/27)$, which equals $\frac{1}{2}\sqrt{3}$.

28. Since $f'(x) = -\pi\sin\pi x < 0$ for x in $(\frac{1}{3}, 1)$, f has no critical numbers in $(\frac{1}{3}, 1)$. Thus f can have an extreme value on $(\frac{1}{3}, 1]$ only at 1. Observe that for $\frac{1}{3} < x \leq 1$ we have $f(x) = \cos\pi x \geq -1 = f(1)$, so that the minimum value of f on $(\frac{1}{3}, 1]$ is $f(1)$, which equals -1, and there is no maximum value.

29. Since $f'(x) = \frac{1}{2}\sec^2(x/2) > 0$ for x in $(-\pi/2, \pi/6)$, f has no critical numbers in $(-\pi/2, \pi/6)$. Along with the fact that $(-\pi/2, \pi/6)$ has no endpoints, this means that f has no extreme value on $(-\pi/2, \pi/6)$.

30. Since $f'(x) = -3\csc 3x\cot 3x$, the only critical number of f in $(\pi/18, \pi/4)$ is $\pi/6$. Thus the extreme values of f on $[\pi/18, \pi/4]$ can occur only at $\pi/18$, $\pi/6$, or $\pi/4$. Since $f(\pi/18) = 2$, $f(\pi/6) = 1$ and $f(\pi/4) = \sqrt{2}$, the minimum value of f on $[\pi/18, \pi/4]$ is $f(\pi/6)$, which is 1, and the minimum value is $f(\pi/18)$, which is 2.

31. Since $f'(x) = e^x + xe^x = (1+x)e^x$, the only critical number of f in $(-2, 0)$ is -1. Thus the extreme values of f on $[-2, 0]$ can occur only at -2, -1, or 0. Since $f(-2) = -2e^{-2}$, $f(-1) = -e^{-1}$, and $f(0) = 0$, the minimum value of f on $[-2, 0]$ is $f(-1)$, which equals $-e^{-1}$, and the maximum value of f on $[-2, 0]$ is $f(0)$, which equals 0.

32. Since $f'(x) = e^x - 2e^{2x} = e^x(1 - 2e^x)$ and since $1 - 2e^x < 0$ for x in $(0, 1)$, f has no critical numbers in $(0, 1)$. Thus the extreme values of f on $[0, 1]$ occur at the endpoints 0 and 1. Since $f(0) = 0$ and $f(1) = e - e^2$, the minimum value of f on $[0, 1]$ is $f(1)$, which equals $e - e^2$, and the maximum value of f on $[0, 1]$ is $f(0)$, which equals 0.

33. Since $f'(x) = 1 - 2/x$, f has no critical numbers in $(\frac{1}{2}, 2)$. Thus the extreme values of f on $[\frac{1}{2}, 2]$ occur at the endpoints $\frac{1}{2}$ and 2. Since $f'(x) < 0$ for $\frac{1}{2} < x < 2$, f is decreasing on $[\frac{1}{2}, 2]$. Thus the minimum value of f on $[\frac{1}{2}, 2]$ is $f(2)$, which equals $2 - 2\ln 2$, and the maximum value of f on $[\frac{1}{2}, 2]$ is $f(\frac{1}{2})$, which equals $\frac{1}{2} - 2\ln\frac{1}{2} = \frac{1}{2} + 2\ln 2$.

34. Since $f(x) = \ln x - \ln(x^2 + 1)$ and thus $f'(x) = 1/x - 2x/(x^2 + 1) = (1 - x^2)/[x(x^2 + 1)]$, the only critical number of f in $(\frac{1}{2}, 3)$ is 1. Thus the extreme values of f on $[\frac{1}{2}, 3]$ can occur only at $\frac{1}{2}$, 1, or 3. Since $f(\frac{1}{2}) = \ln\frac{2}{5}$, $f(1) = \ln\frac{1}{2}$, and $f(3) = \ln\frac{3}{10}$, the minimum value of f on $[\frac{1}{2}, 3]$ is $f(3)$, which equals $\ln\frac{3}{10}$, and the maximum value of f on $[\frac{1}{2}, 3]$ is $f(1)$, which equals $\ln\frac{1}{2}$.

35. $f'(x) = x^3 + 3x^2 - 1$ and $f''(x) = 3x^2 + 6x$. The Newton-Raphson method yields (approximate) critical numbers -2.879385242 and $.5320888862$.

36. $f'(x) = \cos x - x\sin x$ and $f''(x) = -2\sin x - x\cos x$. The Newton-Raphson method yields (approximate) critical numbers -3.425618459, $-.860333589$, 0, $.860333589$, and 3.425618459.

37. $f'(x) = 2x + e^x$ and $f''(x) = 2 + e^x$. The Newton-Raphson method yields approximately $-.3517337112$ as the only critical number of f in $[-1, 1]$. Since $f(-1) = 1 + e^{-1}$, $f(-.3517337112) \approx .8271840261$, and $f(1) = 1 + e$, we conclude that $f(-.3517337112)$, which is approximately $.8271840261$, is the (approximate) minimum value of f, and $f(1)$, which is $1 + e$, is the maximum value of f on $[-1, 1]$.

38. $f'(x) = x^3 + 3x^2 + 2$ and $f''(x) = 3x^2 + 6x$. The Newton-Raphson method yields approximately -3.195823345 as the only critical number in $[-4, 0]$. Since

$$f(-4) = -2, \quad f(-3.195823345) \approx -6.95370016, \quad \text{and} \quad f(0) = 6,$$

we conclude that $f(-3.195823345)$, which is approximately -6.95370016, is the (approximate) minimum value of f, and $f(0)$, which is 6, is the maximum value of f on $[-4, 0]$.

39. $f'(x) = \dfrac{a(cx+d) - (ax+b)c}{(cx+d)^2} = \dfrac{ad - bc}{(cx+d)^2}$

If $ad - bc \neq 0$, then $f'(x) \neq 0$ for all x in the domain of f. Thus if $ad - bc \neq 0$, then f has no critical numbers. Now assume that $ad - bc = 0$. If $d \neq 0$, then $a = bc/d$, so that

$$f(x) = \frac{(bc/d)x + b}{cx + d} = \frac{b}{d}\left(\frac{cx+d}{cx+d}\right) = \frac{b}{d}$$

and thus f is a constant function. If $d = 0$, then $c \neq 0$ (since not both c and d are 0 by hypothesis), so $b = 0$ (because $ad - bc = 0$) and thus $f(x) = ax/(cx) = a/c$. Therefore if $ad - bc = 0$, then f is a constant function.

40. $f(x_0)$ is the maximum value of f on I if and only if $f(x) \leq f(x_0)$ for x in I if and only if $-f(x) \geq -f(x_0)$ for x in I if and only if $g(x) \geq g(x_0)$ for x in I if and only if $g(x_0)$ is the minimum value of g on I.

41. Assume that $f'(c) = \lim_{x\to c}[f(x) - f(c)]/(x - c) < 0$. Then for x in some open interval I about c the inequality $[f(x) - f(c)]/(x - c) < 0$ holds. If x is in I and $x > c$, then $x - c > 0$, so that

$$f(x) - f(c) = (x - c)\left(\frac{f(x) - f(c)}{x - c}\right) < 0.$$

Therefore $f(x) < f(c)$, so $f(c)$ is not a minimum value. If x is in I and $x < c$, then $x - c < 0$, so that

$$f(x) - f(c) = (x - c)\left(\frac{f(x) - f(c)}{x - c}\right) > 0.$$

Therefore $f(x) > f(c)$, so $f(c)$ is not a maximum value. Thus if $f'(c) < 0$, then f does not have an extreme value at c.

42. In the proof it is assumed that $[f(x) - f(c)]/(x - c) > 0$ for all $x \neq c$ in some open interval I containing c. Each such x is contained in the domain of f, and hence in I. Thus c must be an interior number of I.

43. Let $g(x) = f(x) - mx$ for $a \leq x \leq b$. Since $g'(x) = f'(x) - m$ and $f'(a) < m < f'(b)$, we have $g'(a) = f'(a) - m < 0$ and $g'(b) = f'(b) - m > 0$. Since $g'(a) < 0$, we must have $[g(x) - g(a)]/(x - a) < 0$ for x in an interval $(a, a + \delta)$. But then

$$(x - a)\left(\frac{g(x) - g(a)}{x - a}\right) < 0$$

so $g(x) < g(a)$ for x in $(a, a + \delta)$. Similarly, since $g'(b) > 0$, we must have

$$\frac{[g(x) - g(b)]}{x - b} > 0$$

for x in an interval $(b - \delta, b)$. But then

$$g(x) - g(b) = (x - b)\left(\frac{g(x) - g(b)}{x - b}\right) < 0 \quad \text{for } b - \delta < x < b$$

and hence $g(x) < g(b)$ for x in $(b - \delta, b)$. Thus g does not assume its minimum value at a or b. But since g is continuous on $[a, b]$, the Maximum-Minimum Theorem says that g has a minimum value on $[a, b]$, which must occur on (a, b). Since g is differentiable on (a, b), Theorem 4.3 says that there is a number c in (a, b) such that $g'(c) = 0$. But $g'(c) = f'(c) - m$. Thus $f'(c) = m$.

44. a. If the house is placed along one of the sides, then, in effect, the fencing becomes 30 meters longer. Thus we can follow the solution of Example 2, with 2000 replaced by 2030. We have $x + 2y = 2030$, so that $y = 1015 - \frac{1}{2}x$. The area A fenced in is given by $A(x) = xy = x(1015 - \frac{1}{2}x) = 1015x - \frac{1}{2}x^2$. Thus we seek the maximum value of A on $[0, 2030]$. Since $A'(x) = 1015 - x$, the only critical number of A in $[0, 2030]$ is 1015. Thus A can have its maximum only at 0, 1015, or 2030. Since $A(0) = 0$ and $A(2030) = 0$, A is maximum for $x = 1015$. The corresponding value of y is $1015 - \frac{1}{2}(1015) = 507.5$. Thus the field should be 1015 meters long and 507.5 meters wide.

b. Suppose the house is placed as in the diagram and let x and y be as in the diagram. Since the area of the triangle cut off from the field by the house is constant, we can maximize the area of the field by maximizing the area xy of the rectangle with sides of length x and y. Since there is no fencing along the dashed part of the rectangle in the diagram, one has, in effect, an additional $30\sqrt{2}$ meters of fencing. Thus one can again follow the solution of Example 2, with 2000 replaced by $2000 + 30\sqrt{2}$. This time one finds that $x = 1000 + 15\sqrt{2}$ and $y = 500 + \frac{1}{2}(15\sqrt{2})$ maximize the area. Thus the field should be $1000 + 15\sqrt{2}$ meters long and $500 + \frac{1}{2}(15\sqrt{2})$ meters wide.

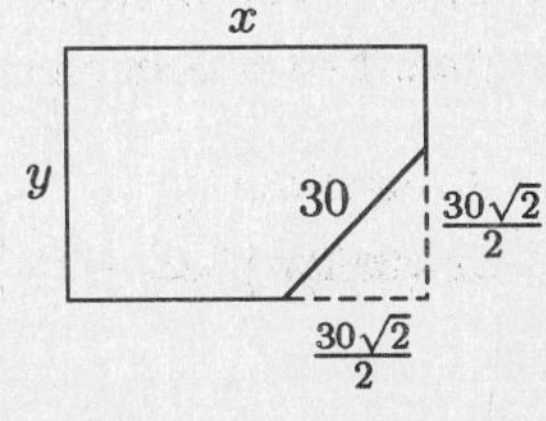

45. Since $P(x_0)$ is the maximum of P on $[0, \infty)$, it is also the maximum value of P on $[0, 2x_0]$. By Theorem 4.3, $P'(x_0) = 0$, and since $P'(x_0) = R'(x_0) - C'(x_0)$, it follows that $R'(x_0) = C'(x_0)$.

46. Let $f(x) = x(1 - x)$ for $0 \leq x \leq 1$. We are to find the largest value of f on $[0, 1]$. Now $f'(x) = 1 - 2x$, so that $f'(x) = 0$ only for $x = \frac{1}{2}$. Thus the maximum value of f can occur only at 0, $\frac{1}{2}$, or 1. Since $f(0) = f(1) = 0$ and $f(\frac{1}{2}) = \frac{1}{4}$, the maximum value of f, and hence the largest product, is $\frac{1}{4}$. The smallest product is 0, which occurs for $x = 0$ and $y = 1$, or $x = 1$ and $y = 0$.

47. Since $x(t+\pi) = x(t)$, the maximum value of x equals its maximum value on $[0, \pi]$. Now $x'(t) = 2\cos 2t - 2\sqrt{3}\sin 2t$, so that $x'(t) = 0$ only if $2\cos 2t - 2\sqrt{3}\sin 2t = 0$, or $\tan 2t = 1/\sqrt{13}$. Thus the only critical number of x in $(0, \pi)$ is $\pi/12$. Thus the maximum value of x on $[0, \pi]$ can occur only at 0, $\pi/12$, or π. Since $x(0) = x(\pi) = \sqrt{3}$, and $x(\pi/12) = \frac{1}{2} + \frac{3}{2} = 2$, the maximum value of x is 2. Consequently the maximum distance from the origin is 2.

48. $dM/dx = \frac{1}{2}w(L-x) - \frac{1}{2}wx = \frac{1}{2}w(L-2x)$, so $dM/dx = 0$ only for $x = L/2$. Thus the extreme values of M on $[0, L]$ can occur only at 0, $L/2$, or L. Since $M = 0$ if $x = 0$ or $x = L$, M is largest for $x = L/2$, that is, at the midpoint of the beam.

49. a. $R'(\theta) = (2v_0^2/g)\cos 2\theta$, so that $R'(\theta) = 0$ if $2\theta = \pi/2$, or $\theta = \pi/4$. Thus the extreme values of R on $[0, \pi/2]$ can occur only at 0, $\pi/4$, or $\pi/2$. Since $R = 0$ if $\theta = 0$ or $\theta = \pi/2$, the maximum value of R is its value for $\theta = \pi/4$, that is, $(v_0^2/g)\sin(\pi/2)$, which equals v_0^2/g.

    b. We seek a value of θ for which $R(\theta) = 144$. Since $v_0 = 30$ and $g = 9.8$, this means that $(30^2/9.8)\sin 2\theta = 50$, or $\sin 2\theta - \frac{49}{90} = 0$. By the Newton-Raphson method, $\theta \approx .287863324$ radian, or approximately $16.5°$.

    c. Since the maximum value of $\sin^2\theta$ occurs for $\theta = \pi/2$, the maximum value of y_{max} occurs for $\theta = \pi/2$ also. This means that the ball would be hit straight up and eventually strike the batter.

50. Let $f(x) = x^m(1-x)^{n-m}$. Then

$$f'(x) = mx^{m-1}(1-x)^{n-m} - (n-m)x^m(1-x)^{n-m-1} = x^{m-1}(1-x)^{n-m-1}(m-nx),$$

so that $f'(x) = 0$ if $x = m/n$. Since $f(0) = 0$ and $f(1) = 0$, it follows that f has a maximum value on $[0, 1]$ at $x = m/n$, so m/n is the maximum likelihood estimate.

51. We must determine the maximum value of P on $[0, 4]$. Now $P'(t) = -6(20-t)^2t + 2(20-t)^3 = (20-t)^2(-6t + 40 - 2t) = (20-t)^2(40-8t)$, so $P'(t) > 0$ for $0 \le t \le 4$. Thus the net profit increases the longer the stocks are kept, so the company should retain them the full four-year period.

52. a. $F'(r) = k(4r_0r^3 - 5r^4) = kr^3(4r_0 - 5r)$, so that $F'(r) = 0$ for $r = \frac{4}{5}r_0$. Thus the only critical number of F in $(\frac{1}{2}r_0, r_0)$ is $\frac{4}{5}r_0$. Therefore the extreme values of F on $[\frac{1}{2}r_0, r_0]$ can occur only at $\frac{1}{2}r_0$, $\frac{4}{5}r_0$, or r_0. Since $F(\frac{1}{2}r_0) = \frac{1}{32}kr_0^5$, $F(\frac{4}{5}r_0) = \frac{256}{3125}kr_0^5$, and $F(r_0) = 0$, the flow F is maximized for $r = \frac{4}{5}r_0$.

    b. $dv/dt = (k/\pi)(2r_0r - 3r^2) = (k/\pi)r(2r_0 - 3r)$, so that $dv/dt = 0$ for $r = \frac{2}{3}r_0$. Thus the only critical number of v in $(\frac{1}{2}r_0, r_0)$ is $\frac{2}{3}r_0$. Therefore the extreme values of v on $[\frac{1}{2}r_0, r_0]$ can occur only at $\frac{1}{2}r_0$, $\frac{2}{3}r_0$, or r_0. Since $v(\frac{1}{2}r_0) = \frac{1}{8}(k/\pi)r_0^3$, $v(\frac{2}{3}r_0) = \frac{4}{27}(k/\pi)r_0^3$, and $v(r_0) = 0$, the velocity v is maximized for $r = \frac{2}{3}r_0$.

    c. Yes since both the flow and the velocity can be larger when the windpipe is contracted than when it is relaxed.

53. Let x be the length of the sides of the base of the crate and y the height. We are given that the volume $V = x^2y$ of the crate is 6 cubic feet, and we would like to minimize the cost $C = 5x^2 + 2(4xy) + 1(x^2)$.

Since $x^2y = V = 6$, we have $y = 6/x^2$, so that $C = 6x^2 + 8x(6/x^2) = 6x^2 + 48/x$. Since the length of the base is to be between 1 and 2, the domain of C is $[1,2]$. We have $C'(x) = 12x - 48/x^2$, so that $C'(x) = 0$ if $12x^3 = 48$, or $x = \sqrt[3]{4}$. Thus the extreme values of C on $[1,2]$ can occur only at 1, $\sqrt[3]{4}$, or 2. Since $C(1) = 54$, $C(\sqrt[3]{4}) = 6\sqrt[3]{16} + 48/\sqrt[3]{4} \approx 45.4$, and $C(2) = 48$, the minimum value of C on $[1,2]$ occurs for $x = \sqrt[3]{4}$. The corresponding value of y is $6/x^2 = 6/\sqrt[3]{16}$. Thus for minimum cost the base should be $\sqrt[3]{4}$ feet square and the height should be $6/\sqrt[3]{16}$ feet.

54. Let x be the distance shown in the diagram, so that $0 \le x \le 200$. By the Pythagorean Theorem the distance from the station to each of the houses not adjacent to the road is $\sqrt{x^2 + 50^2}$. Therefore we must minimize the total length $L = 200 - x + 2\sqrt{x^2 + 50^2}$ on $[0, 200]$. Since

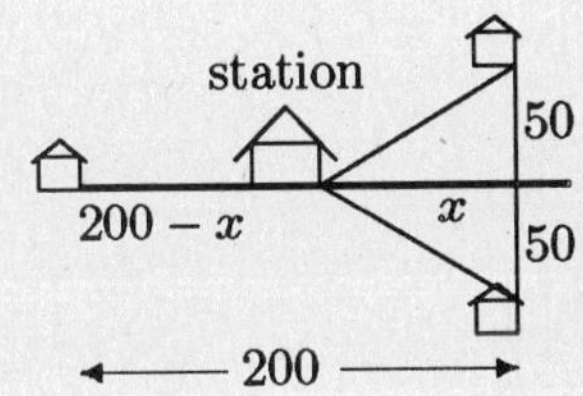

$$L'(x) = -1 + 2\frac{1}{2\sqrt{x^2 + 50^2}}(2x) = -1 + \frac{2x}{\sqrt{x^2 + 50^2}},$$

we have $L'(x) = 0$ if $2x = \sqrt{x^2 + 50^2}$, or $4x^2 = x^2 + 50^2$, or $x = 50/\sqrt{3}$. Thus the extreme values of L on $[0, 200]$ can occur only at 0, $50/\sqrt{3}$, or 200. Since $L(0) = 300$, $L(50/\sqrt{3}) = 200 - 50/\sqrt{3} + 2\sqrt{(50^2/3) + 50^2} = 200 + 50\sqrt{3} \approx 286.6$, and $L(200) = 2\sqrt{200^2 + 50^2} = 100\sqrt{17} \approx 412.3$, the total length is minimized for $x = 50/\sqrt{3} \approx 28.9$, that is, if the station is placed approximately 171.1 feet from the house adjacent to the street.

55. Let x be the length of the base, y the common length of the other two sides, and A the area of the triangle. We must maximize A. By hypothesis, $x + 2y = 3$, so $y = \frac{3}{2} - \frac{1}{2}x$, so by the Pythagorean Theorem, the height h of the triangle is given by $h = \sqrt{y^2 - \frac{1}{4}x^2} = \sqrt{(\frac{3}{2} - \frac{1}{2}x)^2 - \frac{1}{4}x^2} = \frac{1}{2}\sqrt{9 - 6x}$. Thus $A = \frac{1}{2}xh = \frac{1}{2}x(\frac{1}{2}\sqrt{9 - 6x}) = \frac{1}{4}x\sqrt{9 - 6x}$ for $0 \le x \le \frac{3}{2}$. Now

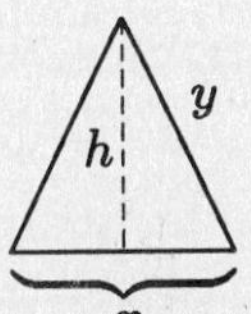

$$A'(x) = \frac{1}{4}\sqrt{9 - 6x} - \frac{3x}{4\sqrt{9 - 6x}} = \frac{9 - 9x}{4\sqrt{9 - 6x}}$$

so $A'(x) = 0$ if $9 - 9x = 0$, that is, $x = 1$. Thus the extreme values of A on $[0, \frac{3}{2}]$ can occur only at 0, 1, or $\frac{3}{2}$. Since $A(0) = 0$, $A(1) = \frac{1}{4}\sqrt{3}$, and $A(\frac{3}{2}) = 0$, the area A is maximum if $x = 1$. Then $y = \frac{3}{2} - \frac{1}{2} \cdot 1 = 1$, making the triangle equilateral.

56. Let x be the length of the sides of the square (so that $0 \le x \le L/4$), r the radius of the circle, and A the sum of the areas of the square and circle. Thus $A = x^2 + \pi r^2$, and we are to maximize and minimize A. Notice that $L = 4x + 2\pi r$, so $r = (L - 4x)/(2\pi)$. Thus

$$A = x^2 + \pi\left(\frac{L - 4x}{2\pi}\right)^2 \quad \text{for } 0 \le x \le \frac{L}{4}.$$

Then

$$A'(x) = 2x + 2\pi\left(\frac{L - 4x}{2\pi}\right)\left(-\frac{4}{2\pi}\right) = 2x - \frac{2L}{\pi} + \frac{8x}{\pi}$$

so $A'(x) = 0$ if $x - L/\pi + 4x/\pi = 0$, that is, $x = L/\pi \cdot 1/(1 + 4/\pi) = L/(\pi + 4)$. Thus the extreme values of A on $[0, L/4]$ can occur only at 0, $L/(\pi + 4)$, or $L/4$. Since

$$A(0) = \pi\left(\frac{L}{2\pi}\right)^2 = \frac{L^2}{4\pi},$$

$$A\left(\frac{L}{\pi+4}\right) = \left(\frac{L}{\pi+4}\right)^2 + \pi\left(\frac{L - 4L/(\pi+4)}{2\pi}\right)^2 = \frac{L^2}{(\pi+4)^2} + \frac{\pi L^2}{4(\pi+4)^2} = \frac{L^2}{4(\pi+4)},$$

and

$$A\left(\frac{L}{4}\right) = \left(\frac{L}{4}\right)^2 + \pi(0) = \frac{L^2}{16},$$

$A(L/(\pi + 4))$ is the minimum value of A. Also, $A(0)$ is the maximum value of A, so that there is no maximum value if the wire is actually cut.

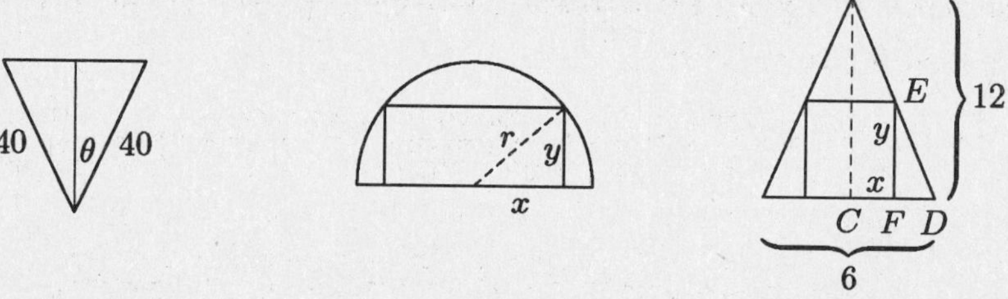

Exercise 57 Exercise 58 Exercise 59

57. a. The cross-section of the trough is the triangle in the figure above, with height equal to $40\cos\theta$ and width equal to $80\sin\theta$. Its area equals $\frac{1}{2}(80\sin\theta)(40\cos\theta) = 1600\sin\theta\cos\theta$. Thus $V = 1000(1600\sin\theta\cos\theta) = 1.6 \times 10^6\sin\theta\cos\theta = .8 \times 10^6 \sin 2\theta$ for $0 \le \theta \le \pi/2$. Thus $V'(\theta) = 1.6 \times 10^5\cos 2\theta$, so that $V'(\theta) = 0$ if $\cos 2\theta = 0$, or $2\theta = \pi/2$, or $\theta = \pi/4$. Thus the extreme value of V on $[0, \pi/2]$ can occur only at 0, $\pi/4$, or $\pi/2$. Since $V(0) = 0$, $V(\pi/4) = 800$, and $V(\pi/2) = 0$ the maximum value of V occurs for $\theta = \pi/4$. The corresponding depth is $40\cos(\pi/4) = 20\sqrt{2}$ (centimeters).

   b. By (a), the maximum volume is $V(\pi/4) = 800$ (cubic centimeters).

58. Let x and y be as in the diagram. Then $x^2 + y^2 = r^2$ and the area A of the rectangle is given by $A = 2xy$. Since $y = \sqrt{r^2 - x^2}$, we have $A = 2x\sqrt{r^2 - x^2}$ for $0 \le x \le r$. Thus

$$A'(x) = 2\sqrt{r^2 - x^2} + 2x\frac{1}{2\sqrt{r^2 - x^2}}(-2x) = 2\sqrt{r^2 - x^2} - \frac{2x^2}{\sqrt{r^2 - x^2}} = \frac{2(r^2 - 2x^2)}{\sqrt{r^2 - x^2}}.$$

It follows that $A'(x) = 0$ if $r^2 - 2x^2 = 0$, or $x = r/\sqrt{2}$. Thus the extreme values of A on $[0, r]$ can occur only at 0, $r/\sqrt{2}$, or r. Since $A(0) = 0$, $A(r/\sqrt{2}) = (2r/\sqrt{2})\sqrt{r^2 - r^2/2} = r^2$, and $A(r) = 0$, the maximum possible area of the rectangle is r^2.

59. Let x be $\frac{1}{2}$ the length of the base of the rectangle, y the height, and A the area. We are to maximize A. Since triangles BCD and EFD are similar, it follows that $\frac{12}{3} = y/(3-x)$, so that $y = 4(3-x) = 12-4x$. Thus $A = 2xy = 2x(12 - 4x) = 24x - 8x^2$ for $0 \le x \le 3$. Now $A'(x) = 24 - 16x$, so $A'(x) = 0$ if $x = \frac{3}{2}$. Thus the extreme values of A on $[0, 3]$ can occur only at 0, $\frac{3}{2}$, or 3. Since $A(0) = 0$, $A(\frac{3}{2}) = 24(\frac{3}{2}) - 8(\frac{3}{2})^2 = 18$, and $A(3) = 0$, the maximum area of an inscribed rectangle is 18.

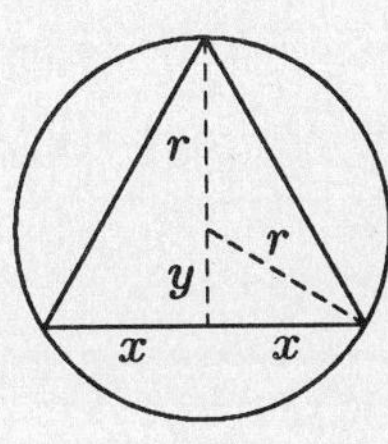

Exercise 60

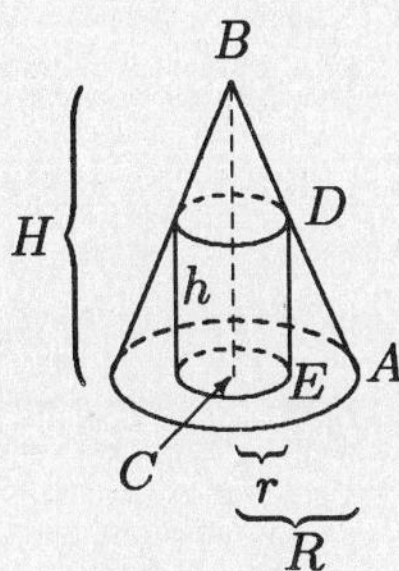

Exercise 61

60. Let x be $\frac{1}{2}$ the length of the base, $y+r$ the height of the triangle, as in the figure, and A the area. We are to maximize A. By the Pythagorean Theorem, $y = \sqrt{r^2-x^2}$, so that $A = \frac{1}{2}(2x)(y+r) = x(\sqrt{r^2-x^2}+r)$ for $0 \le x \le r$. Now

$$A'(x) = \sqrt{r^2-x^2} + r + \frac{x(-x)}{\sqrt{r^2-x^2}} = \sqrt{r^2-x^2} + r - \frac{x^2}{\sqrt{r^2-x^2}}$$

so $A'(x) = 0$ if

$$r = \frac{x^2}{\sqrt{r^2-x^2}} - \sqrt{r^2-x^2} = \frac{x^2-(r^2-x^2)}{\sqrt{r^2-x^2}} = \frac{2x^2-r^2}{\sqrt{r^2-x^2}}$$

so that $r^2(r^2-x^2) = (2x^2-r^2)^2$, or equivalently, $r^4 - r^2x^2 = 4x^4 - 4x^2r^2 + r^4$, and thus $3r^2x^2 = 4x^4$. Thus $x = 0$ or $x = \frac{1}{2}\sqrt{3}\,r$. Therefore the extreme values of A on $[0, r]$ can occur only at 0, $\frac{1}{2}\sqrt{3}\,r$, or r. Since $A(0) = 0$, $A(r) = r^2$ and $A(\frac{1}{2}\sqrt{3}\,r) = \frac{1}{2}\sqrt{3}\,r(\sqrt{r^2-\frac{3}{4}r^2}+r) = \frac{1}{2}\sqrt{3}\,r(\frac{1}{2}r+r) = \frac{3}{4}\sqrt{3}\,r^2$, it follows that the maximum area of an inscribed triangle is $\frac{3}{4}\sqrt{3}\,r^2$.

61. Let V be the volume of the cylinder, h its height, and r its radius. We are to maximize V. From similar triangles ABC and ADE, we deduce that $H/R = h/(R-r)$, so that $h = (H/R)(R-r)$ and thus $V = \pi r^2 h = \pi r^2[(H/R)(R-r)] = \pi H r^2 - (\pi H/R)r^3$ for $0 \le r \le R$. Now $V'(r) = 2\pi H r - (3\pi H/R)r^2$, so $V'(r) = 0$ if $2\pi H r - (3\pi H/R)r^2 = 0$, that is, $r = 0$ or $r = \frac{2}{3}R$. Thus the extreme values of V on $[0, R]$ can occur only at 0, $\frac{2}{3}R$, or R. Since $V(0) = 0 = V(R)$ and $V(\frac{2}{3}R) = \pi H(\frac{2}{3}R)^2 - (\pi H/R)(\frac{2}{3}R)^3 = \frac{4}{27}\pi R^2 H$, it follows that the maximum possible volume is $\frac{4}{27}\pi R^2 H$.

4.2 The Mean Value Theorem

1. $\dfrac{f(4)-f(0)}{4-0} = \dfrac{-8-0}{4} = -2$; $f'(x) = 2x-6$

   We must find c in $(0, 4)$ such that $f'(c) = -2$, which means that $2c - 6 = -2$, or $c = 2$.

2. $\dfrac{f(3)-f(-1)}{3-(-1)} = \dfrac{-24-(-4)}{4} = -5$; $f'(x) = 1-6x$

   We must find c in $(-1, 3)$ such that $f'(c) = -5$, which means that $1 - 6c = -5$, or $c = 1$.

3. $\dfrac{f(0)-f(-2)}{0-(-2)} = \dfrac{0-4}{2} = -2$; $f'(x) = 3x^2-6$

   We must find c in $(-2, 0)$ such that $f'(c) = -2$, which means that $3c^2 - 6 = -2$, or $c^2 = \frac{4}{3}$. Since $-2 < c < 0$, we have $c = -\frac{2}{3}\sqrt{3}$.

4. $\dfrac{f(2)-f(-2)}{2-(-2)} = \dfrac{-4-4}{4} = -2$; $f'(x) = 3x^2 - 6$

We must find c in $(-2,2)$ such that $f'(c) = -2$, which means that $3c^2 - 6 = -2$, or $c^2 = \frac{4}{3}$. Since $-2 < c < 2$, we have $c = -\frac{2}{3}\sqrt{3}$ or $c = \frac{2}{3}\sqrt{3}$.

5. $\dfrac{f(1)-f(-2)}{1-(-2)} = \dfrac{5-(-4)}{3} = 3$; $f'(x) = 3x^2$

We must find c in $(-2,1)$ such that $f'(c) = 3$, which means that $3c^2 = 3$, or $c^2 = 1$. Since $-2 < c < 1$, we have $c = -1$.

6. $\dfrac{f(3)-f(-3)}{3-(-3)} = \dfrac{25-(-29)}{6} = 9$; $f'(x) = 3x^2$

We must find c in $(-3,3)$ such that $f'(c) = 9$, which means that $3c^2 = 9$, or $c^2 = 3$. Since $-3 < c < 3$, we have $c = -\sqrt{3}$ or $c = \sqrt{3}$.

7. $\dfrac{f(2)-f(-2)}{2-(-2)} = \dfrac{3-(-25)}{4} = 7$; $f'(x) = 3x^2 - 6x + 3$

We must find c in $(-2,2)$ such that $f'(c) = 7$, which means that $3c^2 - 6c + 3 = 7$, or $3c^2 - 6c - 4 = 0$. The roots are $1 + \sqrt{21}/3$ and $1 - \sqrt{21}/3$. Since $-2 < c < 2$, we have $c = 1 - \sqrt{21}/3$.

8. $\dfrac{f(1)-f(0)}{1-0} = \dfrac{-2-(-3)}{1} = 1$; $f'(x) = \dfrac{1}{2\sqrt{x}}$

We must find c in $(0,1)$ such that $f'(c) = 1$, which means that $(1/2\sqrt{c}) = 1$, or $\sqrt{c} = \frac{1}{2}$, so that $c = \frac{1}{4}$.

9. $\dfrac{f(8)-f(1)}{8-1} = \dfrac{3-2}{7} = \dfrac{1}{7}$; $f'(x) = \frac{1}{3}x^{-2/3}$

We must find c in $(1,8)$ such that $f'(c) = \frac{1}{7}$, which means that $\frac{1}{3}c^{-2/3} = \frac{1}{7}$, so that $c = (\frac{7}{3})^{3/2}$.

10. $\dfrac{f(3)-f(\frac{1}{3})}{3-(\frac{1}{3})} = \dfrac{10-10}{\frac{8}{3}} = 0$; $f'(x) = 3(1-(1/x^2))$

We must find c in $(\frac{1}{3},3)$ such that $f'(c) = 0$. Thus $3(1-(1/c^2)) = 0$, or $c^2 = 1$. Since $\frac{1}{3} < c < 3$, $c = 1$.

11. $m = \dfrac{f(2)-f(1)}{2-1} = \dfrac{3-(-1)}{1} = 4$; $f'(x) = 2x + 2/x^2$

Thus we seek a solution in $(1,2)$ of $2c + 2/c^2 = 4$, or $-4 + 2c + 2/c^2 = 0$. By the Newton-Raphson method we find that $c \approx 1.618033989$.

12. $m = \dfrac{f(1)-f(-1)}{1-(-1)} = \dfrac{1-(-1)}{1-(-1)} = 1$; $f'(x) = (\pi/2)\cos(\pi x/2)$

Thus we seek a solution in $(-1,1)$ of $(\pi/2)\cos(\pi x/2) = 1$, or $\cos(\pi x/2) - 2/\pi = 0$. By the Newton-Raphson method we find that $c \approx .5606641806$.

13. a. Since $f'(x) = 2Ax + B$, c must satisfy the equation

$$2Ac + B = \frac{(Ab^2 + Bb + C) - (Aa^2 + Ba + C)}{b-a} = \frac{A(b^2-a^2) + B(b-a)}{b-a} = A(b+a) + B.$$

Therefore $c = (b+a)/2$, the midpoint of $[a,b]$.

b. It means geometrically that the line that connects any two distinct points P and Q on a parabola is parallel to the line that is tangent to the point on the parabola whose x coordinate is the average of the x coordinates of P and Q.

14. $f(-2) = |-2| = 2 = |2| = f(2)$. Next, $f'(x) = 1$ for $x > 0$ and $f'(x) = -1$ for $x < 0$, but f is not differentiable at 0. Therefore $f'(x)$ is never 0. Since Rolle's Theorem requires that f be differentiable on $(-2, 2)$ and $f(x) = |x|$ is not differentiable at 0, Rolle's Theorem is not contradicted.

15. By the Mean Value Theorem, there exists a number c in (a, b) such that

$$\frac{f(b)-f(a)}{b-a} = f'(c), \quad \text{so that} \quad \left|\frac{f(b)-f(a)}{b-a}\right| = |f'(c)| \le M.$$

Thus $|f(b) - f(a)| \le M|b-a|$. Equivalently, $f(a) - M(b-a) \le f(b) \le f(a) + M(b-a)$.

16. If $f(x) = \sqrt{x}$, then $f'(x) = 1/(2\sqrt{x})$, and for $100 \le x \le 101$, we have $|f'(x)| \le \frac{1}{20}$. From Exercise 15, $|\sqrt{101} - \sqrt{100}| = |f(101) - f(100)| \le \frac{1}{20}(101 - 100) = 0.05$. Thus $10 - 0.05 \le \sqrt{101} \le 10 + .05$. But $\sqrt{101} > 10$, so $10 < \sqrt{101} \le 10.05$.

17. If $f(x) = x^{2/3}$, then $f'(x) = \frac{2}{3}x^{-1/3}$, and for $27 \le x \le 28$, we have $|f'(x)| \le \frac{2}{9}$. From Exercise 15, $|28^{2/3} - 27^{2/3}| \le \frac{2}{9}(28-27) = \frac{2}{9}$. Thus $9 - \frac{2}{9} \le 28^{2/3} \le 9 + \frac{2}{9} = \frac{83}{9}$. But $28^{2/3} > 9$, so $9 < 28^{2/3} \le \frac{83}{9}$.

18. If $f(x) = x^{1/5}$, then $f'(x) = \frac{1}{5}x^{-4/5}$, and for $32 \le x \le 33$, we have $|f'(x)| \le \frac{1}{5}(32)^{-4/5} = \frac{1}{80}$. From Exercise 15, $|33^{1/5} - 32^{1/5}| \le \frac{1}{80}(33-32) = \frac{1}{80}$. Thus $2 - \frac{1}{80} \le 33^{1/5} \le 2 + \frac{1}{80}$. But $33^{1/5} > 2$, so $2 < 33^{1/5} < 2 + \frac{1}{80}$.

19. Let $f(x) = \sqrt{x}$. If x is in $[2.89, 3]$, then

$$|f'(x)| = \left|\frac{1}{2\sqrt{x}}\right| \le \frac{1}{2\sqrt{2.89}} = \frac{1}{3.4}.$$

With $a = 2.89$ and $b = 3$, Exercise 15 implies that $|\sqrt{3} - 1.7| = |f(3) - f(2.89)| \le (1/3.4)(3 - 2.89) = \frac{11}{340} \approx 0.0323529412$.

20. Let $f(x) = \sqrt{x}$. Then $f'(x) = 1/(2\sqrt{x})$, and for $4.84 \le x \le 5$, we have

$$|f'(x)| \le \frac{1}{2\sqrt{4.84}} = \frac{1}{2(2.2)} = \frac{1}{4.4}.$$

From Exercise 15 we find that $|\sqrt{5} - 2.2| = |f(5) - f(4.84)| \le (1/4.4)(0.16) = \frac{2}{55} \approx 0.0363636364$.

21. Let $f(x) = (x-1)\sin x$. Then f is continuous on $[0, 1]$ and differentiable on $(0, 1)$. Since $f(0) = f(1) = 0$ and $f'(x) = \sin x + (x-1)\cos x$, Rolle's Theorem implies the existence of a number c in $(0, 1)$ such that $\sin c + (c-1)\cos c = 0$, or $\tan c = 1 - c$.

22. Let $f(x) = x\cos x$. Then f is continuous on $[0, \pi/2]$ and differentiable on $(0, \pi/2)$. Since $f(0) = 0 = f(\pi/2)$ and $f'(x) = \cos x - x\sin x$, Rolle's Theorem implies the existence of a number c in $(0, \pi/2)$ such that $\cos c - c\sin c = 0$. Since $\sin c \ne 0$, it follows that $c = (\cos c)/(\sin c) = \cot c$.

23. Let $f(x) = x + \sin x$, so that $f(\pi) = \pi$. Then $f'(x) = 1 + \cos x$, so that $0 < f'(c) < 1$ for $\pi/2 < c < \pi$ and for $\pi < c < 3\pi/2$. For any x with $\pi/2 < x < \pi$ or $\pi < x < 3\pi/2$, the Mean Value Theorem implies that there is c between x and π such that $f(x) - f(\pi) = f'(c)(x - \pi)$. Therefore $|x + \sin x - \pi| = f'(c)|x - \pi| < |x - \pi|$.

24. For $x = 3.14$, the value of $x + \sin x$ given by calculator is 3.141592653. This value agrees with the first 10 digits in the decimal expansion of π.

25. a. Suppose b and d are fixed points, with $b < d$. Then $f(b) = b$ and $f(d) = d$. Now apply the Mean Value Theorem to f on the interval $[b, d]$ to find that there is a number c such that

$$f'(c) = \frac{f(d) - f(b)}{d - b} = \frac{d - b}{d - b} = 1$$

which contradicts the assumption that $f'(x) \neq 1$ for every number x. Thus f has at most one fixed point.

b. Since $f'(x) = \frac{1}{2}\cos 2x \leq \frac{1}{2} < 1$, we conclude from part (a) that f has at most one fixed point. Since $f(0) = \sin 0 = 0$, 0 is the only fixed point.

26. a. Suppose x and y are in (a, b) with $x < y$ and $g(x) = g(y) = 0$. By Rolle's Theorem there is a number c in (x, y) and hence in (a, b) such that $g'(c) = 0$.

b. Since $g(-1) = -2$ and $g(0) = 1$, and since $g(0) = 1$ and $g(1) = -44$, the Intermediate Value Theorem guarantees numbers x in $(-1, 0)$ and y in $(0, 1)$ such that $g(x) = 0 = g(y)$. By part (a), there is a number c in (x, y) such that $g'(c) = 0$. But then $4c^3 - 60c^2 - 50c - 1 = g'(c) = 0$.

27. a. Since $f(-1) = 0$ and $f'(-1) = 1$, $f(x)$ must be positive for all x in some interval $(-1, c)$. Since $f(1) = 0$ and $f'(1) = 1$, $f(x)$ must be negative for all x in some interval $(d, 1)$. Thus f assumes both positive and negative values on $(-1, 1)$. The Intermediate Value Theorem implies that f must also assume the value 0 on $(-1, 1)$.

b. We know $f(1) = 0 = f(-1)$, and by part (a), there is a number r in $(-1, 1)$ such that $f(r) = 0$. Applying the Mean Value Theorem to f on $[-1, r]$ and on $[r, 1]$, we find that there are numbers s and t in $(-1, r)$ and $(r, 1)$, respectively, such that $f'(s) = 0 = f'(t)$. Both s and t are in $(-1, 1)$, so f' has at least two zeros in $(-1, 1)$.

28. Since the graph of f is not a line, there is a point $(r, f(r))$ with $a < r < b$ on the graph of f that is not on the line l joining $(a, f(a))$ and $(b, f(b))$. Without loss of generality, suppose $(r, f(r))$ lies above l. By the Mean Value Theorem there is a number s in (a, r) such that $f'(s) =$ slope of the line l_1 joining $(a, f(a))$ and $(r, f(r))$. Since $(r, f(r))$ lies above l, $f'(s) =$ slope of $l_1 >$ slope of $l = (f(b) - f(a))/(b - a)$. Next, the slope of the line l_2 joining $(r, f(r))$ and $(b, f(b))$ is less than the slope of l. By the Mean Value Theorem there is a number t in (r, b) such that $f'(t) =$ slope of $l_2 <$ slope of $l = [f(b) - f(a)]/(b - a)$.

29. f satisfies the hypothesis of Rolle's Theorem. Thus there is c in $(0, 1)$ such that $f'(c) = 0$. Since $f'(x) = mx^{m-1}(x-1)^n + nx^m(x-1)^{n-1} = x^{m-1}(x-1)^{n-1}[m(x-1) + nx]$, the only value of c in $(0, 1)$

for which $f'(c) = 0$ satisfies $m(c-1) + nc = 0$, that is, $c = m/(m+n)$. The point $m/(m+n)$ divides the interval $[0,1]$ into the intervals $[0, m/(m+n)]$ and $[m/(m+n), 1]$. The lengths of these intervals are $m/(m+n)$ and $1 - m/(m+n) = n/(m+n)$. Thus the ratio of the lengths is m/n.

30. Assume that $a < x < y < z < b$ and $g(x) = g(y) = g(z) = 0$. By Rolle's Theorem there are numbers c in (x,y) and d in (y,z) such that $g'(c) = 0$ and $g'(d) = 0$.

31. Assume a line with slope m intersects the graph of f at $n+2$ points, $(x_1, f(x_1))$, $(x_2, f(x_2))$, $\ldots$, $(x_{n+2}, f(x_{n+2}))$, where $x_1 < x_2 < \cdots < x_{n+2}$. Then by the Mean Value Theorem there exist points $c_1, c_2, \ldots, c_{n+1}$ such that $x_i < c_i < x_{i+1}$ for $i = 1, 2, \ldots, n+1$, and

$$f'(c_i) = \frac{f(x_{i+1}) - f(x_i)}{x_{i+1} - x_i} = m.$$

Thus there are $n+1$ distinct numbers x such that $f'(x) = m$. Since our assumption is that there are no more than n such numbers, we conclude that the line can intersect the graph at most $n+1$ times.

32. Let $f(t)$ be the distance in feet that the car skidded in t seconds after the skid began. Then $f(0) = 0$ and $f(9) = 400$. Assuming that f is continuous on $[0,9]$ and differentiable on $(0,9)$, we conclude from the Mean Value Theorem that for some t_0 in $(0,9)$, $f'(t_0) = [f(9) - f(0)]/(9-0) = \frac{400}{9} > 44$. That is, at some instant *after* the brakes were applied, the velocity was greater than 44 feet per second, or 30 miles per hour. Therefore the car must have been speeding before it skidded.

33. Since 2400 feet equals $\frac{2400}{5280}$ miles, and 12 seconds equals $\frac{12}{3600}$ hours, the average velocity of the racing car was $\frac{2400}{5280} \cdot \frac{3600}{12}$, or rather, $\frac{1500}{11}$, miles per hour. Notice that $\frac{1500}{11} > 130$. Assuming that the function giving the position of the car at any instant is differentiable, we use the Mean Value Theorem to conclude that at some instant the car must have been traveling at least 130 miles per hour.

34. Let the parabola have equation $y = ax^2 + bx + c$. Since $(0,2)$, $(1,0)$, and $(2,1)$ are on the parabola, we have $2 = a \cdot 0^2 + b \cdot 0 + c$, $0 = a \cdot 1^2 + b \cdot 1 + c$, and $1 = a \cdot 2^2 + b \cdot 2 + c$. The first of these equations implies that $c = 2$, so that the other two become $a + b = -2$ and $4a + 2b = -1$. These imply that $a = \frac{3}{2}$ and $b = -\frac{7}{2}$. Therefore an equation of the parabola is $y = \frac{3}{2}x^2 - \frac{7}{2}x + 2$. Since the slope of l is $(2-1)/(0-2) = -\frac{1}{2}$, an equation of l is $y = 2 - \frac{1}{2}x$. Thus for $0 \le x \le 2$, the vertical distance V between the point on l and the point on the parabola corresponding to x is given by

$$V = \left(2 - \frac{1}{2}x\right) - \left(\frac{3}{2}x^2 - \frac{7}{2}x + 2\right) = 3x - \frac{3}{2}x^2.$$

Since $dV/dx = 3 - 3x$, we have $dV/dx = 0$ for $x = 1$. Consequently V can assume its extreme values on $[0,2]$ only at 0, 1, or 2. Since $V(0) = 0 = V(2)$ and $V(1) = \frac{3}{2}$, the vertical distance is maximum for $x = 1$. Thus the point $(1,0)$ on the parabola has maximum vertical distance from the line l.

4.3 Applications of the Mean Value Theorem

1. C
2. $-2x + C$
3. $\frac{3}{2}x^2 + C$
4. $-3x^2 + 5x + C$
5. $-\frac{1}{3}x^3 + C$
6. $\frac{4}{3}x^3 + 3x^2 - x + C$
7. $-\cos x + C$
8. $(-1/\pi)\cot \pi x + C$
9. $\frac{1}{2}\sin^2 x + C$
10. $\dfrac{1}{n+1}x^{n+1} + C$
11. $e^x + C$
12. $-e^{-x} + C$
13. Let $g(x) = -2x$. Then $g'(x) = -2 = f'(x)$, so $f(x) = g(x) + C = -2x + C$ for the appropriate constant C. Since $f(0) = 0$, we have $0 = f(0) = -2(0) + C = C$. Thus $f(x) = -2x$.
14. Let $g(x) = \frac{1}{4}x^2$. Then $g'(x) = \frac{1}{2}x = f'(x)$, so $f(x) = g(x) + C = \frac{1}{4}x^2 + C$ for the appropriate constant C. Since $f(\frac{1}{2}) = -1$, we have $-1 = f(\frac{1}{2}) = \frac{1}{4}(\frac{1}{2})^2 + C$, so that $C = -\frac{17}{16}$. Thus $f(x) = \frac{1}{4}x^2 - \frac{17}{16}$.
15. Let $g(x) = \frac{1}{3}x^3$. Then $g'(x) = x^2 = f'(x)$, so $f(x) = g(x) + C = \frac{1}{3}x^3 + C$ for the appropriate constant C. Since $f(0) = -5$, we have $-5 = f(0) = \frac{1}{3}(0)^3 + C = C$, so that $C = -5$. Thus $f(x) = \frac{1}{3}x^3 - 5$.
16. Let $g(x) = -\frac{1}{2}x^3$. Then $g'(x) = -\frac{3}{2}x^2 = f'(x)$, so $f(x) = g(x) + C = -\frac{1}{2}x^3 + C$ for the appropriate constant C. Since $f(-1) = -\frac{1}{2}$, we have $-\frac{1}{2} = f(-1) = -\frac{1}{2}(-1)^3 + C$, so $C = -1$. Thus $f(x) = -\frac{1}{2}x^3 - 1$.
17. Let $g(x) = \sin x$. Then $g'(x) = \cos x = f'(x)$, so $f(x) = g(x) + C = \sin x + C$ for the appropriate constant C. Since $f(\pi/3) = 1$, we have $1 = f(\pi/3) = \sin(\pi/3) + C = (\sqrt{3}/2) + C$, so $C = 1 - (\sqrt{3}/2)$. Thus $f(x) = \sin x + 1 - \sqrt{3}/2$.
18. Let $g(x) = 2\sec(x/2)$. Then $g'(x) = \sec(x/2)\tan(x/2) = f'(x)$, so $f(x) = g(x) + C = 2\sec(x/2) + C$ for the appropriate constant C. Since $f(\pi/2) = 2$, we have $2 = f(\pi/2) = 2\sec(\pi/4) + C = 2\sqrt{2} + C$, so $C = 2 - 2\sqrt{2}$. Thus $f(x) = 2\sec(x/2) + 2 - 2\sqrt{2}$.
19. Let $g(x) = e^x$. Then $g'(x) = e^x = f'(x)$, so $f(x) = g(x) + C = e^x + C$ for the appropriate constant C. Since $f(0) = 10$, we have $10 = f(0) = e^0 + C = 1 + C$, so that $C = 9$. Thus $f(x) = e^x + 9$.
20. Let $g(x) = \ln x$. Then $g'(x) = 1/x = f'(x)$, so $f(x) = g(x) + C = \ln x + C$ for the appropriate constant C. Since $f(e) = -3$, we have $-3 = f(e) = \ln e + C = 1 + C$, so that $C = -4$. Thus $f(x) = \ln x - 4$.
21. Let $g(x) = 0$. Then $g'(x) = 0 = f''(x) = (f')'(x)$, so by Theorem 4.6, $f'(x) = g(x) + C_1 = C_1$ for some constant C_1. Now let $h(x) = C_1 x$. Then $h'(x) = C_1 = f'(x)$, so by Theorem 4.6, $f(x) = h(x) + C_2 = C_1 x + C_2$ for some constant C_2.
22. By Exercise 21, $f(x) = C_1 x + C_2$, where C_1 and C_2 are constants. Thus $f'(x) = C_1$. Since $f'(-2) = 1$ by hypothesis, it follows that $C_1 = 1$, so that $f(x) = x + C_2$.
23. By Exercise 21, $f(x) = C_1 x + C_2$, where C_1 and C_2 are constants. Thus $f'(x) = C_1$. Since $f'(0) = -1$ and $f(0) = 2$ by hypothesis, it follows that $C_1 = -1$ and $2 = f(0) = C_1 \cdot 0 + C_2 = C_2$. Thus $f(x) = -x + 2$.

24. By Exercise 21, $f(x) = C_1x + C_2$, where C_1 and C_2 are constants. Thus $f'(x) = C_1$. Since $f'(2) = 3$ and $f(-1) = 1$ by hypothesis, it follows that $C_1 = 3$ and $1 = f(-1) = C_1(-1) + C_2 = 3(-1) + C_2$, so that $C_2 = 4$. Thus $f(x) = 3x + 4$.

25. Let $g(x) = -\cos x$. Then $g'(x) = \sin x = f''(x) = (f')'(x)$, so by Theorem 4.6, $f'(x) = g(x) + C_1 = -\cos x + C_1$ for some constant C_1. Now let $h(x) = -\sin x + C_1x$. Then $h'(x) = -\cos x + C_1 = f'(x)$, so by Theorem 4.6, $f(x) = h(x) + C_2 = -\sin x + C_1x + C_2$ for some constant C_2. Since $f'(\pi) = -2$, we have $-2 = f'(\pi) = -\cos\pi + C_1 = 1 + C_1$, so $C_1 = -3$. Since $f(0) = 4$, we have $4 = f(0) = -\sin 0 + C_1 \cdot 0 + C_2$, so $C_2 = 4$. Thus $f(x) = -\sin x - 3x + 4$.

26. Since $f^{(3)}(x) = (f')''(x)$, it follows (as in the solution of Exercise 21) from two applications of Theorem 4.6 that $f'(x) = D_1x + D_2$, where D_1 and D_2 are constants. Now let $g(x) = \frac{1}{2}D_1x^2 + D_2x$. Then $g'(x) = D_1x + D_2 = f'(x)$, so by Theorem 4.6, $f(x) = g(x) + D_3 = \frac{1}{2}D_1x^2 + D_2x + D_3$, where D_3 is some constant. Letting $C_1 = \frac{1}{2}D_1$, $C_2 = D_2$, and $C_3 = D_3$, we have $f(x) = C_1x^2 + C_2x + C_3$.

27. Since $f^{(4)}(x) = (f')^{(3)}(x)$, it follows from the solution of Exercise 26 that $f'(x) = D_1x^2 + D_2x + D_3$, where D_1, D_2, and D_3 are constants. Now let $g(x) = \frac{1}{3}D_1x^3 + \frac{1}{2}D_2x^2 + D_3x$. Then $g'(x) = D_1x^2 + D_2x + D_3 = f'(x)$, so by Theorem 4.6, $f(x) = g(x) + D_4 = \frac{1}{3}D_1x^3 + \frac{1}{2}D_2x^2 + D_3x + D_4$, where D_4 is some constant. Letting $C_1 = \frac{1}{3}D_1$, $C_2 = \frac{1}{2}D_2$, $C_3 = D_3$, and $C_4 = D_4$, we have $f(x) = C_1x^3 + C_2x^2 + C_3x + C_4$.

28. Following the pattern of Exercises 21, 26 and 27, we use Theorem 4.6 n times to obtain

$$f(x) = \frac{1}{(n-1)(n-2)\cdots 1}C_1x^{n-1} + \frac{1}{(n-2)(n-3)\cdots 1}C_2x^{n-2} + \cdots + \frac{1}{2}C_{n-2}x^2 + C_{n-1}x + C_n.$$

29. $f'(x) = 2x + 1$, so $f'(x) < 0$ for $x < -\frac{1}{2}$ and $f'(x) > 0$ for $x > -\frac{1}{2}$. Moreover, $f'(x) = 0$ only for $x = -\frac{1}{2}$. By Theorem 4.7, f is decreasing on $(-\infty, -\frac{1}{2}]$ and increasing on $[-\frac{1}{2}, \infty)$.

30. $f'(x) = 3x^2 - 12 = 3(x+2)(x-2)$, so $f'(x) > 0$ for $x < -2$ and for $x > 2$, and $f'(x) < 0$ for $-2 < x < 2$. Moreover, $f'(x) = 0$ only for $x = -2$ or 2. By Theorem 4.7, f is increasing on $(-\infty, -2]$ and on $[2, \infty)$, and is decreasing on $[-2, 2]$.

31. $f'(x) = 3x^2 - 2x + 1 = 3(x - \frac{1}{3})^2 + \frac{2}{3} > 0$ for all x. By Theorem 4.7, f is increasing on $(-\infty, \infty)$.

32. $f'(x) = 12x^2 - 12x - 9 = 3(2x-3)(2x+1)$, so $f'(x) > 0$ for $x < -\frac{1}{2}$ and for $x > \frac{3}{2}$, and $f'(x) < 0$ for $-\frac{1}{2} < x < \frac{3}{2}$. Moreover, $f'(x) = 0$ only for $x = -\frac{1}{2}$ or $\frac{3}{2}$. By Theorem 4.7, f is increasing on $(-\infty, -\frac{1}{2}]$ and on $[\frac{3}{2}, \infty)$, and is decreasing on $[-\frac{1}{2}, \frac{3}{2}]$.

33. $f'(x) = 4x^3 - 6x^2 = 2x^2(2x-3)$, so $f'(x) < 0$ for $x < \frac{3}{2}$, and $f'(x) > 0$ for $x > \frac{3}{2}$. Moreover, $f'(x) = 0$ only for $x = 0$ or $\frac{3}{2}$. By Theorem 4.7, f is decreasing on $(-\infty, \frac{3}{2}]$ and is increasing on $[\frac{3}{2}, \infty)$.

34. $f'(x) = 5x^4 + 3x^2 + 2 > 0$ for all x. By Theorem 4.7, f is increasing on $(-\infty, \infty)$.

35. $f'(x) = 5x^4 + 3x^2 - 2 = (x^2+1)(5x^2-2)$, so $f'(x) < 0$ for $-\sqrt{2/5} < x < \sqrt{2/5}$, and $f'(x) > 0$ for $x < -\sqrt{2/5}$ and for $x > \sqrt{2/5}$. Moreover, $f'(x) = 0$ only for $x = -\sqrt{2/5}$ or $\sqrt{2/5}$. By Theorem 4.7, f is increasing on $(-\infty, -\sqrt{2/5}]$ and on $[\sqrt{2/5}, \infty)$, and is decreasing on $[-\sqrt{2/5}, \sqrt{2/5}]$.

36. Since $f(x) = x^2$ for $x > 0$ and $f(x) = -x^2$ for $x < 0$, it follows that $f'(x) = 2x > 0$ for $x > 0$ and $f'(x) = -2x > 0$ for $x < 0$. Also

$$f'(0) = \lim_{x\to 0} \frac{x|x| - 0}{x - 0} = \lim_{x\to 0} |x| = 0.$$

Since $f'(x) > 0$ for all x except $x = 0$, and $f'(0) = 0$, it follows from Theorem 4.7 that f is increasing on $(-\infty, \infty)$.

37. Notice that the domain of g is $[-4, 4]$. Also $g'(x) = -x/\sqrt{16 - x^2}$, so $g'(x) > 0$ for $-4 < x < 0$ and $g'(x) < 0$ for $0 < x < 4$. Moreover, $g'(x) = 0$ only for $x = 0$. By Theorem 4.7, g is increasing on $[-4, 0]$ and is decreasing on $[0, 4]$.

38. Notice that the domain of g consists of all numbers x such that $|x| \geq \frac{2}{3}$. For $|x| > \frac{2}{3}$ we have $g'(x) = 9x/\sqrt{9x^2 - 4}$, so $g'(x) > 0$ for $x > \frac{2}{3}$ and $g'(x) < 0$ for $x < -\frac{2}{3}$. By Theorem 4.7, g is increasing on $[\frac{2}{3}, \infty)$ and is decreasing on $(-\infty, -\frac{2}{3}]$.

39. Notice that -3 is not in the domain of g. Also $g'(x) = -1/(x+3)^2 < 0$ for $x \neq -3$. We conclude from Theorem 4.7 that g is decreasing on $(-\infty, -3)$ and on $(-3, \infty)$.

40. Notice that 1 is not in the domain of g. Also

$$g'(x) = \frac{(1)(x-1) - (x-2)(1)}{(x-1)^2} = \frac{1}{(x-1)^2} > 0 \quad \text{for } x \neq 1.$$

We conclude from Theorem 4.7 that g is increasing on $(-\infty, 1)$ and on $(1, \infty)$.

41. $k'(x) = -2x/(x^2+1)^2$, so $k'(x) > 0$ for $x < 0$ and $k'(x) < 0$ for $x > 0$. Moreover, $k'(x) = 0$ only for $x = 0$. By Theorem 4.7, k is increasing on $(-\infty, 0]$ and is decreasing on $[0, \infty)$

42. Notice that -2 and 2 are not in the domain of k. Also $k'(x) = -2x/(x^2-4)^2$, so $k'(x) > 0$ for $x < -2$ or $-2 < x < 0$, and $k'(x) < 0$ for $0 < x < 2$ or $x > 2$. By Theorem 4.7, k is increasing on $(-\infty, -2)$ and on $(-2, 0]$, and is decreasing on $[0, 2)$ and on $(2, \infty)$.

43. Notice that $f(t)$ is not defined for $t = \pi/2 + n\pi$ for any integer n. Also $f'(t) = \sec^2 t > 0$ for all t in the domain of f. By Theorem 4.7, f is increasing on each interval of the form $(\pi/2 + n\pi, \pi/2 + (n+1)\pi)$, where n is any integer.

44. $f'(t) = \cos t$, so $f'(t) > 0$ for $-\pi/2 + 2n\pi < t < \pi/2 + 2n\pi$ for any integer n, and $f'(t) < 0$ for $\pi/2 + 2n\pi < t < 3\pi/2 + 2n\pi$ for any integer n. By Theorem 4.7, f is increasing on $[-\pi/2 + 2n\pi, \pi/2 + 2n\pi]$ for any integer n and is decreasing on $[\pi/2 + 2n\pi, 3\pi/2 + 2n\pi]$ for any integer n.

45. $f'(t) = -2\sin t - 1$, so $f'(t) < 0$ if $\sin t > -\frac{1}{2}$ and $f'(t) > 0$ if $\sin t < -\frac{1}{2}$. Thus $f'(t) < 0$ for $-\pi/6 + 2n\pi < t < 7\pi/6 + 2n\pi$ for any integer n, and $f'(t) > 0$ for $7\pi/6 + 2n\pi < t < 11\pi/6 + 2n\pi$ for any integer n. By Theorem 4.7, f is decreasing on $[-\pi/6 + 2n\pi, 7\pi/6 + 2n\pi]$ for any integer n and is increasing on $[7\pi/6 + 2n\pi, 11\pi/6 + 2n\pi]$ for any integer n.

46. $f'(t) = \cos t - \sin t$, so $f'(t) > 0$ for $-3\pi/4 + 2n\pi < t < \pi/4 + 2n\pi$ for any integer n, and $f'(t) < 0$ for $\pi/4 + 2n\pi < t < 5\pi/4 + 2n\pi$ for any integer n. By Theorem 4.7, f is increasing on $[-3\pi/4 + 2n\pi, \pi/4 + 2n\pi]$ for any integer n and is decreasing on $[\pi/4 + 2n\pi, 5\pi/4 + 2n\pi]$ for any integer n.

47. $f'(x) = e^x + xe^x = (1 + x)e^x$. Since $e^x > 0$ for all x, we have $f'(x) < 0$ for $x < -1$, and $f'(x) > 0$ for $x > -1$. By Theorem 4.7, f is decreasing on $(-\infty, -1]$ and is increasing on $[-1, \infty)$.

48. $f'(x) = e^x - 3$, so $f'(x) < 0$ if $e^x < 3$, and $f'(x) > 0$ if $e^x > 3$. Thus $f'(x) < 0$ for $x < \ln 3$, and $f'(x) > 0$ for $x > \ln 3$. By Theorem 4.7, f is decreasing on $(-\infty, \ln 3]$ and is increasing on $[\ln 3, \infty)$.

49. Notice that the domain of f is $(0, \infty)$. We have $f'(x) = 1 - 1/x$, so $f'(x) > 0$ for $x > 1$, and $f'(x) < 0$ for $0 < x < 1$. By Theorem 4.7, f is decreasing on $(0, 1]$ and is increasing on $[1, \infty)$.

50. Notice that the domain of f is $(0, \infty)$. We have $f'(x) = [(1/x)x - 1 \cdot \ln x]/x^2 = (1 - \ln x)/x^2$, so $f'(x) < 0$ if $\ln x > 1$, and $f'(x) > 0$ if $\ln x < 1$. Thus $f'(x) < 0$ for $x > e$, and $f'(x) > 0$ for $x < e$. By Theorem 4.7, f is increasing on $(0, e]$ and is decreasing on $[e, \infty)$.

51. f is decreasing on $[-1, 1]$.

52. f is increasing on $[-2, -1]$ and $[1, 2]$, and f is decreasing on $[-1, 1]$.

53. f is increasing on $[-1, 0]$, and f is decreasing on $[0, 1]$.

54. f is increasing on $[-2, 0]$, and f is decreasing on $[0, 2]$.

55. Let $f(x) = x^4 - 4x$. Then $f'(x) = 4x^3 - 4 = 4(x^3 - 1) > 0$ for $x > 1$. By Theorem 4.7, f is increasing on $[1, \infty)$. Therefore $x^4 - 4x = f(x) > f(1) = -3$ for $x > 1$.

56. Let $f(x) = 4x^2 + 1/x$. Then $f'(x) = 8x - 1/x^2 = (8x^3 - 1)/x^2 > 0$ for $x > 1$. By Theorem 4.7, f is increasing on $[1, \infty)$. Therefore $4x^2 + 1/x = f(x) > f(1) = 5$ for $x > 1$.

57. Let $f(x) = \frac{1}{4}x + 1/x$. Then $f'(x) = \frac{1}{4} - 1/x^2 = (x^2 - 4)/4x^2 > 0$ for $x > 2$. By Theorem 4.7, f is increasing on $[2, \infty)$. Therefore $\frac{1}{4}x + 1/x = f(x) > f(2) = 1$ for $x > 2$.

58. Let $f(x) = 1/x + \tan(1/x)$. Then $f'(x) = -1/x^2 + [\sec^2(1/x)](-1/x^2) = -[1 + \sec^2(1/x)](1/x^2) < 0$ for all x in the domain of f. Since $0 < 1/x < \pi/4$ for $x > 4/\pi$, x is in the domain of f if $x > 4/\pi$. By Theorem 4.7, f is decreasing on $[4/\pi, \infty)$. Thus $1/x + \tan(1/x) = f(x) < f(4/\pi) = 1 + \pi/4$ for $x > 4/\pi$.

59. a. Let $f(x) = e^x - (\frac{1}{2}x^2 + x + 1)$. Then $f'(x) = e^x - (x + 1) > 0$ for $x > 0$ by Example 7. By Theorem 4.7, f is increasing on $[0, \infty)$. Therefore $f(x) > f(0) = 0$ for $x > 0$. Thus $e^x - (\frac{1}{2}x^2 + x + 1) > 0$, or $e^x > \frac{1}{2}x^2 + x + 1$ for $x > 0$.

    b. Let $f(x) = e^x - (\frac{1}{6}x^3 + \frac{1}{2}x^2 + x + 1)$. Then $f'(x) = e^x - (\frac{1}{2}x^2 + x + 1) > 0$ for $x > 0$ by part (a). By Theorem 4.7, f is increasing on $[0, \infty)$. Therefore $f(x) > f(0) = 0$ for $x > 0$. Thus $e^x - (\frac{1}{6}x^3 + \frac{1}{2}x^2 + x + 1) > 0$, or $e^x > \frac{1}{6}x^3 + \frac{1}{2}x^2 + x + 1$ for $x > 0$.

60. a. Let $u < v$. Then $f'(x) = 1 - \cos x \geq 0$ for all x in $[u, v]$ and is zero for only finitely many values (any of the form $2n\pi$ for some integer n) in $[u, v]$. By Theorem 4.7, f is increasing on $[u, v]$. Therefore $f(u) < f(v)$. Since u, v were arbitrary numbers, f is increasing on $(-\infty, \infty)$.

    b. Since f is increasing by part (a), if $x < 0$ then $x - \sin x = f(x) < f(0) = 0$. Therefore $x < \sin x$ on $(-\infty, 0)$. For $x > 0$, $x - \sin x = f(x) > f(0) = 0$ by part (a). Thus $x > \sin x$ on $(0, \infty)$.

61. Let $h(x) = f(x) - g(x)$, so that by hypothesis, $h(a) = f(a) - g(a) \geq 0$. Fix $z > a$. Then $h'(x) = f'(x) - g'(x) > 0$ for all x in (a, z), so by Theorem 4.7, h is increasing on $[a, z]$. Thus $f(z) - g(z) = h(z) > h(a) = f(a) - g(a) \geq 0$, or $f(z) > g(z)$. Since z was an arbitrary number greater than a, $f(x) > g(x)$ for all $x > a$.

62. Let $f(x) = \tan x - x$. Then $f'(x) = \sec^2 x - 1 \geq 0$ for x in $[0, \pi/2)$, with $f'(x) \neq 0$ for x in $(0, \pi/2)$. By Theorem 4.7, f is increasing on $[0, \pi/2)$. Since $f(0) = 0$, it follows that $f(x) > f(0) = 0$ for x in $(0, \pi/2)$. Thus $\tan x - x > 0$, or equivalently $\tan x > x$, for x in $(0, \pi/2)$.

63. Let $f(x) = (1 + x)^n - (1 + nx)$. Then $f'(x) = n(1 + x)^{n-1} - n$, so that if $x > 0$, then $f'(x) > 0$. By Theorem 4.7, f is increasing on $[0, \infty)$, so $f(x) > f(0) = 0$ for x in $(0, \infty)$. Hence $(1 + x)^n > 1 + nx$ for x in $(0, \infty)$.

64. Let $f(x) = \cos x$ and $g(x) = 1 - x^2/2$. Then $f(0) = 1 = g(0)$, and by Exercise 60(b), $f'(x) = -\sin x > -x = g'(x)$ for $x > 0$. It follows from Exercise 61 that $\cos x = f(x) > g(x) = 1 - x^2/2$ for $x > 0$.

65. Let $f(x) = \sin x$ and $g(x) = x - x^3/6$. Then $f(0) = 0 = g(0)$, and by Exercise 64, $f'(x) = \cos x > 1 - x^2/2 = g'(x)$ for $x > 0$. By Exercise 61, $\sin x = f(x) > g(x) = x - x^3/6$ for $x > 0$.

66. a. Let $f(x) = \cos x - 2x$. Since $f(0) = 1$, $f(\pi/2) = -\pi$, and f is continuous on $[0, \pi/2]$, there is an x in $(0, \pi/2)$ such that $f(x) = 0$ by the Intermediate Value Theorem. If there were two numbers, u and v, with $f(u) = f(v) = 0$, then by Rolle's Theorem there would be a number c between them such that $f'(c) = 0$. But $f'(x) = -\sin x - 2 \leq -1 < 0$ for all x, so there can be no such c. Therefore there is at most one x such that $f(x) = 0$. We conclude that there is exactly one x such that $f(x) = 0$, which is equivalent to $\cos x - 2x = 0$, or $\cos x = 2x$.

    b. Let $f(x) = \cos x - 2x$, so that $f'(x) = -\sin x - 2$. Letting the initial value of c be 1 and using the Newton-Raphson method, we obtain 0.4501836113 as the desired approximate zero of f, and hence approximate solution of $\cos x = 2x$.

67. $f'(x) = 3x^2 + 2ax + b$

    a. Since $3x^2 + 2ax + b = 3(x + a/3)^2 + b - a^2/3$, $f'(x) \geq b - a^2/3$ for all x, and $f'(x) \geq 0$ for all x if $b - a^2/3 \geq 0$ or $a^2 \leq 3b$. In that case, $f'(x) = 0$ only for $x = -a/3$, so Theorem 4.7 implies that f is increasing on $(-\infty, \infty)$.

    b. $f'(x) = 0$ for $x = (-a \pm \sqrt{a^2 - 3b})/3$, and $f'(x) > 0$ on $(-\infty, (-a - \sqrt{a^2 - 3b})/3)$ and on $(-a + \sqrt{a^2 - 3b})/3, \infty)$, while $f'(x) < 0$ on $((-a - \sqrt{a^2 - 3b})/3, (-a + \sqrt{a^2 - 3b})/3)$. The result now follows from Theorem 4.7.

68. 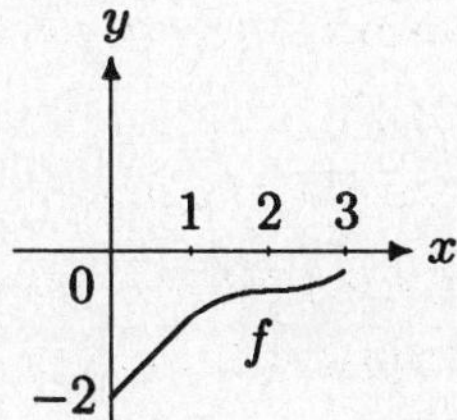

69. a. 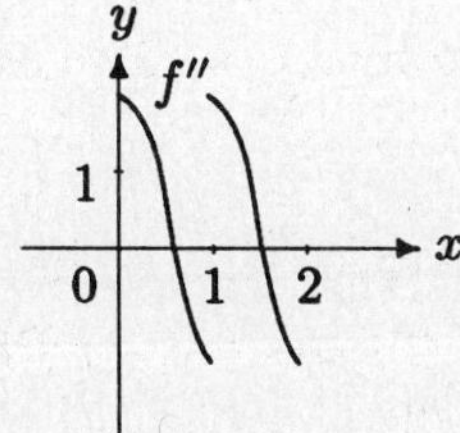

b. We do not have enough information. We would have enough information if we knew the value of f at some number in $[0,2]$. Assume $f(0)=0$. Then the graph of f would be roughly as follows:

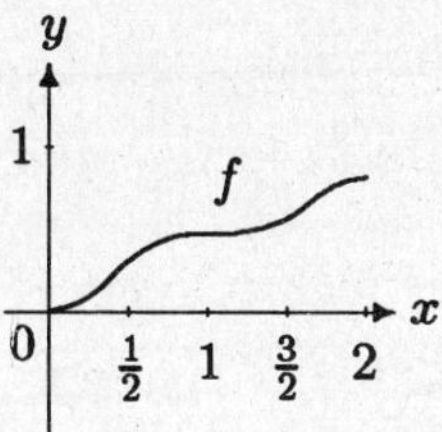

70. a. Since $F'=f$ and $G'=g$, we have $(F+G)'=F'+G'=f+g$. Thus $F+G$ is an antiderivative of $f+g$.

b. Since $F'=f$ we have $(cF)'=cF'=cf$. Thus cF is an antiderivative of cf.

c. No. If $f(x)=g(x)=x$, then $(fg)(x)=x^2$. If $F(x)=G(x)=\frac{1}{2}x^2$, then $F'=f$ and $G'=g$, $(FG)(x)=\frac{1}{4}x^4$, and $(FG)'(x)=x^3$. Thus $(FG)'\neq fg$.

d. No. If $f(x)=g(x)=x$, then $(f/g)(x)=1$ for $x\neq 0$. If $F(x)=G(x)=\frac{1}{2}x^2$, then $F'=f$ and $G'=g$, $(F/G)(x)=1$ and $(F/G)'(x)=0$ for $x\neq 0$. Thus $(F/G)'\neq f/g$.

71. Taking $x=y=0$ in the equation $f(x+y)=f(x)+f(y)$, we have $f(0)=f(0)+f(0)$, so that $f(0)=0$. Taking $y=h$ in the equation $f(x+y)=f(x)+f(y)$, we find that $f(x+h)=f(x)+f(h)$, so that $f(x+h)-f(x)=f(h)$. It now follows from (2) in Section 3.2 that for any x,

$$f'(x)=\lim_{h\to 0}\frac{f(x+h)-f(x)}{h}=\lim_{h\to 0}\frac{f(h)}{h}=\lim_{h\to 0}\frac{f(h)-f(0)}{h}=f'(0).$$

Letting $f'(0)=c$, we have $f'(x)=c$, so that by Theorem 4.6, $f(x)=cx+C$ for some constant C. Since $f(0)=0$, it follows that $C=0$, and thus that $f(x)=cx$ for all x.

72. If f is constant, then for all x and y, $|f(x) - f(y)| = 0 \le |x - y|^2$, so constant functions satisfy the inequality. If f satisfies the inequality, then

$$\left|\frac{f(x) - f(y)}{x - y}\right| \le |x - y| \quad \text{for } x \ne y$$

so

$$|f'(y)| = \left|\lim_{x \to y} \frac{f(x) - f(y)}{x - y}\right| \le \lim_{x \to y} |x - y| = 0 \quad \text{for all } y.$$

By Theorem 4.6, f is constant. The result is true if 2 is replaced by any other rational power greater than 1.

73. Let the time period be from t_1 to t_2, and let $f(t)$ be the position of the particle at any time t. Then by hypothesis, $f'(t) = v(t) = 0$ for $t_1 < t < t_2$. It follows from Theorem 4.8 that f is constant on $[t_1, t_2]$; that is, for t between t_1 and t_2, we have $f(t) = f(t_1)$, which means that the particle stands still during that period.

74. $v'(x) = k(a - x) - kx = ka - 2kx$, so that $v'(x) > 0$ for $0 < x < a/2$ and $v'(x) < 0$ for $a/2 < x < a$. Thus v is increasing on $[0, a/2]$ and decreasing on $[a/2, a]$.

75. a. $\dfrac{dT}{dW} = \dfrac{1}{3\sqrt{1 - S^2/3L^2}} > 0$ for all W, so T is an increasing function of W.

b. $$\frac{dT}{dS} = \left(\frac{-1}{2}\right)\left(\frac{W}{3}\right)\left(1 - \frac{S^2}{3L^2}\right)^{-3/2}\left(\frac{-2S}{3L^2}\right) = \frac{WS}{9L^2}\left(1 - \frac{S^2}{3L^2}\right)^{-3/2} > 0$$

so T is an increasing function of S.

c. $$\frac{dT}{dL} = \left(\frac{-1}{2}\right)\left(\frac{W}{3}\right)\left(1 - \frac{S^2}{3L^2}\right)^{-3/2}\left(\frac{2S^2}{3L^3}\right) = \frac{-WS^2}{9L^3}\left(1 - \frac{S^2}{3L^2}\right)^{-3/2} < 0$$

so T is a decreasing function of L.

76. $$\frac{d}{d\omega} i_{\text{max}} = \left(\frac{-V_0}{2}\right)\left[\left(\frac{1}{\omega C} - \omega L\right)^2 + R^2\right]^{-3/2}\left[2\left(\frac{1}{\omega C} - \omega L\right)\left(\frac{-1}{\omega^2 C} - L\right)\right]$$

Thus $\dfrac{d}{d\omega} i_{\text{max}} > 0$ if and only if $\left(\dfrac{1}{\omega C} - \omega L\right)\left(\dfrac{1}{\omega^2 C} + L\right) > 0$, that is, $1/(\omega C) - \omega L > 0$, since all constants are positive. Consequently

$$\frac{d}{d\omega} i_{\text{max}} > 0 \quad \text{if and only if} \quad 0 < \omega < \sqrt{\frac{1}{CL}}$$

and i_{max} is therefore increasing on $(0, \sqrt{1/(CL)}]$ by Theorem 4.7.

77. If $U = \frac{1}{2}kx^2$, then $dU/dx = kx$, so that $f(x) = -dU/dx$.

78. Let $U = -\frac{1}{2}m\omega^2 r^2/l$. Then $dU/dr = -m\omega^2 r/l$, so that $dU/dr = dT/dr$. By Theorem 4.6, $T = U + C = -\frac{1}{2}m\omega^2 r^2/l + C$ for the appropriate constant C. Since $T = 0$ for $r = l$, we have $0 = 0 + C$, so that $C = 0$. Therefore $T = -\frac{1}{2}m\omega^2 r^2/l$.

79. By (11) in Section 2.2, the height of the high jumper on earth is given by $h(t) = -4.9t^2 + v_0 t$, where v_0 is the initial velocity. Thus $h'(t) = -9.8t + v_0$, so that $h'(t) = 0$ for $t = v_0/9.8$. It follows that the jumper is 2 meters above the ground at time $t = v_0/9.8$. Thus $2 = h(v_0/9.8) = -4.9(v_0/9.8)^2 + v_0(v_0/9.8) = v_0^2/19.6$, so that $v_0 = \sqrt{39.2}$. Let $f(t)$ be the height of the high jumper on the moon at time t. Then $f''(t)$ is the acceleration, which we are assuming to be -1.6. Thus $f''(t) = -1.6$. Therefore Theorem 4.6 implies that $v(t) = f'(t) = -1.6t+C$ for the appropriate constant C. Since the initial velocity is assumed to be the same on the moon as on earth, $v(0) = \sqrt{39.2}$, so that $\sqrt{39.2} = v(0) = -1.6 \cdot 0 + C = C$. Thus $f'(t) = v(t) = -1.6t + \sqrt{39.2}$. By Theorem 4.6, $f(t) = -.8t^2 + \sqrt{39.2}\,t + C_1$ for the appropriate constant C_1. Since $f(0) = 0$, we have $C_1 = 0$, so that $f(t) = -.8t^2 + \sqrt{39.2}\,t$. The maximum height occurs when $f'(t) = 0$, that is $t = \sqrt{39.2}/1.6$. Therefore the maximum height is $f(\sqrt{39.2}/1.6) = -.8(\sqrt{39.2}/1.6)^2 + \sqrt{39.2} \cdot \sqrt{39.2}/1.6 = 39.2/3.2 = 12.25$ (meters). We conclude that the person can high jump 12.25 meters on the moon.

4.4 Exponential Growth and Decay

1. a. By (4) we have $f(t) = 4f(0)$ if $f(0)e^{kt} = 4f(0)$, or $e^{kt} = 4$. Since $k = \frac{1}{2}\ln 2$ by the solution of Example 1, this means that $e^{(t/2)\ln 2} = 4$, or $2^{t/2} = 4$. Thus $t/2 = 2$, or $t = 4$. Therefore it takes 4 days for the algae to quadruple in number.

   b. As in (a), if $f(t) = 3f(0)$, then $2^{t/2} = 3$, so $(t/2)\ln 2 = \ln 3$, or $t = (2\ln 3)/\ln 2 \approx 3.17$. Therefore it takes approximately 3.17 days for the algae to triple in number.

2. Let $f(t)$ be the number of bacteria t hours after there are 4000 bacteria. Then $f(0) = 4000$ and $f(12) = 6000$. By (4), $6000 = f(12) = f(0)e^{12k} = 4000e^{12k}$, so that $e^{12k} = 1.5$, or $k = \frac{1}{12}\ln 1.5$. We seek the value of t for which $f(t) = 2f(0)$. By (4) this means that $2f(0) = f(0)e^{kt}$, or $e^{kt} = 2$, so that $t = (1/k)\ln 2 = (12\ln 2)/\ln 1.5 \approx 20.51$. Thus the doubling time is approximately 20.51 hours.

3. Let $f(t)$ be the number of beetles t days after there are 1200 beetles. Then $f(0) = 1200$, and we seek the value of t for which $f(t) = 1500$. Since the doubling time is 6 days and 20 hours, which is the same as $\frac{41}{6}$ days, we have $f(\frac{41}{6}) = 2f(0)$, so by (4), $2f(0) = f(\frac{41}{6}) = f(0)e^{41k/6}$. Thus $e^{41k/6} = 2$, so that $k = (6\ln 2)/41$. If $f(t) = 1500$, then by (4), $1500 = f(0)e^{kt} = 1200e^{kt}$, or $e^{kt} = \frac{5}{4}$, so that $t = (1/k)\ln 1.25 = (41\ln 1.25)/(6\ln 2) \approx 2.2$. Thus there were 1200 beetles approximately 2.2 days ago.

4. Let $f(t)$ be the population t years after 1962. We desire $f(38)$. Notice that $f(0) = 3.15 \times 10^9$, $f(16) = 4.238 \times 10^9$, and $f(t) = f(0)e^{kt}$ for some constant k and all $t \geq 0$. Then

$$\frac{f(16)}{f(0)} = \frac{4.238 \times 10^9}{3.15 \times 10^9} = e^{16k}$$

so that $k = \frac{1}{16}\ln(4.238/3.15)$. Thus $f(38) = (3.15 \times 10^9)e^{38[(1/16)\ln(4.238/3.15)]} \approx 6.372799433 \times 10^9$, so that in the year 2000 the world population would be approximately 6,373,000,000.

5. Let $f(t)$ be the population in millions of the country with a doubling time of 20 years t years after its population is 50,000,000, and let $g(t)$ be the population of the country with a doubling time of 10 years. From the hypotheses we notice that $f(0) = 50$ and $g(0) = 20$. We seek the value of t for which $f(t) = g(t)$. By (4), there are constants k_1 and k_2 such that $f(t) = f(0)e^{k_1 t} = 50e^{k_1 t}$ and $g(t) = 20e^{k_2 t}$. Since $f(20) = 2f(0)$, we have $2f(0) = f(20) = f(0)e^{20k_1}$, or $e^{20k_1} = 2$, so that $k_1 = \frac{1}{20}\ln 2$. Similarly, since $g(10) = 2g(0)$, we have $k_2 = \frac{1}{10}\ln 2$. Now if $f(t) = g(t)$, then $50e^{k_1 t} = 20e^{k_2 t}$, or $e^{(k_2 - k_1)t} = 2.5$, so that

$$t = \frac{\ln 2.5}{k_2 - k_1} = \frac{\ln 2.5}{\frac{1}{10}\ln 2 - \frac{1}{20}\ln 2} = \frac{20\ln 2.5}{\ln 2} \approx 26.44.$$

Thus it will be approximately 26.44 years until the two countries have the same population.

6. a. The population doubles in any time interval of duration $(\ln 2)/k$ if for any time t, $f(t + (\ln 2)/k) = 2f(t)$. By hypothesis, $f(t)$ grows exponentially, so that

$$f\left(t + \frac{\ln 2}{k}\right) = f(0)e^{k[t+(\ln 2)/k]} = f(0)e^{kt+\ln 2} = f(0)e^{kt}e^{\ln 2} = f(t)\cdot 2 = 2f(t).$$

   b. Since $d = (\ln 2)/k$, we have $k = (\ln 2)/d$, so that $f(t) = f(0)e^{kt} = f(0)e^{(\ln 2)t/d} = f(0)(e^{\ln 2})^{t/d} = f(0)2^{t/d}$.

7. a. The population halves in any time interval of duration $-(\ln 2)/k$ if for any time t, $f(t + (-\ln 2)/k) = \frac{1}{2}f(t)$. By hypothesis, $f(t)$ decays exponentially, so that

$$f\left(t - \frac{\ln 2}{k}\right) = f(0)e^{k[t-(\ln 2)/k]} = f(0)e^{kt-\ln 2} = f(0)e^{kt}e^{-\ln 2} = f(t)\frac{1}{2} = \frac{1}{2}f(t).$$

   b. Since $h = -(\ln 2)/k$, we have $k = -(\ln 2)/h$, so that $f(t) = f(0)e^{kt} = f(0)e^{-(\ln 2)t/h} = f(0)(e^{-\ln 2})^{t/h} = f(0)(\frac{1}{2})^{t/h}$.

8. The number of counts per minute on a Geiger counter is proportional to the amount of the radioactive substance. Since the number of counts per minute drops from 4000 to 500 in 4 days, and since $\frac{500}{4000} = \frac{1}{8} = (\frac{1}{2})^3$, a period of 4 days is the same as three half-lives of the substance. Therefore the half-life is $\frac{4}{3}$ days.

9. Let $f(t)$ be the amount of radium remaining after t years. Then $f(t) \approx f(0)e^{kt}$, where $1590 \approx (-\ln 2)/k$, or $k \approx (-\ln 2)/1590$, by Exercise 7. We seek t such that $f(t)/f(0) = \frac{9}{10}$. We have $\frac{9}{10} = f(t)/f(0) \approx e^{(-\ln 2/1590)t}$, so that $t \approx [-1590/(\ln 2)]\ln\frac{9}{10} \approx 241.7$ (years).

10. By (7) with $t = 5300$ the amount of C^{14} left in the Iceman is given approximately by $f(5300) = f(0)e^{-(\ln 2)5300/5730}$, so that $f(5300)/f(0) = e^{-(\ln 2)5300/5730} \approx .52$. Thus approximately 52% of the original C^{14} remains in the Iceman.

11. Let $f(t)$ be the amount of C^{14} present t years after 13,000 B.C. and let $g(t)$ be the amount of C^{14} present t years after 12,300 B.C. Then $f(t) = f(0)e^{kt}$ and $g(t) = g(0)e^{kt}$ for $t \geq 0$, where $k = -(\ln 2)/5730$

(by Example 2) and $f(0) = g(0)$. The amounts present in 2000 A.D. are $f(15{,}000)$ and $g(14{,}300)$. Furthermore,

$$\frac{g(14{,}300)}{g(0)} - \frac{f(15{,}000)}{f(0)} = e^{14{,}300k} - e^{15{,}000k} \approx 0.0143962542.$$

Thus the difference is approximately 1.44%.

12. From Example 2 the amount of C^{14} present t years after death is given by $f(t) = f(0)e^{-(\ln 2)t/5730}$ for $t \geq 0$. The fraction of C^{14} remaining after 1,800,000 years is

$$\frac{f(1.8 \times 10^6)}{f(0)} = e^{-(\ln 2)(1.8\times 10^6)/5730} = e^{-217} \approx 0.$$

13. Let $f(t)$ be the amount (in milligrams) of iodine 131 t days after delivery. We are to determine $f(0)$, and are given that $f(2) = 100$ and $f(8.14) = \frac{1}{2}f(0)$. By (4), $\frac{1}{2}f(0) = f(8.14) = f(0)e^{8.14k}$, or $e^{8.14k} = \frac{1}{2}$, so that $k = (1/8.14)\ln\frac{1}{2}$. Also by (4) and the hypothesis, $100 = f(2) = f(0)e^{2k}$, so that $f(0) = 100e^{-2k} = 100e^{-(2/8.14)\ln(1/2)} = 100e^{(\ln 2)/4.07} \approx 119$. Thus approximately 119 milligrams of iodine 131 should be purchased.

14. Let $f(t)$ be the amount of radon gas in the laboratory t days after the radiation level is 50% above the safe level. We seek the value of t for which $f(t) = \frac{2}{3}f(0)$. Since the half-life of radon is 3.8 days, (4) implies that $\frac{1}{2}f(0) = f(3.8) = f(0)e^{3.8k}$, or $e^{3.8k} = \frac{1}{2}$, so that $k = (1/3.8)\ln\frac{1}{2}$. If $f(t) = \frac{2}{3}f(0)$, then by (4), $\frac{2}{3}f(0) = f(t) = f(0)e^{kt}$, or $e^{kt} = \frac{2}{3}$, so that $t = (1/k)\ln\frac{2}{3} = 3.8(\ln\frac{2}{3})/(\ln\frac{1}{2}) \approx 2.2$. Therefore the laboratory should remain vacated approximately 2.2 days

15. By (8), $f(t) \approx e^{(-1.25\times 10^{-4})t}$, so that $f(1600) \approx e^{(-1.25\times 10^{-4})1600} = e^{-0.2} \approx 0.819$.

16. The air pressure at 7000 meters is $f(7000) \approx e^{(-1.25\times 10^{-4})7000} = e^{-0.875} \approx 0.417$ (atmospheres).

17. a. $p(0) \approx 29.92$ (inches of mercury)

    b. $p(5) \approx (29.92)e^{(-.2)5} \approx 11.01$ (inches of mercury)

    c. $p(10) \approx (29.92)e^{(-.2)10} \approx 4.049$ (inches of mercury)

18. Since 20 miles per hour is 1760 feet per minute, let $dt/d\tau = -1760$ (feet per minute), where τ denotes time. If $t = 10{,}560$ (feet), then

$$\frac{dp}{d\tau} \approx 2140(-0.000035)e^{-0.000035t}\frac{dt}{d\tau}$$

$$\left.\frac{dp}{d\tau}\right|_{t=10{,}560} = -2140(0.000035)e^{(-0.000035)(10{,}560)}(-1760) \approx 91 \text{ (pounds per square foot per minute).}$$

19. Let $f(t)$ be the amount of sodium pentobarbitol in the blood stream after t hours. Then $f(t) = f(0)e^{kt}$ for $t \geq 0$. By hypothesis, $f(5) = \frac{1}{2}f(0)$, so that $k = (-\ln 2)/5$. To anesthetize a 10 kilogram dog for one-half hour we need $f(\frac{1}{2}) = 20(10) = 200$ milligrams, so that $200 = f(\frac{1}{2}) = f(0)e^{-[(\ln 2)/5](1/2)} = f(0)e^{-(\ln 2)/10}$ and thus $f(0) = 200e^{(\ln 2)/10} \approx 214$ (milligrams).

20. If $p = 6$ and $t = 10$, then $A(10) = Se^{(.06)10} = Se^{0.6}$.

21. For $A(10) = 2S$, we need p to satisfy $2 = A(10)/S = e^{10p/100} = e^{p/10}$, and thus $p = 10 \ln 2 \approx 6.93$ (%).

22. If $S = 100$, $p = 4$, and $t = 75$, then $A(75) = 100e^{(.04)75} \approx 2{,}008.55$ (dollars). If $S = 100$, $p = 3$, and $t = 200$, then $A(200) = 100e^{(.03)200} \approx 40{,}342.88$ (dollars).

23. Let $f(t)$ be the amount of sugar after t minutes. Then $f(t) = f(0)e^{kt} = e^{kt}$ for $t \geq 0$. By hypothesis $f(1) = \frac{3}{4}$, so that $\frac{3}{4} = e^{1k} = e^{k}$, and thus $k = \ln \frac{3}{4}$. Consequently $f(t) = \frac{1}{2} = e^{(\ln 3/4)t}$ if $t = (\ln \frac{1}{2})/(\ln \frac{3}{4}) \approx 2.41$ (minutes).

24. Let $f(t)$ denote the amount of charge t seconds after 4 seconds ago. Then $f(t) = f(0)e^{kt}$, and by hypothesis, $f(0) = 5 \times 10^{-2}$ and $f(4) = 10^{-3}$, so that $f(4)/f(0) = 10^{-3}/(5 \times 10^{-2}) = \frac{1}{50} = e^{4k}$, and thus $k = (-\ln 50)/4$. Consequently the charge one second ago was $f(3) = (5 \times 10^{-2})e^{(-(\ln 50)/4)3} \approx 2.6591479 \times 10^{-3}$ (coulombs).

25. Since $D(t) = P(0) - P(t)$ and $P(0) = e^{\lambda t}P(t)$, we have $D(t) = P(t)(e^{\lambda t} - 1)$, or $D(t)/P(t) = e^{\lambda t} - 1$. Thus

$$\lambda t = \ln\left(\frac{D(t)}{P(t)} + 1\right), \quad \text{or} \quad t = \frac{1}{\lambda} \ln\left(\frac{D(t)}{P(t)} + 1\right).$$

26. a. $t = \dfrac{1}{1.39 \times 10^{-11}} \ln\left(\dfrac{3.96}{202} + 1\right) \approx 1.40 \times 10^{9}$ (years)

b. $\dfrac{D(t)}{P(t)} = e^{\lambda t} - 1 = e^{(1.39 \times 10^{-11})(4.53 \times 10^{9})} - 1 \approx 0.0650$

27. a. $t = (1.885)10^{9} \ln\left[9.068\left(\dfrac{1.95 \times 10^{-12}}{2.885 \times 10^{-8}}\right) + 1\right] \approx 1{,}150{,}000$ (years)

b. $\dfrac{D(t)}{P(t)} = \dfrac{1}{9.068}(e^{4.19/1.885} - 1) \approx 0.908$

4.5 The First and Second Derivative Tests

1. $f'(x) = 2x + 6 = 2(x + 3)$, so f' changes from negative to positive at -3.

2. $f'(x) = 3x^2 - 2x - 1 = (3x + 1)(x - 1)$, so f' changes from positive to negative at $-\frac{1}{3}$ and from negative to positive at 1.

3. $f'(x) = 8x^3 - 8x = 8x(x - 1)(x + 1)$, so f' changes from negative to positive at -1 and 1, and from positive to negative at 0.

4. $f'(x) = \dfrac{(x^3 - 2) - x(3x^2)}{(x^3 - 2)^2} = \dfrac{-2(x^3 + 1)}{(x^3 - 2)^2} = \dfrac{-2(x + 1)(x^2 - x + 1)}{(x^3 - 2)^2}$

Since $x^2 > x + 1 > 0$ for all x and $(x^3 - 2)^2 \geq 0$ for all x, f' changes from positive to negative at -1.

5. $f'(t) = \dfrac{(2t - 1)(t^2 + t + 1) - (t^2 - t + 1)(2t + 1)}{(t^2 + t + 1)^2} = \dfrac{2(t + 1)(t - 1)}{(t^2 + t + 1)^2}$

so that f' changes from positive to negative at -1 and from negative to positive at 1.

6. $f'(t) = -\frac{1}{2}(t - t^2)^{-3/2}(1 - 2t)$, so f' changes from negative to positive at $\frac{1}{2}$.

7. $f'(t) = \cos t + \frac{1}{2}$, so $f'(t) > 0$ if $\cos t > -\frac{1}{2}$, and $f'(t) < 0$ if $\cos t < -\frac{1}{2}$. Thus f' changes from positive to negative at $2\pi/3 + 2n\pi$ for any integer n, and changes from negative to positive at $4\pi/3 + 2n\pi$ for any integer n.

8. $f'(t) = \cos t + \sin t$, so $f'(t) > 0$ if $\cos t > -\sin t$, and $f'(t) < 0$ if $\cos t < -\sin t$. Thus f' changes from positive to negative at $3\pi/4 + 2n\pi$ for any integer n, and from negative to positive at $-\pi/4 + 2n\pi$ for any integer n.

9. $f'(x) = -6x + 3 = 3(1 - 2x)$, so f' changes from positive to negative at $\frac{1}{2}$. By the First Derivative Test, $f(\frac{1}{2}) = \frac{31}{4}$ is a relative maximum value of f.

10. $f'(x) = 3x^2 - 12 = 3(x+2)(x-2)$, so f' changes from positive to negative at -2 and from negative to positive at 2. By the First Derivative Test, $f(-2) = 18$ is a relative maximum value and $f(2) = -14$ is a relative minimum value of f.

11. $f'(x) = 3x^2 + 6x = 3x(x + 2)$, so f' changes from positive to negative at -2 and from negative to positive at 0. By the First Derivative Test, $f(-2) = 8$ is a relative maximum value and $f(0) = 4$ is a relative minimum value of f.

12. $f'(x) = 4x^3 - 16x = 4x(x + 2)(x - 2)$, so f' changes from negative to positive at -2 and 2, and from positive to negative at 0. By the First Derivative Test, $f(-2) = f(2) = -15$ is a relative minimum value and $f(0) = 1$ is a relative maximum value of f.

13. $g'(x) = 8x + \dfrac{1}{x^2} = \dfrac{8x^3 + 1}{x^2} = \dfrac{(2x + 1)(4x^2 - 2x + 1)}{x^2}$

    Since $4x^2 - 2x + 1 > 0$ for all x, g' changes from negative to positive at $-\frac{1}{2}$. By the First Derivative Test, $g(-\frac{1}{2}) = 3$ is a relative minimum value of g.

14. $g'(x) = -2x/(1 + x^2)^2$, so g' changes from positive to negative at 0. By the First Derivative Test, $g(0) = 1$ is a relative maximum value of g.

15. $f'(x) = \dfrac{(16 + x^3) - x(3x^2)}{(16 + x^3)^2} = \dfrac{16 - 2x^3}{(16 + x^3)^2} = \dfrac{-2(x - 2)(x^2 + 2x + 4)}{(16 + x^3)^2}$

    Since $x^2 + 2x + 4 > 0$ for all x, f' changes from positive to negative at 2. By the First Derivative Test, $f(2) = 1/12$ is a relative maximum value of f.

16. $f'(x) = \dfrac{1}{2\sqrt{|x| + 1}}$ for $x > 0$ and $f'(x) = \dfrac{-1}{2\sqrt{|x| + 1}}$ for $x < 0$

    so f' changes from negative to positive at 0. By the First Derivative Test, $f(0) = 1$ is a relative minimum value of f. (Notice that f is not differentiable at $x = 0$.)

17. $f'(x) = \sqrt{1 - x^2} - \dfrac{x^2}{\sqrt{1 - x^2}} = \dfrac{1 - 2x^2}{\sqrt{1 - x^2}} = \dfrac{(1 - \sqrt{2}\,x)(1 + \sqrt{2}\,x)}{\sqrt{1 - x^2}}$

so f' changes from negative to positive at $-\frac{1}{2}\sqrt{2}$ and from positive to negative at $\frac{1}{2}\sqrt{2}$. By the First Derivative Test, $f(-\frac{1}{2}\sqrt{2}) = -\frac{1}{2}$ is a relative minimum value and $f(\frac{1}{2}\sqrt{2}) = \frac{1}{2}$ is a relative maximum value of f.

18. $f'(x) = \dfrac{(2x+1)(x^2-x+1)-(2x-1)(x^2+x+1)}{(x^2-x+1)^2} = \dfrac{-2x^2+2}{(x^2-x+1)^2} = \dfrac{-2(x-1)(x+1)}{(x^2-x+1)^2}$
so f' changes from negative to positive at -1 and from positive to negative at 1. By the First Derivative Test, $f(-1) = \frac{1}{3}$ is a relative minimum value and $f(1) = 3$ is a relative maximum value of f.

19. $k'(x) = -\sin x + \frac{1}{2}$, so $k'(x) > 0$ if $\sin x < \frac{1}{2}$, and $k'(x) < 0$ if $\sin x > \frac{1}{2}$. Thus k' changes from positive to negative at $\pi/6 + 2n\pi$ for any integer n, and from negative to positive at $5\pi/6 + 2n\pi$ for any integer n. By the First Derivative Test, $k(\pi/6 + 2n\pi) = \frac{1}{2}\sqrt{3} + \pi/12 + n\pi$ is a relative maximum value of k for any integer n, and $k(5\pi/6 + 2n\pi) = -\frac{1}{2}\sqrt{3} + 5\pi/12 + n\pi$ is a relative minimum value of k for any integer n.

20. $k'(x) = \cos x - \frac{1}{2}\sqrt{3}$, so $k'(x) > 0$ if $\cos x > \frac{1}{2}\sqrt{3}$, and $k'(x) < 0$ if $\cos x < \frac{1}{2}\sqrt{3}$. Thus k' changes from positive to negative at $\pi/6 + 2n\pi$ for any integer n, and from negative to positive at $11\pi/6 + 2n\pi$ for any integer n. By the First Derivative Test, $k(\pi/6 + 2n\pi) = \frac{1}{2} - \frac{1}{2}\sqrt{3}(\pi/6 + 2n\pi)$ is a relative maximum value of k for any integer n, and $k(11\pi/6 + 2n\pi) = -\frac{1}{2} - \frac{1}{2}\sqrt{3}(11\pi/6 + 2n\pi)$ is a relative minimum value of k for any integer n.

21. $k'(x) = \cos\left(\dfrac{x^2}{1+x^2}\right)\dfrac{2x(1+x^2)-x^2(2x)}{(1+x^2)^2} = \dfrac{2x}{(1+x^2)^2}\cos\left(\dfrac{x^2}{1+x^2}\right)$
Since $0 \le x^2/(1+x^2) \le 1 < \pi/2$, we have $\cos(x^2/(1+x^2)) > 0$ for all x. Thus k' changes from negative to positive at 0. By the First Derivative Test, $k(0) = 0$ is a relative minimum value of k.

22. $$k'(x) = \frac{(-\sin x)(1+\sin x)-(\cos x)(\cos x)}{(1+\sin x)^2} = \frac{-\sin x - (\sin^2 x + \cos^2 x)}{(1+\sin x)^2} = \frac{-\sin x - 1}{(1+\sin x)^2} = -\frac{1}{1+\sin x} < 0$$
for all x in the domain of k. Thus k is decreasing on every interval in its domain and hence has no relative extreme values.

23. $f'(x) = 2xe^{-x} - x^2e^{-x} = xe^{-x}(2-x)$. Thus f' changes from negative to positive at 0, and from positive to negative at 2. By the First Derivative Test, $f(0) = 0$ is a relative minimum value and $f(2) = 4e^{-2}$ is a relative maximum value.

24. The domain of f is $(0, \infty)$, and
$$f'(x) = \frac{1}{x} - \frac{1}{x^2+1}(2x) = \frac{1-x^2}{x(x^2+1)} = \frac{(1+x)(1-x)}{x(x^2+1)}.$$
Thus f' changes from positive to negative at 1. By the First Derivative Test, $f(1) = -\ln 2$ is a relative maximum value.

25. $f'(x) = -8x + 3$, so $f'(x) = 0$ if $x = \frac{3}{8}$. Since $f''(x) = -8 < 0$ for all x, the Second Derivative Test implies that $f(\frac{3}{8}) = -\frac{7}{16}$ is a relative maximum value of f.

26. $f'(x) = 3x^2 + 12x = 3x(x+4)$, so $f'(x) = 0$ if $x = 0$ or $x = -4$. Since $f''(x) = 6x + 12$, so that $f''(0) = 12 > 0$ and $f''(-4) = -12 < 0$, the Second Derivative Test implies that $f(0) = 9$ is a relative minimum value of f, and $f(-4) = 41$ is a relative maximum value of f.

27. $f'(x) = 3x^2 - 6x - 24 = 3(x-4)(x+2)$, so $f'(x) = 0$ if $x = 4$ or $x = -2$. Since $f''(x) = 6x - 6$, so that $f''(4) = 18 > 0$ and $f''(-2) = -18 < 0$, the Second Derivative Test implies that $f(4) = -79$ is a relative minimum value of f, and $f(-2) = 29$ is a relative maximum value of f.

28. $f'(x) = 4x^3 + \frac{1}{2}$, so that $f'(x) = 0$ if $x = -\frac{1}{2}$. Since $f''(x) = 12x^2$, so that $f''(-\frac{1}{2}) = 3 > 0$, the Second Derivative Test implies that $f(-\frac{1}{2}) = -\frac{3}{16}$ is a relative minimum value of f.

29. $f'(x) = 12x^3 - 12x^2 - 9x = 3x(2x+1)(2x-3)$, so $f'(x) = 0$ if $x = 0$, $x = -\frac{1}{2}$, or $x = \frac{3}{2}$. Since $f''(x) = 36x^2 - 24x - 9$, so that $f''(0) = -9 < 0$, $f''(-\frac{1}{2}) = 12 > 0$ and $f''(\frac{3}{2}) = 36 > 0$, the Second Derivative Test implies that $f(0) = \frac{1}{2}$ is a relative maximum value of f, $f(-\frac{1}{2}) = \frac{1}{16}$ is a relative minimum value of f, and $f(\frac{3}{2}) = -\frac{127}{16}$ is a relative minimum value of f.

30. $g'(x) = 6(x^2+2)^5(2x) = 12x(x^2+2)^5$, so $g'(x) = 0$ if $x = 0$. Since $g''(x) = 12(x^2+2)^5 + (12x)[5(x^2+2)^4(2x)]$, so that $g''(0) = 12 \cdot 32 > 0$, the Second Derivative Test implies that $g(0) = 64$ is a relative minimum value of g.

31. $f'(t) = 2t - 1/t^2$, so $f'(t) = 0$ if $2t = 1/t^2$, or $t^3 = \frac{1}{2}$, or $t = 1/\sqrt[3]{2}$. Since $f''(t) = 2 + 2/t^3$, so that $f''(1/\sqrt[3]{2}) = 2 + 2/\frac{1}{2} = 6 > 0$, the Second Derivative Test implies that $f(1/\sqrt[3]{2}) = 1/(2^{2/3}) + \sqrt[3]{2} + 1$ is a relative minimum value of f.

32. $f'(t) = 3t^2 + 96/t^3 = (3/t^3)(t^5 + 32)$, so $f'(t) = 0$ if $t = -2$. Since $f''(t) = 6t - 288/t^4 = (6/t^4)(t^5 - 48)$, so that $f''(-2) = \frac{6}{16}(-80) = -30 < 0$, the Second Derivative Test implies that $f(-2) = -20$ is a relative maximum value of f.

33. $f'(t) = \cos t - \sin t$, so $f'(t) = 0$ if $\sin t = \cos t$, that is, if $x = \pi/4 + n\pi$ for any integer n. Next, $f''(t) = \sin t - \cos t$. If n is even, then $f''(\pi/4 + n\pi) = f''(\pi/4) = -\sqrt{2} < 0$, so the Second Derivative Test implies that $f(\pi/4 + n\pi) = \sqrt{2}$ is a relative maximum value of f. Analogously, if n is odd, then $f''(\pi/4 + n\pi) = f''(\pi/4 + \pi) = f''(5\pi/4) = \sqrt{2} > 0$, so the Second Derivative Test implies that $f(\pi/4 + n\pi) = -\sqrt{2}$ is a relative minimum value of f.

34. $f'(t) = 1 - 2\sin 2t$, so $f'(t) = 0$ if $\sin 2t = \frac{1}{2}$, that is, if $2t = \pi/6 + 2n\pi$ or $2t = 5\pi/6 + 2n\pi$ for any integer n, that is, if $t = \pi/12 + n\pi$ or $t = 5\pi/12 + n\pi$ for any integer n. Since $f''(t) = -4\cos 2t$, we find that $f''(\pi/12 + n\pi) = -4\cos(\pi/6 + 2n\pi) = -4\cos(\pi/6) = -2\sqrt{3} < 0$, and thus the Second Derivative Test implies that $f(\pi/12 + n\pi) = \pi/12 + n\pi + \cos(\pi/6 + 2n\pi) = \pi/12 + n\pi + \frac{1}{2}\sqrt{3}$ is a relative maximum value of f for any integer n. Analogously, $f''(5\pi/12 + n\pi) = -4\cos 5\pi/6 = 2\sqrt{3} > 0$, so that the Second Derivative Test implies that $f(5\pi/12 + n\pi) = 5\pi/12 + n\pi + \cos(5\pi/6 + 2n\pi) = 5\pi/12 + n\pi - \frac{1}{2}\sqrt{3}$ is a relative minimum value of f for any integer n.

35. $f'(t) = e^t - (e^{-t})(-1) = e^t + e^{-t}$, so that $f'(t) > 0$ for all t. Therefore f is increasing on $(-\infty, \infty)$ and hence has no relative extreme values.

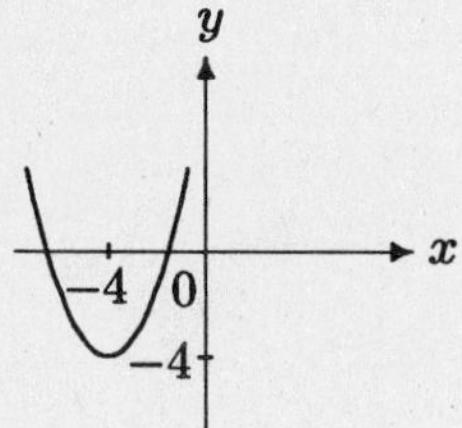

Exercise 37

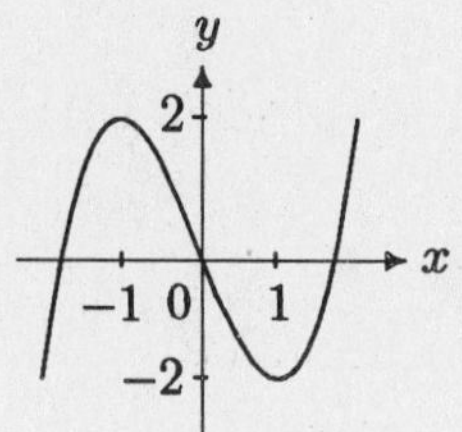

Exercise 38

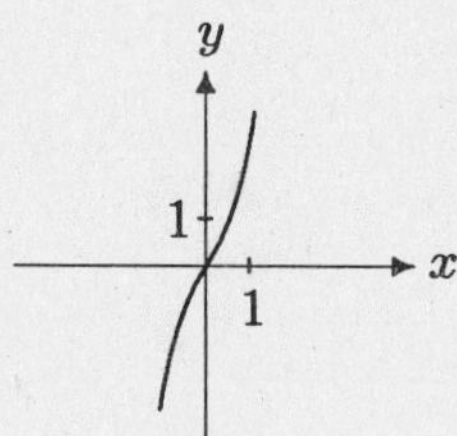

Exercise 39

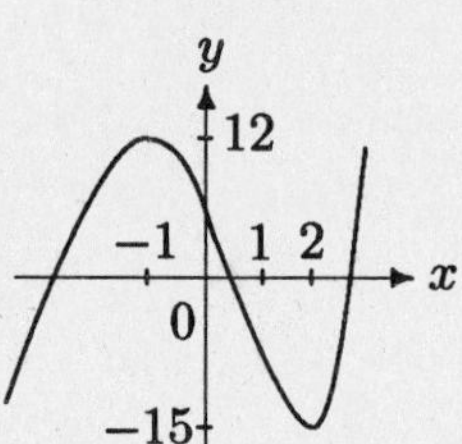

Exercise 40

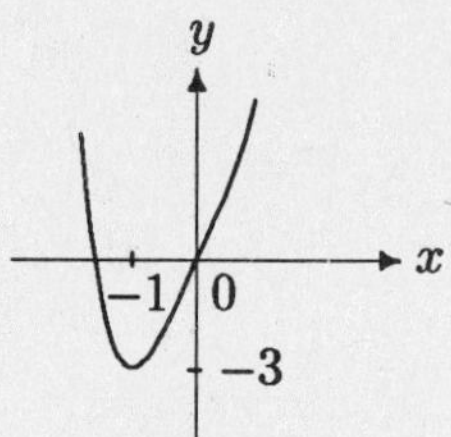

Exercise 41

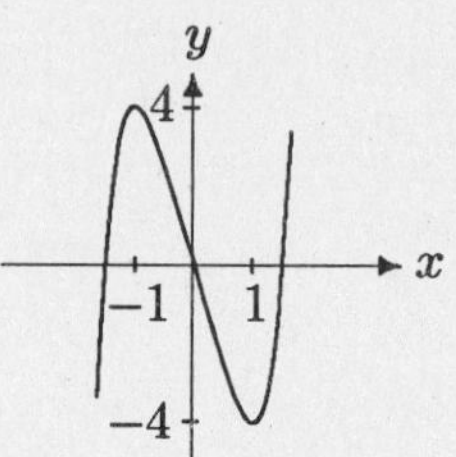

Exercise 42

36. The domain of f is $(0, \infty)$, and $f'(t) = 2t - 8/t = 2(t^2 - 4)/t = 2(t+2)(t-2)/t$. Thus $f'(t) = 0$ for $t = 2$. Since $f''(t) = 2 + 8/t^2$, so that $f''(2) = 4 > 0$, the Second Derivative Test implies that $f(2) = 4 - 8\ln 2$ is a relative minimum value of f.

37. $f'(x) = 2x + 8 = 2(x+4)$, so that $f'(x) = 0$ for $x = -4$. Also $f''(x) = 2 > 0$ for all x. By the Second Derivative Test, $f(-4) = -4$ is a relative minimum value of f.

38. $f'(x) = 3x^2 - 3 = 3(x+1)(x-1)$, so that $f'(x) = 0$ for $x = 1$ or $x = -1$. Next, $f''(x) = 6x$, so that $f''(1) = 6 > 0$ and $f''(-1) = -6 < 0$. By the Second Derivative Test, $f(1) = -2$ is a relative minimum value of f, and $f(-1) = 2$ is a relative maximum value of f.

39. $f'(x) = 3x^2 + 3 = 3(x^2 + 1) > 0$ for all x, so that f has no critical numbers, and therefore no relative extreme values.

40. $f'(x) = 6x^2 - 6x - 12 = 6(x-2)(x+1)$, so that $f'(x) = 0$ for $x = 2$ or $x = -1$. Next $f''(x) = 12x - 6$, so that $f''(2) = 18 > 0$ and $f''(1) = -18 < 0$. By the Second Derivative Test, $f(2) = -15$ is a relative minimum value of f, and $f(-1) = 12$ is a relative maximum value of f.

41. $f'(x) = 4x^3 + 4 = 4(x+1)(x^2 - x + 1)$, so that since $x^2 - x + 1 > 0$ for all x, $f'(x) = 0$ for $x = -1$. Next, $f''(x) = 12x^2$, so that $f''(-1) = 12 > 0$. By the Second Derivative Test, $f(-1) = -3$ is a relative minimum value of f.

42. $f'(x) = 5x^4 - 5 = 5(x^2 + 1)(x+1)(x-1)$, so that $f'(x) = 0$ for $x = 1$ or $x = -1$. Next, $f''(x) = 20x^3$, so that $f''(1) = 20 > 0$ and $f''(-1) = -20 < 0$. By the Second Derivative Test, $f(1) = -4$ is a relative minimum value of f, and $f(-1) = 4$ is a relative maximum value of f.

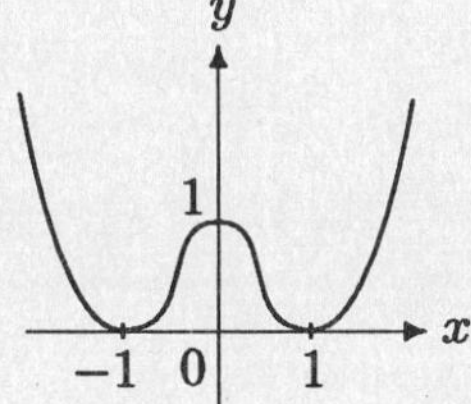

Exercise 43

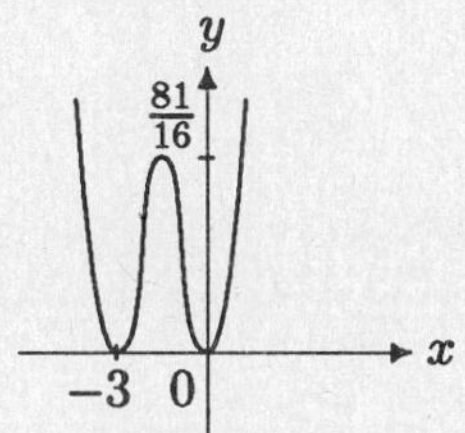

Exercise 44

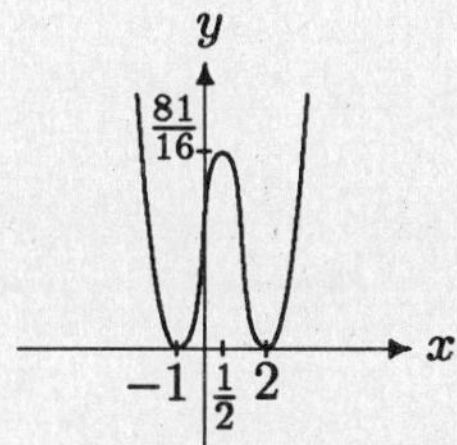

Exercise 45

Exercise 46

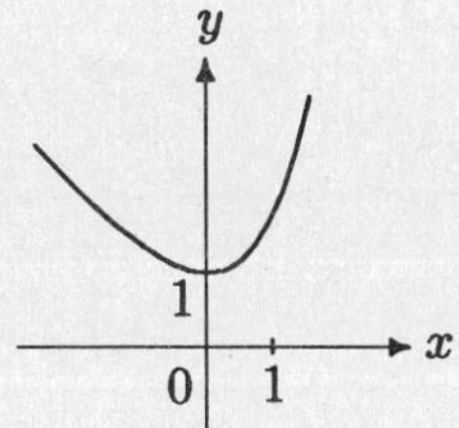

Exercise 47

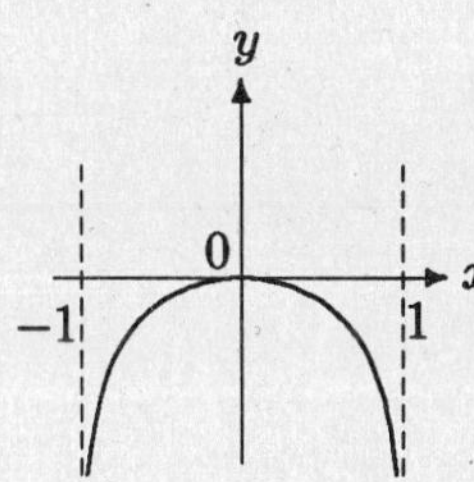

Exercise 48

43. $f'(x) = 2(x^2 - 1)(2x) = 4x(x+1)(x-1)$, so that $f'(x) = 0$ for $x = 0$, $x = 1$, or $x = -1$. Next, $f''(x) = 12x^2 - 4$, so that $f''(0) = -4 < 0$, $f''(1) = 8 > 0$, and $f''(-1) = 8 > 0$. By the Second Derivative Test, $f(0) = 1$ is a relative maximum value of f, and $f(1) = f(-1) = 0$ is a relative minimum value of f.

44. $f'(x) = 2x(x+3)^2 + x^2[2(x+3)] = 4x^3 + 18x^2 + 18x = 2x(2x+3)(x+3)$, so that $f'(x) = 0$ for $x = 0$, $x = -\frac{3}{2}$, or $x = -3$. Next $f''(x) = 12x^2 + 36x + 18$, so that $f''(0) = 18 > 0$, $f''(-\frac{3}{2}) = -9 < 0$, and $f''(-3) = 18 > 0$. By the Second Derivative Test, $f(0) = f(-3) = 0$ is a relative minimum value of f, and $f(-\frac{3}{2}) = \frac{81}{16}$ is a relative maximum value of f.

45. $f'(x) = 2(x-2)(x+1)^2 + (x-2)^2 2(x+1) = 2(x-2)(x+1)(2x-1)$, so that $f'(x) = 0$ for $x = 2$, $x = -1$, or $x = \frac{1}{2}$. Since f' changes from negative to positive at -1 and 2, and positive to negative at $\frac{1}{2}$, the First Derivative Test implies that $f(-1) = f(2) = 0$ is a relative minimum value of f, and $f(\frac{1}{2}) = \frac{81}{16}$ is a relative maximum value of f. (The graph in this exercise is the same as that in Exercise 44 shifted right 2 units.)

46. $f'(x) = (1-2x)/(2\sqrt{x - x^2})$, so that $f'(x) = 0$ for $x = \frac{1}{2}$. Since f' changes from positive to negative at $\frac{1}{2}$, the First Derivative Test implies that $f(\frac{1}{2}) = \frac{1}{2}$ is a relative maximum value of f.

47. $f'(x) = e^x - 1$, so that $f'(0) = 0$. Since f' changes from negative to positive at 0, the First Derivative Test implies that $f(0) = 1$ is a relative minimum value of f.

48. The domain of f is $(-1, 1)$, and

$$f'(x) = \frac{1}{1+x} + \frac{1}{1-x}(-1) = \frac{-2x}{(1+x)(1-x)},$$

so $f'(x) = 0$ for $x = 0$. Since f' changes from positive to negative at 0, the First Derivative Test implies that $f(0) = 0$ is a relative maximum value.

49. $f'(x) = 5x^4$ and $f''(x) = 20x^3$, so that $f'(0) = f''(0) = 0$. But $f'(x) > 0$ if $x \neq 0$, so f is increasing, and thus has no relative extreme values.

50. $f'(x) = \frac{7}{3}x^{4/3}$ and $f''(x) = \frac{28}{9}x^{1/3}$, so that $f'(0) = f''(0) = 0$. But $f'(x) > 0$ if $x \neq 0$, so f is increasing, and thus has no relative extreme values.

51. $f'(x) = 5x^4 - 3x^2 = x^2(5x^2 - 3)$ and $f''(x) = 20x^3 - 6x = 2x(10x^2 - 3)$, so that $f'(0) = f''(0) = 0$. But $f'(x) < 0$ for x in $(-\sqrt{\frac{3}{5}}, \sqrt{\frac{3}{5}})$ and $x \neq 0$, so that f is decreasing on $[-\sqrt{\frac{3}{5}}, \sqrt{\frac{3}{5}}]$, and thus f has no relative extreme value at 0.

52. $f'(x) = 3(x-2)^2$ and $f''(x) = 6(x-2)$, so $f'(2) = f''(2) = 0$. But $f'(x) > 0$ if $x \neq 2$, so that f is increasing, and thus has no relative extreme values.

53. $f'(x) = 3x^2e^x + x^3e^x = x^2e^x(3+x)$ and $f''(x) = 6xe^x + 3x^2e^x + 3x^2e^x + x^3e^x = xe^x(6 + 6x + x^2)$, so that $f'(0) = f''(0) = 0$. But $f'(x) > 0$ for $x > -3$, so that f is increasing on $[-3, \infty)$, and thus f has no relative extreme value at 0.

54. $f'(x) = 1 + \cos x$ and $f''(x) = -\sin x$, so that $f''(\pi) = f''(\pi) = 0$. But $f'(x) > 0$ if x is in $(0, 2\pi)$ and $x \neq \pi$, so that by Theorem 4.7, f is increasing on $[0, 2\pi]$, and thus has no relative extreme value at π.

55. Relative maximum value at -0.5; relative minimum value at 0.

56. Relative maximum value at 0.8; relative minimum value at -0.7.

57. Relative maximum value at -5.0 and at 1.2; relative minimum value at -1.2 and at 5.0.

58. Relative maximum value at -4.7; relative minimum value at -1.7.

59. Assume that $f''(c) > 0$. Since $f'(c) = 0$, $f'(x)/(x-c) = [f'(x) - f'(c)]/(x-c) > 0$ for all x in some interval $(c-\delta, c+\delta)$. Therefore if $c - \delta < x < c$, then $f'(x) < 0$ since $x - c < 0$, while if $c < x < c + \delta$, then $f'(x) > 0$ since $x - c > 0$. This means that f' changes from negative to positive at c, and hence by the First Derivative Test, f has a relative minimum value at c.

60. a. Let $f(x) = x^{4/3}$. Then $f'(x) = (\frac{4}{3})x^{1/3}$, so $f'(0) = 0$. Since

$$\lim_{x\to 0} \frac{f'(x) - f'(0)}{x - 0} = \lim_{x\to 0} \left(\frac{4}{3}\right) x^{-2/3} = \infty$$

$f''(0)$ does not exist. Now $f'(x) < 0$ for $x < 0$ and $f'(x) > 0$ for $x > 0$, so $f(0) = 0$ is a relative minimum value for f.

b. Let $f(x) = x^{5/3}$. Then $f'(x) = (\frac{5}{3})x^{2/3}$, so $f'(0) = 0$. But $[f'(x) - f'(0)]/(x-0) = (\frac{5}{3})x^{-1/3}$, and since $\lim_{x\to 0} x^{-1/3}$ does not exist, likewise $\lim_{x\to 0}[f'(x) - f'(0)]/(x-0)$ and hence $f''(0)$ do not exist. Since $f(x) < 0$ if $x < 0$ and $f(x) > 0$ if $x > 0$, $f(0)$ is not a relative extreme value.

4.6 Extreme Values on an Arbitrary Interval

1. Let $r(x) = kx(a - x)$. Then $r'(x) = ka - 2kx$, so $r'(x) = 0$ if $ka - 2kx = 0$, that is, $x = a/2$. Since $r''(x) = -2k < 0$, (1) and the Second Derivative Test imply that $r(x)$ is maximized for $x = a/2$. Thus the value of x for which dx/dt is maximum is $a/2$.

2. a. If $C(x) = cx$ and $c < p$, then $P(x) = px - cx = (p - c)x$ and $p - c > 0$, so there is no maximum profit.

   b. If $C(x) = (x - 1)^2 + 2$, then $P(x) = px - C(x) = px - (x - 1)^2 - 2$. Thus $P'(x) = p - 2(x - 1)$, so $P'(x) = 0$ for $x = 1 + p/2$. Since $P''(x) = -2 < 0$, (1) and the Second Derivative Test imply that $P(1 + p/2)$ is the maximum value of P. Thus the maximum profit is $P(1 + p/2) = p(1 + p/2) - [(1 + p/2) - 1]^2 - 2 = p^2/4 + p - 2$.

3. $$\frac{dP}{dR} = \frac{E^2(R+r)^2 - 2E^2R(R+r)}{(R+r)^4} = \frac{E^2(r-R)}{(R+r)^3}$$
   Therefore $dP/dR = 0$ only for $R = r$, and dP/dR changes from positive to negative at r. By (1) and the First Derivative Test, the maximum value of P occurs for $R = r$.

4. $$\frac{dE}{dI} = \frac{V(VI + P + I^2R) - VI(V + 2IR)}{(VI + P + I^2R)^2} = \frac{V(P - I^2R)}{(VI + P + I^2R)^2}$$
   Therefore $dE/dI = 0$ only for $I = \sqrt{P/R}$, and dE/dI changes from positive to negative at $\sqrt{P/R}$. By (1) and the First Derivative Test, the efficiency E is maximum for $I = \sqrt{P/R}$.

5. $$P'(r) = \frac{\pi}{6a^5}\left[4r^3e^{-r/a} + r^4e^{-r/a}\left(-\frac{1}{a}\right)\right] = \frac{\pi r^3}{6a^5}e^{-r/a}\left(4 - \frac{r}{a}\right)$$
   Therefore $P'(r) = 0$ only for $r = 4a$, and P' changes from positive to negative at $4a$. By (1) and the First Derivative Test, the maximum value of P occurs at $4a$. Thus the most probable distance of the electron from the center of the atom is $4a$ (exactly 4 times the most probable state, as in Example 3).

6. b. Since $R = Ax\ln B - Ax\ln x$, we have
   $$\frac{dR}{dx} = A\ln B - A\ln x - Ax\cdot\frac{1}{x} = A(\ln B - \ln x - 1) = A\left(\ln\frac{B}{x} - 1\right) \quad\text{and}\quad \frac{d^2R}{dx^2} = -\frac{A}{x}.$$
   Thus $dR/dx = 0$ only if $\ln(B/x) = 1$, or $B/x = e$, or $x = B/e$. Since $d^2R/dx^2 < 0$ for $x = B/e$, it follows from (1) and the Second Derivative Test that the maximum value of R occurs for $x = B/e$. Thus the tumor is growing most rapidly when the radius is B/e.

7. $ds/dx = -2kx\ln x - kx^2(1/x) = -kx(2\ln x + 1)$, so that $ds/dx = 0$ only if $\ln x = -\frac{1}{2}$, or $x = e^{-1/2}$. Since ds/dx changes from positive to negative at $e^{-1/2}$, it follows from (1) and the First Derivative Test that the maximum value of s occurs for $x = e^{-1/2}$.

8. a. $dy/dt = c(-be^{-bt} + ae^{-at})$, so $dy/dt = 0$ only if $be^{-bt} = ae^{-at}$, or $e^{(a-b)t} = a/b$, or $(a - b)t = \ln(a/b)$, or $t = [1/(a - b)]\ln(a/b)$. Since
   $$\frac{d^2y}{dt^2} = b^2e^{-bt} - a^2e^{-at} = e^{-at}\left(b^2e^{(a-b)t} - a^2\right),$$

we see that for $t = [1/(a-b)]\ln(a/b)$, the value of d^2y/dt^2 is

$$e^{-at}\left(b^2 e^{\ln(a/b)} - a^2\right) = e^{-at}\left(b^2 \cdot \frac{a}{b} - a^2\right) = e^{-at}(ba - a^2) < 0$$

since $e^{-at} > 0$ and $a > b$. By (1) and the Second Derivative Test, the maximum value of y occurs for $t = [1/(a-b)]\ln(a/b)$. Thus the concentration is maximum at time $[1/(a-b)]\ln(a/b)$.

b. Let $r(t)$ be the rate of increase of the concentration with respect to time. Then $r(t) = dy/dt = c(-be^{-bt} + ae^{-at})$, and we wish to find the time t at which $r(t)$ is maximized. Since $r'(t) = c(b^2e^{-bt} - a^2e^{-at})$, we have $r'(t) = 0$ only if

$$b^2e^{-bt} = a^2e^{-at}, \quad \text{or} \quad e^{(a-b)t} = \frac{a^2}{b^2}, \quad \text{or} \quad t = \frac{1}{b-a}\ln\frac{a^2}{b^2} = \frac{2}{b-a}\ln\frac{a}{b}.$$

Since

$$r''(t) = c(-b^3e^{-bt} + a^3e^{-at}) = ce^{-at}(-b^3e^{(a-b)t} + a^3),$$

the value of $r''(t)$ for $t = [2/(b-a)]\ln(a/b)$ is

$$ce^{-at}\left(-b^3e^{2\ln(a/b)} + a^3\right) = ce^{-at}\left(-b^3 \cdot \frac{a^2}{b^2} + a^3\right) = ce^{-at}(a^3 - ba^2) < 0$$

since $ce^{-at} > 0$ and $a > b$. By (1) and the Second Derivative Test, the maximum value of r occurs for $t = [1/(b-a)]\ln(a^2/b^2)$. Thus the concentration is increasing most rapidly at time $[2/(b-a)]\ln(a/b)$.

9. Let x and y be the positive numbers, so $0 < x < 18$ and $0 < y < 18$. If P denotes their product, we seek to maximize P. Since $x + y = 18$, we have $P = xy = x(18-x) - 18x - x^2$. Now $P'(x) = 18 - 2x$, so $P'(x) = 0$ for $x = 9$. Since $P''(x) = -2 < 0$ for all x, by (1) and the Second Derivative Test we know that the maximum value of P occurs for $x = 9$. The corresponding value of y is $y = 18 - 9 = 9$. The numbers are 9 and 9.

10. Let x and y be the numbers, and P their product. We must minimize P. Since $x - y = 16$, we have $P = xy = x(x-16) = x^2 - 16x$. Thus $P'(x) = 2x - 16$, so $P'(x) = 0$ for $x = 8$. Since $P''(x) = 2 > 0$ for all x, by (1) and the Second Derivative Test we know that the minimum value of P occurs for $x = 8$. The corresponding value of y is $y = 8 - 16 = -8$. The numbers are 8 and -8.

11. Let x be the length of a side of the base, h the height, V the volume, and S the surface area. We must minimize S. By hypothesis $S = 4xh + x^2$ and $4 = V = x^2h$, so $h = 4/x^2$. Thus $S = 4x(4/x^2) + x^2 = 16/x + x^2$. Next, $S'(x) = -16/x^2 + 2x$, so $S'(x) = 0$ if $-16/x^2 + 2x = 0$, that is, $2x^3 = 16$, or $x = 2$. Since $S''(x) = 32/x^3 + 2 > 0$ for all $x > 0$, it follows from (1) and the Second Derivative Test that the surface area is minimum for $x = 2$. Then $h = 4/2^2 = 1$, so the dimensions are 2 meters on a side of the base, and 1 meter in height.

12. Let x be the length of a side of the base, h the height, V the volume, and S the surface area. We must minimize S. By hypothesis, $4 = V = x^2h$, so that $S = 4xh + 2x^2 = 16/x + 2x^2$. Then $S'(x) = -16/x^2 + 4x$, so $S'(x) = 0$ if $-16/x^2 + 4x = 0$, that is, $4x^3 = 16$, or $x = 4^{1/3}$. Since

$S''(x) = 32/x^3 + 4 > 0$ for all $x > 0$, it follows from (1) and the Second Derivative Test that the surface area is minimum for $x = 4^{1/3}$. Then $h = 4/(4^{1/3})^2 = 4/4^{2/3} = 4^{1/3}$, and thus the crate is a cube, $4^{1/3}$ meters on a side.

13. Let r be the radius of the two semicircles, and x the length of the rectangular portion of the field. Our goal is to maximize the area $A = 2rx$ of the rectangular portion. Since the perimeter of the entire field is to be 440 yards, we have $2x + 2\pi r = 440$, so that $x = 220 - \pi r$. Therefore $A = 2rx = 2r(220 - \pi r) = 440r - 2\pi r^2$ for $0 \le r \le 220/\pi$. Thus $dA/dr = 440 - 4\pi r$, so that $dA/dr = 0$ only for $r = 110/\pi$. Since $d^2A/dr^2 = -4\pi < 0$, it follows from (1) and the Second Derivative Test that the maximum value of A occurs for $r = 110/\pi$. The corresponding value of x is $220 - \pi(110/\pi) = 110$. Thus the area of the rectangular portion is maximum if the length of the rectangle is 110 yards and the radius of the semicircles is $110/\pi$ yards.

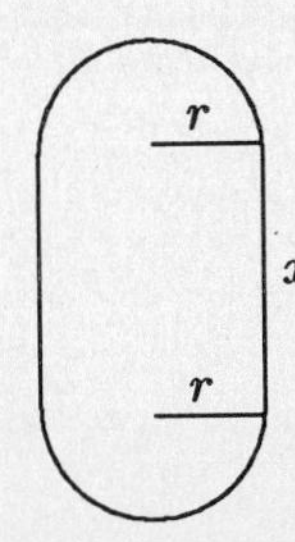

14. Let P denote the perimeter and A the area of the window. Since the amount of light to enter is proportional to the area, we are to maximize the area. By hypothesis $A = 2rh + \frac{1}{2}\pi r^2$ and $12 = P = 2h + 2r + \pi r = 2h + (2+\pi)r$. Then $h = 6 - \frac{1}{2}(2+\pi)r$, so $A = r(12 - (2+\pi)r) + \frac{1}{2}\pi r^2 = 12r - 2r^2 - \frac{1}{2}\pi r^2$. Now $A'(r) = 12 - 4r - \pi r$, so $A'(r) = 0$ if $12 - 4r - \pi r = 0$, that is, $4r + \pi r = 12$, or $r = 12/(4+\pi)$. Since $A''(r) = -4 - \pi < 0$ for all r, it follows from (1) and the Second Derivative Test that the area A is maximum if $r = 12/(4+\pi)$. Since

$$h = 6 - \frac{1}{2}(2+\pi)\frac{12}{4+\pi} = 6 - \frac{12+6\pi}{4+\pi} = \frac{12}{4+\pi}$$

the maximum amount of light will enter if $r = 12/(4+\pi)$ feet and $h = 12/(4+\pi)$ feet.

15. Let x and h be as in the figure, and let P be the perimeter and A the area. We are to maximize A. By hypothesis the triangle is equilateral, so its altitude is $\frac{1}{2}\sqrt{3}x$. Thus $A = xh + \frac{1}{2}x(\frac{1}{2}\sqrt{3}x) = xh + \frac{1}{4}\sqrt{3}x^2$ and $12 = P = 2h + 3x$. Then $h = 6 - \frac{3}{2}x$, so $A = x(6 - \frac{3}{2}x) + \frac{1}{4}\sqrt{3}x^2 = 6x + (\frac{1}{4}\sqrt{3} - \frac{3}{2})x^2$ for $0 < x \le 4$. Now $A'(x) = 6 + (\frac{1}{2}\sqrt{3} - 3)x$, so $A'(x) = 0$ if $x = -6/(\sqrt{3}/2 - 3) = 12/(6 - \sqrt{3})$. Since $A''(x) = \frac{1}{2}\sqrt{3} - 3 < 0$ for all x, it follows from (1) and the Second Derivative Test that A is maximum if $x = 12/(6-\sqrt{3})$. Since

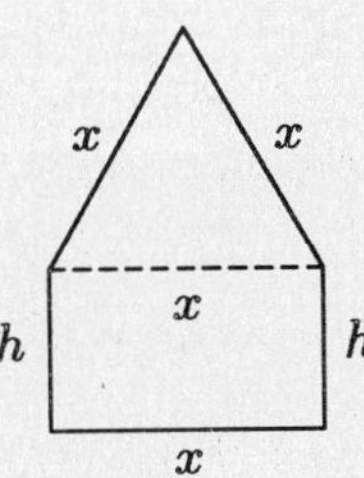

$$h = 6 - \frac{3}{2}\,\frac{12}{6-\sqrt{3}} = \frac{18 - 6\sqrt{3}}{6-\sqrt{3}}$$

the maximum amount of light will enter if

$$x = \frac{12}{6-\sqrt{3}} \approx 2.8\,(\text{feet}) \quad \text{and} \quad h = \frac{18-6\sqrt{3}}{6-\sqrt{3}} \approx 1.8\,(\text{feet}).$$

16. Let $t = 0$ correspond to 3 p.m. and set up a coordinate system as in the diagram, with the origin at the location of the oil tanker at time 0. At any time t the position of the oil tanker on the x axis is

$-15t$ and the position of the luxury liner on the y axis is $25 + 25t$. Thus the distance D between them is given by

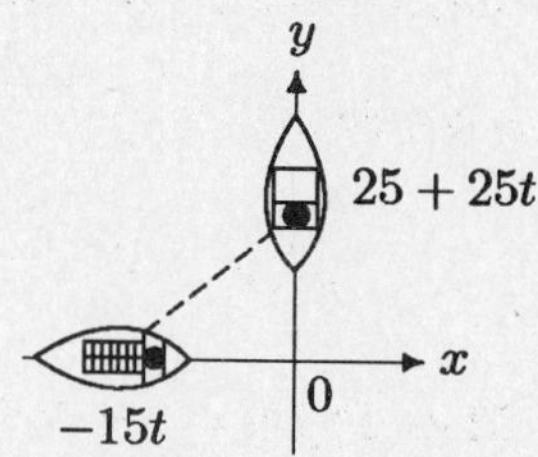

$$D = \sqrt{(0 + 15t)^2 + (25 + 25t - 0)^2}.$$

We will minimize $E = D^2 = 225t^2 + 625(1+t)^2$. Now

$$E'(t) = 450t + 1250(1+t) = 1700t + 1250,$$

so $E'(t) = 0$ if $1700t = -1250$, or $t = -\frac{1250}{1700} = -\frac{25}{34}$. Since $E''(t) = 1700 > 0$ for all t, it follows from (1) and the Second Derivative Test that E and hence D is minimum if $t = -\frac{25}{34}$, which corresponds to approximately 44 minutes before 3 p.m., that is 2:16 p.m.

17. Let x be the length in kilometers of the side along the highway, and y the length in kilometers of the sides perpendicular to the highway. Let k be the cost per kilometer of fence for the cheaper wood. Then the cost of the two sides perpendicular to the highway is $ky + ky = 2ky$, and the cost of the other two sides is $kx + 3kx = 4kx$. By hypothesis, $xy = 1$, so that $y = 1/x$. Thus the total cost of the fence is given by $C = 4kx + 2ky = 4kx + 2k/x$ for $x > 0$. Then $C'(x) = 4k - 2k/x^2$, so that $C'(x) = 0$ if $x^2 = \frac{1}{2}$, or $x = \frac{1}{2}\sqrt{2}$. Since $C''(x) = 4k/x^3 > 0$ for $x > 0$, it follows from (1) and the Second Derivative Test that the cost is minimized if $x = \frac{1}{2}\sqrt{2}$. The corresponding value of y is $1/(\frac{1}{2}\sqrt{2}) = \sqrt{2}$. Thus the cost is minimized if the side of the fence along the highway is $\frac{1}{2}\sqrt{2}$ kilometers long and the sides perpendicular to the highway are $\sqrt{2}$ kilometers long.

18. Let the length of the base be x, the height y, the volume V, the total cost C. We are to minimize C. Let the cost per square inch for the sides be k, so the cost per square inch of the top and bottom is $2k$. Then the total cost of the container is given by $C = 2k(2x^2) + k(4xy) = 4kx^2 + 4kxy$. By hypothesis, $250 = V = x^2y$, so $y = 250/x^2$, and thus $C = 4kx^2 + 4kx(250/x^2) = 4kx^2 + 1000k/x$. Now $C'(x) = 8kx - 1000k/x^2$, so $C'(x) = 0$ if $8kx - 1000k/x^2 = 0$, that is, $8x^3 = 1000$, or $x = (\frac{1000}{8})^{1/3} = 5$. Then $y = 250/5^2 = 10$. Since $C''(x) = 8k + 2000k/x^3 > 0$ for $x > 0$, (1) and the Second Derivative Test tells us that the cost is minimized if the bottoms are 5 inches square and the heights are 10 inches.

19. $f'(\theta) = q\csc^2\theta - \dfrac{r\cos\theta}{\sin^2\theta} = \dfrac{q - r\cos\theta}{\sin^2\theta}$ so that $f'(\theta) = 0$ if $\cos\theta = q/r$. Also

$$f''(\theta) = \frac{r\sin\theta(\sin^2\theta) - (q - r\cos\theta)2\sin\theta\cos\theta}{\sin^4\theta} = \frac{r(\sin^2\theta + 2\cos^2\theta) - 2q\cos\theta}{\sin^3\theta}$$

$$= \frac{r(1+\cos^2\theta) - 2q\cos\theta}{\sin^3\theta} > \frac{r(1+\cos^2\theta - 2\cos\theta)}{\sin^3\theta} = \frac{r(1-\cos\theta)^2}{\sin^3\theta} > 0 \quad \text{for } \theta \text{ in } (0, \pi/2).$$

By (1) and the Second Derivative Test, $f(\theta)$ is minimum for the value of θ in $(0, \pi/2)$ satisfying $\cos\theta = q/r$.

20. If we let $p = ka/r_1^4$, $q = kb/r_1^4$, and $r = kb/r_2^4$ in Exercise 19, then since $q < r$, Exercise 19 implies that the minimum value of $\mathcal{R}$ is attained for θ_0 such that $\cos\theta_0 = q/r = r_2^4/r_1^4$.

21. If we let $p = 6ab$, $q = 3b^2/2$, and $r = 3\sqrt{3}\,b^2/2$ in Exercise 19, then $q < r$, so Exercise 19 implies that the minimum value of S is attained for θ_0 such that $\cos\theta_0 = q/r = 1/\sqrt{3}$.

22. Since $E(x) < 0$ for $x < 0$ and $E(x) > 0$ for $x > 0$, it suffices to find the maximum value of E on $[0, \infty)$.

$$E'(x) = \frac{Q(x^2+a^2)^{3/2} - Qx(x^2+a^2)^{1/2}(3x)}{(x^2+a^2)^3} = \frac{Q(x^2+a^2) - 3Qx^2}{(x^2+a^2)^{5/2}} = \frac{-2Qx^2+Qa^2}{(x^2+a^2)^{5/2}}.$$

Thus $E'(x) = 0$ if $Qa^2 = 2Qx^2$, or $x = a/\sqrt{2}$. Since $E'(x) > 0$ if $0 < x < a/\sqrt{2}$ and $E'(x) < 0$ if $x > a/\sqrt{2}$, it follows from (1) and the First Derivative Test that

$$E(a/\sqrt{2}) = \frac{Q(a/\sqrt{2})}{(a^2/2+a^2)^{3/2}} = \frac{2\sqrt{3}\,Q}{9a^2}$$

is the maximum value of E on $[0, \infty)$, and hence on $(-\infty, \infty)$.

23. a. E is continuous on $[0, \infty)$, and since $E'(r) = c > 0$ for $0 < r < a$ and $E'(r) = -ca^2/r^2 < 0$ for $r > a$, E is increasing on $[0, a]$ and is decreasing on $[a, \infty)$. Therefore $E(a)$ is the maximum value of E.

b. Since

$$\lim_{r\to a^-} \frac{E(r)-E(a)}{r-a} = \lim_{r\to a^-} \frac{c(r-a)}{r-a} = c$$

and

$$\lim_{r\to a^+} \frac{E(r)-E(a)}{r-a} = \lim_{r\to a^+} \frac{(ca^2/r)-ca}{r-a} = \lim_{r\to a^+} \frac{-ca}{r} = -c$$

E is not differentiable at a.

24. Since $y = 2x - 4$ for any point (x, y) on the line, the distance between (x, y) and $(1, 3)$ is

$$\sqrt{(x-1)^2 + [(2x-4)-3]^2} = \sqrt{(x-1)^2 + (2x-7)^2}.$$

This distance is minimized for the same value of x that minimizes the square E of the distance, so let $E = (x-1)^2 + (2x-7)^2$. Then $E'(x) = 2(x-1) + 4(2x-7) = 10x - 30 = 10(x-3)$. Thus $E'(x) = 0$ for $x = 3$. Since $E'(x) < 0$ for $x < 3$ and $E'(x) > 0$ for $x > 3$, it follows from (1) and the First Derivative Test that E has its minimum value at 3. If $x = 3$, then $y = 2(3) - 4 = 2$. Thus $(3, 2)$ is the point on the line $y = 2x - 4$ that is closest to the point $(1, 3)$.

25. The distance between a point (x, y) on the parabola and the point $(-1, 0)$ is given by

$$D = \sqrt{(x+1)^2 + y^2} = \sqrt{x^2 + 2x + 1 + y^2} = \sqrt{y + 1 + y^2}.$$

This distance is minimized for the same value of y that minimizes the square E of the distance, so we let $E = D^2 = y + 1 + y^2$. Then $E'(y) = 1 + 2y$, so $E'(y) = 0$ if $y = -\frac{1}{2}$. Since $E'(y) < 0$ for $y < -\frac{1}{2}$ and $E(y) > 0$ for $y > -\frac{1}{2}$, it follows from (1) and the First Derivative Test that E has its minimum value at $-\frac{1}{2}$. If $y = -\frac{1}{2}$, then $-\frac{1}{2} + 1 = x^2 + 2x + 1 = (x+1)^2$, so that $x + 1 = \sqrt{\frac{1}{2}} = \sqrt{2}/2$ or $x + 1 = -\sqrt{\frac{1}{2}} = -\sqrt{2}/2$. Thus $x = -1 + \sqrt{2}/2$ or $x = -1 - \sqrt{2}/2$. Therefore $(-1 + \sqrt{2}/2, -\frac{1}{2})$ and $(-1 - \sqrt{2}/2, -\frac{1}{2})$ are the points on the parabola $y = x^2 + 2x$ closest to the point $(-1, 0)$.

26. Let x and y be as in the figure. Since triangles ABC and OBD are similar, we have $y/x = 1/(x-1)$, so $y = x/(x-1)$. Thus the area A of triangle OBD is given by $A = \frac{1}{2}xy = x^2/[2(x-1)]$ for $x > 1$. Then

$$A'(x) = \frac{(2x)(x-1) - 2x^2}{4(x-1)^2} = \frac{2x^2 - 4x}{4(x-1)^2} = \frac{x(x-2)}{2(x-1)^2} \quad \text{for } x > 1.$$

Thus $A'(x) = 0$ for $x = 2$. Since $A'(x) < 0$ for $1 < x < 2$ and $A'(x) > 0$ for $x > 2$, it follows from (1) and the First Derivative Test that A has its minimum value at 2. If $x = 2$, then $y = 2/(2-1) = 2$, and the length of the hypotenuse BD is $\sqrt{2^2 + 2^2} = 2\sqrt{2}$. Thus the lengths of the sides of the triangle with smallest area are 2, 2, and $2\sqrt{2}$.

27. a. For any point (x, x^2) on the parabola $y = x^2$, let $f(x)$ denote the square of the distance between $(0, p)$ and (x, x^2). Thus $f(x) = (x-0)^2 + (x^2-p)^2 = x^2 + (x^2-p)^2$, so that $f'(x) = 2x + 2(x^2-p)(2x) = 4x^3 + 2x(1-2p) = 2x[2x^2 + (1-2p)]$. This implies that $f'(0) = 0$ and if $1-2p \geq 0$, then $f'(x) = 0$ only for $x = 0$, and f' changes from negative to positive at 0. Thus if $1 - 2p \geq 0$, then (1) and the First Derivative Test imply that the maximum value of f occurs for $x = 0$. For any $x \neq 0$, we have $f'(x) \neq 0$, so f assumes its maximum only at 0. Thus if $1 - 2p \geq 0$, or equivalently, $p \leq \frac{1}{2}$, then the origin is the only point on the parabola that is closest to $(0, p)$.

b. Recall from part (a) that $f'(x) = 2x[2x^2 + (1-2p)]$. Thus if $1 - 2p < 0$, then $f'(x) = 0$ for $x = 0$, for $x = -\sqrt{p - \frac{1}{2}}$, and for $x = \sqrt{p - \frac{1}{2}}$. Since $f''(x) = 12x^2 + 2(1-2p)$, we have $f''(0) = 2(1-2p) < 0$, so by the Second Derivative Test, f has a relative maximum value at 0. But $f''(\sqrt{p - \frac{1}{2}}) = 12(p - \frac{1}{2}) + 2(1-2p) > 0$. Since $\sqrt{p - \frac{1}{2}}$ is the only critical number of f in $(0, \infty)$, it follows from (1) and the Second Derivative Test that f assumes its maximum value on $[0, \infty)$ at $\sqrt{p - \frac{1}{2}}$. Since $f(-x) = f(x)$, it follows that f assumes its maximum value on $(-\infty, \infty)$ at $-\sqrt{p - \frac{1}{2}}$ and $\sqrt{p - \frac{1}{2}}$. Thus if $1 - 2p < 0$, or equivalently, $p > \frac{1}{2}$, then there are two points on the parabola that are closest to $(0, p)$.

28. a. As in the figure, let the width of the base be x, the height y, and the volume V. We are to maximize V, which is given by $V = 2x(x)y = 2x^2y$. By hypothesis the total length of wire, and hence of edges, is 12, so $12 = 4x + 8x + 4y$, and thus $y = (12 - 12x)/4 = 3 - 3x$. Therefore $V = 2x^2(3-3x) = 6x^2 - 6x^3$ for $0 \leq x \leq 1$. Now $V'(x) = 12x - 18x^2$, so $V'(x) = 0$ if $12x - 18x^2 = 0$, that is, $x = 0$ or $x = \frac{2}{3}$. Since $V(0) = 0 = V(1)$ and $V(\frac{2}{3}) = 6(\frac{2}{3})^2 - 6(\frac{2}{3})^3 = \frac{8}{9}$, it follows that the maximum volume is obtained if $x = \frac{2}{3}$ (foot) and thus $y = 3 - 3(\frac{2}{3}) = 1$ (foot). Thus the wire should be cut so that 4 pieces are $\frac{2}{3}$ foot long, 4 are $\frac{4}{3}$ feet long, and 4 are 1 foot long.

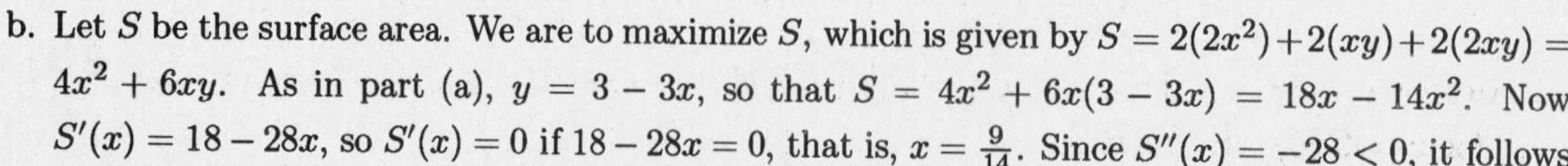

b. Let S be the surface area. We are to maximize S, which is given by $S = 2(2x^2) + 2(xy) + 2(2xy) = 4x^2 + 6xy$. As in part (a), $y = 3 - 3x$, so that $S = 4x^2 + 6x(3-3x) = 18x - 14x^2$. Now $S'(x) = 18 - 28x$, so $S'(x) = 0$ if $18 - 28x = 0$, that is, $x = \frac{9}{14}$. Since $S''(x) = -28 < 0$, it follows from (1) and the Second Derivative Test that the maximum volume is obtained if $x = \frac{9}{14}$. Then $y = 3 - 3(\frac{9}{14}) = \frac{15}{14}$. Thus the wire should be cut so that 4 pieces are $\frac{9}{14}$ foot long, 4 are $\frac{9}{7}$ feet long, and 4 are $\frac{15}{14}$ feet long.

29. a. Following the solution of Example 4 but with 10 replacing 5, we find that T is given by

$$T = \frac{\sqrt{x^2+4}}{3} + \frac{10-x}{4} \quad \text{for } 0 < x < 10.$$

Thus $T'(x)$ is the same as in Example 4, so $T'(x) = 0$ for $x = \frac{6}{7}\sqrt{7}$. As in Example 4, it follows from (1) and the Second Derivative Test that T is minimized for $x = \frac{6}{7}\sqrt{7}$. Thus the ranger should walk toward the point $\frac{6}{7}\sqrt{7}$ miles down the road.

b. This time T is given by

$$T = \frac{\sqrt{x^2+4}}{3} + \frac{\frac{1}{2}-x}{4} \quad \text{for } 0 \le x \le \tfrac{1}{2}.$$

Thus $T'(x)$ is the same as in Example 4. However, since $\frac{6}{7}\sqrt{7} > \frac{1}{2}$, there are no critical numbers of T in $(0, \frac{1}{2})$, so the minimum value of T must occur at 0 or $\frac{1}{2}$. Since

$$T(0) = \frac{\sqrt{0^2+4}}{3} + \frac{\frac{1}{2}-0}{4} = \frac{19}{24} \quad \text{and} \quad T(\tfrac{1}{2}) = \frac{\sqrt{(\frac{1}{2})^2+4}}{3} + 0 = \frac{\sqrt{17}}{6}$$

it follows that T is minimized for $x = \frac{1}{2}$. Thus the ranger should walk directly toward the car.

c. T is given by

$$T = \frac{\sqrt{x^2+4}}{3} + \frac{c-x}{4} \quad \text{for } 0 \le x \le c$$

so $T'(x)$ is as given in Example 4. If $c > \frac{6}{7}\sqrt{7}$, it follows as in Example 4 that the ranger should walk toward the point $\frac{6}{7}\sqrt{7}$ miles down the road. However, if $c \le \frac{6}{7}\sqrt{7}$, it follows as in part (b) that the ranger should walk directly toward the car.

30. Let x be as in Figure 4.56. Then the pigeon flies a distance $\sqrt{x^2 + (500)^2}$ over water and $1200 - x$ over land. The total flying time is given for $0 \le x \le 1200$ by

$$T(x) = \frac{(x^2+(500)^2)^{1/2}}{9} + \frac{1200-x}{10}.$$

Then

$$T'(x) = \frac{x(x^2+(500)^2)^{-1/2}}{9} - \frac{1}{10}$$

so $T'(x) = 0$ if $9 = 10x(x^2+(500)^2)^{-1/2}$, or $81(x^2+(500)^2) = 100x^2$. It follows that $x = 4500/\sqrt{19}$. Since

$$T''(x) = \frac{(x^2+(500)^2)^{-1/2}}{9} - \frac{x^2(x^2+(500)^2)^{-3/2}}{9} = \frac{(500)^2(x^2+(500)^2)^{-3/2}}{9}$$

we have $T''(x) > 0$ for $0 < x < 1200$, so (1) and the Second Derivative Test imply that T is minimum for $x = 4500/\sqrt{19}$ (meters).

31. Let x and y denote, respectively, the width and length of the printing on the page. We are to minimize the area A of the page. By hypothesis $xy = 35$, so $y = 35/x$, and thus $A = (x+2)(y+4) = (x+2)(35/x+4) = 43+70/x+4x$ for $x > 0$. Now $A'(x) = -70/x^2 + 4$, so $A'(x) = 0$ if $x^2 = \frac{70}{4}$, or $x = \frac{1}{2}\sqrt{70}$. Since $A''(x) = 140/x^3 > 0$ for $x > 0$, it follows from (1) and the Second Derivative Test that the minimum value of A is

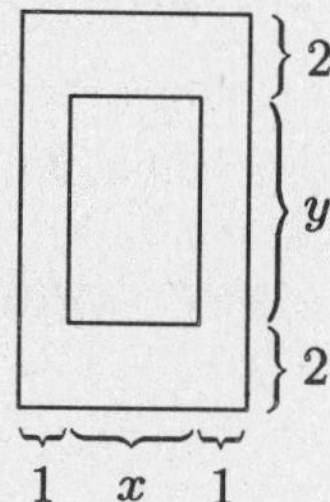

$$A(\tfrac{1}{2}\sqrt{70}) = 43 + 70/(\tfrac{1}{2}\sqrt{70}) + 4(\tfrac{1}{2}\sqrt{70}) = 43 + 4\sqrt{70}.$$

Thus the minimum area is $43 + 4\sqrt{70}$ square inches.

32. a. If the height y is less than the length x of the sides of the square base, then the largest volume will occur when $4x + y = 108$, so that $y = 108 - 4x$. Since $y \geq x$, we have $108 = 4x + y \geq 4x + x = 5x$, so $x \leq 21.6$. The volume is given by $V = x^2y = x^2(108 - 4x)$ for $0 \leq x \leq 21.6$. Now $V'(x) = 216x - 12x^2 = 12x(18 - x)$, so that $V'(x) = 0$ if $x = 18$. Since $V'(x) > 0$ if $0 < x < 18$ and $V'(x) < 0$ if $x > 18$, the dimensions of the largest parcel are $x = 18$ (inches) and $y = 108 - 4(18) = 36$ (inches), and the volume is 11,664 cubic inches. If the height y is less than the length x of one side of the square base, then the largest volume will occur when $x+(2y+2x) = 108$, so that $y = (108-3x)/2$ and $21.6 < x \leq 36$. Then $V = x^2y = x^2((108-3x)/2)$ for $21.6 < x \leq 36$. Now $V'(x) = 108x - \frac{9}{2}x^2 = \frac{9}{2}x(24 - x)$, so that $V'(x) = 0$ if $x = 24$. Since $V'(x) > 0$ if $x < 24$ and $V'(x) < 0$ if $x > 24$, (1) and the First Derivative Test imply that the largest volume is attained if $x = 24$ (inches). Then $y = [108 - 3(24)]/2 = 18$ (inches), and the volume is 10,368 cubic inches. Comparing the volume with that in the first case we see that the dimensions producing the largest volume are $x = 18$ (inches) and $y = 36$ (inches).

b. Let r be the radius of the cylinder and h the height. If $2r \leq h$, then the largest volume will occur when $h + 2\pi r = 108$, so that $h = 108 - 2\pi r$. Since $2r \leq h$, we have $108 = h + 2\pi r \geq 2r + 2\pi r$, so $r \leq 54/(1 + \pi)$. Then $V = \pi r^2 h = \pi r^2(108 - 2\pi r)$ for $0 < r \leq 54/(1+\pi)$. Now $V'(r) = 216\pi r - 6\pi^2 r^2 = 6\pi r(36 - \pi r)$, so that $V'(r) = 0$ if $r = 36/\pi$. Since $V'(r) > 0$ if $0 < r < 36/\pi$ and $V'(r) < 0$ if $r > 36/\pi$, (1) and the First Derivative Test imply that the largest volume is attained if $r = 36/\pi$ (inches). Then $h = 108 - 2\pi(36/\pi) = 36$ (inches), and the volume is $46{,}656/\pi$ cubic inches. If $2r > h$, then the largest volume will occur when $2r+(2h+4r) = 108$, so $h = 54-3r$. Then $V = \pi r^2 h = \pi r^2(54 - 3r)$ for $54/(1 + \pi) < r \leq 18$. Now $V'(r) = 108\pi r - 9\pi r^2 = 9\pi r(12 - r)$, so that $V'(r) = 0$ if $r = 12$. Since $V'(r) > 0$ for $54/(1 + \pi) < r < 12$ and $V'(r) < 0$ for $12 < r < 18$, (1) and the First Derivative Test imply that the largest volume is attained if $r = 12$ and $h = 54 - 3(12) = 18$, and the volume is 2592π. Comparing the volume with that in the first case, we see that the dimensions producing the largest volume are $r = 36/\pi$ (inches) and $h = 36$ (inches).

c. Let x be the length of one side of the cube. Then the largest volume will occur when $x+4x = 108$, so that $x = \frac{108}{5} = 21.6$ (inches).

d. The maximum volume of a rectangular parallelepiped in part (a) is 11,664 cubic inches, whereas the maximum volume of a cylinder in part (b) is $46{,}656/\pi \approx 14{,}851.1$ cubic inches, and the maximum volume of a cube in part (c) is $(21.6)^3 = 10{,}077.696$ cubic inches.

33. Let r and h denote the radius and height of the can. Since the volume is to be V, we have $\pi r^2 h = V$, so that $h = V/\pi r^2$. Since the area of the bottom is πr^2 and the area of the sides is $2\pi rh$, it follows that the surface area S of the can is given by

$$S = \pi r^2 + 2\pi rh = \pi r^2 + 2\pi r\frac{V}{\pi r^2} = \pi r^2 + \frac{2V}{r}.$$

Therefore $dS/dr = 2\pi r - 2V/r^2$, so that $dS/dr = 0$ only if $2\pi r = 2V/r^2$, or $r^3 = V/\pi$, or $r = \sqrt[3]{V/\pi}$. Since $d^2S/dr^2 = 2\pi + 4V/r^3 > 0$ for all $r > 0$, it follows from (1) and the Second Derivative Test that the surface area S is minimum for $r = \sqrt[3]{V/\pi}$.

34. Let h be the height, r the radius of the base, and V the volume of the cylinder. We are to maximize V. By the figure, $r^2 = R^2 - (h/2)^2$, so that $V = \pi r^2 h = \pi(R^2 - h^2/4)h = \pi R^2 h - (\pi/4)h^3$. Now $V'(h) = \pi R^2 - (3\pi/4)h^2$, so $V'(h) = 0$ if $\pi R^2 - (3\pi/4)h^2 = 0$, that is, $h = \frac{2}{3}\sqrt{3}\,R$. Since $V''(h) = -(3\pi/2)h < 0$ for $h > 0$, it follows from (1) and the Second Derivative Test that the maximum volume is attained for $h = \frac{2}{3}\sqrt{3}\,R$.

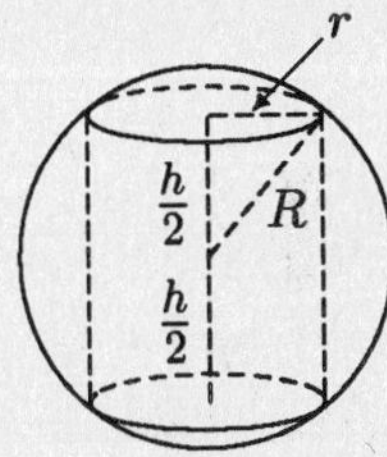

35. Let r be the radius, h the height, and S the surface area of the cone. We must minimize S. By hypothesis the volume is V. Since $V = \frac{1}{3}\pi r^2 h$, it follows that $h = 3V/(\pi r^2)$. Thus

$$S = \pi r\sqrt{r^2 + h^2} = \pi r\sqrt{r^2 + \left(\frac{3V}{\pi r^2}\right)^2} = \pi r\sqrt{r^2 + \frac{9V^2}{\pi^2 r^4}} = \frac{1}{r}\sqrt{\pi^2 r^6 + 9V^2}.$$

Now

$$S'(r) = -\frac{1}{r^2}\sqrt{\pi^2 r^6 + 9V^2} + \frac{6\pi^2 r^5}{2r\sqrt{\pi^2 r^6 + 9V^2}} = \frac{2\pi^2 r^6 - 9V^2}{r^2\sqrt{\pi^2 r^2 + 9V^2}}$$

so $S'(r) = 0$ only if $2\pi^2 r^6 - 9V^2 = 0$, that is, $r = [9V^2/(2\pi^2)]^{1/6}$. Since $S'(r) < 0$ for $r < [9V^2/(2\pi^2)]^{1/6}$ and $S'(r) > 0$ for $r > [9V^2/(2\pi^2)]^{1/6}$, (1) and the First Derivative Test imply that the minimum surface area occurs for $r = [9V^2/(2\pi^2)]^{1/6}$.

36. In order for the pipe to fit around the corner, its length must be less than or equal to the length of any pipe that touches the two outside walls (as in the figure), no matter what angle θ it makes with respect to the inside wall. Thus we must find the minimum length of a pipe that touches the walls, as in the figure, with $0 < \theta < \pi/2$. Then the length L of the pipe is given by $L = L_1 + L_2 = 10\csc\theta + 10\sec\theta$. Therefore

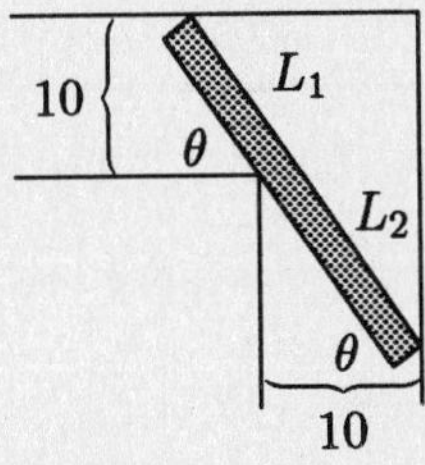

$$\frac{dL}{d\theta} = -10\csc\theta\cot\theta + 10\sec\theta\tan\theta = 10\left(-\frac{\cos\theta}{\sin^2\theta} + \frac{\sin\theta}{\cos^2\theta}\right) = \frac{10}{\sin^2\theta\cos^2\theta}(\sin^3\theta - \cos^3\theta)$$

so that $dL/d\theta = 0$ if and only if $\sin^3\theta = \cos^3\theta$, or $\tan^3\theta = 1$, or $\tan\theta = 1$, or $\theta = \pi/4$. Since $dL/d\theta < 0$ for $0 < \theta < \pi/4$ and $dL/d\theta > 0$ for $\pi/4 < \theta < \pi/2$, it follows from (1) and the First Derivative Test that L assumes its minimum value for $\theta = \pi/4$. Thus the longest pipe that can be carried around the corner has length $10\csc(\pi/4) + 10\sec(\pi/4) = 20\sqrt{2}$ (feet).

37. Let x be the distance from the person to the quieter highway, so $300 - x$ is the distance to the noisier highway. The total intensity of noise is given for $0 < x < 300$ by

$$f(x) = k\left(\frac{1}{x^2}\right) + k\left(\frac{8}{(300-x)^2}\right)$$

where k is a positive constant. Then

$$f'(x) = \frac{-2k}{x^3} + \frac{16k}{(300-x)^3} = 2k\,\frac{8x^3 - (300-x)^3}{x^3(300-x)^3}.$$

Thus $f'(x) = 0$ only if $8x^3 - (300-x)^3 = 0$, or $2x = 300 - x$, so that $x = 100$. Since

$$f''(x) = \frac{6}{x^4} + \frac{48k}{(300-x)^4}$$

we have $f''(x) > 0$ for $0 < x < 300$. It follows from (1) and the Second Derivative Test that $f(100)$ is the minimum value of f, so the person should sit 100 meters from the quieter highway.

38. Let x be the loan interest rate. Then the amount the firm can lend is k/x^2, where $k > 0$, and the profit is given by $P(x) = (k/x^2)(x - .05) = (k/x) - [k(.05)/x^2]$ for $.05 \le x$. Thus

$$P'(x) = \frac{-k}{x^2} + \frac{k(.1)}{x^3} = \frac{k}{x^3}(-x + .1)$$

and $P'(x) = 0$ if $x = .1$. Since $P'(x) > 0$ if $.05 < x < .1$, and $P'(x) < 0$ if $x > .1$, it follows from (1) and the First Derivative Test that the profit is maximized if $x = .1$, that is, if the loan interest rate is 10%.

39. The total cost per day is given by $C(x) = 5000 + 3x + x^2/2{,}500{,}000$, so the total cost per unit is given by $U(x) = 5000/x + 3 + x/2{,}500{,}000$. Now $U'(x) = -5000/x^2 + 1/2{,}500{,}000$, so that $U'(x) = 0$ only if $x^2 = (5000)(2{,}500{,}000) = 125 \times 10^8$, or $x = 5\sqrt{5} \times 10^4$. Since $U'(x) < 0$ if $x < 5\sqrt{5} \times 10^4$ and $U'(x) > 0$ if $x > 5\sqrt{5} \times 10^4$, it follows from (1) and the First Derivative Test that U has a minimum value at $x = 5\sqrt{5} \times 10^4$.

40. The annual stocking cost is $bx/2$ and the annual reordering cost is $1000c/x$. The inventory cost is given by $f(x) = bx/2 + 1000c/x$. Now $f'(x) = b/2 - 1000c/x^2$, so that $f'(x) = 0$ only if $x^2 = 2000c/b$, or $x = 20\sqrt{5c/b}$. Since $f'(x) < 0$ if $x < 20\sqrt{5c/b}$ and $f'(x) > 0$ if $x > 20\sqrt{5c/b}$, it follows from (1) and the First Derivative Test that f has a minimum value at $x = 20\sqrt{5c/b}$.

41. Let x be the number of pickers, and t the amount of time (in hours) needed for harvesting. The wages of the pickers amount to $6xt$, the wages of the supervisor amount to $10t$, and the union collects $10x$. Thus the total cost C is given for $x > 0$ by $C = 6xt + 10t + 10x$. Since 62,500 tomatoes are to be picked,

$625xt = 62{,}500$, so that $t = 100/x$. Thus $C(x) = 600 + 1000/x + 10x$. Then $C'(x) = -1000/x^2 + 10$, and $C'(x) = 0$ if $x = 10$. Since $C''(x) = 2000/x^3$, it follows that $C''(x) > 0$ for $x > 0$. Thus (1) and the Second Derivative Test imply that the minimum cost occurs when the farmer hires 10 pickers. The minimum cost is $C(10) = \$800$.

42. Let a and b be the distances from A and B, respectively, to the line separating the two media, and let l be the distance shown in the diagram. Then a, b, and l are constants, and $a\tan\theta + b\tan\varphi = l$. Differentiating implicitly with respect to θ, we find that

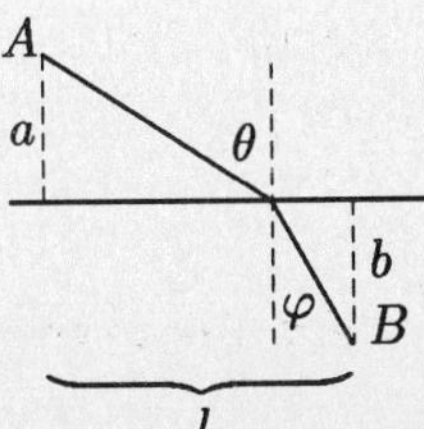

$$a\sec^2\theta + b\sec^2\varphi\frac{d\varphi}{d\theta} = 0 \quad\text{so that}\quad \frac{d\varphi}{d\theta} = -\frac{a\sec^2\theta}{b\sec^2\varphi}.$$

Our goal is to minimize the time T it takes the light to travel from A to B. In the first medium the distance traveled is $a\sec\theta$, so the time the light travels in the first medium is distance/velocity = $(a\sec\theta)/u$. Similarly the time of travel in the second medium is $(b\sec\varphi)/v$. Thus

$$T = \frac{a\sec\theta}{u} + \frac{b\sec\varphi}{v}$$

so that

$$\frac{dT}{d\theta} = \frac{a\sec\theta\tan\theta}{u} + \frac{b\sec\varphi\tan\varphi}{v}\frac{d\varphi}{d\theta} = \frac{a\sec\theta\tan\theta}{u} + \frac{b\sec\varphi\tan\varphi}{v}\left(-\frac{a\sec^2\theta}{b\sec^2\varphi}\right)$$

$$= a\sec^2\theta\left(\frac{\tan\theta}{u\sec\theta} - \frac{\tan\varphi}{v\sec\varphi}\right) = a\sec^2\theta\left(\frac{\sin\theta}{u} - \frac{\sin\varphi}{v}\right).$$

Thus

$$\frac{dT}{d\theta} = 0 \quad\text{if and only if}\quad \frac{\sin\theta}{u} = \frac{\sin\varphi}{v}.$$

Because $d\varphi/d\theta = -(a\sec^2\theta)/(b\sec^2\varphi) < 0$, φ is a decreasing function of θ. It follows that $(\sin\theta)/u - (\sin\varphi)/v$ is an increasing function of θ. Therefore $dT/d\theta$ is an increasing function of θ and hence $d^2T/d\theta^2 > 0$. By (1) and the Second Derivative Test, T is minimized if θ and φ satisfy $(\sin\theta)/u = (\sin\varphi)/v$.

4.7 Concavity and Inflection Points

1. $f'(x) = -3x + 1$; $f''(x) = -3$. Thus the graph is concave downward on $(-\infty, \infty)$.

2. $f'(x) = 2x + 2 = 2(x+1)$; $f''(x) = 2$. Thus the graph is concave upward on $(-\infty, \infty)$.

3. $g'(x) = 3x^2 - 12x + 12 = 3(x-2)^2$; $g''(x) = 6x - 12 = 6(x-2)$. Thus the graph is concave upward on $(2, \infty)$ and concave downward on $(-\infty, 2)$.

4. $g'(x) = 4x^3 - 12x = 4x(x^2 - 3)$; $g''(x) = 12x^2 - 12 = 12(x+1)(x-1)$. Thus the graph is concave upward on $(-\infty, -1)$ and $(1, \infty)$ and concave downward on $(-1, 1)$.

5. $f'(x) = \dfrac{(x^2+1)-2x^2}{(x^2+1)^2} = \dfrac{1-x^2}{(x^2+1)^2} = \dfrac{(1+x)(1-x)}{(x^2+1)^2}$

$f''(x) = \dfrac{(x^2+1)^2(-2x)-4x(x^2+1)(1-x^2)}{(x^2+1)^4} = \dfrac{2x(x^2-3)}{(x^2+1)^3}$

Thus the graph is concave upward on $(-\sqrt{3}, 0)$ and $(\sqrt{3}, \infty)$ and concave downward on $(-\infty, -\sqrt{3})$ and $(0, \sqrt{3})$.

6. Note: The domain of f consists of all numbers x such that $x \geq 1$.

$$f'(x) = \sqrt{x-1} + \frac{x}{2\sqrt{x-1}} = \frac{3x-2}{2\sqrt{x-1}}$$

$$f''(x) = \frac{6\sqrt{x-1}-(3x-2)/\sqrt{x-1}}{4(x-1)} = \frac{3x-4}{4(x-1)^{3/2}}$$

Thus the graph is concave upward on $(\frac{4}{3}, \infty)$ and concave downward on $(1, \frac{4}{3})$.

7. $g'(x) = e^x + xe^x = (1+x)e^x$; $g''(x) = e^x + (1+x)e^x = (2+x)e^x$. Since $e^x > 0$ for all x, the graph is concave upward on $(-2, \infty)$ and concave downward on $(-\infty, -2)$.

8. $g'(x) = 2xe^{-x} + x^2(-e^{-x}) = (2x - x^2)e^{-x}$; $g''(x) = (2-2x)e^{-x} + (2x-x^2)(-e^{-x}) = (2-4x+x^2)e^{-x}$. Since $x^2 - 4x + 2 = 0$ for $x = (4 \pm \sqrt{(-4)^2 - 4(1)(2)})/2 = 2 \pm \sqrt{2}$, it follows that $g''(x) = (x - 2 - \sqrt{2})(x - 2 + \sqrt{2})e^{-x}$. Since $e^{-x} > 0$ for all x, the graph is concave upward on $(-\infty, 2-\sqrt{2})$ and on $(2+\sqrt{2}, \infty)$, and concave downward on $(2-\sqrt{2}, 2+\sqrt{2})$.

9. The domain of f consists of all positive numbers, and $f'(x) = \ln x + x(1/x) = \ln x + 1$ and $f''(x) = 1/x$. Thus the graph is concave upward on $(0, \infty)$.

10. The domain of f consists of all positive numbers, and $f'(x) = 2x + 1/x$ and $f''(x) = 2 - 1/x^2 = (2x^2-1)/x^2$. Thus the graph is concave upward on $(\sqrt{2}/2, \infty)$ and concave downward on $(0, \sqrt{2}/2)$.

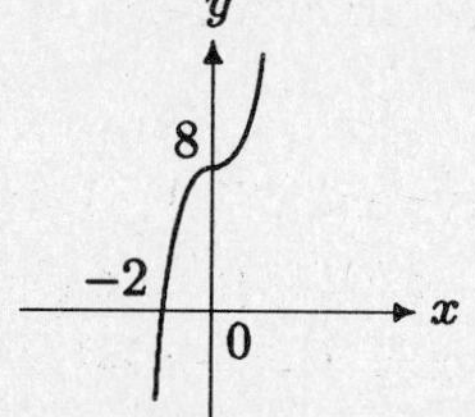

Exercise 11

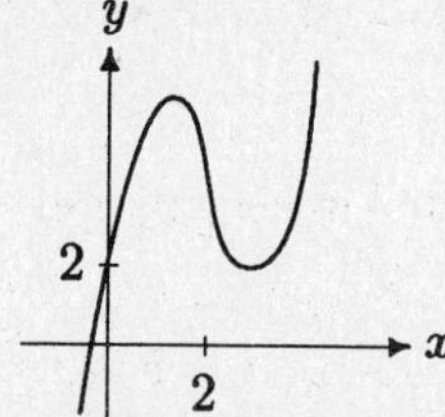

Exercise 12

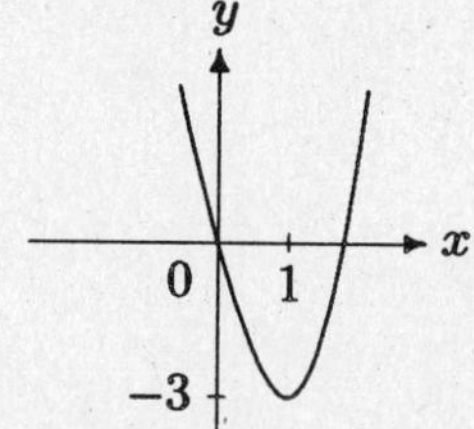

Exercise 13

11. $f'(x) = 3x^2$; $f''(x) = 6x$. Thus the graph is concave upward on $(0, \infty)$ and concave downward on $(-\infty, 0)$.

12. $f'(x) = 3x^2 - 12x + 9 = 3(x-3)(x-1)$; $f''(x) = 6x - 12 = 6(x-2)$. Thus the graph is concave upward on $(2, \infty)$ and concave downward on $(-\infty, 2)$. Also, $f(1) = 6$ is a relative maximum value, and $f(3) = 2$ is a relative minimum value.

13. $g'(x) = 4x^3 - 4 = 4(x-1)(x^2+x+1)$; $g''(x) = 12x^2$. Thus the graph is concave upward on $(-\infty, \infty)$. Also, $g(1) = -3$ is the minimum value of g.

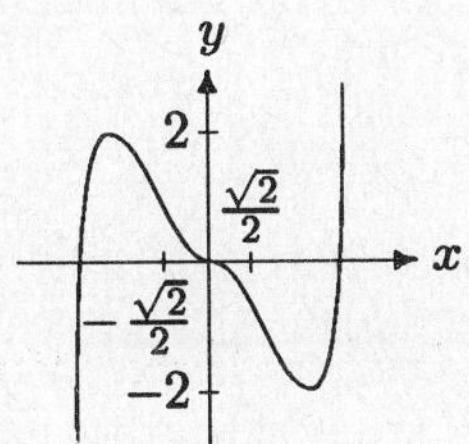

Exercise 14

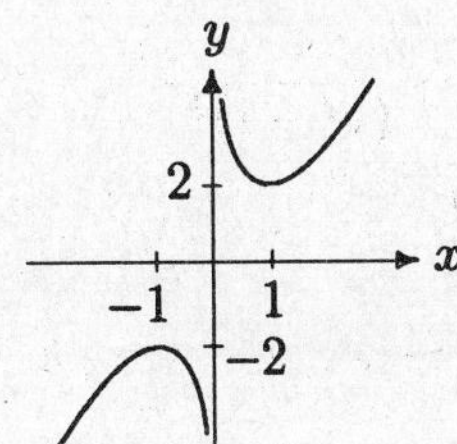

Exercise 15

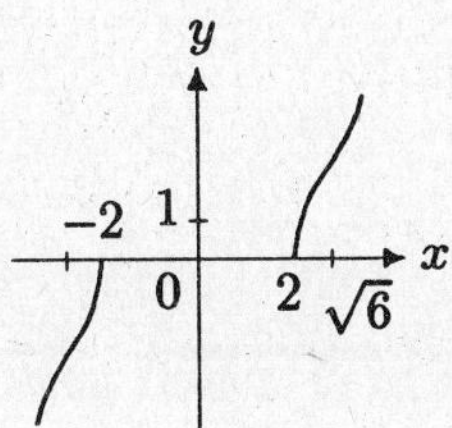

Exercise 16

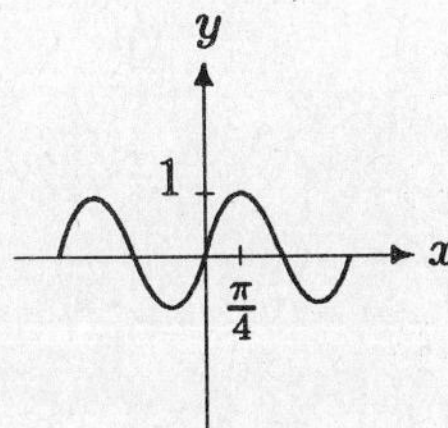

Exercise 17

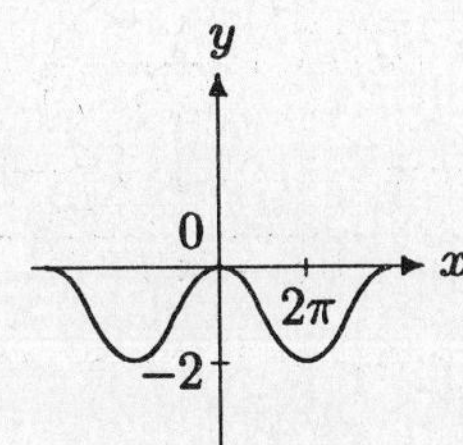

Exercise 18

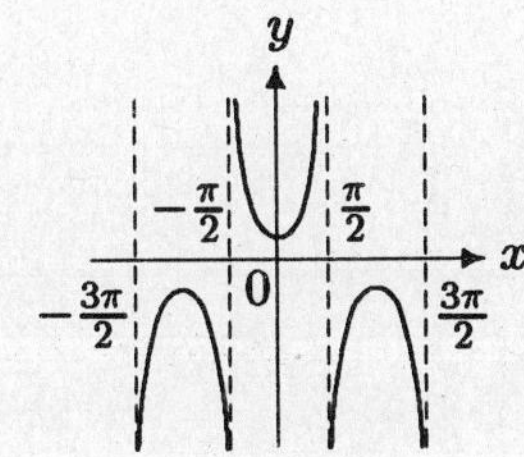

Exercise 19

14. $g'(x) = 15x^4 - 15x^2 = 15x^2(x+1)(x-1)$; $g''(x) = 60x^3 - 30x = 30x(2x^2 - 1)$. Thus the graph is concave upward on $(-\sqrt{2}/2, 0)$ and $(\sqrt{2}/2, \infty)$ and concave downward on $(-\infty, -\sqrt{2}/2)$ and $(0, \sqrt{2}/2)$. Also, $g(-1) = 2$ is a relative maximum value, and $g(1) = -2$ is a relative minimum value.

15. $f'(x) = 1-(1/x)^2$; $f''(x) = 2/x^3$. Thus the graph is concave upward on $(0, \infty)$ and concave downward on $(-\infty, 0)$. Also, $f(-1) = -2$ is a relative maximum value, and $f(1) = 2$ is a relative minimum value.

16. Note: The domain of f consists of all numbers x such that $|x| \geq 2$.

$$f'(x) = \sqrt{x^2-4} + \frac{x^2}{\sqrt{x^2-4}} = \frac{2(x^2-2)}{\sqrt{x^2-4}}; f''(x) = \frac{4x\sqrt{x^2-4} - (2x^3-4x)/\sqrt{x^2-4}}{x^2-4} = \frac{2x(x^2-6)}{(x^2-4)^{3/2}}.$$

Thus the graph is concave upward on $(-\sqrt{6}, -2)$ and $(\sqrt{6}, \infty)$ and concave downward on $(-\infty, -\sqrt{6})$ and $(2, \sqrt{6})$.

17. Refer to Example 4 and the paragraph following it. We have $f'(x) = 2\cos 2x$ and $f''(x) = -4\sin 2x = -4f(x)$. Thus the graph is concave upward on $(n\pi + \pi/2, (n+1)\pi)$ for any integer n and concave downward on $(n\pi, n\pi + \pi/2)$ for any integer n. Furthermore, for any integer n, $f(n\pi + \pi/4) = 1$ is the maximum value, and $f(n\pi - \pi/4) = -1$ the minimum value of f.

18. $f'(x) = -\frac{1}{2}\sin(x/2)$; $f''(x) = -\frac{1}{4}\cos(x/2)$. Thus the graph is concave upward on $((2n-1)\pi, (2n+1)\pi)$ for any odd integer n and concave downward on $((2n-1)\pi, (2n+1)\pi)$ for any even integer n. For any integer n, $f(4n\pi) = 0$ is the maximum value, and $f((4n+2)\pi) = -2$ is the minimum value of f.

19. $f'(x) = \sec x \tan x$; $f''(x) = \sec x \tan^2 x + \sec^3 x = \sec x\left((\sec^2 x - 1) + \sec^2 x\right) = \sec x\,(2\sec^2 x - 1)$. Since $|\sec x| \geq 1$ for all x in the domain, $2\sec^2 x - 1 > 0$ for all x in the domain, so f and f'' have the same sign. Thus the graph of f is concave upward on $(-\pi/2 + 2n\pi, \pi/2 + 2n\pi)$ and concave downward on $(\pi/2 + 2n\pi, 3\pi/2 + 2n\pi)$ for any integer n. Also $f(2n\pi) = 1$ is a relative minimum value and $f((2n+1)\pi) = -1$ is a relative maximum value of f.

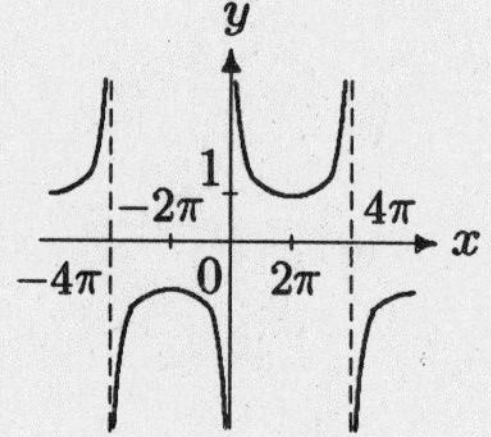

Exercise 20

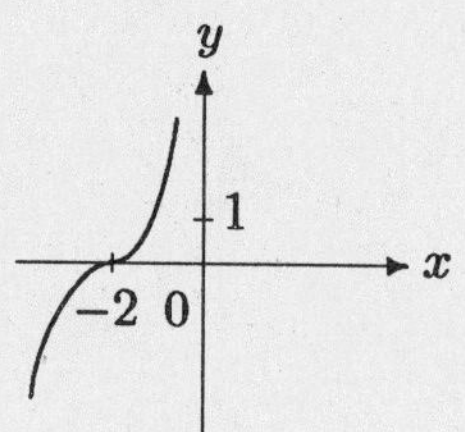

Exercise 21

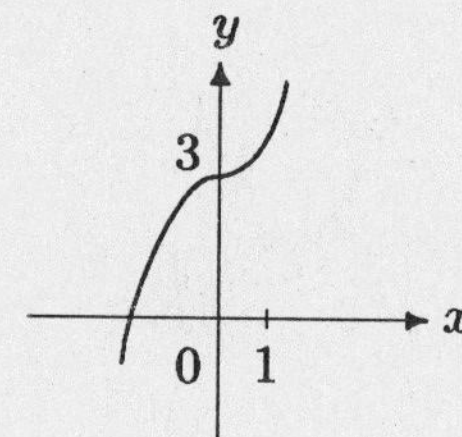

Exercise 22

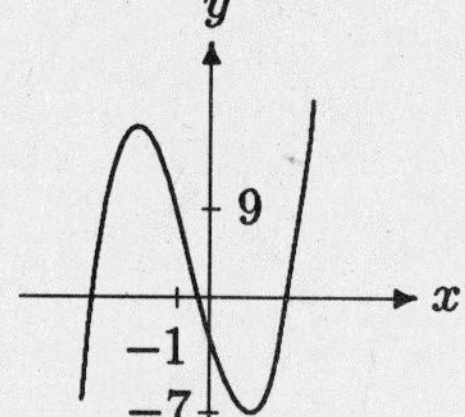

Exercise 23

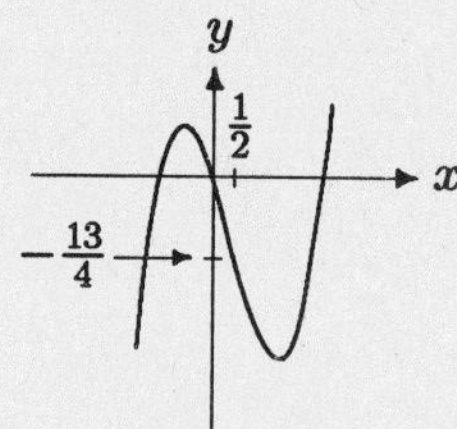

Exercise 24

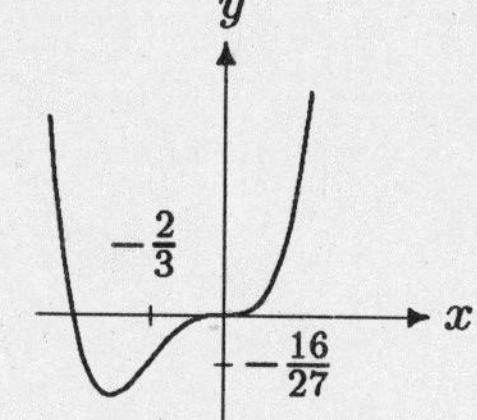

Exercise 25

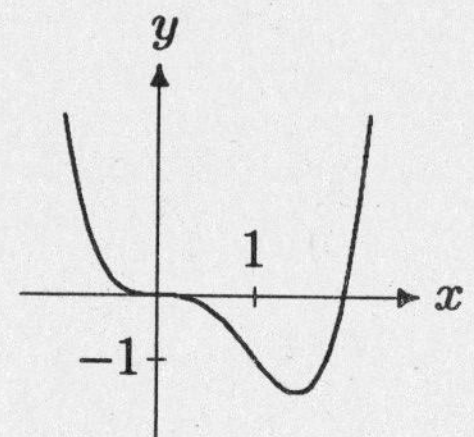

Exercise 26

20. $f'(x) = \dfrac{-1}{4}\csc\dfrac{x}{4}\cot\dfrac{x}{4}$

$$f''(x) = \frac{1}{16}\left(\csc\frac{x}{4}\cot^2\frac{x}{4} + \csc^3\frac{x}{4}\right) = \frac{1}{16}\csc\frac{x}{4}\left(\left(\csc^2\frac{x}{4} - 1\right) + \csc^2\frac{x}{4}\right) = \frac{1}{16}\csc\frac{x}{4}\left(2\csc^2\frac{x}{4} - 1\right)$$

Since $|\csc x| \geq 1$ for all x in the domain, $2\csc^2(x/4) - 1 > 0$ for all x in the domain, so f and f'' have the same sign. Thus the graph of f is concave upward on $(8n\pi, 8n\pi + 4\pi)$ and concave downward on $(8n\pi + 4\pi, 8n\pi + 8\pi)$ for any integer n. Also $f(8n\pi + 2\pi) = 1$ is a relative minimum value and $f(8n\pi + 6\pi) = -1$ is a relative maximum value of f.

21. $f'(x) = 3(x+2)^2$ and $f''(x) = 6(x+2)$. Thus f'' changes sign at -2, so $(-2, 0)$ is an inflection point.

22. $f'(x) = 3x^2$ and $f''(x) = 6x$. Thus f'' changes sign at 0, so $(0, 3)$ is an inflection point.

23. $f'(x) = 3x^2 + 6x - 9 = 3(x+3)(x-1)$ and $f''(x) = 6x + 6 = 6(x+1)$. Thus f'' changes sign at -1, so $(-1, 9)$ is an inflection point. Also $f(-3) = 25$ is a relative maximum value and $f(1) = -7$ is a relative minimum value of f.

24. $f'(x) = 3x^2 - 3x - 6 = 3(x-2)(x+1)$ and $f''(x) = 6x - 3 = 3(2x-1)$. Thus f'' changes sign at $\frac{1}{2}$, so $(\frac{1}{2}, -\frac{13}{4})$ is an inflection point. Also, $f(-1) = \frac{7}{2}$ is a relative maximum value and $f(2) = -10$ is a relative minimum value of f.

25. $g'(x) = 12x^3 + 12x^2 = 12x^2(x+1)$ and $g''(x) = 36x^2 + 24x = 12x(3x+2)$. Thus g'' changes sign at 0 and $-\frac{2}{3}$, so $(0, 0)$ and $(-\frac{2}{3}, -\frac{16}{27})$ are inflection points. Also $g(-1) = -1$ is the minimum value of g.

26. $g'(x) = 4x^3 - 6x^2 = 2x^2(2x-3)$ and $g''(x) = 12x^2 - 12x = 12x(x-1)$. Thus g'' changes sign at 0 and 1, so $(0, 0)$ and $(1, -1)$ are inflection points. Also $g(\frac{3}{2}) = -\frac{27}{16}$ is the minimum value of g.

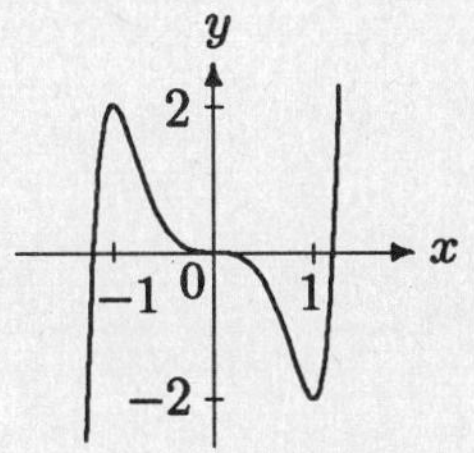

Exercise 27

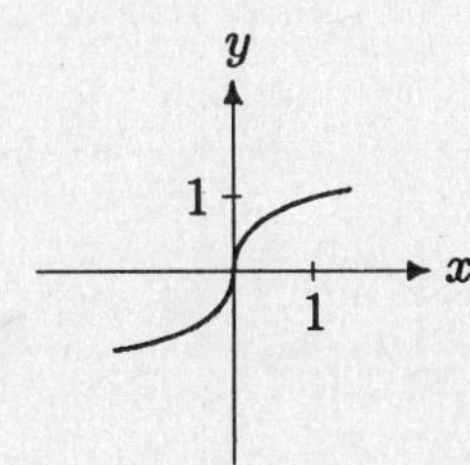

Exercise 28

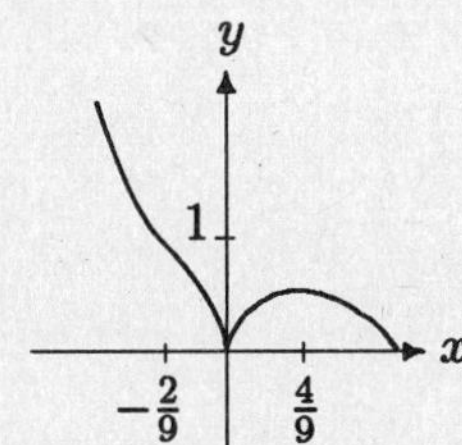

Exercise 29

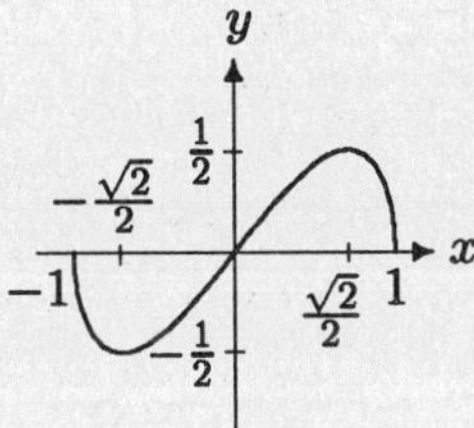

Exercise 30

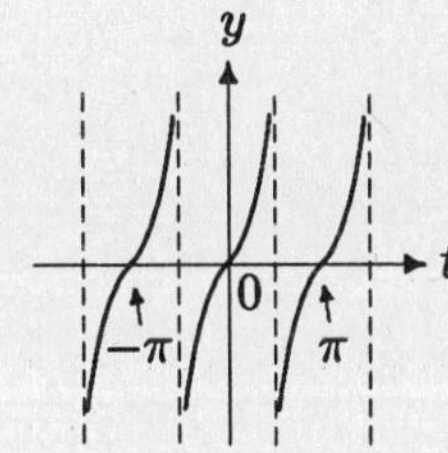

Exercise 31

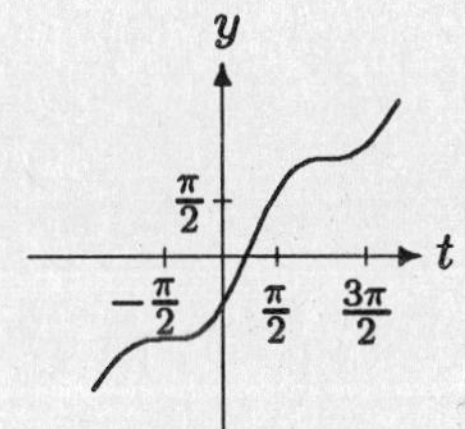

Exercise 32

27. $g'(x) = 9x^8 - 9x^2 = 9x^2(x^6 - 1)$ and $g''(x) = 72x^7 - 18x = 18x(4x^6 - 1)$. Thus g'' changes sign at $-1/\sqrt[3]{2}$, 0, and $1/\sqrt[3]{2}$, so that $(-1/\sqrt[3]{2}, \frac{11}{8})$, $(0,0)$, and $(1/\sqrt[3]{2}, -\frac{11}{8})$ are inflection points. Also $g(-1) = 2$ is a relative maximum value and $g(1) = -2$ is a relative minimum value of g.

28. $g'(x) = \frac{1}{3}x^{-2/3}$ and $g''(x) = -\frac{2}{9}x^{-5/3}$. Thus g'' changes sign at 0. Since the graph of g has a vertical tangent at $(0,0)$, it follows that $(0,0)$ is an inflection point.

29. $g'(x) = \frac{4}{9}x^{-1/3} - x^{2/3} = x^{-1/3}(\frac{4}{9} - x)$ and $g''(x) = -\frac{4}{27}x^{-4/3} - \frac{2}{3}x^{-1/3} = -\frac{2}{3}x^{-4/3}(\frac{2}{9} + x)$ for $x \neq 0$. Since g'' changes from positive to negative at $-\frac{2}{9}$, the point $(-\frac{2}{9}, g(-\frac{2}{9})) = (-\frac{2}{9}, \frac{4}{5}(\frac{2}{9})^{2/3})$ is a point of inflection. Finally $g(\frac{4}{9}) = \frac{2}{5}(\frac{4}{9})^{2/3}$ is a relative maximum value of g.

30. The domain of g is $[-1, 1]$.

$$g'(x) = \sqrt{1 - x^2} - \frac{x^2}{\sqrt{1 - x^2}} = \frac{1 - 2x^2}{\sqrt{1 - x^2}}$$

$$g''(x) = \frac{-4x\sqrt{1 - x^2} - (1 - 2x^2)(-x/\sqrt{1 - x^2})}{1 - x^2} = \frac{x(2x^2 - 3)}{(1 - x^2)^{3/2}}$$

Thus g'' changes sign at 0, so $(0,0)$ is an inflection point. Also $g(\sqrt{2}/2) = \frac{1}{2}$ is the maximum value and $g(-\sqrt{2}/2) = -\frac{1}{2}$ is the minimum value of g.

31. $f'(t) = \sec^2 t$ and $f''(t) = 2\sec^2 t \tan t$. Thus f'' changes sign at $n\pi$, for any integer n, so $(n\pi, 0)$ is an inflection point for any integer n.

32. $f'(t) = 1 + \sin t$ and $f''(t) = \cos t$. Thus f'' changes sign at $\pi/2 + n\pi$, for any integer n, so $(\pi/2 + n\pi, \pi/2 + n\pi)$ is an inflection point for any integer n. Since $f'(t) > 0$ if $t \neq 2n\pi + 3\pi/2$, f is increasing.

33. $f'(x) = 7x^6 - 5x^4 + 3x^2 + 6x$, $f''(x) = 42x^5 - 20x^3 + 6x + 6$, and $f^{(3)}(x) = 210x^4 - 60x^2 + 6$. By the Newton-Raphson method applied to f'', we find that f'' changes sign at $c \approx -.7492409172$, so $(c, f(c))$ is an inflection point.

34. $f'(x) = 2x\cos x^2$, $f''(x) = 2\cos x^2 - 4x^2 \sin x^2$, and $f^{(3)}(x) = -4x\sin x^2 - 8x\sin x^2 - 8x^3\cos x^2 = -12x\sin x^2 - 8x^3\cos x^2$. By the Newton-Raphson method applied to f'', we find that f'' changes sign at $c \approx .8082519329$ and at $c \approx -.8082519329$. Thus $(c, f(c))$ is an inflection point for these values of c.

35. $f'(x) = e^x - \cos x$, $f''(x) = e^x + \sin x$, and $f^{(3)}(x) = e^x + \cos x$. By the Newton-Raphson method applied to f'', we find that f'' changes sign at $c \approx -.588532744$, so $(c, f(c))$ is an inflection point.

36. a. Concave upward on $(0, 2)$ and concave downward on $(-2, 0)$.

    b. Since f' is increasing on $(-2, -1)$ and $(1, 2)$, we know that f'' is positive on $(-2, -1)$ and $(1, 2)$. Thus the graph of f is concave upward on $(-2, -1)$ and $(1, 2)$. Similarly, since f' is decreasing on $(-1, 1)$, we know that f'' is negative on $(-1, 1)$ and hence the graph of f is concave downward on $(-1, 1)$.

    c. Since f'' is positive on $(-2, 0)$ and negative on $(0, 2)$, the graph of f is concave upward on $(-2, 0)$ and concave downward on $(0, 2)$.

37. a. Since f' is positive on (a, c), it follows that f is increasing on $[a, c]$. Therefore $f(c) > f(b) > f(a)$. Since f' is negative on $[c, d]$, it follows that f is decreasing on $[c, d]$. Therefore $f(c) \geq f(d)$. Thus f has the largest value at c.

    b. From the solution of part (a), only $f(a)$ or $f(d)$ could be the smallest.

    c. Since $f'' = (f')'$, we consider the slope of f' at a, b, c, d. At c and d the slope is negative. At a and b the slope is positive and larger at b. Thus f'' is largest at b.

    d. Since the graph of f' is steeper at d and both $f''(c)$ and $f''(d)$ are negative, it follows that $f''(d)$ is the smallest value of f'' at a, b, c, and d.

    e. The graph of f has an inflection point at a number r if f'' changes from positive to negative at r. This is the case if f' has a relative maximum at r. This is true if $r = e$. Thus f has an inflection point at e.

38. a. Since $f'(x)$ is the slope of f at x, we consider the slope of f at a, b, c, and d. The largest is at b, so $f'(b)$ is the largest of $f'(a)$, $f'(b)$, $f'(c)$, and $f'(d)$.

    b. Proceeding as in part (a), we see that $f'(d)$ is the smallest of $f'(a)$, $f'(b)$, $f'(c)$, and $f'(d)$.

    c. The graph of f changes from concave upward to concave downward at b, and from concave downward to concave upward at d, so $(b, f(b))$ and $(d, f(d))$ are inflection points.

39. a.

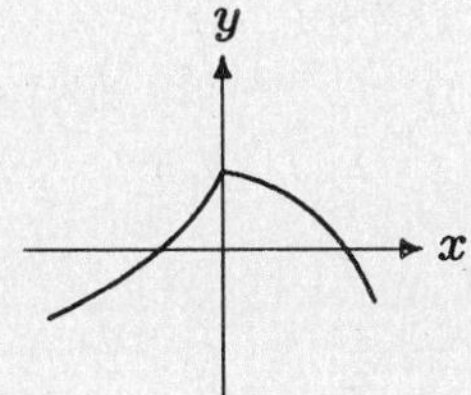

b.

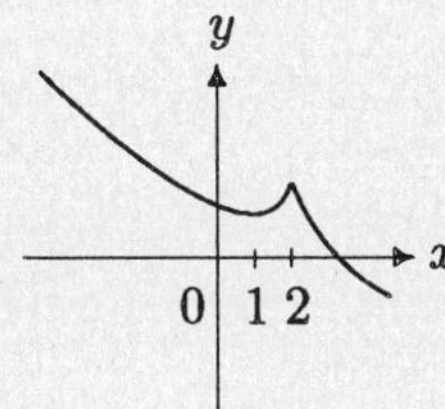

c.

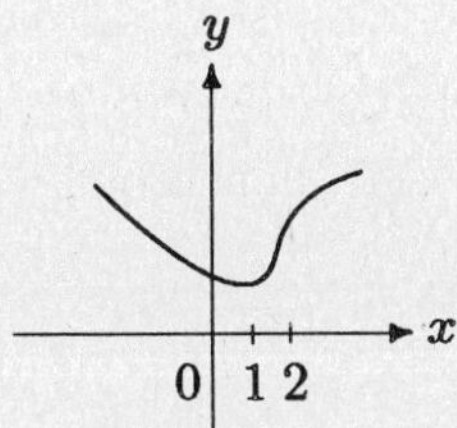

d.

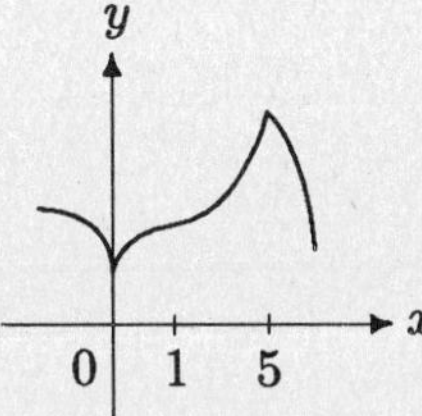

40. $f'(x) = \dfrac{-2x}{(1+x^2)^2}$; $f''(x) = \dfrac{-2(1+x^2)^2 - (-2x)2(1+x^2)(2x)}{(1+x^2)^4} = \dfrac{6x^2-2}{(1+x^2)^3}$; $f''(0) = -2$; $g'(x) = -xe^{-x^2/2}$; $g''(x) = -e^{-x^2/2} + (-x)e^{-x^2/2}(-x) = (x^2-1)e^{-x^2/2}$; $g''(0) = -1$. Thus $|f''(0)| > |g''(0)|$, which corresponds to the greater concavity of the graph of f at $(0,1)$ than that of g.

41. a. Since $f(x) = f(-x)$, $f'(x) = -f'(-x)$ and $f''(x) = f''(-x)$. Thus the graph is concave upward on $(-\infty, 0)$.

    b. Since $f(x) = -f(-x)$, $f'(x) = f'(-x)$ and $f''(x) = -f''(-x)$. Thus the graph is concave downward on $(-\infty, 0)$.

42. Let $g = -f$. Then $g' = -f'$ and $g'' = -f''$. Thus the concavity of the graph of $-f$ is the opposite of the concavity of the graph of f.

43. Let $f(x) = g(x) = x^2 - 1$, for $-1 < x < 1$. Then $f''(x) = g''(x) = 2$, so the graphs of f and g are concave upward on $(-1,1)$. If $k(x) = f(x)g(x) = x^4 - 2x^2 + 1$, then $k'(x) = 4x^3 - 4x$ and $k''(x) = 12x^2 - 4$, so that $k''(x) < 0$ for $-1/\sqrt{3} < x < 1/\sqrt{3}$. Thus the graph of k is concave downward on $(-1/\sqrt{3}, 1/\sqrt{3})$.

44. For $x \neq 0$, $f'(x) = (\frac{1}{3})x^{-2/3}$ and $f''(x) = (-\frac{2}{9})x^{-5/3}$. Since

$$\lim_{x\to 0} \frac{f(x) - f(0)}{x - 0} = \lim_{x\to 0} x^{-2/3} = \infty,$$

$f'(0)$ does not exist, although the line $x = 0$ is tangent to the graph of f at $(0,0)$. Since $f'(0)$ does not exist, $f''(0)$ cannot exist. But f'' changes sign at 0, so $(0, f(0)) = (0,0)$ is an inflection point.

45. Any second degree polynomial can be given by $f(x) = ax^2 + bx + c$. Then $f'(x) = 2ax + b$ and $f''(x) = 2a$, so that f'' does not change sign. Thus the graph of a second degree polynomial does not have an inflection point.

46. $f'(x) = 3ax^2 + 2bx + c$ and $f''(x) = 6ax + 2b$. Thus f'' changes sign only at $-b/(3a)$, so

$$\left(-\frac{b}{3a}, \frac{2b^3}{27a^2} - \frac{bc}{3a} + d\right)$$

is the only inflection point.

47. $f'(x) = 5x^4 - 3cx^2$; $f''(x) = 20x^3 - 6cx = x(20x^2 - 6c)$. If $c = 0$ then $f''(x) = 20x^3$, and f'' changes sign at 0. If $c \neq 0$ then $20x^2 - 6c \neq 0$ for all x such that $x^2 < \frac{3}{10}|c|$, that is, $|x| < \sqrt{\frac{3}{10}|c|}$, so f'' changes sign at 0. Thus regardless of the value of c, f'' changes sign at 0, so f has an inflection point at $(0, 0)$.

48. a. $f'(x) = 4ax^3 + 3bx^2 + 2cx + d$; $f''(x) = 12ax^2 + 6bx + 2c$. If f'' has two zeros, then f'' will change sign at each of the zeros, so there will be two inflection points on the graph of f. By the quadratic formula, $12ax^2 + 6bx + 2c$ has two zeros if $(6b)^2 - 4(12a)(2c) > 0$. Thus if $36b^2 - 96ac > 0$, or equivalently $9b^2 - 24ac > 0$, then there are two inflection points on the graph of f.

    b. If f'' has no zeros or one zero, then f'' will not change sign and hence there will be no inflection points on the graph of f. By the quadratic formula and part (a), this occurs if $9b^2 - 24ac \leq 0$.

    c. Notice that as a polynomial of degree 2, f'' has two, one, or no zeros. If f'' has two zeros, then the graph of f has two inflection points by part (a). If f'' has no zeros or one zero, then there are no inflection points by part (b). Therefore the graph of f has either two or no inflection points.

49. The graph of f has either one or three inflection points.

50. $f'(x) = nx^{n-1}$ and $f''(x) = n(n-1)x^{n-2}$. For $n \geq 2$, f'' changes sign at zero if $n - 2$ is a positive odd integer, that is, if n is an odd integer greater than 1. Thus $(0, 0)$ is a point of inflection of f if n is an odd integer greater than 1. If n is an even integer, $f''(x) \geq 0$ for all x, so there is no point of inflection. Thus there is at most one inflection point. If $n = 1$, then $f(x) = x$, so f has no inflection point.

51. If f is a polynomial of degree n, $n \geq 2$, then f'' is a polynomial of degree $n - 2$. Since f'' is defined for all x and has at most $n - 2$ real zeros, the graph of f can have at most $n - 2$ inflection points.

52. a. $f'(x) = \dfrac{x\cos x - \sin x}{x^2}$

$$f''(x) = \frac{x^2(\cos x - x\sin x - \cos x) - 2x(x\cos x - \sin x)}{x^4} = \frac{-x^2\sin x - 2x\cos x + 2\sin x}{x^3} = \frac{g(x)}{x^3}$$

    b. Since

$$g'(x) = -2x\sin x - x^2\cos x - 2\cos x + 2x\sin x + 2\cos x = -x^2\cos x$$

    it follows that $g'(x) < 0$ for $0 < x < \pi/2$. Thus g is decreasing on $(0, \pi/2)$ by Theorem 4.7, so $g(x) < g(0) = 0$ for x in $(0, \pi/2)$. Consequently the graph of f is concave downward on $(0, \pi/2)$.

    c. The graph of f is concave upward on $(\pi/2 + 2n\pi, 3\pi/2 + 2n\pi)$ and concave downward on $(3\pi/2 + 2n\pi, 5\pi/2 + 2n\pi)$, for any nonnegative integer n. Thus

$$\left(\frac{\pi}{2}+2n\pi, \frac{1}{\pi/2+2n\pi}\right) \quad \text{and} \quad \left(\frac{3\pi}{2}+2n\pi, \frac{-1}{3\pi/2+2n\pi}\right)$$

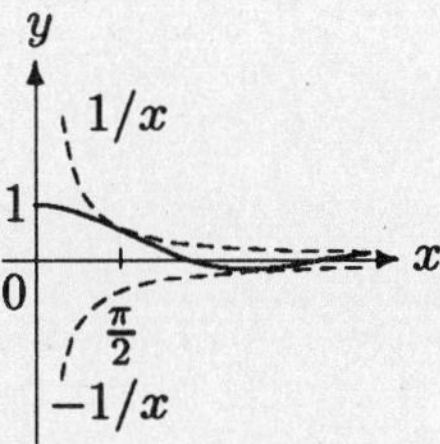

are inflection points. The graph of f touches the graph of $y = 1/x$ at $(x, f(x))$ if $\sin x = 1$, that is, for $x = \pi/2 + 2n\pi$ for any positive integer n. Similarly, the graph of f touches the graph of $y = -1/x$ at $(x, f(x))$ if $x = -\pi/2 + 2n\pi$ for any positive integer n.

53. Suppose that $f''(c) > 0$. Since f'' is continuous on an open interval containing c, there is an open interval I centered at c such that $f'' > 0$ on I. Thus f'' does not change sign at c, and hence f does not have an inflection point at $(c, f(c))$, as assumed. Similarly, the assumption that $f''(c) < 0$ leads to a contradiction. Therefore $f''(c) = 0$.

54. a. By (1) in Section 1.3, $h(t) = -4.9t^2 + v_0t + h_0$. Thus $h'(t) = -9.8t + v_0$ and $h''(t) = -9.8 < 0$ for all t. Therefore the graph of h is concave downward.

b. Since $v(t) = h'(t) = -9.8t + v_0$, the velocity constantly decreases.

4.8 Limits at Infinity

1. $\displaystyle \lim_{x\to\infty} \frac{2}{x-3} = \lim_{x\to\infty} \frac{2/x}{1-3x} = \frac{0}{1-0} = 0$

2. $\displaystyle \lim_{x\to\infty} \frac{4}{2-x} = \lim_{x\to\infty} \frac{4/x}{2/x-1} = \frac{0}{0-1} = 0$

3. $\displaystyle \lim_{x\to\infty} \frac{x}{3x+2} = \lim_{x\to\infty} \frac{1}{3+2/x} = \frac{1}{3+0} = \frac{1}{3}$

4. $\displaystyle \lim_{x\to\infty} \frac{4x^2}{\sqrt{2}\,x-3} = \lim_{x\to\infty} \left(\frac{4x}{\sqrt{2}\,x-3}\cdot x\right) = \lim_{x\to\infty} \left(\frac{4}{\sqrt{2}-3/x}\cdot x\right) = \infty$

5. $\displaystyle \lim_{x\to\infty} \frac{2x^2+x-1}{x^2-x+4} = \lim_{x\to\infty} \frac{2+1/x-1/x^2}{1-1/x+4/x^2} = \frac{2+0-0}{1-0+0} = 2$

6. $\displaystyle \lim_{t\to\infty} \frac{(t-1)(2t+1)}{(3t-2)(t+4)} = \lim_{t\to\infty} \frac{(1-1/t)(2+1/t)}{(3-2/t)(1+4/t)} = \frac{(1-0)(2+0)}{(3-0)(1+0)} = \frac{2}{3}$

7. $\displaystyle \lim_{t\to\infty} \frac{t}{t^{1/2}+2t^{-1/2}} = \lim_{t\to\infty} \left(\frac{t}{t+2}\cdot t^{1/2}\right) = \lim_{t\to\infty} \left(\frac{1}{1+2/t}\cdot t^{1/2}\right) = \infty$

8. Since $-1/x \le (\sin x)/x \le 1/x$ for $x > 0$ and since $\lim_{x\to\infty}(-1/x) = 0 = \lim_{x\to\infty} 1/x$, the Squeezing Theorem for limits at ∞ implies $\lim_{x\to\infty}(\sin x)/x = 0$.

9. Since

$$-\frac{1}{\sqrt{x^2-1}} \le \frac{\cos x}{\sqrt{x^2-1}} \le \frac{1}{\sqrt{x^2-1}} \quad \text{for } x < -1$$

and since

$$\lim_{x\to-\infty} -\frac{1}{\sqrt{x^2-1}} = \lim_{x\to-\infty} \frac{1}{\sqrt{x^2-1}} = 0$$

the Squeezing Theorem for limits at $-\infty$ implies that $\lim_{x\to-\infty}(\cos x)/\sqrt{x^2-1} = 0$.

10. $\lim_{x\to-\infty} \dfrac{x-\frac{1}{2}}{\frac{1}{2}x+1} = \lim_{x\to-\infty} \dfrac{1-1/(2x)}{1/2+1/x} = \dfrac{1-0}{\frac{1}{2}+0} = 2$

11. $\lim_{x\to-\infty} \dfrac{x^2}{4x^3-9} = \lim_{x\to-\infty} \dfrac{1/x}{4-9/x^3} = \dfrac{0}{4-0} = 0$

12. $\lim_{x\to-\infty} \dfrac{2-3x-4x^2}{3x^2+6x+10} = \lim_{x\to-\infty} \dfrac{2/x^2-3/x-4}{3+6/x+10/x^2} = \dfrac{0-0-4}{3+0+0} = -\dfrac{4}{3}$

13. For $x > \frac{1}{2}$,

$$x - \sqrt{4x^2-1} = (x - \sqrt{4x^2-1})\frac{x+\sqrt{4x^2-1}}{x+\sqrt{4x^2-1}} = \frac{1-3x^2}{x+\sqrt{4x^2-1}} = \frac{1/x-3x}{1+\sqrt{4-1/x^2}}$$

so

$$\lim_{x\to\infty}(x-\sqrt{4x^2-1}) = \lim_{x\to\infty}\frac{1/x-3x}{1+\sqrt{4-1/x^2}} = -\infty.$$

The exercise can also be solved as follows:

$$\lim_{x\to\infty}(x-\sqrt{4x^2-1}) = \lim_{x\to\infty}\left(x - x\sqrt{4-\frac{1}{x^2}}\right) = \lim_{x\to\infty} x\left(1-\sqrt{4-\frac{1}{x^2}}\right) = -\infty.$$

14. $\lim_{x\to\infty}\left(3\sqrt{\dfrac{x^2}{4}-1}-\dfrac{3}{2}x\right) = \lim_{x\to\infty}\left(\dfrac{3}{2}\sqrt{x^2-4}-\dfrac{3}{2}x\right) = \dfrac{3}{2}\lim_{x\to\infty}(\sqrt{x^2-4}-x) = \dfrac{3}{2}\cdot 0 = 0$ by Example 3.

15. Since $\lim_{x\to\infty} 1/x = 0$, the Substitution Theorem for limits at ∞ (with $y = 1/x$) implies that $\lim_{x\to\infty} \tan 1/x = \lim_{y\to 0^+} \tan y = \lim_{y\to 0} \tan y = \tan 0 = 0$.

16. Since $\lim_{x\to-\infty} 1/x = 0$, the Substitution Theorem for limits at ∞ (with $y = 1/x$) implies that

$$\lim_{x\to-\infty} x\tan\frac{1}{x} = \lim_{y\to 0^-}\frac{\tan y}{y} = \lim_{y\to 0^-}\left(\frac{\sin y}{y}\cdot\frac{1}{\cos y}\right) = \left(\lim_{y\to 0}\frac{\sin y}{y}\right)\left(\frac{1}{\lim_{y\to 0}\cos y}\right) = 1\cdot\frac{1}{1} = 1.$$

17. Since $\lim_{x\to\infty} e^x = \infty$, we have $\lim_{x\to\infty} e^{-x} = \lim_{x\to\infty} 1/e^x = 1/\lim_{x\to\infty} e^x = 0$.

18. Since $\lim_{x\to-\infty} x^2 = \infty$, it follows from the Substitution Theorem for limits at ∞ (with $y = x^2$) and the solution of Exercise 17 that $\lim_{x\to-\infty} e^{-(x^2)} = \lim_{y\to\infty} e^{-y} = 0$.

19. Since $-1/x > 0$ if $x < 0$, and since $\lim_{x\to-\infty}(-1/x) = 0$, the Substitution Theorem for limits at ∞ (with $y = -1/x$) implies that $\lim_{x\to-\infty} e^{-1/x} = \lim_{y\to 0^+} e^y = \lim_{y\to 0} e^y = e^0 = 1$.

20. Since $1/x > 0$ for $x > 0$, and since $\lim_{x\to 0^+} \ln x = -\infty$, the Substitution Theorem for limits at ∞ (with $y = 1/x$) implies that $\lim_{x\to\infty} \ln(1/x) = \lim_{y\to 0^+} \ln y = -\infty$.

21. Since $\lim_{x\to\infty} \ln x = \infty$, the Substitution Theorem for limits at ∞ (with $y = \ln x$) implies that $\lim_{x\to\infty} 1/\ln x = \lim_{y\to\infty} 1/y = 0$.

22. Since $\lim_{x\to\infty} e^x = \infty$ and $\lim_{x\to\infty} \ln x = \infty$, we have $\lim_{x\to\infty} e^x \ln x = \infty$.

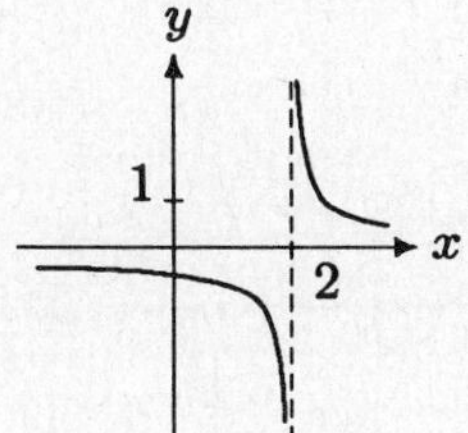

Exercise 23

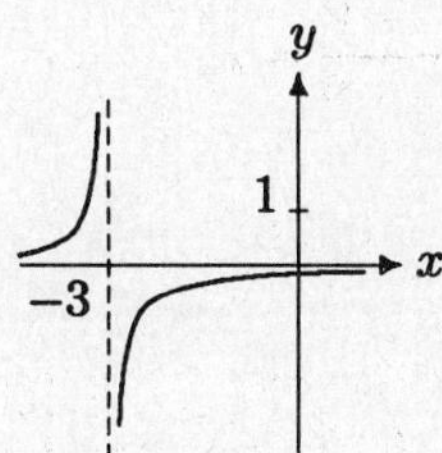

Exercise 24

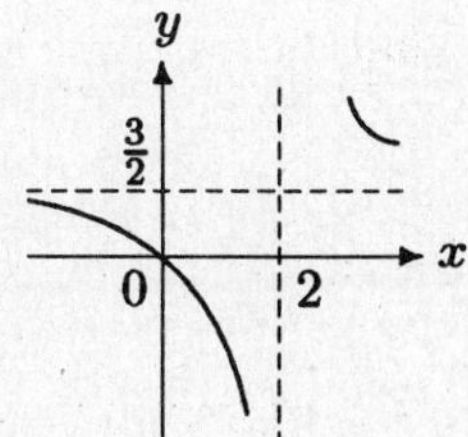

Exercise 25

23. $\lim\limits_{x\to\infty} \dfrac{1}{x-2} = \lim\limits_{x\to-\infty} \dfrac{1}{x-2} = 0$

so $y = 0$ is a horizontal asymptote; $f'(x) = -1/(x-2)^2 < 0$ for $x \neq 2$, so f is decreasing on $(-\infty, 2)$ and $(2, \infty)$; $f''(x) = 2/(x-2)^3$, so the graph of f is concave upward on $(2, \infty)$ and concave downward on $(-\infty, 2)$;

$$\lim_{x\to2^+} \frac{1}{x-2} = \infty \quad \text{and} \quad \lim_{x\to2^-} \frac{1}{x-2} = -\infty$$

so $x = 2$ is a vertical asymptote.

24. $\lim\limits_{x\to\infty} -\dfrac{1}{x+3} = \lim\limits_{x\to-\infty} -\dfrac{1}{x+3} = 0$

so $y = 0$ is a horizontal asymptote; $f'(x) = 1/(x+3)^2 > 0$ for $x \neq -3$, so f is increasing on $(-\infty, -3)$ and $(-3, \infty)$; $f''(x) = -2/(x+3)^3$, so the graph of f is concave upward on $(-\infty, -3)$ and concave downward on $(-3, \infty)$;

$$\lim_{x\to-3^+} -\frac{1}{x+3} = -\infty \quad \text{and} \quad \lim_{x\to-3^-} -\frac{1}{x+3} = \infty$$

so $x = -3$ is a vertical asymptote.

25. $\lim\limits_{x\to\infty} \dfrac{3x}{2x-4} = \lim\limits_{x\to-\infty} \dfrac{3x}{2x-4} = \dfrac{3}{2}$

so $y = \frac{3}{2}$ is a horizontal asymptote;

$$f'(x) = \frac{3(2x-4) - 3x(2)}{(2x-4)^2} = \frac{-12}{(2x-4)^2} = \frac{-3}{(x-2)^2} \quad \text{for } x \neq 2$$

so f is decreasing on $(-\infty, 2)$ and $(2, \infty)$; $f''(x) = 6/(x-2)^3$, so the graph of f is concave upward on $(2, \infty)$ and concave downward on $(-\infty, 2)$;

$$\lim_{x\to2^+} \frac{3x}{2x-4} = \infty \quad \text{and} \quad \lim_{x\to2^-} \frac{3x}{2x-4} = -\infty$$

so $x = 2$ is a vertical asymptote.

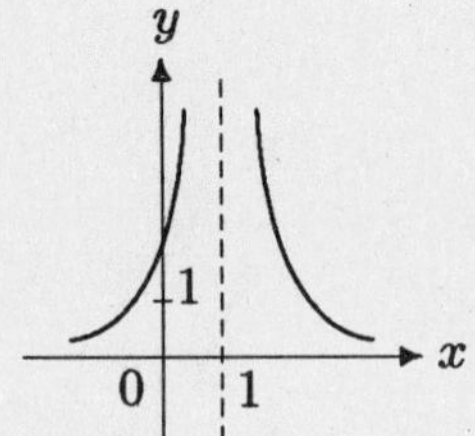

Exercise 26

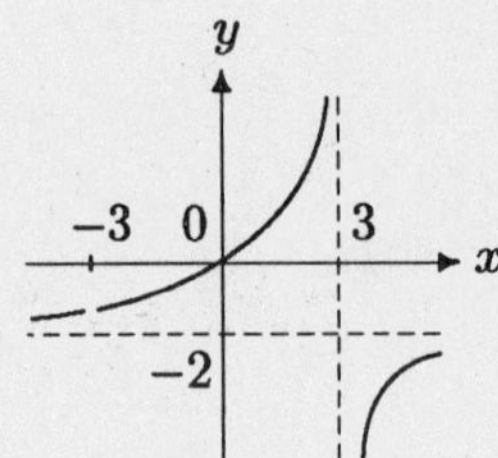

Exercise 27

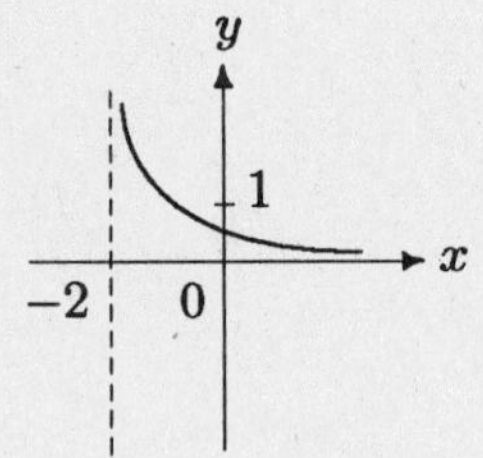

Exercise 28

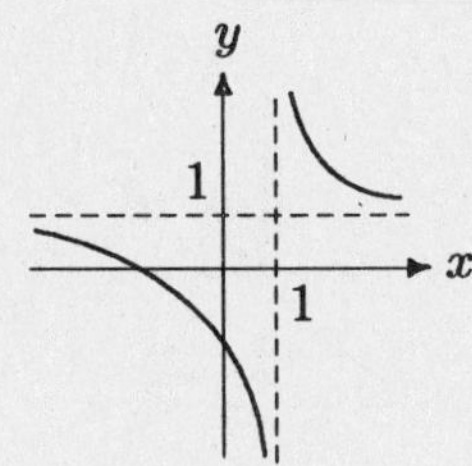

Exercise 29

26. $\lim_{x\to\infty} \dfrac{4}{(1-x)^2} = \lim_{x\to-\infty} \dfrac{4}{(1-x)^2} = 0$
so $y = 0$ is a horizontal asymptote; $f'(x) = 8/(1-x)^3$, so f is increasing on $(-\infty, 1)$ and decreasing on $(1, \infty)$; $f''(x) = 24/(1-x)^4$, so the graph of f is concave upward on $(-\infty, 1)$ and on $(1, \infty)$; $\lim_{x\to1} 4/(1-x)^2 = \infty$, so $x = 1$ is a vertical asymptote.

27. For $x \neq -3$ and 3, $f(x) = \dfrac{2x(x+3)}{(3-x)(3+x)} = \dfrac{2x}{3-x}$,
so $\lim_{x\to\infty} f(x) = \lim_{x\to-\infty} f(x) = -2$ and thus $y = -2$ is a horizontal asymptote;

$$f'(x) = \frac{2(3-x) - 2x(-1)}{(3-x)^2} = \frac{6}{(3-x)^2} > 0 \quad \text{for } x \neq -3 \text{ and } 3$$

so f is increasing on $(-\infty, -3)$, $(-3, 3)$, and $(3, \infty)$; $f''(x) = 12/(3-x)^3$ for $x \neq -3$ and 3, so the graph of f is concave upward on $(-\infty, -3)$ and $(-3, 3)$ and concave downward on $(3, \infty)$; $\lim_{x\to3^+} 2x/(3-x) = -\infty$ and $\lim_{x\to3^-} 2x/(3-x) = \infty$, so $x = 3$ is a vertical asymptote.

28. The domain is $(-2, \infty)$ and

$$f(x) = \frac{1}{(x+2)^{3/2}}; \quad \lim_{x\to\infty} \frac{1}{(x+2)^{3/2}} = \lim_{x\to-\infty} \frac{1}{(x+2)^{3/2}} = 0$$

so $y = 0$ is a horizontal asymptote; $f'(x) = -\frac{3}{2}(x+2)^{-5/2} < 0$ for $x > -2$, so f is decreasing on $(-2, \infty)$; $f''(x) = \frac{15}{4}(x+2)^{-7/2} > 0$ for $x > -2$, so the graph of f is concave upward on $(-2, \infty)$; $\lim_{x\to-2^+} 1/(x+2)^{3/2} = \infty$, so $x = -2$ is a vertical asymptote.

29. $\lim_{x\to\infty} \dfrac{x+2}{x-1} = \lim_{x\to-\infty} \dfrac{x+2}{x-1} = 1$
so $y = 1$ is a horizontal asymptote;

$$f'(x) = \frac{1(x-1) - (x+2)(1)}{(x-1)^2} = \frac{-3}{(x-1)^2} < 0 \quad \text{for } x \neq 1$$

so f is decreasing on $(-\infty, 1)$ and $(1, \infty)$; $f''(x) = 6/(x-1)^3$, so the graph of f is concave upward on $(1, \infty)$ and concave downward on $(-\infty, 1)$;

$$\lim_{x\to1^+} \frac{x+2}{x-1} = \infty \quad \text{and} \quad \lim_{x\to1^-} \frac{x+2}{x-1} = -\infty$$

so $x = 1$ is a vertical asymptote.

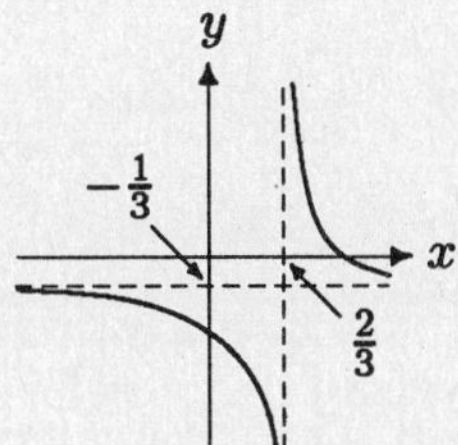

Exercise 30

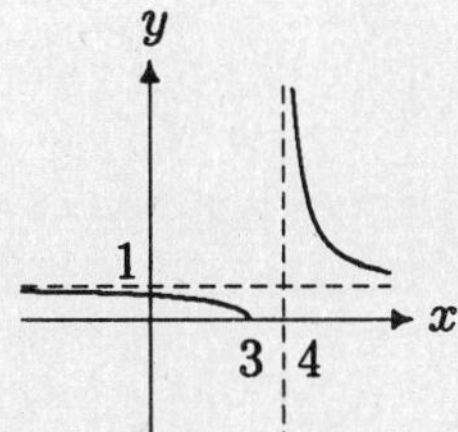

Exercise 31

30. $\displaystyle\lim_{x\to\infty}\frac{2x-3}{4-6x} = \lim_{x\to-\infty}\frac{2x-3}{4-6x} = -\frac{1}{3}$
so $y = -\frac{1}{3}$ is a horizontal asymptote;

$$f'(x) = \frac{2(4-6x)-(2x-3)(-6)}{(4-6x)^2} = \frac{-10}{(4-6x)^2} = \frac{-5}{2(2-3x)^2} < 0 \quad \text{for } x \neq \tfrac{2}{3}$$

so f is decreasing on $(-\infty, \frac{2}{3})$ and $(\frac{2}{3}, \infty)$; $f''(x) = -15/(2-3x)^3$, so the graph of f is concave downward on $(-\infty, \frac{2}{3})$ and concave upward on $(\frac{2}{3}, \infty)$;

$$\lim_{x\to 2/3+}\frac{2x-3}{4-6x} = \infty \quad \text{and} \quad \lim_{x\to 2/3-}\frac{2x-3}{4-6x} = -\infty$$

so $x = \frac{2}{3}$ is a vertical asymptote.

31. The domain of f consists of all x for which $(3-x)/(4-x) \geq 0$, that is, all x for which $3-x=0$, or $3-x$ and $4-x$ have the same sign. Thus the domain of f consists of $(-\infty, 3]$ and $(4, \infty)$.

$$\lim_{x\to\infty}\sqrt{\frac{3-x}{4-x}} = \lim_{x\to-\infty}\sqrt{\frac{3-x}{4-x}} = 1$$

so $y = 1$ is a horizontal asymptote;

$$f'(x) = \frac{1}{2}\left(\frac{3-x}{4-x}\right)^{-1/2}\left[\frac{-(4-x)-(3-x)(-1)}{(4-x)^2}\right] = \frac{-1}{2(4-x)^2}\left(\frac{3-x}{4-x}\right)^{-1/2}$$

so f is decreasing on $(-\infty, 3]$ and $(4, \infty)$;

$$f''(x) = \frac{-1}{(4-x)^3}\left(\frac{3-x}{4-x}\right)^{-1/2} + \frac{1}{4(4-x)^2}\left(\frac{3-x}{4-x}\right)^{-3/2}\left[\frac{-(4-x)-(3-x)(-1)}{(4-x)^2}\right]$$

$$= \frac{-1}{(4-x)^3}\left(\frac{3-x}{4-x}\right)^{-1/2}\left[1+\frac{1}{4(4-x)}\left(\frac{3-x}{4-x}\right)^{-1}\right] = \frac{-1}{(4-x)^3}\left(\frac{3-x}{4-x}\right)^{-1/2}\left[1+\frac{1}{4(3-x)}\right]$$

$$= \frac{4x-13}{4(3-x)(4-x)^3}\left(\frac{3-x}{4-x}\right)^{-1/2}$$

so the graph of f is concave upward on $(4, \infty)$ and concave downward on $(-\infty, 3)$;
$\lim_{x\to 4+}\sqrt{(3-x)/(4-x)} = \infty$, so $x = 4$ is a vertical asymptote.

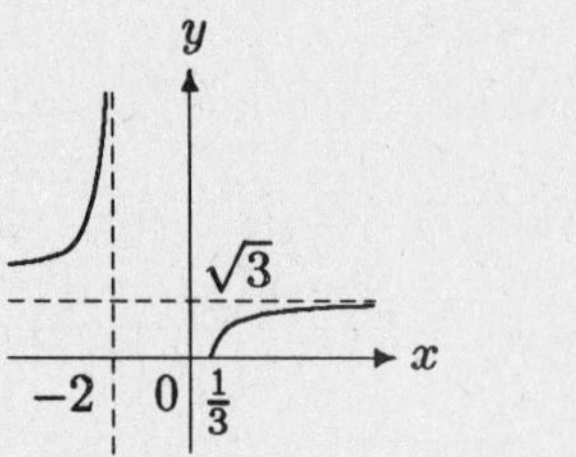

Exercise 32

Exercise 33

32. The domain of f consists of all x for which $(1-3x)/(-2-x) \geq 0$, that is, all x for which $1-3x=0$, or $1-3x$ and $-2-x$ have the same sign. Thus the domain of f consists of $(-\infty,-2)$ and $[\frac{1}{3},\infty)$;

$$\lim_{x\to\infty}\sqrt{\frac{1-3x}{-2-x}} = \lim_{x\to-\infty}\sqrt{\frac{1-3x}{-2-x}} = \sqrt{3}$$

so $y=\sqrt{3}$ is a horizontal asymptote;

$$f'(x) = \frac{1}{2}\left(\frac{1-3x}{-2-x}\right)^{-1/2}\left[\frac{-3(-2-x)-(1-3x)(-1)}{(-2-x)^2}\right] = \frac{7}{2(2+x)^2}\left(\frac{1-3x}{-2-x}\right)^{-1/2}$$

so f is increasing on $(-\infty,-2)$ and $[\frac{1}{3},\infty)$;

$$f''(x) = \frac{-7}{(2+x)^3}\left(\frac{1-3x}{-2-x}\right)^{-1/2} - \frac{7}{4(2+x)^2}\left(\frac{1-3x}{-2-x}\right)^{-3/2}\left[\frac{-3(-2-x)-(1-3x)(-1)}{(-2-x)^2}\right]$$

$$= \frac{-7}{(2+x)^3}\left(\frac{1-3x}{-2-x}\right)^{-1/2}\left[1+\frac{7}{4(2+x)}\left(\frac{1-3x}{-2-x}\right)^{-1}\right] = \frac{-7}{(2+x)^3}\left(\frac{1-3x}{-2-x}\right)^{-1/2}\left[1+\frac{7}{4(3x-1)}\right]$$

$$= \frac{-21(4x+1)}{4(3x-1)(2+x)^3}\left(\frac{1-3x}{-2-x}\right)^{-1/2}$$

so the graph of f is concave upward on $(-\infty,-2)$ and concave downward on $(\frac{1}{3},\infty)$;
$\lim_{x\to-2^-}(1-3x)/(-2-x)=\infty$, so $x=-2$ is a vertical asymptote.

33. $\displaystyle\lim_{x\to\infty}\frac{1}{x^2-4} = \lim_{x\to-\infty}\frac{1}{x^2-4} = 0$
so $y=0$ is a horizontal asymptote; $f'(x) = -2x/(x^2-4)^2$, so f is increasing on $(-\infty,-2)$ and $(-2,0]$, and decreasing on $[0,2)$ and $(2,\infty)$;

$$f''(x) = \frac{-2(x^2-4)^2-(-2x)2(x^2-4)(2x)}{(x^2-4)^4} = \frac{2(3x^2+4)}{(x^2-4)^3}$$

so the graph of f is concave upward on $(-\infty,-2)$ and $(2,\infty)$ and concave downward on $(-2,2)$;

$$\lim_{x\to2^+}\frac{1}{x^2-4} = \lim_{x\to-2^-}\frac{1}{x^2-4} = \infty \quad\text{and}\quad \lim_{x\to2^-}\frac{1}{x^2-4} = \lim_{x\to-2^+}\frac{1}{x^2-4} = -\infty$$

so $x=2$ and $x=-2$ are vertical asymptotes.

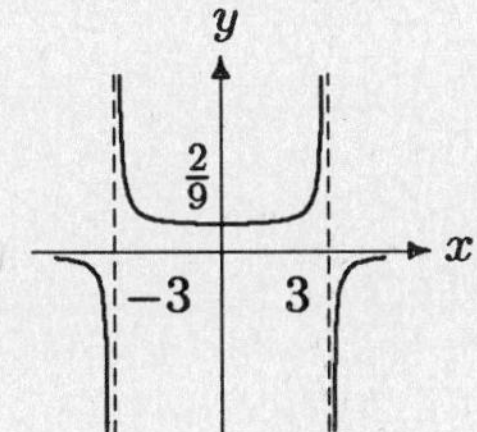

Exercise 34

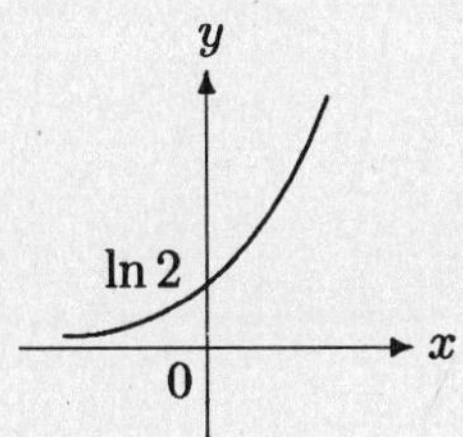

Exercise 35

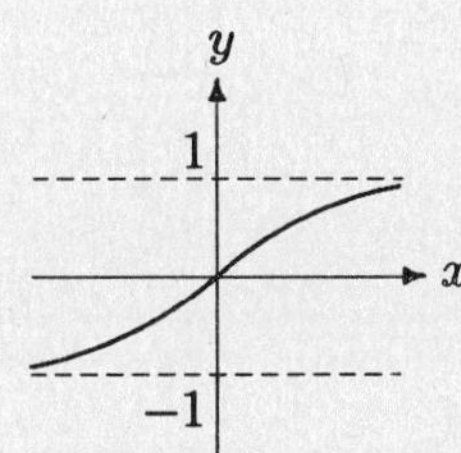

Exercise 36

34. $\lim\limits_{x\to\infty} \dfrac{-2}{x^2-9} = \lim\limits_{x\to-\infty} \dfrac{-2}{x^2-9} = 0$

so $y = 0$ is a horizontal asymptote; $f'(x) = 4x/(x^2-9)^2$, so f is increasing on $[0,3)$ and $(3,\infty)$ and decreasing on $(-\infty,-3)$ and $(-3,0]$;

$$f''(x) = \frac{4(x^2-9)^2 - (4x)2(x^2-9)(2x)}{(x^2-9)^4} = \frac{-12(x^2+3)}{(x^2-9)^3}$$

so the graph of f is concave upward on $(-3,3)$ and concave downward on $(-\infty,-3)$ and $(3,\infty)$;

$$\lim_{x\to 3^+} \frac{-2}{x^2-9} = \lim_{x\to -3^-} \frac{-2}{x^2-9} = -\infty \quad \text{and} \quad \lim_{x\to 3^-} \frac{-2}{x^2-9} = \lim_{x\to -3^+} \frac{-2}{x^2-9} = \infty$$

so $x = 3$ and $x = -3$ are vertical asymptotes.

35. $\lim\limits_{x\to\infty} \ln(1+e^x) = \infty$ and $\lim\limits_{x\to-\infty} \ln(1+e^x) = \ln 1 = 0$

so $y = 0$ is a horizontal asymptote; $f'(x) = e^x/(1+e^x) > 0$ for all x, so f is increasing on $(-\infty,\infty)$;

$$f''(x) = \frac{e^x(1+e^x) - e^x e^x}{(1+e^x)^2} = \frac{e^x}{(1+e^x)^2} > 0 \quad \text{for all } x$$

so the graph of f is concave upward on $(-\infty,\infty)$.

36. $f(-x) = -f(x)$, so the graph is symmetric with respect to the origin;

$$\lim_{x\to\infty} \frac{e^x - e^{-x}}{e^x + e^{-x}} = \lim_{x\to\infty} \frac{1 - e^{-2x}}{1 + e^{-2x}} = \frac{1-0}{1+0} = 1,$$

so $y = 1$ is a horizontal asymptote;

$$f'(x) = \frac{(e^x + e^{-x})(e^x + e^{-x}) - (e^x - e^{-x})(e^x - e^{-x})}{(e^x + e^{-x})^2} = \frac{4}{(e^x + e^{-x})^2} > 0 \quad \text{for all } x$$

so f is increasing on $(-\infty,\infty)$;

$$f''(x) = \frac{-8(e^x - e^{-x})}{(e^x + e^{-x})^3},$$

so the graph of f is concave upward on $(-\infty,0)$ and concave downward on $(0,\infty)$.

37. Horizontal asymptote: $y = 1/\sqrt{2}$; vertical asymptotes: $x = -4$ and $x = 4$.

38. No horizontal asymptotes; vertical asymptotes: $x = \pi/2 + n\pi$ for any integer n.

39. No horizontal asymptotes; vertical asymptotes: $x = -1$ and $x = 1$.

40. Horizontal asymptotes: $y = 0$ and $y = \frac{1}{3}$; no vertical asymptotes.

41. No horizontal asymptotes; vertical asymptote: $x = 0$.

42. Horizontal asymptote: $y = 1$; vertical asymptotes: $x = -8$ and $x = 8$.

43. $\lim_{x\to\infty} \dfrac{2x^2+1}{3x^2-5} = \lim_{x\to 0+} \dfrac{2(1/x)^2+1}{3(1/x)^2+5} = \lim_{x\to 0} \dfrac{2+x^2}{3+5x^2} = \dfrac{2}{3}$

44. $\lim_{x\to-\infty} \dfrac{4x^3-9x^2}{-7x^3+17} = \lim_{x\to 0-} \dfrac{4(1/x)^3-9(1/x)^2}{-7(1/x)^3+17} = \lim_{x\to 0} \dfrac{4-9x}{-7+17x^3} = -\dfrac{4}{7}$

45. $\lim_{x\to\infty} \dfrac{\sqrt{1+x^2}}{x} = \lim_{x\to 0+} \dfrac{\sqrt{1+(1/x)2}}{1/x} = \lim_{x\to 0+} \sqrt{x^2}\sqrt{1+1/x^2} = \lim_{x\to 0} \sqrt{x^2+1} = 1$

46. Since $x = -\sqrt{x^2}$ for $x < 0$,

$$\lim_{x\to-\infty} \frac{\sqrt{1+x^2}}{x} = \lim_{x\to 0-} \frac{\sqrt{1+(1/x)^2}}{1/x} = \lim_{x\to 0-} -\sqrt{x^2}\sqrt{1+1/x^2} = \lim_{x\to 0} -\sqrt{x^2+1} = -1.$$

47. If $x > 0$, then

$$f(x) = \frac{x^2}{x^2+1} = \frac{1}{1+(1/x^2)}, \quad \text{so} \quad \lim_{x\to\infty} f(x) = 1.$$

Thus $y = 1$ is a horizontal asymptote. If $x < 0$, then $f(x) = -x^2/(x^2+1)$, so $\lim_{x\to-\infty} f(x) = -1$. Thus $y = -1$ is a horizontal asymptote.

48. Since $\lim_{x\to\infty} 2/x^2 = 0$ and $\lim_{x\to-\infty} 2/x^2 = 0$, it follows that

$$\lim_{x\to\infty} \frac{\sqrt{2+4x^2}}{x} = \lim_{x\to\infty} \sqrt{\frac{2}{x^2}+4} = 2 \quad \text{and} \quad \lim_{x\to-\infty} \frac{\sqrt{2+4x^2}}{x} = \lim_{x\to-\infty} -\sqrt{\frac{2}{x^2}+4} = -2.$$

Therefore the lines $y = 2$ and $y = -2$ are horizontal asymptotes of the graph of f.

49. Let $N > 0$ and choose $M < 0$ such that if $x < M$, then $f(x)/g(x) > \frac{1}{2}$ and $g(x) > 2N$. It follows that if $x < M$, then $f(x) = [f(x)/g(x)]g(x) > \frac{1}{2} \cdot 2N = N$. Thus $\lim_{x\to-\infty} f(x) = \infty$.

50. Let $\varepsilon > 0$. If $L = 0$, we choose $M_1 \geq M$ so that if $x \geq M_1$, then $[f(x)]^2 < \varepsilon^2$. This implies that if $x \geq M_1$, then $0 \leq f(x) \leq \varepsilon$, so that $\lim_{x\to\infty} f(x) = 0 = \sqrt{L}$. If $L > 0$, we choose $M_1 \geq M$ so that if $x \geq M_1$, then $|[f(x)]^2 - L| < \varepsilon\sqrt{L}$. This implies that if $x \geq M_1$, then

$$|f(x) - \sqrt{L}| = \frac{|[f(x)]^2 - L|}{f(x)+\sqrt{L}} \leq \frac{|[f(x)]^2 - L|}{\sqrt{L}} < \frac{\varepsilon\sqrt{L}}{\sqrt{L}} = \varepsilon$$

so that $\lim_{x\to\infty} f(x) = \sqrt{L}$.

51. a. $f(10^2) \approx 96.86$, $f(10^3) \approx 996.9$, $f(10^4) \approx 9997$.

b. For any positive integer n, $f(2n) = 2n - \pi$ and $f(2n+1) = -(2n+1-\pi)$. Thus $f(x)$ assumes arbitrarily large positive values and $f(x)$ assumes negative values arbitrarily large in absolute value as x tends to ∞. Therefore $\lim_{x\to\infty} f(x)$ does not exist as a number, as ∞, or as $-\infty$.

52. a. $\lim_{r\to\infty} v(r) = \lim_{r\to\infty} \sqrt{\frac{192{,}000}{r} + 8^2 - 48} = \lim_{r\to\infty} \sqrt{\frac{192{,}000}{r} + 16} = \sqrt{16} = 4$ (miles per second)

b. Since

$$\lim_{r\to\infty} v(r) = \lim_{r\to\infty} \sqrt{\frac{192{,}000}{r} + v_0^2 - 48} = \sqrt{v_0^2 - 48} \quad \text{for } v_0^2 \geq 48$$

it follows that if $\lim_{r\to\infty} v(r) = 0$, then $\sqrt{v_0^2 - 48} = 0$, so $v_0 = \sqrt{48} = 4\sqrt{3}$ (miles per second).

53. a. Since $a > 0$, $\lim_{t\to\infty} e^{-at} = 0$. Therefore $\lim_{t\to\infty} v(t) = \lim_{t\to\infty} v^*(1 - e^{-at}) = v^*(1-0) = v^*$.

b. As time progresses, the velocity approaches the number v^*. Thus v^* is the "terminal," or "limiting," velocity of the falling parachutist.

54. Assuming that the end of the universe is "at infinity," we compute the work required as

$$\lim_{x\to\infty} W(x) = \lim_{x\to\infty} GMm\left(\frac{1}{3960} - \frac{1}{x}\right) = \frac{GMm}{3960}.$$

55. $\lim_{t\to\infty} S(t) = \lim_{t\to\infty} \left(\frac{a}{t} + b\right) = b$

56. Since $\lim_{t\to\infty} e^{-1.0235t} = 0$, we have

$$\lim_{t\to\infty} \frac{449}{1 + e^{5.4094 - 1.0235t}} = \lim_{t\to\infty} \frac{449}{1 + e^{5.4094}e^{-1.0235t}} = \frac{449}{1 + e^{5.4094} \cdot (0)} = 449.$$

Thus the carrying capacity of the medium is 449.

57. $\lim_{t\to\infty} \left(I(t) - 3\sin\frac{30t}{\pi}\right) = \lim_{t\to\infty} \frac{100}{1+t^2} = 0$

58. Voyager 2 traveled approximately 2,791,000,000 − 1,780,000,000 = 1,011,000,000 miles in approximately 3 years and 7 months, or 3.6 years. Thus the average velocity was approximately 1,011,000,000/3.6 miles per year, or approximately 32,000 miles per hour. Thus Voyager 2 had sufficient velocity to escape the earth's gravity.

59. a. Let $u = gt/v_T$. Then $\lim_{t\to\infty} gt/v_T = \lim_{u\to\infty} u = \infty$, so that $\lim_{t\to\infty} e^{-gt/v_T} = \lim_{u\to\infty} e^{-u} = 0$. Therefore $\lim_{t\to\infty} v_T(1 - e^{-gt/v_T}) = v_T - v_T \lim_{t\to\infty} e^{-gt/v_T} = v_T - v_T \cdot 0 = v_T$.

b. We must solve $\frac{1}{2} = 1 - e^{-(9.8)t/(2.7\times 10^{-2})}$ for t. This is equivalent to

$$\frac{1}{2} = e^{-(9.8)t/(2.7\times 10^{-2})}, \quad \text{or} \quad \ln 2 = \left(\frac{9.8}{2.7\times 10^{-2}}\right)t.$$

Thus $t = (2.7\times 10^{-2})(\ln 2)/9.8 \approx .0019096912$. Consequently it takes approximately .002 seconds for the droplet to reach half its terminal speed.

4.9 Graphing

1. $f'(x) = 3(x^2+1)$; $f''(x) = 6x$; increasing on $(-\infty, \infty)$; concave upward on $(0, \infty)$ and concave downward on $(-\infty, 0)$; inflection point is $(0, 2)$.

2. $f'(x) = 3x^2 - 16x + 16$; $f''(x) = 6x - 16$; relative maximum value is $f(\frac{4}{3}) = \frac{175}{27}$; relative minimum value is $f(4) = -3$; increasing on $(-\infty, \frac{4}{3}]$ and $[4, \infty)$; decreasing on $[\frac{4}{3}, 4]$; concave upward on $(\frac{8}{3}, \infty)$ and concave downward on $(-\infty, \frac{8}{3})$; inflection point is $(\frac{8}{3}, \frac{47}{27})$.

3. $f'(x) = 4x^3 + 24x^2 + 72x$; $f''(x) = 12x^2 + 48x + 72$; relative minimum value is $f(0) = -3$; increasing on $[0, \infty)$ and decreasing on $(-\infty, 0]$; concave upward on $(-\infty, \infty)$.

4. $f'(x) = 4x^3 - 12x$; $f''(x) = 12x^2 - 12$; relative maximum value is $f(0) = 0$; relative minimum value is $f(-\sqrt{3}) = f(\sqrt{3}) = -9$; increasing on $[-\sqrt{3}, 0]$ and $[\sqrt{3}, \infty)$, and decreasing on $(-\infty, -\sqrt{3})$ and $[0, \sqrt{3}]$; concave upward on $(-\infty, -1)$ and $(1, \infty)$, and concave downward on $(-1, 1)$; inflection points are $(-1, -5)$ and $(1, -5)$; symmetry with respect to the y axis.

5. $g'(x) = 1 - 4/x^2$; $g''(x) = 8/x^3$; relative maximum value is $g(-2) = -4$; relative minimum value is $g(2) = 4$; increasing on $(-\infty, -2]$ and $[2, \infty)$, and decreasing on $[-2, 0)$ and $(0, 2]$; concave upward on $(0, \infty)$ and concave downward on $(-\infty, 0)$; vertical asymptote is $x = 0$; symmetry with respect to the origin.

6. $g'(x) = -2/x^3$; $g''(x) = 6/x^4$; increasing on $(-\infty, 0)$ and decreasing on $(0, \infty)$; concave upward on $(-\infty, 0)$ and on $(0, \infty)$; vertical asymptote is $x = 0$; horizontal asymptote is $y = 2$; symmetry with respect to the y axis.

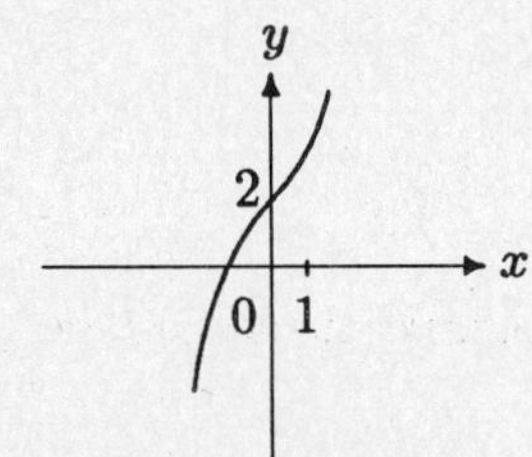

Exercise 1

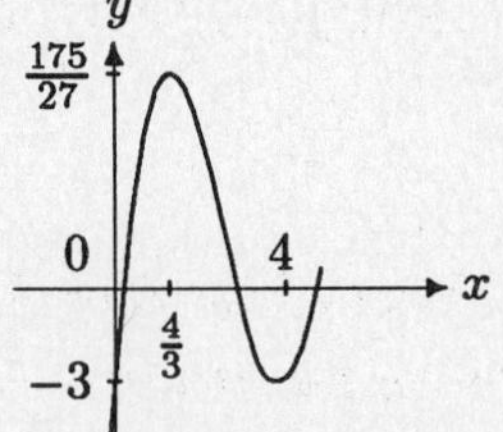

Exercise 2

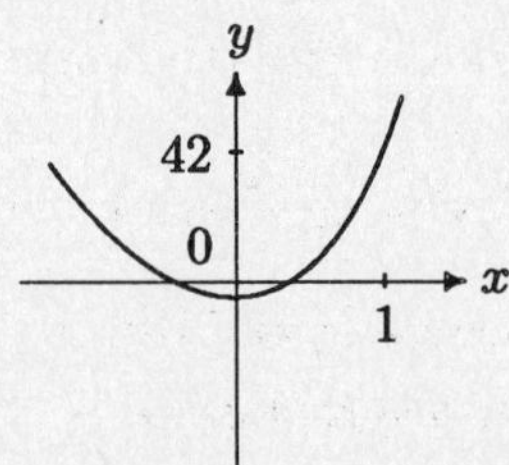

Exercise 3

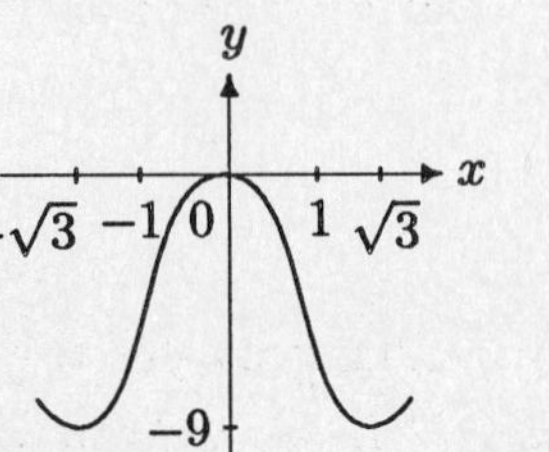

Exercise 4

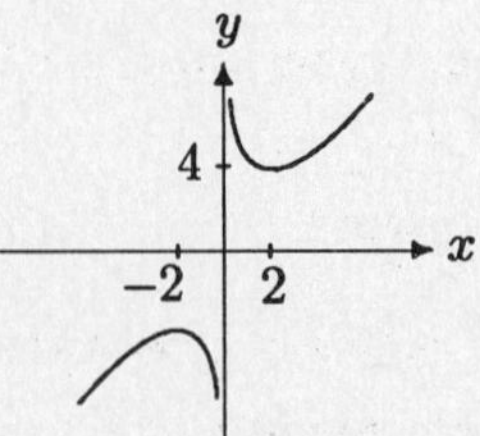

Exercise 5

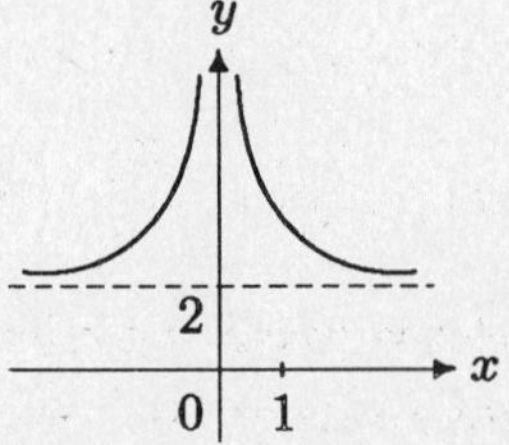

Exercise 6

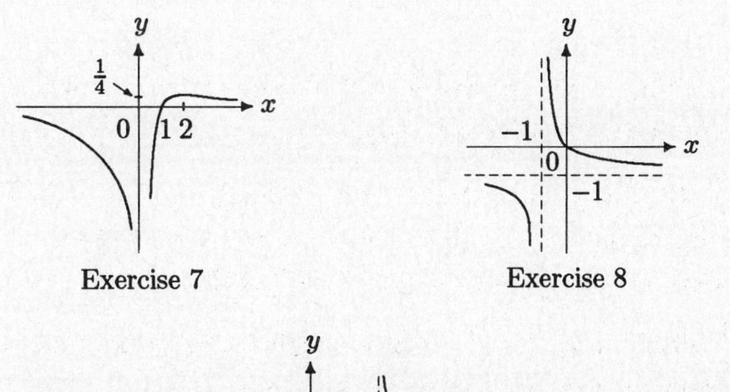

Exercise 7 Exercise 8

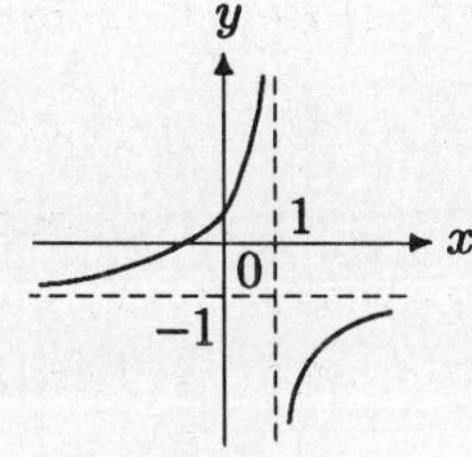

Exercise 9

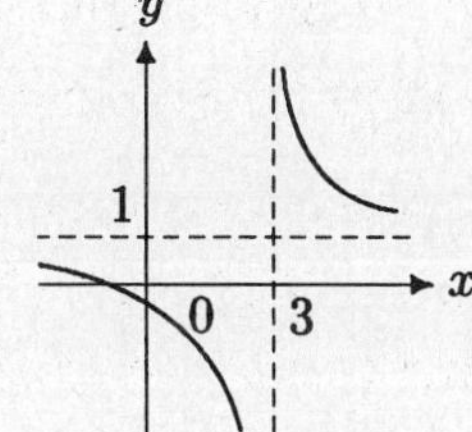

Exercise 10

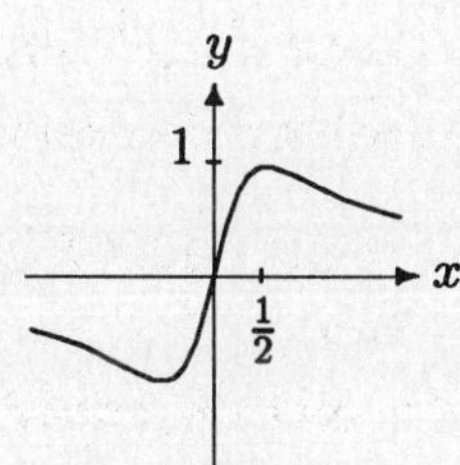

Exercise 11

7. $g'(x) = \dfrac{2-x}{x^3}$; $g''(x) = \dfrac{2(x-3)}{x^4}$

relative maximum value is $g(2) = \frac{1}{4}$; increasing on $(0, 2]$, and decreasing on $(-\infty, 0)$ and on $[2, \infty)$; concave upward on $(3, \infty)$ and concave downward on $(-\infty, 0)$ and $(0, 3)$; inflection point is $(3, \frac{2}{9})$; vertical asymptote is $x = 0$; horizontal asymptote is $y = 0$.

8. $g(x) = -1 + \dfrac{1}{x+1}$, so $g'(x) = \dfrac{-1}{(x+1)^2}$; $g''(x) = \dfrac{2}{(x+1)^3}$

decreasing on $(-\infty, -1)$ and on $(-1, \infty)$; concave upward on $(-1, \infty)$ and concave downward on $(-\infty, -1)$; vertical asymptote is $x = -1$; horizontal asymptote is $y = -1$.

9. $k'(x) = \dfrac{2}{(1-x)^2}$; $k''(x) = \dfrac{4}{(1-x)^3}$

increasing on $(-\infty, 1)$ and $(1, \infty)$; concave upward on $(-\infty, 1)$ and concave downward on $(1, \infty)$; vertical asymptote is $x = 1$; horizontal asymptote is $y = -1$.

10. $k'(x) = \dfrac{-5}{(x-3)^2}$; $k''(x) = \dfrac{10}{(x-3)^3}$

decreasing on $(-\infty, 3)$ and $(3, \infty)$; concave downward on $(-\infty, 3)$ and concave upward on $(3, \infty)$; vertical asymptote is $x = 3$; horizontal asymptote is $y = 1$.

11. $k'(x) = \dfrac{4(1-4x^2)}{(1+4x^2)^2}$; $k''(x) = \dfrac{32x(-3+4x^2)}{(1+4x^2)^3}$

relative maximum value is $k(\frac{1}{2}) = 1$; relative minimum value is $k(-\frac{1}{2}) = -1$; increasing on $[-\frac{1}{2}, \frac{1}{2}]$, and decreasing on $(-\infty, -\frac{1}{2}]$ and $[\frac{1}{2}, \infty)$; concave upward on $(-\sqrt{3}/2, 0)$ and $(\sqrt{3}/2, \infty)$, and concave downward on $(-\infty, -\sqrt{3}/2)$ and $(0, \sqrt{3}/2)$; inflection points are $(-\sqrt{3}/2, -\sqrt{3}/2)$, $(0, 0)$, and $(\sqrt{3}/2, \sqrt{3}/2)$; horizontal asymptote is $y = 0$; symmetry with respect to the origin.

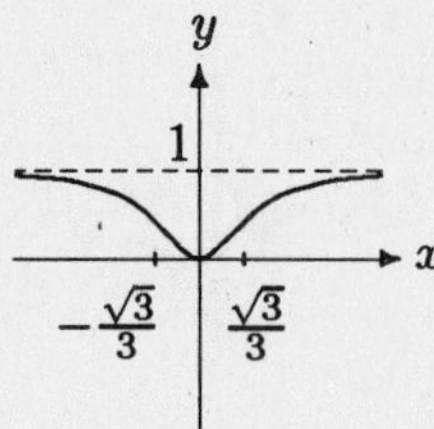

Exercise 12

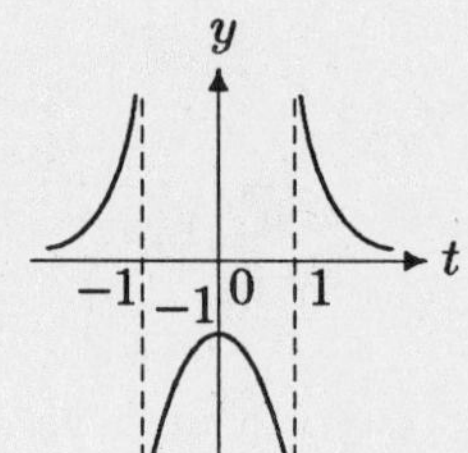

Exercise 13

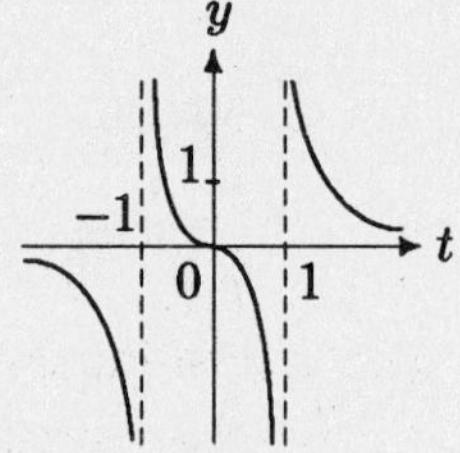

Exercise 14

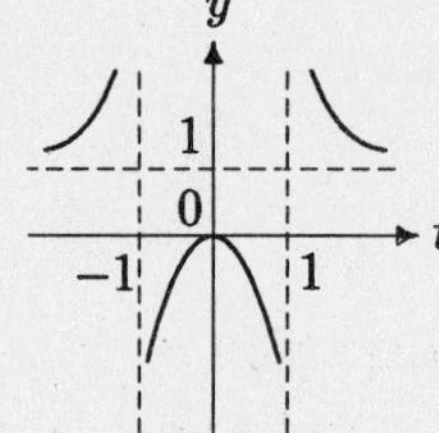

Exercise 15

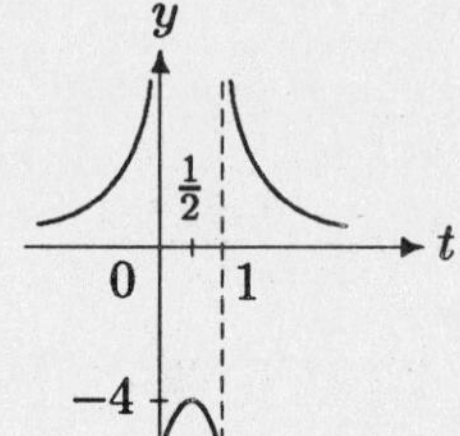

Exercise 16

12. $k'(x) = \dfrac{2x}{(1+x^2)^2}$; $k''(x) = \dfrac{2(1-3x^2)}{(1+x^2)^3}$

    relative minimum value is $k(0) = 0$; increasing on $[0, \infty)$ and decreasing on $(-\infty, 0]$; concave upward on $(-\sqrt{3}/3, \sqrt{3}/3)$, and concave downward on $(-\infty, -\sqrt{3}/3)$ and $(\sqrt{3}/3, \infty)$; inflection points are $(-\sqrt{3}/3, \frac{1}{4})$ and $(\sqrt{3}/3, \frac{1}{4})$; horizontal asymptote is $y = 1$; symmetry with respect to the y axis.

13. $f'(t) = \dfrac{-2t}{(t^2-1)^2}$; $f''(t) = \dfrac{6t^2+2}{(t^2-1)^3}$

    relative maximum value is $f(0) = -1$; increasing on $(-\infty, -1)$ and $(-1, 0]$, and decreasing on $[0, 1)$ and $(1, \infty)$; concave upward on $(-\infty, -1)$ and $(1, \infty)$, and concave downward on $(-1, 1)$; vertical asymptotes are $t = -1$ and $t = 1$; horizontal asymptote is $y = 0$; symmetry with respect to the y axis.

14. $f'(t) = \dfrac{-1-t^2}{(t^2-1)^2}$; $f''(t) = \dfrac{2t(t^2+3)}{(t^2-1)^3}$

    decreasing on $(-\infty, -1)$, $(-1, 1)$, and on $(1, \infty)$; concave upward on $(-1, 0)$ and $(1, \infty)$, and concave downward on $(-\infty, -1)$ and on $(0, 1)$; inflection point is $(0, 0)$; vertical asymptotes are $t = -1$ and $t = 1$; horizontal asymptote is $y = 0$; symmetry with respect to the origin.

15. Since $t^2/(t^2-1) = 1 + 1/(t^2-1)$, the graph is the same as the graph in Exercise 13, but translated upward one unit.

16. $f'(t) = \dfrac{1-2t}{(t^2-t)^2}$; $f''(t) = \dfrac{6t^2-6t+2}{(t^2-t)^3}$

    relative maximum value is $f(\frac{1}{2}) = -4$; increasing on $(-\infty, 0)$ and $(0, \frac{1}{2}]$, and decreasing on $[\frac{1}{2}, 1)$ and $(1, \infty)$; concave upward on $(-\infty, 0)$ and $(1, \infty)$, and concave downward on $(0, 1)$; vertical asymptotes are $t = 0$ and $t = 1$; horizontal asymptote is $y = 0$.

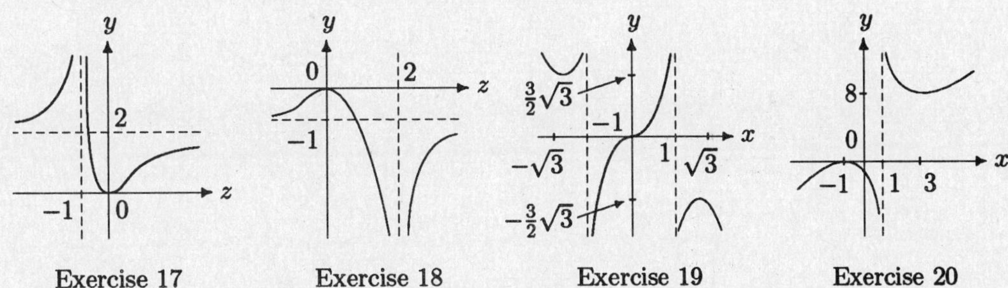

Exercise 17 Exercise 18 Exercise 19 Exercise 20

17. $f'(z) = \dfrac{4z}{(z+1)^3}$; $f''(z) = \dfrac{4(1-2z)}{(z+1)^4}$

relative minimum value is $f(0) = 0$; increasing on $(-\infty, -1)$ and $[0, \infty)$, and decreasing on $(-1, 0]$; concave upward on $(-\infty, -1)$ and $(-1, \frac{1}{2})$, and concave downward on $(\frac{1}{2}, \infty)$; inflection point is $(\frac{1}{2}, \frac{2}{9})$; vertical asymptote is $z = -1$; horizontal asymptote is $y = 2$.

18. $f'(z) = \dfrac{-4z}{(2-z)^3}$; $f''(z) = \dfrac{-8(1+z)}{(2-z)^4}$

relative maximum value is $f(0) = 0$; increasing on $(-\infty, 0]$ and $(2, \infty)$, and decreasing on $[0, 2)$; concave upward on $(-\infty, -1)$ and concave downward on $(-1, 2)$ and $(2, \infty)$; inflection point is $(-1, -\frac{1}{9})$; vertical asymptote is $z = 2$; horizontal asymptote is $y = -1$.

19. $f'(x) = \dfrac{x^2(3-x^2)}{(1-x^2)^2}$; $f''(x) = \dfrac{2x(x^2+3)}{(1-x^2)^3}$

relative maximum value is $f(\sqrt{3}) = -\frac{3}{2}\sqrt{3}$; relative minimum value is $f(-\sqrt{3}) = \frac{3}{2}\sqrt{3}$; increasing on $[-\sqrt{3}, -1)$, $(-1, 1)$, and $(1, \sqrt{3}]$, and decreasing on $(-\infty, -\sqrt{3}]$ and on $(\sqrt{3}, \infty)$; concave upward on $(-\infty, -1)$ and on $(0, 1)$,and concave downward on $(-1, 0)$ and $(1, \infty)$; inflection point is $(0, 0)$; vertical asymptotes are $x = -1$ and $x = 1$; symmetry with respect to the origin.

20. $f'(x) = \dfrac{x^2-2x-3}{(x-1)^2}$; $f''(x) = \dfrac{8}{(x-1)^3}$

relative maximum value is $f(-1) = 0$; relative minimum value is $f(3) = 8$; increasing on $(-\infty, -1]$ and $[3, \infty)$, and decreasing on $[-1, 1)$ and $(1, 3]$; concave upward on $(1, \infty)$, and concave downward on $(-\infty, 1)$; vertical asymptote is $x = 1$.

21. $f'(x) = \dfrac{-3x^2}{(x^3-1)^2}$; $f''(x) = \dfrac{6x(2x^3+1)}{(x^3-1)^3}$

decreasing on $(-\infty, 1)$ and $(1, \infty)$; concave upward on $(-\sqrt[3]{\frac{1}{2}}, 0)$ and $(1, \infty)$, and concave downward on $(-\infty, -\sqrt[3]{\frac{1}{2}})$ and $(0, 1)$; inflection points are $(-\sqrt[3]{\frac{1}{2}}, -\frac{2}{3})$ and $(0, -1)$; vertical asymptote is $x = 1$; horizontal asymptote is $y = 0$.

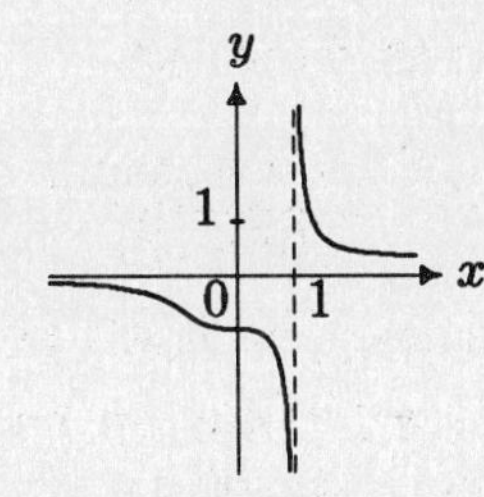

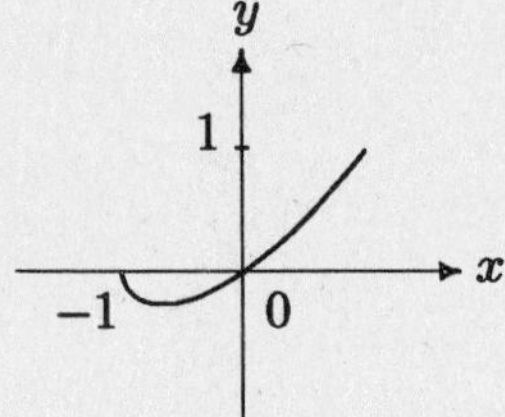

Exercise 22

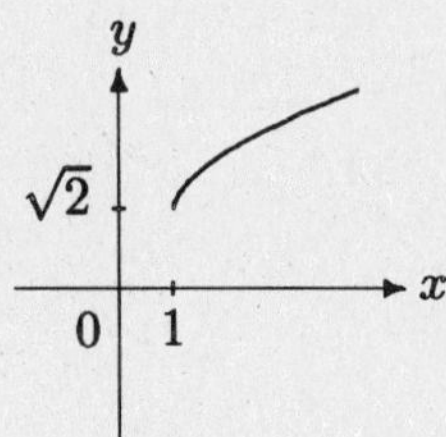

Exercise 23

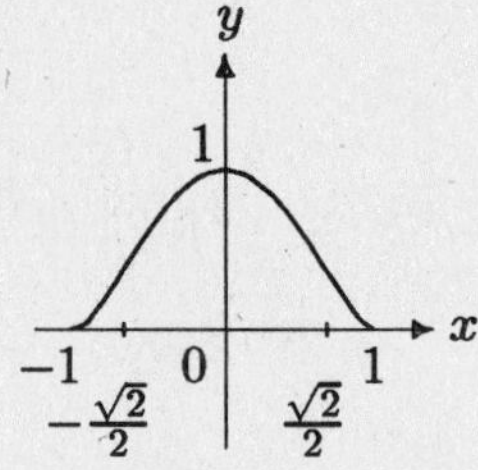

Exercise 24

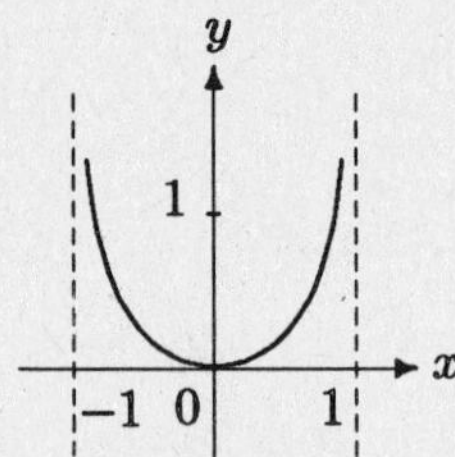

Exercise 25

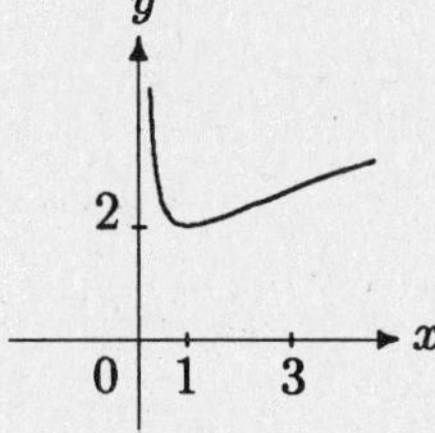

Exercise 26

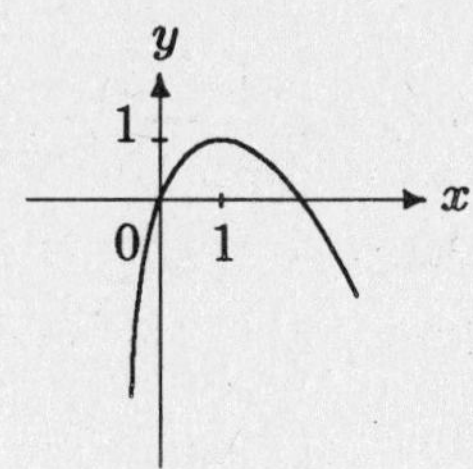

Exercise 27

22. $f'(x) = \dfrac{2+3x}{2\sqrt{1+x}}$; $f''(x) = \dfrac{4+3x}{4(1+x)^{3/2}}$

domain is $[-1,\infty)$; relative minimum value is $f(-\frac{2}{3}) = -2\sqrt{3}/9$; increasing on $[-\frac{2}{3},\infty)$, and decreasing on $[-1,-\frac{2}{3}]$; concave upward on $(-1,\infty)$.

23. $f'(x) = \frac{1}{2}(x-1)^{-1/2} + \frac{1}{2}(x+1)^{-1/2}$; $f''(x) = -\frac{1}{4}(x-1)^{-3/2} - \frac{1}{4}(x+1)^{-3/2}$;

domain is $[1,\infty)$; increasing on $[1,\infty)$; concave downward on $(1,\infty)$.

24. $f'(x) = -3x(1-x^2)^{1/2}$; $f''(x) = \dfrac{3(2x^2-1)}{(1-x^2)^{1/2}}$

domain is $[-1,1]$; relative maximum value is $f(0) = 1$; increasing on $[-1,0]$ and decreasing on $[0,1]$; concave upward on $(-1,-\sqrt{2}/2)$ and $(\sqrt{2}/2,1)$, and concave downward on $(-\sqrt{2}/2,\sqrt{2}/2)$; inflection points are $(\sqrt{2}/2,\sqrt{2}/4)$ and $(-\sqrt{2}/2,\sqrt{2}/4)$; symmetry with respect to the y axis.

25. $f'(x) = \dfrac{x(2-x^2)}{(1-x^2)^{3/2}}$; $f''(x) = \dfrac{2+x^2}{(1-x^2)^{5/2}}$

domain is $(-1,1)$; relative minimum value is $f(0) = 0$; increasing on $[0,1)$ and decreasing on $(-1,0]$; concave upward on $(-1,1)$; vertical asymptotes are $x=-1$ and $x=1$; symmetry with respect to the y axis.

26. $f'(x) = \dfrac{x-1}{2x^{3/2}}$; $f''(x) = \dfrac{3-x}{4x^{5/2}}$

relative minimum value is $f(1) = 2$; increasing on $[1,\infty)$ and decreasing on $(0,1]$; concave upward on $(0,3)$ and concave downward on $(3,\infty)$; inflection point is $(3,\frac{4}{3}\sqrt{3})$; vertical asymptote is $x=0$.

27. $f'(x) = 4(1-x^{1/3})$; $f''(x) = -\frac{4}{3}x^{-2/3}$

relative maximum value is $f(1) = 1$; increasing on $(-\infty,1]$ and decreasing on $[1,\infty)$; concave downward on $(-\infty,\infty)$.

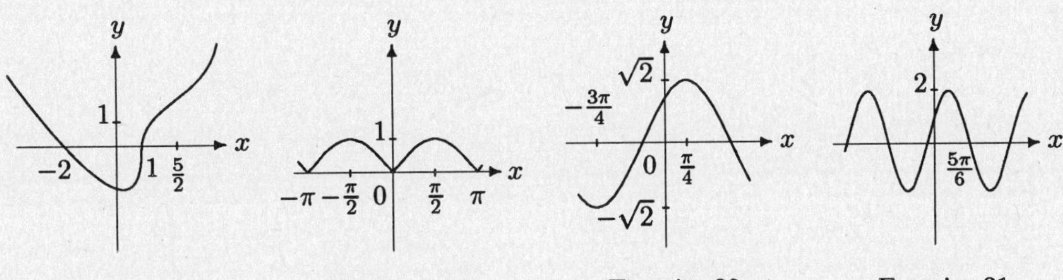

Exercise 28 Exercise 29 Exercise 30 Exercise 31

28. $f'(x) = \dfrac{4x-1}{3(x-1)^{2/3}}$; $f''(x) = \dfrac{2(2x-5)}{9(x-1)^{5/3}}$

relative minimum value is $f(\frac{1}{4}) = -\frac{9}{4}(\frac{3}{4})^{1/3}$; increasing on $[\frac{1}{4}, \infty)$ and decreasing on $(-\infty, \frac{1}{4}]$; concave upward on $(-\infty, 1)$ and $(\frac{5}{2}, \infty)$; concave downward on $(1, \frac{5}{2})$; inflection point is $(\frac{5}{2}, \frac{9}{2}(\frac{3}{2})^{1/3})$.

29. $g'(x) = \left\{ \begin{array}{ll} \cos x & \text{for } 2n\pi < x < (2n+1)\pi \\ -\cos x & \text{for } (2n+1)\pi < x < (2n+2)\pi \end{array} \right\}$, for any integer n

$g''(x) = -|\sin x|$ for $x \neq n\pi$, for any integer n.

relative maximum value is $g(\pi/2 + n\pi) = 1$; relative minimum value is $g(n\pi) = 0$; increasing on $[n\pi, \pi/2 + n\pi]$ and decreasing on $[\pi/2 + n\pi, (n+1)\pi]$; concave downward on $(n\pi, (n+1)\pi)$; symmetry with respect to the y axis.

30. $g'(x) = \cos x - \sin x$; $g''(x) = -\sin x - \cos x$

relative maximum value is $g(2n\pi + \pi/4) = \sqrt{2}$ for any integer n; relative minimum value is $g(2n\pi + \frac{5}{4}\pi) = -\sqrt{2}$, for any integer n; increasing on $[2n\pi - \frac{3}{4}\pi, 2n\pi + \frac{1}{4}\pi]$ and decreasing on $[2n\pi + \frac{1}{4}\pi, 2n\pi + \frac{5}{4}\pi]$; concave upward on $(2n\pi + \frac{3}{4}\pi, 2n\pi + \frac{7}{4}\pi)$ and concave downward on $(2n\pi - \frac{1}{4}\pi, 2n\pi + \frac{3}{4}\pi)$; inflection points are $(n\pi + \frac{3}{4}\pi, 0)$.

31. $g'(x) = \sqrt{3}\cos x - \sin x$; $g''(x) = -\sqrt{3}\sin x - \cos x = -g(x)$

relative maximum value is $g(\pi/3 + 2n\pi) = 2$ for any integer n; relative minimum value is $g(-2\pi/3 + 2n\pi) = -2$ for any integer n; increasing on $[-2\pi/3 + 2n\pi, \pi/3 + 2n\pi]$ and decreasing on $[\pi/3 + 2n\pi, 4\pi/3 + 2n\pi]$; concave upward on $(-7\pi/6 + 2n\pi, -\pi/6 + 2n\pi)$ and concave downward on $(-\pi/6 + 2n\pi, 5\pi/6 + 2n\pi)$; inflection points are $(-\pi/6 + n\pi, 0)$.

32. $g'(x) = \frac{1}{2} + \cos x$; $g''(x) = -\sin x$

relative maximum values are $g(2n\pi + \frac{2}{3}\pi) = n\pi + \frac{1}{3}\pi + \sqrt{3}/2$ for any integer n; relative minimum values are $g(2n\pi + \frac{4}{3}\pi) = n\pi + \frac{2}{3}\pi - \sqrt{3}/2$ for any integer n; increasing on $[2n\pi - \frac{2}{3}\pi, 2n\pi + \frac{2}{3}\pi]$ and decreasing on $[2n\pi + \frac{2}{3}\pi, 2n\pi + \frac{4}{3}\pi]$; concave upward on $((2n+1)\pi, (2n+2)\pi)$; concave downward on $(2n\pi, (2n+1)\pi)$; inflection points are $(n\pi, n\pi/2)$; symmetry with respect to the origin.

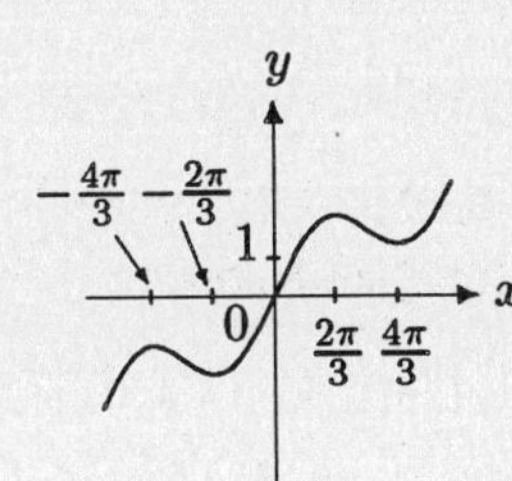

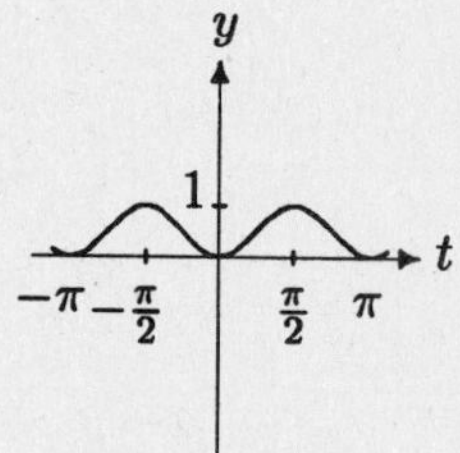

Exercise 33

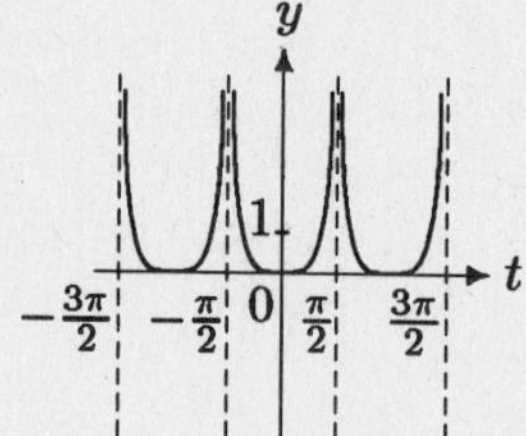

Exercise 34

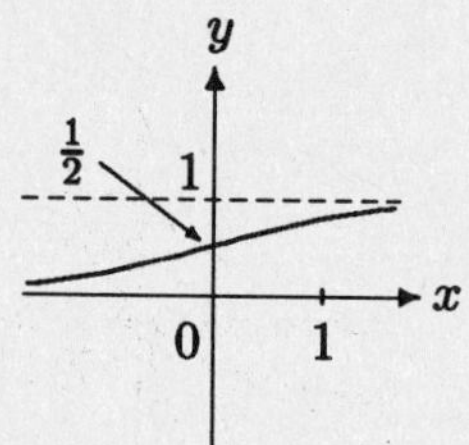

Exercise 35

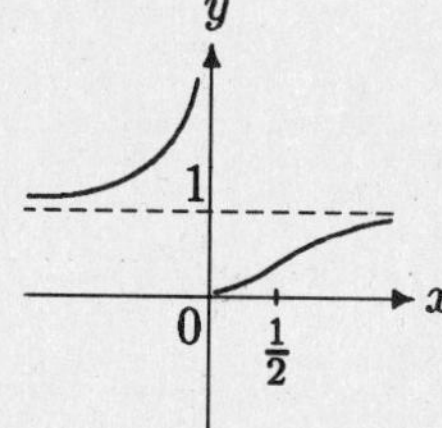

Exercise 36

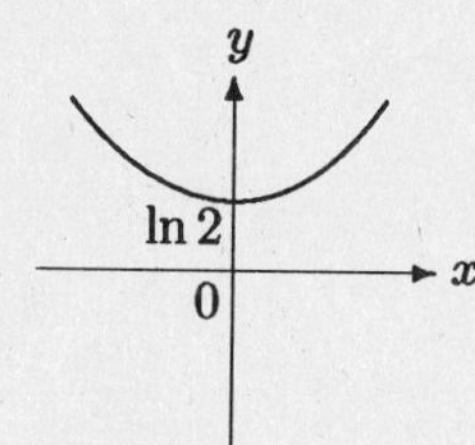

Exercise 37

33. $g'(t) = 2\sin t\,\cos t = \sin 2t$; $g''(t) = 2\cos 2t$

relative maximum value is $g(n\pi + \pi/2) = 1$ for any integer n; relative minimum value is $g(n\pi) = 0$ for any integer n; increasing on $[n\pi, n\pi + \pi/2]$ and decreasing on $[n\pi + \pi/2, (n+1)\pi]$; concave upward on $(n\pi - \pi/4, n\pi + \pi/4)$ and concave downward on $(n\pi + \pi/4, n\pi + 3\pi/4)$; inflection points are $(\pi/4 + n\pi/2, \frac{1}{2})$; symmetry with respect to the y axis.

34. $g'(t) = 2\tan t\,\sec^2 t$; $g''(t) = 2\sec^4 t + 4\tan^2 t\,\sec^2 t$; relative minimum value is $g(n\pi) = 0$ for any integer n; increasing on $[n\pi, n\pi + \pi/2]$ and decreasing on $(n\pi + \pi/2, (n+1)\pi]$; concave upward on $(n\pi - \pi/2, n\pi + \pi/2)$; vertical asymptotes are $t = n\pi + \pi/2$; symmetry with respect to the y axis.

35. $f'(x) = \dfrac{e^x}{(1+e^x)^2}$; $f''(x) = \dfrac{e^x - e^{2x}}{(1+e^x)^3}$

increasing on $(-\infty, \infty)$; $f''(x) = 0$ if $e^x(1 - e^x) = 0$, or $x = 0$; concave upward on $(-\infty, 0)$ and concave downward on $(0, \infty)$; inflection point is $(0, \frac{1}{2})$;

$$\lim_{x\to\infty} \frac{e^x}{1+e^x} = \lim_{x\to\infty} \frac{1}{e^{-x}+1} = 1 \quad \text{and} \quad \lim_{x\to-\infty} \frac{e^x}{1+e^x} = 0$$

so that $y = 1$ and $y = 0$ are horizontal asymptotes.

36. $f'(x) = \dfrac{1}{x^2}e^{-1/x}$; $f''(x) = \dfrac{e^{-1/x}}{x^4}(1 - 2x)$

increasing on $(-\infty, 0)$ and $(0, \infty)$; concave upward on $(-\infty, 0)$ and $(0, \frac{1}{2})$, and concave downward on $(\frac{1}{2}, \infty)$; inflection point is $(\frac{1}{2}, e^{-2})$; vertical asymptote is $x = 0$; horizontal asymptote is $y = 1$.

37. $f'(x) = \dfrac{e^x - e^{-x}}{e^x + e^{-x}} = \dfrac{e^{-x}(e^{2x} - 1)}{e^x + e^{-x}}$; $f''(x) = \dfrac{4}{(e^x + e^{-x})^2}$

increasing on $[0, \infty)$ and decreasing on $(-\infty, 0]$; minimum value is $f(0) = \ln 2$; concave upward on $(-\infty, \infty)$; symmetry with respect to the y axis.

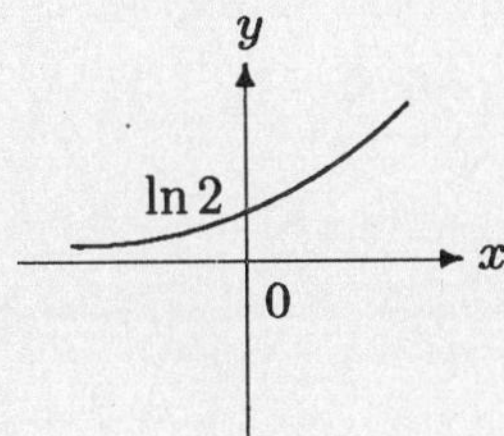

Exercise 38

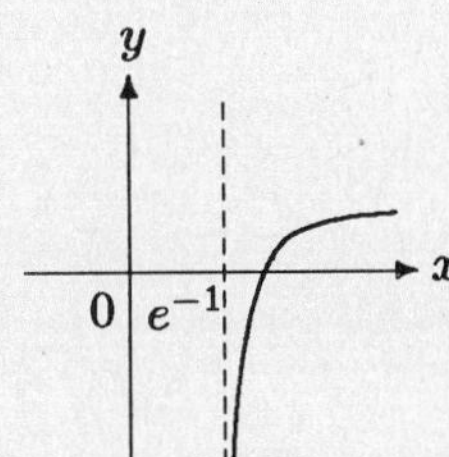

Exercise 39

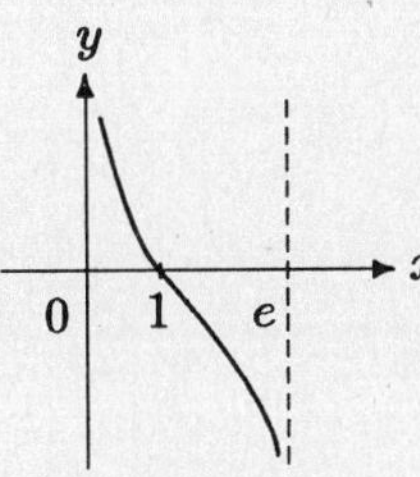

Exercise 40

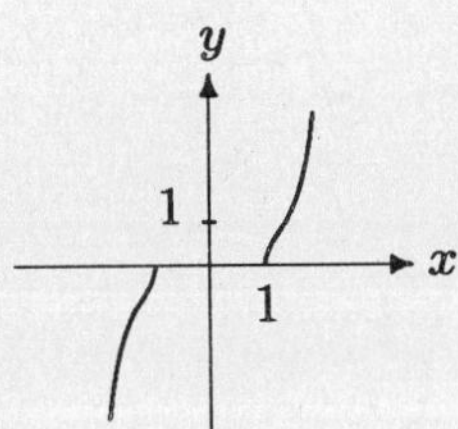

Exercise 41

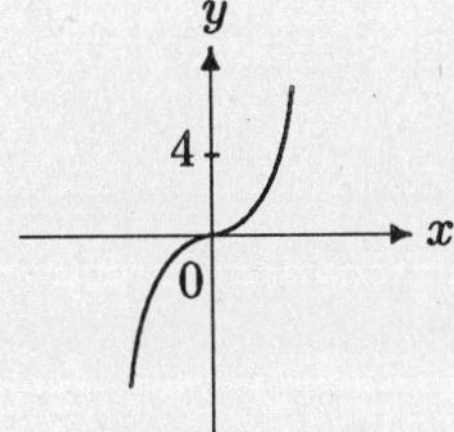

Exercise 42

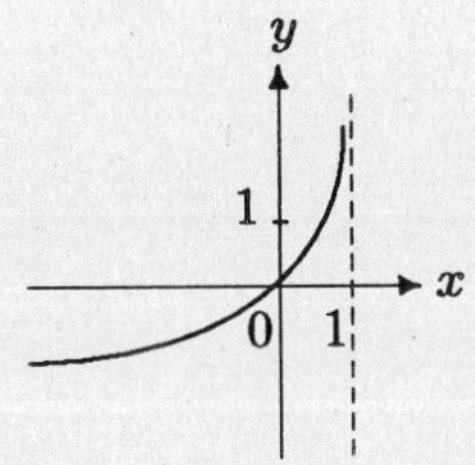

Exercise 43

38. $f'(x) = \dfrac{e^x}{1+e^x}$; $f''(x) = \dfrac{e^x}{(1+e^x)^2}$
increasing on $(-\infty, \infty)$; concave upward on $(-\infty, \infty)$; horizontal asymptote is $y = 0$.

39. $f'(x) = \dfrac{1}{x(1+\ln x)}$; $f''(x) = \dfrac{-(2+\ln x)}{x^2(1+\ln x)^2}$
domain is (e^{-1}, ∞); increasing on (e^{-1}, ∞); concave downward on (e^{-1}, ∞); vertical asymptote is $x = e^{-1}$.

40. $f'(x) = \dfrac{-1}{x(1-\ln x)}$; $f''(x) = \dfrac{-\ln x}{x^2(1-\ln x)^2}$
domain is $(0, e)$; decreasing on $(0, e)$; concave upward on $(0, 1)$ and concave downward on $(1, e)$; inflection point is $(1, 0)$; vertical asymptotes are $x = 0$ and $x = e$.

41. $f'(x) = \dfrac{2x^2-1}{\sqrt{x^2-1}}$; $f''(x) = \dfrac{x(2x^2-3)}{(x^2-1)^{3/2}}$
increasing on $(-\infty, -1]$ and $[1, \infty)$; concave upward on $(-\sqrt{\frac{3}{2}}, -1)$ and $(\sqrt{\frac{3}{2}}, \infty)$, and concave downward on $(-\infty, -\sqrt{\frac{3}{2}})$ and $(1, \sqrt{\frac{3}{2}})$; inflection points are $(\sqrt{\frac{3}{2}}, \sqrt{\frac{3}{4}})$ and $(-\sqrt{\frac{3}{2}}, -\sqrt{\frac{3}{4}})$; symmetry with respect to the origin.

42. $f'(x) = \dfrac{1+2x^2}{(1+x^2)^{1/2}}$; $f''(x) = \dfrac{x(3+2x^2)}{(1+x^2)^{3/2}}$
increasing on $(-\infty, \infty)$; concave upward on $(0, \infty)$, and concave downward on $(-\infty, 0)$; inflection point is $(0, 0)$; symmetry with respect to the origin.

43. $f'(x) = \dfrac{2-x}{2(1-x)^{3/2}}$; $f''(x) = \dfrac{4-x}{4(1-x)^{5/2}}$
domain is $(-\infty, 1)$; increasing on $(-\infty, 1)$; concave upward on $(-\infty, 1)$; vertical asymptote is $x = 1$.

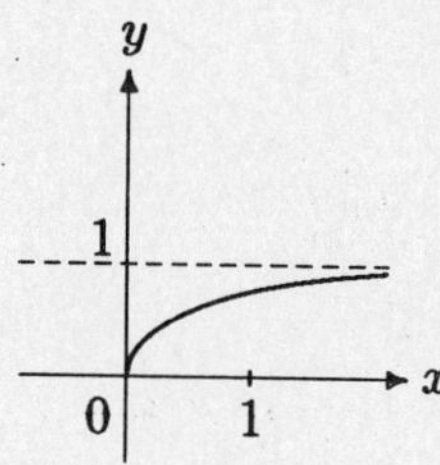

Exercise 44

Exercise 45

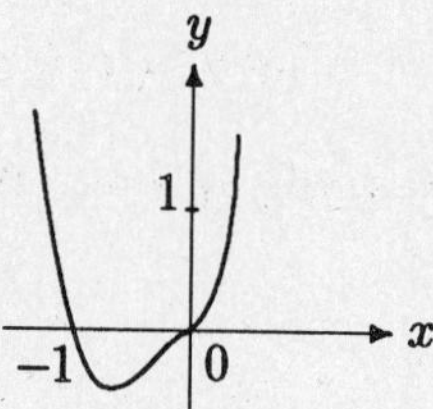

Exercise 46

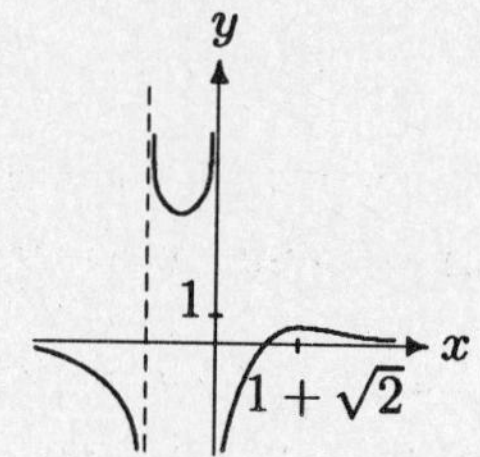

Exercise 47

44. $f'(x) = \dfrac{x^{-1/2}}{2(1+x^{1/2})^2}$; $f''(x) = \dfrac{-(x^{-3/2}+3x^{-1})}{4(1+x^{1/2})^3}$
increasing on $[0,\infty)$; concave downward on $(0,\infty)$; horizontal asymptote is $y=1$.

45. $f'(x) = 4x^3+12x^2+8x = 4x(x+1)(x+2)$; $f''(x) = 12x^2+24x+8 = 12(x+1-\frac{1}{3}\sqrt{3})(x+1+\frac{1}{3}\sqrt{3})$
by the Newton-Raphson method, the zeros of f are approximately -2.554 and 0.554; relative maximum value is $f(-1) = -1$; relative minimum value is $f(-2) = f(0) = -2$; increasing on $[-2,-1]$ and $[0,\infty)$, and decreasing on $(-\infty,-2]$ and $[-1,0]$; concave upward on $(-\infty,-1-\frac{1}{3}\sqrt{3})$ and $(-1+\frac{1}{3}\sqrt{3},\infty)$, and concave downward on $(-1-\frac{1}{3}\sqrt{3},-1+\frac{1}{3}\sqrt{3})$; inflection points are $(-1-\frac{1}{3}\sqrt{3},-\frac{14}{9})$ and $(-1+\frac{1}{3}\sqrt{3},-\frac{14}{9})$.

46. $f'(x) = 8x^3+3x^2+1$; $f''(x) = 24x^2+6x = 6x(4x+1)$
by the Newton-Raphson method, the critical point c is approximately -0.661, and the relative minimum value is $f(c) \approx -0.568$; increasing on (c,∞) and decreasing on $(-\infty,c)$; concave upward on $(-\infty,-\frac{1}{4})$ and $(0,\infty)$, and concave downward on $(-\frac{1}{4},0)$; inflection points are $(-\frac{1}{4},-\frac{33}{128})$ and $(0,0)$.

47. $f'(x) = \dfrac{-x^2+2x+1}{x^2(x+1)^2}$; $f''(x) = \dfrac{2x^3-6x^2-6x-2}{x^3(x+1)^3}$
relative minimum value is $f(1-\sqrt{2}) = \sqrt{2}/(3\sqrt{2}-4)$; relative maximum value is $f(1+\sqrt{2}) = \sqrt{2}/(4+3\sqrt{2})$; increasing on $[1-\sqrt{2},0)$ and $(0,1+\sqrt{2})$, and decreasing on $(-\infty,-1)$, $(-1,1-\sqrt{2}]$ and $(1+\sqrt{2},\infty)$; by the Newton-Raphson method the zero c of f'' is approximately 3.847; concave upward on $(-1,0)$ and (c,∞), and concave downward on $(-\infty,-1)$ and $(0,c)$; inflection point is $(c,f(c))$, which is approximately $(3.847, 0.153)$; vertical asymptotes are $x=-1$ and $x=0$; horizontal asymptote is $y=0$.

48. No asymptotes; relative maximum value: $f(-1.06) \approx 2.10$; relative minimum value: $f(.840) \approx -.305$.

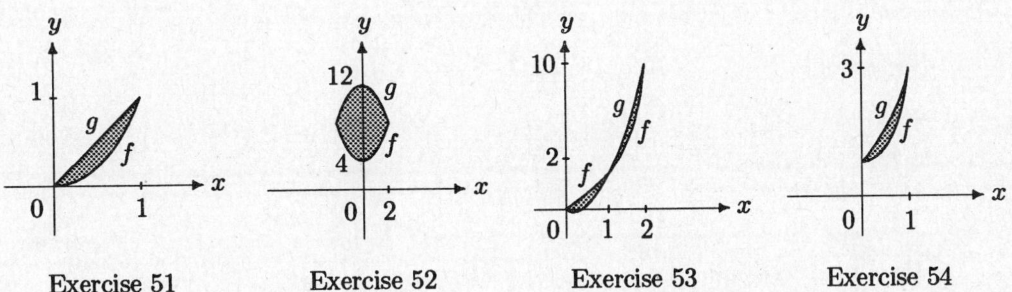

49. Vertical asymptotes: $x = 0$, $x = 1$, and $x = 2$; horizontal asymptote: $y = 0$; no relative extreme values.

50. Vertical asymptotes: $x = 0$, $x = 1$, and $x = 2$; horizontal asymptote: $y = 0$; relative maximum value: $f(1.49) \approx -3.33$; relative minimum value: $f(.514) \approx 3.33$.

51. The graphs intersect at (x, y) such that $x^2 = y = x$, or $x^2 - x = 0$, or $x = 0$ and $x = 1$. For $0 \le x \le 1$, $f(x) \le g(x)$. Since $g'(x) = 1$ and $f'(x) = 2x$, both functions are increasing on $[0, 1]$. The graph of f is concave upward on $(0, 1)$.

52. The graphs intersect at (x, y) such that $x^2 + 4 = y = 12 - x^2$, or $2x^2 = 8$, or $x = \pm 2$. For $-2 \le x \le 2$, $f(x) \le g(x)$. Since $f'(x) = 2x$ and $f''(x) = 2$, f is increasing on $[0, 2]$ and decreasing on $[-2, 0]$; its graph is concave upward on $(-2, 2)$. Since $g'(x) = -2x$ and $g''(x) = -2$, g is increasing on $[-2, 0]$ and decreasing on $[0, 2]$; its graph is concave downward on $(-2, 2)$.

53. The graphs intersect at (x, y) such that $x^3 + x = y = 3x^2 - x$, or $x^3 - 3x^2 + 2x = 0$, or $x = 0$, 1, and 2. For $0 < x < 1$, $f(x) \ge g(x)$, and for $1 < x < 2$, $f(x) \le g(x)$. Since $f'(x) = 3x^2 + 1$ and $f''(x) = 6x$, f is increasing on $[0, 2]$ and its graph is concave upward on $(0, 2)$. Since $g'(x) = 6x - 1$ and $g''(x) = 6$, g is increasing on $[\frac{1}{6}, 2]$ and decreasing on $[0, \frac{1}{6}]$; relative minimum value is $g(\frac{1}{6}) = -\frac{1}{12}$; its graph is concave upward on $(0, 2)$.

54. The graphs intersect at (x, y) such that $x^3 + x^2 + 1 = y = x^3 + x + 1$, or $x^2 - x = 0$, or $x = 0$ and $x = 1$. For $0 < x < 1$, $f(x) \le g(x)$. Since $f'(x) = 3x^2 + 2x$ and $f''(x) = 6x + 2$, f is increasing on $[0, 1]$ and its graph is concave upward on $(0, 1)$. Since $g'(x) = 3x^2 + 1$ and $g''(x) = 6x$, g is increasing on $[0, 1]$ and its graph is concave upward on $(0, 1)$.

55. The graphs intersect at (x, y) such that

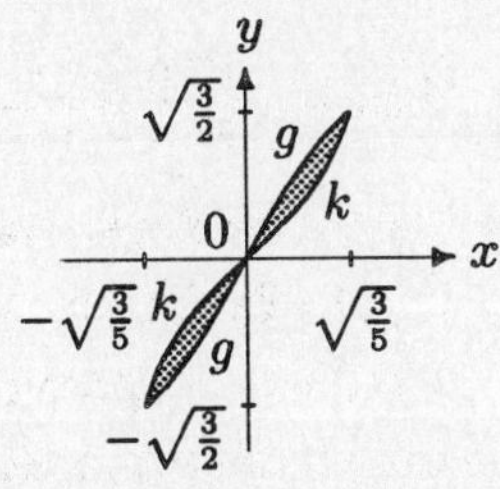

$$\frac{2x}{\sqrt{1+x^2}} = y = \frac{x}{\sqrt{1-x^2}}, \quad \text{or} \quad \frac{4x^2}{1+x^2} = \frac{x^2}{1-x^2},$$

or $3x^2 = 5x^4$ so that $x = 0$ and $x = \pm\sqrt{\frac{3}{5}}$. Since

$$g'(x) = 2/(1+x^2)^{3/2} \quad \text{and} \quad g''(x) = -6x/(1+x^2)^{5/2}$$

g is increasing on $[-\sqrt{\frac{3}{5}}, \sqrt{\frac{3}{5}}]$, and the graph of g is concave upward on $[-\sqrt{\frac{3}{5}}, 0)$ and concave downward on $(0, \sqrt{\frac{3}{5}})$. Since

$$k'(x) = \frac{1}{(1-x^2)^{3/2}} \quad \text{and} \quad k''(x) = \frac{3x}{(1-x^2)^{5/2}}$$

k is increasing on $[-\sqrt{\frac{3}{5}}, \sqrt{\frac{3}{5}}]$, and the graph of k is concave downward on $(-\sqrt{\frac{3}{5}}, 0)$ and concave upward on $(0, \sqrt{\frac{3}{5}})$.

56. The graphs intersect at (t, y) such that $t - \cos t = y = t + \sin t$, or $\sin t = -\cos t$, and thus for $t = \frac{3}{4}\pi + n\pi$, for $n = -1$, 0, and 1. Since $g'(t) = 1 + \sin t$ and $g''(t) = \cos t$, g is increasing on $[-\pi/4, 7\pi/4]$, and is concave upward on $(-\pi/4, \pi/2)$ and $(3\pi/2, 7\pi/4)$, and concave downward on $(\pi/2, 3\pi/2)$. Since $k'(t) = 1 + \cos t$ and $k''(t) = -\sin t$, k is increasing on $[-\pi/4, 7\pi/4]$, and is concave upward on $(-\pi/4, 0)$ and $(\pi, 7\pi/4)$, and concave downward on $(0, \pi)$.

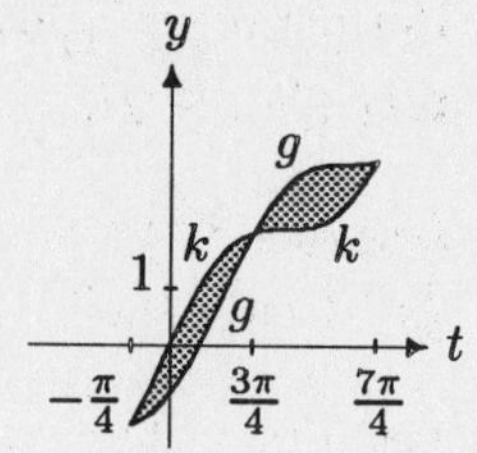

Chapter 4 Review

1. The domain of f is $(-\infty, 2]$;

$$f'(x) = 2x\sqrt{2-x} - \frac{x^2}{2\sqrt{2-x}} = \frac{x(8-5x)}{2\sqrt{2-x}}$$

so $f'(x) = 0$ for $x = 0$ and $\frac{8}{5}$, and $f'(x)$ is undefined for $x = 2$. Critical numbers: 0, $\frac{8}{5}$, 2.

2. $f'(x) = -\frac{1}{3}x^{-2/3}\sin x^{1/3}$, so $f'(x) = 0$ for $x = n^3\pi^3$ for any integer n except 0, and $f'(x)$ is undefined for $x = 0$. Critical numbers: $n^3\pi^3$ for any integer n.

3. Since $f'(x) = 2x + 1$, the only critical number in $(-2, 2)$ is $-\frac{1}{2}$. Thus the extreme values of f on $[-2, 2]$ can occur only at -2, $-\frac{1}{2}$ and 2. Since $f(-2) = 3$, $f(-\frac{1}{2}) = \frac{3}{4}$, and $f(2) = 7$, the minimum value is $f(-\frac{1}{2})$, which is $\frac{3}{4}$, and the maximum value is $f(2)$, which is 7.

4. Since $f'(x) = (3-x^2)/(3+x^2)^2$, the only critical numbers in $(-4, 4)$ are $-\sqrt{3}$ and $\sqrt{3}$. Thus the extreme values of f on $[-4, 4]$ can occur only at -4, $-\sqrt{3}$, $\sqrt{3}$, and 4. Since $f(-4) = -\frac{4}{19}$, $f(-\sqrt{3}) = -\frac{1}{6}\sqrt{3}$, $f(\sqrt{3}) = \frac{1}{6}\sqrt{3}$, and $f(4) = \frac{4}{19}$, the minimum value is $f(-\sqrt{3})$, which is $-\frac{1}{6}\sqrt{3}$, and the maximum value is $f(\sqrt{3})$, which is $\frac{1}{6}\sqrt{3}$.

5. Since $f'(x) = 1 + x/\sqrt{1-x^2}$, the only critical number in $(-1, 1)$ is $-\frac{1}{2}\sqrt{2}$. Thus the extreme values of f on $[-1, 1]$ can occur only at -1, $-\frac{1}{2}\sqrt{2}$, and 1. Since $f(-1) = -1$, $f(-\frac{1}{2}\sqrt{2}) = -\sqrt{2}$, and $f(1) = 1$, the minimum value is $f(-\frac{1}{2}\sqrt{2})$, which is $-\sqrt{2}$, and the maximum value is $f(1)$, which is 1.

6. Since $f'(x) = \frac{2}{3}x^{-1/3} - 1$ for $x \neq 0$, the only critical number in $(-\frac{1}{8}, \frac{1}{8})$ is 0. Thus the extreme values of f on $[-\frac{1}{8}, \frac{1}{8}]$ can occur only at $-\frac{1}{8}$, 0, and $\frac{1}{8}$. Since $f(-\frac{1}{8}) = (-\frac{1}{8})^{2/3} + \frac{1}{8} = \frac{3}{8}$, $f(0) = 0$, and $f(\frac{1}{8}) = (\frac{1}{8})^{2/3} - \frac{1}{8} = \frac{1}{8}$, the minimum value is $f(0)$, which is 0, and the maximum value is $f(-\frac{1}{8})$, which is $\frac{3}{8}$.

7. a. $f(-1) = (-1) + 1 = 0$ and $f(1) = 1 - 1 = 0$, and $f'(x) = 1$ for x in $(-1, 1)$ with $x \neq 0$. Also $f'(0)$ does not exist.

   b. This does not contradict Rolle's Theorem because f is not continuous at 0.

8. Since $f(2) > f(0)$, the Mean Value Theorem implies that there is a number c in $(0,2)$ such that $f'(c) = [f(2) - f(0)]/(2-0) > 0$. Thus f' takes on positive values on $(0,2)$. Since f is not increasing on $[0,2]$, there are numbers a, b such that $0 \le a < b \le 2$ and $f(a) > f(b)$. Therefore $[f(b) - f(a)]/(b-a) < 0$. But the Mean Value Theorem guarantees the existence of a number c in (a,b), and hence in $(0,2)$, such that $f'(c) = [f(b) - f(a)]/(b-a) < 0$. Thus f' also takes on negative values on $(0,2)$.

9. Let $g(x) = \frac{1}{3}x^3 + \cos x$. Then $g'(x) = x^2 - \sin x = f'(x)$, so by Theorem 4.6, $f(x) = g(x) + C = \frac{1}{3}x^3 + \cos x + C$.

10. Let $g(x) = 5x$. Then $g'(x) = 5 = f'(x)$, so by Theorem 4.6, $f(x) = g(x) + C = 5x + C$ for the appropriate constant C. Since $f(0) = -3$, we have $-3 = f(0) = 5(0) + C = C$.Thus $f(x) = 5x - 3$.

11. Let $g(x) = \frac{1}{3}x^3 - 4x$. Then $g'(x) = x^2 - 4 = f''(x) = (f')'(x)$ so by Theorem 4.6, $f'(x) = g(x) + C_1 = \frac{1}{3}x^3 - 4x + C_1$ for some constant C_1. Now let $h(x) = \frac{1}{12}x^4 - 2x^2 + C_1x$. Then $h'(x) = \frac{1}{3}x^3 - 4x + C_1 = f'(x)$, so by Theorem 4.6, $f(x) = h(x) + C_2 = \frac{1}{12}x^4 - 2x^2 + C_1x + C_2$ for some constant C_2.

12. Let $g(x) = 0$. Then $g'(x) = 0 = f''(x) = (f')'(x)$, so by Theorem 4.6, $f'(x) = g(x) + C_1 = C_1$, for the appropriate constant C_1. Now let $h(x) = C_1x$. Then $h'(x) = C_1 = f'(x)$, so by Theorem 4.6, $f(x) = h(x) + C_2 = C_1x + C_2$ for the appropriate constant C_2. Since $f(0) = 0$, we have $C_2 = 0$, and since $f(1) = -1$, we have $-1 = f(1) = C_1(1) = C_1$. Thus $f(x) = -x$.

13. $f'(x) = x^2 - 2x + 1 = (x-1)^2$, so $f'(x) \ge 0$ for all x, and $f'(x) > 0$ except for $x = 1$. By Theorem 4.7, f is increasing on $(-\infty, \infty)$.

14. $f'(x) = \frac{1}{3}x^{-2/3} - 1$, so $f'(x) < 0$ on $(-\infty, -\sqrt{3}/9)$ and on $(\sqrt{3}/9, \infty)$, and $f'(x) > 0$ on $(-\sqrt{3}/9, 0)$ and on $(0, \sqrt{3}/9)$. By Theorem 4.7, f is decreasing on $(-\infty, -\sqrt{3}/9]$ and on $[\sqrt{3}/9, \infty)$, and is increasing on $[-\sqrt{3}/9, \sqrt{3}/9]$.

15. $f'(x) = \cos x - \frac{1}{8}\sec^2 x$, so $f'(x) > 0$ if $\cos x > \frac{1}{8}\sec^2 x$, or $\cos^3 x > \frac{1}{8}$, or $\cos x > \frac{1}{2}$. By Theorem 4.7, f is increasing on $[2n\pi - \pi/3, 2n\pi + \pi/3]$ and decreasing on $[2n\pi + \pi/3, 2n\pi + \pi/2)$, on $(2n\pi + \pi/2, 2n\pi + 3\pi/2)$, and on $(2n\pi + 3\pi/2, 2n\pi + 5\pi/3]$, for any integer n.

16. $f'(x) = 4x^3 + 3x^2 + 2x + 1$; by the Newton-Raphson method, f' has an approximate zero at -0.606, and f' is an increasing function since $f''(x) = 12x^2 + 6x + 2 > 0$ for all x. Thus f is increasing on (c, ∞) and decreasing on $(-\infty, c)$, where $c \approx -0.606$.

17. Let $f(x) = \sqrt{x+3} - \sqrt{3} - x/4$ for $0 \le x \le 1$. Then $f'(x) = 1/(2\sqrt{x+3}) - \frac{1}{4}$. Thus f' is decreasing, and $f'(x) > 1/(2\sqrt{1+3}) - \frac{1}{4} = 0$ for $0 < x < 1$. We conclude from Theorem 4.7 that f is increasing on $[0,1]$. Since $f(0) = 0$, it follows that $\sqrt{x+3} \ge \sqrt{3} + x/4$ for $0 \le x \le 1$.

18. Let $f(x) = \sin x - (2/\pi)x$. Then $f'(x) = \cos x - 2/\pi$ and $f''(x) = -\sin x$. Since $f'(0) = 1 - 2/\pi > 0$ and $f'(\pi/2) = -2/\pi < 0$, the Intermediate Value Theorem implies that there is at least one x_0 in $[0, \pi/2]$ such that $f'(x_0) = 0$. Since $f''(x) < 0$ for x in $(0, \pi/2)$, f' is decreasing on $[0, \pi/2]$. Thus $f'(x) > 0$ for $0 < x < x_0$ and $f'(x) < 0$ for $x_0 < x < \pi/2$, so f is increasing on $[0, x_0]$ and decreasing

on $[x_0, \pi/2]$. Therefore $f(x) \geq f(0) = 0$ for $0 \leq x \leq x_0$ and $f(x) \geq f(\pi/2) = 0$ for $x_0 \leq x \leq \pi/2$. Thus $\sin x - (2/\pi)x = f(x) \geq 0$, so $\sin x \geq (2/\pi)x$ for $0 \leq x \leq \pi/2$.

19. $f'(x) = 12x^3 - 30x^2 + 12x = 6x(2x-1)(x-2)$; $f''(x) = 36x^2 - 60x + 12$. The relative extreme values (if any) must occur at the critical numbers 0, $\frac{1}{2}$, and 2. Since $f''(0) = 12 > 0$, $f''(\frac{1}{2}) = -9 < 0$, and $f''(2) = 36 > 0$, the Second Derivative Test implies that $f(0) = 3$ is a relative minimum value, $f(\frac{1}{2}) = \frac{55}{16}$ is a relative maximum value, and $f(2) = -5$ is a relative minimum value.

20. $f'(x) = \dfrac{x^2 + 3 - (x-1)2x}{(x^2+3)^2} = \dfrac{-x^2 + 2x + 3}{(x^2+3)^2} = \dfrac{-(x-3)(x+1)}{(x^2+3)^2}$

The relative extreme values (if any) must occur at the critical numbers -1 and 3. Since $f'(x) < 0$ for x in $(-\infty, -1)$ or $(3, \infty)$, and since $f'(x) > 0$ for x in $(-1, 3)$, the First Derivative Test implies that $f(-1) = -\frac{1}{2}$ is a relative minimum value, and $f(3) = \frac{1}{6}$ is a relative maximum value.

21. $f'(x) = 2(x+1)(x-2)^4 + 4(x+1)^2(x-2)^3 = 6x(x+1)(x-2)^3$. The relative extreme values (if any) must occur at the critical numbers -1, 0, and 2. Since $f'(x) < 0$ for x in $(-\infty, -1)$ or $(0, 2)$, and since $f'(x) > 0$ for x in $(-1, 0)$ or $(2, \infty)$, the First Derivative Test implies that $f(-1) = f(2) = 0$ is a relative minimum value, and $f(0) = 16$ is a relative maximum value.

22. The domain of f is $[1, \infty)$. Next,

$$f'(x) = \frac{1}{\sqrt{x+1}} - \frac{1}{2\sqrt{x-1}}, \quad f''(x) = \frac{-1}{2(x+1)^{3/2}} + \frac{1}{4(x-1)^{3/2}}.$$

Now $f'(x) = 0$ if $1/\sqrt{x+1} = 1/(2\sqrt{x-1})$, that is, if $2\sqrt{x-1} = \sqrt{x+1}$, or $4(x-1) = x+1$, or $x = \frac{5}{3}$. Thus the relative extreme value (if any) must occur at $\frac{5}{3}$. Since

$$f''\left(\frac{5}{3}\right) = \frac{-1}{2(8/3)^{3/2}} + \frac{1}{4(2/3)^{3/2}} = \frac{-1}{16(2/3)^{3/2}} + \frac{1}{4(2/3)^{3/2}} > 0$$

the Second Derivative Test implies that

$$f\left(\frac{5}{3}\right) = 2\sqrt{\frac{8}{3}} - \sqrt{\frac{2}{3}} = \frac{2\sqrt{8} - \sqrt{2}}{\sqrt{3}} = \frac{3\sqrt{2}}{\sqrt{3}} = \sqrt{6}$$

is a relative minimum value.

23. $f'(x) = 2x^3 + 3x^2 - 12x$; $f''(x) = 6x^2 + 6x - 12 = 6(x+2)(x-1)$. Thus the graph is concave upward on $(-\infty, -2)$ and $(1, \infty)$, and concave downward on $(-2, 1)$.

24. $f'(x) = \dfrac{1}{2\sqrt{x}} - \dfrac{1}{x^2}$ and $f''(x) = \dfrac{-1}{4x^{3/2}} + \dfrac{2}{x^3} = \dfrac{8 - x^{3/2}}{4x^3}$

Thus the graph is concave upward on $(0, 4)$ and concave downward on $(4, \infty)$.

25. $f'(x) = \dfrac{-4x^3}{(1+x^4)^2}$ and $f''(x) = \dfrac{4x^2(5x^4 - 3)}{(1+x^4)^3}$

Thus the graph is concave upward on $(-\infty, -\sqrt[4]{\frac{3}{5}})$ and on $(\sqrt[4]{\frac{3}{5}}, \infty)$, and concave downward on $(-\sqrt[4]{\frac{3}{5}}, \sqrt[4]{\frac{3}{5}})$.

26. $f'(x) = \cos x + \frac{1}{2}\cos 2x$; $f''(x) = -\sin x - \sin 2x = -\sin x\,(1+2\cos x)$. For the moment let $-\pi \le x \le \pi$. We see that $\sin x > 0$ for $0 < x < \pi$ and that $1 + 2\cos x > 0$ for $-2\pi/3 < x < 2\pi/3$. Thus $f''(x) > 0$ for $-2\pi/3 < x < 0$ and $2\pi/3 < x < \pi$, whereas $f''(x) < 0$ for $-\pi < x < -2\pi/3$ and $0 < x < 2\pi/3$. From the periodicity, the graph is concave upward on $(-2\pi/3 + 2n\pi, 2n\pi)$ and $(2\pi/3 + 2n\pi, \pi + 2n\pi)$ for any integer n, and concave downward on $(-\pi + 2n\pi, -2\pi/3 + 2n\pi)$ and $(2n\pi, 2\pi/3 + 2n\pi)$ for any integer n.

27. Since $f'(x) = (x-1)^3(x+1)$ is positive on $(-\infty, -1)$ and $(1, \infty)$, f is increasing on $(-\infty, -1]$ and $[1, \infty)$. Since $f'(x) < 0$ on $(-1, 1)$, f is decreasing on $[-1, 1]$. Also $f''(x) = 3(x-1)^2(x+1) + (x-1)^3 = (x-1)^2(4x+2)$. Thus the graph of f is concave upward on $(-\frac{1}{2}, \infty)$ and concave downward on $(-\infty, -\frac{1}{2})$.

28. Since $f'(x) = xe^x$ is positive on $(0, \infty)$, f is increasing on $[0, \infty)$. Since $f'(x)$ is negative on $(-\infty, 0)$, f is decreasing on $(-\infty, 0]$. Also $f''(x) = (x+1)e^x$. Thus the graph of f is concave upward on $(-1, \infty)$ and concave downward on $(-\infty, -1)$.

29. $f'(x) = 3x^2 - 6$; $f''(x) = 6x$; relative maximum value is $f(-\sqrt{2}) = 4\sqrt{2} - 1$; relative minimum value is $f(\sqrt{2}) = -4\sqrt{2} - 1$; increasing on $(-\infty, -\sqrt{2}]$ and $[\sqrt{2}, \infty)$, and decreasing on $[-\sqrt{2}, \sqrt{2}]$; concave upward on $(0, \infty)$ and concave downward on $(-\infty, 0)$; inflection point is $(0, -1)$.

30. $f'(x) = 2x^2(2x+3)$; $f''(x) = 12x(x+1)$; relative minimum value is $f(-\frac{3}{2}) = -\frac{11}{16}$; increasing on $[-\frac{3}{2}, \infty)$ and decreasing on $(-\infty, -\frac{3}{2}]$; concave upward on $(-\infty, -1)$ and $(0, \infty)$, and concave downward on $(-1, 0)$; inflection points are $(-1, 0)$ and $(0, 1)$.

31. $f'(x) = \dfrac{x^2 - 3}{x^4}$; $f''(x) = \dfrac{12 - 2x^2}{x^5}$
relative maximum value is $f(-\sqrt{3}) = \frac{2}{9}\sqrt{3}$; relative minimum value is $f(\sqrt{3}) = -\frac{2}{9}\sqrt{3}$; increasing on $(-\infty, -\sqrt{3}]$ and $[\sqrt{3}, \infty)$, and decreasing on $[-\sqrt{3}, 0)$ and $(0, \sqrt{3}]$; concave upward on $(-\infty, -\sqrt{6})$ and $(0, \sqrt{6})$, and concave downward on $(-\sqrt{6}, 0)$ and $(\sqrt{6}, \infty)$; inflection points are $(-\sqrt{6}, \frac{5}{36}\sqrt{6})$ and $(\sqrt{6}, -\frac{5}{36}\sqrt{6})$; vertical asymptote is $x = 0$; horizontal asymptote is $y = 0$; symmetry with respect to the origin.

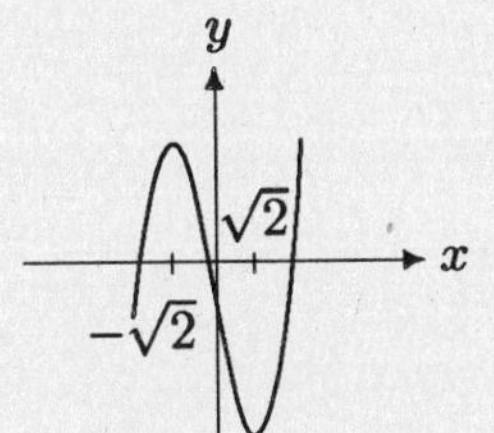

Exercise 29

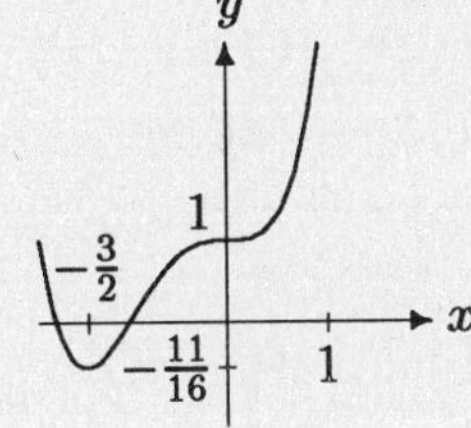

Exercise 30

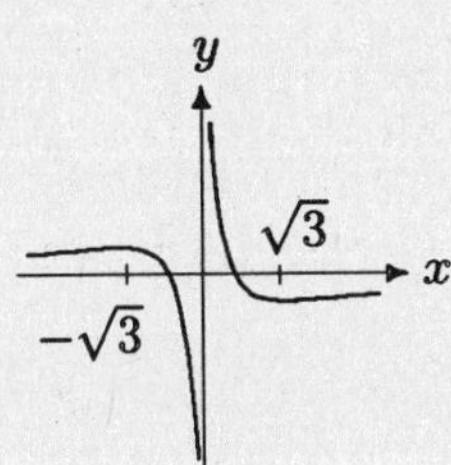

Exercise 31

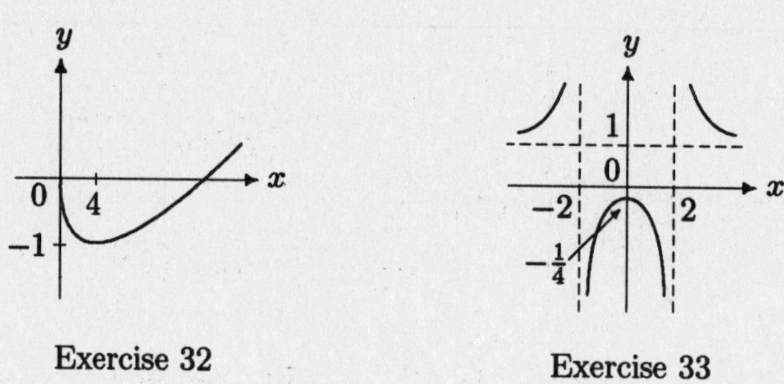

Exercise 32

Exercise 33

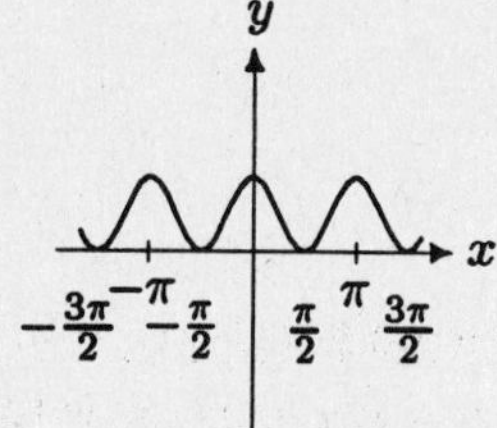

Exercise 34

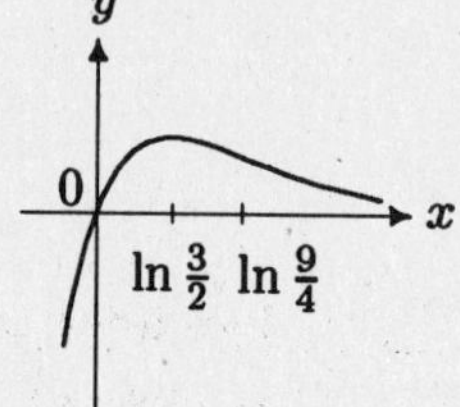

Exercise 35

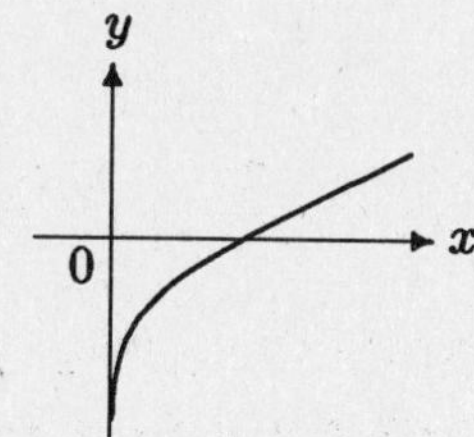

Exercise 36

32. $f'(x) = \dfrac{\sqrt{x}-2}{4\sqrt{x}}$; $f''(x) = \frac{1}{4}x^{-3/2}$
relative minimum value is $f(4) = -1$; increasing on $[4, \infty)$, and decreasing on $[0, 4]$; concave upward on $(0, \infty)$.

33. $k'(x) = \dfrac{-10x}{(x^2-4)^2}$; $k''(x) = \dfrac{10(3x^2+4)}{(x^2-4)^3}$
relative maximum value is $k(0) = -\frac{1}{4}$; increasing on $(-\infty, -2)$ and $(-2, 0]$, and decreasing on $[0, 2)$ and $(2, \infty)$; concave upward on $(-\infty, -2)$ and $(2, \infty)$, and concave downward on $(-2, 2)$; vertical asymptotes are $x = -2$ and $x = 2$; horizontal asymptote is $y = 1$; symmetry with respect to the y axis.

34. $f'(x) = -2\sin x\cos x = -\sin 2x$; $f''(x) = -2\cos 2x$; relative maximum value is $f(n\pi) = 1$ for any integer n; relative minimum value is $f(n\pi+\pi/2) = 0$ for any integer n; increasing on $[n\pi+\pi/2, (n+1)\pi]$ and decreasing on $[n\pi, n\pi+\pi/2]$; concave upward on $(\pi/4+n\pi, 3\pi/4+n\pi)$, and concave downward on $(3\pi/4+n\pi, 5\pi/4+n\pi)$; inflection points are $(\pi/4+n\pi, \frac{1}{2})$ and $(3\pi/4+n\pi, \frac{1}{2})$; symmetry with respect to the y axis.

35. $f'(x) = -2e^{-2x} + 3e^{-3x} = e^{-3x}(3-2e^x)$; $f''(x) = 4e^{-2x} - 9e^{-3x} = e^{-3x}(4e^x - 9)$
relative maximum value is $f(\ln\frac{3}{2}) = -\frac{9}{8}$; increasing on $(-\infty, \ln\frac{3}{2}]$, and decreasing on $[\ln\frac{3}{2}, \infty)$; concave upward on $(\ln\frac{9}{4}, \infty)$ and concave downward on $(-\infty, \ln\frac{9}{4})$; inflection point is $(\ln\frac{9}{4}, \frac{80}{729})$.

36. $f'(x) = \dfrac{e^x+e^{-x}}{e^x-e^{-x}}$; $f''(x) = \dfrac{-4}{e^x-e^{-x}}$
domain is $(0, \infty)$; increasing on $(0, \infty)$; concave downward on $(0, \infty)$; vertical asymptote is $x = 0$.

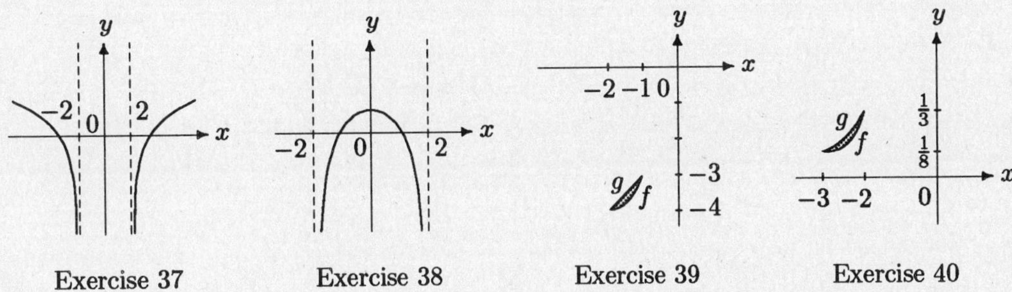

37. $f'(x) = \dfrac{2x}{x^2-4}$; $f''(x) = \dfrac{-2(x^2+4)}{(x^2-4)^2}$

domain is the union of $(-\infty, -2)$ and $(2, \infty)$; increasing on $(2, \infty)$ and decreasing on $(-\infty, -2)$; concave downward on $(-\infty, -2)$ and $(2, \infty)$; vertical asymptotes are $x = -2$ and $x = 2$; symmetry with respect to the y axis.

38. $f'(x) = \dfrac{2x}{x^2-4}$; $f''(x) = \dfrac{-2(x^2+4)}{(x^2-4)^2}$

domain is $(-2, 2)$; relative maximum value is $f(0) = \ln 4$; increasing on $(-2, 0]$ and decreasing on $[0, 2)$; concave downward on $(-2, 2)$; vertical asymptotes are $x = -2$ and $x = 2$; symmetry with respect to the y axis.

39. The graphs intersect at (x, y) such that $x^2 + 4x = y = x - 2$, or $x^2 + 3x + 2 = 0$, or $x = -2$ or $x = -1$. For $-2 \le x \le -1$, $f(x) \le g(x)$. Since $f'(x) = 2x + 4$ and $f''(x) = 2$, f has a relative minimum value at -2, and the graph of f is concave upward on $(-2, -1)$; g is increasing on $[-2, -1]$.

40. The graphs intersect at (x, y) such that $-8/(7+5x) = 8/(x^2-1)$, or $1 - x^2 = 7 + 5x$, or $x^2 + 5x + 6 = 0$, or $x = -3$ or $x = -2$. For $-3 \le x \le -2$, $f(x) \le g(x)$. (Check that $f(-\frac{5}{2}) < g(-\frac{5}{2})$.) Since $f'(x) = 40/(7+5x)^2$ and $f''(x) = -400/(7+5x)^3$, f is increasing on $[-3, -2]$ and its graph is concave upward on $(-3, -2)$. Since

$$g'(x) = \frac{-16x}{(x^2-1)^2} \quad \text{and} \quad g''(x) = \frac{16(3x^2+1)}{(x^2-1)^3}$$

g is increasing on $[-3, -2]$ and its graph is concave upward on $(-3, -2)$.

41. $f'(x) = mx^{m-1}(x-1)^n + nx^m(x-1)^{n-1} = x^{m-1}(x-1)^{n-1}[m(x-1) + nx]$, so $f'(x) = 0$ for $x = 0$, 1, and $m/(m+n)$. If $f(\frac{1}{4})$ is to be a relative extreme value, then $m/(m+n) = \frac{1}{4}$, so that $4m = m + n$, or $n = 3m$. Furthermore, if $f(0)$ and $f(1)$ are relative extreme values, then f' must change sign at 0 and 1, which requires $m - 1$ and $n - 1$ to be odd, that is, m and n even. Thus if $f(0)$, $f(\frac{1}{4})$, and $f(1)$ are relative extreme values, then $n = 3m$ with m even.

42. For the area to be maximum the fourth side must have length greater than L. Let x be as in the diagram. By the Pythagorean Theorem the length of the dashed lines is $\sqrt{L^2 - x^2}$. Thus the area A of the trapezoid, which is the sum of the areas of the rectangle and the two triangles, is given by

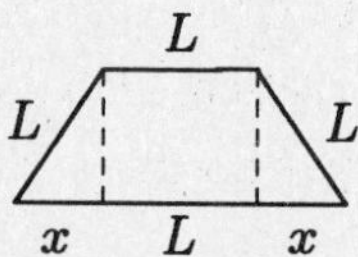

$$A = L\sqrt{L^2 - x^2} + 2 \cdot \tfrac{1}{2} \cdot L\sqrt{L^2 - x^2} = (L + x)\sqrt{L^2 - x^2}$$

for $0 < x < L$. Since

$$\frac{dA}{dx} = \sqrt{L^2 - x^2} - \frac{(L + x)x}{\sqrt{L^2 - x^2}} = \frac{L - Lx - 2x^2}{\sqrt{L^2 - x^2}} = \frac{(L - 2x)(L + x)}{\sqrt{L^2 - x^2}}$$

we have $dA/dx = 0$ only for $x = L/2$. Since $dA/dx > 0$ for $0 < x < L/2$ and $dA/dx < 0$ for $L/2 < x < L$, (1) of Section 4.6 and the First Derivative Test imply that $x = L/2$ yields the trapezoid with maximum area.

43. The area A of the rectangle in Figure 4.88 is given by $A = xy = xe^{-x}$ for $x > 0$. Thus $dA/dx = e^{-x} - xe^{-x} = (1 - x)e^{-x}$, so that $dA/dx = 0$ only for $x = 1$. Since $dA/dx > 0$ for $0 < x < 1$ and $dA/dx < 0$ for $x > 1$, (1) of Section 4.6 and the First Derivative Test imply that A is maximum for $x = 1$. The maximum area is $(1)e^{-1} = e^{-1}$.

44. The square of the distance between the point $(4, 0)$ and the point $(x, x^{1/2})$ on the curve $y = x^{1/2}$ is given by $f(x) = (x - 4)^2 + (x^{1/2} - 0)^2 = x^2 - 7x + 16$. We will minimize f in order to find the closest point on the graph. Now $f'(x) = 2x - 7$, so that $f'(x) = 0$ only if $x = \frac{7}{2}$. Since $f''(x) = 2$ for $x > 0$, (1) of Section 4.6 and the Second Derivative Test imply that the minimum square of the distance, and hence the minimum distance, occurs at $(\frac{7}{2}, \sqrt{\frac{7}{2}})$.

45. a. By Theorem 4.8, the amount of Uranium 238 is given by $f(t) = f(0)e^{kt}$ for some constant k. Since $f(10^9) = .85719f(0)$, we have $f(0)e^{k \cdot 10^9} = .85719f(0)$, so that $e^{k \cdot 10^9} = .85719$, or $k = 10^{-9} \ln .85719$. We seek the value of t for which $f(t) = \frac{1}{2}f(0)$, or $f(0)e^{kt} = \frac{1}{2}f(0)$, so that

$$t = \frac{\ln(1/2)}{k} = \frac{-\ln 2}{10^{-9} \ln .85719} \approx 4.4982 \times 10^9.$$

Thus the half-life of Uranium 238 is approximately 4.5 billion years.

b. Taking $t = 10^7$ in $f(t) = f(0)e^{kt}$, we find that $f(10^7) = f(0)e^{k \cdot 10^7} = f(0)e^{10^{-2} \ln .85719}$. Thus $f(10^7)/f(0) = e^{10^{-2} \ln .85719} \approx .99846$. This means that after 10 million years, approximately 99.8% of the Uranium 238 would remain.

46. Since the interest rate r is 8% and the bond will be worth $B = 5000$ in $t = 6$ years, its present value is $Be^{-rt/100} = 5000e^{-(8)(6)/100} = 5000e^{-.48} \approx 3093.92$ (dollars). Thus it is a good deal for you to pay \$3000 for the bond.

47. $D'(v) = \dfrac{\sqrt{3}}{48}\left(120v^{1/2} - \dfrac{5}{2}v^{3/2}\right) = \dfrac{5\sqrt{3}}{96}v^{1/2}(48 - v)$

so $D'(v) = 0$ only if $v = 48$. Since $D'(v) > 0$ for $0 < v < 48$ and $D'(v) < 0$ for $48 < v < 75$, (1) of Section 4.6 and the First Derivative Test imply that the maximum value of D occurs for $v = 48$ (miles per hour).

48. Let V be the volume of the capsule. We are to maximize V. Notice that $V = \frac{4}{3}\pi r^3 + \pi r^2 h$. Also, the surface area is given by $S = 4\pi r^2 + 2\pi r h$, so that $h = S/(2\pi r) - 2r$. Therefore $V(r) = \frac{4}{3}\pi r^3 + \pi r^2[S/(2\pi r) - 2r] = \frac{1}{2}Sr - \frac{2}{3}\pi r^3$ for $r > 0$, so $V'(r) = \frac{1}{2}S - 2\pi r^2$. Thus $V'(r) = 0$ only for $r = \frac{1}{2}\sqrt{S/\pi}$. Since $V'(r) > 0$ for $0 < r < \frac{1}{2}\sqrt{S/\pi}$ and $V'(r) < 0$ for $r > \frac{1}{2}\sqrt{S/\pi}$, (1) of Section 4.6 and the First Derivative Test imply that the maximum value of V occurs for $r = \frac{1}{2}\sqrt{S/\pi}$.

49. Let x be the length in feet of one side of the base, y the height in feet of the toolshed, and C the cost of the material. We are to minimize C. Since the volume is 800 cubic feet, we have $x^2 y = 800$, so that $y = 800/x^2$. Since the floor costs $6x^2$ dollars, the roof costs $2x^2$ dollars, and each side $5xy$ dollars, C is given by $C(x) = 6x^2 + 2x^2 + 4(5xy) = 8x^2 + 20x(800/x^2) = 8(x^2 + 2000/x)$ for $x > 0$. Thus $C'(x) = 8(2x - 2000/x^2)$, so that $C'(x) = 0$ only if $2x = 2000/x^2$, that is, for $x^3 = 1000$, or $x = 10$. Since $C''(x) = 16 + 32{,}000/x^3$ for $x > 0$, (1) of Section 4.6 and the Second Derivative Test imply that the minimum value of C is $C(10)$. For $x = 10$ we have $y = 800/10^2 = 8$, so the base should be 10 feet on a side, and the shed should be 8 feet tall.

50. The revenue per bottle is $15(\frac{4}{3}\pi r^3) = 20\pi r^3$ and the cost is $10 + 60\pi r^2$, so the profit is given by $P(r) = 20\pi r^3 - 10 - 60\pi r^2$ for $0 \le r \le 5$. Then $P'(r) = 60\pi r^2 - 120\pi r$, and thus $P'(r) = 0$ for r in $(0, 5)$ only if $r = 2$. Also $P(0) = -10$, $P(2) = -80\pi - 10$, and $P(5) = 1000\pi - 10$.

a. A radius of 5 centimeters will maximize the profit.

b. A radius of 2 centimeters will minimize the profit.

51. The revenue the company receives from x passengers is given by $R(x) = x(1000 - 2x) = 1000x - 2x^2$. We are to maximize R. Since $R'(x) = 1000 - 4x$, we find that $R'(x) = 0$ only for $x = 250$. Since $R''(x) = -4 < 0$ for $x > 0$, (1) of Section 4.6 and the Second Derivative Test imply that the maximum revenue is $R(250) = 125{,}000$ dollars.

52. Let x and y be the length and width of the rectangle (see the figure), and let P denote the perimeter. We are to maximize P. Since the area of the pool is $5000/\pi$, we have $5000/\pi = xy + (\pi/4)y^2$. Thus y cannot equal 0, and we obtain $x = 5000/(\pi y) - (\pi/4)y$, so that

$$P(y) = 2x + \pi y = 2\left(\frac{5000}{\pi y} - \frac{\pi}{4}y\right) + \pi y = \frac{10{,}000}{\pi y} + \frac{\pi y}{2} \quad \text{for } y > 0.$$

Thus $P'(y) = -10{,}000/(\pi y^2) + \pi/2$, so that $P'(y) = 0$ if $y = (100/\pi)\sqrt{2}$. Since $P''(y) = 20{,}000/(\pi y^3) > 0$ for $y > 0$, (1) of Section 4.6 and the Second Derivative Test imply that the minimum value of P occurs for $y = (100/\pi)\sqrt{2}$. Then

$$x = \frac{5{,}000}{\pi[100\sqrt{2}/\pi]} - \frac{\pi}{4}\left(\frac{100\sqrt{2}}{\pi}\right) = 0.$$

Thus the minimum perimeter occurs when the pool is circular.

53. $f'(v) = \frac{v}{c^2}\left(1 - \frac{v^2}{c^2}\right)^{-3/2}$

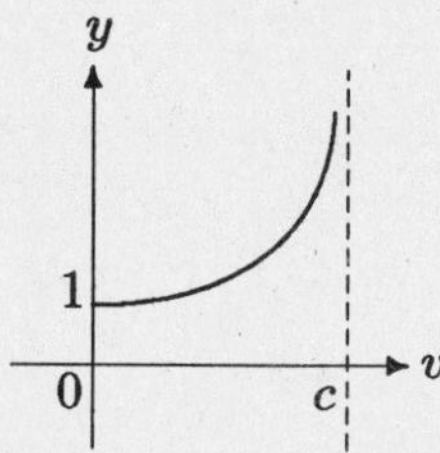

and $f''(v) = \frac{1}{c^2}\left(1 - \frac{v^2}{c^2}\right)^{-3/2} + \frac{3v^2}{c^4}\left(1 - \frac{v^2}{c^2}\right)^{-5/2}$

$= \frac{1}{c^2}\left(1 + \frac{2v^2}{c^2}\right)\left(1 - \frac{v^2}{c^2}\right)^{-5/2}$

The function is increasing and concave upward on $(0, c)$. The line $v = c$ is a vertical asymptote.

54. We are to maximize the intensity I of the lamp. Using the hint and the notation in Figure 4.89, we find that

$$I = \frac{k\cos\theta}{r^2} = \frac{k\cos\theta\sin^2\theta}{25}$$

for some positive constant k. Moreover, $0 < \theta < \pi/2$ since the bulb is above the floor. Now

$$I'(\theta) = \frac{-k\sin^3\theta}{25} + \frac{2k\cos^2\theta\sin\theta}{25} = \frac{k\sin\theta}{25}(2\cos^2\theta - \sin^2\theta)$$

so $I'(\theta) = 0$ only if $2\cos^2\theta - \sin^2\theta = 0$. Since $0 < \theta < \pi/2$, this means that $\tan\theta = \sqrt{2}$. Since $I'(\theta)$ changes from positive to negative at the value of θ for which $\tan\theta = \sqrt{2}$, (1) of Section 4.6 and the First Derivative Test imply that the maximum value of I occurs for $\tan\theta = \sqrt{2}$. The corresponding height is given by $x = 5\cot\theta = (5\sqrt{2})/2$ (feet).

55. Let x be the length of the fence parallel to the river, y the length of each fence perpendicular to the river, and P the total length of fence. We are to minimize P. Then $xy = 6400$, so that $y = 6400/x$, and thus $P(x) = x + 4y = x + 4(6400/x) = x + 25{,}600/x$ for $x > 0$. Since $P'(x) = 1 - 25{,}600/x^2$, we have $P'(x) = 0$ only if $x = 160$. Since $P''(x) = 51{,}200/x^3$, we have $P''(x) > 0$ for all $x > 0$. Thus (1) of Section 4.6 and the Second Derivative Test imply that the total length of fence is minimized if $x = 160$ feet.

56. a. Since the maximum daily production is 100 barrels, and since $P(100) = -40{,}000$, it follows that a \$40,000 loss will result.

b. $P'(x) = 100 - 10x$, so that $P'(x) = 0$ only for $x = 10$. Since $P''(x) = -10 < 0$, (1) of Section 4.6 and the Second Derivative Test imply that the maximum profit is $P(10) = 500$ (dollars), from 10 barrels.

57. Since $C_a(x) = C(x)/x$, we have $C_a'(x) = (xC'(x) - C(x))/x^2$. Assuming that $C_a'(x) = 0$ when C_a is minimized, we find that $xC'(x) - C(x) = 0$, so that $C'(x) = C(x)/x = C_a(x)$.

58. a. Since $h'(x) = (-g/v_0^2)(\sec^2\theta)x + (\tan\theta)$, it follows that $h'(x) = 0$ only for $x = (v_0^2\tan\theta)/(g\sec^2\theta)$. Since h' changes from positive to negative at that value of x, (1) of Section 4.6 and the First

Derivative Test imply that the height is maximum for $x = (v_0^2 \tan\theta)/(g\sec^2\theta)$. For that value of x,

$$h(x) = -\frac{g}{2v_0^2}(\sec^2\theta)\frac{v_0^4\tan^2\theta}{g^2\sec^4\theta} + (\tan\theta)\frac{v_0^2\tan\theta}{g\sec^2\theta} + h_0 = \frac{v_0^2\tan^2\theta}{2g\sec^2\theta} + h_0 = \frac{v_0^2}{2g}\sin^2\theta + h_0.$$

b. The range $R(\theta)$ is the positive value of x for which $h(x) = 0$. By the quadratic formula, that value is

$$R(\theta) = \frac{-\tan\theta - \sqrt{\tan^2\theta + (2gh_0/v_0^2)\sec^2\theta}}{(-g/v_0^2)\sec^2\theta} = \frac{v_0^2}{g}\cos^2\theta\left(\tan\theta + \sqrt{\tan^2\theta + (2gh_0/v_0^2)\sec^2\theta}\right).$$

If $h_0 = 0$, this reduces to

$$R(\theta) = \frac{v_0^2}{g}\cos^2\theta\left(\tan\theta + \sqrt{\tan^2\theta}\right) = \frac{2v_0^2}{g}\cos^2\theta\,\tan\theta = \frac{2v_0^2}{g}\sin\theta\,\cos\theta = \frac{v_0^2}{g}\sin 2\theta$$

which is consistent with Exercise 49 of Section 4.1.

59. a. If the pigeon flies across the river perpendicular to the shore, then the angle θ in Figure 4.91 is 0. If the pigeon flies directly toward the nest, then θ is the angle $\theta_{\max}$ with $\theta_{\max} = k/a$. Suppose the pigeon lies at an angle θ with $0 \le \theta \le \theta_{\max}$. Then the distance flown over water is $a\sec\theta$, so that the time of flight over water is $(a\sec\theta)/v$. The distance flown over land is $k - a\tan\theta$, so that the time of flight over land is $(k - a\tan\theta)/w$. Thus

$$T = \frac{a\sec\theta}{v} + \frac{k - a\tan\theta}{w} \quad \text{for } 0 \le \theta \le \theta_{\max}.$$

b. Since

$$T'(\theta) = \frac{a\sec\theta\tan\theta}{v} - \frac{a\sec^2\theta}{w} = a\sec\theta\left(\frac{\tan\theta}{v} - \frac{\sec\theta}{w}\right)$$
$$= \frac{a}{\cos\theta}\left(\frac{\sin\theta}{v\cos\theta} - \frac{1}{w\cos\theta}\right) = \frac{a}{\cos^2\theta}\left(\frac{\sin\theta}{v} - \frac{1}{w}\right)$$

it follows that $T'(\theta) = 0$ if $\sin\theta = v/w$.

c. For Jo, $a = 1000$, $k = 3000$, $v = 20$, and $w = 24$. Thus $\tan\theta_{\max} = 3000/1000 = 3$. By part (b), $T'(\theta_0) = 0$ if $\sin\theta_0 = \frac{20}{24} = \frac{5}{6}$. Then $\tan\theta_0 = \sin\theta_0/\cos\theta_0 = (5/6)/\sqrt{1-(5/6)^2} = 5/\sqrt{11}$ and $\sec\theta_0 = 6/\sqrt{11}$. Since $\tan\theta_0 = 5/\sqrt{11} < 3 = \tan\theta_{\max}$, we have $0 < \theta_0 < \theta_{\max}$. By the formula for $T'(\theta)$ in part (b), it follows that T' changes from negative to positive at θ_0. Thus (1) in Section 4.6 and the First Derivative Test imply that, for Jo, the time is minimized for $\theta = \theta_0$. Since

$$T(\theta_0) = \frac{1000(6/\sqrt{11})}{20} + \frac{3000 - 1000(5/\sqrt{11})}{24} \approx 153\,\text{(seconds)}$$

it takes Jo about 153 seconds to fly to the nest.

For Mo, $a = 1000$, $k = 3000$, $v = 18$, and $w = 26$. Thus $\tan\theta_{\max} = 3$. By part (b), $T'(\theta_1) = 0$ if $\sin\theta_1 = \frac{18}{26} = \frac{9}{13}$. Then $\tan\theta_1 = \sin\theta_1/\cos\theta_1 = (9/13)/\sqrt{1-(9/13)^2} = 9/\sqrt{88}$ and $\sec\theta_1 = 13/\sqrt{88}$. Since $\tan\theta_1 = 9/\sqrt{88} < 3 = \tan\theta_{\max}$, we have $0 < \theta_1 < \theta_{\max}$. By the formula for $T'(\theta)$ in part (b) it follows that T' changes from negative to positive at θ_1. Thus (1) in Section 4.6 and the First Derivative Test imply that, for Mo, the time is minimized for $\theta = \theta_1$. Since

$$T(\theta_1) = \frac{1000(13/\sqrt{88})}{18} + \frac{3000 - 1000(9/\sqrt{88})}{26} \approx 155 \text{ (seconds)}$$

it takes Mo about 155 seconds to fly to the nest. Therefore Jo arrives at the nest first.

60. We are to minimize C. Now $C'(x) = a - b/x^2$, so that $C'(x) = 0$ for $x > 0$ only if $x = \sqrt{b/a}$. Since $C''(x) = 2b/x^3$, and $C''(x) > 0$ for all $x > 0$, (1) of Section 4.6 and the Second Derivative Test imply that the total cost is minimized if the cross-sectional area of the wire is $\sqrt{b/a}$. The purchase price of the wire of cross-sectional area $\sqrt{b/a}$ is $a\sqrt{b/a} = \sqrt{ab}$, and the cost due to power loss is $b/\sqrt{b/a} = \sqrt{ab}$, so the purchase price and cost due to power loss are the same if the cross-sectional area is $\sqrt{b/a}$, and hence when the total cost is minimized.

61. Let the radius of the barrel be r, and V the volume. We are to maximize V. The length of the barrel is $2\sqrt{l^2 - 4r^2}$, and the volume is given by $V(r) = \pi r^2(2\sqrt{l^2 - 4r^2}) = 2\pi r^2\sqrt{l^2 - 4r^2}$. Now

$$V'(r) = 4\pi r\sqrt{l^2 - 4r^2} - \frac{8\pi r^3}{\sqrt{l^2 - 4r^2}} = \frac{4\pi r(l^2 - 6r^2)}{\sqrt{l^2 - 4r^2}}$$

so that $V'(r) = 0$ for $r > 0$ only if $r = (l/6)\sqrt{6}$. Since $V'(r) > 0$ if $0 < r < (l/6)\sqrt{6}$, and $V'(r) < 0$ if $(l/6)\sqrt{6} < r < l/2$, (1) of Section 4.6 and the First Derivative Test imply that the barrel has maximum volume if the radius is $(l/6)\sqrt{6}$; the length is then $2\sqrt{l^2 - \frac{4}{6}l^2} = \frac{2}{3}\sqrt{3}\,l$.

62. Let P denote the profit; we are to maximize P. If the firm borrows money at x percent, then it can borrow kx^2 dollars, where k is a constant. Its income from lending kx^2 dollars is $\frac{18}{100}(kx^2)$ dollars, whereas the cost of borrowing kx^2 dollars is $(x/100)(kx^2)$ dollars. Therefore the profit in dollars is given by $P(x) = \frac{18}{100}kx^2 - (k/100)x^3 = (k/100)(18x^2 - x^3)$. Thus $P'(x) = (k/100)(36x - 3x^2) = (3kx/100)(12 - x)$, so that $P'(x) = 0$ for $x > 0$ only if $x = 12$. Since $P'(x) > 0$ for $0 < x < 12$ and $P'(x) < 0$ for $x > 12$, (1) of Section 4.6 and the First Derivative Test imply that the maximum profit occurs for $x = 12$, so the firm should borrow at 12% in order to maximize its annual profit.

63. Let x be the distance shown in the figure to the right, and L the total length of wire required. We are to minimize L. Now L is given by $L(x) = \sqrt{x^2 + 50^2} + \sqrt{(150 - x)^2 + 75^2}$ for $0 \le x \le 150$, so that

$$L'(x) = \frac{x}{\sqrt{x^2 + 50^2}} + \frac{x - 150}{\sqrt{(150 - x)^2 + 75^2}}.$$

Thus $L'(x) = 0$ if

$$\frac{x}{\sqrt{x^2 + 50^2}} = \frac{150 - x}{\sqrt{(150 - x)^2 + 75^2}}$$

or $x\sqrt{(150 - x)^2 + 75^2} = (150 - x)\sqrt{x^2 + 50^2}$, or $x^2(150 - x)^2 + 75^2x^2 = (150 - x)^2x^2 + (150 - x)^2 \cdot 50^2$, or $75^2x^2 = (150 - x)^2 \cdot 50^2$, or $75x = (150 - x)50$, or $x = 60$. If we replace "=" by ">" in the preceding argument, the resulting inequalities are valid. Thus $L'(x) > 0$ if $x > 60$. Similarly, $L'(x) < 0$ if $x < 60$.

Thus (1) of Section 4.6 and the First Derivative Test imply that the minimum value of L occurs for $x = 60$. Consequently the telephone pole should be located 60 feet down the street from the house that is 50 feet from the street.

64. Since the initial velocity of a droplet is 0, (2) of Section 1.3 (with $v_0 = 0$ and $h_0 = h$) implies that the height at time t_0 is 0 if $-16t_0^2 + H - h = 0$, that is, if $t_0 = \sqrt{(H-h)/16}$. Therefore by the hint,

$$R = \sqrt{2gh}\sqrt{\frac{H-h}{16}} = \sqrt{\frac{gh(H-h)}{8}}.$$

We wish to find the maximum value of R as a function of h. Now

$$R'(h) = \frac{1}{2}\left(\frac{gh(H-h)}{8}\right)^{-1/2}\left[\frac{g}{8}(H-2h)\right] = 0 \quad \text{only if} \quad h = \frac{H}{2}.$$

Since $R'(h) > 0$ if $h < H/2$ and $R'(h) < 0$ if $h > H/2$, (1) of Section 4.6 and the First Derivative Test imply that R is maximum for $h = H/2$. Since

$$R\left(\frac{H}{2}\right) = \sqrt{\frac{g(H/2)(H-H/2)}{8}} = \frac{H}{4}\sqrt{\frac{g}{2}}$$

it follows that $(H/4)\sqrt{g/2}$ is the maximum value of R. Taking $g = 32$, we obtain $R(H/2) = (H/4)\sqrt{\frac{32}{2}} = H$. Thus the maximum value of R is H.

65. Let $t = 0$ correspond to the time of the accident. Since the amount of alcohol in the person's system decreases exponentially with time, it is given as a function of time t (in hours) by $f(t) = f(0)e^{kt}$ for some constant k. We are given that $f(2) = .0007$ and $f(4) = .0005$. Thus

$$f(0)e^{2k} = .0007 \quad \text{and} \quad f(0)e^{4k} = .0005.$$

Dividing and canceling $f(0)$, we have

$$\frac{e^{4k}}{e^{2k}} = \frac{.0005}{.0007}, \quad \text{or} \quad e^{2k} = \frac{5}{7}.$$

Thus $.0007 = f(0)e^{2k} = \frac{5}{7}f(0)$, so that $f(0) = \frac{7}{5}(.0007) = .00098 < .0001$. We conclude that the driver was not intoxicated at the time of the accident.

Cumulative Review(Chapters 1–3)

1. Since $4x^6 - 1 = 0$ for $x = -1/\sqrt[3]{2}$ and $x = 1/\sqrt[3]{2}$, it follows that $4x^6 - 1 > 0$ for $x < -1/\sqrt[3]{2}$ and for $x > 1/\sqrt[3]{2}$, and $4x^6 - 1 < 0$ for $-1/\sqrt[3]{2} < x < 1/\sqrt[3]{2}$. From the diagram we see that the solution of the given inequality is the union of $(-1/\sqrt[3]{2}, 0)$ and $(1/\sqrt[3]{2}, \infty)$.

x	−	−	−	−	−	0	+	+	+	+	+
$4x^6-1$	+	+	0	−	−	−	−	−	0	+	+
$18x(4x^6-1)$	−	−	0	+	+	0	−	−	0	+	+

$-\frac{1}{\sqrt[3]{2}}$ 0 $\frac{1}{\sqrt[3]{2}}$ x

2. The given inequality is equivalent to $3-4 \le |x| \le 3+4$, or $-1 \le |x| \le 7$. Since $|x| \ge 0$ for all x, the solution is $[-7, 7]$.

3. The given inequality is equivalent to $2 \le 1 + x^4 < 16$, or $1 \le x^4 < 15$. Thus the solution is the union of $(-\sqrt[4]{15}, -1]$ and $[1, \sqrt[4]{15})$.

4. The given inequality is equivalent to $\sin x \ge 2(1-\sin^2 x) - 1$, or $2\sin^2 x + \sin x - 1 \ge 0$, or $(2\sin x - 1)(\sin x + 1) \ge 0$. Since $\sin x + 1 \ge 0$ for all x, the solution consists of all x such that $\sin x = -1$ or $2\sin x - 1 \ge 0$ (that is, $\sin x \ge \frac{1}{2}$). Thus x is a solution if and only if $x = 3\pi/2 + 2n\pi$ or x is in $[\pi/6 + 2n\pi, 5\pi/6 + 2n\pi]$ for some integer n.

5. a. The domain of f is $(-3, \infty)$ and the domain of g consists of all numbers except $\frac{1}{2}$. Thus the domain of $f \circ g$ consists of all x except $\frac{1}{2}$ such that

$$\frac{1}{2x-1} > -3, \quad \text{or} \quad \frac{1}{2x-1} + 3 > 0, \quad \text{or} \quad \frac{2(3x-1)}{2x-1} > 0.$$

From the diagram we see that the solution of this inequality, and hence the domain of $f \circ g$, is the union of $(-\infty, \frac{1}{3})$ and $(\frac{1}{2}, \infty)$.

$3x-1$	$-$	$-$	0	$+$	$+$	$+$	$+$	$+$	$+$	$+$	$+$
$2x-1$	$-$	$-$	$-$	$-$	$-$	$-$	$-$	$-$	0	$+$	$+$
$\frac{2(3x-1)}{2x-1}$	$+$	$+$	0	$-$	$-$	$-$	$-$	$-$		$+$	$+$

x; $\frac{1}{3}$; $\frac{1}{2}$

b. $$(f \circ g)(x) = f(g(x)) = f\left(\frac{1}{2x-1}\right) = \frac{1}{\sqrt{1/(2x-1)+3}} = \sqrt{\frac{2x-1}{6x-2}}$$

6. Let $f(x) = 1 + \sin x$ and $g(x) = 3x^2 - 2$. Then $h(x) = 1 + \sin(g(x)) = f(g(x))$. Alternatively, let $f(x) = 1 + x$ and $g(x) = \sin(3x^2 - 2)$.

7. $$\lim_{x\to 4^+} \frac{x(x+4)}{16-x^2} = \lim_{x\to 4^+} \frac{x(x+4)}{(4-x)(4+x)} = \lim_{x\to 4^+} \frac{x}{4-x} = -\infty$$

8. Since $|x| = -x$ for $x < -3$, we have

$$\lim_{x\to -3^-} \frac{3|x|+9}{x^2-9} = \lim_{x\to -3^-} \frac{3(-x)+9}{(x+3)(x-3)} = \lim_{x\to -3^-} \frac{-3}{x+3} = \infty.$$

9. $$\lim_{x\to 0^+} \frac{\sin 2x - 2\sqrt{x}\,\sin x + 4x^2}{x} = \lim_{x\to 0^+} \left(\frac{\sin 2x}{x} - 2\sqrt{x}\,\frac{\sin x}{x} + 4x\right)$$

$$= \lim_{x\to 0^+} 2\,\frac{\sin 2x}{2x} - 2 \lim_{x\to 0^+} \sqrt{x} \lim_{x\to 0^+} \frac{\sin x}{x} + 4 \lim_{x\to 0^+} x = 2(1) - 2(0)(1) + 4(0) = 2$$

10. Since $\lim_{x\to 0^+} \ln 2x = -\infty$, it follows that $\lim_{x\to 0^+}(1 - \ln 2x) = \infty$. Thus the Substitution Theorem for infinite limits (with $y = 1 - \ln 2x$) implies that $\lim_{x\to 0^+} \ln(1 - \ln 2x) = \lim_{y\to\infty} \ln y = \infty$.

11. Since the slope of the line $y-2x=8$ is 2, we seek (a,b) on the graph of f at which the slope is the negative reciprocal of 2, that is, $-\frac{1}{2}$. But $f'(x)=2(x-4)$, so a must satisfy $2(a-4)=-\frac{1}{2}$. Thus $a=4-\frac{1}{4}=\frac{15}{4}$, and $b=f(a)=(\frac{15}{4}-4)^2+1=\frac{17}{16}$. Therefore the point is $(\frac{15}{4},\frac{17}{16})$.

12. a. $\lim_{x\to 1^-} f(x)=\lim_{x\to 1^-}(x-1)^2=0$; $\lim_{x\to 1^+} f(x)=\lim_{x\to 1^+}(x^3-x^2)=0$

Thus $\lim_{x\to 1} f(x)=0=f(1)$, so f is continuous at 1.

b. $$\lim_{x\to 1^-}\frac{f(x)-f(1)}{x-1}=\lim_{x\to 1^-}\frac{(x-1)^2-0}{x-1}=\lim_{x\to 1^-}(x-1)=0$$

$$\lim_{x\to 1^+}\frac{f(x)-f(1)}{x-1}=\lim_{x\to 1^+}\frac{x^3-x^2}{x-1}=\lim_{x\to 1^+}\frac{x^2(x-1)}{x-1}=\lim_{x\to 1^+}x^2=1$$

since the two one-sided limits differ, it follows that $\lim_{x\to 1}[f(x)-f(1)]/(x-1)$ fails to exist, so f is not differentiable at 1.

13. $$f'(4)=\lim_{x\to 4}\frac{f(x)-f(4)}{x-4}=\lim_{x\to 4}\frac{2/x^{1/2}-1}{x-4}=\lim_{x\to 4}\frac{2-x^{1/2}}{x^{1/2}(x^{1/2}-2)(x^{1/2}+2)}$$
$$=\lim_{x\to 4}\frac{-1}{x^{1/2}(x^{1/2}+2)}=\frac{-1}{2(2+2)}=-\frac{1}{8}$$

14. $f'(x)=[\cos(\cos x^3)](-\sin x^3)(3x^2)=(-3x^2\sin x^3)\cos(\cos x^3)$

15. $$f'(x)=\frac{-(1-e^{\tan x}\sec^2 x)}{(x-e^{\tan x})^2}$$

16. a. The domain of f consists of all x satisfying $-4/(1-e^x)>0$, or equivalently, $1-e^x<0$. The latter inequality is equivalent to $e^x>1$, or $x>0$.

b. $f(x)=\ln\dfrac{-4}{1-e^x}=\ln\dfrac{4}{e^x-1}=\ln 4-\ln(e^x-1)$, so $f'(x)=\dfrac{-e^x}{e^x-1}=\dfrac{e^x}{1-e^x}$.

c. Since $f(x)=\ln 4-\ln(e^x-1)$ by part (b), and since $\lim_{x\to 0^+}(e^x-1)=e^0-1=0$, the Substitution Theorem for infinite limits (with $y=e^x-1$) implies that

$$\lim_{x\to 0^+} f(x)=\lim_{x\to 0^+}(\ln 4-\ln(e^x-1))=\lim_{y\to 0^+}(\ln 4-\ln y)=\infty.$$

17. $$\frac{d}{dx}[3(2x+1)^{5/2}-5(2x+1)^{3/2}]=3\left(\frac{5}{2}\right)(2x+1)^{3/2}(2)-5\left(\frac{3}{2}\right)(2x+1)^{1/2}(2)$$
$$=15(2x+1)^{1/2}[(2x+1)-1]=30x(2x+1)^{1/2}$$

18. a. The velocity is given by

$$v(t)=f'(t)=\frac{1(t^2+1)-t(2t)}{(t^2+1)^2}=\frac{1-t^2}{(t^2+1)^2}.$$

Thus $v(t)>0$ for $0<t<1$ and $v(t)<0$ for $t>1$, so the direction of motion changes at time 1.

b. The acceleration is given by

$$a(t)=v'(t)=\frac{-2t(t^2+1)^2-(1-t^2)2(t^2+1)(2t)}{(t^2+1)^4}.$$

Therefore

$$a(1)=\frac{-2(2)^2-0}{2^4}=-\frac{1}{2}.$$

19. Differentiating the given equation implicitly, we have

$$y^2 + 2xy\frac{dy}{dx} + 3\frac{dy}{dx} - 4 = 0, \quad \text{so} \quad \frac{dy}{dx} = \frac{4 - y^2}{2xy + 3}.$$

20. Differentiating the given equation implicitly, we have

$$2x\frac{dx}{dt} - 4y\frac{dy}{dt} = 0, \quad \text{so} \quad \frac{dx}{dt} = \frac{2y}{x}\frac{dy}{dt}.$$

Since $dy/dt = -3$ by hypothesis, it follows that $dx/dt = (2y/x)(-3) = -6y/x$. When the point is located at $(\sqrt{3}, -1)$, $dx/dt = -6(-1)/\sqrt{3} = 2\sqrt{3}$ (units per second).

21. The area A is given by $A = \pi r^2$. Differentiating implicitly, we have $dA/dt = 2\pi r(dr/dt)$. Since $dA/dt = 2\pi\sqrt{r}$ by hypothesis, it follows that $2\pi\sqrt{r} = dA/dt = 2\pi r(dr/dt)$, so $dr/dt = 1/\sqrt{r}$. When the radius is increasing at the rate of 2 feet per minute, we have $2 = dr/dt = 1/\sqrt{r}$, so $r = (\frac{1}{2})^2 = \frac{1}{4}$. At that time, $A = \pi(\frac{1}{4})^2 = \frac{1}{16}\pi$ (square feet).

22. $f'(x) = 4x^3 - 3x^2 + 1$. Letting the initial value of c be -1 and using the Newton-Raphson method, we obtain 1.308571201 for the approximate zero of f.

23. By (1) of Section 1.3, the height of the baton in meters is given by $h(t) = -4.9t^2 + v_0 t$. Thus $h'(t) = -9.8t + v_0$, so $h'(t) = 0$ for $t = v_0/9.8$. Thus $h(v_0/9.8)$ is the maximum height. Since there are $7 \times 24 \times 60 \times 60 = 604{,}800$ seconds in a week, we have $0 = h(604{,}800) = -4.9(604{,}800)^2 + v_0(604{,}800)$, so that $v_0 = 4.9(604{,}800)$. Thus $h(v_0/9.8) = h(302{,}400) = -4.9(302{,}400)^2 + 4.9(604{,}800)(302{,}400) = 4.9(302{,}400)^2 \approx 4.5 \times 10^{11}$ (meters). Thus the baton would have gone about 4.5×10^8 kilometers high!

Chapter 5

The Integral

5.1 Preparation for the Definite Integral

1. From the figures, $\Delta x_1 = \Delta x_2 = \Delta x_3 = 1$. Moreover, $m_1 = 1 = m_2$, and $m_3 = 2$; $M_1 = 2 = M_2$, and $M_3 = 5$. Thus

$$L_f(P) = 1\cdot 1 + 1\cdot 1 + 2\cdot 1 = 4 \quad \text{and} \quad U_f(P) = 2\cdot 1 + 2\cdot 1 + 5\cdot 1 = 9.$$

2. From the figures, $\Delta x_1 = \Delta x_2 = \Delta x_3 = \Delta x_4 = 1$. Moreover, $m_1 = 0$, $m_2 = 3 = m_3$, and $m_4 = 0$; $M_1 = 3$, $M_2 = 4 = M_3$, and $M_4 = 3$. Thus

$$L_f(P) = 0\cdot 1 + 3\cdot 1 + 3\cdot 1 + 0\cdot 1 = 6 \quad \text{and} \quad U_f(P) = 3\cdot 1 + 4\cdot 1 + 4\cdot 1 + 3\cdot 1 = 14.$$

3. From the figures, $\Delta x_1 = \Delta x_2 = \Delta x_3 = \Delta x_4 = \pi/4$. Moreover, $m_1 = 0$, $m_2 = \sqrt{2}/2 = m_3$, and $m_4 = 0$; $M_1 = \sqrt{2}/2$, $M_2 = 1 = M_3$, and $M_4 = \sqrt{2}/2$. Thus

$$L_f(P) = 0\cdot\frac{\pi}{4} + \frac{\sqrt{2}}{2}\cdot\frac{\pi}{4} + \frac{\sqrt{2}}{2}\cdot\frac{\pi}{4} + 0\cdot\frac{\pi}{4} = \frac{\sqrt{2}\pi}{4} \quad \text{and} \quad U_f(P) = \frac{\sqrt{2}}{2}\cdot\frac{\pi}{4} + 1\cdot\frac{\pi}{4} + 1\cdot\frac{\pi}{4} + \frac{\sqrt{2}}{2}\cdot\frac{\pi}{4} = (\sqrt{2}+2)\frac{\pi}{4}.$$

4. From the figures, $\Delta x_1 = \Delta x_2 = \Delta x_3 = 1$. Moreover, $m_1 = \frac{1}{2}$, $m_2 = \frac{1}{3}$, and $m_3 = \frac{1}{4}$; $M_1 = 1$, $M_2 = \frac{1}{2}$, and $M_3 = \frac{1}{3}$. Thus

$$L_f(P) = \frac{1}{2}\cdot 1 + \frac{1}{3}\cdot 1 + \frac{1}{4}\cdot 1 = \frac{13}{12} \quad \text{and} \quad U_f(P) = 1\cdot 1 + \frac{1}{2}\cdot 1 + \frac{1}{3}\cdot 1 = \frac{11}{6}.$$

5. Since $x+2$ is increasing on $[-1, 2]$,

$$L_f(P) = 1\left(\frac{-1}{2} - (-1)\right) + \frac{3}{2}\left(0 - \left(\frac{-1}{2}\right)\right) + 2\left(\frac{1}{2} - 0\right) + \frac{5}{2}\left(1 - \frac{1}{2}\right) + 3\left(\frac{3}{2} - 1\right) + \frac{7}{2}\left(2 - \frac{3}{2}\right) = \frac{27}{4},$$

$$U_f(P) = \frac{3}{2}\left(\frac{-1}{2} - (-1)\right) + 2\left(0 - \left(\frac{-1}{2}\right)\right) + \frac{5}{2}\left(\frac{1}{2} - 0\right) + 3\left(1 - \frac{1}{2}\right) + \frac{7}{2}\left(\frac{3}{2} - 1\right) + 4\left(2 - \frac{3}{2}\right) = \frac{33}{4}.$$

6. Since x^2 is decreasing on $[-1, 0]$ and increasing on $[0, 2]$,

$$L_f(P) = \frac{1}{4}\left(\frac{-1}{2} - (-1)\right) + 0\left(0 - \left(\frac{-1}{2}\right)\right) + 0\left(\frac{1}{2} - 0\right) + \frac{1}{4}\left(1 - \frac{1}{2}\right) + 1\left(\frac{3}{2} - 1\right) + \frac{9}{4}\left(2 - \frac{3}{2}\right) = \frac{15}{8},$$

$$U_f(P) = 1\left(\frac{-1}{2} - (-1)\right) + \frac{1}{4}\left(0 - \left(\frac{-1}{2}\right)\right) + \frac{1}{4}\left(\frac{1}{2} - 0\right) + 1\left(1 - \frac{1}{2}\right) + \frac{9}{4}\left(\frac{3}{2} - 1\right) + 4\left(2 - \frac{3}{2}\right) = \frac{35}{8}.$$

7. Since x^4 is decreasing on $[-1, 0]$ and increasing on $[0, 2]$,

$$\begin{aligned} L_f(P) &= \frac{1}{16}\left(\frac{-1}{2} - (-1)\right) + 0\left(0 - \left(\frac{-1}{2}\right)\right) + 0\left(\frac{1}{2} - 0\right) \\ &\quad + \frac{1}{16}\left(1 - \frac{1}{2}\right) + 1\left(\frac{3}{2} - 1\right) + \frac{81}{16}\left(2 - \frac{3}{2}\right) = \frac{99}{32}, \\ U_f(P) &= 1\left(\frac{-1}{2} - (-1)\right) + \frac{1}{16}\left(0 - \left(\frac{-1}{2}\right)\right) + \frac{1}{16}\left(\frac{1}{2} - 0\right) \\ &\quad + 1\left(1 - \frac{1}{2}\right) + \frac{81}{16}\left(\frac{3}{2} - 1\right) + 16\left(2 - \frac{3}{2}\right) = \frac{371}{32}. \end{aligned}$$

8. Since $-1/x$ is increasing on $[-4, -1]$,

$$L_f(P) = \frac{1}{4}(-3 - (-4)) + \frac{1}{3}(-2 - (-3)) + \frac{1}{2}(-1 - (-2)) = \frac{13}{12},$$

$$U_f(P) = \frac{1}{3}(-3 - (-4)) + \frac{1}{2}(-2 - (-3)) + 1(-1 - (-2)) = \frac{11}{6}.$$

9. Since $\sin x$ is increasing on $[0, \pi/2]$,

$$L_f(P) = 0\left(\frac{\pi}{4} - 0\right) + \frac{\sqrt{2}}{2}\left(\frac{\pi}{2} - \frac{\pi}{4}\right) = \frac{\pi\sqrt{2}}{8},$$

$$U_f(P) = \frac{\sqrt{2}}{2}\left(\frac{\pi}{4} - 0\right) + 1\left(\frac{\pi}{2} - \frac{\pi}{4}\right) = \frac{\pi}{4}\left(\frac{\sqrt{2}}{2} + 1\right).$$

10. Since $\sin x$ is increasing on $[0, \pi/2]$,

$$L_f(P) = 0\left(\frac{\pi}{6} - 0\right) + \frac{1}{2}\left(\frac{\pi}{4} - \frac{\pi}{6}\right) + \frac{\sqrt{2}}{2}\left(\frac{\pi}{3} - \frac{\pi}{4}\right) + \frac{\sqrt{3}}{2}\left(\frac{\pi}{2} - \frac{\pi}{3}\right) = \frac{\pi}{24}(1 + \sqrt{2} + 2\sqrt{3}),$$

$$U_f(P) = \frac{1}{2}\left(\frac{\pi}{6} - 0\right) + \frac{\sqrt{2}}{2}\left(\frac{\pi}{4} - \frac{\pi}{6}\right) + \frac{\sqrt{3}}{2}\left(\frac{\pi}{3} - \frac{\pi}{4}\right) + 1\left(\frac{\pi}{2} - \frac{\pi}{3}\right) = \frac{\pi}{24}(6 + \sqrt{2} + \sqrt{3}).$$

11. Since $\cos x$ is increasing on $[-\pi/3, 0]$ and decreasing on $[0, \pi/3]$,

$$L_f(P) = \frac{1}{2}\left(\frac{-\pi}{6} - \left(\frac{-\pi}{3}\right)\right) + \frac{\sqrt{3}}{2}\left(0 - \left(\frac{-\pi}{6}\right)\right) + \frac{\sqrt{3}}{2}\left(\frac{\pi}{6} - 0\right) + \frac{1}{2}\left(\frac{\pi}{3} - \frac{\pi}{6}\right) = \frac{\pi}{6}(1 + \sqrt{3}),$$

$$U_f(P) = \frac{\sqrt{3}}{2}\left(\frac{-\pi}{6} - \left(\frac{-\pi}{3}\right)\right) + 1\left(0 - \left(\frac{-\pi}{6}\right)\right) + 1\left(\frac{\pi}{6} - 0\right) + \frac{\sqrt{3}}{2}\left(\frac{\pi}{3} - \frac{\pi}{6}\right) = \frac{\pi}{6}(\sqrt{3} + 2).$$

12. Since $f'(x) = \cos x - \sin x$, so that $f'(x) > 0$ on $(0, \pi/4)$ and $f'(x) < 0$ on $(\pi/4, \pi/2)$, we know that f is increasing on $[0, \pi/4]$ and decreasing on $[\pi/4, \pi/2]$. Thus

$$L_f(P) = 1\left(\frac{\pi}{4} - 0\right) + 1\left(\frac{\pi}{2} - \frac{\pi}{4}\right) = \frac{\pi}{2} \quad \text{and} \quad U_f(P) = \sqrt{2}\left(\frac{\pi}{4} - 0\right) + \sqrt{2}\left(\frac{\pi}{2} - \frac{\pi}{4}\right) = \frac{\sqrt{2}\,\pi}{2}.$$

13. Since $f'(x) = 3x^2 + 3 > 0$ for all x, f is increasing on $[-2, 2]$. Thus

$$L_f(P) = -11(1) - 1(1) + 3(1) + 7(1) = -2$$

$$U_f(P) = -1(1) + 3(1) + 7(1) + 17(1) = 26.$$

14. Since $f'(x) = 4x^3 - 4x = 4x(x+1)(x-1)$, f is decreasing on $(-\infty, -1]$ and on $[0, 1]$, and is increasing on $[-1, 0]$ and on $[1, \infty)$. Thus

$$L_f(P) = -1(1) - 1(1) - 1(1) - 1(1) = -4$$

$$U_f(P) = 8(1) + 0(1) + 0(1) + 8(1) = 16.$$

15. Since $\Delta x_k = \frac{1}{9}$ for $1 \le k \le 9$ and f is increasing on $[0, 1]$,

$$\begin{aligned} L_f(P) &= 0\left(\frac{1}{9}\right) + \frac{1}{3}\left(\frac{1}{9}\right) + \frac{\sqrt{2}}{3}\left(\frac{1}{9}\right) + \frac{\sqrt{3}}{3}\left(\frac{1}{9}\right) + \frac{\sqrt{4}}{3}\left(\frac{1}{9}\right) + \frac{\sqrt{5}}{3}\left(\frac{1}{9}\right) \\ &\quad + \frac{\sqrt{6}}{3}\left(\frac{1}{9}\right) + \frac{\sqrt{7}}{3}\left(\frac{1}{9}\right) + \frac{\sqrt{8}}{3}\left(\frac{1}{9}\right) \approx 0.6039259454 \\ U_f(P) &= \frac{1}{3}\left(\frac{1}{9}\right) + \frac{\sqrt{2}}{3}\left(\frac{1}{9}\right) + \frac{\sqrt{3}}{3}\left(\frac{1}{9}\right) + \frac{\sqrt{4}}{3}\left(\frac{1}{9}\right) + \frac{\sqrt{5}}{3}\left(\frac{1}{9}\right) \\ &\quad + \frac{\sqrt{6}}{3}\left(\frac{1}{9}\right) + \frac{\sqrt{7}}{3}\left(\frac{1}{9}\right) + \frac{\sqrt{8}}{3}\left(\frac{1}{9}\right) + \frac{\sqrt{9}}{3}\left(\frac{1}{9}\right) \approx 0.7150370565. \end{aligned}$$

16. Since $\Delta x_k = \frac{1}{4}$ for $1 \le k \le 8$, and f is increasing on $[-1, 0]$ and decreasing on $[0, 1]$, we obtain

$$\begin{aligned} L_f(P) &= 0\left(\frac{1}{4}\right) + \sqrt{\frac{7}{16}}\left(\frac{1}{4}\right) + \sqrt{\frac{3}{4}}\left(\frac{1}{4}\right) + \sqrt{\frac{15}{16}}\left(\frac{1}{4}\right) + \sqrt{\frac{15}{16}}\left(\frac{1}{4}\right) \\ &\quad + \sqrt{\frac{3}{4}}\left(\frac{1}{4}\right) + \sqrt{\frac{7}{16}}\left(\frac{1}{4}\right) + 0\left(\frac{1}{4}\right) \approx 1.247854534 \\ U_f(P) &= \sqrt{\frac{7}{16}}\left(\frac{1}{4}\right) + \sqrt{\frac{3}{4}}\left(\frac{1}{4}\right) + \sqrt{\frac{15}{16}}\left(\frac{1}{4}\right) + 1\left(\frac{1}{4}\right) + 1\left(\frac{1}{4}\right) \\ &\quad + \sqrt{\frac{15}{16}}\left(\frac{1}{4}\right) + \sqrt{\frac{3}{4}}\left(\frac{1}{4}\right) + \sqrt{\frac{7}{16}}\left(\frac{1}{4}\right) \approx 1.747854534. \end{aligned}$$

17. Since f is decreasing on $[-1, 0]$ and increasing on $[0, 1]$,

$$L_f(P) = \sqrt{\frac{97}{81}}\left(\frac{1}{3}\right) + \sqrt{\frac{17}{16}}\left(\frac{1}{6}\right) + 1\left(\frac{1}{2}\right) + 1\left(\frac{1}{4}\right) + \sqrt{\frac{257}{256}}\left(\frac{1}{4}\right) + \sqrt{\frac{17}{16}}\left(\frac{1}{6}\right) + \sqrt{\frac{97}{81}}\left(\frac{1}{3}\right)$$

$$\approx 2.073624963$$

$$U_f(P) = \sqrt{2}\left(\frac{1}{3}\right) + \sqrt{\frac{97}{81}}\left(\frac{1}{6}\right) + \sqrt{\frac{17}{16}}\left(\frac{1}{2}\right) + \sqrt{\frac{257}{256}}\left(\frac{1}{4}\right) + \sqrt{\frac{17}{16}}\left(\frac{1}{4}\right) + \sqrt{\frac{97}{81}}\left(\frac{1}{6}\right) + \sqrt{2}\left(\frac{1}{3}\right)$$

$$\approx 2.331151663.$$

18. Since f is increasing on $[0, \pi/2]$,

$$L_f(P) = 0\left(\frac{\pi}{6}\right) + \left(\frac{\pi}{6}\sin\frac{\pi}{6}\right)\left(\frac{\pi}{12}\right) + \left(\frac{\pi}{4}\sin\frac{\pi}{4}\right)\left(\frac{\pi}{12}\right) + \left(\frac{\pi}{3}\sin\frac{\pi}{3}\right)\left(\frac{\pi}{6}\right) \approx 0.6887834868$$

$$U_f(P) = \left(\frac{\pi}{6}\sin\frac{\pi}{6}\right)\left(\frac{\pi}{6}\right) + \left(\frac{\pi}{4}\sin\frac{\pi}{4}\right)\left(\frac{\pi}{12}\right) + \left(\frac{\pi}{3}\sin\frac{\pi}{3}\right)\left(\frac{\pi}{12}\right) + \left(\frac{\pi}{2}\sin\frac{\pi}{2}\right)\left(\frac{\pi}{6}\right) \approx 1.342363658.$$

19. Since f is increasing on $[0, 1]$,

$$L_f(P) = e^0(.1) + e^{.1}(.1) + e^{.2}(.1) + \cdots + e^{.9}(.1) \approx 1.6337994$$

$$U_f(P) = e^{.1}(.1) + e^{.2}(.1) + e^{.3}(.1) + \cdots + e^1(.1) \approx 1.805627583.$$

20. Since f is decreasing on $[1, 2]$,

$$L_f(P) = [\ln(2.9)](.1) + \cdots + [\ln 2](.1) \approx 0.889130385$$

$$U_f(P) = [\ln 3](.1) + [\ln(2.9)](.1) + \cdots + [\ln(2.1)](.1) \approx 0.9296768958.$$

21. $L_f(P) = 0(0 - (-1)) + 1(2 - 0) = 2$
$U_f(P) = 1(0 - (-1)) + 3(2 - 0) = 7$
$L_f(P') = 0(0 - (-1)) + 1(1 - 0) + 2(2 - 1) = 3$
$U_f(P') = 1(0 - (-1)) + 2(1 - 0) + 3(2 - 1) = 6$

22. $L_f(P) = 0(\frac{1}{2} - 0) + \frac{1}{4}(1 - \frac{1}{2}) = \frac{1}{8}$
$U_f(P) = \frac{1}{4}(\frac{1}{2} - 0) + 1(1 - \frac{1}{2}) = \frac{5}{8}$
$L_f(P') = 0(\frac{1}{4} - 0) + \frac{1}{16}(\frac{1}{2} - \frac{1}{4}) + \frac{1}{4}(\frac{3}{4} - \frac{1}{2}) + \frac{9}{16}(1 - \frac{3}{4}) = \frac{7}{32}$
$U_f(P') = \frac{1}{16}(\frac{1}{4} - 0) + \frac{1}{4}(\frac{1}{2} - \frac{1}{4}) + \frac{9}{16}(\frac{3}{4} - \frac{1}{2}) + 1(1 - \frac{3}{4}) = \frac{15}{32}$

23. $L_f(P) = 0\left(\frac{\pi}{2} - 0\right) + 0\left(\pi - \frac{\pi}{2}\right) = 0$
$U_f(P) = 1\left(\frac{\pi}{2} - 0\right) + 1\left(\pi - \frac{\pi}{2}\right) = \pi$
$L_f(P') = 0\left(\frac{\pi}{4} - 0\right) + \frac{\sqrt{2}}{2}\left(\frac{\pi}{2} - \frac{\pi}{4}\right) + \frac{\sqrt{2}}{2}\left(\frac{3\pi}{4} - \frac{\pi}{2}\right) + 0\left(\pi - \frac{3\pi}{4}\right) = \frac{\sqrt{2}\pi}{4}$
$U_f(P') = \frac{\sqrt{2}}{2}\left(\frac{\pi}{4} - 0\right) + 1\left(\frac{\pi}{2} - \frac{\pi}{4}\right) + 1\left(\frac{3\pi}{4} - \frac{\pi}{2}\right) + \frac{\sqrt{2}}{2}\left(\pi - \frac{3\pi}{4}\right) = \frac{\pi}{4}(\sqrt{2} + 2)$

24. $L_f(P) = \frac{1}{2}\left(\frac{\pi}{3} - 0\right) + 0\left(\frac{\pi}{2} - \frac{\pi}{3}\right) = \frac{\pi}{6}$

$U_f(P) = 1\left(\frac{\pi}{3} - 0\right) + \frac{1}{2}\left(\frac{\pi}{2} - \frac{\pi}{3}\right) = \frac{5\pi}{12}$

$L_f(P') = \frac{\sqrt{3}}{2}\left(\frac{\pi}{6} - 0\right) + \frac{1}{2}\left(\frac{\pi}{3} - \frac{\pi}{6}\right) + 0\left(\frac{\pi}{2} - \frac{\pi}{3}\right) = \frac{\pi}{12}(\sqrt{3} + 1)$

$U_f(P') = 1\left(\frac{\pi}{6} - 0\right) + \frac{\sqrt{3}}{2}\left(\frac{\pi}{3} - \frac{\pi}{6}\right) + \frac{1}{2}\left(\frac{\pi}{2} - \frac{\pi}{3}\right) = \frac{\pi}{12}(\sqrt{3} + 3)$

25. $L_f(P) = 0\left(\frac{\pi}{2} - 0\right) + \left(\frac{\pi}{2} + 1\right)\left(\pi - \frac{\pi}{2}\right) = \left(\frac{\pi}{2} + 1\right)\frac{\pi}{2}$

$U_f(P) = \left(\frac{\pi}{2} + 1\right)\left(\frac{\pi}{2} - 0\right) + \pi\left(\pi - \frac{\pi}{2}\right) = \left(\frac{3\pi}{2} + 1\right)\frac{\pi}{2}$

$L_f(P') = 0\left(\frac{\pi}{4} - 0\right) + \left(\frac{\pi}{4} + \frac{\sqrt{2}}{2}\right)\left(\frac{\pi}{2} - \frac{\pi}{4}\right) + \left(\frac{\pi}{2} + 1\right)\left(\frac{3\pi}{4} - \frac{\pi}{2}\right)$

$+ \left(\frac{3\pi}{4} + \frac{\sqrt{2}}{2}\right)\left(\pi - \frac{3\pi}{4}\right) = \frac{\pi}{4}\left(\frac{3\pi}{2} + \sqrt{2} + 1\right)$

$U_f(P') = \left(\frac{\pi}{4} + \frac{\sqrt{2}}{2}\right)\left(\frac{\pi}{4} - 0\right) + \left(\frac{\pi}{2} + 1\right)\left(\frac{\pi}{2} - \frac{\pi}{4}\right) + \left(\frac{3\pi}{4} + \frac{\sqrt{2}}{2}\right)\left(\frac{3\pi}{4} - \frac{\pi}{2}\right)$

$+\pi\left(\pi - \frac{3\pi}{4}\right) = \frac{\pi}{4}\left(\frac{5\pi}{2} + \sqrt{2} + 1\right)$

26. a. $L_f(P) = 0(2) + 0(2) = 0$; $U_f(P) = 2(2) + 2(2) = 8$

b. $L_f(P') = 0(2) + \sqrt{3}\,(1) + 0(1) = \sqrt{3}$; $U_f(P') = 2(2) + 2(1) + \sqrt{3}\,(1) = 6 + \sqrt{3}$

c. $L_f(P'') = 0(1) + \sqrt{3}\,(1) + \sqrt{3}\,(1) + 0(1) = 2\sqrt{3}$; $U_f(P'') = \sqrt{3}\,(1) + 2(1) + 2(1) + \sqrt{3}\,(1) = 4 + 2\sqrt{3}$

27. $L_f(P) = \frac{4}{9}(\frac{1}{2}) + \frac{1}{4}(\frac{1}{2}) + \frac{4}{25}(\frac{1}{2}) + \frac{1}{9}(\frac{1}{2}) = \frac{869}{1800}$. Thus the area is approximately $\frac{869}{1800}$.

28. Because $L_f(P)$ cannot be greater than $U_f(P)$.

29. a. $L_f(P) = 0(1) + 1(5) + 6(1) = 11$; $L_f(P') = 0(4) + 4(3) = 12$. Thus $L_f(P) \neq L_f(P')$.

b. $L_f(P'') = 0\left(\frac{7 - \sqrt{5}}{2}\right) + \left(\frac{7 - \sqrt{5}}{2}\right)\left(\frac{7 + \sqrt{5}}{2}\right) = \frac{49 - 5}{4} = 11$. Thus $L_f(P) = L_f(P'')$.

30. $L_f(P) = 0(c) + c(7 - c) = 7c - c^2$; $U_f(P) = c(c) + 7(7 - c) = 49 - 7c + c^2$.

Since the equation $2c^2 - 14c + 49 = 0$ has no roots, $L_f(P) \neq U_f(P)$ for every c in $(0, 7)$.

31. Let $P = \{x_0, x_1, \ldots, x_n\}$. In order to find $U_f(P)$ we must be able to find the maximum value of f on $[x_0, x_1] = [0, x_1]$, and this is not possible since $\lim_{x\to 0^+} 1/x = \infty$. We can find the minimum value of f on each subinterval determined by P. Thus we can find $L_f(P)$.

32. Let $P = \{x_0, x_1, \ldots, x_n\}$ be a partition of $[a, b]$. Let $m_k(f)$ and $m_k(g)$ be the minimum values of f and g, respectively, on $[x_{k-1}, x_k]$, and $M_k(f)$ and $M_k(g)$ the maximum values of f and g, respectively,

on $[x_{k-1}, x_k]$. Since $f(x) \le g(x)$ for $a \le x \le b$, we have $m_k(f) \le m_k(g)$ and $M_k(f) \le M_k(g)$. Thus

$$\begin{aligned} L_f(P) &= m_1(f)\Delta x_1 + m_2(f)\Delta x_2 + \cdots + m_n(f)\Delta x_n \\ &\le m_1(g)\Delta x_1 + m_2(g)\Delta x_2 + \cdots + m_n(g)\Delta x_n \\ &= L_g(P) \end{aligned}$$

$$\begin{aligned} U_f(P) &= M_1(f)\Delta x_1 + M_2(f)\Delta x_2 + \cdots + M_n(f)\Delta x_n \\ &\le M_1(g)\Delta x_1 + M_2(g)\Delta x_2 + \cdots + M_n(g)\Delta x_n \\ &= U_g(P). \end{aligned}$$

33. Let P be a partition such that $L_f(P) = U_f(P)$. Then $m_k = M_k$ for each k, so that f is constant on each subinterval $[x_{k-1}, x_k]$. Moreover, $f(a) = f(x_1) = f(x_2) = \cdots = f(x_n)$. Thus f is constant on $[a, b]$.

34. Let $P = \{x_0, x_1, \ldots, x_n\}$ be a partition of $[a, b]$ such that $\Delta x_k = (b-a)/n$ for $1 \le k \le n$. Since f is increasing on $[a, b]$,

$$U_f(P) = f(x_1)\frac{b-a}{n} + f(x_2)\frac{b-a}{n} + \cdots + f(x_n)\frac{b-a}{n}$$

$$L_f(P) = f(x_0)\frac{b-a}{n} + f(x_1)\frac{b-a}{n} + \cdots + f(x_{n-1})\frac{b-a}{n}.$$

Using the fact that $x_0 = a$ and $x_n = b$, we conclude that

$$U_f(P) - L_f(P) = f(x_n)\frac{b-a}{n} - f(x_0)\frac{b-a}{n} = [f(b) - f(a)]\frac{b-a}{n}.$$

35. Notice that

$$f'(x) = \frac{10^4(1+x^2) - 10^4(2x^2)}{(1+x^2)^2} = \frac{10^4(1+x)(1-x)}{(1+x^2)^2},$$

so that f is increasing on $[0, 1]$ and decreasing on $[1, 4]$.

a. Let $P = \{0, 1, 2, 3, 4\}$. Then

$$L_f(P) = 0(1) + \frac{10^4(2)}{5}(1) + \frac{10^4(3)}{10}(1) + \frac{10^4(4)}{17}(1) = \frac{159}{170} \times 10^4 \approx 0.9352941176 \times 10^4.$$

b. Let $P' = \left\{0, \frac{1}{2}, 1, \frac{3}{2}, 2, \frac{5}{2}, 3, \frac{7}{2}, 4\right\}$. Then

$$L_f(P') = 0\left(\frac{1}{2}\right) + \frac{10^4(\frac{1}{2})}{\frac{5}{4}}\left(\frac{1}{2}\right) + \frac{10^4(\frac{3}{2})}{\frac{13}{4}}\left(\frac{1}{2}\right) + \frac{10^4(2)}{5}\left(\frac{1}{2}\right) + \frac{10^4(\frac{5}{2})}{\frac{29}{4}}\left(\frac{1}{2}\right)$$

$$+\frac{10^4(3)}{10}\left(\frac{1}{2}\right) + \frac{10^4(\frac{7}{2})}{\frac{53}{4}}\left(\frac{1}{2}\right) + \frac{10^4(4)}{17}\left(\frac{1}{2}\right) \approx 1.202905554 \times 10^4.$$

5.2 The Definite Integral

1. From the figures, $\Delta x_1 = \Delta x_2 = \Delta x_3 = 1$. From the figures, $m_1 = -\frac{1}{2}$, $m_2 = \frac{1}{2}$, and $m_3 = \frac{3}{2}$; $M_1 = \frac{1}{2}$, $M_2 = \frac{3}{2}$, and $M_3 = \frac{5}{2}$. We obtain $L_f(P) = -\frac{1}{2}\cdot 1 + \frac{1}{2}\cdot 1 + \frac{3}{2}\cdot 1 = \frac{3}{2}$ and $U_f(P) = \frac{1}{2}\cdot 1 + \frac{3}{2}\cdot 1 + \frac{5}{2}\cdot 1 = \frac{9}{2}$.

2. From the figures, $\Delta x_1 = \Delta x_2 = \Delta x_3 = \Delta x_4 = 1$. From the figures, $m_1 = -2$, $m_2 = -\frac{1}{4}$, $m_3 = 0$, and $m_4 = \frac{1}{4}$; $M_1 = -\frac{1}{4}$, $M_2 = 0$, $M_3 = \frac{1}{4}$, and $M_4 = 2$. We obtain $L_f(P) = -2\cdot 1 - \frac{1}{4}\cdot 1 + 0\cdot 1 + \frac{1}{4}\cdot 1 = -2$ and $U_f(P) = -\frac{1}{4}\cdot 1 + 0\cdot 1 + \frac{1}{4}\cdot 1 + 2\cdot 1 = 2$.

3. From the figures, we have $\Delta x_1 = \Delta x_2 = \Delta x_3 = \frac{1}{2}$. From the figures, $m_1 = 0$, $m_2 = 0$, and $m_3 = (\frac{3}{2})^2 - (\frac{3}{2})^3 = -\frac{9}{8}$. Since $f'(x) = 2x - 3x^2 = x(2-3x)$, the maximum value of f on $[\frac{1}{2}, 1]$ occurs at $\frac{2}{3}$. From this and the figures, $M_1 = (\frac{1}{2})^2 - (\frac{1}{2})^3 = \frac{1}{8}$, $M_2 = (\frac{2}{3})^2 - (\frac{2}{3})^3 = \frac{4}{27}$, and $M_3 = 0$. We obtain $L_f(P) = 0\cdot\frac{1}{2} + 0\cdot\frac{1}{2} + (-\frac{9}{8})\cdot\frac{1}{2} = -\frac{9}{16}$ and $U_f(P) = \frac{1}{8}\cdot\frac{1}{2} + \frac{4}{27}\cdot\frac{1}{2} + 0\cdot\frac{1}{2} = \frac{59}{432}$.

4. From the figures, we have $\Delta x_1 = \Delta x_2 = \cdots = \Delta x_8 = \pi/4$.

$$L_f(P) = \frac{\pi}{4}\left(\cos\frac{\pi}{4} + \cos\frac{\pi}{2} + \cos\frac{3\pi}{4} + \cos\pi + \cos\pi + \cos\frac{5\pi}{4} + \cos\frac{3\pi}{2} + \cos\frac{7\pi}{4}\right)$$

$$= \frac{\pi}{4}\left(\frac{\sqrt{2}}{2} + 0 - \frac{\sqrt{2}}{2} - 1 - 1 - \frac{\sqrt{2}}{2} + 0 + \frac{\sqrt{2}}{2}\right) = -\frac{\pi}{2}$$

and

$$U_f(P) = \frac{\pi}{4}\left(\cos 0 + \cos\frac{\pi}{4} + \cos\frac{\pi}{2} + \cos\frac{3\pi}{4} + \cos\frac{5\pi}{4} + \cos\frac{3\pi}{2} + \cos\frac{7\pi}{4} + \cos 2\pi\right)$$

$$= \frac{\pi}{4}\left(1 + \frac{\sqrt{2}}{2} + 0 - \frac{\sqrt{2}}{2} - \frac{\sqrt{2}}{2} + 0 + \frac{\sqrt{2}}{2} + 1\right) = \frac{\pi}{2}.$$

5. Since $2x$ is increasing on $[-1,3]$, $L_f(P) = -2(1) + 0(1) + 2(1) + 4(1) = 4$, $U_f(P) = 0(1) + 2(1) + 4(1) + 6(1) = 12$.

6. Since x^2 is decreasing on $[-2,0]$ and increasing on $[0,1]$, $L_f(P) = 1(1) + 0(1) + 0(1) = 1$, $U_f(P) = 4(1) + 1(1) + 1(1) = 6$.

7. Since $|x|$ is decreasing on $[-1,0]$ and increasing on $[0,3]$, $L_f(P) = \frac{1}{2}(\frac{1}{2}) + 0(\frac{1}{2}) + 0(\frac{1}{2}) + \frac{1}{2}(\frac{1}{2}) + 1(\frac{1}{2}) + \frac{3}{2}(\frac{1}{2}) + 2(\frac{1}{2}) + \frac{5}{2}(\frac{1}{2}) = 4$, $U_f(P) = 1(\frac{1}{2}) + \frac{1}{2}(\frac{1}{2}) + \frac{1}{2}(\frac{1}{2}) + 1(\frac{1}{2}) + \frac{3}{2}(\frac{1}{2}) + 2(\frac{1}{2}) + \frac{5}{2}(\frac{1}{2}) + 3(\frac{1}{2}) = 6$.

8. Since $-\cos x$ is decreasing on $[-\pi/4, 0]$ and increasing on $[0, \pi/4]$,

$$L_f(P) = (-1)\left(\frac{\pi}{4}\right) + (-1)\left(\frac{\pi}{4}\right) = \frac{-\pi}{2} \quad\text{and}\quad U_f(P) = \frac{-\sqrt{2}}{2}\left(\frac{\pi}{4}\right) + \left(\frac{-\sqrt{2}}{2}\right)\left(\frac{\pi}{4}\right) = \frac{-\sqrt{2}}{4}\pi.$$

9. Since $3\sin x$ is increasing on $[-\pi/4, \pi/4]$,

$$L_f(P) = \left(\frac{-3\sqrt{2}}{2}\right)\left(\frac{\pi}{4}\right) + 0\left(\frac{\pi}{4}\right) = \frac{-3\sqrt{2}\pi}{8} \quad\text{and}\quad U_f(P) = 0\left(\frac{\pi}{4}\right) + \frac{3\sqrt{2}}{2}\left(\frac{\pi}{4}\right) = \frac{3\sqrt{2}\pi}{8}.$$

10. Since $|x-1|$ is decreasing on $[0,1]$ and increasing on $[1,2]$,

$$L_f(P) = \frac{1}{2}\left(\frac{1}{2}\right) + 0\left(\frac{1}{2}\right) + 0\left(\frac{1}{2}\right) + \frac{1}{2}\left(\frac{1}{2}\right) = \frac{1}{2}$$

and

$$U_f(P) = 1\left(\frac{1}{2}\right) + \frac{1}{2}\left(\frac{1}{2}\right) + \frac{1}{2}\left(\frac{1}{2}\right) + 1\left(\frac{1}{2}\right) = \frac{3}{2}.$$

11. Since $\ln x$ is increasing on $[0.5, 2]$,

$$L_f(P) = (\ln 0.5)(0.25) + (\ln 0.75)(0.25) + \cdots + (\ln 1.5)(0.25) + (\ln 1.75)(0.25) \approx 0.0518487986;$$

$$U_f(P) = (\ln 0.75)(0.25) + (\ln 1)(0.25) + \cdots + (\ln 1.75)(0.25) + (\ln 2)(0.25) \approx 0.3984223889.$$

12. Since $e^{-2x} - 1$ is decreasing,

$$L_f(P) = (e^{-2(-.8)} - 1)(.2) + (e^{-2(-.6)} - 1)(.2) + \cdots + (e^{-2(1)} - 1)(.2) \approx 0.9497179993;$$

$$U_f(P) = (e^{-2(-1)} - 1)(.2) + (e^{-2(-.8)} - 1)(.2) + \cdots + (e^{-2(.8)} - 1)(.2) \approx 2.400462162.$$

13. By Example 1, $\int_{-2}^{3} 4\,dx = 4[3-(-2)] = 20$.

14. By Example 2, $\int_{-3}^{3} x\,dx = \frac{1}{2}[3^2 - (-3)^2] = 0$.

15. By (1), $\int_{2.7}^{2.9} -x\,dx = -\frac{1}{2}[(2.9)^2 - (2.7)^2] = -0.56$.

16. By (2), $\int_{-5}^{0} -3x^2\,dx = -\frac{3}{3}[0^3 - (-5)^3] = -125$.

17. By (2), $\int_{-1}^{4} \pi x^2\,dx = (\pi/3)[4^3 - (-1)^3] = \frac{65}{3}\pi$.

18. a. $1/x$ is not defined at 0, so $U_f(P)$ is not meaningful.
    b. The interval $[0, \infty)$ formed by the limits of integration is unbounded, so $U_f(P)$ is not meaningful.
    c. Tan x is not defined at $\pi/2$, so $U_f(P)$ is not meaningful.
    d. $\sqrt{x}$ is not defined on $[-1, 0)$, so $U_f(P)$ is not meaningful.

19. $A = \int_{-2}^{3} \frac{5}{2}\,dx = \frac{5}{2}(3-(-2)) = \frac{25}{2}$

20. $A = \int_{\sqrt{3}}^{3\sqrt{3}} \sqrt{3}\,dx = \sqrt{3}(3\sqrt{3} - \sqrt{3}) = 6$

21. $A = \int_{1}^{4} x\,dx = \frac{1}{2}(4^2 - 1^2) = \frac{15}{2}$

22. $A = \int_{-3}^{-1} -x\,dx = -\frac{1}{2}[(-1)^2 - (-3)^2] = 4$

23. Let $f(x) = x^2 - x$ for $1 \le x \le 3$.
    left sum: $f(1)(1) + f(2)(1) = 0(1) + 2(1) = 2$
    right sum: $f(2)(1) + f(3)(1) = 2(1) + 6(1) = 8$
    midpoint sum: $f(\frac{3}{2})(1) + f(\frac{5}{2})(1) = \frac{3}{4}(1) + \frac{15}{4}(1) = \frac{9}{2}$

24. Let $f(x) = x - 3$ for $0 \le x \le 4$.

left sum: $f(0)(1) + f(1)(1) + f(2)(1) + f(3)(1) = (-3)(1) + (-2)(1) + (-1)(1) + 0(1) = -6$

right sum: $f(1)(1) + f(2)(1) + f(3)(1) + f(4)(1) = (-2)(1) + (-1)(1) + 0(1) + 1(1) = -2$

midpoint sum: $f(\frac{1}{2})(1) + f(\frac{3}{2})(1) + f(\frac{5}{2})(1) + f(\frac{7}{2})(1) = (-\frac{5}{2})(1) + (-\frac{3}{2})(1) + (-\frac{1}{2})(1) + \frac{1}{2}(1) = -4$

25. Let $f(x) = \sin \pi x$ for $0 \le x \le 2$.

left sum: $f(0)\left(\frac{1}{2}\right) + f\left(\frac{1}{2}\right)\left(\frac{1}{2}\right) + f(1)(1) = (\sin 0)\left(\frac{1}{2}\right) + \left(\sin \frac{\pi}{2}\right)\left(\frac{1}{2}\right) + (\sin \pi)(1)$
$= 0\left(\frac{1}{2}\right) + 1\left(\frac{1}{2}\right) + 0(1) = \frac{1}{2}$

right sum: $f\left(\frac{1}{2}\right)\left(\frac{1}{2}\right) + f(1)\left(\frac{1}{2}\right) + f(2)(1) = \left(\sin \frac{\pi}{2}\right)\left(\frac{1}{2}\right) + (\sin \pi)\left(\frac{1}{2}\right) + (\sin 2\pi)(1)$
$= 1\left(\frac{1}{2}\right) + 0\left(\frac{1}{2}\right) + 0(1) = \frac{1}{2}$

midpoint sum: $f\left(\frac{1}{4}\right)\left(\frac{1}{2}\right) + f\left(\frac{3}{4}\right)\left(\frac{1}{2}\right) + f\left(\frac{3}{2}\right)(1) = \left(\sin \frac{\pi}{4}\right)\left(\frac{1}{2}\right) + \left(\sin \frac{3\pi}{4}\right)\left(\frac{1}{2}\right) + \left(\sin \frac{3\pi}{2}\right)(1)$
$= \frac{\sqrt{2}}{2}\left(\frac{1}{2}\right) + \frac{\sqrt{2}}{2}\left(\frac{1}{2}\right) + (-1)(1) = \frac{\sqrt{2}}{2} - 1$

26. Let $f(x) = \cos x$ for $-\pi \le x \le 0$.

left sum: $f(-\pi)\left(\frac{\pi}{3}\right) + f\left(-\frac{2\pi}{3}\right)\left(\frac{\pi}{3}\right) + f\left(-\frac{\pi}{3}\right)\left(\frac{\pi}{3}\right) = (\cos(-\pi))\left(\frac{\pi}{3}\right) + \left(\cos\left(-\frac{2\pi}{3}\right)\right)\left(\frac{\pi}{3}\right)$
$+ \left(\cos\left(-\frac{\pi}{3}\right)\right)\left(\frac{\pi}{3}\right) = -\frac{\pi}{3} - \frac{\pi}{6} + \frac{\pi}{6} = -\frac{\pi}{3}$

right sum: $f\left(-\frac{2\pi}{3}\right)\left(\frac{\pi}{3}\right) + f\left(-\frac{\pi}{3}\right)\left(\frac{\pi}{3}\right) + f(0)\left(\frac{\pi}{3}\right) = \left(\cos\left(-\frac{2\pi}{3}\right)\right)\left(\frac{\pi}{3}\right) + \left(\cos\left(-\frac{\pi}{3}\right)\right)\left(\frac{\pi}{3}\right)$
$+ (\cos 0)\left(\frac{\pi}{3}\right) = -\frac{\pi}{6} + \frac{\pi}{6} + \frac{\pi}{3} = \frac{\pi}{3}$

midpoint sum: $f\left(-\frac{5\pi}{6}\right)\left(\frac{\pi}{3}\right) + f\left(-\frac{\pi}{2}\right)\left(\frac{\pi}{3}\right) + f\left(-\frac{\pi}{6}\right)\left(\frac{\pi}{3}\right) = \left(\cos\left(-\frac{5\pi}{6}\right)\right)\left(\frac{\pi}{3}\right) + \left(\cos\left(-\frac{\pi}{2}\right)\right)\left(\frac{\pi}{3}\right)$
$+ \left(\cos\left(-\frac{\pi}{6}\right)\right)\left(\frac{\pi}{3}\right)$
$= -\frac{\sqrt{3}}{2}\left(\frac{\pi}{3}\right) + 0\left(\frac{\pi}{3}\right) + \frac{\sqrt{3}}{2}\left(\frac{\pi}{3}\right) = 0$

27. Let $f(x) = 1/x$ for $1 \le x \le 5$.

left sum: $f(1)(1) + f(2)(1) + f(3)(1) + f(4)(1) = 1(1) + \frac{1}{2}(1) + \frac{1}{3}(1) + \frac{1}{4}(1) = \frac{25}{12}$

right sum: $f(2)(1) + f(3)(1) + f(4)(1) + f(5)(1) = \frac{1}{2}(1) + \frac{1}{3}(1) + \frac{1}{4}(1) + \frac{1}{5}(1) = \frac{77}{60}$

midpoint sum: $f(\frac{3}{2})(1) + f(\frac{5}{2})(1) + f(\frac{7}{2})(1) + f(\frac{9}{2})(1) = \frac{2}{3}(1) + \frac{2}{5}(1) + \frac{2}{7}(1) + \frac{2}{9}(1) = \frac{496}{315}$

28. Let $f(x) = 1/(2x + 1)$ for $-2 \le x \le -1$.

left sum: $f(-2)(\frac{1}{2}) + f(-\frac{3}{2})(\frac{1}{4}) + f(-\frac{5}{4})(\frac{1}{4}) = (-\frac{1}{3})(\frac{1}{2}) + (-\frac{1}{2})(\frac{1}{4}) + (-\frac{2}{3})(\frac{1}{4}) = -\frac{11}{24}$

right sum: $f(-\frac{3}{2})(\frac{1}{2}) + f(-\frac{5}{4})(\frac{1}{4}) + f(-1)(\frac{1}{4}) = (-\frac{1}{2})(\frac{1}{2}) + (-\frac{2}{3})(\frac{1}{4}) + (-1)(\frac{1}{4}) = -\frac{2}{3}$

midpoint sum: $f(-\frac{7}{4})(\frac{1}{2}) + f(-\frac{11}{8})(\frac{1}{4}) + f(-\frac{9}{8})(\frac{1}{4}) = (-\frac{2}{5})(\frac{1}{2}) + (-\frac{4}{7})(\frac{1}{4}) + (-\frac{4}{5})(\frac{1}{4}) = -\frac{19}{35}$

29. The midpoint sum yields

$$\int_0^{\pi} \sin x\, dx \approx \frac{\pi - 0}{10}\left[\sin \frac{\pi}{20} + \sin \frac{3\pi}{20} + \sin \frac{5\pi}{20} + \cdots + \sin \frac{19\pi}{20}\right] \approx 2.008248408.$$

30. The left sum yields

$$\int_0^{\pi/4} \tan x\,dx \approx \frac{\pi/4-0}{10}\left[\tan 0+\tan\frac{\pi}{40}+\tan\frac{2\pi}{40}+\cdots+\tan\frac{9\pi}{40}\right] \approx 0.3078169879.$$

31. The midpoint sum yields

$$\int_1^2 \frac{1}{1+x^2}\,dx \approx \frac{2-1}{10}\left[\frac{1}{1+(1.05)^2}+\frac{1}{1+(1.15)^2}+\cdots+\frac{1}{1+(1.95)^2}\right] \approx 0.3216088602.$$

32. The left sum yields

$$\int_0^1 \sqrt{1+\cos x}\,dx \approx \frac{1-0}{20}\left[\sqrt{1+\cos 0}+\sqrt{1+\cos .05}+\sqrt{1+\cos .1}+\cdots+\sqrt{1+\cos .95}\right] \approx 1.360277681.$$

33. The left sum yields

$$\int_2^4 \frac{x^2}{x^{10}-1}\,dx \approx \frac{4-2}{20}\left[\frac{2^2}{2^{10}-1}+\frac{(2.1)^2}{(2.1)^{10}-1}+\cdots+\frac{(3.9)^2}{(3.9)^{10}-1}\right] \approx 0.0013155169.$$

34. The right sum yields

$$\int_{1.1}^{1.2} \ln(1+e^x)\,dx \approx \frac{1.2-1.1}{20}\left[\ln(1+e^{1.105})+\ln(1+e^{1.11})+\cdots+\ln(1+e^{1.2})\right] \approx 0.1427055747.$$

35. The right sum yields

$$\int_2^3 e^{-x}\,dx \approx \frac{3-2}{20}\left[e^{-2.05}+e^{-2.1}+\cdots+e^{-3}\right] \approx 0.0834273313.$$

36. The right sum yields

$$\int_{-1}^1 e^{(x^2)}\,dx \approx \frac{1-(-1)}{20}\left[e^{(-.9)^2}+e^{(-.8)^2}+\cdots+e^{(.9)^2}+e^{(1)^2}\right] \approx 2.934349385.$$

37. $A \approx f(0)(\frac{1}{4})+f(\frac{1}{4})(\frac{1}{4})+f(\frac{1}{2})(\frac{1}{4})+f(\frac{3}{4}(\frac{1}{4}) = 0(\frac{1}{4})+\frac{7}{8}(\frac{1}{4})+2(\frac{1}{4})+\frac{27}{8}(\frac{1}{4}) = \frac{25}{16}$

38. $A \approx f(1)(1)+f(2)(1)+f(3)(1) = 1(1)+\sqrt{2}(1)+\sqrt{3}(1) \approx 4.1462637$

39. $A \approx f(0)(\frac{1}{2})+f(\frac{1}{2})(\frac{1}{2})+f(1)(1) = 0(\frac{1}{2})+\frac{1}{3}(\frac{1}{2})+\frac{1}{2}(1) = \frac{2}{3}$

40. By calculator, $A \approx 7.88$.

41. By calculator, $A \approx 8.27$.

42. a. Let $P = \{x_0, x_1, \ldots, x_n\}$ be any partition of $[a,b]$. Let $m_k(f)$ and $M_k(f)$ be the minimum and maximum values, respectively, of f on $[x_{k-1}, x_k]$. Let $m_k(g)$ and $M_k(g)$ be the minimum and maximum values, respectively, of g on $[x_{k-1}, x_k]$. Then $m_k(f) \le m_k(g)$ and $M_k(f) \le M_k(g)$ for any k between 1 and n. Thus we have

$$\begin{aligned} L_f(P) &= m_1(f)\Delta x_1 + m_2(f)\Delta x_2 + \cdots + m_n(f)\Delta x_n \\ &\le m_1(g)\Delta x_1 + m_2(g)\Delta x_2 + \cdots + m_n(g)\Delta x_n = L_g(P) \end{aligned}$$

and

$$\begin{aligned}U_f(P) &= M_1(f)\Delta x_1 + M_2(f)\Delta x_2 + \cdots + M_n(f)\Delta x_n \\ &\le M_1(g)\Delta x_1 + M_2(g)\Delta x_2 + \cdots + M_n(g)\Delta x_n = U_g(P).\end{aligned}$$

b. (1) and (2): By definition of the definite integral. (3): By part (a).

43. For $0 \le x \le 1$ we have $x^6 \le x$. Thus $\int_0^1 x^6\,dx \le \int_0^1 x\,dx$.

44. For $x \ge 1$ we have $x \le x^6$. Thus $\int_1^2 x\,dx \le \int_1^2 x^6\,dx$.

45. For $x \ge 1$ we have $x^6 \ge x$ and hence $1/x^6 \le 1/x$. Thus $\int_1^2 (1/x^6)\,dx \le \int_1^2 (1/x)\,dx$.

46. For $x \ge 0$ we have $\sin x \le x$. Thus $\int_0^{\pi/2} \sin x\,dx \le \int_0^{\pi/2} x\,dx$.

47. For $0 \le x \le \pi/4$ we have $\sin x \le \sqrt{2}/2 \le \cos x$. Thus $\int_0^{\pi/4} \sin x\,dx \le \int_0^{\pi/4} \cos x\,dx$.

48. Since $M_k = x_k$ and $x_k > \frac{1}{2}(x_k + x_{k-1})$,

$$\begin{aligned}U_f(P) &= M_1\Delta x_1 + M_2\Delta x_2 + \cdots + M_n\Delta x_n \\ &= x_1(x_1 - x_0) + x_2(x_2 - x_1) + \cdots + x_n(x_n - x_{n-1}) \\ &> \tfrac{1}{2}(x_1 + x_0)(x_1 - x_0) + \tfrac{1}{2}(x_2 + x_1)(x_2 - x_1) + \cdots + \tfrac{1}{2}(x_n + x_{n-1})(x_n - x_{n-1}) \\ &= \tfrac{1}{2}(x_1^2 - x_0^2) + \tfrac{1}{2}(x_2^2 - x_1^2) + \cdots + \tfrac{1}{2}(x_n^2 - x_{n-1}^2) = \tfrac{1}{2}(x_n^2 - x_0^2) \\ &= \tfrac{1}{2}(b^2 - a^2)\end{aligned}$$

49. Let $P = \{x_0, x_1, \ldots, x_n\}$ be any partition of $[a, b]$. Then for any k between 1 and n we have $m_k = x_{k-1} + 4$ and $M_k = x_k + 4$. Thus

$$\begin{aligned}L_f(P) &= (x_0 + 4)(x_1 - x_0) + (x_1 + 4)(x_2 - x_1) + \cdots + (x_{n-1} + 4)(x_n - x_{n-1}) \\ &= x_0(x_1 - x_0) + x_1(x_2 - x_1) + \cdots + x_{n-1}(x_n - x_{n-1}) + 4(x_n - x_0) \\ &< \tfrac{1}{2}(b^2 - a^2) + 4(b - a)\end{aligned}$$

and

$$\begin{aligned}U_f(P) &= (x_1 + 4)(x_1 - x_0) + (x_2 + 4)(x_2 - x_1) + \cdots + (x_n + 4)(x_n - x_{n-1}) \\ &= x_1(x_1 - x_0) + x_2(x_2 - x_1) + \cdots + x_n(x_n - x_{n-1}) + 4(x_n - x_0) \\ &> \tfrac{1}{2}(b^2 - a^2) + 4(b - a)\end{aligned}$$

Thus $L_f(P) \le \frac{1}{2}(b^2 - a^2) + 4(b - a) \le U_f(P)$ for any partition P. Definition 5.2 therefore implies that $\int_a^b (x + 4)\,dx = \frac{1}{2}(b^2 - a^2) + 4(b - a)$.

50. Let $P = \{x_0, x_1, \ldots, x_n\}$ be any partition of $[a, b]$, and for any k between 1 and n let $\Delta x_k = x_k - x_{k-1}$. From the first set of inequalities in Example 2,

$$x_0\Delta x_1 + x_1\Delta x_2 + \cdots + x_{n-1}\Delta x_n < \frac{1}{2}(b^2 - a^2).$$

An analogous computation shows that

$$x_1\Delta x_1 + x_2\Delta x_2 + \cdots + x_n\Delta x_n > \frac{1}{2}(b^2 - a^2).$$

Suppose $c > 0$. For any k between 1 and n, $m_k = cx_{k-1}$ and $M_k = cx_k$. Thus $L_f(P) = m_1\Delta x_1 + m_2\Delta x_2 + \cdots + m_n\Delta x_n = cx_0\Delta x_1 + cx_1\Delta x_2 + \cdots + cx_{n-1}\Delta x_n = c[x_0\Delta x_1 + x_1\Delta x_2 + \cdots + x_{n-1}\Delta x_n] < c[\frac{1}{2}(b^2 - a^2)]$, whereas $U_f(P) = M_1\Delta x_1 + M_2\Delta x_2 + \cdots + M_n\Delta x_n = cx_1\Delta x_1 + cx_2\Delta x_2 + \cdots + cx_n\Delta x_n = c[x_1\Delta x_1 + x_2\Delta x_2 + \cdots + x_n\Delta x_n] > c[\frac{1}{2}(b^2 - a^2)]$. Therefore for any partition P of $[a, b]$,

$$L_f(P) \le \frac{c}{2}(b^2 - a^2) \le U_f(P)$$

and we conclude from Definition 5.2 that $\int_a^b cx\,dx = (c/2)(b^2 - a^2)$ if $c > 0$.

Suppose $c < 0$. For any k between 1 and n, $m_k = cx_k$ and $M_k = cx_{k-1}$. Thus $L_f(P) = m_1\Delta x_1 + m_2\Delta x_2 + \cdots + m_n\Delta x_n = cx_1\Delta x_1 + cx_2\Delta x_2 + \cdots + cx_n\Delta x_n = c[x_1\Delta x_1 + x_2\Delta x_2 + \cdots + x_n\Delta x_n] < c[\frac{1}{2}(b^2 - a^2)]$, whereas $U_f(P) = M_1\Delta x_1 + M_2\Delta x_2 + \cdots + M_n\Delta x_n = cx_0\Delta x_1 + cx_1\Delta x_2 + \cdots + cx_{n-1}\Delta x_n = c[x_0\Delta x_1 + x_1\Delta x_2 + \cdots + x_{n-1}\Delta x_n] > c[\frac{1}{2}(b^2 - a^2)]$. Therefore, for any partition P of $[a, b]$,

$$L_f(P) \le \frac{c}{2}(b^2 - a^2) \le U_f(P)$$

and we conclude from Definition 5.2 that $\int_a^b cx\,dx = (c/2)(b^2 - a^2)$ if $c < 0$.

If $c = 0$, then $\int_a^b cx\,dx = \int_a^b 0\,dx = 0(b - a) = 0 = (c/2)(b^2 - a^2)$ by Example 1.

51. a. $\int_1^3 4x\,dx = \frac{4}{2}(3^2 - 1^2) = 16$

    b. $\int_2^6 -\frac{1}{2}x\,dx = \frac{-1/2}{2}(6^2 - 2^2) = -8$

    c. $\int_{-5}^5 \sqrt{3}\,x\,dx = (\sqrt{3}/2)[5^2 - (-5)^2] = 0$

    d. $\int_{-1/\pi}^0 \pi x\,dx = (\pi/2)[0^2 - (-1/\pi)^2] = -1/(2\pi)$

52. Let $P = \{x_0, x_1, \ldots, x_n\}$ be any partition of $[a, b]$. Then for any k between 1 and n we have

$$m_k = x_{k-1}^2, \quad M_k = x_k^2 \quad \text{and} \quad x_{k-1}^2 < \frac{x_k^2 + x_kx_{k-1} + x_{k-1}^2}{3} < x_k^2.$$

Thus

$$\begin{aligned}
L_f(P) &= m_1\Delta x_1 + m_2\Delta x_2 + \cdots + m_n\Delta x_n \\
&= x_0^2(x_1 - x_0) + x_1^2(x_2 - x_1) + \cdots + x_{n-1}^2(x_n - x_{n-1}) \\
&< \frac{x_1^2 + x_1x_0 + x_0^2}{3}(x_1 - x_0) + \frac{x_2^2 + x_2x_1 + x_1^2}{3}(x_2 - x_1) + \cdots \\
&\quad + \frac{x_n^2 + x_nx_{n-1} + x_{n-1}^2}{3}(x_n - x_{n-1}) \\
&= \frac{1}{3}[(x_1^3 - x_0^3) + (x_2^3 - x_1^3) + \cdots + (x_n^3 - x_{n-1}^3)] = \frac{1}{3}(b^3 - a^3).
\end{aligned}$$

Similarly

$$\begin{aligned} U_f(P) &= M_1\Delta x_1 + M_2\Delta x_2 + \cdots + M_n\Delta x_n \\ &= x_1^2(x_1 - x_0) + x_2^2(x_2 - x_1) + \cdots + x_n^2(x_n - x_{n-1}) \\ &> \frac{x_1^2 + x_1x_0 + x_0^2}{3}(x_1 - x_0) + \frac{x_2^2 + x_2x_1 + x_1^2}{3}(x_2 - x_1) + \cdots \\ &\quad + \frac{x_n^2 + x_nx_{n-1} + x_{n-1}^2}{3}(x_n - x_{n-1}) \\ &= \frac{1}{3}(b^3 - a^3). \end{aligned}$$

Since for any partition P of $[a,b]$, $L_f(P) \le \frac{1}{3}(b^3 - a^3) \le U_f(P)$, we conclude from Definition 5.2 that $\int_a^b x^3\,dx = \frac{1}{3}(b^3 - a^3)$.

53. a. $\int_0^2 x^3\,dx = \frac{1}{4}(2^4 - 0^4) = 4$

b. $\int_{-1}^1 x^3\,dx = \frac{1}{4}[1^4 - (-1)^4] = 0$

54. $\displaystyle\int_a^b x^n\,dx = \frac{1}{n+1}(b^{n+1} - a^{n+1})$

55. a. Let $f(x) = 1/x$, so $f'(x) = -1/x^2$. Since $|f'|$ is decreasing on $[1,2]$, let $K = |f'(1)| = 1$. Then

$$E_n^L \le \frac{1}{2n}(2-1)^2 = \frac{1}{2n} \quad \text{and} \quad E_n^R \le \frac{1}{2n}(2-1)^2 = \frac{1}{2n}.$$

b. Let $f(x) = \sin x$, so $f'(x) = \cos x$. Since $|f'| \le 1$ on $[0,3]$ and $|f'(\pi)| = 1$, let $K = 1$. Then

$$E_n^L \le \frac{1}{2n}(3-0)^2 = \frac{9}{2n} \quad \text{and} \quad E_n^R \le \frac{1}{2n}(3-0)^2 = \frac{9}{2n}.$$

c. Let $f(x) = e^{1/x}$, so $f'(x) = (-1/x^2)e^{1/x}$. Since $|f'|$ is decreasing on $[1,2]$, let $K = |f'(1)| = e$. Then

$$E_n^L \le \frac{e}{2n}(2-1)^2 = \frac{e}{2n} \quad \text{and} \quad E_n^R \le \frac{e}{2n}.$$

56. a. Let $f(x) = 1/x$, so $f'(x) = -1/x^2$ and $f''(x) = 2/x^3$. Since $|f''|$ is decreasing on $[1,2]$, $K = |f''(1)| = 2$. Thus

$$E_n^M \le \frac{2}{24n^2}(2-1)^3 = \frac{1}{12n^2}.$$

b. Let $f(x) = \sin x$, so $f'(x) = \cos x$ and $f''(x) = -\sin x$. Since $|f''| \le 1$ and $|f''(\pi/2)| = 1$, let $K = 1$. Then

$$E_n^M \le \frac{1}{24n^2}(3-0)^3 = \frac{9}{8n^2}.$$

c. Let $f(x) = e^{-x^2}$, so $f'(x) = -2xe^{-x^2}$ and $f''(x) = -2e^{-x^2} - 2x(-2xe^{-x^2}) = 2e^{-x^2}(-1 + 2x^2)$. Since $|e^{-x^2}| \le 1$ for $0 \le x \le 1$ and $|-1 + 2x^2| \le 1$ for $0 \le x \le 1$, we have

$$|f''(x)| = 2|e^{-x^2}||-1 + 2x^2| \le 2 \cdot 1 \cdot 1 = 2 \quad \text{for } 0 \le x \le 1.$$

Thus we let $K = 2$. Then

$$E_n^M \le \frac{2}{24n^2}(1-0)^3 = \frac{1}{12n^2}.$$

57. If $[r, s]$ is any interval, then

$$\int_r^s (mx + c)\,dx = \left(\frac{m}{2}x^2 + cx\right)\Big|_r^s = \frac{m}{2}(s^2 - r^2) + c(s - r).$$

Also

$$f\left(\frac{r+s}{2}\right)(s - r) = \left[m\left(\frac{r+s}{2}\right) + c\right](s - r) = \frac{m}{2}(s^2 - r^2) + c(s - r).$$

Thus

$$\int_r^s f(x)\,dx = f\left(\frac{r+s}{2}\right)(s - r).$$

If $P = \{x_0, x_1, \ldots, x_n\}$ is any partition of $[a, b]$, then

$$\int_a^b f(x)\,dx = \int_{x_0}^{x_1} f(x)\,dx + \int_{x_1}^{x_2} f(x)\,dx + \cdots + \int_{x_{n-1}}^{x_n} f(x)\,dx$$

$$= f\left(\frac{x_0 + x_1}{2}\right)\Delta x_1 + f\left(\frac{x_1 + x_2}{2}\right)\Delta x_2 + \cdots + f\left(\frac{x_{n-1} + x_n}{2}\right)\Delta x_n.$$

58. Let t_k be the midpoint of $[x_{k-1}, x_k]$. Then $t_k = -t_{n-k+1}$ for $1 \le k \le n$. Since $f(-x) = -f(x)$, we have $f(t_k) = f(-t_{n-k+1}) = -f(t_{n-k+1})$, so that

$$\sum_{k=1}^n f(t_k)\Delta x_k = \sum_{k=1}^n f(t_k)\frac{2a}{n} = \{[f(t_1) + f(t_n)] + [f(t_2) + f(t_{n-1})] + \cdots\}\frac{2a}{n} = 0 = \int_{-a}^a f(x)\,dx.$$

59. Let $P = \{x_0, x_1, \ldots, x_n\}$ be a partition of $[a, b]$. For any $k = 1, 2, \ldots, n$, apply the Mean Value Theorem to e^x on $[x_{k-1}, x_k]$ to obtain a t_k in $[x_{k-1}, x_k]$ such that

$$\frac{e^{x_k} - e^{x_{k-1}}}{x_k - x_{k-1}} = e^{t_k}.$$

This means that $e^{t_k}(x_k - x_{k-1}) = e^{x_k} - e^{x_{k-1}}$. Since e^x is an increasing function, $e^{x_{k-1}} \le e^{t_k} \le e^{x_k}$. Therefore

$$e^{x_{k-1}}(x_k - x_{k-1}) \le e^{t_k}(x_k - x_{k-1}) = e^{x_k} - e^{x_{k-1}} \le e^{x_k}(x_k - x_{k-1}).$$

Thus

$$L_f(P) \le \sum_{k=1}^n e^{x_{k-1}}(x_k - x_{k-1}) \le \sum_{k=1}^n (e^{x_k} - e^{x_{k-1}}) \le \sum_{k=1}^n e^{x_k}(x_k - x_{k-1}) \le U_f(P).$$

Since $\sum_{k=1}^n (e^{x_k} - e^{x_{k-1}}) = (e^{x_1} - e^{x_0}) + (e^{x_2} - e^{x_1}) + \cdots + (e^{x_n} - e^{x_{n-1}}) = e^{x_n} - e^{x_0} = e^b - e^a$, it follows that $L_f(P) \le e^b - e^a \le U_f(P)$ for all partitions P. Consequently $\int_a^b e^x\,dx = e^b - e^a$.

60. a. $A \approx f(1)(.5) + f(1.5)(.2) + f(1.7)(.4) + f(2.1)(.4) + f(2.5)(.5)$
$= 2(.5) + 1(.2) + (.5)(.4) + (.2)(.4) + 0(.5) = 1.48$

b. $A \approx f(1.5)(.5) + f(1.7)(.2) + f(2.1)(.4) + f(2.5)(.4) + f(3)(.5)$
$= 1(.5) + (.5)(.2) + (.2)(.4) + 0(.4) + (.1)(.5) = 0.73$

61. a. Let $f(x) = \sqrt{1-x^2}$ for $-1 \le x \le 1$. The graph of f is the upper semicircle of radius 1 centered at the origin. Thus $\int_{-1}^{1} \sqrt{1-x^2}\,dx$ is the area of the region bounded above by the semicircle and below by the x axis. Therefore $\int_{-1}^{1} \sqrt{1-x^2}\,dx = \frac{1}{2}A$, so that $A = 2\int_{-1}^{1} \sqrt{1-x^2}\,dx$.

b. left sum $\approx$ 3.138268511

right sum $\approx$ 3.138268511

midpoint sum $\approx$ 3.142565552

c. $A_{100} \approx 3.139525976$ and the corresponding midpoint sum is 3.142565552. Since $\pi \approx 3.141592654$, it follows that the midpoint sum is a little more accurate.

62. a. midpoint sum $\approx$ 18.85539331

b. $A = \pi ab$

63. a. midpoint sum $\approx$ 0.682697558

b. midpoint sum $\approx$ 0.954514133

64. The area is approximately $100 \cdot 200 + 125 \cdot 200 + 110 \cdot 200 = 67{,}000$ (square feet).

65. Let V denote the speed. The total distance during the six seconds is $\int_0^6 v(t)\,dt$. We have the following:

$$\text{left sum} = 0(1) + 20(1) + 37(1) + 45(1) + 50(1) + 53(1) = 205 \text{ (meters)}$$

$$\text{right sum} = 20(1) + 37(1) + 45(1) + 50(1) + 53(1) + 55(1) = 260 \text{ (meters)}$$

They differ by 55 meters.

66. Let v denote the speed in feet per second. Then the total distance during the five seconds is $\int_0^5 v(t)\,dt$. Since 1 mile per hour equals 5280/3600 feet per second, we have the following:

$$\text{left sum} = 0(1) + 16 \cdot \frac{5280}{3600}(1) + 40 \cdot \frac{5280}{3600}(1) + 62 \cdot \frac{5280}{3600}(1) + 82 \cdot \frac{5280}{3600}(1) = \frac{880}{3}$$

$$\text{right sum} = 16 \cdot \frac{5280}{3600}(1) + 40 \cdot \frac{5280}{3600}(1) + 62 \cdot \frac{5280}{3600}(1) + 82 \cdot \frac{5280}{3600}(1) + 100 \cdot \frac{5280}{3600}(1) = 440.$$

Thus the difference in distance is $440 - \frac{880}{3} = \frac{440}{3} \approx 147$ (feet).

67. Let r denote the rate of descent. Then the total change in elevation during the five seconds is $\int_0^5 r(t)\,dt$. We have the following:

$$\text{right sum} = 14(1) + 18(1) - 2(1) + 10(1) + 3(1) = 43 \text{ (feet)}.$$

5.3 Special Properties of the Definite Integral

1. $\displaystyle\int_3^5 7\,dx = 7(5-3) = 14$

2. $\displaystyle\int_{-1}^2 -3\,dx = -3(2-(-1)) = -9$

3. $\int_{2}^{-1} -10\,du = -10(-1-2) = 30$

4. $\int_{1}^{-1} 5\,dx = 5(-1-1) = -10$

5. $\int_{0}^{1} x\,dx = \frac{1}{2}(1^2 - 0^2) = \frac{1}{2}$, $\int_{1}^{2} x\,dx = \frac{1}{2}(2^2 - 1^2) = \frac{3}{2}$, so $\int_{0}^{1} x\,dx + \int_{1}^{2} x\,dx = \frac{1}{2} + \frac{3}{2} = 2$;
$\int_{0}^{2} x\,dx = \frac{1}{2}(2^2 - 0^2) = 2$

6. $\int_{3}^{4} x^2\,dx = -\int_{4}^{3} x^2\,dx$, so $\int_{3}^{4} x^2\,dx + \int_{4}^{3} x^2\,dx = 0$; $\int_{3}^{3} x^2\,dx = 0$

7. $\int_{1}^{0} y^2\,dy = -\int_{0}^{1} y^2\,dy = -\frac{1}{3}(1^3 - 0^3) = -\frac{1}{3}$, $\int_{0}^{2} y^2\,dy = \frac{1}{3}(2^3 - 0) = \frac{8}{3}$,
so $\int_{1}^{0} y^2\,dy + \int_{0}^{2} y^2\,dy = -\frac{1}{3} + \frac{8}{3} = \frac{7}{3}$; $\int_{1}^{2} y^2\,dy = \frac{1}{3}(2^3 - 1^3) = \frac{7}{3}$

8. $\int_{-2}^{-3} -y\,dy = -\int_{-3}^{-2} -y\,dy = \int_{-3}^{-2} y\,dy = \frac{1}{2}[(-2)^2 - (-3)^2] = -\frac{5}{2}$,
$\int_{-3}^{-6} -y\,dy = -\int_{-6}^{-3} -y\,dy = \int_{-6}^{-3} y\,dy = \frac{1}{2}[(-3)^2 - (-6)^2] = -\frac{27}{2}$,
so $\int_{-2}^{-3} -y\,dy + \int_{-3}^{-6} -y\,dy = -\frac{5}{2} - \frac{27}{2} = -16$;
$\int_{-2}^{-6} -y\,dy = -\int_{-6}^{-2} -y\,dy = \int_{-6}^{-2} y\,dy = \frac{1}{2}[(-2)^2 - (-6)^2] = -16$

9. $\int_{0}^{2} f(x)\,dx + \int_{3}^{0} f(x)\,dx = \int_{3}^{0} f(x)\,dx + \int_{0}^{2} f(x)\,dx = \int_{3}^{2} f(x)\,dx$, so $a = 3$ and $b = 2$.

10. $\int_{1/2}^{-1/2} f(x)\,dx + \int_{-1}^{1/2} f(x)\,dx = \int_{-1}^{1/2} f(x)\,dx + \int_{1/2}^{-1/2} f(x)\,dx = \int_{-1}^{-1/2} f(x)\,dx$,
so $a = -1$ and $b = -\frac{1}{2}$.

11. $\int_{a}^{b} f(t)\,dt = \int_{5}^{3} f(t)\,dt + \int_{3}^{1} f(t)\,dt = \int_{5}^{1} f(t)\,dt$, so $a = 5$ and $b = 1$.

12. $\int_{a}^{b} f(t)\,dt = \int_{\pi}^{2\pi} f(t)\,dt - \int_{3\pi}^{2\pi} f(t)\,dt = \int_{\pi}^{2\pi} f(t)\,dt + \int_{2\pi}^{3\pi} f(t)\,dt = \int_{\pi}^{3\pi} f(t)\,dt$,
so $a = \pi$ and $b = 3\pi$.

13. $m = \frac{1}{3}$, $M = \frac{1}{2}$; $\frac{1}{3} = \frac{1}{3}(3-2) \le \int_{2}^{3} \frac{1}{x}\,dx \le \frac{1}{2}(3-2) = \frac{1}{2}$

14. $m = \frac{\sqrt{2}}{2}$, $M = 1$; $\frac{\sqrt{2}\,\pi}{8} = \frac{\sqrt{2}}{2}\left(\frac{\pi}{2} - \frac{\pi}{4}\right) \le \int_{\pi/4}^{\pi/2} \sin x\,dx \le 1\left(\frac{\pi}{2} - \frac{\pi}{4}\right) = \frac{\pi}{4}$

15. $m=\frac{1}{2}$, $M=\frac{\sqrt{2}}{2}$; $\frac{\pi}{24}=\frac{1}{2}\left(\frac{\pi}{3}-\frac{\pi}{4}\right)\leq\int_{\pi/4}^{\pi/3}\cos x\,dx\leq\frac{\sqrt{2}}{2}\left(\frac{\pi}{3}-\frac{\pi}{4}\right)=\frac{\sqrt{2}\pi}{24}$

16. $m=0$, $M=\sqrt{3}$; $0=0\left(\frac{\pi}{3}-0\right)\leq\int_{0}^{\pi/3}\tan t\,dt\leq\sqrt{3}\left(\frac{\pi}{3}-0\right)=\frac{\sqrt{3}\pi}{3}$

17. By (5), $f_{\text{av}}=\frac{1}{1-0}\int_0^1 x\,dx=\frac{1}{2}(1^2-0^2)=\frac{1}{2}$

18. By (5), $f_{\text{av}}=\frac{1}{2-(-2)}\int_{-2}^{2} x\,dx=\frac{1}{4}\left\{\frac{1}{2}[2^2-(-2)^2]\right\}=0$

19. By (5), $f_{\text{av}}=\frac{1}{1-(-1)}\int_{-1}^{1} x^2\,dx=\frac{1}{2}\left\{\frac{1}{3}[1^3-(-1)^3]\right\}=\frac{1}{3}$

20. By (5),

$$f_{\text{av}}=\frac{1}{3-(-2)}\int_{-2}^{3}|x|\,dx=\frac{1}{5}\int_{-2}^{0}(-x)\,dx+\frac{1}{5}\int_0^3 x\,dx=\frac{1}{5}\left\{-\frac{1}{2}[0^2-(-2)^2]\right\}+\frac{1}{5}\left[\frac{1}{2}(3^2-0^2)\right]=\frac{13}{10}$$

21. The mean value of f on $[a,b]$ is

$$\frac{1}{b-a}\int_a^b f(x)\,dx=\frac{1}{b-a}\int_a^b x\,dx=\frac{1}{b-a}\left[\frac{1}{2}(b^2-a^2)\right]=\frac{1}{2}(a+b).$$

22. a. By definition, the mean value of f on $[a,b]$ is

$$\frac{1}{b-a}\int_a^b f(x)\,dx=\frac{1}{b-a}\int_a^b x^2\,dx=\frac{1}{b-a}\left[\frac{1}{3}(b^3-a^3)\right]$$
$$=\frac{1}{3}\frac{b^3-a^3}{b-a}=\frac{1}{3}(b^2+ba+a^2)=\frac{1}{3}(a^2+ab+b^2).$$

b. By the Mean Value Theorem for Integrals there is a number c in $[a,b]$ such that $\int_a^b f(x)\,dx=f(c)(b-a)$, so

$$c^2=f(c)=\frac{1}{b-a}\int_a^b f(x)\,dx=\frac{1}{3}(a^2+ab+b^2).$$

23. $A=\int_{-1}^{1} f(x)\,dx=\int_{-1}^{0}-x\,dx+\int_0^1 x^2\,dx=-\frac{1}{2}[0^2-(-1)^2]+\frac{1}{3}[1^3-0^3]=\frac{5}{6}$

24. $A=\int_0^4 f(x)\,dx=\int_0^1 1\,dx+\int_1^4 x^2\,dx=1(1-0)+\frac{1}{3}(4^3-1^3)=22$

25. b. By Figure 5.35,

$$\text{left sum}=f(-1)(0.2)+f(-0.8)(0.2)+\cdots+f(0.6)(0.2)+f(0.8)(0.2)$$
$$\approx(0.2)(1+1.6+2.02+2.18+2.15+2+1.75+1.5+1.25+1.07)\approx 3.30.$$

Thus the mean value of f on $[0,1]=\frac{1}{2}\int_{-1}^{1}f(x)\,dx\approx\frac{3.30}{2}=1.65$.

26. c. By calculator, the midpoint sum is approximately 0.8948778776. Thus the mean value $f_{av} \approx (1/\sqrt{\pi})(0.8948778776) \approx 0.5048807771$.

27. $\int_0^1 x^7\,dx = \int_0^{1/2} x^7\,dx + \int_{1/2}^1 x^7\,dx$; $\int_0^{1/2} x^7\,dx \geq \int_0^{1/2} 0\,dx = 0$, and since $x^7 \geq (\frac{1}{2})^7$ for $\frac{1}{2} \leq x \leq 1$, we have $\int_{1/2}^1 x^7\,dx \geq \int_{1/2}^1 (\frac{1}{2})^7\,dx = (\frac{1}{2})^7(1-\frac{1}{2}) = (\frac{1}{2})^8$. Therefore $\int_0^1 x^7\,dx \geq 0 + (\frac{1}{2})^8 = (\frac{1}{2})^8 > 0$.

28. $\int_0^{\pi/2} \sin x\,dx = \int_0^{\pi/6} \sin x\,dx + \int_{\pi/6}^{\pi/2} \sin x\,dx$; $\int_0^{\pi/6} \sin x\,dx \geq \int_0^{\pi/6} 0\,dx = 0$, and since $\sin x \geq \frac{1}{2}$ for $\pi/6 \leq x \leq \pi/2$, we have $\int_{\pi/6}^{\pi/2} \sin x\,dx \geq \int_{\pi/6}^{\pi/2} \frac{1}{2}\,dx = \frac{1}{2}(\pi/2 - \pi/6) = \pi/6 > 0$. Therefore $\int_0^{\pi/2} \sin x\,dx \geq 0 + \pi/6 = \pi/6$.

29. a. Since f is continuous on $[a,b]$, the Maximum-Minimum Theorem implies that f assumes its minimum value m on $[a,b]$. Since $f(x) > 0$ for all x in $[a,b]$, $m > 0$. Finally, since $a < b$, the Comparison Property yields $\int_a^b f(x)\,dx \geq m(b-a) > 0$.

    b. For $|x| \leq \pi/6$, $\cos x \geq \sqrt{3}/2$ and $0 \leq x^2 \leq (\pi/6)^2$, so that $\cos x - x^2 \geq \sqrt{3}/2 - (\pi/6)^2 > 0$. From part (a), $\int_{-\pi/6}^{\pi/6}(\cos x - x^2)\,dx > 0$.

30. If $c < a < b$, then by the Addition Property we have

$$\int_c^b f(x)\,dx = \int_c^a f(x)\,dx + \int_a^b f(x)\,dx$$

so that

$$\int_a^b f(x)\,dx = -\int_c^a f(x)\,dx + \int_c^b f(x)\,dx = \int_a^c f(x)\,dx + \int_c^b f(x)\,dx.$$

If $b < a < c$, then by the Addition Property we have

$$\int_b^c f(x)\,dx = \int_b^a f(x)\,dx + \int_a^c f(x)\,dx$$

so that

$$\int_a^b f(x)\,dx = -\int_b^a f(x)\,dx = \int_a^c f(x)\,dx - \int_b^c f(x)\,dx = \int_a^c f(x)\,dx + \int_c^b f(x)\,dx.$$

31. If $m \leq f(x) \leq M$ for all x in $[a,b]$, and we choose c in $[a,b]$ so that $\int_a^b f(x)\,dx = f(c)(b-a)$, then $m(b-a) \leq f(c)(b-a) = \int_a^b f(x)\,dx \leq M(b-a)$.

32. Let T_{mv} denote the mean temperature during the year. Then $T_{mv} = \frac{1}{12}\int_0^{12} T(t)\,dt$. Using the mean monthly temperatures in the table, we obtain $\int_0^{12} T(t)\,dt \approx 32(1)+33(1)+\cdots+36(1) = 653$. Therefore $T_{mv} \approx \frac{1}{12}(653) \approx 54.4$ (degrees Fahrenheit).

33. Let P be a partition of $[0,24]$ into n subintervals of equal length. Then the right sum with respect to P is

$$\frac{1}{n}\left[T\left(\frac{24\cdot 1}{n}\right) + T\left(\frac{24\cdot 2}{n}\right) + \cdots + T\left(\frac{24\cdot n}{n}\right)\right] = \frac{1}{n}\sum_{k=1}^{n} T\left(\frac{24k}{n}\right).$$

By Theorem 5.5 in Section 5.2, if n is large then $\frac{1}{n}\sum_{k=1}^{n} T(\frac{24k}{n})$ is approximately $\frac{1}{24}\int_0^{24} T(t)\,dt$, which is the mean temperature.

5.4 The Fundamental Theorem of Calculus

1. $F'(x) = x(1+x^3)^{29}$

2. $F'(x) = \dfrac{1}{(x+x^3)^{16}}$

3. $F(y) = \int_y^2 \frac{1}{t^3}\,dt = -\int_2^y \frac{1}{t^3}\,dt$, so $F'(y) = -\frac{1}{y^3}$.

4. $F(t) = \int_t^0 x \sin x\,dx = -\int_0^t x\sin x\,dx$, so $F'(t) = -t\sin t$.

5. Let $G(x) = \int_0^x t\sin t\,dt$, so $F(x) = G(x^2)$. Since $G'(x) = x\sin x$, the Chain Rule implies that $F'(x) = [G'(x^2)](2x) = (x^2\sin x^2)(2x) = 2x^3\sin x^2$.

6. Let $G(x) = \int_1^x e^{(t^2)}\,dt$, so $F(x) = G(-x)$. Since $G'(x) = e^{(x^2)}$, the Chain Rule implies that $F'(x) = G'(-x)(-1) = -e^{(x^2)}$.

7. Notice that

$$G(y) = \int_y^{y^2} (1+t^2)^{1/2}\,dt = \int_y^0 (1+t^2)^{1/2}\,dt + \int_0^{y^2} (1+t^2)^{1/2}\,dt$$
$$= -\int_0^y (1+t^2)^{1/2}\,dt + \int_0^{y^2} (1+t^2)^{1/2}\,dt.$$

Let

$$H(y) = \int_0^y (1+t^2)^{1/2}\,dt \quad\text{and}\quad K(y) = \int_0^{y^2} (1+t^2)^{1/2}\,dt.$$

Then $K(y) = H(y^2)$ and $G(y) = -H(y) + K(y)$, so that $G'(y) = -H'(y) + K'(y)$. Now $H'(y) = (1+y^2)^{1/2}$ and by the Chain Rule, $K'(y) = [H'(y^2)](2y) = 2y(1+y^4)^{1/2}$. Therefore

$$G'(y) = -(1+y^2)^{1/2} + 2y(1+y^4)^{1/2}.$$

8. $$F(x) = \int_{x^2}^{x^3} (1+t^2)^{1/2}\,dt = \int_{x^2}^0 (1+t^2)^{1/2}\,dt + \int_0^{x^3} (1+t^2)^{1/2}\,dt$$
$$= -\int_0^{x^2} (1+t^2)^{1/2}\,dt + \int_0^{x^3} (1+t^2)^{1/2}\,dt$$

Let

$$H(x) = \int_0^x (1+t^2)^{1/2}\,dt \quad K(x) = H(x^2) \quad\text{and}\quad L(x) = H(x^3).$$

Then $F(x) = -K(x) + L(x)$, so that $F'(x) = -K'(x) + L'(x)$. By the Chain Rule,

$$K'(x) = [H'(x^2)](2x) = [1+(x^2)^2]^{1/2}(2x) = 2x(1+x^4)^{1/2}$$

and

$$L'(x) = [H'(x^3)](3x^2) = [1+(x^3)^2]^{1/2}(3x^2) = 3x^2(1+x^6)^{1/2}.$$

Thus

$$F'(x) = -2x(1+x^4)^{1/2} + 3x^2(1+x^6)^{1/2}.$$

9. Let $G(x) = \int_0^x (1+t^2)^{4/5}\,dt$. Then $G'(x) = (1+x^2)^{4/5}$ and

$$F(x) = \frac{d}{dx}G(4x) = [G'(4x)](4) = 4(1+16x^2)^{4/5}$$

so that $F'(x) = \frac{16}{5}(1+16x^2)^{-1/5}(32x) = \frac{512}{5}\,x(1+16x^2)^{-1/5}$.

10. Let

$$H(y) = \int_{\sin y}^{2y} \cos t\,dt = \int_{\sin y}^{0} \cos t\,dt + \int_0^{2y} \cos t\,dt = -\int_0^{\sin y} \cos t\,dt + \int_0^{2y} \cos t\,dt.$$

Then $G(y) = H'(y) = -(\cos(\sin y))\cos y + (\cos 2y)2 = -(\cos y)\cos(\sin y) + 2\cos 2y$. Thus

$$\begin{aligned} G'(y) &= (\sin y)\cos(\sin y) + (\cos y)[\sin(\sin y)]\cos y - 4\sin 2y \\ &= (\sin y)\cos(\sin y) + (\cos^2 y)\sin(\sin y) - 4\sin 2y. \end{aligned}$$

11. $\int_0^1 4\,dx = 4x\big|_0^1 = 4$

12. $\int_1^{12} 0\,dx = 0\big|_1^{12} = 0$

13. $\int_1^3 -y\,dy = -\frac{1}{2}y^2\Big|_1^3 = -\frac{9}{2} - \left(-\frac{1}{2}\right) = -4$

14. $\int_5^2 -4t\,dt = -2t^2\big|_5^2 = -8 - (-50) = 42$

15. $\int_1^{-3} 3u\,du = \frac{3}{2}u^2\Big|_1^{-3} = \frac{27}{2} - \frac{3}{2} = 12$

16. $\int_{-b}^{b} x^5\,dx = \frac{1}{6}x^6\Big|_{-b}^{b} = \frac{1}{6}(b^6 - (-b)^6) = 0$

17. $\int_0^1 x^{100}\,dx = \frac{1}{101}x^{101}\Big|_0^1 = \frac{1}{101}$

18. $\int_0^2 u^{1/2}\,du = \frac{2}{3}u^{3/2}\Big|_0^2 = \frac{2}{3}2^{3/2} - 0 = \frac{4}{3}\sqrt{2}$

19. $\int_{-1}^1 u^{1/3}\,du = \frac{3}{4}u^{4/3}\Big|_{-1}^1 = \frac{3}{4} - \frac{3}{4}(-1)^{4/3} = 0$

20. $\int_{16}^2 x^{5/4}\,dx = \frac{4}{9}x^{9/4}\Big|_{16}^2 = \left(\frac{4}{9}\right)2^{9/4} - \left(\frac{4}{9}\right)16^{9/4} = \frac{16}{9}\sqrt[4]{2} - \frac{2048}{9}$

21. $\int_1^4 x^{-7/9}\,dx = \frac{9}{2}x^{2/9}\Big|_1^4 = \frac{9}{2}(4^{2/9} - 1)$

22. $\int_0^1 x^{12/5}\,dx = \frac{5}{17}x^{17/5}\Big|_0^1 = \frac{5}{17}$

23. $\displaystyle\int_{-1.5}^{2\pi}(5-x)\,dx = \left(5x-\frac{1}{2}x^2\right)\Big|_{-1.5}^{2\pi} = (10\pi - 2\pi^2) - (-7.5 - 2.25/2) = 10\pi - 2\pi^2 + 8.625$

24. $\displaystyle\int_0^3\left(\frac{1}{2}x-4\right)\,dx = \left(\frac{1}{4}x^2-4x\right)\Big|_0^3 = \left(\frac{9}{4}-12\right) - 0 = -\frac{39}{4}$

25. $\displaystyle\int_{-4}^{-1}(5x+14)\,dx = \left(\frac{5}{2}x^2+14x\right)\Big|_{-4}^{-1} = \left(\frac{5}{2}-14\right) - (40-56) = \frac{9}{2}$

26. $\displaystyle\int_0^{\pi/6}\cos x\,dx = \sin x|_0^{\pi/6} = \frac{1}{2} - 0 = \frac{1}{2}$

27. $\displaystyle\int_{-\pi}^{\pi/3}\cos x\,dx = \sin x|_{-\pi}^{\pi/3} = \frac{1}{2}\sqrt{3} - 0 = \frac{1}{2}\sqrt{3}$

28. $\displaystyle\int_{\pi/3}^{\pi/4}\sin t\,dt = -\cos t|_{\pi/3}^{\pi/4} = -\frac{1}{2}\sqrt{2} - \left(-\frac{1}{2}\right) = \frac{1}{2} - \frac{1}{2}\sqrt{2}$

29. $\displaystyle\int_{\pi/3}^{-\pi/4}\sin t\,dt = -\cos t|_{\pi/3}^{-\pi/4} = -\frac{1}{2}\sqrt{2} - \left(-\frac{1}{2}\right) = \frac{1}{2} - \frac{1}{2}\sqrt{2}$

30. $\displaystyle\int_2^3\frac{1}{x^3}\,dx = \frac{-1}{2x^2}\Big|_2^3 = \frac{-1}{18} - \left(\frac{-1}{8}\right) = \frac{5}{72}$

31. $\displaystyle\int_1^2\frac{1}{y^4}\,dy = \frac{-1}{3y^3}\Big|_1^2 = \frac{-1}{24} - \left(\frac{-1}{3}\right) = \frac{7}{24}$

32. $\displaystyle\int_{-1}^{-2}\left(x-\frac{5}{x^3}\right)\,dx = \left(\frac{x^2}{2}+\frac{5}{2x^2}\right)\Big|_{-1}^{-2} = \left(2+\frac{5}{8}\right) - \left(\frac{1}{2}+\frac{5}{2}\right) = \frac{-3}{8}$

33. $\displaystyle\int_2^4\frac{1}{x}\,dx = \ln x|_2^4 = \ln 4 - \ln 2 = 2\ln 2 - \ln 2 = \ln 2$

34. $\displaystyle\int_1^e\frac{2}{x}\,dx = 2\ln x|_1^e = 2\ln e - 2\ln 1 = 2 - 0 = 2$

35. $\displaystyle\int_0^2 e^x\,dx = e^x|_0^2 = e^2 - e^0 = e^2 - 1$

36. $\displaystyle\int_1^{\ln 3} e^x\,dx = e^x|_1^{\ln 3} = e^{\ln 3} - e^1 = 3 - e$

37. $\displaystyle\int_{\pi/6}^{\pi/2}\csc^2 t\,dt = -\cot t|_{\pi/6}^{\pi/2} = 0 - (-\sqrt{3}) = \sqrt{3}$

38. $\displaystyle\int_0^{\pi/4}\sec x\,\tan x\,dx = \sec x|_0^{\pi/4} = \sqrt{2} - 1$

39. $\displaystyle\int_0^{\pi/2}\left(\frac{d}{dx}\sin^5 x\right)\,dx = \sin^5 x|_0^{\pi/2} = 1 - 0 = 1$

40. $\displaystyle\int_{-1}^{1}\left(\frac{d}{dx}\sqrt{1+x^4}\right)dx = \sqrt{1+x^4}\Big|_{-1}^{1} = \sqrt{2}-\sqrt{2}=0$

41. $\displaystyle A=\int_{-1}^{1} x^4\,dx = \frac{1}{5}x^5\Big|_{-1}^{1} = \frac{1}{5}-\left(-\frac{1}{5}\right)=\frac{2}{5}$

42. $\displaystyle A=\int_{-2}^{-1}\frac{1}{x^2}\,dx = \frac{-1}{x}\Big|_{-2}^{-1} = 1-\frac{1}{2}=\frac{1}{2}$

43. $\displaystyle A=\int_{0}^{2\pi/3}\sin x\,dx = -\cos x\big|_0^{2\pi/3} = \frac{1}{2}-(-1)=\frac{3}{2}$

44. $\displaystyle A=\int_{-\pi/2}^{\pi/3}\cos x\,dx = \sin x\big|_{-\pi/2}^{\pi/3} = \frac{1}{2}\sqrt{3}-(-1)=\frac{1}{2}\sqrt{3}+1$

45. $\displaystyle A=\int_{1}^{4} x^{1/2}\,dx = \frac{2}{3}x^{3/2}\Big|_1^4 = \frac{16}{3}-\frac{2}{3}=\frac{14}{3}$

46. $\displaystyle A=\int_{1}^{8} x^{1/3}\,dx = \frac{3}{4}x^{4/3}\Big|_1^8 = 12-\frac{3}{4}=\frac{45}{4}$

47. $\displaystyle A=\int_{0}^{\pi/4}\sec^2 x\,dx = \tan x\big|_0^{\pi/4} = 1-0=1$

48. $\displaystyle A=\int_{\pi/4}^{\pi/2}\csc x\,\cot x\,dx = -\csc x\big|_{\pi/4}^{\pi/2} = -1-(-\sqrt{2})=\sqrt{2}-1$

49. $\displaystyle A=\int_{1/e}^{1}\frac{1}{x}\,dx = \ln x\big|_{1/e}^{1} = \ln 1-\ln(1/e)=0-(-1)=1$

50. $\displaystyle A=\int_{0}^{4}(2+e^x)\,dx = (2x+e^x)\big|_0^4 = (2\cdot 4+e^4)-(2\cdot 0+e^0)=8+e^4-1=7+e^4$

51. $\displaystyle A=\int_{0}^{\pi/2}\cos^2 x\,dx = \left(\frac{x}{2}+\frac{\sin 2x}{4}\right)\Big|_0^{\pi/2} = \frac{\pi}{4}-0=\frac{\pi}{4}$

52. $\displaystyle A=\int_{0}^{\pi/3}\sec x\,\tan^3 x\,dx = \left(\frac{\sec^3 x}{3}-\sec x\right)\Big|_0^{\pi/3} = \left(\frac{8}{3}-2\right)-\left(\frac{1}{3}-1\right)=\frac{4}{3}$

53. $\displaystyle \int_{-1}^{1} x^n\,dx = \frac{1}{n+1}x^{n+1}\Big|_{-1}^{1} = \frac{1}{n+1}[1^{n+1}-(-1)^{n+1}] = \frac{1}{n+1}[1-(-1)^{n+1}]$

a. If n is odd, then $(-1)^{n+1}=(-1)^{\text{even}}=1$, so that $\int_{-1}^{1}x^n\,dx=[1/(n+1)](1-1)=0$.

b. If n is even, then $(-1)^{n+1}=(-1)^{\text{odd}}=-1$, so that $\int_{-1}^{1}x^n\,dx=[1/(n+1)][1-(-1)]=2/(n+1)$.

54. Notice that $f'(x)=2x-2$ for $0\le x\le 2$ and $f'(x)=-2x+6$ for $2\le x\le 3$. Then by (5),

$$f(3)-f(1)=\int_1^3 f'(x)\,dx=\int_1^2 f'(x)\,dx+\int_2^3 f'(x)\,dx=\int_1^2(2x-2)\,dx+\int_2^3(-2x+6)\,dx$$

$$=(x^2-2x)\big|_1^2+(-x^2+6x)\big|_2^3=[(4-4)-(1-2)]+[(-9+18)-(-4+12)]=1+1=2.$$

Therefore $f(3)=f(1)+2=10+2=12$.

55. a. $\int_0^x f(t)\,dt = \int_0^x t\,dt = \frac{1}{2}x^2$; $\frac{d}{dx}\int_0^x f(t)\,dt = \frac{d}{dx}\left(\frac{1}{2}x^2\right) = x = f(x)$

b. $\int_0^x f(t)\,dt = \int_0^x -2t^2\,dt = -\left.\frac{2}{3}t^3\right|_0^x = -\frac{2}{3}x^3$; $\frac{d}{dx}\int_0^x f(t)\,dt = \frac{d}{dx}\left(-\frac{2}{3}x^3\right) = -2x^2 = f(x)$

c. $\int_0^x f(t)\,dt = \int_0^x -\sin t\,dt = \cos t|_0^x = \cos x - 1$; $\frac{d}{dx}\int_0^x f(t)\,dt = \frac{d}{dx}(\cos x - 1) = -\sin x = f(x)$

d. $\int_0^x f(t)\,dt = \int_0^x 10t^4\,dt = 2t^5|_0^x = 2x^5$; $\frac{d}{dx}\int_0^x f(t)\,dt = \frac{d}{dx}(2x^5) = 10x^4 = f(x)$

56. a. $F'(x) = 1$; $\int_1^x F'(t)\,dt = \int_1^x 1\,dt = t|_1^x = x - 1 = (x+2) - 3 = F(x) - F(1)$

b. $F'(x) = 3x^2$; $\int_1^x F'(t)\,dt = \int_1^x 3t^2\,dt = t^3|_1^x = x^3 - 1^3 = F(x) - F(1)$

c. $F'(x) = 4x^3$; $\int_{-1}^x F'(t)\,dt = \int_{-1}^x 4t^3\,dt = t^4|_{-1}^x = x^4 - (-1)^4 = F(x) - F(-1)$

57. Since $x^2 + 4x$ is an increasing function on $[1, 2]$, the first sum is the lower sum of $\int_1^2 (x^2 + 4x)\,dx$ for the partition P, and the last sum is the upper sum of $\int_1^2 (x^2+4x)\,dx$ for P. Since $L_f(P) \le I \le U_f(P)$ for every partition P, it follows that

$$I = \int_1^2 (x^2 + 4x)\,dx = \left.\left(\frac{1}{3}x^3 + 2x^2\right)\right|_1^2 = \left(\frac{8}{3} + 8\right) - \left(\frac{1}{3} + 2\right) = \frac{25}{3}.$$

58. Since $\cos x - \sin x$ is a decreasing function on $[0, \pi/2]$, the first sum is the lower sum of $\int_0^{\pi/2} (\cos x - \sin x)\,dx$ for the partition P, and the last sum is the upper sum of $\int_0^{\pi/2} (\cos x - \sin x)\,dx$ for P. Since $L_f(P) \le I \le U_f(P)$ for every partition P, it follows that

$$I = \int_0^{\pi/2} (\cos x - \sin x)\,dx = (\sin x + \cos x)|_0^{\pi/2} = (1 - 0) - (0 + 1) = 0.$$

59. The velocity in miles per second is $v/3600$. The distance D traveled during the first 5 seconds is given (approximately) by

$$D \approx \frac{v(1)}{3600}(1) + \frac{v(2)}{3600}(1) + \frac{v(3)}{3600}(1) + \frac{v(4)}{3600}(1) + \frac{v(5)}{3600}(1)$$

$$= \frac{5}{3600} + \frac{15}{3600} + \frac{50}{3600} + \frac{200}{3600} + \frac{500}{3600} = \frac{770}{3600} \approx 0.21 \text{ (miles)}.$$

60. a. For $0 \le t \le 10$, we have $f(t) - f(0) = \int_0^t v(s)\,ds = \int_0^t (10s - s^2)\,ds = (5s^2 - \frac{1}{3}s^3)|_0^t = 5t^2 - \frac{1}{3}t^3$.

b. $a(t) = v'(t) = 10 - 2t$, so that $a(t) = 0$ if $t = 5$. Since the car is at the origin at $t = 0$, we have $f(0) = 0$, so it follows from (a) that $f(5) = f(5) - f(0) = 5(5^2) - \frac{1}{3}(5^3) = \frac{250}{3}$.

61. $f(t) = f(0) + \int_0^t v(s)\,ds = 1 + \int_0^t (2\sin s + 3\cos s)\,ds$

$= 1 + (-2\cos s + 3\sin s)|_0^t = 1 + (-2\cos t + 3\sin t) - (-2) = 3 - 2\cos t + 3\sin t$

62. The amount of flow per day is $\int_0^{24} F'(t)\,dt$, and by (5) and the hint,

$$\int_0^{24} F'(t)\,dt = -\frac{336{,}000}{\pi}\cos\frac{\pi t}{24}\Big|_0^{24} = -\frac{336{,}000}{\pi}(\cos\pi - \cos 0) = \frac{672{,}000}{\pi}\text{ (tons).}$$

63. a. $t = 2$ and $t = 4$, since at those times v changed from positive to negative and negative to positive, respectively.

b. $t = 8$, since $\int_0^t v(s)\,ds$ is largest when $t = 8$.

c. $t = 1$, 3, and 6, since at those times $v'(t) = 0$.

64. $R(x) - R(1) = \int_1^x m_R(t)\,dt = \int_1^x (4 - 0.02t)\,dt = (4t - 0.01t^2)\big|_1^x = (4x - 0.01x^2) - 3.99$

a. Since $R(1) = 4$, it follows that $R(30) = 4 + [(120 - 9) - 3.99] = 111.01$ (dollars).

b. $m_R(x) = 0$ if $x = 200$; $R(200) = 4 + [(800 - 400) - 3.99] = 400.01$ (dollars).

65. $C(x) - C(2) = \int_2^x m_C(t)\,dt = \int_2^x (3 - 0.1t)\,dt = (3t - 0.05t^2)\big|_2^x = (3x - 0.05x^2) - (6 - 0.2) = 3x - 0.05x^2 - 5.8$. Since $C(2) = 10.98$, it follows that $C(x) = 10.98 + 3x - 0.05x^2 - 5.8$, so that $C(30) = 10.98 + 3(30) - 0.05(30)^2 - 5.8 = 50.18$ (dollars).

66. a. $v(t) = v(0) + \int_0^t a(s)\,ds = v(0) + \int_0^t -32\,ds = v(0) - 32t$
$f(t) = f(0) + \int_0^t v(s)\,ds = f(0) + \int_0^t (v(0) - 32s)\,ds = 528 + (v(0)s - 16s^2)\big|_0^t = 528 + v(0)t - 16t^2$
Since $f(6) = 0$, we have $0 = 528 + v(0)6 - 576$, so that $v(0) = 8$ (feet per second).

b. As in part (a), $f(t) = f(0) + \int_0^t (v(0) - 32s)\,ds$. Since $f(0) = 992$ and $v(0) = 4$, we have $f(t) = 992 + \int_0^t (4 - 32s)\,ds = 992 + (4s - 16s^2)\big|_0^t = 992 + 4t - 16t^2 = 4(4t + 31)(-t + 8)$, so $f(t) = 0$ if $t = 8$ (seconds).

67. We need to coordinate our units of measure—let time be in hours. Then $v(0) = 60$, $v(\frac{1}{30}) = 0$, and the acceleration, which was assumed to be constant, is

$$\frac{v(\frac{1}{30}) - v(0)}{\frac{1}{30} - 0} = \frac{0 - 60}{\frac{1}{30}} = -1800.$$

Therefore $v(t) = v(0) + \int_0^t a(s)\,ds = v(0) + \int_0^t -1800\,ds = 60 - 1800t$, so that if we let $f(0) = 0$, then

$$f(t) = f(0) + \int_0^t v(s)\,ds = f(0) + \int_0^t (60 - 1800s)\,ds = 0 + (60s - 900s^2)\big|_0^t = 60t - 900t^2.$$

After 2 minutes the position of the train is $f(\frac{1}{30})$, and $f(\frac{1}{30}) = 60(\frac{1}{30}) - 900(\frac{1}{30})^2 = 1$. Thus the train was 1 mile from the cow when the brakes were applied.

68. The amount lost between time t_1 and t_2 is $\int_{t_1}^{t_2} R(t)\,dt$.

69. $V = \int_{-r}^{r} \pi(r^2 - x^2)\,dx = \pi\left(r^2x - \frac{x^3}{3}\right)\Big|_{-r}^{r} = \pi\left[\left(r^3 - \frac{r^3}{3}\right) - \left(-r^3 + \frac{r^3}{3}\right)\right] = \frac{4}{3}\pi r^3$

70. a. By the Fundamental Theorem (or by (8)), $f(b) - f(a) = \int_a^b v(t)\,dt$. Then

$$\frac{\int_a^b v(t)\,dt}{b-a} = \frac{f(b)-f(a)}{b-a} = \text{average velocity}$$

as defined in Section 2.1.

b. $$\frac{\int_0^3 v(t)\,dt}{3-0} = \frac{\int_0^3 (-20-32t)\,dt}{3-0} = \frac{(-20t-16t^2)\big|_0^3}{3} = \frac{-60-144}{3} = -68$$

71. a. By the Fundamental Theorem (or by (7)), $C(b) - C(a) = \int_a^b m_C(x)\,dx$. Then

$$\frac{\int_a^b m_C(x)\,dx}{b-a} = \frac{C(b)-C(a)}{b-a} = \text{average cost between the } a\text{th and } b\text{th units produced}$$

as defined in Section 3.1.

b. $$\frac{\int_1^4 m_C(x)\,dx}{4-1} = \frac{\int_1^4 (1/x^{1/2})\,dx}{4-1} = \frac{2x^{1/2}\big|_1^4}{3} = \frac{4-2}{3} = \frac{2}{3} \text{ (thousand dollars per thousand umbrellas)}$$

72. $$\frac{\int_0^\pi V(t)\,dt}{\pi-0} = \frac{\int_0^\pi 110\sin t\,dt}{\pi-0} = \frac{-110}{\pi}\cos t\bigg|_0^\pi = \frac{-110}{\pi}(-1-1) = \frac{220}{\pi} = \text{average voltage}$$

73. $$W = (2500\pi)(62.5)\int_0^{100}(100-y)\,dy = 156{,}250\pi\left(100y - \frac{y^2}{2}\right)\bigg|_0^{100}$$
$$= 156{,}250\pi(10{,}000 - 5{,}000)) = 781{,}250{,}000\pi \text{ (foot-pounds)}$$

74. Let A_1 = area of lower peach portion. Then $A_1 = \int_0^1 x^3\,dx = \frac{1}{4}x^4\big|_0^1 = \frac{1}{4}$. Let A_2 = area of cream portion. Then $A_2 = \int_0^1 x^{1/3}\,dx - A_1 = \frac{3}{4}x^{4/3}\big|_0^1 - A_1 = \frac{3}{4} - \frac{1}{4} = \frac{1}{2}$. Thus $\frac{1}{2}$ square unit of cream enamel will be required. Since the area of the tile is 1 square unit, exactly the same amount of peach and cream enamel will be required.

75. Since $a(t) = -10$ by hypothesis, (9) implies that

$$v(t) - v(0) = \int_0^t -10\,du = -10u\big|_0^t = -10t$$

for all t until the plane stops. Since $v(0) = 150$ by assumption, $v(t) = v(0) - 10t = 150 - 10t$. Notice that $v(t) = 0$ if $150 - 10t = 0$, which occurs if $t = 15$. Next, let $f(t)$ denote the distance the plane travels during t seconds. By (8),

$$f(15) - f(0) = \int_0^{15} v(u)\,du = \int_0^{15}(150-10u)\,du = (150u - 5u^2)\big|_0^{15} = 150(15) - 5(15)^2 = 1125.$$

Since $f(0) = 0$, we have $f(15) = 1125$, which is the stopping distance. Since the airstrip must be 60% longer than the stopping distance, the airstrip needs to be $(1.6)(1125) = 1800$ feet long.

76. By the hint,

$$F = m\frac{d^2s}{dt^2} = ma,$$

where a is the acceleration. By (9), the velocity is given by

$$v(t) - v(0) = \int_0^t a(u)\,du = \int_0^t \frac{F(u)}{m}\,du = \int_0^t \frac{1}{m}(mg\sin\theta - \mu mg\cos\theta)\,du$$

$$= (\sin\theta - \mu\cos\theta)gu\big|_0^t = (\sin\theta - \mu\cos\theta)gt.$$

Since $v(0) = v_0$ by hypothesis, $v(t) = (\sin\theta - \mu\cos\theta)gt + v_0$. Next, by (8) the distance s is given by

$$s(t) - s(0) = \int_0^t v(u)\,du = \int_0^t [(\sin\theta - \mu\cos\theta)gu + v_0]\,du$$

$$= \left[\frac{g}{2}(\sin\theta - \mu\cos\theta)u^2 + v_0u\right]\Bigg|_0^t = \frac{g}{2}(\sin\theta - \mu\cos\theta)t^2 + v_0t.$$

If s represents the distance the carton travels in the time interval $[0, t]$, then $s = \frac{1}{2}(\sin\theta - \mu\cos\theta)gt^2 + v_0t$.

77. a. $p(t_2) - p(t_1) = \int_{t_1}^{t_2} \frac{dp}{dt}\,dt = \int_{t_1}^{t_2} F\,dt$

b. The impulse of the force during the 10^{-3} seconds while the ball is in contact with the floor is given by $p(10^{-3}) - p(0) = (0.1)(4.5) - (0.1)(-5) = 0.95$. Thus the impulse is 0.95 kilogram meter per second per second. The mean force is $0.95/10^{-3} = 950$ Newtons per second per second.

78. Area of shaded region $= \int_0^\pi \sin\theta\,d\theta = -\cos\theta\big|_0^\pi = -(-1-1) = 2$. Area of rectangle is 2π, so the required proportion is $2/(2\pi) = 1/\pi$.

79. If the needle is 2 inches long, then we must have $y \leq 2\sin\theta$. The area of the shaded region $= \int_0^\pi 2\sin\theta\,d\theta = -2\cos\theta\big|_0^\pi = -2(-1-1) = 4$. The area of the rectangle is 2π, so the proportion is $4/(2\pi) = 2/\pi$.

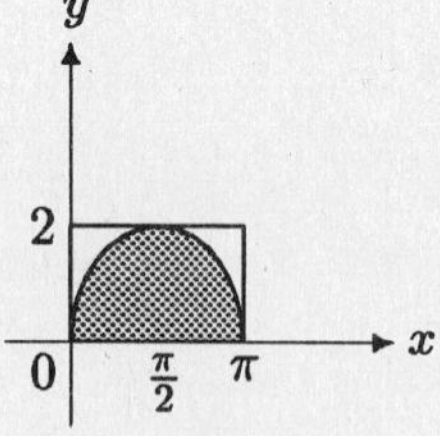

Exercise 79

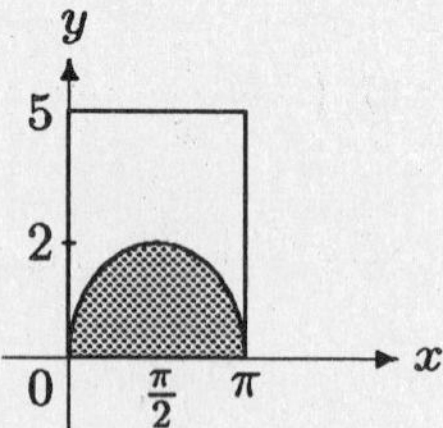

Exercise 80

80. If the needle is 2 inches long, then we must have $y \leq 2\sin\theta$. The area of the shaded region $= \int_0^\pi 2\sin\theta\,d\theta = -2\cos\theta\big|_0^\pi = -2(-1-1) = 4$. The area of the rectangle is 5π, so the proportion is $4/(5\pi)$.

5.5 Indefinite Integrals and Integration Rules

1. $\int (2x - 7)\,dx = x^2 - 7x + C$

2. $\int (2x^2 - 7x^3 + 4x^4)\,dx = \frac{2}{3}x^3 - \frac{7}{4}x^4 + \frac{4}{5}x^5 + C$

3. $\int (2x^{1/3} - 3x^{3/4} + x^{2/5})\,dx = \frac{3}{2}x^{4/3} - \frac{12}{7}x^{7/4} + \frac{5}{7}x^{7/5} + C$

4. $\int (x^{3/2} + 4x^{1/2} - \pi)\,dx = \frac{2}{5}x^{5/2} + \frac{8}{3}x^{3/2} - \pi x + C$

5. $\int \left(t^5 - \frac{1}{t^4}\right) dt = \frac{t^6}{6} + \frac{1}{3t^3} + C$

6. $\int \left(\sqrt{y} + \frac{1}{\sqrt{y}}\right) dy = \frac{2}{3}y^{3/2} + 2\sqrt{y} + C$

7. $\int (2\cos x - 5x)\,dx = 2\sin x - \frac{5}{2}x^2 + C$

8. $\int (\theta^2 + \sec^2\theta)\,d\theta = \frac{1}{3}\theta^3 + \tan\theta + C$

9. $\int (3\csc^2 x - x)\,dx = -3\cot x - \frac{1}{2}x^2 + C$

10. $\int \left(\frac{1}{y^3} - \frac{1}{y^2} + 2y\right) dy = \frac{-1}{2y^2} + \frac{1}{y} + y^2 + C$

11. $\int (2t+1)^2\,dt = \int (4t^2 + 4t + 1)\,dt = \frac{4}{3}t^3 + 2t^2 + t + C$

12. $\int \left(t + \frac{1}{t}\right)^2 dt = \int \left(t^2 + 2 + \frac{1}{t^2}\right) dt = \frac{t^3}{3} + 2t - \frac{1}{t} + C$

13. $\int \left(1 + \frac{1}{x}\right)^2 dx = \int \left(1 + \frac{2}{x} + \frac{1}{x^2}\right) dx = x + 2\ln x - \frac{1}{x} + C$

14. $\int (\sqrt{x} - 3e^x)\,dx = \frac{2}{3}x^{3/2} - 3e^x + C$

15. $\int_{-1}^{2} (3x - 4)\,dx = \left(\frac{3}{2}x^2 - 4x\right)\Big|_{-1}^{2} = -2 - \frac{11}{2} = -\frac{15}{2}$

16. $\int_1^4 \left(\sqrt{x} + \frac{1}{2\sqrt{x}}\right)^2 dx = \int_1^4 \left(x + 1 + \frac{1}{4x}\right) dx = \left(\frac{1}{2}x^2 + x + \frac{1}{4}\ln x\right)\Big|_1^4$

$$= \left(8 + 4 + \frac{1}{4}\ln 4\right) - \left(\frac{1}{2} + 1 + \frac{1}{4}\ln 1\right) = \frac{21}{2} + \frac{1}{4}\ln 4$$

17. $\int_{\pi/4}^{\pi/2} (-7\sin x + 3\cos x)\,dx = (7\cos x + 3\sin x)\big|_{\pi/4}^{\pi/2} = 3 - 5\sqrt{2}$

18. $\displaystyle\int_0^{\pi}(\sin x - 8x^2)\,dx = \left(-\cos x - \frac{8}{3}x^3\right)\Big|_0^{\pi} = \left(1-\frac{8\pi^3}{3}\right) - (-1) = 2 - \frac{8\pi^3}{3}$

19. $\displaystyle\int_{-\pi/4}^{-\pi/2}\left(3x - \frac{1}{x^2} + \sin x\right)dx = \left(\frac{3}{2}x^2 + \frac{1}{x} - \cos x\right)\Big|_{-\pi/4}^{-\pi/2}$

$\displaystyle= \left(\frac{3\pi^2}{8} - \frac{2}{\pi}\right) - \left(\frac{3\pi^2}{32} - \frac{4}{\pi} - \frac{\sqrt{2}}{2}\right) = \frac{9\pi^2}{32} + \frac{2}{\pi} + \frac{\sqrt{2}}{2}$

20. $\displaystyle\int_{-1/4}^{1/4}(4t-3)^2\,dt = \int_{-1/4}^{1/4}(16t^2 - 24t + 9)\,dt = \left(\frac{16}{3}t^3 - 12t^2 + 9t\right)\Big|_{-1/4}^{1/4}$

$\displaystyle= \left(\frac{1}{12} - \frac{3}{4} + \frac{9}{4}\right) - \left(-\frac{1}{12} - \frac{3}{4} - \frac{9}{4}\right) = \frac{14}{3}$

21. $\displaystyle\int_{\pi/3}^{\pi/4}(3\sec^2\theta + 4\csc^2\theta)\,d\theta = (3\tan\theta - 4\cot\theta)\Big|_{\pi/3}^{\pi/4} = -1 - \left(3\sqrt{3} - \frac{4\sqrt{3}}{3}\right) = -1 - \frac{5}{3}\sqrt{3}$

22. $\displaystyle\int_1^2\left(t^2 - \frac{1}{t^2}\right)^2 dt = \int_1^2\left(t^4 - 2 + \frac{1}{t^4}\right)dt = \left(\frac{t^5}{5} - 2t - \frac{1}{3t^3}\right)\Big|_1^2$

$\displaystyle= \left(\frac{32}{5} - 4 - \frac{1}{24}\right) - \left(\frac{1}{5} - 2 - \frac{1}{3}\right) = \frac{539}{120}$

23. $\displaystyle\int_1^{1/3}(3t+2)^3\,dt = \int_1^{1/3}(27t^3 + 54t^2 + 36t + 8)\,dt = \left(\frac{27}{4}t^4 + 18t^3 + 18t^2 + 8t\right)\Big|_1^{1/3} = \frac{-136}{3}$

24. $\displaystyle\int_{-\pi/4}^{0}(\sec\theta)(\tan\theta + \sec\theta)\,d\theta = \int_{-\pi/4}^{0}(\sec\theta\,\tan\theta + \sec^2\theta)\,d\theta$

$\displaystyle= (\sec\theta + \tan\theta)\Big|_{-\pi/4}^{0} = 1 - (\sqrt{2} - 1) = 2 - \sqrt{2}$

25. $\displaystyle\int_{\pi/2}^{\pi}\left(\pi\sin x - 2x + \frac{5}{x^2} + 2\pi\right)dx = \left(-\pi\cos x - x^2 - \frac{5}{x} + 2\pi x\right)\Big|_{\pi/2}^{\pi} = \pi + \frac{5}{\pi} + \frac{\pi^2}{4}$

26. $\displaystyle\int_1^0 x(2x+5)\,dx = \int_1^0(2x^2 + 5x)\,dx = \left(\frac{2}{3}x^3 + \frac{5}{2}x^2\right)\Big|_1^0 = -\frac{2}{3} - \frac{5}{2} = -\frac{19}{6}$

27. $\displaystyle\int_{-1}^1(2x+5)(2x-5)\,dx = \int_{-1}^1(4x^2 - 25)\,dx = \left(\frac{4}{3}x^3 - 25x\right)\Big|_{-1}^1 = -\frac{142}{3}$

28. $\displaystyle\int_2^1(x+3)^2(x+1)\,dx = \int_2^1(x^3 + 7x^2 + 15x + 9)\,dx = \left(\frac{1}{4}x^4 + \frac{7}{3}x^3 + \frac{15}{2}x^2 + 9x\right)\Big|_2^1 = -\frac{619}{12}$

29. $\displaystyle\int_4^7|x-5|\,dx = \int_4^5(5-x)\,dx + \int_5^7(x-5)\,dx = \left(5x - \frac{1}{2}x^2\right)\Big|_4^5 + \left(\frac{1}{2}x^2 - 5x\right)\Big|_5^7 = \frac{1}{2} + 2 = \frac{5}{2}$

30. $\displaystyle\int_1^0|2x-1|\,dx = \int_1^{1/2}(2x-1)\,dx + \int_{1/2}^0(1-2x)\,dx = (x^2 - x)\Big|_1^{1/2} + (x - x^2)\Big|_{1/2}^0 = -\frac{1}{4} - \frac{1}{4} = -\frac{1}{2}$

31. $\displaystyle\int_0^\pi (\sin x - 2e^x)\,dx = (-\cos x - 2e^x)\Big|_0^\pi = (-\cos\pi - 2e^\pi) - (-\cos 0 - 2e^0)$
$= (1 - 2e^\pi) - (-1 - 2) = 4 - 2e^\pi$

32. $\displaystyle\int_{1/2}^2 \frac{x-1}{x}\,dx = \int_{1/2}^2 \left(1 - \frac{1}{x}\right)dx = (x - \ln x)\Big|_{1/2}^2 = (2 - \ln 2) - \left(\frac{1}{2} - \ln\frac{1}{2}\right) = \frac{3}{2} - 2\ln 2$

33. $\displaystyle\int_4^6 f(x)\,dx = \int_4^5 2x\,dx + \int_5^6 (20 - 2x)\,dx = x^2\Big|_4^5 + (20x - x^2)\Big|_5^6 = 9 + 9 = 18$

34. $\displaystyle\int_0^{\pi/2} f(x)\,dx = \int_0^{\pi/4} \sec^2 x\,dx + \int_{\pi/4}^{\pi/2} \csc^2 x\,dx = \tan x\Big|_0^{\pi/4} - \cot x\Big|_{\pi/4}^{\pi/2} = 1 + 1 = 2$

35. Since $F'(x) = 20x(1+x^2)^9$, we have $\int 20x(1+x^2)^9\,dx = (1+x^2)^{10} + C$.

36. Since $F'(x) = 1 + x$, we have $\int (1+x)\,dx = \frac{1}{2}(1+x^2)^2 + C$.

37. Since $F'(x) = x\cos x + 2\sin x$, we have $\int (x\cos x + 2\sin x)\,dx = x\sin x - \cos x + C$.

38. Since $F'(x) = 2\sec^2(2x+1)$, we have $\int 2\sec^2(2x+1)\,dx = \tan(2x+1) + C$.

39. Since $F'(x) = 21\sin^6 x\,\cos x$, we have $\int 21\sin^6 x\,\cos x\,dx = 3\sin^7 x + C$.

40. Since $F'(x) = \sin x\,\cos x + x(\cos^2 x - \sin^2 x)$, we have $\int [\sin x\,\cos x + x(\cos^2 x - \sin^2 x)]\,dx =$ $x\sin x\,\cos x + C$.

41. Since $F'(x) = 2xe^{(x^2)} + e^{-x}$, we have $\int (2xe^{(x^2)} + e^{-x})\,dx = e^{(x^2)} - e^{-x} + C$.

42. Since $F'(x) = \ln x + 1 - 1 = \ln x$, we have $\int \ln x\,dx = x\ln x - x + C$.

43. $\displaystyle A = \int_{-1}^1 (3x^2 + 4)\,dx = (x^3 + 4x)\Big|_{-1}^1 = 5 - (-5) = 10$

44. $\displaystyle A = \int_1^2 \left(\frac{1}{2}x^3 + 3x\right)dx = \left(\frac{1}{8}x^4 + \frac{3}{2}x^2\right)\Big|_1^2 = (2 + 6) - \left(\frac{1}{8} + \frac{3}{2}\right) = \frac{51}{8}$

45. $\displaystyle A = \int_1^4 \left(3\sqrt{x} - \frac{1}{\sqrt{x}}\right)dx = (2x^{3/2} - 2x^{1/2})\Big|_1^4 = (16 - 4) - (2 - 2) = 12$

46. $\displaystyle A = \int_1^8 (8x^{1/3} - x^{-1/3})\,dx = \left(6x^{4/3} - \frac{3}{2}x^{2/3}\right)\Big|_1^8 = (96 - 6) - \left(6 - \frac{3}{2}\right) = \frac{171}{2}$

47. $\displaystyle A = \int_{\pi/4}^{\pi/2} (2\sin x + 3\cos x)\,dx = (-2\cos x + 3\sin x)\Big|_{\pi/4}^{\pi/2}$
$\displaystyle = (0 + 3) - \left[-2\left(\frac{\sqrt{2}}{2}\right) + 3\left(\frac{\sqrt{2}}{2}\right)\right] = 3 - \frac{\sqrt{2}}{2}$

48. $\displaystyle A = \int_{-2}^0 |x+1|\,dx = \int_{-2}^{-1} -(x+1)\,dx + \int_{-1}^0 (x+1)\,dx$
$\displaystyle = \left(-\frac{1}{2}x^2 - x\right)\Big|_{-2}^{-1} + \left(\frac{1}{2}x^2 + x\right)\Big|_{-1}^0 = \left(\frac{1}{2} - 0\right) + \left(0 + \frac{1}{2}\right) = 1$

49. $A = \int_2^4 \left(2x - \frac{4}{x}\right) dx = (x^2 - 4\ln x)\Big|_2^4 = (16 - 4\ln 4) - (4 - 4\ln 2)$

$= 12 - 4\ln 4 + 4\ln 2 = 12 - 8\ln 2 + 4\ln 2 = 12 - 4\ln 2$

50. $A = \int_0^3 \left(\frac{1}{2}e^x - \frac{1}{3}x\right) dx = \left(\frac{1}{2}e^x - \frac{1}{6}x^2\right)\Big|_0^3 = \left(\frac{1}{2}e^3 - \frac{3}{2}\right) - \frac{1}{2}e^0 = \frac{1}{2}e^3 - 2$

51. a. Since $0 \le \sin x \le x$ for $0 \le x \le 1$, we have $0 \le \sin x^2 \le x^2$ for $0 \le x \le 1$. Then by Corollary 5.19, $0 \le \int_0^1 \sin(x^2)\, dx \le \int_0^1 x^2\, dx = \frac{1}{3}x^3\big|_0^1 = \frac{1}{3}$.

b. Since $0 \le \sin x \le x$ for $0 \le x \le 1$, we have $0 \le \sin^{3/2} x \le x^{3/2}$ for $0 \le x \le 1$. Then by Corollary 5.19, $0 \le \int_0^{\pi/6} \sin^{3/2} x\, dx \le \int_0^{\pi/6} x^{3/2}\, dx = \frac{2}{5}x^{5/2}\big|_0^{\pi/6} = \frac{2}{5}(\pi/6)^{5/2}$.

52. Since $0 \le \sin x \le x$ for $0 \le x \le \frac{1}{2}$, we have $0 \le x \sin x \le x^2$. From Corollary 5.19, $0 \le \int_0^{1/2} x \sin x\, dx \le \int_0^{1/2} x^2\, dx = \frac{1}{3}x^3\big|_0^{1/2} = \frac{1}{24}$.

53. $\int_0^2 f(x)\, dx = \int_0^2 (1-x)\, dx = (x - \frac{1}{2}x^2)\big|_0^2 = (2-2) - 0 = 0$, so $\left|\int_0^2 f(x)\, dx\right| = 0$. However, $\int_0^2 |f(x)|\, dx = \int_0^1 (1-x)\, dx + \int_1^2 -(1-x)\, dx = (x - \frac{1}{2}x^2)\big|_0^1 - (x - \frac{1}{2}x^2)\big|_1^2 = (\frac{1}{2} - 0) - (0 - \frac{1}{2}) = 1$. Thus

$$\left|\int_0^2 f(x)\, dx\right| < \int_0^2 |f(x)|\, dx.$$

54. By (5), we have $\left|\int_a^b f(x)\, dx\right| \le \int_a^b |f(x)|\, dx$ and by the Comparison Property, $\int_a^b |f(x)|\, dx \le M(b-a)$. Thus $\left|\int_a^b f(x)\, dx\right| \le M(b-a)$.

55. Since $\tan x$ is an increasing function on $(-\pi/2, \pi/2)$, it follows that $-\sqrt{3} = \tan(-\pi/3) \le \tan x \le \tan(-\pi/4) = -1$ for x in $[-\pi/3, -\pi/4]$. Thus for x in $[-\pi/3, -\pi/4]$, we have $|\tan x| \le \sqrt{3}$. By Exercise 54,

$$\left|\int_{-\pi/3}^{-\pi/4} \tan x\, dx\right| \le \sqrt{3}\left(-\frac{\pi}{4} + \frac{\pi}{3}\right) = \frac{1}{12}\sqrt{3}\,\pi.$$

56. By the hint, $0 \le \sin x \le x$ for $0 \le x \le \frac{1}{2}$. Thus for $0 \le x \le \frac{1}{2}$ we have $0 \le x \sin x \le x^2$, so that

$$0 = \int_0^\varepsilon 0\, dx \le \int_0^\varepsilon x \sin x\, dx \le \int_0^\varepsilon x^2\, dx = \frac{x^3}{3}\Big|_0^\varepsilon = \frac{\varepsilon^3}{3}$$

for $0 \le \varepsilon \le \frac{1}{2}$. Consequently

$$0 \le \frac{1}{\varepsilon}\int_0^\varepsilon x \sin x\, dx \le \frac{\varepsilon^2}{3}.$$

Since $\lim_{\varepsilon \to 0^+} 0 = \lim_{\varepsilon \to 0^+} \varepsilon^3/3 = 0$, it follows from the Squeezing Theorem that

$$\lim_{\varepsilon \to 0^+} \frac{1}{\varepsilon}\int_0^\varepsilon x \sin x\, dx = 0.$$

57. a. Fix any x in $[a, b]$. By the Mean Value Theorem there is a number c in (a, x) such that $[f(x) - f(a)]/(x-a) = f'(c)$. Since $|f'(c)| \le M$ and $f(a) = 0$ by hypothesis, we have

$$\frac{|f(x)|}{|x-a|} = \frac{|f(x)-f(a)|}{|x-a|} = |f'(c)| \le M, \quad \text{or} \quad |f(x)| \le M|x-a| = M(x-a).$$

b. By (a) and (5) we have

$$\left|\int_a^b f(x)\,dx\right| \le \int_a^b |f(x)|\,dx \le \int_a^b M(x-a)\,dx = M\int_a^b (x-a)\,dx = M\left.\frac{(x-a)^2}{2}\right|_a^b = M\frac{(b-a)^2}{2}.$$

58. a. $\dfrac{d}{dx}(x^2-1)^{3/2} = \dfrac{3}{2}(x^2-1)^{1/2}(2x) = 3x(x^2-1)^{1/2}$, and

$$0 \le 3x(x^2-1)^{1/2} \le 3\sqrt{5}\left[\left(\sqrt{5}\right)^2 - 1\right]^{1/2} = 6\sqrt{5} \quad \text{for } 1 \le x \le \sqrt{5}.$$

By Exercise 57(b), we have

$$\int_1^{\sqrt{5}} (x^2-1)^{3/2}\,dx \le \frac{6\sqrt{5}}{2}\left(\sqrt{5}-1\right)^2 = 18\sqrt{5} - 30.$$

b. $\dfrac{d}{dx}\sin^{3/2} x = \dfrac{3}{2}\sin^{1/2} x \cos x$, and

$$\left|\frac{3}{2}\sin^{1/2} x \cos x\right| \le \frac{3}{2}\sqrt{\frac{1}{2}}\,1 = \frac{3}{4}\sqrt{2} \quad \text{for } 0 \le x \le \pi/6.$$

By Exercise 57(b), we have

$$\int_0^{\pi/6} \sin^{3/2} x\,dx \le \frac{3}{4}\sqrt{2}\,\frac{(\pi/6)^2}{2} = \frac{\sqrt{2}}{96}\pi^2.$$

59. Let $f(x) = ax^3 + bx^2 + cx + d$. Then $f(-1/\sqrt{3}) + f(1/\sqrt{3}) = a(-1/\sqrt{3})^3 + b(-1/\sqrt{3})^2 + c(-1/\sqrt{3}) + d + a(1/\sqrt{3})^3 + b(1/\sqrt{3})^2 + c(1/\sqrt{3}) + d = \frac{2}{3}b + 2d$. Since $\int_{-1}^1 x^n\,dx = 0$ whenever n is odd (see Exercise 53(a) of Section 5.4), we have $\int_{-1}^1 ax^3\,dx = 0 = \int_{-1}^1 cx\,dx$, so that

$$\int_{-1}^1 f(x)\,dx = \int_{-1}^1 (ax^3 + bx^2 + cx + d)\,dx = \int_{-1}^1 (bx^2 + d)\,dx$$

$$= \left.\left(\frac{b}{3}x^3 + dx\right)\right|_{-1}^1 = \left(\frac{b}{3} + d\right) - \left(-\frac{b}{3} - d\right) = \frac{2}{3}b + 2d.$$

Thus (6) is valid.

60. By Exercise 59 with $f(x) = e^{-x^2/2}$, $\int_{-1}^1 e^{-x^2/2}\,dx \approx e^{-(-1/\sqrt{3})^2/2} + e^{-(1/\sqrt{3})^2/2} = 2e^{-1/6} \approx 1.69296345$.

61. If $g(x) \le f(x)$ for $b \le x \le a$, then $-f(x) \le -g(x)$, so that Corollary 5.19 implies that

$$\int_a^b g(x)\,dx = \int_b^a -g(x)\,dx \ge \int_b^a -f(x)\,dx = \int_a^b f(x)\,dx.$$

62. $\int [f(x) - g(x)]\,dx = \int [f(x) + (-g(x))]\,dx = \int f(x)\,dx + \int -g(x)\,dx = \int f(x)\,dx - \int g(x)\,dx$

63. We will use induction. The result is valid for $n = 2$ by Theorem 5.16. Assume the result is valid for $n - 1$ functions, and let $f_1, f_2, \ldots, f_n$ be continuous on an interval I. Then

$$\int [f_1(x) + f_2(x) + \cdots + f_{n-1}(x) + f_n(x)]\,dx = \int [f_1(x) + f_2(x) + \cdots + f_{n-1}(x)]\,dx + \int f_n(x)\,dx$$

$$= \left[\int f_1(x)\,dx + \int f_2(x)\,dx + \cdots + \int f_{n-1}(x)\,dx\right] + \int f_n(x)\,dx$$

which is equivalent to the desired equation.

64. Since $2x + 2y(dy/dx) = 0$, so that $dy/dx = -x/y$, the slope of the tangent line at $(\sqrt{3}/2, \frac{1}{2})$ is

$$\left.\frac{dy}{dx}\right|_{x=\sqrt{3}/2} = \frac{-\sqrt{3}/2}{1/2} = -\sqrt{3}.$$

The equation of the tangent line is $y - \frac{1}{2} = -\sqrt{3}\,(x - \sqrt{3}/2)$, or $y = 2 - \sqrt{3}\,x$. Since $0 \le \sqrt{1 - x^2} \le 2 - \sqrt{3}\,x$, we have

$$\int_0^1 \sqrt{1 - x^2}\,dx \le \int_0^1 (2 - \sqrt{3}\,x)\,dx = \left(2x - \frac{\sqrt{3}}{2}x^2\right)\Big|_0^1 = 2 - \frac{\sqrt{3}}{2}.$$

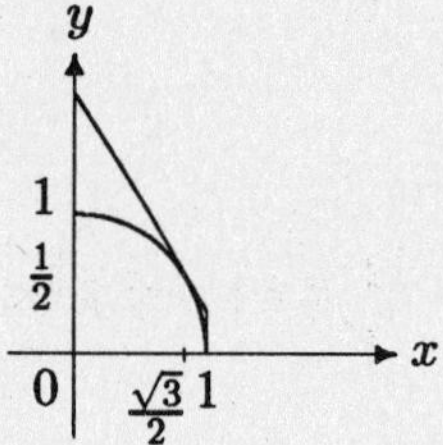

Exercise 64

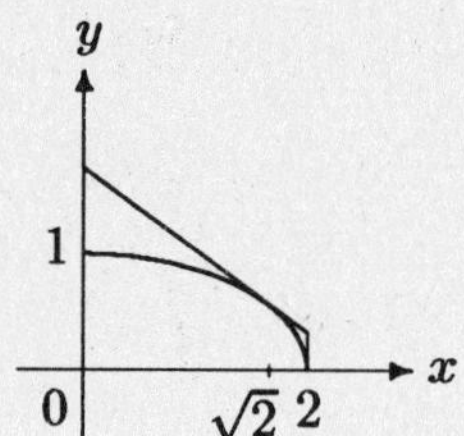

Exercise 65

65. a. Since $(x/2) + 2y(dy/dx) = 0$, so that $dy/dx = -x/4y$, the slope of the tangent line at $(\sqrt{2}, 1/\sqrt{2})$ is

$$\left.\frac{dy}{dx}\right|_{x=\sqrt{2}} = \frac{-\sqrt{2}}{4/\sqrt{2}} = \frac{-1}{2}.$$

The equation of the tangent line is $y - 1/\sqrt{2} = (-1/2)(x - \sqrt{2})$, or $y = \sqrt{2} - \frac{1}{2}x$. Since $\sqrt{1 - (x^2/4)} \le \sqrt{2} - \frac{1}{2}x$ for $0 \le x \le 2$, we have

$$\int_0^2 \sqrt{1 - \frac{x^2}{4}}\,dx \le \int_0^2 \left(\sqrt{2} - \frac{1}{2}x\right)dx = \left(\sqrt{2}\,x - \frac{1}{4}x^2\right)\Big|_0^2 = 2\sqrt{2} - 1.$$

b. The triangle inscribed in the quarter ellipse has vertices $(0,0)$, $(2,0)$, $(0,1)$, so the area of the triangle is 1.

66. $A = \int_a^b (cx + d)\,dx = \left(\frac{c}{2}x^2 + dx\right)\Big|_a^b = \left(\frac{cb^2}{2} + db\right) - \left(\frac{ca^2}{2} + da\right) = \left(\frac{cb}{2} + \frac{ca}{2} + d\right)(b - a).$

Since
$$\frac{f(a) + f(b)}{2} = \frac{ca + d}{2} + \frac{cb + d}{2} = \frac{cb}{2} + \frac{ca}{2} + d$$
we conclude that
$$A = \left(\frac{f(a) + f(b)}{2}\right)(b - a).$$

67. Let $p(r) = \int_a^b [f(x) + rg(x)]^2\,dx$. Then by the Addition Property and (2),
$$p(r) = \int_a^b \left[(f(x))^2 + 2rf(x)g(x) + r^2(g(x))^2\right] dx$$
$$= \int_a^b (f(x))^2\,dx + 2r\int_a^b f(x)g(x)\,dx + r^2\int_a^b (g(x))^2\,dx = Ar^2 + Br + C$$
where $A = \int_a^b (g(x))^2\,dx$, $B = 2\int_a^b f(x)g(x)\,dx$ and $C = \int_a^b (f(x))^2\,dx$. For any given real number r we have $[f(x) + rg(x)]^2 \ge 0$ for all x in $[a, b]$, so by Corollary 5.10, $p(r) \ge 0$ for any r. But then p has at most one zero, so by the quadratic formula the discriminant of p, which is $B^2 - 4AC$, is nonpositive. Thus $B^2 \le 4AC$. This is equivalent to the desired inequality.

68. $V = \int_0^r \frac{k}{l}x(r^2 - x^2)\,dx = \int_0^r \frac{k}{l}(xr^2 - x^3)\,dx = \frac{k}{l}\left(\frac{x^2r^2}{2} - \frac{x^4}{4}\right)\Big|_0^r = \frac{k}{l}\left(\frac{r^4}{2} - \frac{r^4}{4}\right) = \frac{kr^4}{4l}$

5.6 Integration by Substitution

1. Let $u = 4x - 5$, so that $du = 4\,dx$. Then
$$\int \sqrt{4x - 5}\,dx = \int \sqrt{u}\,\frac{1}{4}\,du = \frac{1}{4}\int \sqrt{u}\,du = \frac{1}{4}\left(\frac{2}{3}u^{3/2}\right) + C = \frac{1}{6}(4x - 5)^{3/2} + C.$$

2. Let $u = 1 - 5x^2$, so that $du = -10x\,dx$. Then
$$\int (1 - 5x^2)^{2/3}(10x)\,dx = \int u^{2/3}(-1)\,du = -\int u^{2/3}\,du = -\frac{3}{5}u^{5/3} + C = -\frac{3}{5}(1 - 5x^2)^{5/3} + C.$$

3. Let $u = \pi x$, so that $du = \pi\,dx$. Then
$$\int \cos \pi x\,dx = \int (\cos u)\frac{1}{\pi}\,du = \frac{1}{\pi}\int \cos u\,du = \frac{1}{\pi}\sin u + C = \frac{1}{\pi}\sin \pi x + C.$$

4. Let $u = -2x$, so that $du = -2\,dx$. Then
$$\int 3\sin(-2x)\,dx = \int 3(\sin u)\left(-\frac{1}{2}\right)du = -\frac{3}{2}\int \sin u\,du = -\frac{3}{2}(-\cos u) + C = \frac{3}{2}\cos(-2x) + C.$$

5. Let $u = x^2$, so that $du = 2x\,dx$. Then
$$\int x\cos x^2\,dx = \int (\cos u)\frac{1}{2}\,du = \frac{1}{2}\int \cos u\,du = \frac{1}{2}\sin u + C = \frac{1}{2}\sin x^2 + C.$$

6. Let $u = \sin t$, so that $du = \cos t\, dt$. Then

$$\int \sin^3 t \cos t\, dt = \int u^3\, du = \frac{1}{4}u^4 + C = \frac{1}{4}\sin^4 t + C.$$

7. Let $u = \cos t$, so that $du = -\sin t\, dt$. Then

$$\int \cos^{-4} t \sin t\, dt = \int u^{-4}(-1)\, du = \frac{1}{3}u^{-3} + C = \frac{1}{3}\cos^{-3} t + C.$$

8. Let $u = t^2 - 3t + 1$, so that $du = (2t - 3)\, dt$. Then

$$\int \frac{2t-3}{(t^2-3t+1)^2}\, dt = \int \frac{1}{u^2}\, du = \int u^{-2}\, du = -u^{-1} + C = \frac{-1}{t^2-3t+1} + C.$$

9. Let $u = t^2 - 3t + 1$, so that $du = (2t - 3)\, dt$. Then

$$\int \frac{2t-3}{(t^2-3t+1)^{7/2}}\, dt = \int \frac{1}{u^{7/2}}\, du = \int u^{-7/2}\, du = -\frac{2}{5}u^{-5/2} + C = -\frac{2}{5}\frac{1}{(t^2-3t+1)^{5/2}} + C.$$

10. Let $v = x - 1$, so that $dv = dx$ and $x = v + 1$. Then

$$\int x\sqrt{x-1}\, dx = \int (v+1)\sqrt{v}\, dv = \int (v^{3/2}+v^{1/2})\, dv = \frac{2}{5}v^{5/2}+\frac{2}{3}v^{3/2}+C = \frac{2}{5}(x-1)^{5/2}+\frac{2}{3}(x-1)^{3/2}+C.$$

11. Let $v = x + 1$, so that $dv = dx$ and $x - 1 = v - 2$. Then

$$\int (x-1)\sqrt{x+1}\, dx = \int (v-2)\sqrt{v}\, dv = \int (v^{3/2} - 2v^{1/2})\, dv$$

$$= \frac{2}{5}v^{5/2} - 2\left(\frac{2}{3}v^{3/2}\right) + C = \frac{2}{5}(x+1)^{5/2} - \frac{4}{3}(x+1)^{3/2} + C.$$

12. Let $v = x + 3$, so that $dv = dx$ and $x^2 = (v - 3)^2$. Then

$$\int x^2\sqrt{x+3}\, dx = \int (v-3)^2\sqrt{v}\, dv = \int (v^{5/2} - 6v^{3/2} + 9v^{1/2})\, dv$$

$$= \frac{2}{7}v^{7/2} - 6\left(\frac{2}{5}v^{5/2}\right) + 9\left(\frac{2}{3}v^{3/2}\right) + C = \frac{2}{7}(x+3)^{7/2} - \frac{12}{5}(x+3)^{5/2} + 6(x+3)^{3/2} + C.$$

13. Let $u = 3 + \sec x$, so that $du = \sec x \tan x\, dx$. Then

$$\int \sec x \tan x \sqrt{3+\sec x}\, dx = \int \sqrt{u}\, du = \frac{2}{3}u^{3/2} + C = \frac{2}{3}(3+\sec x)^{3/2} + C.$$

14. Let $u = \sqrt[3]{x} + 1$, so that $du = \frac{1}{3}x^{-2/3}\, dx$. Since $3x^{2/3}\, du = dx$, we have $\sqrt[3]{x}\, dx = 3x\, du = 3(u-1)^3\, du$. Then

$$\int \frac{\sqrt[3]{x}}{(\sqrt[3]{x}+1)^5}\, dx = \int \frac{3(u-1)^3}{u^5}\, du = 3\int \frac{u^3 - 3u^2 + 3u - 1}{u^5}\, du$$

$$= 3\int (u^{-2} - 3u^{-3} + 3u^{-4} - u^{-5})\, du = 3\left(-u^{-1} + \frac{3}{2}u^{-2} - u^{-3} + \frac{1}{4}u^{-4}\right) + C$$

$$= 3u^{-4}\left(-u^3 + \frac{3}{2}u^2 - u + \frac{1}{4}\right) + C = \frac{3}{(\sqrt[3]{x}+1)^4}\left(-(\sqrt[3]{x}+1)^3 + \frac{3}{2}(\sqrt[3]{x}+1)^2 - (\sqrt[3]{x}+1) + \frac{1}{4}\right) + C.$$

15. Let $u = x^2$, so that $du = 2x\,dx$. Then

$$\int xe^{(x^2)}\,dx = \int e^u \frac{1}{2}\,du = \frac{1}{2}e^u + C = \frac{1}{2}e^{(x^2)} + C.$$

16. Let $u = 1 + e^x$, so that $du = e^x\,dx$. Then

$$\int \frac{e^x}{1+e^x}\,dx = \int \frac{1}{u}\,du = \ln u + C = \ln(1+e^x) + C.$$

17. Let $u = x^2 + 1$, so that $du = 2x\,dx$. Then

$$\int \frac{x}{x^2+1}\,dx = \int \frac{1}{u}\frac{1}{2}\,du = \frac{1}{2}\ln u + C = \frac{1}{2}\ln(x^2+1) + C.$$

18. Let $u = \sqrt{x} + 1$, so that $du = (1/2\sqrt{x})\,dx$. Then

$$\int \frac{1}{x+\sqrt{x}}\,dx = \int \frac{1}{\sqrt{x}+1}\frac{1}{\sqrt{x}}\,dx = \int \frac{1}{u}2\,du = 2\ln u + C = 2\ln(\sqrt{x}+1) + C.$$

19. Let $u = x^3 + 1$, so that $du = 3x^2\,dx$. Then

$$\int 3x^2(x^3+1)^{12}\,dx = \int u^{12}\,du = \frac{1}{13}u^{13} + C = \frac{1}{13}(x^3+1)^{13} + C.$$

20. Let $u = 2 - 5x^4$, so that $du = -20x^3\,dx$. Then

$$\int x^3(2-5x^4)^7\,dx = \int u^7\left(-\frac{1}{20}\right)du = -\frac{1}{20}\int u^7\,du$$

$$= -\frac{1}{20}\left(\frac{1}{8}u^8\right) + C = -\frac{1}{160}u^8 + C = -\frac{1}{160}(2-5x^4)^8 + C.$$

21. Let $u = 4 + x^{3/2}$, so that $du = \frac{3}{2}x^{1/2}\,dx$. Then

$$\int \sqrt{x}(4+x^{3/2})\,dx = \int u\frac{2}{3}\,du = \frac{1}{3}u^2 + C = \frac{1}{3}(4+x^{3/2})^2 + C.$$

22. Let $u = x + 1/x$, so that $du = (1 - 1/x^2)\,dx$. Then

$$\int \left(1-\frac{1}{x^2}\right)\left(x+\frac{1}{x}\right)^{-3}dx = \int u^{-3}\,du = -\frac{1}{2}u^{-2} + C = -\frac{1}{2}\left(x+\frac{1}{x}\right)^{-2} + C.$$

23. Let $u = 3x + 7$, so that $du = 3\,dx$. Then

$$\int \sqrt{3x+7}\,dx = \int u^{1/2}\frac{1}{3}\,du = \frac{1}{3}\int u^{1/2}\,du = \frac{1}{3}\left(\frac{2}{3}u^{3/2}\right) + C = \frac{2}{9}(3x+7)^{3/2} + C.$$

24. Let $u = 4 - 2x$, so that $du = -2\,dx$. Then

$$\int \sqrt{4-2x}\,dx = \int (\sqrt{u})\left(-\frac{1}{2}\right)du = -\frac{1}{2}\int u^{1/2}\,du = -\frac{1}{2}\left(\frac{2}{3}u^{3/2}\right) + C = -\frac{1}{3}(4-2x)^{3/2} + C.$$

25. Let $u = 1 + 2x + 4x^2$, so that $du = (2 + 8x)\,dx$. Then

$$\int (1+4x)\sqrt{1+2x+4x^2}\,dx = \int (\sqrt{u})\frac{1}{2}\,du = \frac{1}{2}\int u^{1/2}\,du = \frac{1}{2}\left(\frac{2}{3}u^{3/2}\right) + C = \frac{1}{3}(1+2x+4x^2)^{3/2} + C.$$

26. Let $u = 7x$, so that $du = 7\,dx$. Then

$$\int \cos 7x\,dx = \int (\cos u)\frac{1}{7}\,du = \frac{1}{7}\int \cos u\,du = \frac{1}{7}\sin u + C = \frac{1}{7}\sin 7x + C.$$

27. Let $u = \pi x$, so that $du = \pi\,dx$. If $x = -1$, then $u = -\pi$; if $x = 3$, then $u = 3\pi$. Thus

$$\int_{-1}^{3} \sin \pi x\,dx = \int_{-\pi}^{3\pi} (\sin u)\frac{1}{\pi}\,du = \frac{1}{\pi}\int_{-\pi}^{3\pi} \sin u\,du = \frac{1}{\pi}(-\cos u)\Big|_{-\pi}^{3\pi} = \frac{1}{\pi}[-(-1) + (-1)] = 0.$$

28. Let $u = t^{10}$, so that $du = 10t^9\,dt$. If $t = 0$, then $u = 0$; if $t = 1$, then $u = 1$. Thus

$$\int_0^1 t^9 \sin t^{10}\,dt = \int_0^1 (\sin u)\frac{1}{10}\,du = \frac{1}{10}\int_0^1 \sin u\,du = \frac{1}{10}(-\cos u)\Big|_0^1 = \frac{1}{10}(-\cos 1 + 1)) = \frac{1}{10}(1 - \cos 1).$$

29. Let $u = \sin t$, so that $du = \cos t\,dt$. Then

$$\int \sin^6 t\,\cos t\,dt = \int u^6\,du = \frac{1}{7}u^7 + C = \frac{1}{7}\sin^7 t + C.$$

30. Let $u = \cos t$, so that $du = -\sin t\,dt$. Then

$$\int \cos^{-3} t\,\sin t\,dt = \int u^{-3}(-1)\,du = -\int u^{-3}\,du = (-1)\left(-\frac{1}{2}u^{-2}\right) + C = \frac{1}{2}\cos^{-2} t + C.$$

31. Let $u = \sin 2z$, so that $du = 2\cos 2z\,dz$. Then

$$\int \sqrt{\sin 2z}\,\cos 2z\,dz = \int \sqrt{u}\,\frac{1}{2}\,du = \frac{1}{2}\int \sqrt{u}\,du = \frac{1}{2}\left(\frac{2}{3}u^{3/2}\right) + C = \frac{1}{3}(\sin 2z)^{3/2} + C.$$

32. Let $u = 1 - \cos 3z$, so that $du = 3\sin 3z\,dz$. Then

$$\int \sin 3z\,\sqrt{1 - \cos 3z}\,dz = \int \sqrt{u}\,\frac{1}{3}\,du = \frac{1}{3}\int \sqrt{u}\,du = \frac{1}{3}\left(\frac{2}{3}u^{3/2}\right) + C = \frac{2}{9}(1 - \cos 3z)^{3/2} + C.$$

33. Let $u = \cos z$, so that $du = -\sin z\,dz$. If $z = 0$, then $u = 1$; if $z = \pi/4$, then $u = \sqrt{2}/2$. Thus

$$\int_0^{\pi/4} \frac{\sin z}{\cos^2 z}\,dz = \int_1^{\sqrt{2}/2} \frac{1}{u^2}(-1)\,du = \frac{1}{u}\Big|_1^{\sqrt{2}/2} = \frac{1}{\sqrt{2}/2} - 1 = \sqrt{2} - 1.$$

34. Let $u = \sin z$, so that $du = \cos z\,dz$. If $z = \pi/2$, then $u = 1$; if $z = \pi/6$, then $u = \frac{1}{2}$. Thus

$$\int_{\pi/2}^{\pi/6} \frac{\cos z}{\sin^3 z}\,dz = \int_1^{1/2} \frac{1}{u^3}\,du = -\frac{1}{2u^2}\Big|_1^{1/2} = -\left(2 - \frac{1}{2}\right) = -\frac{3}{2}.$$

35. Let $u = \sqrt{z}$, so that $du = (1/2\sqrt{z})\,dz$. Then

$$\int \frac{1}{\sqrt{z}} \sec^2 \sqrt{z}\, dz = \int (\sec^2 u)(2)\, du = 2\int \sec^2 u\, du = 2\tan u + C = 2\tan\sqrt{z} + C.$$

36. Let $u = 1/z$, so that $du = (-1/z^2)\,dz$. Then

$$\int \frac{1}{z^2} \csc^2 \frac{1}{z}\, dz = \int (\csc^2 u)(-1)\, du = -\int \csc^2 u\, du = -(-\cot u) + C = \cot\frac{1}{z} + C.$$

37. Let $u = w^2 + 1$, so that $du = 2w\,dw$. Then

$$\int w\left(\sqrt{w^2+1} + \frac{1}{\sqrt{w^2+1}}\right) dw = \int \left(\sqrt{u} + \frac{1}{\sqrt{u}}\right)\frac{1}{2}\, du = \frac{1}{2}\int \left(\sqrt{u} + \frac{1}{\sqrt{u}}\right) du$$

$$= \frac{1}{2}\left(\frac{2}{3}u^{3/2} + 2u^{1/2}\right) + C = \frac{1}{3}(w^2+1)^{3/2} + (w^2+1)^{1/2} + C.$$

38. Let $u = 1 + \sqrt{x}$, so that $du = (1/2\sqrt{x})\,dx$. If $x = 4$, then $u = 3$; if $x = 1$, then $u = 2$. Thus

$$\int_4^1 \frac{\sqrt{1+\sqrt{x}}}{\sqrt{x}}\, dx = \int_3^2 \sqrt{u}\,(2)\, du = 2\int_3^2 \sqrt{u}\, du = 2\left(\frac{2}{3}u^{3/2}\right)\Big|_3^2 = \frac{4}{3}(2\sqrt{2} - 3\sqrt{3}).$$

39. Let $u = 1 + 4x^{1/3}$, so that $du = \frac{4}{3}x^{-2/3}$. If $x = 1$, then $u = 5$; if $x = 8$, then $u = 9$. Thus

$$\int_1^8 x^{-2/3}\sqrt{1+4x^{1/3}}\, dx = \int_5^9 \sqrt{u}\left(\frac{3}{4}\right) du = \frac{3}{4}\int_5^9 \sqrt{u}\, du = \frac{3}{4}\left(\frac{2}{3}u^{3/2}\right)\Big|_5^9 = \frac{1}{2}(27 - 5\sqrt{5}).$$

40. $$\int_{-1}^0 w\left(\sqrt{1-w^2} + \sin \pi w^2\right) dw = \int_{-1}^0 \left(w\sqrt{1-w^2} + w\sin \pi w^2\right) dw$$

$$= \int_{-1}^0 w\sqrt{1-w^2}\, dw + \int_{-1}^0 w\sin \pi w^2\, dw$$

To evaluate $\int_{-1}^0 w\sqrt{1-w^2}\, dw$, let $v = 1 - w^2$, so that $dv = -2w\,dw$. If $w = -1$, then $v = 0$; if $w = 0$, then $v = 1$. Thus

$$\int_{-1}^0 w\sqrt{1-w^2}\, dw = \int_0^1 \sqrt{v}\left(-\frac{1}{2}\right) dv = -\frac{1}{2}\int_0^1 \sqrt{v}\, dv = -\frac{1}{2}\left(\frac{2}{3}v^{3/2}\right)\Big|_0^1 = -\frac{1}{2}\left(\frac{2}{3} - 0\right) = -\frac{1}{3}.$$

To evaluate $\int_{-1}^0 w\sin \pi w^2\, dw$, let $u = \pi w^2$, so that $du = 2\pi w\, dw$. If $w = -1$, then $u = \pi$; if $w = 0$, then $u = 0$. Thus

$$\int_{-1}^0 w\sin \pi w^2\, dw = \int_\pi^0 (\sin u)\left(\frac{1}{2\pi}\right) du = \frac{1}{2\pi}\int_\pi^0 \sin u\, du$$

$$= \frac{1}{2\pi}(-\cos u)\Big|_\pi^0 = \frac{1}{2\pi}[(-\cos 0) - (-\cos \pi)] = \frac{1}{2\pi}(-1-1) = -\frac{1}{\pi}.$$

Therefore

$$\int_{-1}^0 w\left(\sqrt{1-w^2} + \sin \pi w^2\right) dw = \int_{-1}^0 w\sqrt{1-w^2}\, dw + \int_{-1}^0 w\sin \pi w^2\, dw = -\frac{1}{3} - \frac{1}{\pi}.$$

41. Let $u = 1 + e^{2x}$, so that $du = 2e^{2x}\,dx$. Then

$$\int e^{2x}\sin(1+e^{2x})\,dx = \int (\sin u)\frac{1}{2}\,du = -\frac{1}{2}\cos u + C = -\frac{1}{2}\cos(1+e^{2x}) + C.$$

42. Let $u = \sqrt{x}$, so that $du = (1/2\sqrt{x})\,dx$. Then

$$\int \frac{e^{\sqrt{x}}}{\sqrt{x}}\,dx = \int e^u(2)\,du = 2e^u + C = 2e^{\sqrt{x}} + C.$$

43. Let $u = 1 + x^4$, so that $du = 4x^3\,dx$. Then

$$\int \frac{x^3}{1+x^4}\,dx = \int \frac{1}{u}\frac{1}{4}\,du = \frac{1}{4}\ln u + C = \frac{1}{4}\ln(1+x^4) + C.$$

44. Let $u = \ln x$, so that $du = (1/x)\,dx$. Then

$$\int \frac{(\ln x)^2}{x}\,dx = \int u^2\,du = \frac{1}{3}u^3 + C = \frac{1}{3}(\ln x)^3 + C.$$

45. Let $u = x + 2$, so that $du = dx$ and $x = u - 2$. Then

$$\int x\sqrt{x+2}\,dx = \int (u-2)\sqrt{u}\,du = \int (u^{3/2} - 2u^{1/2})\,du$$

$$= \frac{2}{5}u^{5/2} - \frac{4}{3}u^{3/2} + C = \frac{2}{5}(x+2)^{5/2} - \frac{4}{3}(x+2)^{3/2} + C.$$

46. Let $u = x + 3$, so that $du = dx$ and $x = u - 3$. Then

$$\int \frac{x}{\sqrt{x+3}}\,dx = \int \frac{u-3}{\sqrt{u}}\,du = \int \left(\sqrt{u} - \frac{3}{\sqrt{u}}\right)du = \frac{2}{3}u^{3/2} - 6u^{1/2} + C = \frac{2}{3}(x+3)^{3/2} - 6(x+3)^{1/2} + C.$$

47. Let $u = 6 - 2x$, so that $du = -2\,dx$ and $4x = 2(6-u)$. If $x = 1$, then $u = 4$; if $x = 3$, then $u = 0$. Thus

$$\int_1^3 4x\sqrt{6-2x}\,dx = \int_4^0 2(6-u)\sqrt{u}\left(-\frac{1}{2}\right)du = -\int_4^0 (6u^{1/2} - u^{3/2})\,du$$

$$= \int_0^4 (6u^{1/2} - u^{3/2})\,du = \left(4u^{3/2} - \frac{2}{5}u^{5/2}\right)\Big|_0^4 = \left[4(8) - \frac{2}{5}(32)\right] - 0 = \frac{96}{5}.$$

48. Let $u = x + 4$, so that $du = dx$ and $x^2 = (u-4)^2$. Then

$$\int x^2\sqrt{x+4}\,dx = \int (u-4)^2\sqrt{u}\,du = \int (u^{5/2} - 8u^{3/2} + 16u^{1/2})\,du$$

$$= \frac{2}{7}u^{7/2} - \frac{16}{5}u^{5/2} + \frac{32}{3}u^{3/2} + C = \frac{2}{7}(x+4)^{7/2} - \frac{16}{5}(x+4)^{5/2} + \frac{32}{3}(x+4)^{3/2} + C.$$

49. Let $u = 1 - 8t$, so that $du = -8\,dt$ and $t^2 = \frac{1}{64}(1-u)^2$. Then

$$\int t^2\sqrt{1-8t}\,dt = \int \frac{1}{64}(1-u)^2\sqrt{u}\left(-\frac{1}{8}\right)du = -\frac{1}{512}\int (u^{1/2} - 2u^{3/2} + u^{5/2})\,du$$

$$= -\frac{1}{512}\left(\frac{2}{3}u^{3/2} - \frac{4}{5}u^{5/2} + \frac{2}{7}u^{7/2}\right) + C = -\frac{1}{256}\left[\frac{1}{3}(1-8t)^{3/2} - \frac{2}{5}(1-8t)^{5/2} + \frac{1}{7}(1-8t)^{7/2}\right] + C.$$

50. Let $u = 1 + e^t$, so that $du = e^t\,dt$ and $e^t = u - 1$. Then

$$\int e^{3t}\sqrt{1+e^t}\,dt = \int e^{2t}\sqrt{1+e^t}\,e^t\,dt = \int (u-1)^2\sqrt{u}\,du = \int (u^{5/2} - 2u^{3/2} + u^{1/2})\,du$$
$$= \frac{2}{7}u^{7/2} - \frac{4}{5}u^{5/2} + \frac{2}{3}u^{3/2} + C = \frac{2}{7}(1+e^t)^{7/2} - \frac{4}{5}(1+e^t)^{5/2} + \frac{2}{3}(1+e^t)^{3/2} + C.$$

51. Let $u = t + 2$, so that $du = dt$ and $t^2 = (u-2)^2$. If $t = -1$, then $u = 1$; if $t = 2$, then $u = 4$. Thus

$$\int_{-1}^{2} \frac{t^2}{\sqrt{t+2}}\,dt = \int_1^4 \frac{(u-2)^2}{\sqrt{u}}\,du = \int_1^4 (u^{3/2} - 4u^{1/2} + 4u^{-1/2})\,du$$
$$= \left(\frac{2}{5}u^{5/2} - \frac{8}{3}u^{3/2} + 8u^{1/2}\right)\Big|_1^4 = \left[\frac{2}{5}(32) - \frac{8}{3}(8) + 8(2)\right] - \left[\frac{2}{5} - \frac{8}{3} + 8\right] = \frac{26}{15}.$$

52. Let $u = 1 + \sqrt{x}$, so that $\sqrt{x} = u - 1$ and $du = 1/(2\sqrt{x})\,dx$, and thus $2(u-1)\,du = dx$. If $x = 0$, then $u = 1$; if $x = 1$, then $u = 2$. Thus

$$\int_0^1 \frac{\sqrt{x}}{\sqrt{1+\sqrt{x}}}\,dx = \int_1^2 \frac{u-1}{\sqrt{u}}\,2(u-1)\,du = 2\int_1^2 \frac{(u-1)^2}{\sqrt{u}}\,du = 2\int_1^2 (u^{3/2} - 2u^{1/2} + u^{-1/2})\,du$$
$$= 2\left(\frac{2}{5}u^{5/2} - \frac{4}{3}u^{3/2} + 2u^{1/2}\right)\Big|_1^2 = 2\left\{\left[\frac{2}{5}(4\sqrt{2}) - \frac{4}{3}(2\sqrt{2}) + 2\sqrt{2}\right] - \left[\frac{2}{5} - \frac{4}{3} + 2\right]\right\} = \frac{4}{15}\left(7\sqrt{2} - 8\right).$$

53. $A = \int_0^3 \sqrt{x+1}\,dx$. Let $u = x + 1$, so that $du = dx$. If $x = 0$, then $u = 1$; if $x = 3$, then $u = 4$. Thus

$$A = \int_0^3 \sqrt{x+1}\,dx = \int_1^4 \sqrt{u}\,du = \frac{2}{3}\left(4^{3/2} - 1^{3/2}\right) = \frac{14}{3}.$$

54. $A = \int_0^1 \sin \pi x\,dx$. Let $u = \pi x$, so that $du = \pi\,du$. If $x = 0$, then $u = 0$; if $x = 1$, then $u = \pi$. Thus

$$A = \int_0^1 \sin \pi x\,dx = \int_0^\pi (\sin u)\frac{1}{\pi}\,du = \frac{1}{\pi}\int_0^\pi \sin u\,du = -\frac{1}{\pi}\cos u\Big|_0^\pi = -\frac{1}{\pi}(-1-1) = \frac{2}{\pi}.$$

55. $A = \int_1^2 [x/(x^2+1)^2]\,dx$. Let $u = x^2 + 1$, so that $du = 2x\,dx$. If $x = 1$, then $u = 2$; if $x = 2$, then $u = 5$. Thus

$$A = \int_1^2 \frac{x}{(x^2+1)^2}\,dx = \int_2^5 \frac{1}{u^2}\left(\frac{1}{2}\right)du = \frac{1}{2}\int_2^5 \frac{1}{u^2}\,du = -\frac{1}{2}\frac{1}{u}\Big|_2^5 = -\frac{1}{2}\left(\frac{1}{5} - \frac{1}{2}\right) = \frac{3}{20}.$$

56. $A = \int_3^5 x\sqrt{x^2-9}\,dx$. Let $u = x^2 - 9$, so that $du = 2x\,dx$. If $x = 3$, then $u = 0$; if $x = 5$, then $u = 16$. Thus

$$A = \int_3^5 x\sqrt{x^2-9}\,dx = \int_0^{16} u^{1/2}\left(\frac{1}{2}\right)du = \frac{1}{2}\int_0^{16} u^{1/2}\,du = \frac{1}{3}u^{3/2}\Big|_0^{16} = \frac{64}{3}.$$

57. $A = \int_{1/8}^{1/3} (1/x^2)(1 + 1/x)^{1/2}\,dx$. Let $u = 1 + 1/x$, so that $du = -(1/x^2)\,dx$. If $x = \frac{1}{8}$, then $u = 9$; if $x = \frac{1}{3}$, then $u = 4$. Thus

$$A = \int_{1/8}^{1/3} \frac{1}{x^2}\left(1 + \frac{1}{x}\right)^{1/2} dx = \int_9^4 u^{1/2}(-1)\,du = -\int_9^4 u^{1/2}\,du = -\frac{2}{3}u^{3/2}\Big|_9^4 = \frac{38}{3}.$$

58. $A = \int_{-1}^{0} -x^{1/3}(1+x^{4/3})^{1/3}\,dx$. Let $u = 1 + x^{4/3}$, so that $du = \frac{4}{3}x^{1/3}\,dx$. If $x = -1$, then $u = 2$; if $x = 0$, then $u = 1$. Thus

$$A = \int_{-1}^{0} -x^{1/3}(1+x^{4/3})^{1/3}\,dx = \int_{2}^{1} -u^{1/3}\left(\frac{3}{4}\right)du = \frac{3}{4}\int_{2}^{1} -u^{1/3}\,du = -\left.\frac{9}{16}u^{4/3}\right|_{2}^{1} = \frac{9}{16}\left(2^{4/3}-1\right).$$

59. a. We have

$$\int_{a}^{a+k\pi} \sin^2 x\,dx = \left.\left(\frac{1}{2}x - \frac{1}{4}\sin 2x\right)\right|_{a}^{a+k\pi}$$

$$= \left[\frac{1}{2}(a+k\pi) - \frac{1}{4}\sin 2(a+k\pi)\right] - \left[\frac{1}{2}a - \frac{1}{4}\sin 2a\right] = \frac{1}{2}k\pi.$$

b. We have

$$\int_{a}^{a+k\pi} \cos^2 x\,dx = \left.\left(\frac{1}{2}x + \frac{1}{4}\sin 2x\right)\right|_{a}^{a+k\pi}$$

$$= \left[\frac{1}{2}(a+k\pi) + \frac{1}{4}\sin 2(a+k\pi)\right] - \left[\frac{1}{2}a + \frac{1}{4}\sin 2a\right] = \frac{1}{2}k\pi.$$

60. a. Let $u = 1 - x$, so that $du = -dx$. If $x = 0$, then $u = 1$; if $x = 1$, then $u = 0$. Thus $\int_0^1 x^n(1-x)^m\,dx = \int_1^0 (1-u)^n u^m(-1)\,du = \int_0^1 x^m(1-x)^n\,dx$.

b. By part (a),

$$\int_0^1 x^2(1-x)^{10}\,dx = \int_0^1 x^{10}(1-x)^2\,dx = \int_0^1 (x^{10} - 2x^{11} + x^{12})\,dx$$

$$= \left.\left(\frac{1}{11}x^{11} - \frac{2}{12}x^{12} + \frac{1}{13}x^{13}\right)\right|_0^1 = \frac{1}{11} - \frac{1}{6} + \frac{1}{13} = \frac{1}{858} \approx 0.0011655012.$$

61. By the trigonometric identity $\sin^2 x = \frac{1}{2} - \frac{1}{2}\cos 2x$ we have

$$\int \sin^2 x\,dx = \int\left(\frac{1}{2} - \frac{1}{2}\cos 2x\right)dx = \int \frac{1}{2}\,dx - \frac{1}{2}\int \cos 2x\,dx.$$

Let $u = 2x$, so that $du = 2\,dx$. Then

$$\int \sin^2 x\,dx = \frac{1}{2}x - \frac{1}{2}\int (\cos u)\frac{1}{2}\,du = \frac{1}{2}x - \frac{1}{4}\sin u + C = \frac{1}{2}x - \frac{1}{4}\sin 2x + C.$$

62. a. Let $u = a - x$, so that $du = -dx$. If $x = 0$, then $u = a$; if $x = a$, then $u = 0$. Thus

$$\int_0^a \frac{f(x)}{f(x)+f(a-x)}\,dx = \int_a^0 \frac{f(a-u)}{f(a-u)+f(u)}(-1)\,du = \int_0^a \frac{f(a-u)}{f(u)+f(a-u)}\,du.$$

b. By the result of part (a),

$$2\int_0^a \frac{f(x)}{f(x)+f(a-x)}\,dx = \int_0^a \frac{f(x)}{f(x)+f(a-x)}\,dx + \int_0^a \frac{f(x)}{f(x)+f(a-x)}\,dx$$

$$= \int_0^a \frac{f(x)}{f(x)+f(a-x)}\,dx + \int_0^a \frac{f(a-u)}{f(u)+f(a-u)}\,du$$

$$= \int_0^a \frac{f(x)}{f(x)+f(a-x)}\,dx + \int_0^a \frac{f(a-x)}{f(x)+f(a-x)}\,dx$$

$$= \int_0^a \frac{f(x)+f(a-x)}{f(x)+f(a-x)}\,dx = \int_0^a 1\,dx = a.$$

Dividing by 2, we conclude that

$$\int_0^a \frac{f(x)}{f(x)+f(a-x)}\,dx = \frac{a}{2}.$$

c. Applying part (b) with $f(x) = x^4$ and $a = 1$, we have

$$\int_0^1 \frac{x^4}{x^4+(1-x)^4}\,dx = \frac{1}{2}.$$

63. a. Let $u = ax + b$, so that $du = a\,dx$. Then

$$\int f(ax+b)\,dx = \int f(u)\frac{1}{a}\,du = \frac{1}{a}\int f(u)\,du = \frac{1}{a}F(u) + C = \frac{1}{a}F(ax+b) + C.$$

b. If $f(x) = \sin x$, then since $\int \sin x\,dx = -\cos x + C$, part (a) implies that

$$\int \sin(ax+b)\,dx = -\frac{1}{a}\cos(ax+b) + C.$$

c. If $f(x) = x^n$ with $n \neq 0, -1$, then since $\int x^n\,dx = [1/(n+1)]x^{n+1} + C$, part (a) implies that

$$\int (ax+b)^n\,dx = \frac{1}{a}\left[\frac{1}{n+1}(ax+b)^{n+1}\right] + C = \frac{1}{a(n+1)}(ax+b)^{n+1} + C.$$

64. Let $u = x/c$, so that $du = (1/c)\,dx$ and $x = cu$. If $x = ca$, then $u = a$; if $x = cb$, then $u = b$. Thus

$$\int_{ca}^{cb} \frac{1}{x}\,dx = \int_a^b \frac{1}{cu}c\,du = \int_a^b \frac{1}{u}\,du = \int_a^b \frac{1}{x}\,dx$$

where we have replaced u by x in the last equation.

65. Let $u = -x$, so that $du = -dx$. If $x = -a$, then $u = a$; if $x = 0$, then $u = 0$. Thus

$$\int_{-a}^0 f(x)\,dx = \int_a^0 [f(-u)](-1)\,du = \int_0^a f(-u)\,du = \int_0^a f(-x)\,dx$$

where we have replaced u by x in the last equation.

66. a. By the Addition Property and Exercise 65,

$$\int_{-a}^a f(x)\,dx = \int_{-a}^0 f(x)\,dx + \int_0^a f(x)\,dx = \int_0^a f(-x)\,dx + \int_0^a f(x)\,dx = \int_0^a [f(x)+f(-x)]\,dx.$$

b. By (a) and the hint,

$$\int_{-a}^a f(x)\,dx = \int_0^a [f(x)+f(-x)]\,dx = \int_0^a [f(x)-f(x)]\,dx = \int_0^a 0\,dx = 0.$$

c. By (a) and the hint,

$$\int_{-a}^{a} f(x)\,dx = \int_0^a [f(x)+f(-x)]\,dx = \int_0^a [f(x)+f(x)]\,dx = 2\int_0^a f(x)\,dx.$$

67. a. Since $\sin x$ is odd, it follows from Exercise 66(b) that $\int_{-\pi/3}^{\pi/3} \sin x\,dx = 0$.

b. Since $\cos t$ is even, it follows from Exercise 66(c) that

$$\int_{-\pi/4}^{\pi/4} \cos t\,dt = 2\int_0^{\pi/4} \cos t\,dt = 2(\sin t)\big|_0^{\pi/4} = 2\left(\frac{\sqrt{2}}{2} - 0\right) = \sqrt{2}.$$

68. The problem with the argument is that if $u = 1/x$, then u is not continuous (much less differentiable) on $[-1, 1]$, as required by Theorem 5.20 and also (4).

69. a. mean power $= \dfrac{1}{t^*}\displaystyle\int_0^{t^*} (V_0 \sin 3t)(I_0 \sin 3t)\,dt = \frac{V_0 I_0}{t^*}\int_0^{t^*} \sin^2 3t\,dt$

Let $u = 3t$, so that $du = 3\,dt$. If $t = 0$, then $u = 0$; if $t = t^*$, then $u = 3t^*$. By (3),

$$\int_0^{t^*} \sin^2 3t\,dt = \int_0^{3t^*} (\sin^2 u)\frac{1}{3}\,du = \frac{1}{3}\left(\frac{1}{2}u - \frac{1}{4}\sin 2u\right)\bigg|_0^{3t^*} = \frac{1}{2}t^* - \frac{1}{12}\sin 6t^*.$$

Therefore

$$\text{mean power} = \frac{V_0 I_0}{t^*}\left(\frac{1}{2}t^* - \frac{1}{12}\sin 6t^*\right) = \frac{1}{2}V_0 I_0 - \frac{V_0 I_0}{12t^*}\sin 6t^*.$$

b. mean power $= \dfrac{1}{t^*}\displaystyle\int_0^{t^*} (V_0 \sin 3t)(I_0 \cos 3t)\,dt = \frac{V_0 I_0}{t^*}\int_0^{t^*} \sin 3t\,\cos 3t\,dt$

Let $u = \sin 3t$, so that $du = 3\cos 3t\,dt$. If $t = 0$, then $u = 0$; if $t = t^*$, then $u = \sin 3t^*$. Then

$$\int_0^{t^*} \sin 3t\,\cos 3t\,dt = \int_0^{\sin 3t^*} u\frac{1}{3}\,du = \frac{1}{6}u^2\bigg|_0^{\sin 3t^*} = \frac{1}{6}\sin^2(3t^*).$$

Therefore

$$\text{mean power} = \frac{V_0 I_0}{t^*}\left[\frac{1}{6}\sin^2(3t^*)\right] = \frac{V_0 I_0}{6t^*}\sin^2(3t^*).$$

70. a. Let $u = 2\pi x$, so that $du = 2\pi\,dx$. If $x = 0$, then $u = 0$; if $x = \frac{1}{4}$, then $u = \pi/2$. Then by (3),

$$\int_0^{1/4} 2\sin^2(2\pi x)\,dx = \int_0^{\pi/2} (2\sin^2 u)\frac{1}{2\pi}\,du = \frac{1}{\pi}\int_0^{\pi/2} \sin^2 u\,du$$

$$= \frac{1}{\pi}\left(\frac{1}{2}u - \frac{1}{4}\sin 2u\right)\bigg|_0^{\pi/2} = \frac{1}{\pi}\left(\frac{\pi}{4} - \frac{1}{4}\sin\pi\right) = \frac{1}{4}.$$

b. Using the result of part (a) with $u = 2\pi$ when $x = 1$, we have

$$\int_0^1 |\psi(x)|^2\,dx = \int_0^1 2\sin^2(2\pi x)\,dx = \frac{1}{\pi}\left(\frac{1}{2}u - \frac{1}{4}\sin 2u\right)\bigg|_0^{2\pi} = 1.$$

The physical significance of this result is that the electron is certain to be in the interval $[0, 1]$.

71. Let $u = -s/\lambda$, so that $du = -(1/\lambda)\,ds$. If $s = 0$, then $u = 0$; if $s = t$, then $u = -t/\lambda$. Thus

$$P(t) = \int_0^t \frac{1}{\lambda} e^{-s/\lambda}\,ds = \int_0^{-t/\lambda} \frac{1}{\lambda} e^u(-\lambda)\,du = -\int_0^{-t/\lambda} e^u\,du = -e^u\Big|_0^{-t/\lambda} = 1 - e^{-t/\lambda}.$$

a. $\lim_{t\to\infty} P(t) = \lim_{t\to\infty}(1 - e^{-t/\lambda}) = 1$

b. If $\lambda = 2$ and $t = 1$, then $P(1) = 1 - e^{-1/2} \approx 0.393493403$. Thus the probability is approximately 0.4.

c. We must find t^* such that $P(t^*) = \frac{1}{2}$, or equivalently, $1 - e^{-t^*/\lambda} = \frac{1}{2}$. Thus $\frac{1}{2} = e^{-t^*/\lambda}$, so that $\ln\frac{1}{2} = -t^*/2$, so $t^* = 2\ln 2 \approx 1.386294361$. Consequently there is a 50% chance the battery will last at most 1.39 years.

72. Let $u = x - a$, so that $du = dx$. If $x = x_1$, then $u = x_1 - a$; if $x = x_2$, then $u = x_2 - a$. Thus

$$W = \int_{x_1}^{x_2} \frac{Gm_1m_2}{(x-a)^2}\,dx = \int_{x_1-a}^{x_2-a} \frac{Gm_1m_2}{u^2}\,du = Gm_1m_2\int_{x_1-a}^{x_2-a} \frac{1}{u^2}\,du = Gm_1m_2\left(-\frac{1}{u}\right)\Big|_{x_1-a}^{x_2-a}$$

$$= Gm_1m_2\left(-\frac{1}{x_2-a} + \frac{1}{x_1-a}\right) = \frac{Gm_1m_2(x_2-x_1)}{(x_1-a)(x_2-a)}.$$

5.7 The Logarithm

1. $\displaystyle\int_2^8 \frac{1}{x}\,dx = \ln x\Big|_2^8 = \ln 8 - \ln 2 = \ln\frac{8}{2} = \ln 4$

2. $\displaystyle\int_{1/9}^{1/4} \frac{-1}{3x}\,dx = -\frac{1}{3}\int_{1/9}^{1/4} \frac{1}{x}\,dx = -\frac{1}{3}\ln x\Big|_{1/9}^{1/4} = -\frac{1}{3}\left(\ln\frac{1}{4} - \ln\frac{1}{9}\right) = -\frac{1}{3}(-\ln 4 + \ln 9) = \frac{1}{3}\ln\frac{4}{9}$

3. $\displaystyle\int_{-4}^{-12} \frac{2}{t}\,dt = 2\int_{-4}^{-12} \frac{1}{t}\,dt = 2\ln|t|\Big|_{-4}^{-12} = 2(\ln 12 - \ln 4) = 2\ln 3$

4. $\displaystyle\int_{-1/16}^{-1/8} \frac{1}{t}\,dt = \ln|t|\Big|_{-1/16}^{-1/8} = \ln\frac{1}{8} - \ln\frac{1}{16} = -\ln 8 + \ln 16 = \ln 2$

5. The domain is $(-1, \infty)$; $f'(x) = 1/(x+1)$.

6. Since $(t^2+4)^3 > 0$ for all t, the domain consists of all real numbers; since $k(t) = 3\ln(t^2+4)$, we have

$$k'(t) = 3\left[\frac{1}{t^2+4}(2t)\right] = \frac{6t}{t^2+4}.$$

7. The domain consists of all x such that $(x-3)/(x-2) > 0$, that is, the union of $(-\infty, 2)$ and $(3, \infty)$; since $f(x) = \frac{1}{2}\ln[(x-3)/(x-2)]$, it follows that

$$f'(x) = \frac{1}{2}\,\frac{1}{(x-3)/(x-2)}\,\frac{1(x-2) - 1(x-3)}{(x-2)^2} = \frac{1}{2(x-3)(x-2)}.$$

8. The domain consists of $(0, 1)$ and $(1, \infty)$;

$$f'(x) = \frac{(1/x)(x-1) - \ln x}{(x-1)^2} = \frac{x - 1 - x\ln x}{x(x-1)^2}.$$

9. The domain is $(0, \infty)$; $f'(t) = [\cos(\ln t)](1/t)$.

10. The domain consists of all u such that $\sin u > 0$, that is, all intervals $(2n\pi, (2n+1)\pi)$ for any integer n; $g'(u) = [1/(\sin u)] \cos u = \cot u$.

11. The domain consists of all x such that $\ln x > 0$, that is, $(1, \infty)$; $f'(x) = [1/(\ln x)](1/x) = 1/(x \ln x)$.

12. The domain consists of all x in $(-\infty, -1]$ or $[1, \infty)$ such that $x + \sqrt{x^2-1} > 0$. Since $\sqrt{x^2-1} < \sqrt{x^2} = |x|$, it follows that $x + \sqrt{x^2-1} < 0$ for $x \le -1$. Thus the domain is $[1, \infty)$;

$$f'(x) = \frac{1}{x+\sqrt{x^2-1}}\left(1 + \frac{2x}{2\sqrt{x^2-1}}\right) = \frac{1}{\sqrt{x^2-1}}.$$

13. By implicit differentiation,

$$\ln(y^2+x) + x\left[\frac{1}{y^2+x}\left(2y\frac{dy}{dx}+1\right)\right] = 5\frac{dy}{dx}$$

so that

$$\left(5 - \frac{2xy}{y^2+x}\right)\frac{dy}{dx} = \ln(y^2+x) + \frac{x}{y^2+x}, \quad \text{and thus} \quad \frac{dy}{dx} = \frac{(y^2+x)\ln(y^2+x)+x}{5(y^2+x)-2xy}.$$

14. By implicit differentiation,

$$\frac{dy}{dx}\ln\frac{y}{x} + y\left[\frac{1}{y/x}\left(\frac{(dy/dx)x - y}{x^2}\right)\right] = 2y(\cos y^2)\frac{dy}{dx}.$$

Thus

$$\frac{dy}{dx}\left(\ln\frac{y}{x}\right) + \frac{dy}{dx} - \frac{y}{x} = 2y\,(\cos y^2)\frac{dy}{dx}, \quad \text{so that} \quad \frac{dy}{dx} = \frac{y/x}{\ln(y/x)+1-2y\cos y^2}.$$

15. The domain consists of $(-\infty, 0)$ and $(0, \infty)$.

$$f(x) = \begin{cases} \ln x & \text{for } x > 0 \\ \ln(-x) & \text{for } x < 0 \end{cases}$$

$$f'(x) = \frac{1}{x}; \quad f''(x) = \frac{-1}{x^2}$$

No critical numbers or inflection points; concave downward on $(-\infty, 0)$ and on $(0, \infty)$; vertical asymptote is $x = 0$; symmetric with respect to the y axis.

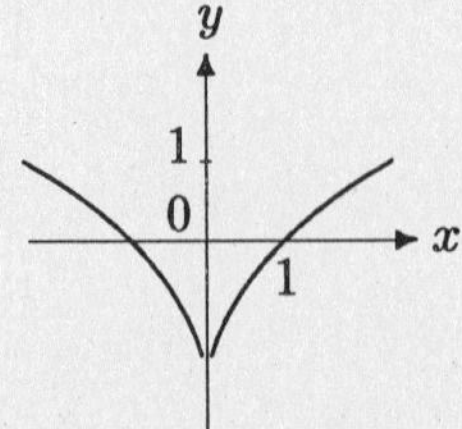

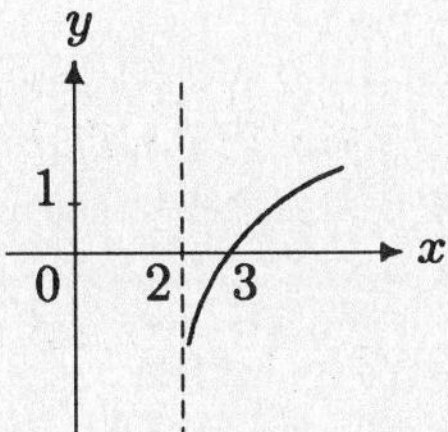

Exercise 16

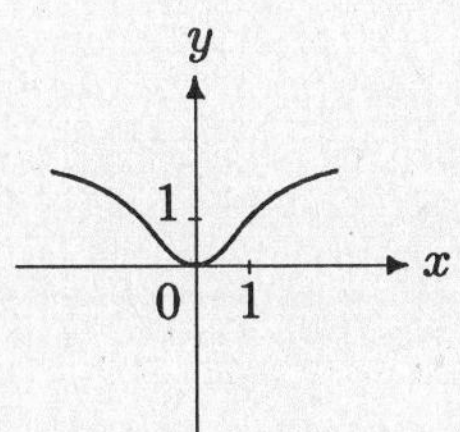

Exercise 17

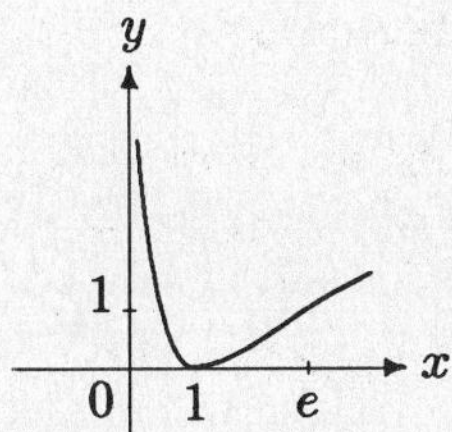

Exercise 18

16. The domain is $(2, \infty)$.

$$f'(x) = \frac{1}{x-2}; \quad f''(x) = \frac{-1}{(x-2)^2}$$

No critical numbers or inflection points; concave downward on $(2, \infty)$; vertical asymptote is $x = 2$.

17. The domain is $(-\infty, \infty)$.

$$f'(x) = \frac{2}{x^2+1}; \quad f''(x) = \frac{2-2x^2}{(x^2+1)^2}$$

Relative minimum value is $f(0) = 0$; inflection points are $(-1, \ln 2)$ and $(1, \ln 2)$; concave downward on $(-\infty, -1)$ and $(1, \infty)$, and concave upward on $(-1, 1)$; symmetric with respect to the y axis.

18. The domain is $(0, \infty)$.

$$f'(x) = 2\frac{\ln x}{x}; \quad f''(x) = \frac{2(1/x)x - 2\ln x}{x^2} = \frac{2(1-\ln x)}{x^2}$$

Relative minimum value is $f(1) = 0$; inflection point is $(e, 1)$; concave upward on $(0, e)$ and concave downward on (e, ∞); vertical asymptote is $x = 0$.

19. Let

$$g(x) = x - \frac{f(x)}{f'(x)} = x - \frac{x^{-2} - \ln x}{-2x^{-3} - 1/x} = \frac{3x + x^3 - x^3 \ln x}{2 + x^2},$$

and begin the Newton-Raphson method by letting $c_1 = 1$. A zero of f is approximately 1.531584394.

20. We will find an approximate zero of f'. Since $f'(x) = 2x + \ln x + 1$ and $f''(x) = 2 + 1/x$, let

$$g(x) = x - \frac{f'(x)}{f''(x)} = x - \frac{2x + \ln x + 1}{2 + 1/x}$$

and begin the Newton-Raphson method by letting $c_1 = .6$. A zero of f' is approximately 0.2315277567. Since $f''(x) > 0$ for $x > 0$, this value is a relative maximum value of f.

21. Let $u = x - 1$, so that $du = dx$. Then

$$\int \frac{1}{x-1}\,dx = \int \frac{1}{u}\,du = \ln|u| + C = \ln|x-1| + C.$$

22. Let $u = 1 - 4x$, so that $du = -4\,dx$. Then

$$\int \frac{2}{1-4x}\,dx = \int \frac{2}{u}\left(-\frac{1}{4}\right)du = -\frac{1}{2}\int \frac{1}{u}\,du = -\frac{1}{2}\ln|u| + C = -\frac{1}{2}\ln|1-4x| + C.$$

23. Let $u = x^2 + 4$, so that $du = 2x\,dx$. Then

$$\int \frac{x}{x^2+4}\,dx = \int \frac{1}{u}\frac{1}{2}\,du = \frac{1}{2}\int \frac{1}{u}\,du = \frac{1}{2}\ln|u| + C = \frac{1}{2}\ln(x^2+4) + C.$$

24. Let $u = 1 - x^3$, so that $du = -3x^2\,dx$. Then

$$\int \frac{x^2}{1-x^3}\,dx = \int \frac{1}{u}\left(-\frac{1}{3}\right)du = -\frac{1}{3}\int \frac{1}{u}\,du = -\frac{1}{3}\ln|u| + C = -\frac{1}{3}\ln|1-x^3| + C.$$

25. Let $u = 1 - 3\cos x$, so that $du = 3\sin x\,dx$. If $x = 0$, then $u = -2$; if $x = \pi/3$, then $u = -\frac{1}{2}$. Thus

$$\int_0^{\pi/3} \frac{\sin x}{1-3\cos x}\,dx = \int_{-2}^{-1/2} \frac{1}{u}\left(\frac{1}{3}\right)du = \frac{1}{3}\int_{-2}^{-1/2} \frac{1}{u}\,du = \frac{1}{3}\ln|u|\Big|_{-2}^{-1/2} = \frac{1}{3}\left(\ln\frac{1}{2} - \ln 2\right) = -\frac{2}{3}\ln 2.$$

26. Let $u = 1 + \ln x$, so that $du = (1/x)\,dx$. Then

$$\int \frac{1}{x(1+\ln x)}\,dx = \int \frac{1}{u}\,du = \ln|u| + C = \ln|1+\ln x| + C.$$

27. Let $u = x^2 + 4x - 1$, so that $du = (2x+4)\,dx = 2(x+2)\,dx$. If $x = -1$, then $u = -4$; if $x = 0$, then $u = -1$. Thus

$$\int_{-1}^{0} \frac{x+2}{x^2+4x-1}\,dx = \int_{-4}^{-1} \frac{1}{u}\left(\frac{1}{2}\right)du = \frac{1}{2}\int_{-4}^{-1} \frac{1}{u}\,du = \frac{1}{2}\ln|u|\Big|_{-4}^{-1} = -\frac{1}{2}\ln 4 = -\ln 2.$$

28. Let $u = 1 + \sqrt{x}$, so that $du = (1/2\sqrt{x})\,dx$. If $x = 1$, then $u = 2$; if $x = 4$, then $u = 3$. Thus

$$\int_1^4 \frac{1}{\sqrt{x}\,(1+\sqrt{x})}\,dx = \int_2^3 \frac{1}{u}(2)\,du = 2\int_2^3 \frac{1}{u}\,du = 2\ln|u|\Big|_2^3 = 2(\ln 3 - \ln 2) = 2\ln\frac{3}{2}.$$

29. Let $u = \ln z$, so that $du = (1/z)\,dz$. Then

$$\int \frac{\ln z}{z}\,dz = \int u\,du = \frac{1}{2}u^2 + C = \frac{1}{2}(\ln z)^2 + C.$$

30. Let $u = \ln z$, so that $du = (1/z)\,dz$. Then

$$\int \frac{(\ln z)^5}{z}\,dz = \int u^5\,du = \frac{1}{6}u^6 + C = \frac{1}{6}(\ln z)^6 + C.$$

31. Let $u = \ln(\ln t)$, so that

$$du = \frac{1}{\ln t}\cdot\frac{1}{t}\,dt = \frac{1}{t\ln t}\,dt.$$

Then

$$\int \frac{\ln(\ln t)}{t\ln t}\,dt = \int u\,du = \frac{1}{2}u^2 + C = \frac{1}{2}(\ln(\ln t))^2 + C.$$

32. Let $u = \sqrt{t}$, so that $du = (1/2\sqrt{t})\,dt$. Then

$$\int \frac{\tan\sqrt{t}}{\sqrt{t}}\,dt = \int 2\tan u\,du = 2\int \tan u\,du.$$

But $\int \tan u\,du = -\ln|\cos u| + C$. Thus

$$\int \frac{\tan\sqrt{t}}{\sqrt{t}}\,dt = -2\ln|\cos u| + C = -2\ln\cos\sqrt{t} + C.$$

33. Note that $\int \cot t\,dt = \int (\cos t/\sin t)\,dt$. Let $u = \sin t$, so that $du = \cos t\,dt$. Then

$$\int \cot\,dt = \int \frac{\cos t}{\sin t}\,dt = \int \frac{1}{u}\,du = \ln|u| + C = \ln|\sin t| + C.$$

34. Let $u = 1 + x^{1/3}$, so that $du = \frac{1}{3}x^{-2/3}\,dx$. Since $x^{1/3} = u - 1$, we have $x^{2/3} = (u-1)^2$, so that

$$\int \frac{1}{1+x^{1/3}}\,dx = \int \frac{x^{2/3}}{1+x^{1/3}}x^{-2/3}\,dx = \int \frac{(u-1)^2}{u}(3)\,du = 3\int\left(u - 2 + \frac{1}{u}\right)du$$

$$= 3\left(\frac{1}{2}u^2 - 2u + \ln|u|\right) + C = \frac{3}{2}(1+x^{1/3})^2 - 6(1+x^{1/3}) + 3\ln|1+x^{1/3}| + C.$$

35. Note that

$$\int \frac{x}{1+x\tan x}\,dx = \int \frac{x}{1+x\dfrac{\sin x}{\cos x}}\,dx = \int \frac{x\cos x}{\cos x + x\sin x}\,dx.$$

Let $u = \cos x + x\sin x$, so that $du = (-\sin x + \sin x + x\cos x)\,dx = x\cos x\,dx$. Then

$$\int \frac{x}{1+x\tan x}\,dx = \int \frac{x\cos x}{\cos x + x\sin x}\,dx = \int \frac{1}{u}\,du = \ln|u| + C = \ln|\cos x + x\sin x| + C.$$

36. Note that $(d/dx)(\csc x + \cot x) = -\csc x\,\cot t - \csc^2 x = -\csc x\,(\csc x + \cot x)$. Thus

$$\int \csc x\,dx = -\int \frac{-\csc x\,(\csc x + \cot x)}{\csc x + \cot x}\,dx.$$

Letting $u = \csc x + \cot x$, we see from our calculation above that

$$\int \csc x\,dx = -\int \frac{1}{u}\,du = -\ln|u| + C = -\ln|\csc x + \cot x| + C.$$

37. $A = \int_e^{e^2} (1/x)\,dx = \ln|x|\Big|_e^{e^2} = \ln e^2 - \ln e = 2 - 1 = 1$

38. $A = \int_{-2}^{-\sqrt{3}} [x/(2-x^2)]\,dx$. Let $u = 2 - x^2$, so that $du = -2x\,dx$. If $x = -2$, then $u = -2$; if $x = -\sqrt{3}$, then $u = -1$. Thus

$$A = \int_{-2}^{-\sqrt{3}} \frac{x}{2-x^2}\,dx = \int_{-2}^{-1} \frac{1}{u}\left(-\frac{1}{2}\right)du = -\frac{1}{2}\int_{-2}^{-1}\frac{1}{u}\,du = -\frac{1}{2}\ln|u|\Big|_{-2}^{-1} = -\frac{1}{2}(\ln 1 - \ln 2) = \frac{1}{2}\ln 2.$$

39. $A = \int_{\pi/4}^{\pi/3} \frac{\sin^3 x}{\cos x}\,dx = \int_{\pi/4}^{\pi/3} \frac{(1-\cos^2 x)\sin x}{\cos x}\,dx = \int_{\pi/4}^{\pi/3} (\tan x - \sin x \cos x)\,dx$

$$= \left(-\ln|\cos x| - \frac{1}{2}\sin^2 x\right)\Big|_{\pi/4}^{\pi/3} = \left[-\ln\frac{1}{2} - \frac{1}{2}\left(\frac{1}{2}\sqrt{3}\right)^2\right] - \left[-\ln\frac{1}{2}\sqrt{2} - \frac{1}{2}\left(\frac{1}{2}\sqrt{2}\right)^2\right] = \frac{1}{2}\ln 2 - \frac{1}{8}$$

40. a. Let P be the partition of $[1, 2.9]$ into 19 subintervals of length 0.1. Since $1/t$ is decreasing on $[1, 2.9]$, the corresponding right sum for $\int_1^{2.9}(1/t)\,dt$ is no greater than the integral. However,

$$\text{right sum} = \frac{1}{10}\left(\frac{1}{1.1} + \frac{1}{1.2} + \frac{1}{1.3} + \cdots + \frac{1}{2.9}\right) \approx 1.032685544.$$

Thus $\int_1^{2.9}(1/t)\,dt \geq 1.032685544 > 1$.

b. Since $1/t > 0$ on $[1, \infty)$, $\int_e^{2.9}(1/t)\,dt > 0$ only if $e < 2.9$. By part (a) and the fact that $\int_1^e(1/t)\,dt = \ln e = 1$, we have $\int_e^{2.9}(1/t)\,dt = \int_1^{2.9}(1/t)\,dt - \int_1^e(1/t)\,dt > 1 - 1 = 0$. Thus $e < 2.9$.

41. Since $\ln|f(x)| = \ln|x+1|^{1/5} + \ln|2x+3|^2 + \ln|7-4x|^{-1/2} = \frac{1}{5}\ln|x+1| + 2\ln|2x+3| - \frac{1}{2}\ln|7-4x|$, we have

$$\frac{d}{dx}\ln|f(x)| = \frac{1}{5}\frac{1}{x+1} + \frac{4}{2x+3} + \frac{2}{7-4x}.$$

Then (18) yields

$$f'(x) = \left[(x+1)^{1/5}(2x+3)^2(7-4x)^{-1/2}\right]\left[\frac{1}{5(x+1)} + \frac{4}{2x+3} + \frac{2}{7-4x}\right].$$

42. Since $\ln|f(x)| = \ln(1+\cos x)^{2/3} + \ln(x^2+x+1)^{4/5} + \ln x^{1.1} = \frac{2}{3}\ln(1+\cos x) + \frac{4}{5}\ln(x^2+x+1) + 1.1\ln x$, we have

$$\frac{d}{dx}\ln|f(x)| = \frac{2}{3}\frac{-\sin x}{1+\cos x} + \frac{4}{5}\frac{2x+1}{x^2+x+1} + \frac{1.1}{x}.$$

Thus (18) yields

$$f'(x) = (1+\cos x)^{2/3}(x^2+x+1)^{4/5}x^{1.1}\left[\frac{-2\sin x}{3(1+\cos x)} + \frac{8x+4}{5(x^2+x+1)} + \frac{1.1}{x}\right].$$

43. Since $\ln|y| = \ln|x+3|^{2/3} + \ln|2x-1|^{1/3} - \ln|4x+5|^{4/3} = \frac{2}{3}\ln|x+3| + \frac{1}{3}\ln|2x-1| - \frac{4}{3}\ln|4x+5|$, we have

$$\frac{d}{dx}\ln|y| = \frac{2}{3}\frac{1}{x+3} + \frac{1}{3}\frac{2}{2x-1} - \frac{4}{3}\frac{4}{4x+5}.$$

Then (18) yields

$$\frac{dy}{dx} = \sqrt[3]{\frac{(x+3)^2(2x-1)}{(4x+5)^4}}\left(\frac{2}{3x+9} + \frac{2}{6x-3} - \frac{16}{12+15}\right).$$

44. Since

$$\ln|y| = \ln(x^2+1)^{1/2} + \ln|\sin x|^3 - \ln x^2 - \ln(2x^2+1)^{1/2}$$
$$= \frac{1}{2}\ln(x^2+1) + 3\ln|\sin x| - 2\ln|x| - \frac{1}{2}\ln(2x^2+1)$$

we have

$$\frac{d}{dx}\ln|y| = \frac{x}{x^2+1} + \frac{3\cos x}{\sin x} - \frac{2}{x} - \frac{2x}{2x^2+1}.$$

Then (18) yields

$$\frac{dy}{dx} = \frac{\sqrt{x^2+1}\,\sin^3 x}{x^2\sqrt{2x^2+1}}\left(\frac{x}{x^2+1} + 3\cot x - \frac{2}{x} - \frac{2x}{2x^2+1}\right).$$

45. Since $\ln|y| = \ln x^{3/2} + \ln e^{-x^2} - \ln|1-e^x| = \frac{3}{2}\ln|x| - x^2 - \ln|1-e^x|$, we have

$$\frac{d}{dx}\ln|y| = \frac{3}{2x} - 2x - \frac{-e^x}{1-e^x}.$$

Then (18) yields

$$\frac{dy}{dx} = \frac{x^{3/2}e^{-x^2}}{1-e^x}\left(\frac{3}{2x} - 2x + \frac{e^x}{1-e^x}\right).$$

46. Since $\ln|y| = \ln x^2 + \ln|\ln x| - \ln|2x+1|^{3/2} - \ln|\cos x| = 2\ln|x| + \ln|\ln x| - \frac{3}{2}\ln|2x+1| - \ln|\cos x|$, we have

$$\frac{d}{dx}\ln|y| = \frac{2}{x} + \frac{1}{x\ln x} - \frac{3}{2x+1} - \frac{-\sin x}{\cos x}.$$

Then (18) yields

$$\frac{dy}{dx} = \frac{x^2\ln x}{(2x+1)^{3/2}\cos x}\left(\frac{2}{x} + \frac{1}{x\ln x} - \frac{3}{2x+1} + \tan x\right).$$

47. Let $f(x) = \ln x^r$ and $g(x) = r\ln x$. Then $f'(x) = (1/x^r)rx^{r-1} = r/x$ and $g'(x) = r/x$, so $f'(x) = g'(x)$. Moreover, $f(1) = \ln 1^r = \ln 1 = 0$ and $g(1) = r\ln 1 = 0$. By Theorem 4.6(b), $f = g$, so $\ln b^r = r\ln b$.

48. a. Let $r = -1$. Then (11) becomes $\ln b^{-1} = -\ln b$, that is, $\ln(1/b) = -\ln b$.

b. Let $f(x) = \ln(1/x)$ and $g(x) = -\ln x$. Then

$$f'(x) = \frac{1}{1/x}\left(-\frac{1}{x^2}\right) = -\frac{1}{x} \quad\text{and}\quad g(x) = -\frac{1}{x}, \quad\text{so}\quad f'(x) = g'(x).$$

Moreover, $f(1) = \ln(1/1) = \ln 1 = 0$ and $g(1) = -\ln 1 = 0$. By Theorem 4.6(b), $f = g$, so $\ln(1/b) = -\ln b$.

49. a. By the Law of Logarithms, $\ln(b/c) = \ln b(1/c) = \ln b + \ln(1/c)$, and by (12), $\ln(1/c) = -\ln c$. Therefore $\ln(b/c) = \ln b - \ln c$.

b. Let $f(x) = \ln(x/c)$ and $g(x) = \ln x - \ln c$. Then

$$f'(x) = \frac{1}{x/c}\left(\frac{1}{c}\right) = \frac{1}{x} \quad\text{and}\quad g'(x) = \frac{1}{x}$$

so $f'(x) = g'(x)$. Moreover, $f(c) = \ln(c/c) = \ln 1 = 0$ and $g(c) = \ln c - \ln c = 0$. By Theorem 4.6(b), $f = g$, so $\ln(b/c) = \ln b - \ln c$.

50. By Example 1, $\ln 3 > 1$. If n is any positive integer, then it follows from Exercise 47 that $\ln 3^n = n\ln 3 > n$, so that if $x > 3^n$, then $\ln x > \ln 3^n > n$. Thus $\lim_{x\to\infty} \ln x = \infty$. Moreover if $0 < x < 1/3^n$, then by Exercise 48, $\ln x < \ln 1/3^n = -\ln 3^n < -n$. Consequently $\lim_{x\to 0^+} \ln x = -\infty$.

51. We have $\ln n = \int_1^n (1/t)\,dt$. Let P be the partition of $[1, n]$ with subintervals of length 1. Then

$$\text{lower sum} = \frac{1}{2} + \frac{1}{3} + \cdots + \frac{1}{n} \quad \text{and} \quad \text{upper sum} = 1 + \frac{1}{2} + \frac{1}{3} + \cdots + \frac{1}{n-1}.$$

Thus

$$\frac{1}{2} + \frac{1}{3} + \frac{1}{4} + \cdots + \frac{1}{n} < \ln n < 1 + \frac{1}{2} + \frac{1}{3} + \cdots + \frac{1}{n-1}.$$

52. a. $\ln n > 20$ if $n > e^{20}$. So let n be any integer $> e^{20} \approx 485{,}165{,}195$.

b. $\ln n > 100$ if $n > e^{100}$. So let n be any integer $> e^{100} \approx 2.688117142 \times 10^{43}$.

53. Since $dy/dt = -1/t^2$, an equation of the tangent line at $(1, 1)$ is $y - 1 = -1(x-1)$, or $y = -x + 2$. For $0 < h < 1$, the area of the region below the line $y = -x + 2$ on $[1, 1+h]$ equals $\int_1^{1+h} (-x+2)\,dx = \left(-\frac{1}{2}x^2 + 2x\right)\Big|_1^{1+h} = h - \frac{1}{2}h^2$. For $-1 < h < 0$, the area of the region below the line $y = -x + 2$ on $[1+h, 1]$ equals $\int_{1+h}^1 (-x+2)\,dx = -\int_1^{1+h}(-x+2)\,dx = -\left(h - \frac{1}{2}h^2\right)$.

54. a. $\ln 1.1 \approx (0.1) - \frac{1}{2}(0.1)^2 = 0.095$

b. $\ln 0.9 \approx (-0.1) - \frac{1}{2}(-0.1)^2 = -0.105$

c. $\ln 1.02 \approx (0.02) - \frac{1}{2}(0.02)^2 = 0.0198$

d. $\ln 0.98 \approx (-0.02) - \frac{1}{2}(-0.02)^2 = -0.0202$

55. a. Since $1/t \le 1/\sqrt{t}$ for $t \ge 1$, we have

$$\ln x = \int_1^x \frac{1}{t}\,dt \le \int_1^x \frac{1}{\sqrt{t}}\,dt = 2\sqrt{t}\Big|_1^x = 2\left(\sqrt{x} - 1\right) \quad \text{for } x \ge 1.$$

b. Since $0 \le \ln x \le 2(\sqrt{x} - 1)$ for $x \ge 1$ by (a), we have $0 \le (\ln x)/x \le \left(2\sqrt{x} - 2\right)/x$. But $\lim_{x\to\infty} \left(2\sqrt{x} - 2\right)/x = \lim_{x\to\infty} \left(2/\sqrt{x} - 2/x\right) = 0$. Thus by the Squeezing Theorem,

$$\lim_{x\to\infty} \frac{\ln x}{x} = 0.$$

c. By (b) and (12),

$$\lim_{x\to 0^+} x \ln x = \lim_{y\to\infty} \frac{1}{y} \ln \frac{1}{y} = \lim_{y\to\infty} \frac{-\ln y}{y} = 0.$$

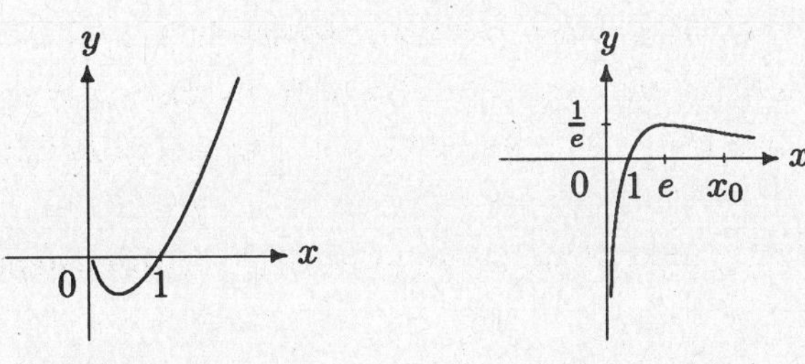

Exercise 56 Exercise 57

56. Let $f(x) = x \ln x$. Then $f'(x) = \ln x + 1$ and $f''(x) = 1/x$. Thus the graph is concave upward on $(0, \infty)$. Since $f'(x) = 0$ if $\ln x = -1$, it follows that f has a minimum value at $1/e$, which is approximately 0.37.

57. a. $f'(x) = \dfrac{(1/x)x - \ln x}{x^2} = \dfrac{1 - \ln x}{x^2}$
Since $\ln e = 1$ and $\ln x$ is increasing, we have $f'(x) > 0$ for $0 < x < e$ and $f'(x) < 0$ for $x > e$. Thus f is increasing on $(0, e]$ and decreasing on $[e, \infty)$.

b. By (a), $f(e) = 1/e$ is the maximum value of f.

c. $f''(x) = \dfrac{-(1/x)x^2 - 2x(1 - \ln x)}{x^4} = \dfrac{-3 + 2\ln x}{x^3}$
If $\ln x_0 = \frac{3}{2}$, then $x_0 \approx 4.5$, and the graph is concave downward on $(0, x_0)$ and concave upward on (x_0, ∞). By Exercise 55(b), $y = 0$ is a horizontal asymptote of f. Since $\lim_{x \to 0^+} \ln x = -\infty$ and $\lim_{x \to 0^+} 1/x = \infty$, we have $\lim_{x \to 0^+} (\ln x)/x = -\infty$, so that the line $x = 0$ is a vertical asymptote.

58. a. Since $\ln x$ is an increasing function, the inequality $a^b > b^a$ is equivalent to $\ln a^b > \ln b^a$, that is, $b \ln a > a \ln b$. This latter inequality is equivalent to $(\ln a)/a > (\ln b)/b$ since $a > 0$ and $b > 0$.

b. By Exercise 57(a), $(\ln x)/x$ is increasing on $(0, e]$, so that if $b < a \le e$, then $(\ln a)/a > (\ln b)/b$. By (a) this means that $a^b > b^a$. By Exercise 57(a), $(\ln x)/x$ is decreasing on $[e, \infty)$, so that if $e \le a < b$, then $(\ln a)/a > (\ln b)/b$. By (a), this means that $a^b > b^a$.

c. Yes, since $x^4 > 4^x$ if $e < x < 4$.

59. If $f(x) = \ln x$, then $f'(x) = 1/x$, so that $f(x) \ge 0$ and $|f'(x)| \le 1$ on $[1, 2]$. Thus by Exercise 57(b) of Section 5.5,

$$0 \le \int_1^2 \ln x\, dx = \left| \int_1^2 \ln x\, dx \right| \le \frac{1}{2}(2-1)^2 = \frac{1}{2}.$$

60. a. By (20), $f(1) = f(1 \cdot 1) = f(1) + f(1) = 2f(1)$. Therefore $f(1) = 0$.

b. By (20), $f(y) = f(x \cdot y/x) = f(x) + f(y/x)$. Thus $f(y/x) = f(y) - f(x)$.

c. If $0 < |h| < x$, then $x + h > 0$, so that $x + h$ is in the domain of f. By part (b), $f((x+h)/x) = f(x+h) - f(x)$. Thus

$$\frac{f(x+h) - f(x)}{h} = \frac{f((x+h)/x)}{h} = \frac{f(1+h/x)}{h} = \frac{1}{x}\,\frac{f(1+h/x) - f(1)}{h/x}.$$

d. Fix $x > 0$. Since $\lim_{h\to 0}(h/x) = 0$, it follows from (c) and the Substitution Rule (with $y = h/x$) that

$$\lim_{h\to 0}\frac{f(x+h)-f(x)}{h} = \frac{1}{x}\lim_{h\to 0}\frac{f(1+h/x)-f(1)}{h/x} = \frac{1}{x}\lim_{y\to 0}\frac{f(1+y)-f(1)}{y} = \frac{1}{x}f'(1).$$

61. $W = \int_{V_1}^{V_2} P\,dV = \int_{V_1}^{V_2} \frac{c}{V}\,dV = (c\ln V)\Big|_{V_1}^{V_2} = c(\ln V_2 - \ln V_1) = c\ln\frac{V_2}{V_1}$

62. a. By (6) of Section 5.4, $R(x) = R(0) + \int_0^x [2/(t+1)]\,dt = 0 + 2\ln(t+1)|_0^x = 2\ln(x+1)$ for $x \geq 0$.

b. Since $m_R(x) = 2/(x+1) > 0$ for $x > 0$, R is increasing. Since $R''(x) = -2/(x+1)^2 < 0$ for all $x > 0$, the graph of R is concave downward.

63. a. $\ln w = 4.4974 + 3.135\ln 1 = 4.4974$, so $w \approx 89.7834$ (kilograms)

b. $\ln w = 4.4974 + 3.135\ln\frac{1}{2}$, so $w \approx 10.2204$ (kilograms)

64. a. $\frac{1}{y}\frac{dy}{dx} + \frac{1}{341.5-y}\frac{dy}{dx} = c$, so $\frac{dy}{dx}\left[\frac{341.5}{y(341.5-y)}\right] = c.$

Thus

$$\frac{dy}{dx} = \frac{cy(341.5-y)}{341.5} > 0 \quad \text{for } 0 < y < 341.5.$$

b. Differentiating the first equation in (a), we obtain

$$\left[\frac{-1}{y^2} + \frac{1}{(341.5-y)^2}\right]\left(\frac{dy}{dx}\right)^2 + \left[\frac{1}{y} + \frac{1}{341.5-y}\right]\frac{d^2y}{dx^2} = 0.$$

Since $dy/dx > 0$, if $d^2y/dx^2 = 0$ then we must have $-1/y^2 + 1/(341.5-y)^2 = 0$ and thus $(341.5-y)^2 = y^2$, so $2y = 341.5$. Thus the maximum of dy/dx is attained when $y = 170.75$ (ounces). Solving for x in the given equation, we find that $x_0 = 1.66$ (months).

5.8 Another Look at Area

1. $x^2 - 2x \leq 0$ on $[0, 2]$. Thus

$$A = \int_0^2 -(x^2-2x)\,dx = -\left(\frac{1}{3}x^3 - x^2\right)\Big|_0^2 = -\left(\frac{8}{3}-4\right) = \frac{4}{3}.$$

2. The function $y = x^3 - x$ is an odd function, and $x^3 - x \leq 0$ on $[0, 1]$. Thus

$$A = 2\int_0^1 -(x^3-x)\,dx = -2\left(\frac{1}{4}x^4 - \frac{1}{2}x^2\right)\Big|_0^1 = -2\left(\frac{1}{4}-\frac{1}{2}\right) = \frac{1}{2}.$$

3. The function $y = x\sqrt{1-x^2}$ is an odd function on $[-1, 1]$, and $x\sqrt{1-x^2} \geq 0$ on $[0, 1]$. Thus $A = 2\int_0^1 x\sqrt{1-x^2}\,dx$. Let $u = 1 - x^2$, so that $du = -2x\,dx$. If $x = 0$, then $u = 1$; if $x = 1$, then $u = 0$. Thus

$$A = 2\int_0^1 x\sqrt{1-x^2}\,dx = 2\int_1^0 \sqrt{u}\left(-\frac{1}{2}\right)du = -\frac{2}{3}u^{3/2}\Big|_1^0 = \frac{2}{3}.$$

4. $\tan x \le 0$ on $[-\pi/4, 0]$, whereas $\tan x \ge 0$ on $[0, \pi/6]$. Thus

$$A = \int_{-\pi/4}^{0} (-\tan x)\,dx + \int_{0}^{\pi/6} \tan x\,dx = \ln|\cos x|\Big|_{-\pi/4}^{0} - \ln|\cos x|\Big|_{0}^{\pi/6}$$

$$= \left(\ln 1 - \ln\frac{\sqrt{2}}{2}\right) - \left(\ln\frac{\sqrt{3}}{2} - \ln 1\right) = -\frac{1}{2}\ln 2 + \ln 2 - \frac{1}{2}\ln 3 + \ln 2 = \frac{3}{2}\ln 2 - \frac{1}{2}\ln 3.$$

5. Let $f(x) = |x|$ and $g(x) = x^2$. Notice that f and g are even functions, and $[-1, 1]$ is symmetric with respect to the origin. Thus $A = 2\int_0^1 |f(x) - g(x)|\,dx$. Since $f(x) \ge g(x)$ for $0 \le x \le 1$, we find that

$$A = 2\int_0^1 (f(x) - g(x))\,dx = 2\int_0^1 (x - x^2)\,dx = 2\left(\frac{1}{2}x^2 - \frac{1}{3}x^3\right)\Big|_0^1 = 2\left(\frac{1}{6}\right) = \frac{1}{3}.$$

6. Let $f(x) = e^x$ and $g(x) = e^{-x}$. Since $f(x) \ge g(x)$ for $0 \le x \le 1$, we find that

$$A = \int_0^1 [f(x) - g(x)]\,dx = \int_0^1 (e^x - e^{-x})\,dx = (e^x + e^{-x})\big|_0^1 = e + e^{-1} - 2.$$

7. $x^2 + 2x = x(x+2) \le 0$ on $[-1, 0]$, whereas $x^2 + 2x \ge 0$ on $[0, 3]$. Thus

$$A = \int_{-1}^{0} -(x^2 + 2x)\,dx + \int_0^3 (x^2 + 2x)\,dx = -\left(\frac{1}{3}x^3 + x^2\right)\Big|_{-1}^{0} + \left(\frac{1}{3}x^3 + x^2\right)\Big|_0^3 = \frac{2}{3} + 18 = \frac{56}{3}.$$

8. $\cos x - \sin x \ge 0$ on $[0, \pi/4]$, whereas $\cos x - \sin x \le 0$ on $[\pi/4, \pi/3]$. Thus

$$A = \int_0^{\pi/4} (\cos x - \sin x)\,dx + \int_{\pi/4}^{\pi/3} (\sin x - \cos x)\,dx = (\sin x + \cos x)\big|_0^{\pi/4} + (-\cos x - \sin x)\big|_{\pi/4}^{\pi/3}$$

$$= (\sqrt{2} - 1) + \left(\frac{-1}{2} - \frac{\sqrt{3}}{2} + \sqrt{2}\right) = 2\sqrt{2} - \frac{3}{2} - \frac{\sqrt{3}}{2}.$$

9. $x/\sqrt{1+x^2} \ge 0$ on $[0, \sqrt{7}]$, whereas $x/\sqrt{1+x^2} \le 0$ on $[-1, 0]$. Thus

$$A = \int_{-1}^{0} \frac{-x}{\sqrt{1+x^2}}\,dx + \int_0^{\sqrt{7}} \frac{x}{\sqrt{1+x^2}}\,dx \overset{u=1+x^2}{=} \int_2^1 -\frac{1}{2\sqrt{u}}\,du + \int_1^8 \frac{1}{2\sqrt{u}}\,du$$

$$= -\sqrt{u}\big|_2^1 + \sqrt{u}\big|_1^8 = (\sqrt{2} - 1) + (\sqrt{8} - 1) = 3\sqrt{2} - 2.$$

10. $x/(x^2 - 1) \ge 0$ on $[-\frac{1}{2}, 0]$, whereas $x/(x^2 - 1) \le 0$ on $[0, \frac{1}{3}]$. Thus

$$A = \int_{-1/2}^{0} \frac{x}{x^2 - 1}\,dx + \int_0^{1/3} \frac{-x}{x^2 - 1}\,dx \overset{u=x^2-1}{=} \int_{-3/4}^{-1} \frac{1}{2u}\,du + \int_{-1}^{-8/9} -\frac{1}{2u}\,du$$

$$= \frac{1}{2}\ln|u|\Big|_{-3/4}^{-1} + \left(-\frac{1}{2}\ln|u|\right)\Big|_{-1}^{-8/9} = -\frac{1}{2}\ln\frac{3}{4} - \frac{1}{2}\ln\frac{8}{9} = \frac{1}{2}(\ln 3 - \ln 2).$$

11. $(\ln x)/x \le 0$ on $[\frac{1}{2}, 1]$, whereas $(\ln x)/x \ge 0$ on $[1, 2]$. Thus

$$A = \int_{1/2}^{1} -\frac{\ln x}{x}\,dx + \int_{1}^{2} \frac{\ln x}{x}\,dx \overset{u=\ln x}{=} \int_{-\ln 2}^{0} -u\,du + \int_{0}^{\ln 2} u\,du$$

$$= -\frac{1}{2}u^2\Big|_{-\ln 2}^{0} + \frac{1}{2}u^2\Big|_{0}^{\ln 2} = \frac{1}{2}(\ln 2)^2 + \frac{1}{2}(\ln 2)^2 = (\ln 2)^2.$$

12. $e^{-x} - 1 \le 0$ if and only if $e^{-x} \le 1$, or equivalently, $1 \le e^x$, which occurs on $[0, 3]$. Thus

$$A = \int_0^3 -(e^{-x} - 1)\,dx = (e^{-x} + x)\Big|_0^3 = (e^{-3} + 3) - (1 + 0) = e^{-3} + 2.$$

13. $f(x) \ge g(x)$ for $-2 \le x \le 1$, so

$$A = \int_{-2}^{1} (x^2 - x^3)\,dx = \left(\frac{1}{3}x^3 - \frac{1}{4}x^4\right)\Big|_{-2}^{1} = \frac{1}{12} + \frac{20}{3} = \frac{27}{4}.$$

14. $f(x) \le g(x)$ for $\frac{1}{2} \le x \le 1$ and $f(x) \ge g(x)$ for $1 \le x \le 2$, so

$$A = \int_{1/2}^{1} \left(\frac{1}{x^2} - \frac{1}{x}\right) dx + \int_{1}^{2} \left(\frac{1}{x} - \frac{1}{x^2}\right) dx$$

$$= \left(\frac{-1}{x} - \ln|x|\right)\Big|_{1/2}^{1} + \left(\ln|x| + \frac{1}{x}\right)\Big|_{1}^{2} = \left(-1 + 2 + \ln\frac{1}{2}\right) + \left(\ln 2 + \frac{1}{2} - 1\right) = \frac{1}{2}.$$

15. $g(x) - k(x) = x^2 + 3x + 2 = (x + 1)(x + 2)$, so $g(x) - k(x) \ge 0$ for $-3 \le x \le -2$ and for $-1 \le x \le 0$, whereas $g(x) - k(x) \le 0$ for $-2 \le x \le -1$. Thus

$$A = \int_{-3}^{-2} (x^2 + 3x + 2)\,dx + \int_{-2}^{-1} (-x^2 - 3x - 2)\,dx + \int_{-1}^{0} (x^2 + 3x + 2)\,dx$$

$$= \left(\frac{1}{3}x^3 + \frac{3}{2}x^2 + 2x\right)\Big|_{-3}^{-2} + \left(\frac{-1}{3}x^3 - \frac{3}{2}x^2 - 2x\right)\Big|_{-2}^{-1} + \left(\frac{1}{3}x^3 + \frac{3}{2}x^2 + 2x\right)\Big|_{-1}^{0} = \frac{5}{6} + \frac{1}{6} + \frac{5}{6} = \frac{11}{6}.$$

16. $g(x) - k(x) = 2x^2 + 2x = 2x(x + 1)$, so $g(x) - k(x) \ge 0$ for $-4 \le x \le -1$ and $0 \le x \le 2$, whereas $g(x) - k(x) \le 0$ for $-1 \le x \le 0$. Thus

$$A = \int_{-4}^{-1} (2x^2 + 2x)\,dx + \int_{-1}^{0} -(2x^2 + 2x)\,dx + \int_{0}^{2} (2x^2 + 2x)\,dx$$

$$= \left(\frac{2}{3}x^3 + x^2\right)\Big|_{-4}^{-1} + \left(-\frac{2}{3}x^3 - x^2\right)\Big|_{-1}^{0} + \left(\frac{2}{3}x^3 + x^2\right)\Big|_{0}^{2} = 27 + \frac{1}{3} + \frac{28}{3} = \frac{110}{3}.$$

17. Since $\sec x \ge \tan x$ and $\sec x \ge 0$ for $-\pi/3 \le x \le \pi/6$, we have $f(x) \ge g(x)$ for $-\pi/3 \le x \le \pi/6$. Thus

$$A = \int_{-\pi/3}^{\pi/6} (\sec^2 x - \sec x \tan x)\,dx = (\tan x - \sec x)\Big|_{-\pi/3}^{\pi/6}$$

$$= \left(\frac{1}{3}\sqrt{3} - \frac{2}{3}\sqrt{3}\right) - \left(-\sqrt{3} - 2\right) = \frac{2}{3}\sqrt{3} + 2.$$

18. The graphs intersect at (x, y) with x in $[\pi/3, 2\pi/3]$ if

$$\sin 2x = y = 2\cot x, \text{ or } 2\sin x\,\cos x = 2(\cos x/\sin x), \quad \text{so that} \quad \cos x = 0 \text{ or } \sin^2 x = 1.$$

Thus $x = \pi/2$. Also $g(x) \geq f(x)$ on $[\pi/3, \pi/2]$ and $f(x) \geq g(x)$ on $[\pi/2, 2\pi/3]$. Using $(\cos x)/(\sin x)$ for $\cot x$ and $2\sin x\,\cos x$ for $\sin 2x$, we find that

$$A = \int_{\pi/3}^{\pi/2}\left(2\frac{\cos x}{\sin x} - 2\sin x\,\cos x\right)dx + \int_{\pi/2}^{2\pi/3}\left(2\sin x\,\cos x - 2\frac{\cos x}{\sin x}\right)dx$$

$$\overset{u=\sin x}{=} 2\int_{\sqrt{3}/2}^{1}\left(\frac{1}{u} - u\right)du + 2\int_{1}^{\sqrt{3}/2}\left(u - \frac{1}{u}\right)du = 4\int_{1}^{\sqrt{3}/2}\left(u - \frac{1}{u}\right)du$$

$$= 4\left(\frac{1}{2}u^2 - \ln u\right)\Big|_1^{\sqrt{3}/2} = 4\left(\frac{3}{8} - \ln\frac{\sqrt{3}}{2} - \frac{1}{2}\right) = 4\ln 2 - 2\ln 3 - \frac{1}{2}.$$

19. $g(x) - k(x) = \sin^2 x - (\sin x)/(\cos x) = (\sin x)(\sin x - \sec x)$. Since $\sin x - \sec x < 0$ for all x in $[-\pi/4, \pi/4]$, it follows that $g(x) \geq k(x)$ for $-\pi/4 \leq x \leq 0$ and $g(x) \leq k(x)$ for $0 \leq x \leq \pi/4$. Thus

$$A = \int_{-\pi/4}^{0}\left(\frac{1}{2} - \frac{1}{2}\cos 2x - \tan x\right)dx + \int_{0}^{\pi/4} -\left(\frac{1}{2} - \frac{1}{2}\cos 2x - \tan x\right)dx$$

$$= \left(\frac{x}{2} - \frac{\sin 2x}{4} + \ln|\cos x|\right)\Big|_{-\pi/4}^{0} + \left(-\frac{x}{2} + \frac{\sin 2x}{4} - \ln|\cos x|\right)\Big|_0^{\pi/4}$$

$$= \left(\frac{\pi}{8} - \frac{1}{4} - \ln\frac{\sqrt{2}}{2}\right) + \left(-\frac{\pi}{8} + \frac{1}{4} - \ln\frac{\sqrt{2}}{2}\right) = -2\ln\frac{\sqrt{2}}{2} = \ln 2.$$

20. $g(x) - k(x) = x^3 - 4x^2 + 3x = x(x-3)(x-1)$, so $g(x) - k(x) \geq 0$ for $0 \leq x \leq 1$, whereas $g(x) - k(x) \leq 0$ for $-1 \leq x \leq 0$ and $1 \leq x \leq 2$. Thus

$$A = \int_{-1}^{0} -(x^3 - 4x^2 + 3x)\,dx + \int_0^1 (x^3 - 4x^2 + 3x)\,dx + \int_1^2 -(x^3 - 4x^2 + 3x)\,dx$$

$$= \left(-\frac{1}{4}x^4 + \frac{4}{3}x^3 - \frac{3}{2}x^2\right)\Big|_{-1}^{0} + \left(\frac{1}{4}x^4 - \frac{4}{3}x^3 + \frac{3}{2}x^2\right)\Big|_0^1 + \left(-\frac{1}{4}x^4 + \frac{4}{3}x^3 - \frac{3}{2}x^2\right)\Big|_1^2 = \frac{37}{12} + \frac{5}{12} + \frac{13}{12} = \frac{55}{12}.$$

21. $g(x) - f(x) = x^2 - x\sqrt{2x+3} = x(x - \sqrt{2x+3})$. Now if $x \geq 0$, then $x \geq \sqrt{2x+3}$ if $x^2 \geq 2x + 3$, or $x^2 - 2x - 3 \geq 0$, or $(x-3)(x+1) \geq 0$, which happens if $x \geq 3$. Thus $f(x) \geq g(x)$ for $0 \leq x \leq 3$. If $x < 0$, then $x - \sqrt{2x+3} \leq 0$, so $x(x - \sqrt{2x+3}) \geq 0$. Hence $g(x) \geq f(x)$ for $-1 \leq x \leq 0$. Thus

$$A = \int_{-1}^{0}(x^2 - x\sqrt{2x+3})\,dx + \int_0^3 -(x^2 - x\sqrt{2x+3})\,dx$$

$$= \frac{1}{3}x^3\Big|_{-1}^{0} - \int_{-1}^{0} x\sqrt{2x+3}\,dx - \frac{1}{3}x^3\Big|_0^3 + \int_0^3 x\sqrt{2x+3}\,dx$$

$$\overset{u=2x+3}{=} \frac{1}{3} - \int_1^3 \frac{1}{2}(u-3)\sqrt{u}\,\frac{1}{2}\,du - 9 + \int_3^9 \frac{1}{2}(u-3)\sqrt{u}\,\frac{1}{2}\,du$$

$$= \frac{1}{3} - \frac{1}{4}\left(\frac{2}{5}u^{5/2} - 2u^{3/2}\right)\Big|_1^3 - 9 + \frac{1}{4}\left(\frac{2}{5}u^{5/2} - 2u^{3/2}\right)\Big|_3^9$$

$$= \frac{1}{3} - \frac{1}{4}\left[\left(\frac{18\sqrt{3}}{5} - 6\sqrt{3}\right) - \left(\frac{2}{5} - 2\right)\right] - 9 + \frac{1}{4}\left[\left(\frac{2}{5}\cdot 243 - 54\right) - \left(\frac{18\sqrt{3}}{3} - 6\sqrt{3}\right)\right] = \frac{6}{5}\sqrt{3} + \frac{26}{15}.$$

22. The graphs intersect for $x = 0$. If $|x| \le 1$ then $x^3 + 1 \le x^2 + 1$, so $(x^3+1)^5 \le (x^2+1)^5$. Thus $x^2(x^3+1)^5 \le x(x^2+1)^5$ on $[0,1]$, and $x^2(x^3+1)^5 \ge 0 \ge x(x^2+1)^5$ on $[-1,0]$. Therefore

$$A = \int_{-1}^{0} [x^2(x^3+1)^5 - x(x^2+1)^5]\,dx + \int_0^1 [x(x^2+1)^5 - x^2(x^3+1)^5]\,dx$$

$$= \int_{-1}^{0} x^2(x^3+1)^5\,dx - \int_{-1}^{0} x(x^2+1)^5\,dx + \int_0^1 x(x^2+1)^5\,dx - \int_0^1 x^2(x^3+1)^5\,dx$$

$$\overset{\substack{u=x^3+1\\ v=x^2+1}}{=} \int_0^1 u^5\left(\frac{1}{3}\right)du - \int_2^1 v^5\left(\frac{1}{2}\right)dv + \int_1^2 v^5\left(\frac{1}{2}\right)dv - \int_1^2 u^5\left(\frac{1}{3}\right)du$$

$$= \frac{1}{18}u^6\Big|_0^1 - \frac{1}{12}v^6\Big|_2^1 + \frac{1}{12}v^6\Big|_1^2 - \frac{1}{18}u^6\Big|_1^2 = \frac{1}{18} + \frac{63}{12} + \frac{63}{12} - \frac{63}{18} = \frac{127}{18}.$$

23. The graphs intersect if $e^{2x} = e^x$, which occurs for $x = 0$. Since $2x \le x$ for $-1 \le x \le 0$ and $2x \ge x$ for $0 \le x \le 1$, we have $f(x) \le g(x)$ for $-1 \le x \le 0$, whereas $f(x) \ge g(x)$ for $0 \le x \le 1$. Thus

$$A = \int_{-1}^{0} (e^x - e^{2x})\,dx + \int_0^1 (e^{2x} - e^x)\,dx = \left(e^x - \frac{1}{2}e^{2x}\right)\Big|_{-1}^0 + \left(\frac{1}{2}e^{2x} - e^x\right)\Big|_0^1$$

$$= \left[\left(1 - \frac{1}{2}\right) - \left(e^{-1} - \frac{1}{2}e^{-2}\right)\right] + \left[\left(\frac{1}{2}e^2 - e\right) - \left(\frac{1}{2} - 1\right)\right] = 1 - e^{-1} + \frac{1}{2}e^{-2} + \frac{1}{2}e^2 - e.$$

24. The graphs intersect if $e^x = 1/e^x$, which occurs for $x = 0$. Notice that $f(x) \le g(x)$ for $-1 \le x \le 0$, whereas $f(x) \ge g(x)$ for $0 \le x \le 2$. Thus

$$A = \int_{-1}^{0} \left(\frac{1}{e^x} - e^x\right)dx + \int_0^2 \left(e^x - \frac{1}{e^x}\right)dx = \int_{-1}^{0} (e^{-x} - e^x)\,dx + \int_0^2 (e^x - e^{-x})\,dx$$

$$= (-e^{-x} - e^x)\Big|_{-1}^0 + (e^x + e^{-x})\Big|_0^2 = [(-1-1) - (-e - e^{-1})] + [(e^2 + e^{-2}) - (1+1)]$$

$$= (-2 + e + e^{-1}) + (e^2 + e^{-2} - 2) = e^2 + e + e^{-1} + e^{-2} - 4.$$

25. The graphs intersect at (x, y) if $x^3 = y = x^{1/3}$, or $x^9 = x$, or $x = -1$, 0, or 1. Also $f(x) \ge g(x)$ on $[-1, 0]$ and $g(x) \ge f(x)$ on $[0, 1]$. Thus

$$A = \int_{-1}^{0} (x^3 - x^{1/3})\,dx + \int_0^1 (x^{1/3} - x^3)\,dx = \left(\frac{1}{4}x^4 - \frac{3}{4}x^{4/3}\right)\Big|_{-1}^0 + \left(\frac{3}{4}x^{4/3} - \frac{1}{4}x^4\right)\Big|_0^1 = \frac{1}{2} + \frac{1}{2} = 1.$$

26. The graphs intersect at (x, y) if $x^2 + 3 = y = 12 - x^2$, or $x^2 = \frac{9}{2}$, or $x = \pm\frac{3}{2}\sqrt{2}$. Also $g(x) \geq f(x)$ on $[-\frac{3}{2}\sqrt{2}, \frac{3}{2}\sqrt{2}]$. Thus

$$A = \int_{-3\sqrt{2}/2}^{3\sqrt{2}/2} [(12 - x^2) - (x^2 + 3)]\, dx = \int_{-3\sqrt{2}/2}^{3\sqrt{2}/2} (9 - 2x^2)\, dx$$

$$= \left(9x - \frac{2}{3}x^3\right)\Big|_{-3\sqrt{2}/2}^{3\sqrt{2}/2} = \left(\frac{27}{2}\sqrt{2} - \frac{9}{2}\sqrt{2}\right) - \left(-\frac{27}{2}\sqrt{2} + \frac{9}{2}\sqrt{2}\right) = 18\sqrt{2}.$$

27. The graphs intersect at (x, y) if $x^2 + 1 = y = 2x + 9$, or $x^2 - 2x - 8 = 0$, or $x = -2$ or $x = 4$. Also $g(x) \geq f(x)$ on $[-2, 4]$. Thus

$$A = \int_{-2}^{4} [(2x + 9) - (x^2 + 1)]\, dx = \int_{-2}^{4} (2x - x^2 + 8)\, dx = \left(x^2 - \frac{1}{3}x^3 + 8x\right)\Big|_{-2}^{4}$$

$$= \left(16 - \frac{64}{3} + 32\right) - \left(4 + \frac{8}{3} - 16\right) = 36.$$

28. The graphs intersect at (x, y) if $x^3 + x = y = 3x^2 - x$, or $x^3 - 3x^2 + 2x = 0$, or $x(x-1)(x-2) = 0$, or $x = 0$, 1, or 2. Also $f(x) \geq g(x)$ on $[0, 1]$ and $g(x) \geq f(x)$ on $[1, 2]$. Thus

$$A = \int_0^1 (x^3 - 3x^2 + 2x)\, dx + \int_1^2 (-x^3 + 3x^2 - 2x)\, dx$$

$$= \left(\frac{1}{4}x^4 - x^3 + x^2\right)\Big|_0^1 + \left(-\frac{1}{4}x^4 + x^3 - x^2\right)\Big|_1^2 = \frac{1}{4} + \frac{1}{4} = \frac{1}{2}.$$

29. The graphs intersect at (x, y) if $x^3 + 1 = y = (x+1)^2$, or $x^3 - x^2 - 2x = 0$, or $x(x+1)(x-2) = 0$, or $x = -1$, 0, or 2. Also$f(x) \geq g(x)$ on $[-1, 0]$ and $g(x) \geq f(x)$ on $[0, 2]$. Thus

$$A = \int_{-1}^{0} [(x^3+1) - (x+1)^2]\, dx + \int_0^2 [(x+1)^2 - (x^3+1)]\, dx = \int_{-1}^{0} (x^3 - x^2 - 2x)\, dx + \int_0^2 (-x^3 + x^2 + 2x)\, dx$$

$$= \left(\frac{1}{4}x^4 - \frac{1}{3}x^3 - x^2\right)\Big|_{-1}^{0} + \left(-\frac{1}{4}x^4 + \frac{1}{3}x^3 + x^2\right)\Big|_0^2 = -\left(\frac{1}{4} + \frac{1}{3} - 1\right) + \left(-4 + \frac{8}{3} + 4\right) = \frac{37}{12}.$$

30. The graphs intersect at (x, y) if $2 - \sqrt{x} = (\sqrt{x}+1)/(2\sqrt{x})$, or $4\sqrt{x} - 2x = \sqrt{x} + 1$, or $2x - 3\sqrt{x} + 1 = 0$, or $(2\sqrt{x} - 1)(\sqrt{x} - 1) = 0$, so that $\sqrt{x} = \frac{1}{2}$ or 1, and thus $x = \frac{1}{4}$ or 1. Also $f(x) \geq g(x)$ on $[\frac{1}{4}, 1]$. Thus

$$A = \int_{1/4}^{1} \left[(2 - \sqrt{x}) - \frac{\sqrt{x}+1}{2\sqrt{x}}\right] dx = \int_{1/4}^{1} \left(\frac{3}{2} - \sqrt{x} - \frac{1}{2\sqrt{x}}\right) dx$$

$$= \left(\frac{3}{2}x - \frac{2}{3}x^{3/2} - x^{1/2}\right)\Big|_{1/4}^{1} = \left(\frac{3}{2} - \frac{2}{3} - 1\right) - \left(\frac{3}{8} - \frac{1}{12} - \frac{1}{2}\right) = \frac{1}{24}.$$

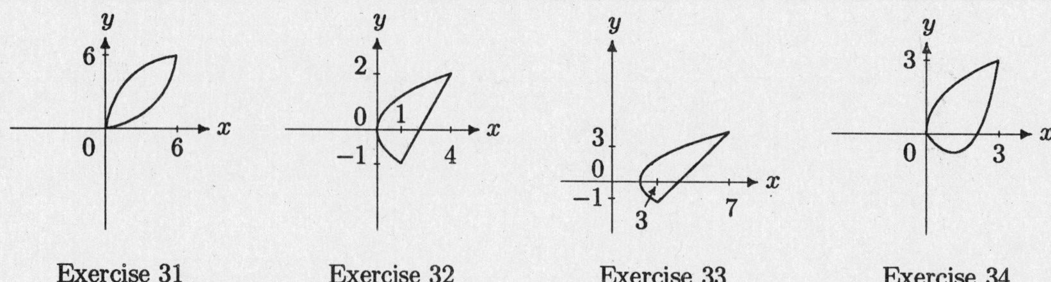

31. The graphs intersect at (x, y) if $6x = y^2 = (x^2/6)^2$, or $x^4 = 216x$, or $x = 0$ or 6. Thus the graphs intersect at $(0,0)$ and $(6,6)$, so

$$A = \int_0^6 \left(\sqrt{6x} - \frac{1}{6}x^2\right) dx = \left(\frac{2\sqrt{6}}{3}x^{3/2} - \frac{1}{18}x^3\right)\Bigg|_0^6 = \left(\frac{2\sqrt{6}}{3}\right)(6\sqrt{6}) - 12 = 12.$$

32. The graphs intersect at (x, y) if $y^2 = x = y + 2$, or $y^2 - y - 2 = 0$, or $y = -1$, or 2. Thus the graphs intersect at $(1, -1)$ and $(4, 2)$, so

$$A = \int_{-1}^2 (y + 2 - y^2)\, dy = \left(\frac{1}{2}y^2 + 2y - \frac{1}{3}y^3\right)\Bigg|_{-1}^2 = \left(2 + 4 - \frac{8}{3}\right) - \left(\frac{1}{2} - 2 + \frac{1}{3}\right) = \frac{9}{2}.$$

33. The graphs intersect at (x, y) if $\frac{1}{2}(y^2 + 5) = x = y + 4$, or $y^2 - 2y - 3 = 0$, or $y = -1$ or 3. Thus the graphs intersect at $(3, -1)$ and $(7, 3)$. Thus

$$A = \int_{-1}^3 \left[(y + 4) - \frac{1}{2}(y^2 + 5)\right] dy = \int_{-1}^3 \left(y - \frac{1}{2}y^2 + \frac{3}{2}\right) dy$$

$$= \left(\frac{1}{2}y^2 - \frac{1}{6}y^3 + \frac{3}{2}y\right)\Bigg|_{-1}^3 = \left(\frac{9}{2} - \frac{9}{2} + \frac{9}{2}\right) - \left(\frac{1}{2} + \frac{1}{6} - \frac{3}{2}\right) = \frac{16}{3}.$$

34. $A = \displaystyle\int_0^3 [\sqrt{3x} - (x^2 - 2x)]\, dx = \left(\frac{2}{3}\sqrt{3}x^{3/2} - \frac{1}{3}x^3 + x^2\right)\Bigg|_0^3 = \left(\frac{2}{3}\sqrt{3}\right)(3\sqrt{3}) - 9 + 9 = 6$

35. The graphs of $y = x + 2$ and $y = \frac{1}{3}(2 - x)$ intersect at $(-1, 1)$; the graphs of $y = x + 2$ and $y = -3x + 6$ intersect at $(1, 3)$; the graphs of $y = \frac{1}{3}(2 - x)$ and $y = -3x + 6$ intersect at $(2, 0)$. We obtain

$$A = \int_{-1}^1 \left[(x + 2) - \frac{1}{3}(2 - x)\right] dx + \int_1^2 \left[(-3x + 6) - \frac{1}{3}(2 - x)\right] dx$$

$$= \int_{-1}^1 \left(\frac{4}{3}x + \frac{4}{3}\right) dx + \int_1^2 \left(\frac{16}{3} - \frac{8}{3}x\right) dx$$

$$= \frac{1}{3}(2x^2 + 4x)\Bigg|_{-1}^1 + \frac{1}{3}(16x - 4x^2)\Bigg|_1^2 = \frac{8}{3} + \frac{4}{3} = 4.$$

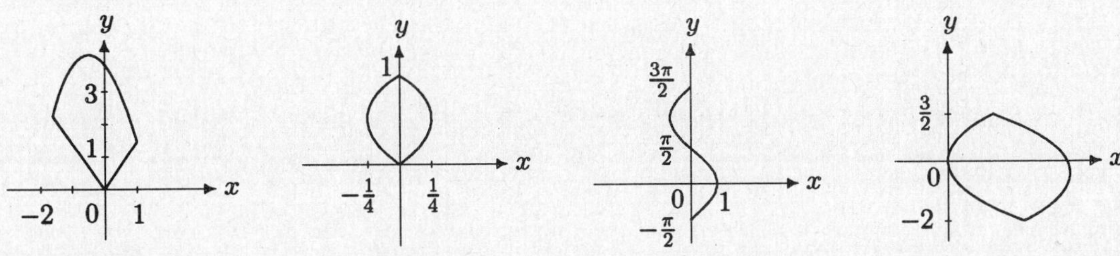

Exercise 36 Exercise 37 Exercise 38 Exercise 39

36. The graphs of $y = -\frac{3}{2}x$ for $x \le 0$ and $y = -x^2 - \frac{3}{2}x + 4$ intersect at (x, y) if $-\frac{3}{2}x = y = -x^2 - \frac{3}{2}x + 4$, or $-x^2 + 4 = 0$ or $x = -2$; the graphs of $y = -\frac{3}{2}x$ and $y = \frac{3}{2}x$ intersect at $(0, 0)$; the graphs of $y = \frac{3}{2}x$ for $x \ge 0$ and $y = -x^2 - \frac{3}{2}x + 4$ intersect at (x, y) if $\frac{3}{2}x = y = -x^2 - \frac{3}{2}x + 4$, or $x^2 + 3x - 4 = 0$, or $x = 1$. Thus

$$A = \int_{-2}^{0} \left[\left(-x^2 - \frac{3}{2}x + 4\right) - \left(-\frac{3}{2}x\right)\right] dx + \int_0^1 \left[\left(-x^2 - \frac{3}{2}x + 4\right) - \frac{3}{2}x\right] dx$$
$$= \int_{-2}^{0} (-x^2 + 4)\, dx + \int_0^1 (-x^2 - 3x + 4)\, dx$$
$$= \left(-\frac{1}{3}x^3 + 4x\right)\Big|_{-2}^{0} + \left(-\frac{1}{3}x^3 - \frac{3}{2}x^2 + 4x\right)\Big|_0^1 = \frac{16}{3} + \frac{13}{6} = \frac{15}{2}.$$

37. The graphs intersect at (x, y) if $y^2 - y = x = y - y^2$, or $2(y^2 - y) = 0$, or $y = 0$ or 1. Thus

$$A = \int_0^1 [(y - y^2) - (y^2 - y)]\, dy = \int_0^1 2(y - y^2)\, dy = \left(y^2 - \frac{2}{3}y^3\right)\Big|_0^1 = \frac{1}{3}.$$

38. $A = \displaystyle\int_{-\pi/2}^{\pi/2} \cos y\, dy + \int_{\pi/2}^{3\pi/2} -\cos y\, dy = \sin y\Big|_{-\pi/2}^{\pi/2} + (-\sin y)\Big|_{\pi/2}^{3\pi/2} = 2 + 2 = 4$

39. The graphs intersect at (x, y) if $y^2 = x = 6 - y - y^2$, or $2y^2 + y - 6 = 0$, or $(2y - 3)(y + 2) = 0$, or $y = -2$, or $\frac{3}{2}$. Thus

$$A = \int_{-2}^{3/2} [(6 - y - y^2) - y^2]\, dy = \int_{-2}^{3/2} (6 - y - 2y^2)\, dy = \left(6y - \frac{1}{2}y^2 - \frac{2}{3}y^3\right)\Big|_{-2}^{3/2}$$
$$= \left(9 - \frac{9}{8} - \frac{9}{4}\right) - \left(-12 - 2 + \frac{16}{3}\right) = \frac{343}{24}.$$

40. Since $A_b = \int_0^b e^{-x}\, dx = -e^{-x}\big|_0^b = 1 - e^{-b}$, we have $\lim_{b\to\infty} A_b = \lim_{b\to\infty}(1 - e^{-b}) = 1$.

41. Let A_R denote the area of R_a, so that $A_R = \frac{1}{2}(\text{base})(\text{height}) = \frac{1}{2}(2a)(a^2) = a^3$. Next, let A_S denote the area of S_a. Since the line joining $(0, 0)$ and (a, a^2) has equation $y = ax$, we find that

$$A_S = 2\int_0^a (ax - x^2)\, dx = 2\left(\frac{1}{2}ax^2 - \frac{1}{3}x^3\right)\Big|_0^a = 2\left(\frac{1}{2}a^3 - \frac{1}{3}a^3\right) = \frac{1}{3}a^3.$$

Thus $r_a = A_R/A_S = a^3/(a^3/3) = 3$ so that r_a is independent of a.

42. The area between the graphs of $f + h$ and $g + h$ equals

$$\int_a^b |(f(x) + h(x)) - (g(x) + h(x))|\, dx = \int_a^b |f(x) - g(x)|\, dx$$

which equals the area between the graphs of f and g.

43. The profit is given by

$$\int_0^4 [(\sqrt{t} + 3) - (t^{1/3} + 2)]\, dt = \int_0^4 (\sqrt{t} - t^{1/3} + 1)\, dt = \left(\frac{2}{3}t^{3/2} - \frac{3}{4}t^{4/3} + t\right)\Big|_0^4$$

$$= \frac{2}{3}(8) - \frac{3}{4}(4)^{4/3} + 4 = \frac{28}{3} - 3(4)^{1/3} \approx 4.57113.$$

Thus it is not possible to make a profit of \$5000 during the four-month period.

Chapter 5 Review

1. left sum:

$$f(0)\left(\frac{\pi}{3}\right) + f\left(\frac{\pi}{3}\right)\left(\frac{\pi}{3}\right) + f\left(\frac{2\pi}{3}\right)\left(\frac{\pi}{3}\right) + f(\pi)\left(\frac{\pi}{2}\right)$$

$$= 0\left(\frac{\pi}{3}\right) + \left(\frac{\pi}{3}\frac{\sqrt{3}}{2}\right)\left(\frac{\pi}{3}\right) + \left(\frac{2\pi}{3}\frac{\sqrt{3}}{2}\right)\left(\frac{\pi}{3}\right) + 0\left(\frac{\pi}{2}\right) = \frac{\pi^2\sqrt{3}}{6}$$

right sum:

$$f\left(\frac{\pi}{3}\right)\left(\frac{\pi}{3}\right) + f\left(\frac{2\pi}{3}\right)\left(\frac{\pi}{3}\right) + f(\pi)\left(\frac{\pi}{3}\right) + f\left(\frac{3\pi}{2}\right)\left(\frac{\pi}{2}\right)$$

$$= \left(\frac{\pi}{3}\frac{\sqrt{3}}{2}\right)\left(\frac{\pi}{3}\right) + \left(\frac{2\pi}{3}\frac{\sqrt{3}}{2}\right)\left(\frac{\pi}{3}\right) + 0\left(\frac{\pi}{3}\right) + \left(-\frac{3\pi}{2}\right)\left(\frac{\pi}{2}\right) = \frac{\pi^2\sqrt{3}}{6} - \frac{3\pi^2}{4}$$

midpoint sum:

$$f\left(\frac{\pi}{6}\right)\left(\frac{\pi}{3}\right) + f\left(\frac{\pi}{2}\right)\left(\frac{\pi}{3}\right) + f\left(\frac{5\pi}{6}\right)\left(\frac{\pi}{3}\right) + f\left(\frac{5\pi}{4}\right)\left(\frac{\pi}{2}\right)$$

$$= \left(\frac{\pi}{6}\frac{1}{2}\right)\left(\frac{\pi}{3}\right) + \left(\frac{\pi}{2}\right)\left(\frac{\pi}{3}\right) + \left(\frac{5\pi}{6}\frac{1}{2}\right)\left(\frac{\pi}{3}\right) + \left(-\frac{5\pi}{4}\frac{\sqrt{2}}{2}\right)\left(\frac{\pi}{2}\right) = \frac{\pi^2}{3} - \frac{5\sqrt{2}\pi^2}{16}$$

2. midpoint sum: 1.622739957

3. $\int \left(x^{3/5} - 8x^{5/3}\right) dx = \frac{5}{8}x^{8/5} - 8\left(\frac{3}{8}x^{8/3}\right) + C = \frac{5}{8}x^{8/5} - 3x^{8/3} + C$

4. $\int (3\cos x - 2\sin x)\, dx = 3\int \cos x\, dx - 2\int \sin x\, dx = 3\sin x + 2\cos x + C$

5. $\int \left(x^3 - 3x + 2 - \frac{2}{x}\right) dx = \frac{1}{4}x^4 - \frac{3}{2}x^2 + 2x - 2\ln|x| + C$

6. Let $u = 4 - x$, so that $du = -dx$. Then

$$\int (4-x)^9\,dx = \int u^9(-1)\,du = -\int u^9\,du = -\frac{1}{10}u^{10} + C = -\frac{1}{10}(4-x)^{10} + C.$$

7. Let $u = 1 + \sqrt{x+1}$, so that $du = 1/(2\sqrt{x+1})\,dx$. Then

$$\int \frac{1+\sqrt{x+1}}{\sqrt{x+1}}\,dx = \int u(2)\,du = 2\int u\,du = 2\left(\frac{1}{2}u^2\right) + C = (1+\sqrt{x+1})^2 + C.$$

8. Let $u = 1/x$, so that $du = -1/x^2$. Thus

$$\int \frac{1}{x^2}\,e^{1/x}\,dx = \int e^u(-1)\,du = -e^u + C = -e^{1/x} + C.$$

9. Let $u = \cos 3t$, so that $du = -3\sin 3t\,dt$. Then

$$\int \cos^3 3t\,\sin 3t\,dt = \int u^3\left(-\frac{1}{3}\right)du = -\frac{1}{3}\int u^3\,du = -\frac{1}{3}\left(\frac{1}{4}u^4\right) + C = -\frac{1}{12}\cos^4 3t + C.$$

10. Let $x = \ln t$, so that $dx = (1/t)\,dt$. Then

$$\int \frac{\tan(\ln t)}{t}\,dt = \int \tan x\,dx.$$

But $\int \tan x\,dx = -\ln|\cos x| + C$. Thus

$$\int \frac{\tan(\ln t)}{t}\,dt = -\ln|\cos x| + C = -\ln|\cos(\ln t)| + C.$$

11. Let $u = 1 + \sqrt{x}$, so that $du = 1/(2\sqrt{x})\,dx$ and $2\sqrt{x} = 2(u-1)$. Then

$$\int \sqrt{1+\sqrt{x}}\,dx = \int \sqrt{1+\sqrt{x}}\,2\sqrt{x}\left(\frac{1}{2\sqrt{x}}\right)dx = \int \sqrt{u}\,[2(u-1)]\,du = \int 2(u^{3/2} - u^{1/2})\,du$$

$$= 2\left(\frac{2}{5}u^{5/2} - \frac{2}{3}u^{3/2}\right) + C = \frac{4}{5}(1+\sqrt{x})^{5/2} - \frac{4}{3}(1+\sqrt{x})^{3/2} + C.$$

12. Let $u = x - \tan x$, so that $du = (1 - \sec^2 x)\,dx = (-\tan^2 x)\,dx$. Then

$$\int \frac{\tan^2 x}{x - \tan x}\,dx = \int \frac{1}{u}(-1)\,du = -\ln|u| + C = -\ln|x - \tan x| + C.$$

13. $$\int_{-1}^{-2}\left(x^{2/3} - \frac{5}{x^3}\right)dx = \left(\frac{3}{5}x^{5/3} + \frac{5}{2x^2}\right)\Bigg|_{-1}^{-2} = \frac{3}{5}[(-2)^{5/3} - (-1)^{5/3}] + \frac{5}{2}\left[\frac{1}{(-2)^2} - \frac{1}{(-1)^2}\right]$$

$$= \frac{3}{5}[(-2)2^{2/3} + 1] + \frac{5}{2}\left(\frac{1}{4} - 1\right) = -\frac{51}{40} - \frac{6}{5}(2^{2/3})$$

14. $$\int_1^2 \frac{x^2 + 2x + 3}{x}\,dx = \int_1^2\left(x + 2 + \frac{3}{x}\right)dx = \left(\frac{1}{2}x^2 + 2x + 3\ln x\right)\Bigg|_1^2$$

$$= \left[\frac{1}{2}(2)^2 + 2(2) + 3\ln 2\right] - \left[\frac{1}{2}(1)^2 + 2(1) + 3\ln 1\right] = \frac{7}{2} + 3\ln 2$$

15. Let $u = x^3 + 9x + 1$, so that $du = (3x^2 + 9)\,dx = 3(x^2+3)\,dx$. If $x = 0$, then $u = 1$; if $x = 2$, then $u = 27$. Thus

$$\int_0^2 (x^2+3)(x^3+9x+1)^{1/3}\,dx = \int_1^{27} u^{1/3}\frac{1}{3}\,du = \frac{1}{3}\int_1^{27} u^{1/3}\,du = \frac{1}{3}\left(\frac{3}{4}u^{4/3}\right)\bigg|_1^{27} = \frac{1}{4}(81-1) = 20.$$

16. $\displaystyle\int_0^\pi (\sqrt{x} - 3\sin x)\,dx = \left(\frac{2}{3}x^{3/2} + 3\cos x\right)\bigg|_0^\pi = \left[\frac{2}{3}\pi^{3/2} + 3\cos\pi\right] - \left[\frac{2}{3}(0) + 3\cos 0\right] = \frac{2}{3}\pi^{3/2} - 6$

17. $\displaystyle\int_{-8}^{-2} \frac{-1}{5u}\,du = -\frac{1}{5}\ln|u|\bigg|_{-8}^{-2} = -\frac{1}{5}\ln 2 + \frac{1}{5}\ln 8 = -\frac{1}{5}\ln 2 + \frac{1}{5}\ln 2^3 = -\frac{1}{5}\ln 2 + \frac{3}{5}\ln 2 = \frac{2}{5}\ln 2$

18. $\displaystyle\int_{-3}^{2} (u+|u|)\,du = \int_{-3}^{0} (u+|u|)\,du + \int_0^2 (u+|u|)\,du = \int_{-3}^0 0\,du + \int_0^2 2u\,du = 0 + (u^2)\big|_0^2 = 4$

19. Let $u = x + e^x$, so that $du = (1+e^x)\,dx$. If $x = 0$, then $u = 1$; if $x = 1$, then $u = 1 + e$. Thus

$$\int_0^1 \frac{1+e^x}{x+e^x}\,dx = \int_1^{1+e} \frac{1}{u}\,du = \ln u\big|_1^{1+e} = \ln(1+e) - \ln 1 = \ln(1+e).$$

20. Let $u = 1 - t^2$, so that $du = -2t\,dt$ and $t^4 = (t^2)^2 = (1-u)^2$. If $t = 0$, then $u = 1$; if $t = 1$, then $u = 0$. Thus

$$\int_0^1 t^5\sqrt{1-t^2}\,dt = \int_0^1 t^4\sqrt{1-t^2}\,t\,dt = \int_1^0 (1-u)^2\sqrt{u}\left(-\frac{1}{2}\right)du = -\frac{1}{2}\int_1^0 (u^{1/2} - 2u^{3/2} + u^{5/2})\,du$$

$$= -\frac{1}{2}\left[\frac{2}{3}u^{3/2} - 2\left(\frac{2}{5}u^{5/2}\right) + \frac{2}{7}u^{7/2}\right]\bigg|_1^0 = -\frac{1}{2}(0) + \frac{1}{2}\left(\frac{2}{3} - \frac{4}{5} + \frac{2}{7}\right) = \frac{8}{105}.$$

21. Let $u = 1 + \sin t$, so that $du = \cos t\,dt$. If $t = -\pi/4$ then $u = 1 - \sqrt{2}/2$, and if $t = \pi/2$ then $u = 2$. Thus

$$\int_{-\pi/4}^{\pi/2} \frac{\cos t}{1+\sin t}\,dt = \int_{1-\sqrt{2}/2}^{2} \frac{1}{u}\,du = \ln u\big|_{1-\sqrt{2}/2}^{2} = \ln 2 - \ln\left(\frac{2-\sqrt{2}}{2}\right) = 2\ln 2 - \ln(2-\sqrt{2}).$$

22. Let $u = x - 1$, so that $du = dx$ and $x = u + 1$. If $x = 2$, then $u = 1$; if $x = 5$, then $u = 4$. Thus

$$\int_2^5 \frac{x}{\sqrt{x-1}}\,dx = \int_1^4 \frac{u+1}{\sqrt{u}}\,du = \int_1^4 \left(\sqrt{u} + \frac{1}{\sqrt{u}}\right)du = \left(\frac{2}{3}u^{3/2} + 2u^{1/2}\right)\bigg|_1^4$$

$$= \left[\frac{2}{3}(4)^{3/2} + 2(4)^{1/2}\right] - \left[\frac{2}{3}(1)^{3/2} + 2(1)^{1/2}\right] = \frac{20}{3}.$$

23. Let $u = x/(x+1)$, so that

$$du = \frac{(x+1)-x}{(x+1)^2}\,dx = \frac{1}{(x+1)^2}\,dx.$$

If $x = \frac{1}{26}$ then $u = \frac{1}{27}$, and if $x = \frac{1}{7}$ then $u = \frac{1}{8}$. Thus

$$\int_{1/26}^{1/7} \frac{1}{x^2}\left(\frac{x+1}{x}\right)^{1/3} dx = \int_{1/26}^{1/7} \left(\frac{x+1}{x}\right)^2\left(\frac{x+1}{x}\right)^{1/3}\frac{1}{(x+1)^2}\,dx = \int_{1/27}^{1/8} u^{-7/3}\,du$$

$$= -\frac{3}{4}u^{-4/3}\bigg|_{1/27}^{1/8} = -\frac{3}{4}(16-81) = \frac{195}{4}.$$

24. $\int_{-1}^{\pi/2} f(x)\,dx = \int_{-1}^{0} (x^3 - 2x^2)\,dx + \int_{0}^{\pi/2} \sin x\,dx = \left(\frac{1}{4}x^4 - \frac{2}{3}x^3\right)\Big|_{-1}^{0} - \cos x\Big|_0^{\pi/2}$

$$= \left[0 - \left(\frac{1}{4} + \frac{2}{3}\right)\right] - (0 - 1) = \frac{1}{12}$$

25. $A = \int_2^4 \left(\frac{7}{4}x^2\sqrt{x} + \frac{1}{\sqrt{x}}\right) dx = \int_2^4 \left(\frac{7}{4}x^{5/2} + x^{-1/2}\right) dx = \left(\frac{1}{2}x^{7/2} + 2x^{1/2}\right)\Big|_2^4$

$= (64 + 4) - (4\sqrt{2} + 2\sqrt{2}) = 68 - 6\sqrt{2}$

26. $x + 2\sin x \le 0$ on $[-\pi/2, 0]$ and $x + 2\sin x \ge 0$ on $[0, \pi]$. Thus

$$A = \int_{-\pi/2}^{0} -(x + 2\sin x)\,dx + \int_0^{\pi} (x + 2\sin x)\,dx = -\left(\frac{1}{2}x^2 - 2\cos x\right)\Big|_{-\pi/2}^{0} + \left(\frac{1}{2}x^2 - 2\cos x\right)\Big|_0^{\pi}$$

$$= -\left(-2 - \frac{1}{8}\pi^2\right) + \left(\frac{1}{2}\pi^2 + 2 + 2\right) = 6 + \frac{5}{8}\pi^2.$$

27. Notice that

$$\frac{e^x - e^{2x}}{1 + e^x} = \frac{e^x(1 - e^x)}{1 + e^x}.$$

Let $u = 1 + e^x$, so that $du = e^x\,dx$ and $1 - e^x = 2 - (1 + e^x) = 2 - u$. If $x = 1$, then $u = 1 + e$; if $x = \ln 3$, then $u = 1 + e^{\ln 3} = 1 + 3 = 4$. Finally, $(e^x - e^{2x})/(1 + e^x) < 0$ on $[1, \ln 3]$. Thus

$$A = \int_1^{\ln 3} -\frac{e^x - e^{2x}}{1 + e^x}\,dx = \int_1^{\ln 3} -\frac{e^x(1 - e^x)}{1 + e^x}\,dx = \int_{1+e}^{4} -\frac{2 - u}{u}\,du = \int_{1+e}^{4} \left(1 - \frac{2}{u}\right) du$$

$$= (u - 2\ln u)\Big|_{1+e}^{4} = (4 - 2\ln 4) - (1 + e - 2\ln(1 + e)) = 3 - e + \ln\frac{(1 + e)^2}{16} \approx 0.1356528243.$$

28. $f(x) \le 0$ on $[1, 3]$ and $f(x) \ge 0$ on $[3, 4]$. Thus

$$A = \int_1^3 -(x - 3)\,dx + \int_3^4 (x^2 - 9)\,dx = \left(-\frac{1}{2}x^2 + 3x\right)\Big|_1^3 + \left(\frac{1}{3}x^3 - 9x\right)\Big|_3^4$$

$$= \left[\left(-\frac{9}{2} + 9\right) - \left(-\frac{1}{2} + 3\right)\right] + \left[\left(\frac{64}{3} - 36\right) - (9 - 27)\right] = \frac{16}{3}.$$

29. The graphs intersect at (x, y) if $2x^5 + 5x^4 = y = 2x^5 + 20x^2$, or $5x^4 - 20x^2 = 0$, or $x = -2$, 0, or 2. Also $g(x) \ge f(x)$ on $[-2, 2]$. Thus

$$A = \int_{-2}^{2} [(2x^5 + 20x^2) - (2x^5 + 5x^4)]\,dx = \int_{-2}^{2} (20x^2 - 5x^4)\,dx = \left(\frac{20}{3}x^3 - x^5\right)\Big|_{-2}^{2}$$

$$= \left(\frac{160}{3} - 32\right) - \left(-\frac{160}{3} + 32\right) = \frac{128}{3}.$$

30. The graphs intersect at (x, y) if $(x^2+2)/\sqrt{x+1} = y = (3x+2)/\sqrt{x+1}$, or $x^2+2 = 3x+2$, or $x = 0$ or 3. Also $(3x+2)/\sqrt{x+1} \geq (x^2+2)/\sqrt{x+1}$ on $[0, 3]$. Thus

$$A = \int_0^3 \left(\frac{3x+2}{\sqrt{x+1}} - \frac{x^2+2}{\sqrt{x+1}}\right) dx = \int_0^3 \frac{-x^2+3x}{\sqrt{x+1}}\, dx \overset{u=x+1}{=} \int_1^4 \frac{-(u-1)^2+3(u-1)}{\sqrt{u}}\, du$$

$$= \int_1^4 (-u^{3/2} + 5u^{1/2} - 4u^{-1/2})\, du = \left(-\frac{2}{5}u^{5/2} + \frac{10}{3}u^{3/2} - 8u^{1/2}\right)\Big|_1^4$$

$$= \left(-\frac{64}{5} + \frac{80}{3} - 16\right) - \left(-\frac{2}{5} + \frac{10}{3} - 8\right) = \frac{44}{15}.$$

31. The graphs intersect at (x, y) if $2y^3+y^2+5y-7 = x = y^3+4y^2+3y-7$, or $y^3-3y^2+2y = 0$, or $y = 0$, 1, or 2. Also $2y^3+y^2+5y-7 \geq y^3+4y^2+3y-7$ on $[0, 1]$, and $y^3+4y^2+3y-7 \geq 2y^3+y^2+5y-7$ on $[1, 2]$. Thus

$$A = \int_0^1 [(2y^3+y^2+5y-7) - (y^3+4y^2+3y-7)]\, dy + \int_1^2 [(y^3+4y^2+3y-7) - (2y^3+y^2+5y-7)]\, dy$$

$$= \int_0^1 (y^3 - 3y^2 + 2y)\, dy + \int_1^2 (-y^3 + 3y^2 - 2y)\, dy$$

$$= \left(\frac{1}{4}y^4 - y^3 + y^2\right)\Big|_0^1 + \left(-\frac{1}{4}y^4 + y^3 - y^2\right)\Big|_1^2$$

$$= \left(\frac{1}{4} - 1 + 1\right) + \left[(-4+8-4) - \left(-\frac{1}{4} + 1 + 1\right)\right] = \frac{1}{2}.$$

32. The average value of f on $[0, \pi]$ is

$$\frac{1}{\pi - 0}\int_0^\pi (x + 2\sin x)\, dx = \frac{1}{\pi}\left(\frac{1}{2}x^2 - 2\cos x\right)\Big|_0^\pi = \frac{1}{\pi}\left[\left(\frac{1}{2}\pi^2 + 2\right) + 2\right] = \frac{1}{2}\pi + \frac{4}{\pi}.$$

33. The domain is the union of $(-\infty, -2)$ and $(2, \infty)$.

$$f'(x) = \frac{2x}{x^2-4}; \quad f''(x) = \frac{-8-2x^2}{(x^2-4)^2}$$

decreasing on $(-\infty, -2)$ and increasing on $(2, \infty)$; concave downward on $(-\infty, -2)$ and $(2, \infty)$; vertical asymptotes are $x = -2$ and $x = 2$; symmetric with respect to the y axis.

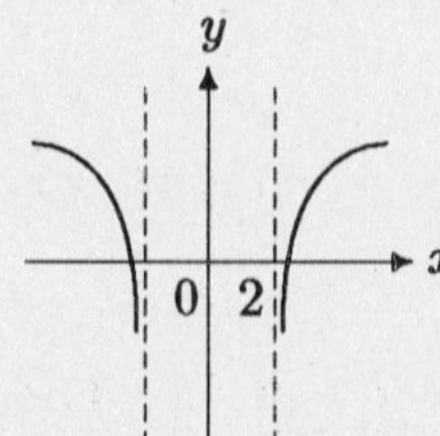

34. Since $2-x-x^2 = -(x^2+x-2) = -(x+2)(x-1) > 0$ if $-2 < x < 1$, the domain is $(-2,1)$. Since $2-x-x^2 = 1$ if $x^2+x-1=0$, so that $x = -\frac{1}{2} \pm \frac{1}{2}\sqrt{5}$, the x intercepts are $-\frac{1}{2}-\frac{1}{2}\sqrt{5}$ and $-\frac{1}{2}+\frac{1}{2}\sqrt{5}$. The y intercept is $\ln 2$. Next,

$$f'(x) = \frac{-1-2x}{2-x-x^2}; \quad f''(x) = \frac{-5-2x-2x^2}{(2-x-x^2)^2}$$

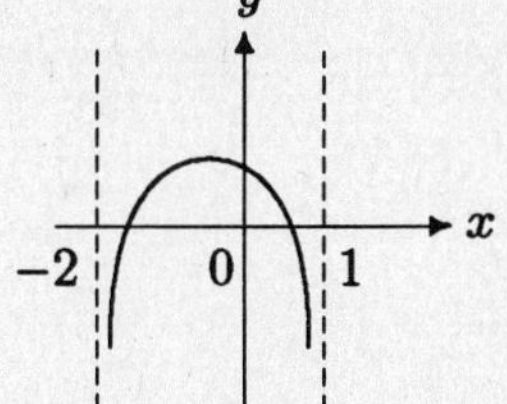

relative maximum value is $f(-\frac{1}{2}) = \ln\frac{9}{4}$; increasing on $(-2,-\frac{1}{2})$ and decreasing on $(-\frac{1}{2},1)$; concave downward on $(-2,1)$; vertical asymptotes are $x=-2$ and $x=1$.

35. $F'(x) = x\sqrt{1+x^5}$

36. Notice that

$$G(y) = \int_{2y}^{0} t\sin^2 t\,dt + \int_0^{\sin y} t\sin^2 t\,dt = -\int_0^{2y} t\sin^2 t\,dt + \int_0^{\sin y} t\sin^2 t\,dt.$$

Let $F(x) = \int_0^x t\sin^2 t\,dt$, so that $F'(x) = x\sin^2 x$ and $G(y) = -F(2y)+F(\sin y)$. Then the Chain Rule implies that

$$\begin{aligned} G'(y) &= -[F'(2y)](2) + [F'(\sin y)](\cos y) = -2(2y\sin^2 2y) + \sin y\,\sin^2(\sin y)\,\cos y \\ &= -4y\sin^2 2y + \sin y\,\cos y\,\sin^2(\sin y). \end{aligned}$$

37. Let $G(x) = \int_1^x (1/t)\,dt$, so that $F(x) = G(\ln x)$. Since $G'(x) = 1/x$, the Chain Rule implies that

$$F'(x) = [G'(\ln x)]\frac{1}{x} = \frac{1}{\ln x}\cdot\frac{1}{x} = \frac{1}{x\ln x}.$$

38. $f'(x) = \dfrac{1}{\tan x + \sec x}(\sec^2 x + \sec x\,\tan x) = \sec x$

39. $f'(x) = \dfrac{1}{x} + \dfrac{1}{1/x}\left(\dfrac{-1}{x^2}\right) = \dfrac{1}{x} - \dfrac{1}{x} = 0.$

Alternatively, $f(x) = \ln x - \ln x = 0$, so $f'(x) = 0$.

40. $f'(x) = \dfrac{1}{\ln(\ln x)}\cdot\dfrac{1}{\ln x}\dfrac{1}{x} = \dfrac{1}{x\ln x\ln(\ln x)}$

41. Since

$$\begin{aligned} \ln|f(x)| &= \ln(4-\cos x)^{1/3} + \ln|2x-5|^{1/2} - \ln|x+5|^{1/3} \\ &= \frac{1}{3}\ln(4-\cos x) + \frac{1}{2}\ln|2x-5| - \frac{1}{3}\ln|x+5| \end{aligned}$$

we have

$$\frac{d}{dx}\ln|f(x)| = \frac{1}{3}\cdot\frac{1}{4-\cos x}\cdot\sin x + \frac{1}{2}\cdot\frac{1}{2x-5}\cdot 2 - \frac{1}{3}\cdot\frac{1}{x+5}.$$

Thus (18) of Section 5.7 yields

$$f'(x) = \frac{(4-\cos x)^{1/3}\sqrt{2x-5}}{\sqrt[3]{x+5}}\left(\frac{\sin x}{12-3\cos x} + \frac{1}{2x-5} - \frac{1}{3x+15}\right).$$

42. Since

$$\ln|f(x)| = \ln|3x+7|^{1/3} + \ln|x^2-1|^{2/3} - \ln|x|^{2/3} - \ln\left(e^{2x}\right)^{1/3}$$
$$= \frac{1}{3}\ln|3x+7| + \frac{2}{3}\ln|x^2-1| - \frac{2}{3}\ln|x| - \frac{2}{3}x$$

we have

$$\frac{d}{dx}\ln|f(x)| = \frac{1}{3}\frac{3}{3x+7} + \frac{2}{3}\frac{2x}{x^2-1} - \frac{2}{3x} - \frac{2}{3}.$$

Thus (18) of Section 5.7 yields

$$f'(x) = \sqrt[3]{\frac{(3x+7)(x^2-1)^2}{x^2e^{2x}}}\left(\frac{1}{3x+7} + \frac{4x}{3x^2-3} - \frac{2}{3x} - \frac{2}{3}\right).$$

43. The integrals in (a) and (c) cannot be easily evaluated by substitution. For the integral in (b) let $u = x^2+6$, so that $du = 2x\,dx$. Then

$$\int x\sqrt{x^2+6}\,dx = \int \sqrt{u}\,\frac{1}{2}\,du = \frac{1}{3}u^{3/2} + C = \frac{1}{3}(x^2+6)^{3/2} + C.$$

44. The integrals in (a) and (b) cannot be easily evaluated by substitution. For the integral in (c) let $u = \sqrt{x}$, so that $du = 1/(2\sqrt{x})\,dx$. Then

$$\int \frac{1}{\sqrt{x}}\sin\sqrt{x}\,dx = \int (\sin u)2\,du = -2\cos u + C = -2\cos\sqrt{x} + C.$$

45. The integrals in (a) and (b) cannot be easily evaluated by substitution. For the integral in (c) let $u = \ln(x+1)$, so that $du = [1/(x+1)]\,dx$. Then

$$\int \frac{\ln(x+1)}{x+1}\,dx = \int u\,du = \frac{1}{2}u^2 + C = \frac{1}{2}[\ln(x+1)]^2 + C.$$

46. The integrals in (a) and (b) cannot be easily integrated by substitution. For the integral in (c) let $u = e^{2x}$, so that $du = 2e^{2x}\,dx$. Then

$$\int e^{2x}\sin(e^{2x})\,dx = \int (\sin u)\frac{1}{2}\,du = -\frac{1}{2}\cos u + C = -\frac{1}{2}\cos(e^{2x}) + C.$$

47. By the General Comparison Property,

$$\frac{26}{3} = \frac{1}{3}x^3\bigg|_1^3 = \int_1^3 \sqrt{x^4}\,dx \le \int_1^3 \sqrt{1+x^4}\,dx \le \int_1^3 \sqrt{2x^4}\,dx = \frac{\sqrt{2}}{3}x^3\bigg|_1^3 = \frac{26}{3}\sqrt{2}.$$

48. Replacing x by $\sqrt{x}$ in the given inequality yields $1 - \frac{1}{2}x \le \cos\sqrt{x} \le 1 - \frac{1}{2}\sqrt{x} + \frac{1}{24}x^2$, for $0 \le x \le 1$. Since

$$\int_0^1 \left(1 - \frac{1}{2}x\right)dx = \left(x - \frac{1}{4}x^2\right)\bigg|_0^1 = \frac{3}{4}$$

and

$$\int_0^1 \left(1 - \frac{1}{2}x + \frac{1}{24}x^2\right)dx = \left(x - \frac{1}{4}x^2 + \frac{1}{72}x^3\right)\bigg|_0^1 = \frac{55}{72},$$

it follows from the General Comparison Property that $\frac{3}{4} \le \int_0^1 \cos\sqrt{x}\,dx \le \frac{55}{72}$.

49. a. If $1 \le t \le x$, then $1/t \le 1$, so the General Comparison Property implies that $\int_1^x (1/t)\,dt \le \int_1^x 1\,dt$.

b. Since $\int_1^x (1/t)\,dt = \ln x$ and $\ln x \ge 0$ for $x \ge 1$, and since $\int_1^x 1\,dt = x - 1$, part (a) implies that $0 \le \ln x \le x - 1$.

c. From (b) we find that if $x \ge 1$, then $0 \le x \ln x \le x(x-1) = x^2 - x$. Thus $0 \le \int_1^2 x \ln x\,dx \le \int_1^2 (x^2 - x)\,dx = \left(\frac{1}{3}x^3 - \frac{1}{2}x^2\right)\Big|_1^2 = \frac{5}{6}$.

50. a. For $x \ge 1$,

$$\ln x = \int_1^x \frac{1}{t}\,dt \le \int_1^x t^r\,dt = \frac{1}{r+1}t^{r+1}\Big|_1^x = \frac{1}{r+1}(x^{r+1} - 1).$$

b. For $x \ge 1$,

$$\ln x = \int_1^x \frac{1}{t}\,dt \ge \int_1^x t^s\,dt = \frac{1}{s+1}t^{s+1}\Big|_1^x = \frac{1}{s+1}(x^{s+1} - 1).$$

c. Yes

51. Let $f(x) = rx + s$ for $a \le x \le b$, and let $P = \{x_0, x_1, \ldots, x_n\}$ be a partition of $[a, b]$. Then

$$\begin{aligned}
\frac{1}{2}(\text{left sum} + \text{right sum}) &= \frac{1}{2}\{[f(x_0)\Delta x_1 + f(x_1)\Delta x_2 + \cdots + f(x_{n-1})\Delta x_n] \\
&\quad + [f(x_1)\Delta x_1 + f(x_2)\Delta x_2 + \cdots + f(x_n)\Delta x_n]\} \\
&= \frac{f(x_0) + f(x_1)}{2}\Delta x_1 + \cdots + \frac{f(x_{n-1}) + f(x_n)}{2}\Delta x_n \\
&= \frac{(rx_0 + s) + (rx_1 + s)}{2}\Delta x_1 + \cdots + \frac{(rx_{n-1} + s) + (rx_n + s)}{2}\Delta x_n \\
&= \left[r\left(\frac{x_0 + x_1}{2}\right) + s\right]\Delta x_1 + \cdots + \left[r\left(\frac{x_{n-1} + x_n}{2}\right) + s\right]\Delta x_n \\
&= f\left(\frac{x_0 + x_1}{2}\right)\Delta x_1 + \cdots + f\left(\frac{x_{n-1} + x_n}{2}\right)\Delta x_n \\
&= \text{midpoint sum.}
\end{aligned}$$

52. Since the graph of f is concave upward, the average

$$\frac{f(x_{k-1}) + f(x_k)}{2}$$

of the values of f at x_{k-1} and at x_k is greater than $f\big((x_{k-1} + x_k)/2\big)$. Therefore the midpoint sum is less than the average of the left and right sums.

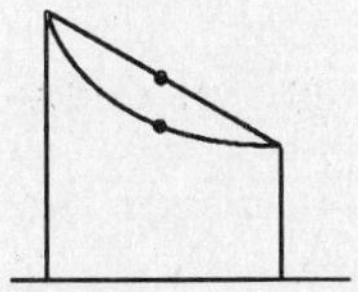

53. a. Since $G'(x) = f(x)$ by Theorem 5.12, positivity of f on I would imply that $G'(x) > 0$ for x in I and hence that f is increasing on I.

b. b is a critical number of G if $G'(b) = 0$. Now $G'(b) = f(b)$ by Theorem 5.12. Therefore b is a critical number of G provided that $f(b) = 0$.

c. By Theorem 4.13, if $G'' > 0$ on I, then the graph of G is concave upward. If f' exists on I, then $G'' = f'$, so that the graph of G is concave upward if $f' > 0$, that is, if f is increasing on I.

54. Since $(x-1)^4$ is a factor of $p(x)+1$ and $(x+1)^4$ is a factor of $p(x)-1$, there are polynomials $f(x)$ and $g(x)$ such that $p(x)+1=(x-1)^4 f(x)$ and $p(x)-1=(x+1)^4 g(x)$. Differentiating both sides of these two equations, we find that

$$p'(x)=4(x-1)^3 f(x)+(x-1)^4 f'(x)=(x-1)^3[4f(x)+(x-1)f'(x)]$$

$$p'(x)=4(x+1)^3 g(x)+(x+1)^4 g'(x)=(x+1)^3[4g(x)+(x+1)g'(x)].$$

It follows that $p'(x)$ is divisible by both $(x-1)^3$ and $(x+1)^3$. But $p'(x)$ is a polynomial of degree 6 since $p(x)$ is a polynomial of degree 7. Thus there is a constant B such that $p'(x)=B(x-1)^3(x+1)^3=B(x^2-1)^3=B(x^6-3x^4+3x^2-1)$. Integrating, we find that there is a constant C such that $p(x)=B(\frac{1}{7}x^7-\frac{3}{5}x^5+x^3-x)+C$. Next, we again use the fact that $p(x)+1$ is divisible by $(x-1)^4$ to deduce that

$$0=(1-1)^4 g(1)=p(1)+1=B(\frac{1}{7}-\frac{3}{5}+1-1)+C+1=-\frac{16}{35}B+C+1.$$

Similarly, $p(x)-1$ is divisible by $(x+1)^4$, so

$$0=(-1+1)^4 g(-1)=p(-1)-1=B\left(-\frac{1}{7}+\frac{3}{5}-1+1\right)+C-1=\frac{16}{35}B+C-1.$$

From these equations it follows that $B=\frac{35}{16}$ and $C=0$. Therefore

$$p(x)=\frac{35}{16}\left(\frac{1}{7}x^7-\frac{3}{5}x^5+x^3-x\right)=\frac{1}{16}(5x^7-21x^5+35x^3-35x).$$

55. $a(t)=-4$, so that $v(t)=v(0)+\int_0^t a(s)\,ds=44+\int_0^t -4\,ds=44-4t$, so that $v(t)=0$ if $t=11$. Let $f(t)$ denote the position of the car at time t. Then the distance traveled by the car before coming to a stop is $f(11)-f(0)=\int_0^{11} v(t)\,dt=\int_0^{11}(44-4t)\,dt=(44t-2t^2)\big|_0^{11}=484-242=242$ (feet).

56. $T(2)-T(0)=\int_0^2(dT/dt)\,dt=\int_0^2(t^2+2t)\,dt=(\frac{1}{3}t^3+t^2)\big|_0^2=\frac{8}{3}+4=\frac{20}{3}$. Since $T(0)=60$ by assumption, $T(2)=T(0)+\frac{20}{3}=60+\frac{20}{3}=\frac{200}{3}\approx 66.7$.

57. Let H denote the average rate of heat production, so

$$H=\frac{\int_0^{1/60}(110\sin 120\pi t)^2 R\,dt}{1/60}=60(110)^2R\int_0^{1/60}\sin^2 120\pi t\,dt.$$

Let $u=120\pi t$, so that $du=120\pi\,dt$. Then

$$H=\frac{60(110)^2R}{120\pi}\int_0^{2\pi}\sin^2 u\,du=\frac{6050}{\pi}R\left(\frac{1}{2}u-\frac{1}{4}\sin 2u\right)\bigg|_0^{2\pi}=6050R.$$

58. $f'(x)=\dfrac{-5(3\ln x-2)}{(3x\ln x-5x+10)^2}$

so $f'(x_0)=0$ if $\ln x_0=\frac{2}{3}$, or $x_0\approx 1.95$ (years). Since $f'(x)>0$ for $x<x_0$ and $f'(x)<0$ for $x>x_0$, it follows that $f(x_0)$ is the maximum value of f. Thus a child learns best at approximately 1.95 years of age.

59. a. Since $dv/dm = -u_0/m$, integration yields $v = -u_0 \ln m + C$. By hypothesis, at $t = 0$ we have $v = v_0$ and $m = m_0$. Therefore $v_0 = -u_0 \ln m_0 + C$, so $C = v_0 + u_0 \ln m_0$. Consequently $v = -u_0 \ln m + (v_0 + u_0 \ln m_0) = v_0 + u_0 \ln(m_0/m)$.

b. By hypothesis, $u_0 = 3 \times 10^3$ and $v - v_0 = 3 \times 10^7$, so the equation $v = v_0 + u_0 \ln(m_0/m)$ becomes $3 \times 10^7 = (3 \times 10^3)\ln(m_0/m)$, or $10^4 = \ln(m_0/m)$. Thus $m_0/m = e^{(10^4)}$, so that $m/m_0 = e^{-(10^4)} \approx 0$.

60. $\displaystyle\int_{r_1}^{r_2} \frac{k}{r^2}\,dr = \left.\frac{-k}{r}\right|_{r_1}^{r_2} = k\left(\frac{1}{r_1} - \frac{1}{r_2}\right)$

so that the mean weight is given by

$$\frac{1}{r_2 - r_1}\int_{r_1}^{r_2} \frac{k}{r^2}\,dr = \frac{k}{r_2 - r_1}\left(\frac{1}{r_1} - \frac{1}{r_2}\right) = \frac{k}{r_1 r_2}.$$

Since $w_1 = k/r_1^2$ and $w_2 = k/r_2^2$, it follows that

$$\sqrt{w_1 w_2} = \sqrt{\frac{k}{r_1^2}\frac{k}{r_2^2}} = \frac{k}{r_1 r_2}.$$

Therefore the mean weight is $\sqrt{w_1 w_2}$.

61. $\displaystyle\int_{20}^{50} H\,dt = \int_{20}^{50} 1945\left(\frac{T}{474}\right)^3 dt = \frac{1945}{(474)^3}\int_{20}^{50} T^3\,dt = \left.\frac{1945}{4(474)^3}T^4\right|_{20}^{50}$

$\displaystyle = \frac{1945}{4(474)^3}(50^4 - 20^4) \approx 27.80621535$

Thus it takes approximately 28 joules per mole.

Cumulative Review(Chapters 1–4)

1. Since $2 + \sin x > 0$ for all x, the given inequality is equivalent to

$$-\frac{1}{(x-3)^2}\left(\frac{2-x}{4-x}\right)^{-1} < 0, \quad \text{or} \quad \frac{x-4}{(x-3)^2(2-x)} < 0.$$

From the diagram we see that the solution is the union of $(-\infty, 2)$ and $(4, \infty)$.

$x-4$	− − − − − − − − − 0 + +
$2-x$	+ + 0 − − − − − − − − −
$(x-3)^2$	+ + + + + 0 + + + + +
$\dfrac{x-4}{(x-3)^2(2-x)}$	− − + + + + 0 − −

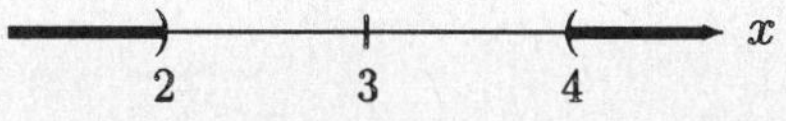

2 3 4 x

2. a. The domain of f consists of all numbers except $-\frac{2}{3}$, and the domain of g consists of all numbers except $\frac{2}{3}$. Thus the domain of $f \circ g$ consists of all x except $\frac{2}{3}$ such that $(2x-1)/(2-3x) \neq -\frac{2}{3}$. But if $(2x-1)/(2-3x) = -\frac{2}{3}$, then $6x - 3 = -4 + 6x$, or $-3 = -4$. Thus $(2x-1)/(2-3x) \neq -\frac{2}{3}$ for all x (except $\frac{2}{3}$), so the domain of $f \circ g$ consists of all numbers except $\frac{2}{3}$. The domain of $g \circ f$ consists of all x except $-\frac{2}{3}$ such that $(2x+1)/(3x+2) \neq \frac{2}{3}$. But if $(2x+1)/(3x+2) = \frac{2}{3}$, then $6x + 3 = 6x + 4$, or $3 = 4$. Thus $(2x+1)/(3x+2) \neq \frac{2}{3}$ for all x (except $-\frac{2}{3}$), so the domain of $g \circ f$ consists of all numbers except $-\frac{2}{3}$.

b. $$(f \circ g)(x) = f(g(x)) = f\left(\frac{2x-1}{2-3x}\right) = \frac{2\left(\dfrac{2x-1}{2-3x}\right)+1}{3\left(\dfrac{2x-1}{2-3x}\right)+2} = \frac{4x-2+2-3x}{6x-3+4-6x} = x$$

$$(g \circ f)(x) = g(f(x)) = g\left(\frac{2x+1}{3x+2}\right) = \frac{2\left(\dfrac{2x+1}{3x+2}\right)-1}{2-3\left(\dfrac{2x+1}{3x+2}\right)} = \frac{4x+2-3x-2}{6x+4-6x-3} = x$$

c. They are not equal since their domains are different.

3. $$\lim_{x\to\pi/2^-} \frac{\cos x}{\sin x - 1} = \lim_{x\to\pi/2^-} \left(\frac{\cos x}{\sin x - 1}\,\frac{\sin x + 1}{\sin x + 1}\right) = \lim_{x\to\pi/2^-} \frac{\cos x\,(\sin x + 1)}{\sin^2 x - 1}$$
$$= \lim_{x\to\pi/2^-} \frac{\cos x\,(\sin x + 1)}{-\cos^2 x} = \lim_{x\to\pi/2^-} \frac{\sin x + 1}{-\cos x} = -\infty$$

4. $$\lim_{x\to\infty} \frac{2x^3+3x^2-2}{-5x^3+x-9} = \lim_{x\to\infty} \frac{2+3/x-2/x^2}{-5+1/x^2-9/x^3} = -\frac{2}{5}$$

5. Let $f(x) = \tan x$, so that $f'(x) = \sec^2 x$. Then

$$\lim_{x\to\pi/4} \frac{\tan x - 1}{x - \pi/4} = \lim_{x\to\pi/4} \frac{f(x) - f(\pi/4)}{x - \pi/4} = f'\left(\frac{\pi}{4}\right) = \sec^2\left(\frac{\pi}{4}\right) = 2.$$

6. a. $\lim_{x\to 0} f(x) = \lim_{x\to 0} \sqrt{\dfrac{x^2(1+x)}{1-x}} = \lim_{x\to 0} |x| \sqrt{\dfrac{1+x}{1-x}} = 0\sqrt{\dfrac{1+0}{1-0}} = 0 = f(0)$,
so f is continuous at 0.

b. $\lim_{x\to 0} \dfrac{f(x)-f(0)}{x-0} = \lim_{x\to 0} \dfrac{\sqrt{[x^2(1+x)]/(1-x)} - 0}{x-0} = \lim_{x\to 0} \dfrac{|x|}{x}\sqrt{\dfrac{1+x}{1-x}}$
Since $\lim_{x\to 0} \sqrt{(1+x)/(1-x)} = 1$ and $\lim_{x\to 0} |x|/x$ does not exist, it follows that

$$\lim_{x\to 0} \frac{|x|}{x}\sqrt{\frac{1+x}{1-x}}$$

does not exist. Thus f is not differentiable at 0.

7. $f'(x) = e^{1/(x^2+1)} \left[\dfrac{-2x}{(x^2+1)^2}\right]$

8. Substituting 0 for x in $x^2+2x+y^2-4y=0$, we find that $y^2-4y=0$, so that $y=0$ or $y=4$. Thus the point on the circle lying on the positive y axis is $(0,4)$. Differentiating the equation $x^2+2x+y^2-4y=0$ with respect to x, we deduce that $2x+2+2y(dy/dx)-4(dy/dx)=0$. Substituting 0 for x and 4 for y, we find that $0+2+8(dy/dx)-4(dy/dx)=0$, so that $dy/dx=-\frac{1}{2}$ at $(0,4)$. Thus the slope of the line tangent at the point on the circle lying on the positive y axis is $-\frac{1}{2}$.

9. $f'(x)=6x^2-18x+14=6\left(x-\frac{3}{2}\right)^2+\frac{1}{2}>0$ for all x, so f is increasing.

10. Let $f(x)=x^{15}+x^9+100x-9$. Since $f(0)=-9<0$ and $f(1)=93>0$, the Intermediate Value Theorem implies that f has a zero in $(0,1)$. However, $f'(x)=15x^{14}+9x^8+100>0$ for all x, so f is increasing. Thus f has exactly one real zero. Equivalently, the equation $x^{15}+x^9+100x-9=0$ has exactly one real solution.

11. Since $f'(x)=c+3/x^4$, the equations $f(x)=0$ and $f'(x)=0$ become $cx-1/x^3-\frac{1}{2}=0$ and $c+3/x^4=0$. From the second of these we conclude that $cx=-3/x^3$, so the first becomes $-3/x^3-1/x^3-\frac{1}{2}=0$, or $x^3=-8$, or $x=-2$. Since $cx=-3/x^3$, this implies that $c=-3/(-2)^4=-\frac{3}{16}$. Thus if $c=-\frac{3}{16}$, then the equations $f(x)=0$ and $f'(x)=0$ have the same root, namely -2.

12. Since f is differentiable, so is $2f$. Since $f'=2f$, this means that f' is differentiable, so that $f''(x)$ exists for all x. Differentiating both sides of the equation $f'(x)=2f(x)$, we find that $f''(x)=2f'(x)=2(2f(x))=4f(x)$.

13.

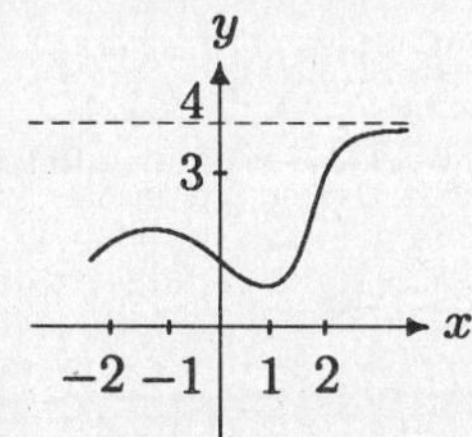

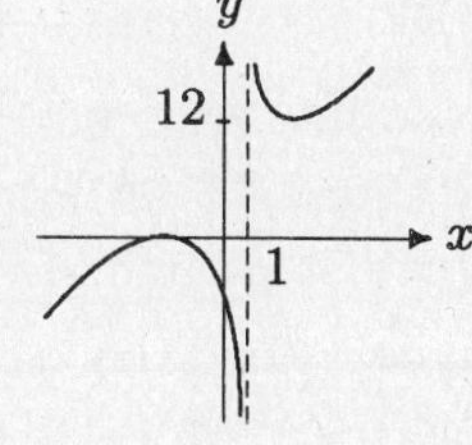

14. $f'(x)=\dfrac{x^2-2x-8}{(x-1)^2}$; $f''(x)=\dfrac{18}{(x-1)^3}$
relative maximum value is $f(-2)=0$; relative minimum value is $f(4)=12$; increasing on $(-\infty,-2]$ and $[4,\infty)$, and decreasing on $[-2,1)$ and $(1,4]$; concave upward on $(1,\infty)$ and concave downward on $(-\infty,1)$; vertical asymptote is $x=1$.

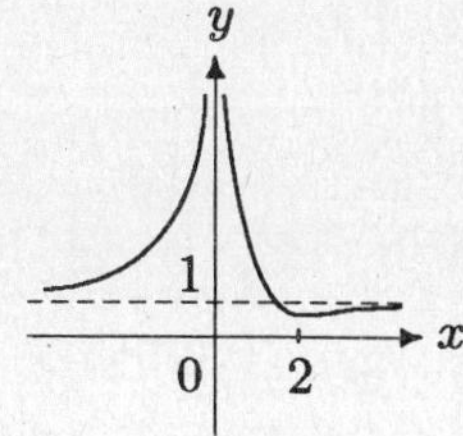

15. $f'(x)=\dfrac{1}{x^2}-\dfrac{2}{x^3}$; $f''(x)=-\dfrac{2}{x^3}+\dfrac{6}{x^4}$
relative minimum value is $f(2)=\frac{3}{4}$; increasing on $(-\infty,0)$ and $[2,\infty)$, and decreasing on $(0,2]$; concave upward on $(-\infty,0)$ and $(0,3)$, and concave downward on $(3,\infty)$; inflection point is $(3,\frac{7}{9})$; vertical asymptote is $x=0$; horizontal asymptote is $y=1$.

16. The surface area S is given by $S = 4\pi r^2$. Differentiating implicitly and using the given information that $dS/dt = -1$, we find that $-1 = dS/dt = 8\pi r(dr/dt)$. When the surface area equals the volume we have $4\pi r^2 = \frac{4}{3}\pi r^3$, so $r = 3$. At that instant, $-1 = 8\pi(3)(dr/dt)$, so $dr/dt = -1/24\pi$ (inch per second).

17. The height of the pot t seconds after it is dropped is given by $h(t) = -16t^2 + h_0$. Let t^* be such that $h(t^*) = 128$. Then the velocity at $t = t^*$ is -32, so $-32t^* = -32$, or $t^* = 1$. Therefore $128 = h(1) = -16(1)^2 + h_0$, so $h_0 = 128 + 16 = 144$. Consequently $h(t) = -16t^2 + 144$.

    a. One second later $t = 2$, and $v(2) = -32(2) = -64$ (feet per second).

    b. The pot hits the ground at t such that $h(t) = 0$. Now $0 = h(t) = -16t^2 + 144$, so that $t = 3$. Since the pot is 128 feet above the ground when $t = 1$, it takes 2 additional seconds for the pot to fall the last 128 feet to the ground.

18. Differentiating the given equation implicitly, we find that

$$3a^2\frac{da}{dt} = 14v\frac{dv}{dt} + \frac{dv}{dt} = (14v + 1)a.$$

When $v = 1$, we have $a^3 = 7 \cdot 1^2 + 1 = 8$, so that $a = 2$. Then $3 \cdot 2^2(da/dt) = (14 \cdot 1 + 1)2$, so that $da/dt = \frac{5}{2}$ when $v = 1$.

19. From the given information it follows that if the toll is set at $3+x$ dollars, then the number of cars using the toll road per day would be $24{,}000 - (20x)300 = 24{,}000 - 6000x$. Thus the total revenue R would be given by $R = (24{,}000 - 6000x)(x+3) = -6000x^2 + 6000x + 72{,}000$. Then $R'(x) = -12{,}000x + 6000 = 0$ for $x = \frac{1}{2}$. Since $R''(x) = -12{,}000 < 0$, the revenue is maximized for $x = \frac{1}{2}$, which means that the toll would be \$3.50.

20. Using the notation in the figure, we have $y/(2-x) = \frac{6}{2} = 3$, so $y = 6-3x$. Thus the area A of the rectangle is given by

$$A = xy = x(6 - 3x) = 6x - 3x^2.$$

Then $A'(x) = 6 - 6x = 0$ for $x = 1$. Since $A''(x) = -6 < 0$, the area is maximized for $x = 1$. The corresponding value of y is $6 - 3(1) = 3$. Thus the dimensions that maximize the area are 1 and 3 inches.

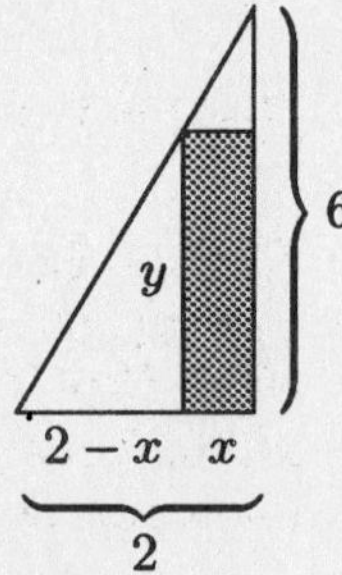

21. We need to find $d\theta/dt$ at the moment that $\varphi = \pi/4$. By Snell's Law, $\sin\theta = \mu\sin\varphi$, so that $(\cos\theta)(d\theta/dt) = (\mu\cos\varphi)(d\varphi/dt)$. Now when $\varphi = \pi/4$, Snell's Law with $\mu = 1.33$ yields $\sin\theta = 1.33\sin(\pi/4) = 1.33\sqrt{2}/2$. Letting $\varphi = \pi/4$, $\mu = 1.33$ and $d\varphi/dt = -\frac{1}{10}$, we obtain

$$\frac{d\theta}{dt} = \frac{\mu\cos\varphi}{\cos\theta}\frac{d\varphi}{dt} = \frac{1.33\cos(\pi/4)}{\sqrt{1-\sin^2\theta}}\left(-\frac{1}{10}\right) = \frac{1.33\sqrt{2}/2}{\sqrt{1-(1.33\sqrt{2}/2)^2}}\left(-\frac{1}{10}\right) \approx -0.2766633735.$$

Since 0.2766633735 radians is approximately 15.9 degrees, the angle of incidence is changing at approximately 15.9 degrees per second.

Chapter 6

Inverse Functions

6.1 Inverse Functions

1. $f'(x) = 5x^4 \geq 0$, and $f'(x) > 0$ for $x \neq 0$, so f has an inverse. Domain of f^{-1}: $(-\infty, \infty)$; range of f^{-1}: $(-\infty, \infty)$.

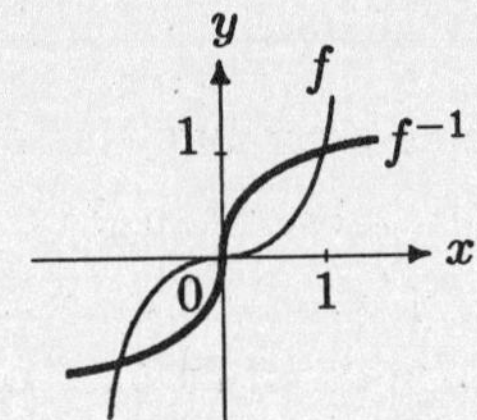

2. $f'(x) = 35x^6 + 12x^2 \geq 0$, and $f'(x) > 0$ for $x \neq 0$, so f has an inverse. Domain of f^{-1}: $(-\infty, \infty)$; range of f^{-1}: $(-\infty, \infty)$.

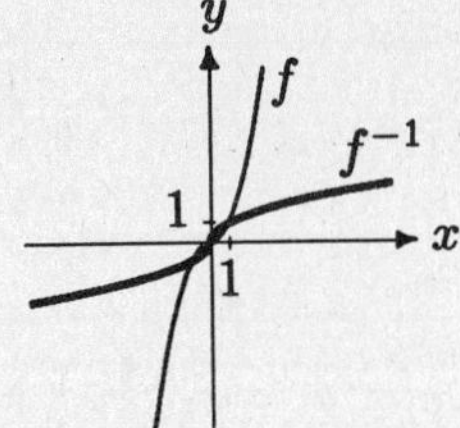

3. $f(-x) = f(x)$ for all x, so f does not have an inverse.

4. $f'(x) = \frac{4}{5}x^{-4/5} > 0$ for $x \neq 0$, so f is increasing on $(-\infty, 0]$ and on $[0, \infty)$. Moreover, $f(x) < 0$ for $x < 0$ and $f(x) > 0$ for $x > 0$. Thus f has an inverse. Domain of f^{-1}: $(-\infty, \infty)$; range of f^{-1}: $(-\infty, \infty)$.

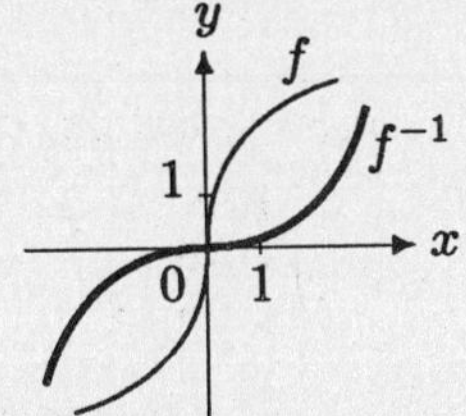

5. $f'(t) = -\frac{1}{2}(4-t)^{-1/2} < 0$ for $t < 4$, so f has an inverse. Domain of f^{-1}: $[0, \infty)$; range of f^{-1}: $(-\infty, 4]$.

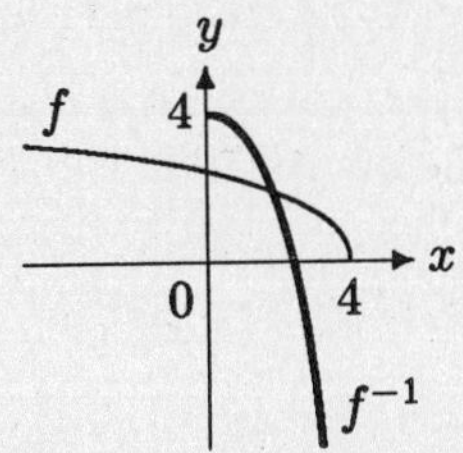

6. $f(-t) = f(t)$ for $-1 \leq t \leq 1$, so f does not have an inverse.

7. $f(x) = 0$ for $x \leq 0$, so f does not have an inverse.

8. $f'(x) = 1 + \cos x \geq 0$, and $f'(x) > 0$ for $x \neq (2n+1)\pi$ for any integer n. Thus f is increasing on any bounded interval and hence on $(-\infty, \infty)$. Therefore f has an inverse. Domain of f^{-1}: $(-\infty, \infty)$; range of f^{-1}: $(-\infty, \infty)$.

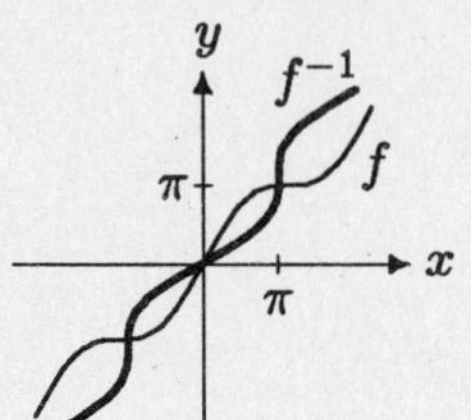

9. $f'(x) = 1 - \cos x \geq 0$, and $f'(x) > 0$ for $x \neq 2n\pi$ for any integer n. Thus f is increasing on any bounded interval and hence on $(-\infty, \infty)$. Therefore f has an inverse. Domain of f^{-1}: $(-\infty, \infty)$; range of f^{-1}: $(-\infty, \infty)$.

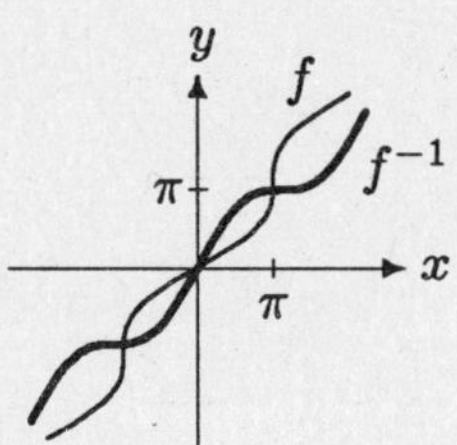

10. $f(-n\pi) = f(n\pi)$ for every integer n, so f does not have an inverse.

11. $f(n\pi) = 0$ for every integer n, so f does not have an inverse.

12. $f'(z) = \sec^2 z > 0$ for $-\pi/2 < z < \pi/2$, so f has an inverse. Domain of f^{-1}: $(-\pi/2, \pi/2)$; range of f^{-1}: $(-\pi/2, \pi/2)$.

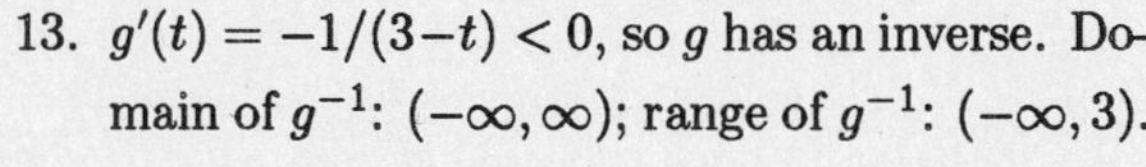
13. $g'(t) = -1/(3-t) < 0$, so g has an inverse. Domain of g^{-1}: $(-\infty, \infty)$; range of g^{-1}: $(-\infty, 3)$.

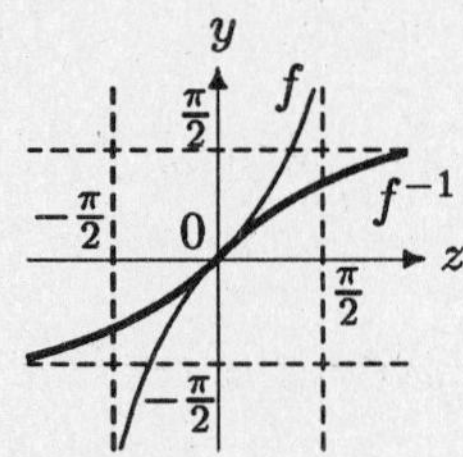

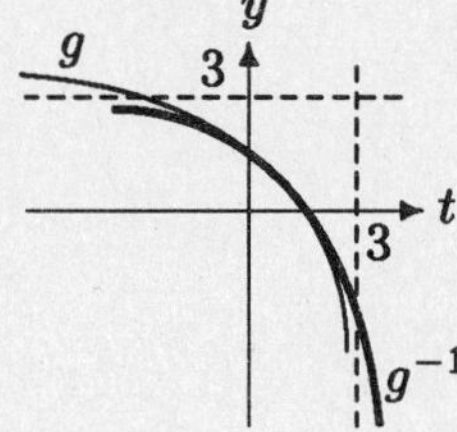

14. $g(-t) = g(t)$ for all $t \neq 0$, so g does not have an inverse.

15. f has no inverse.

16. f has an inverse.

17. f has an inverse.

18. f has no inverse.

19. k is the inverse of f; h is the inverse of g.

20.

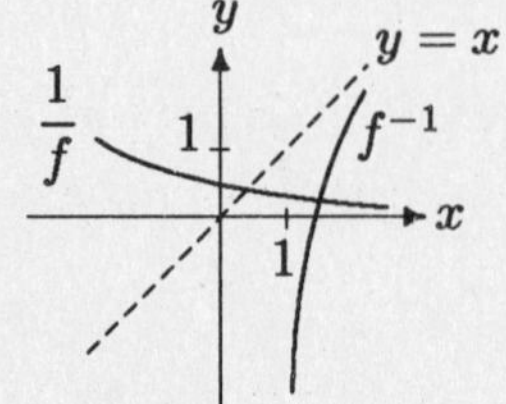

21. Let x_0 be any number in the domain of f. Then $f(a+x_0) = f(x_0)$, but $a+x_0 \neq x_0$ since $a \neq 0$. Thus f does not satisfy (3) and hence does not have an inverse.

22. $f(2\pi + x) = f(x)$ for all x, so f does not have an inverse by Exercise 21.

23. $f(\pi + x) = f(x)$ for all x in the domain of f, so f does not have an inverse by Exercise 21.

24. $f(x+1) = f(x)$ for all x, so f does not have an inverse by Exercise 21.

25. $y = -4x^3 - 1$; $x^3 = \dfrac{y+1}{-4}$; $x = -\sqrt[3]{\dfrac{y+1}{4}}$, so $f^{-1}(x) = -\sqrt[3]{\dfrac{x+1}{4}}$.

26. $y = -2x^5 + \dfrac{9}{4}$; $x^5 = \dfrac{1}{2}\left(\dfrac{9}{4} - y\right)$; $x = \sqrt[5]{\dfrac{9}{8} - \dfrac{y}{2}}$, so $f^{-1}(x) = \sqrt[5]{\dfrac{9}{8} - \dfrac{x}{2}}$.

27. $y = \sqrt{1+x}$; $y^2 = 1+x$; $x = y^2 - 1$, so $g^{-1}(x) = x^2 - 1$ for $x \geq 0$.

28. $y = \sqrt{3-2t}$; $y^2 = 3 - 2t$; $t = \dfrac{3-y^2}{2}$, so $g^{-1}(t) = \dfrac{3-t^2}{2}$ for $t \geq 0$.

29. $y = \dfrac{t-1}{t+1}$; $y(t+1) = t-1$; $t(y-1) = -1-y$; $t = \dfrac{y+1}{1-y}$, so $k^{-1}(t) = \dfrac{t+1}{1-t}$.

30. $y = \dfrac{3t+5}{t-4}$; $y(t-4) = 3t+5$; $t(y-3) = 5+4y$; $t = \dfrac{5+4y}{y-3}$, so $k^{-1}(t) = \dfrac{5+4t}{t-3}$.

31. $f'(x) = 2x$. Since $f'(x) > 0$ for $x > 0$, f has an inverse on $[0, \infty)$. Since $f'(x) < 0$ for $x < 0$, f has an inverse on $(-\infty, 0]$.

32. $f'(x) = 2x - 3$. Since $f'(x) > 0$ for $x > \frac{3}{2}$, f has an inverse on $[\frac{3}{2}, \infty)$. Since $f'(x) < 0$ for $x < \frac{3}{2}$, f has an inverse on $(-\infty, \frac{3}{2}]$.

33. $f'(x) = 3x^2 - 5$. Since $f'(x) > 0$ for $x > \sqrt{\frac{5}{3}}$, f has an inverse on $[\sqrt{\frac{5}{3}}, \infty)$. Since $f'(x) > 0$ for $x < -\sqrt{\frac{5}{3}}$, f has an inverse on $(-\infty, -\sqrt{\frac{5}{3}}]$. Since $f'(x) < 0$ for $-\sqrt{\frac{5}{3}} < x < \sqrt{\frac{5}{3}}$, f has an inverse on $[-\sqrt{\frac{5}{3}}, \sqrt{\frac{5}{3}}]$.

34. $f'(x) = 3x^2 + 5$. Since $f'(x) > 0$ for all x, f has an inverse on $(-\infty, \infty)$.

35. $f'(x) = -2x/(1+x^2)^2$. Since $f'(x) > 0$ for $x < 0$, f has an inverse on $(-\infty, 0]$. Since $f'(x) < 0$ for $x > 0$, f has an inverse on $[0, \infty)$.

36. $f'(x) = (1-x^2)/(1+x^2)^2$. Since $f'(x) > 0$ for $-1 < x < 1$, f has an inverse on $[-1, 1]$. Since $f'(x) < 0$ for $x < -1$ and for $x > 1$, f has an inverse on $(-\infty, -1]$ and f has an inverse on $[1, \infty)$.

37. $f'(x) = -\sin x$. If n is any integer, then $f'(x) < 0$ for $2n\pi < x < (2n+1)\pi$, and $f'(x) > 0$ for $(2n+1)\pi < x < (2n+2)\pi$. Thus f has an inverse on any interval of the form $[n\pi, (n+1)\pi]$, where n is an integer.

38. $f'(x) = \sec^2 x$ for $x \neq \pi/2 + n\pi$ for any integer n. Since $f'(x) > 0$ for $\pi/2 + n\pi < x < \pi/2 + (n+1)\pi$, f has an inverse on any interval of the form $(\pi/2 + n\pi, \pi/2 + (n+1)\pi)$, where n is an integer.

39. $f'(x) = 2\sin x \cos x = \sin 2x$. If n is any integer, then $f'(x) > 0$ for $n\pi < x < n\pi + \pi/2$, and $f'(x) < 0$ for $n\pi + \pi/2 < x < (n+1)\pi$. Thus f has an inverse on any interval of the form $[n\pi/2, (n+1)\pi/2]$, where n is an integer.

40. $f'(x) = \sec x \tan x = (\sin x)/(\cos^2 x)$. If n is any integer, then $f'(x) > 0$ for $2n\pi < x < 2n\pi + \pi/2$ and for $2n\pi + \pi/2 < x < (2n+1)\pi$, and $f'(x) < 0$ for $(2n+1)\pi < x < (2n+1)\pi + \pi/2$ and for $(2n+1)\pi + \pi/2 < x < (2n+2)\pi$. Thus f has an inverse on any interval of the form $[n\pi, n\pi + \pi/2)$ or of the form $(n\pi + \pi/2, (n+1)\pi]$, where n is an integer.

41. $f(-1) = 6$. Since $f'(x) = 3x^2$, we have $f'(-1) = 3$. Thus $(f^{-1})'(6) = 1/[f'(-1)] = \frac{1}{3}$.

42. $f(1) = 9$. Since $f'(x) = 25x^4 + 12x^2$, we have $f'(1) = 37$. Thus $(f^{-1})'(9) = 1/[f'(1)] = \frac{1}{37}$.

43. $f(0) = 0$. Since $f'(x) = 1 + \cos x$, we have $f'(0) = 2$. Thus $(f^{-1})'(0) = 1/[f'(0)] = \frac{1}{2}$.

44. $f(1) = 2$. Since $f'(x) = 1 + \frac{1}{2}x^{-1/2}$, we have $f'(1) = \frac{3}{2}$. Thus $(f^{-1})'(2) = 1/[f'(1)] = \frac{2}{3}$.

45. $f(1) = 0$. Since $f'(x) = 4/x$, we have $f'(1) = 4$. Thus $(f^{-1})'(0) = 1/[f'(1)] = \frac{1}{4}$.

46. $f(\pi/3) = \sqrt{3}$. Since $f'(x) = \sec^2 x$, we have $f'(\pi/3) = 4$. Thus $(f^{-1})'(\sqrt{3}) = 1/[f'(\pi/3)] = \frac{1}{4}$.

47. $f(-1) = -2$. Since $f'(t) = 3 + 3/t^4$, we have $f'(-1) = 6$. Thus $(f^{-1})'(-2) = 1/[f'(-1)] = \frac{1}{6}$.

48. $f(e^2) = e^2 \ln(e^2) = 2e^2$. Since $f'(t) = \ln t + t \cdot 1/t = 1 + \ln t$, we have $f'(e^2) = 1 + \ln(e^2) = 1 + 2 = 3$. Thus $(f^{-1})'(2e^2) = 1/[f'(e^2)] = \frac{1}{3}$.

49. $\dfrac{dx}{dy} = \dfrac{1}{dy/dx} = \dfrac{1}{9x^8 + 7}$.

50. $\dfrac{dx}{dy} = \dfrac{1}{dy/dx} = \dfrac{1}{1 + 2/x^2} = \dfrac{x^2}{x^2 + 2}$ for $x < 0$.

51. $\dfrac{dx}{dy} = \dfrac{1}{dy/dx} = \dfrac{1}{[1/(x^3+1)]3x^2} = \dfrac{x^3 + 1}{3x^2}$

52. $\dfrac{dx}{dy} = \dfrac{1}{dy/dx} = \dfrac{1}{1 - \sin x}$

53. $\dfrac{dx}{dy} = \dfrac{1}{dy/dx} = \dfrac{1}{\cos x}$ for $-\dfrac{\pi}{2} < x < \dfrac{\pi}{2}$

54. $\dfrac{dx}{dy} = \dfrac{1}{dy/dx} = \dfrac{1}{\sec^2 x}$ for $-\dfrac{\pi}{2} < x < \dfrac{\pi}{2}$

55. We apply the criterion that follows Theorem 6.3. Since $f'(x) > 0$ for all x in $(4, 6)$ or in $(8, 9)$, f has an inverse on $[4, 6]$ and on $[8, 9]$. Since $f'(x) < 0$ for all x in $(1, 4)$ or in $(6, 8)$, f has an inverse on $[1, 4]$ and on $[6, 8]$.

56. We apply the criterion that follows Theorem 6.3. Since $f'(0) = -1$, $f'(3) = 0$, and f' is increasing on $[0,4]$, we know that $f'(x) < 0$ for all x in $(0,3)$. Thus f has an inverse on $[0,3]$. Since $f'(3) = 0$, $f'(4) = 2$, and $f'(5) = 0$, and since f' is increasing on $[0,4]$ and decreasing on $[4,6]$, it follows that $f'(x) > 0$ for $3 < x < 5$ and $f'(x) < 0$ for $5 < x < 6$. Therefore f has an inverse on $[3,5]$ and on $[5,6]$.

57. a. By Theorem 5.12, $f'(x) = \sqrt{1+x^4} > 0$ for all x, so f has an inverse.

b. Since $f'(x) = \sqrt{1+x^4}$, we have $f'(1) = \sqrt{2}$. Thus $(f^{-1})'(c) = 1/[f'(1)] = 1/\sqrt{2} = \sqrt{2}/2$.

58. a. Using Theorem 5.12, we have $f'(x) = \left[\sin^6((x^3)^2)\right](3x^2) = 3x^2\sin^6(x^6) \geq 0$ for all x. Also $f'(x) = 0$ only for $x = \sqrt[6]{n\pi}$ for any integer n. It follows from the criterion following Theorem 6.3 that f has an inverse.

b. Using (8) and the derivative in part (a), we have

$$(f^{-1})'(c) = \frac{1}{f'(\sqrt[6]{\pi/6})} = \frac{1}{3(\sqrt[6]{\pi/6})^2\sin^6((\sqrt[6]{\pi/6})^6)} = \frac{1}{3\sqrt[3]{\pi/6}\sin^6(\pi/6)} = \frac{64}{3\sqrt[3]{\pi/6}}.$$

59. By Definition 6.1, the range of f is the same as the domain of f^{-1}. If $f = f^{-1}$, then the domain of f^{-1} is the same as the domain of f. Therefore if $f = f^{-1}$, then the range of f is the same as the domain of f.

60. a. $y = x$; $x = y$, so $f^{-1}(x) = x = f(x)$.

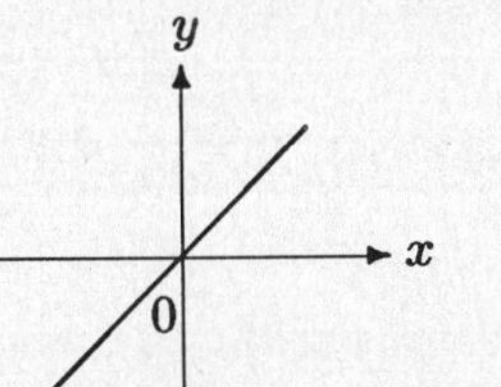

b. $y = -x$; $x = -y$, so $f^{-1}(x) = -x = f(x)$.

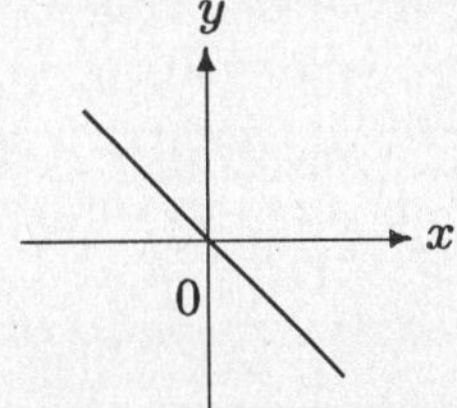

c. $y = \dfrac{1}{x}$; $x = \dfrac{1}{y}$, so $f^{-1}(x) = \dfrac{1}{x} = f(x)$.

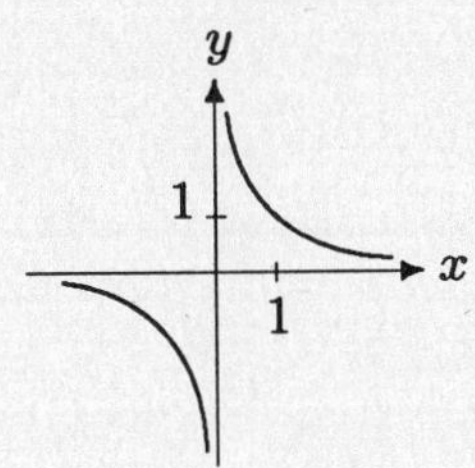

d. $y = \sqrt{1-x^2}$; $y^2 = 1 - x^2$; $x^2 = 1 - y^2$; $x = \sqrt{1-y^2}$, so $f^{-1}(x) = \sqrt{1-x^2} = f(x)$ for $0 \leq x \leq 1$.

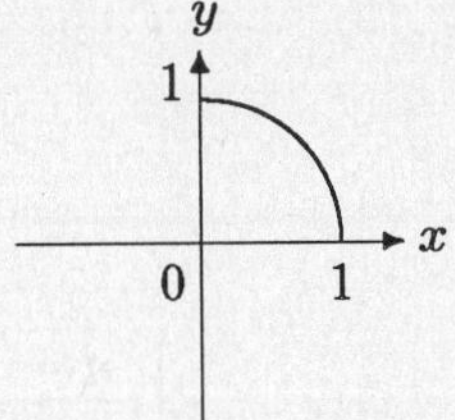

61. a. If f is a polynomial of even degree, then $f(-x) = f(x)$ for all x, so f cannot have an inverse.

b. If f is a polynomial of odd degree, then f can have an inverse. An example is given by $f(x) = x^3 + 5x$.

62. a. The graph of f^{-1} lies in the first quadrant.

b. The graph of f^{-1} lies in the fourth quadrant.

63. Let $y = (g \circ f)(x)$. Then

$$(f^{-1} \circ g^{-1})(y) = (f^{-1} \circ g^{-1})((g \circ f)(x)) = f^{-1}\Big(g^{-1}\big(g(f(x))\big)\Big) = f^{-1}(f(x)) = x.$$

Let $x = (f^{-1} \circ g^{-1})(y)$. Then

$$(g \circ f)(x) = (g \circ f)(f^{-1} \circ g^{-1})(y) = g\Big(f\big(f^{-1}(g^{-1}(y))\big)\Big) = g(g^{-1}(y)) = y.$$

Thus $g \circ f$ has an inverse, and $(g \circ f)^{-1} = f^{-1} \circ g^{-1}$ by Definition 6.1.

64. a. Let $f(x) = (x-1)/(x+1)$ and $g(x) = x^5$. Then $k = g \circ f$. By Exercise 1, g has an inverse, and by Exercise 29, f has an inverse. Thus by Exercise 63, $k = g \circ f$ has an inverse.

b. Let $f(x) = (x-1)/(x+1)$ and $g(x) = \ln x$. Then $k = g \circ f$. By (7), g has an inverse, and by Exercise 29, f has an inverse. Thus by Exercise 63, $k = g \circ f$ has an inverse.

c. Let $f(x) = \ln x$ and $g(x) = (x-1)/(x+1)$. Then $k = g \circ f$. By (7), f has an inverse, and by Exercise 29, g has an inverse. Thus by Exercise 63, $k = g \circ f$ has an inverse.

65. Since f^{-1} exists, Exercise 63 says that $g \circ f$ has an inverse, and since $f^{-1}(x) = -x$, we find that

$$(g \circ f)^{-1}(x) = (f^{-1} \circ g^{-1})(x) = f^{-1}(g^{-1}(x)) = -g^{-1}(x).$$

66. a. Let f be increasing. If f^{-1} were not increasing, then there would be x and z in the domain of f^{-1} with $x < z$ and $f^{-1}(x) \geq f^{-1}(z)$. From the latter inequality and the fact that f is increasing it follows that $x = f(f^{-1}(x)) \geq f(f^{-1}(z)) = z$, which contradicts the fact that $x < z$. Therefore f^{-1} is increasing.

b. Let f be decreasing. If f^{-1} were not decreasing, then there would be x and z in the domain of f^{-1} with $x < z$ and $f^{-1}(x) \leq f^{-1}(z)$. From the latter inequality and the fact that f is decreasing it follows that $x = f(f^{-1}(x)) \geq f(f^{-1}(z)) = z$, which contradicts the fact that $x < z$. Therefore f^{-1} is decreasing.

67. Let $k(x) = f^{-1}(x) - a$. Then $g\big(k(x)\big) = f\big((f^{-1}(x) - a) + a\big) = f\big(f^{-1}(x)\big) = x$, and $k\big(g(x)\big) = f^{-1}\big(f(x) + a)\big) - a = x + a - a = x$. Thus g has an inverse, and $g^{-1}(x) = k(x) = f^{-1}(x) - a$.

68. Let $k(x) = (1/a)f^{-1}(x)$. Then $g\big(k(x)\big) = f\big(a((1/a)f^{-1}(x))\big) = f\big(f^{-1}(x)\big) = x$, and $k\big(g(x)\big) = (1/a)f^{-1}\big(f(ax)\big) = (1/a)(ax) = x$. Thus g has an inverse, and $g^{-1}(x) = k(x) = (1/a)f^{-1}(x)$.

69. $\left.\dfrac{dy}{dx}\right|_{x=2} = 12$ and $\left.\dfrac{dx}{dy}\right|_{y=8} = \dfrac{1}{12} = \dfrac{1}{(dy/dx)|_{x=2}}$ but $\left.\dfrac{dx}{dy}\right|_{y=2} = \dfrac{1}{3(2)^{2/3}} \neq \dfrac{1}{12} = \dfrac{1}{(dy/dx)|_{x=2}}$.

70. If f^{-1} were differentiable at $f(a)$, then differentiating the equation $f^{-1}\big(f(x)\big) = x$ implicitly by the Chain Rule would yield $\big[(f^{-1})'(f(x))\big]f'(x) = 1$. Letting $x = a$, we would obtain $\big[(f^{-1})'(f(a))\big]f'(a) = 1$. But this cannot be, since $f'(a) = 0$ by assumption. Thus f^{-1} is not differentiable at $f(a)$.

71. a. $f(\pi) = \pi$, $f'(x) = 1 + \cos x$, and $f'(\pi) = 1 - 1 = 0$. By Exercise 70, $(f^{-1})(\pi)$ does not exist.

b. $f(0) = -4$, $f'(x) = 5x^4 + 3x^2$, and $f'(0) = 5 \cdot 0 + 3 \cdot 0 = 0$. By Exercise 70, $(f^{-1})'(-4)$ does not exist.

72. a. Notice that the combined area of R_1 and R_2 is $bf(b) - af(a)$, which is the area of the outer rectangle minus that of the inner rectangle. Thus $A_1 + A_2 = bf(b) - af(a)$.

b. Observe that R_1 is the region between the graph of f and the x axis on $[a, b]$, so $A_1 =$ area of $R_1 = \int_a^b f(x)\,dx$. Likewise, R_2 is the region between the graph of f^{-1} and the y axis on $[f(a), f(b)]$, so $A_2 =$ area of $R_2 = \int_{f(a)}^{f(b)} f^{-1}(y)\,dy$. Using the result of part (a), we conclude that

$$\int_a^b f(x)\,dx + \int_{f(a)}^{f(b)} f^{-1}(y)\,dy = A_1 + A_2 = bf(b) - af(a).$$

73. Let $f(x) = \left[(x-1)^{1/3} + 1\right]^{1/2}$. If $y = f(x)$, then $y^2 = (x-1)^{1/3} + 1$, so $x = (y^2 - 1)^3 + 1$. Thus f^{-1} exists, and $f^{-1}(y) = (y^2 - 1)^3 + 1$. Now we use Exercise 72(b), with $a = 0$ and $b = 1$. Since $f(0) = 0$ and $f(1) = 1$, we obtain

$$\int_0^1 \left[(x-1)^{1/3} + 1\right]^{1/2} dx = \int_0^1 f(x)\,dx = 1f(1) - 0f(0) - \int_0^1 f^{-1}(y)\,dy$$

$$= 1 - \int_0^1 [(y^2-1)^3 + 1]\,dy = 1 - \int_0^1 (y^6 - 3y^4 + 3y^2)\,dy = 1 - \left(\frac{1}{7}y^7 - \frac{3}{5}y^5 + y^3\right)\Big|_0^1 = \frac{16}{35}.$$

74. a. $f'(x) = -\frac{1}{2}x^{-1/2}$ and $f''(x) = \frac{1}{4}x^{-3/2}$ for $x > 0$. Thus the graph of f is concave upward on the domain of f. Since $f^{-1}(x) = x^2$ for $x < 0$, $(f^{-1})'(x) = 2x$ and $(f^{-1})''(x) = 2$ for $x < 0$. Thus the graph of f^{-1} is concave upward on the domain of f^{-1}.

b. $f'(x) = \frac{1}{2}x^{-1/2}$ and $f''(x) = -\frac{1}{4}x^{-3/2}$ for $x > 0$. Thus the graph of f is concave downward on $(0, \infty)$. Since $f^{-1}(x) = x^2$ for $x > 0$, we have $(f^{-1})'(x) = 2x$ and $(f^{-1})''(x) = 2$ for $x > 0$. Thus the graph of f^{-1} is concave upward on $(0, \infty)$.

75. From (8) with $a = f^{-1}(x)$ and $c = x$, we have

$$(f^{-1})'(x) = \frac{1}{f'(f^{-1}(x))}.$$

Differentiating both sides of this equation, we obtain

$$(f^{-1})''(x) = \frac{-f''(f^{-1}(x)) \cdot (f^{-1})'(x)}{\left[f'(f^{-1}(x))\right]^2} = \frac{-f''(f^{-1}(x))}{\left[f'(f^{-1}(x))\right]^2} \cdot \frac{1}{f'(f^{-1}(x))} = \frac{-f''(f^{-1}(x))}{\left[f'(f^{-1}(x))\right]^3}.$$

76. a. If f is increasing on I and the graph of f is concave downward on I, then for any x in the domain of f^{-1} we have $f'(f^{-1}(x)) > 0$ and $f''(f^{-1}(x)) < 0$, so that by Exercise 75,

$$(f^{-1})''(x) = \frac{-f''(f^{-1}(x))}{\left[f'(f^{-1}(x))\right]^3} > 0$$

which implies that the graph of f^{-1} is concave upward on its domain. If f is increasing and the graph of f is concave upward on I, then for any x in the domain of f^{-1} we have $f'(f^{-1}(x)) > 0$ and $f''(f^{-1}(x)) > 0$, so that by Exercise 75,

$$(f^{-1})''(x) = \frac{-f''(f^{-1}(x))}{[f'(f^{-1}(x))]^3} < 0$$

which implies that the graph of f^{-1} is concave downward on its domain.

b. The solution is analogous to the solution of part (a). However, in this case, $f'(f^{-1}(x)) < 0$ for all x in the domain of f^{-1}.

c. By (a) and (b), the graph of f^{-1} is concave upward on one side and concave downward on the other side of $f(a)$. Thus the graph of f^{-1} has an inflection point at $f(a)$.

77. For $x \geq 0$ and $y \geq 0$ we have

$$y = 2.54x \quad \text{if and only if} \quad x = \frac{1}{2.54}y.$$

Thus $y = f(x)$ if and only if $x = g(y)$. Therefore f and g are inverses of one another.

78. For $v \geq 0$ and $m \geq m_0$ we have

$$m = \frac{m_0}{\sqrt{1 - \dfrac{v^2}{c^2}}} \quad \text{if and only if} \quad m^2\left(1 - \frac{v^2}{c^2}\right) = m_0^2$$

$$\text{if and only if} \quad \frac{m^2v^2}{c^2} = m^2 - m_0^2$$

$$\text{if and only if} \quad \frac{v^2}{c^2} = 1 - \frac{m_0^2}{m^2}$$

$$\text{if and only if} \quad v = c\sqrt{1 - \frac{m_0^2}{m^2}}.$$

Thus $m = f(v)$ if and only if $v = g(m)$. Therefore f and g are inverses of one another.

6.2 The Natural Exponential Function

1. $f'(x) = \dfrac{1}{e^x + e^{-x}}(e^x - e^{-x}) = \dfrac{e^x - e^{-x}}{e^x + e^{-x}}$

2. $f'(x) = 1 \cdot e^{-x} + (x+1)(-e^{-x}) = -xe^{-x}$

3. $\dfrac{dy}{dx} = \dfrac{e^x(e^x - 1) - (e^x + 1)(e^x)}{(e^x - 1)^2} = \dfrac{-2e^x}{(e^x - 1)^2}$

4. $\dfrac{dy}{dx} = (2e^{2x})(\ln x) + (e^{2x})\left(\dfrac{1}{x}\right) = e^{2x}\left(2\ln x + \dfrac{1}{x}\right)$

5. $2xe^y + x^2e^y \dfrac{dy}{dx} = \dfrac{1}{xy}\left(y + x\dfrac{dy}{dx}\right)$, so $\left(x^2e^y - \dfrac{1}{y}\right)\dfrac{dy}{dx} = \dfrac{1}{x} - 2xe^y$ and thus

$$\frac{dy}{dx} = \frac{1/x - 2xe^y}{x^2e^y - 1/y} = \frac{y - 2x^2ye^y}{x^3ye^y - x}.$$

6. Using (7), we have $e^{xy}\left(y + x\dfrac{dy}{dx}\right) = 2y\dfrac{dy}{dx} - 1$, and thus $\dfrac{dy}{dx} = \dfrac{ye^{xy}+1}{2y - xe^{xy}}$.

7. a. $f(x) = e^x \sin x$; $f'(x) = e^x(\sin x + \cos x)$; $f''(x) = e^x(\sin x + \cos x) + e^x(\cos x - \sin x) = 2e^x \cos x$; $f^{(3)}(x) = 2e^x \cos x - 2e^x \sin x = 2e^x(\cos x - \sin x)$; $f^{(4)}(x) = 2e^x(\cos x - \sin x) + 2e^x(-\sin x - \cos x) = -4e^x \sin x = -4f(x)$. Thus $f^{(8)}(x) = -4f^{(4)}(x) = (-4)(-4f(x)) = 16f(x) = 16e^x \sin x$.

   b. Every 8th derivative of f multiplies f by 16. Thus $f^{(80)}(x) = 16^{10}f(x) = 16^{10}e^x \sin x$.

8. $f'(x) = e^x + xe^x = (1+x)e^x$; $f''(x) = e^x + (1+x)e^x = (2+x)e^x$; $f^{(3)}(x) = e^x + (2+x)e^x = (3+x)e^x$. In general, $f^{(n)}(x) = (n+x)e^x$.

9. $\dfrac{dy}{dx} = e^{2x} + 2xe^{2x} = (1+2x)e^{2x}$, so $x\dfrac{dy}{dx} = (xe^{2x})(1+2x) = y(1+2x)$.

10. $\dfrac{dy}{dx} = e^{-x^2/2} - x^2e^{-x^2/2} = (1-x^2)e^{-x^2/2}$, so $x\dfrac{dy}{dx} = (xe^{-x^2/2})(1-x^2) = y(1-x^2)$.

11. $f'(x) = e^x - e^{-x}$; $f''(x) = e^x + e^{-x}$; $f'(x) = 0$ if $e^x = e^{-x}$, or $e^{2x} = 1$, or $x = 0$; $f''(0) = 2 > 0$; relative minimum value is $f(0) = 2$; concave upward on $(-\infty, \infty)$; symmetric with respect to the y axis.

Exercise 11 Exercise 12

12. $f'(x) = \dfrac{e^x}{(1+e^x)^2}$; $f''(x) = \dfrac{e^x - e^{2x}}{(1+e^x)^3}$;
$f''(x) = 0$ if $e^x(1-e^x) = 0$, or $x = 0$; concave upward on $(-\infty, 0)$ and concave downward on $(0, \infty)$; inflection point: $(0, \frac{1}{2})$;

$$\lim_{x\to\infty} \frac{e^x}{1+e^x} = \lim_{x\to\infty} \frac{1}{e^{-x}+1} = 1 \quad \text{and} \quad \lim_{x\to-\infty} \frac{e^x}{1+e^x} = 0$$

so that $y = 1$ and $y = 0$ are horizontal asymptotes.

13. $\displaystyle\int e^{ex}\,dx \overset{u=ex}{=} \int e^u \cdot \frac{1}{e}\,du = \frac{1}{e}e^u + C = \frac{1}{e}e^{ex} + C = e^{ex-1} + C$

14. $\displaystyle\int e^{\sqrt{2}x+3}\,dx \overset{u=\sqrt{2}x+3}{=} \int \frac{1}{\sqrt{2}}e^u\,du = \frac{1}{\sqrt{2}}e^u + C = \frac{1}{\sqrt{2}}e^{\sqrt{2}x+3} + C$

15. $\displaystyle\int_0^{\pi/3} \frac{e^{\tan y}}{\cos^2 y}\,dy = \int_0^{\pi/3} e^{\tan y}\sec^2 y\,dy \overset{u=\tan y}{=} \int_0^{\sqrt{3}} e^u\,du = e^u\Big|_0^{\sqrt{3}} = e^{\sqrt{3}} - e^0 = e^{\sqrt{3}} - 1$

16. $\displaystyle\int_{-1}^{1} \frac{e^y - e^{-y}}{e^y + e^{-y}}\,dy \overset{u=e^y+e^{-y}}{=} \int_{e^{-1}+e}^{e+e^{-1}} \frac{1}{u}\,du = \int_{e^{-1}+e}^{e^{-1}+e} \frac{1}{u}\,du = 0$

17. $\displaystyle\int \frac{e^{2t}}{\sqrt{e^{2t}-4}}\,dt \overset{u=e^{2t}-4}{=} \int \frac{1}{2\sqrt{u}}\,du = \sqrt{u} + C = \sqrt{e^{2t}-4} + C$

18. $\displaystyle\int e^t e^{(e^t)}\,dt \overset{u=e^t}{=} \int e^u\,du = e^u + c = e^{(e^t)} + C$

19. $\displaystyle\int \frac{e^{-t}\ln(1+e^{-t})}{1+e^{-t}}\,dt \overset{u=\ln(1+e^{-t})}{=} \int -u\,du = -\frac{1}{2}u^2 + C = -\frac{1}{2}[\ln(1+e^{-t})]^2 + C$

20. $\displaystyle\int \sqrt{e^x}\,dx = \int (e^x)^{1/2}\,dx = \int e^{x/2}\,dx \overset{u=x/2}{=} \int 2e^u\,du = 2e^u + C = 2e^{x/2} + C$

21. $\displaystyle\int \frac{1}{1+e^{-x}}\,dx = \int \frac{e^x}{e^x+1}\,dx \overset{u=e^x+1}{=} \int \frac{1}{u}\,du = \ln|u| + C = \ln(e^x+1) + C$

22. $\displaystyle\int \frac{1}{1+e^x}\,dx = \int \frac{e^{-x}}{e^{-x}+1}\,dx \overset{u=e^{-x}+1}{=} \int -\frac{1}{u}\,du = -\ln|u| + C = -\ln(e^{-x}+1) + C$

23. $\displaystyle\int e^{(x-e^x)}\,dx = \int e^x e^{-(e^x)}\,dx \overset{u=e^x}{=} \int e^{-u}\,du = -e^{-u} + C = -e^{-(e^x)} + C$

24. $\displaystyle\int_0^1 e^{(1-t)a}e^{tb}\,dt = \int_0^1 e^{(1-t)a+tb}\,dt = \int_0^1 e^a e^{(b-a)t}\,dt \overset{u=(b-a)t}{=} \int_0^{b-a} e^a e^u \frac{1}{b-a}\,du$

$$= \frac{e^a e^u}{b-a}\Big|_0^{b-a} = \frac{e^a}{b-a}(e^{b-a} - e^0) = \frac{e^b - e^a}{b-a}$$

25. The slope of the line $y = -4x - 7$ is -4, so we seek the value of x for which $(d/dx)(e^{x^2-4}) = -4$. This is equivalent to $2xe^{x^2-4} = -4$, or $xe^{x^2-4} = -2$. Now this equation is satisfied if $x = -2$. The corresponding point on the graph of the equation $y = e^{x^2-4}$ is $(-2, 1)$.

26. Since $e^x > 0$ for all x and $\ln x \le 0$ for $0 < x \le 1$, any point of intersection must lie to the right of the line $x = 1$. However, $f(1) = e > 0 = g(1)$, and $f'(x) = e^x > 1 \ge 1/x = g'(x)$ for $x > 1$. Thus $f(x) > g(x)$ for $x > 1$, so that the graphs do not intersect.

27. $y = \dfrac{e^x-1}{e^x+1}$; $(e^x+1)y = e^x - 1$; $e^x = \dfrac{1+y}{1-y}$; $x = \ln\left(\dfrac{1+y}{1-y}\right)$, so $f^{-1}(x) = \ln\left(\dfrac{1+x}{1-x}\right)$.

28. $y = \dfrac{3e^x-2}{e^x+4}$; $(e^x+4)y = 3e^x - 2$; $e^x = \dfrac{4y+2}{3-y}$; $x = \ln\left(\dfrac{4y+2}{3-y}\right)$, so $f^{-1}(x) = \ln\left(\dfrac{4x+2}{3-x}\right)$

29. The equation $e^{-x} = 2 - x$ is equivalent to $e^{-x} + x - 2 = 0$. Using the Newton-Raphson method with initial value 1, we obtain 1.84140566 as an approximate solution of $e^{-x} = 2 - x$.

30. The equation $e^x = 3x$ is equivalent to $e^x - 3x = 0$. Using the Newton-Raphson method with initial value .5, we obtain .6190612867 as an approximate solution of $e^x = 3x$.

32. $\int_0^c e^{-x}\,dx = -e^{-x}\Big|_0^c = -e^{-c}+1 = 1-e^{-c} = 1-e^{-c}$

We are to find the value of c for which $1-e^{-c} = \frac{1}{2}$, or $e^{-c} = \frac{1}{2}$. Taking natural logarithms, we find that $-c = \ln\frac{1}{2} = -\ln 2$, so that $c = \ln 2$.

33. The graphs intersect at (x,y) if $e^{2x} = y = e^{-2x}$, or $e^{4x} = 1$, or $x = 0$. Since $e^{2x} \geq e^{-2x}$ on $[0, \frac{1}{2}]$, we have

$$A = \int_0^{1/2} (e^{2x} - e^{-2x})\,dx = \left(\frac{1}{2}e^{2x} + \frac{1}{2}e^{-2x}\right)\Bigg|_0^{1/2} = \frac{1}{2}(e+e^{-1}) - 1.$$

34. The curves intersect at (x,y) if $3e^x = y = 2+e^{2x}$, or $e^{2x} - 3e^x + 2 = 0$, or $(e^x)^2 - 3e^x + 2 = 0$, which means that $(e^x-1)(e^x-2) = 0$. If $e^x - 1 = 0$, then $x = 0$; if $e^x - 2 = 0$, then $x = \ln 2$. Also $3e^x \geq 2 + e^{2x}$ on $[0, \ln 2]$. Therefore

$$A = \int_0^{\ln 2} [3e^x - (2+e^{2x})]\,dx = \left(3e^x - 2x - \frac{1}{2}e^{2x}\right)\Bigg|_0^{\ln 2} = (6 - 2\ln 2 - 2) - \left(3 - 0 - \frac{1}{2}\right) = \frac{3}{2} - 2\ln 2.$$

35. Let $f(x) = \ln x$, so that $f^{-1}(y) = e^y$. Also let $a = 1$ and $b = e$, so that $f(a) = \ln 1 = 0$ and $f(b) = \ln e = 1$. Therefore by the formula,

$$\int_1^e \ln x\,dx = e\ln e - 1\ln 1 - \int_0^1 f^{-1}(y)\,dy = e - \int_0^1 e^y\,dy = e - e^y\Big|_0^1 = e - (e-1) = 1.$$

36. From the hint, $R\sin x \geq 2Rx/\pi$ for $0 \leq x \leq \pi/2$. Since the function e^{-x} is decreasing, we have $e^{-R\sin x} \leq e^{-2Rx/\pi}$ for $0 \leq x \leq \pi/2$. By the Comparison Property,

$$\int_0^{\pi/2} e^{-R\sin x}\,dx \leq \int_0^{\pi/2} e^{-2Rx/\pi}\,dx = -\frac{\pi}{2R}e^{-2Rx/\pi}\Big|_0^{\pi/2} = \frac{\pi}{2R} - \frac{\pi}{2R}e^{-R} < \frac{\pi}{2R}.$$

37. a. Since $f(x+h) = f(x)f(h)$, $f(0) = 1$, and $f'(0) = 1$, we find that for any x,

$$f'(x) = \lim_{h\to 0}\frac{f(x+h)-f(x)}{h} = \lim_{h\to 0}\frac{f(x)f(h)-f(x)}{h} = f(x)\lim_{h\to 0}\frac{f(h)-1}{h}$$

$$= f(x)\lim_{h\to 0}\frac{f(h)-f(0)}{h-0} = f(x)f'(0) = f(x)\cdot 1 = f(x).$$

b. By (a) and the Product Rule,

$$\frac{d}{dx}(e^{-x}f(x)) = -e^{-x}f(x) + e^{-x}f'(x) = -e^{-x}f(x) + e^{-x}f(x) = 0.$$

c. By (b) and Theorem 4.6, $e^{-x}f(x) = C$ for some constant C. Therefore $f(x) = e^x e^{-x} f(x) = e^x C = Ce^x$. Since $f(0) = 1$, we have $C\cdot e^0 = 1$, so that $C = 1$ and hence $f(x) = Ce^x = e^x$.

38. a. $\dfrac{d}{dx}(e^{-x}e^{b+x}) = -e^{-x}e^{b+x} + e^{-x}e^{b+x} = 0$

b. By (a) and Theorem 4.6, $e^{-x}e^{b+x} = C$ for some constant C. For $x = 0$, this becomes $e^0e^{b+0} = C$, so that $C = e^b$. Therefore $e^{-x}e^{b+x} = e^b$ for all x.

c. Taking $b = 0$ in (b), we have $e^{-x}e^{0+x} = e^0$, so that $e^{-x}e^x = 1$, or $e^{-x} = 1/e^x$.

d. Taking $x = c$ in (b), we have $e^{-c}e^{b+c} = e^b$. Since $e^{-c} = 1/e^c$ by (c), this becomes $(1/e^c)e^{b+c} = e^b$, or $e^{b+c} = e^b e^c$.

39. Let $f(x) = \dfrac{1}{\sigma\sqrt{2\pi}}\, e^{-(x-\mu)^2/2\sigma^2}$. Then

$$f(\mu) = \frac{1}{\sigma\sqrt{2\pi}}\, e^0 = \frac{1}{\sigma\sqrt{2\pi}}.$$

For $x \neq \mu$, we have $-(x-\mu)^2/2\sigma^2 < 0$, so that $e^{-(x-\mu)^2/2\sigma^2} < e^0 = 1$, and hence

$$f(x) = \frac{1}{\sigma\sqrt{2\pi}}\, e^{-(x-\mu)^2/2\sigma^2} < \frac{1}{\sigma\sqrt{2\pi}}.$$

Therefore the maximum value of f is $f(\mu) = 1/\sigma\sqrt{2\pi}$.

40.
$$\begin{aligned} f'(x) &= \frac{1}{\sigma\sqrt{2\pi}}\, e^{-(x-\mu)^2/2\sigma^2}\left(\frac{-2(x-\mu)}{2\sigma^2}\right) = \frac{\mu - x}{\sigma^3\sqrt{2\pi}}\, e^{-(x-\mu)^2/2\sigma^2}; \\ f''(x) &= \frac{-1}{\sigma^3\sqrt{2\pi}}\, e^{-(x-\mu)^2/2\sigma^2} + \frac{\mu - x}{\sigma^3\sqrt{2\pi}}\, e^{-(x-\mu)^2/2\sigma^2}\left(\frac{-2(x-\mu)}{2\sigma^2}\right) \\ &= \left(-\frac{1}{\sigma^3\sqrt{2\pi}} + \frac{(\mu - x)^2}{\sigma^5\sqrt{2\pi}}\right) e^{-(x-\mu)^2/2\sigma^2} \end{aligned}$$

Therefore $f''(x) = 0$ if and only if

$$\frac{(\mu - x)^2}{\sigma^5\sqrt{2\pi}} = \frac{1}{\sigma^3\sqrt{2\pi}}, \quad \text{or} \quad (\mu - x)^2 = \sigma^2, \quad \text{or} \quad x = \mu - \sigma \text{ or } \mu + \sigma.$$

Since f'' changes from positive to negative at $\mu - \sigma$, and f'' changes from negative to positive at $\mu + \sigma$,

$$(\mu - \sigma, f(\mu - \sigma)) = \left(\mu - \sigma, \frac{1}{\sigma\sqrt{2\pi}}\, e^{-1/2}\right) \quad \text{and} \quad (\mu + \sigma, f(\mu + \sigma)) = \left(\mu + \sigma, \frac{1}{\sigma\sqrt{2\pi}}\, e^{-1/2}\right)$$

are inflection points.

41.
$$\begin{aligned} g'(x) &= ae^{-(be^{-cx})}(-be^{-cx})(-c) = abce^{-(be^{-cx})}e^{-cx}; \\ g''(x) &= abce^{-(be^{-cx})}(-be^{-cx})(-c)(e^{-cx}) + abce^{-(be^{-cx})}e^{-cx}(-c) \\ &= ab^2c^2e^{-(be^{-cx})}e^{-2cx} - abc^2e^{-(be^{-cx})}e^{-cx} \\ &= abc^2e^{-(be^{-cx})}e^{-cx}(be^{-cx} - 1) \end{aligned}$$

Therefore $g''(x) = 0$ if $e^{-cx} = 1/b$ or $-cx = \ln(1/b) = -\ln b$, or $x = (1/c)\ln b$. Since $g''(x)$ changes from positive to negative at $(1/c)\ln b$,

$$\left(\frac{1}{c}\ln b, g\left(\frac{1}{c}\ln b\right)\right) = \left(\frac{1}{c}\ln b, \frac{a}{e}\right)$$

is an inflection point.

42. a. $0 = Q(0) = VC + c$, so $c = -VC$.

b. $Q(t) = VC(1 - e^{-t/RC})$; $Q'(t) = \dfrac{V}{R}e^{-t/RC}$; $Q''(t) = \dfrac{-V}{R^2C}e^{-t/RC}$; no relative extreme values; increasing on $[0, \infty)$; concave downward on $(0, \infty)$; $\lim_{t\to\infty} Q(t) = \lim_{t\to\infty} VC(1 - e^{-t/RC}) = VC$, so that $y = VC$ is a horizontal asymptote.

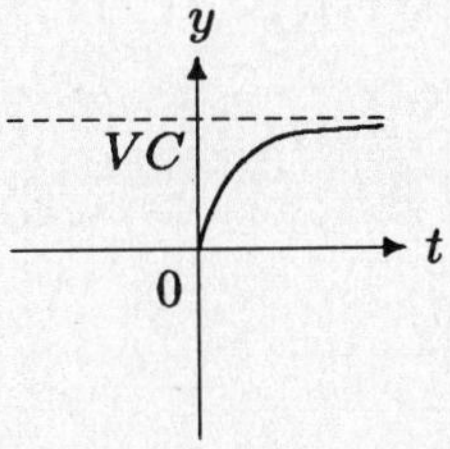

c. If $0.9VC = Q(t) = VC(1 - e^{-t/RC})$, then $.9 = 1 - e^{-t/RC}$, or $e^{-t/RC} = .1$, or $-t/RC = \ln\frac{1}{10} = -\ln 10$, or $t = RC\ln 10$.

6.3 General Exponential and Logarithmic Functions

1. By (6) and the Chain Rule, $g'(x) = (\ln 2)2^{-x}(-1) = (-\ln 2)2^{-x}$.

2. $g'(x) = 1/(x\ln 10)$

3. By (9), $y = t^t = e^{t\ln t}$, so $dy/dt = e^{t\ln t}(\ln t + t\cdot 1/t) = t^t(\ln t + 1)$.

4. By (9), $y = t^{\sin t} = e^{\sin t\ln t}$, so
$$\frac{dy}{dt} = e^{\sin t\ln t}\left[\cos t\,\ln t + (\sin t)\frac{1}{t}\right] = t^{\sin t}\left(\cos t\,\ln t + \frac{\sin t}{t}\right).$$

5. By (9), $y = t^{2/t} = e^{(2\ln t)/t}$, so
$$\frac{dy}{dt} = e^{(2\ln t)/t}\left(\frac{(2/t)t - 2\ln t}{t^2}\right) = t^{2/t}\left(\frac{2 - 2\ln t}{t^2}\right).$$

6. By (9), $y = (1 + 1/t)^t = e^{t\ln(1+1/t)}$, so
$$\frac{dy}{dt} = e^{t\ln(1+1/t)}\left[\ln\left(1 + \frac{1}{t}\right) + t\left(\frac{1}{1+1/t}\right)\left(-\frac{1}{t^2}\right)\right] = \left(1 + \frac{1}{t}\right)^t\left[\ln\left(1 + \frac{1}{t}\right) - \frac{1}{t+1}\right].$$

7. By (9), $f(x) = (\cos x)^{\cos x} = e^{(\cos x)\ln(\cos x)}$, so
$$f'(x) = e^{(\cos x)\ln(\cos x)}\left[(-\sin x)\ln(\cos x) + (\cos x)\left(\frac{-\sin x}{\cos x}\right)\right] = (-\sin x)(\cos x)^{\cos x}[\ln(\cos x) + 1].$$

8. By (9), $f(x) = (\ln x)^{\ln x} = e^{(\ln x)\ln(\ln x)}$, so
$$f'(x) = e^{(\ln x)\ln(\ln x)}\left[\frac{1}{x}\ln(\ln x) + (\ln x)\frac{1}{x\ln x}\right] = \frac{(\ln x)^{\ln x}}{x}[\ln(\ln x) + 1].$$

9. Since $(2x)^{\sqrt{2}} = 2^{\sqrt{2}}x^{\sqrt{2}}$, it follows from (8) that $f'(x) = 2^{\sqrt{2}}\sqrt{2}\,x^{\sqrt{2}-1} = 2\sqrt{2}\,(2x)^{\sqrt{2}-1}$.

10. By (9), $f(x) = (\cos x)^{\pi x^2} = e^{\pi x^2\ln(\cos x)}$, so
$$f'(x) = e^{\pi x^2\ln(\cos x)}\left(2\pi x\ln(\cos x) + \pi x^2\left(\frac{-\sin x}{\cos x}\right)\right) = (\cos x)^{\pi x^2}(2\pi x\ln(\cos x) - \pi x^2\tan x).$$

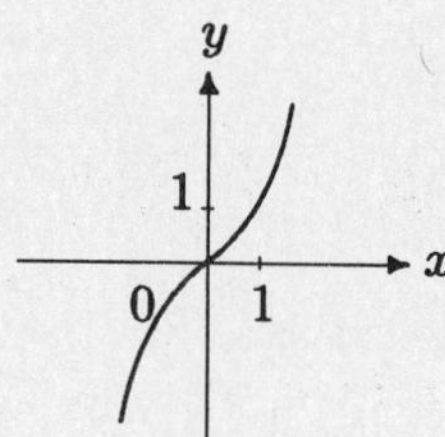

Exercise 11

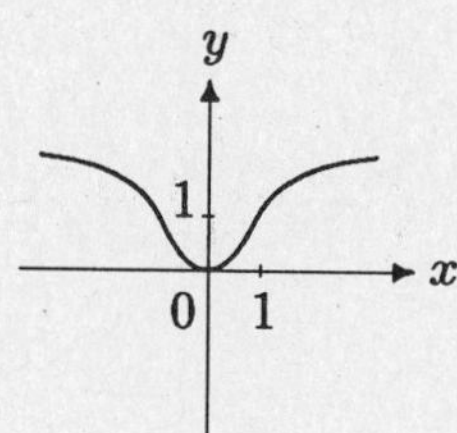

Exercise 12

11. $f'(x) = (\ln 2)(2^x + 2^{-x}) > 0$; increasing on $(-\infty, \infty)$;

$f''(x) = (\ln 2)^2(2^x - 2^{-x})$; $f''(x) = 0$ if $2^x = 2^{-x}$, or $2^{2x} = 1$, or $x = 0$; $f''(x) < 0$ if $x < 0$ and $f''(x) > 0$ if $x > 0$; concave downward on $(-\infty, 0)$ and concave upward on $(0, \infty)$; inflection point: $(0, 0)$; symmetric with respect to the origin.

12. $f'(x) = \dfrac{2x}{(\ln 2)(1 + x^2)}$; $f''(x) = \dfrac{1}{\ln 2}\,\dfrac{2(1 + x^2) - (2x)^2}{(1 + x^2)^2} = \dfrac{2(1 - x^2)}{(\ln 2)(1 + x^2)^2}$;

$f'(x) = 0$ if $x = 0$; $f''(0) = 2/(\ln 2) > 0$, so $f(0) = 0$ is a relative minimum value; concave downward on $(-\infty, -1)$ and $(1, \infty)$, and concave upward on $(-1, 1)$; inflection points: $(-1, \log_2 2) = (-1, 1)$ and $(1, \log_2 2) = (1, 1)$; symmetric with respect to the y axis.

13. By (10), $\displaystyle\int 2^x\,dx = \frac{1}{\ln 2}2^x + C.$

14. By (10), $\displaystyle\int_1^2 10^x\,dx = \frac{1}{\ln 10}10^x\Big|_1^2 = \frac{1}{\ln 10}(10^2 - 10^1) = \frac{90}{\ln 10}.$

15. By (10), $\displaystyle\int_{-2}^0 3^{-x}\,dx \overset{u=-x}{=} \int_2^0 3^u(-1)\,du = \frac{-1}{\ln 3}3^u\Big|_2^0 = -\frac{1}{\ln 3}(1 - 3^2) = \frac{8}{\ln 3}.$

16. By (10), $\displaystyle\int_0^1 4^{3x}\,dx \overset{u=3x}{=} \frac{1}{3}\int_0^3 4^u\,du = \frac{1}{3}\cdot\frac{1}{\ln 4}4^u\Big|_0^3 = \frac{1}{3\ln 4}(4^3 - 4^0) = \frac{21}{\ln 4}.$

17. By (10), $\displaystyle\int x\cdot 5^{-x^2}\,dx \overset{u=-x^2}{=} \int -\frac{1}{2}5^u\,du = -\frac{1}{2}\cdot\frac{1}{\ln 5}5^u + C = \frac{-1}{2\ln 5}5^{-x^2} + C.$

18. By (14), $\displaystyle\int \frac{\log_2 x}{x}\,dx = \int \frac{\ln x}{x\ln 2}\,dx \overset{u=\ln x}{=} \int \frac{u}{\ln 2}\,du = \frac{u^2}{2\ln 2} + C = \frac{(\ln x)^2}{2\ln 2} + C.$

19. By (11), $\displaystyle\int x^{2\pi}\,dx = \frac{1}{2\pi + 1}x^{2\pi+1} + C.$

20. By (11), $\displaystyle\int (\sin x)^e \cos x\,dx \overset{u=\sin x}{=} \int u^e\,du = \frac{1}{e+1}u^{e+1} + C = \frac{1}{e+1}(\sin x)^{e+1} + C.$

21. By (10), $\displaystyle A = \int_1^2 x\cdot 2^{(x^2)}\,dx \overset{u=x^2}{=} \int_1^4 2^u\left(\frac{1}{2}\right)du = \frac{1}{2\ln 2}2^u\Big|_1^4 = \frac{1}{2\ln 2}(2^4 - 2^1) = \frac{7}{\ln 2}.$

22. $2^{-x} - \frac{1}{4} = 0$ for $2^{-x} = \frac{1}{4}$, or $2^x = 4$, or $x = 2$. Thus by (10),

$$A = \int_0^2 \left(2^{-x} - \frac{1}{4}\right) dx \overset{u=-x}{=} \int_0^{-2} \left(2^u - \frac{1}{4}\right)(-1)\, du = -\left(\frac{1}{\ln 2} 2^u - \frac{1}{4} u\right)\Big|_0^{-2}$$

$$= -\left(\frac{1}{4\ln 2} + \frac{1}{2}\right) + \frac{1}{\ln 2} = \frac{3}{4\ln 2} - \frac{1}{2}.$$

23. $3^x \geq 2^x$ on $[0, 2]$, so by (10),

$$A = \int_0^2 (3^x - 2^x)\, dx = \left(\frac{1}{\ln 3} 3^x - \frac{1}{\ln 2} 2^x\right)\Big|_0^2 = \left(\frac{3^2}{\ln 3} - \frac{2^2}{\ln 2}\right) - \left(\frac{1}{\ln 3} 3^0 - \frac{1}{\ln 2} 2^0\right) = \frac{8}{\ln 3} - \frac{3}{\ln 2}.$$

24. The graphs intersect at (x, y) if $3/x = y = (\log_2 x)/x$, that is, $3 = \log_2 x$. But $3 = \log_2 x$ if $x = 2^3 = 8$. Notice that $(\log_2 x)/x \geq 3/x$ on $[8, 16]$. Thus

$$A = \int_8^{16} \left(\frac{\log_2 x}{x} - \frac{3}{x}\right) dx = \int_8^{16} \frac{\ln x}{x \ln 2}\, dx - 3\ln x\Big|_8^{16} \overset{u=\ln x}{=} \int_{\ln 8}^{\ln 16} \frac{u}{\ln 2}\, du - 3\ln 16 + 3\ln 8$$

$$= \frac{u^2}{2\ln 2}\Big|_{\ln 8}^{\ln 16} - 3\ln 16 + 3\ln 8 = \frac{(\ln 16)^2}{2\ln 2} - \frac{(\ln 8)^2}{2\ln 2} - 3\ln 16 + 3\ln 8 = \frac{1}{2}\ln 2.$$

25. By (14), $\log_3 5 = \dfrac{\ln 5}{\ln 3} \approx 1.464973521$.

26. By (14), $\log_{1/2} \frac{1}{3} = \dfrac{\ln(1/3)}{\ln(1/2)} = \dfrac{-\ln 3}{-\ln 2} = \dfrac{\ln 3}{\ln 2} \approx 1.584962501$.

27. By (14), $\log_\pi e = \dfrac{\ln e}{\ln \pi} = \dfrac{1}{\ln \pi} \approx 0.8735685268$.

28. By (14), $\log_{\sqrt{2}} \sqrt{\pi} = \dfrac{\ln\sqrt{\pi}}{\ln\sqrt{2}} = \dfrac{(1/2)\ln \pi}{(1/2)\ln 2} = \dfrac{\ln \pi}{\ln 2} \approx 1.651496129$.

29. Suppose $0 < b < a \leq e$. Since $(\ln x)/x$ is increasing on $(0, e]$, we have $(\ln a)/a > (\ln b)/b$, so $b \ln a > a \ln b$ and thus $\ln a^b > \ln b^a$. Since $\ln x$ is increasing, it follows that $a^b > b^a$. Now suppose $e \leq a < b$. Since $(\ln x)/x$ is decreasing on $[e, \infty)$, it follows that $(\ln a)/a > (\ln b)/b$, so that $b\ln a > a \ln b$ and thus $\ln a^b > \ln b^a$. Because $\ln x$ is increasing, we conclude that $a^b > b^a$.

30. a. Since $e < \pi$, if we let $a = e$ and $b = \pi$ in Exercise 29, we conclude that $e^\pi > \pi^e$, or equivalently, $\pi^e < e^\pi$.

    b. By Exercise 29, with $a = 2$ and $b = \sqrt{x}$, we have $2^{\sqrt{x}} > (\sqrt{x})^2 = x$ for $0 < \sqrt{x} < 2$. This means that $2^{\sqrt{x}} > x$ for $0 < x < 4$.

31. By (14), $f(x) = (x \ln x)/\ln a$, so $f'(x) = (1/\ln a)(\ln x + x \cdot 1/x) = (1/\ln a)(\ln x + 1)$ and $f''(x) = 1/(x \ln a)$. Thus the graph of f is concave upward on $(0, \infty)$ if $\ln a > 0$, that is, $a > 1$, and the graph of f is concave downward on $(0, \infty)$ if $\ln a < 0$, that is, $0 < a < 1$.

32. $y = \dfrac{2^x+1}{2^x-3}$; $(2^x-3)y = 2^x+1$; $2^x = \dfrac{1+3y}{y-1}$; $x = \log_2(2^x) = \log_2\left(\dfrac{1+3y}{y-1}\right)$

Therefore $f^{-1}(x) = \log_2\left(\dfrac{1+3x}{x-1}\right)$.

33. We seek b such that $1.5 + \log_2 x = \log_2(bx) = \log_2 b + \log_2 x$. This implies that $\log_2 b = 1.5$, so that $b = 2^{1.5} = 2\sqrt{2}$.

34. $a^{b+c+d} = a^{(b+c)+d} = a^{b+c}a^d = (a^b a^c)a^d = a^b a^c a^d$

35. a. By (14), $\log_b a \log_a x = \dfrac{\ln a}{\ln b}\dfrac{\ln x}{\ln a} = \dfrac{\ln x}{\ln b} = \log_b x$

b. Taking $b = 4$ and $a = 7$ in part (a), we find that $\log_4 x = \log_4 7 \log_7 x$.

36. Let $f(x) = x^r$ and $g(x) = x^{1/r}$. If $f(x) = y$, then by Theorem 6.7, $g(y) = g(x^r) = (x^r)^{1/r} = x$. If $g(y) = x$, then $f(x) = f(y^{1/r}) = (y^{1/r})^r = y$. Thus by Definition 6.1, f and g are inverses of one another.

37. a. Taking the derivatives of both sides of (15) with respect to t, we obtain $N'(10^7 - P(t))(-P'(t)) = 10^7$. Since $P'(t) = 10^7 - P(t)$, this gives us $N'(10^7 - P(t))(P(t) - 10^7) = 10^7$ for $t > 0$.

b. Let $x = 10^7 - P(t)$. Since $0 \le P(t) < 10^7$, we have $0 < x \le 10^7$. From part (a) we obtain $N'(x)(-x) = 10^7$, or $N'(x) = -10^7/x$ for $0 < x < 10^7$. Since $(d/dx)(-10^7 \ln x) = -10^7/x$, it follows from Theorem 4.6 that $N(x) = -10^7 \ln x + C$ for $0 < x < 10^7$, where C is a constant.

c. Since $N(10^7) = 0$, we have $0 = N(10^7) = -10^7 \ln 10^7 + C$, so that $C = 10^7 \ln 10^7$. Thus $N(x) = -10^7 \ln x + 10^7 \ln 10^7$ for $0 < x \le 10^7$.

d. Let $b = e^{-1/10^7}$. By (14) with $x = e$, we have

$$\log_b e = \frac{1}{\log_e b} = \frac{1}{-1/10^7} = -10^7.$$

Thus by Exercise 35(a), $-10^7 \ln x = \log_b e \ln x = \log_b e \log_e x = \log_b x$.

e. Combining the results of (c) and (d), we have $N(x) = -10^7 \ln x + 10^7 \ln 10^7 = \log_b x + C$ for $0 < x \le 10^7$, where $C = 10^7 \ln 10^7$

38. For the Cantor set, $m = 2$ and $r = \frac{1}{3}$, so the fractal dimension is $\log_{1/r} m = \log_3 2 \approx .63$.

39. For the Sierpinski carpet, $m = 8$ and $r = \frac{1}{3}$, so the fractal dimension is $\log_{1/r} m = \log_3 8 = 3\log_3 2 \approx 1.89$.

41. a. By (6) and the Chain Rule,

$$\frac{dy}{dt} = k(\ln a)a^{(b^t)}(\ln b)b^t = k(\ln a)(\ln b)b^t a^{(b^t)}.$$

Since $0 < a < 1$ and $0 < b < 1$, both $\ln a$ and $\ln b$ are negative. Since $k > 0$, $b^t > 0$, and $a^{(b^t)} > 0$, we conclude that $dy/dt > 0$ for all t.

b. The level of diffusion is increasing.

c. Since $0 < b < 1$, so that $\ln b < 0$, we have $\lim_{t\to\infty} b^t = \lim_{t\to\infty} e^{t\ln b} = 0$. By the Substitution Rule with $y = b^t$, $\lim_{t\to\infty} ka^{(b^t)} = \lim_{y\to 0} ka^y = ka^0 = k$.

42. a. Since $f(0) = 1$, we have $a(\frac{1}{2})^{b\cdot 0} = 1$, so that $a = 1$. Since the half-life is .00014 seconds, $f(.00014) = \frac{1}{2}f(0) = \frac{1}{2}$, so $a(\frac{1}{2})^{b(.00014)} = \frac{1}{2}$, or $(\frac{1}{2})^{b(.00014)} = \frac{1}{2}$. Thus $b = 1/.00014$.

b. Using $a = 1$ and $b = 1/.00014$ from (a), we have $f(1/100) = (\frac{1}{2})^{(1/.00014)(1/100)} = (\frac{1}{2})^{(1/.014)} \approx (\frac{1}{2})^{71.4} \approx 3.15 \times 10^{-22}$. Thus not even a gram would remain after a 1/100-second blink of the eye.

6.4 Hyperbolic Functions

1. $\sinh 0 = \dfrac{e^0 - e^{-0}}{2} = 0$

2. $\cosh 0 = \dfrac{e^0 + e^{-0}}{2} = 1$

3. $\tanh 0 = \dfrac{\sinh 0}{\cosh 0} = \dfrac{e^0 - e^{-0}}{e^0 + e^{-0}} = \dfrac{0}{1} = 0$

4. $\tanh 1 = \dfrac{\sinh 1}{\cosh 1} = \dfrac{e^1 - e^{-1}}{e^1 + e^{-1}} = \dfrac{e^2 - 1}{e^2 + 1}$

5. $\coth(-1) = \dfrac{\cosh(-1)}{\sinh(-1)} = \dfrac{e^{-1} + e^1}{e^{-1} - e^1} = \dfrac{1 + e^2}{1 - e^2}$

6. $\sinh(\ln 2) = \dfrac{e^{\ln 2} - e^{-\ln 2}}{2} = \dfrac{2 - \frac{1}{2}}{2} = \dfrac{3}{4}$

7. $\sinh(\ln 3) = \dfrac{e^{\ln 3} - e^{-\ln 3}}{2} = \dfrac{3 - \frac{1}{3}}{2} = \dfrac{4}{3}$

8. $\cosh(\ln 3) = \dfrac{e^{\ln 3} + e^{-\ln 3}}{2} = \dfrac{3 + \frac{1}{3}}{2} = \dfrac{5}{3}$

9. $\coth(\ln 4) = \dfrac{\cosh(\ln 4)}{\sinh(\ln 4)} = \dfrac{e^{\ln 4} + e^{-\ln 4}}{e^{\ln 4} - e^{-\ln 4}} = \dfrac{4 + \frac{1}{4}}{4 - \frac{1}{4}} = \dfrac{17}{15}$

10. $\operatorname{csch}(\ln \pi^2) = \dfrac{1}{\sinh(\ln \pi^2)} = \dfrac{2}{e^{\ln \pi^2} - e^{-\ln \pi^2}} = \dfrac{2}{\pi^2 - (1/\pi^2)} = \dfrac{2\pi^2}{\pi^4 - 1}$

11. $\operatorname{sech}(\ln \sqrt{2}) = \dfrac{1}{\cosh(\ln \sqrt{2})} = \dfrac{2}{e^{\ln \sqrt{2}} + e^{-\ln \sqrt{2}}} = \dfrac{2}{\sqrt{2} + 1/\sqrt{2}} = \dfrac{2\sqrt{2}}{3}$

12. $\sinh^{-1}\left(\frac{4}{3}\right) = \ln\left(\frac{4}{3} + \sqrt{\left(\frac{4}{3}\right)^2 + 1}\right) = \ln\left(\frac{4}{3} + \frac{5}{3}\right) = \ln 3$

13. $\sinh(\ln x) = \dfrac{e^{\ln x} - e^{-\ln x}}{2} = \dfrac{x - 1/x}{2} = \dfrac{x^2 - 1}{2x}$

14. $\cosh(\ln x) = \dfrac{e^{\ln x} + e^{-\ln x}}{2} = \dfrac{x + 1/x}{2} = \dfrac{x^2 + 1}{2x}$

15. $\tanh(\ln x) = \dfrac{\sinh(\ln x)}{\cosh(\ln x)} = \left(\dfrac{x^2-1}{2x}\right)\bigg/\left(\dfrac{x^2+1}{2x}\right) = \dfrac{x^2-1}{x^2+1}$ from Exercises 13 and 14

16. $\sinh^{-1}\left(\dfrac{1-x^2}{2x}\right) = \ln\left[\dfrac{1-x^2}{2x} + \sqrt{\left(\dfrac{1-x^2}{2x}\right)^2 + 1}\right] = \ln\left[\dfrac{1-x^2}{2x} + \sqrt{\left(\dfrac{1+x^2}{2x}\right)^2}\right]$

$$= \ln\left(\frac{1-x^2}{2x} + \frac{1+x^2}{2|x|}\right) = \begin{cases} \ln(-x) & \text{for } x < 0 \\ -\ln x & \text{for } x > 0 \end{cases}$$

17. $\dfrac{d}{dx}\tanh x = \dfrac{d}{dx}\dfrac{\sinh x}{\cosh x} = \dfrac{\cosh^2 x - \sinh^2 x}{\cosh^2 x} = \dfrac{1}{\cosh^2 x} = \operatorname{sech}^2 x$

18. $\dfrac{d}{dx}\coth x = \dfrac{d}{dx}\dfrac{\cosh x}{\sinh x} = \dfrac{\sinh^2 x - \cosh^2 x}{\sinh^2 x} = \dfrac{-1}{\sinh^2 x} = -\operatorname{csch}^2 x$

19. $\dfrac{d}{dx}\operatorname{sech} x = \dfrac{d}{dx}\dfrac{1}{\cosh x} = \dfrac{-\sinh x}{\cosh^2 x} = -\operatorname{sech} x \tanh x$

20. $\dfrac{d}{dx}\operatorname{csch} x = \dfrac{d}{dx}\dfrac{1}{\sinh x} = \dfrac{-\cosh x}{\sinh^2 x} = -\operatorname{csch} x \coth x$

21. $f'(x) = (-\operatorname{sech}\sqrt{x}\tanh\sqrt{x})\left(\dfrac{1}{2\sqrt{x}}\right) = \dfrac{-1}{2\sqrt{x}}\operatorname{sech}\sqrt{x}\tanh\sqrt{x}$

22. $f'(x) = (\sinh\sqrt{1-x^2})\left(\dfrac{-x}{\sqrt{1-x^2}}\right) = \dfrac{-x}{\sqrt{1-x^2}}\sinh\sqrt{1-x^2}$

23. $f'(x) = (2\sinh\sqrt{1-x^2}\cosh\sqrt{1-x^2})\left(\dfrac{-x}{\sqrt{1-x^2}}\right) = \dfrac{-2x}{\sqrt{1-x^2}}\sinh\sqrt{1-x^2}\cosh\sqrt{1-x^2}$

24. $f'(x) = e^{\operatorname{csch} x}(-\operatorname{csch} x\coth x) = -e^{\operatorname{csch} x}\operatorname{csch} x \coth x$

25. $f'(x) = \left[\sinh(\tan e^{2x})\right](\sec^2 e^{2x})(2e^{2x}) = 2e^{2x}(\sec^2 e^{2x})\sinh(\tan e^{2x})$

26. $f'(x) = \dfrac{1}{\sqrt{(-3x^2)^2+1}}(-6x) = \dfrac{-6x}{\sqrt{9x^4+1}}$

27. Since

$$\frac{dy}{dx} = \frac{\dfrac{1}{\sqrt{1+x^2}}\sqrt{1+x^2} - (\sinh^{-1}x)\left(\dfrac{x}{\sqrt{1+x^2}}\right)}{1+x^2} = \frac{1}{1+x^2} - \frac{xy}{1+x^2},$$

it follows that $(1+x^2)(dy/dx) = 1 - xy$, or $(1+x^2)(dy/dx) + xy = 1$.

28. $\displaystyle\int \operatorname{csch}^2 x\,dx = -\coth x + C$

29. $\displaystyle\int \operatorname{sech}^2 x\,dx = \tanh x + C$

30. $\displaystyle\int \tanh x\,dx = \int \frac{\sinh x}{\cosh x}\,dx = \ln\cosh x + C$

31. $\displaystyle\int 2^x \sinh 2^x\,dx \overset{u=2^x}{=} \int \sinh u \cdot \frac{1}{\ln 2}\,du = \frac{\cosh u}{\ln 2} + C = \frac{\cosh 2^x}{\ln 2} + C$

32. $\int e^x \sinh x\,dx = \int e^x\left(\frac{e^x - e^{-x}}{2}\right)dx = \frac{1}{2}\int (e^{2x}-1)\,dx = \frac{1}{2}\left(\frac{1}{2}e^{2x} - x\right) + C = \frac{1}{4}e^{2x} - \frac{x}{2} + C$

33. $\int_5^{10} \frac{1}{\sqrt{x^2+1}}\,dx = \sinh^{-1} 10 - \sinh^{-1} 5 = \ln(10+\sqrt{101}) - \ln(5+\sqrt{26}) = \ln\left(\frac{10+\sqrt{101}}{5+\sqrt{26}}\right)$

34. $\int_0^1 \frac{x}{\sqrt{1+x^4}}\,dx \overset{u=x^2}{=} \frac{1}{2}\int_0^1 \frac{1}{\sqrt{1+u^2}}\,du = \frac{1}{2}\sinh^{-1} 1 - \frac{1}{2}\sinh^{-1} 0 = \frac{1}{2}\ln(1+\sqrt{2})$

35. $A = \int_{-4}^{4} 4\cosh\frac{x}{4}\,dx \overset{u=x/4}{=} 4\int_{-1}^{1}(\cosh u)\cdot 4\,du = 16\sinh u\Big|_{-1}^{1}$

$= 16(\sinh 1 - \sinh(-1)) = 32\sinh 1 = 16(e - e^{-1})$

36. Since $z + 1/z \geq 2$ for $z > 0$, we have $\cosh x = \frac{1}{2}(e^x + e^{-x}) = \frac{1}{2}(e^x + 1/e^x) \geq \frac{1}{2}\cdot 2 = 1$ for all x.

37. If $x \geq 0$, then $\cosh x = \frac{1}{2}(e^x + e^{-x}) > \frac{1}{2}e^x = \frac{1}{2}e^{|x|}$.
If $x < 0$, then $\cosh x = \frac{1}{2}(e^x + e^{-x}) > \frac{1}{2}e^{-x} = \frac{1}{2}e^{|x|}$.
Thus $\cosh x > \frac{1}{2}e^{|x|}$ for all x.

38. a. $\cosh x + \sinh x = \frac{e^x + e^{-x}}{2} + \frac{e^x - e^{-x}}{2} = \frac{2e^x}{2} = e^x$ for all x.

b. $\cosh x - \sinh x = \frac{e^x + e^{-x}}{2} - \frac{e^x - e^{-x}}{2} = \frac{2e^{-x}}{2} = e^{-x}$ for all x.

39. a. From Exercise 38(a), $(\cosh x + \sinh x)^n = (e^x)^n = e^{nx} = \cosh nx + \sinh nx$ for all x.

b. From Exercise 38(b), $(\cosh x - \sinh x)^n = (e^{-x})^n = e^{-(nx)} = \cosh nx - \sinh nx$ for all x.

40. a. $2\sinh x\cosh x = 2\left(\frac{e^x - e^{-x}}{2}\right)\left(\frac{e^x + e^{-x}}{2}\right) = \frac{e^{2x} - e^{-2x}}{2} = \sinh 2x$

b. $\cosh^2 x + \sinh^2 x = \left(\frac{e^x + e^{-x}}{2}\right)^2 + \left(\frac{e^x - e^{-x}}{2}\right)^2 = \frac{e^{2x} + 2 + e^{-2x}}{4} + \frac{e^{2x} - 2 + e^{-2x}}{4}$

$= \frac{2e^{2x} + 2e^{-2x}}{4} = \frac{e^{2x} + e^{-2x}}{2} = \cosh 2x$

$2\sinh^2 x + 1 = 2\left(\frac{e^x - e^{-x}}{2}\right)^2 + 1 = \frac{e^{2x} - 2 + e^{-2x}}{2} + 1 = \frac{e^{2x} + e^{-2x}}{2} = \cosh 2x$

Thus $\cosh 2x = \cosh^2 x + \sinh^2 x = 2\sinh^2 x + 1$.

41. $f(x) = \frac{1}{2}(1 + \tanh x) = \frac{1}{2}\left(1 + \frac{\sinh x}{\cosh x}\right) = \frac{1}{2}\left(1 + \frac{(e^x - e^{-x})/2}{(e^x + e^{-x})/2}\right)$

$= \frac{1}{2}\left(1 + \frac{e^x - e^{-x}}{e^x + e^{-x}}\right) = \frac{1}{2}\left(\frac{e^x + e^{-x} + e^x - e^{-x}}{e^x + e^{-x}}\right) = \frac{e^x}{e^x + e^{-x}} = \frac{1}{1 + e^{-2x}}$

42. By Exercise 40(b) we know that $\cosh 2u = 2\sinh^2 u + 1$, so that $\sinh^2 u = \frac{1}{2}(\cosh 2u - 1)$. Let $x = \cosh u$, so that if $x = 1$ then $u = 0$, and if $x = \cosh t$ then $u = t$. Noting that $\sqrt{\cosh^2 u - 1} = \sinh u$ for $u \geq 0$, we find that

$$\int_1^{\cosh t} \sqrt{x^2 - 1}\,dx = \int_0^t \sqrt{\cosh^2 u - 1}\,\sinh u\,du = \int_0^t \sinh^2 u\,du$$

$$= \int_0^t \frac{1}{2}(\cosh 2u - 1)\,du = \frac{1}{2}\left(\frac{1}{2}\sinh 2u - u\right)\Big|_0^t = \frac{\sinh 2t}{4} - \frac{t}{2}.$$

43. Let the shaded region have area A. Since the area of the triangle with vertices $(0,0)$, $(\cosh t, 0)$, and $(\cosh t, \sinh t)$ is $\frac{1}{2}(\sinh t)(\cosh t)$, it follows that

$$A = \frac{1}{2}(\sinh t)(\cosh t) - \int_1^{\cosh t} \sqrt{x^2-1}\,dx.$$

From Exercise 40(a) we know that $2\sinh t\,\cosh t = \sinh 2t$, and from Exercise 42 we have

$$\int_1^{\cosh t} \sqrt{x^2-1}\,dx = \frac{\sinh 2t}{4} - \frac{t}{2}.$$

Thus

$$A = \frac{1}{4}\sinh 2t - \left(\frac{\sinh 2t}{4} - \frac{t}{2}\right) = \frac{t}{2}.$$

44. a. $f(0) = c\cosh 0 = c$

b. $y = c\left(\dfrac{e^{x/c}+e^{-x/c}}{2}\right) = \dfrac{c}{2}\left(\dfrac{e^{2x/c}+1}{e^{x/c}}\right)$; $2e^{x/c}y = c(e^{2x/c}+1)$; $(e^{x/c})^2 - \dfrac{2}{c}ye^{x/c} + 1 = 0$;

$$e^{x/c} = \frac{(2/c)y + \sqrt{(4/c^2)y^2 - 4}}{2} = \frac{y+\sqrt{y^2-c^2}}{c};\ \frac{x}{c} = \ln\left(\frac{y+\sqrt{y^2-c^2}}{c}\right);$$

$$f^{-1}(x) = c\ln\left(\frac{x+\sqrt{x^2-c^2}}{c}\right) \quad \text{for } x \ge c$$

45. a. $\sinh^{-1}\sqrt{x^2-1} = \ln\left[\sqrt{x^2-1} + \sqrt{\left(\sqrt{x^2-1}\right)^2+1}\right]$

$$= \ln\left(\sqrt{x^2-1}+\sqrt{x^2}\right) = \ln\left(\sqrt{x^2-1}+x\right) = \cosh^{-1}x \quad \text{for } x \ge 1$$

b. $\cosh^{-1}\sqrt{x^2+1} = \ln\left[\sqrt{x^2+1} + \sqrt{\left(\sqrt{x^2+1}\right)^2-1}\right]$

$$= \ln\left(\sqrt{x^2+1}+\sqrt{x^2}\right) = \ln\left(\sqrt{x^2+1}+x\right) = \sinh^{-1}x \quad \text{for } x \ge 0$$

46. Let $a = \sqrt{\dfrac{kg}{m}}$. Then

$$\lim_{t\to\infty}\tanh\left(\sqrt{\frac{kg}{m}}\,t\right) = \lim_{t\to\infty}\frac{\sinh(at)}{\cosh(at)} = \lim_{t\to\infty}\frac{(e^{at}-e^{-at})/2}{(e^{at}+e^{-at})/2}$$

$$= \lim_{t\to\infty}\frac{e^{at}-e^{-at}}{e^{at}+e^{-at}} = \lim_{t\to\infty}\frac{1-e^{-2at}}{1+e^{-2at}} = \frac{1-0}{1+0} = 1.$$

Therefore

$$\lim_{t\to\infty} v(t) = \lim_{t\to\infty}\left[-\sqrt{\frac{mg}{k}}\tanh\left(\sqrt{\frac{kg}{m}}\,t\right)\right] = -\sqrt{\frac{mg}{k}}.$$

47. a. Since the minimum value of $\cosh x$ is 1, the maximum value of $694 - 69\cosh(x/100)$ is $694 - 69 = 625$.

b. $y = 0$ if $694 - 69\cosh(x/100) = 0$, or $\cosh(x/100) = 694/69$. This is equivalent to

$$\frac{e^{x/100} + e^{-x/100}}{2} = \frac{694}{69},$$

$$\text{or}\quad (e^{x/100})^2 + 1 = (1388/69)e^{x/100}, \quad\text{or}\quad (e^{x/100})^2 - (1388/69)e^{x/100} + 1 = 0.$$

Thus $e^{x/100}$ must be one of the two solutions, say z_1 and z_2, of the quadratic equation $z^2 - (1388/69)z + 1 = 0$. Therefore x must be $100\ln z_1$ or $100\ln z_2$. Using the quadratic formula and a calculator, we find that $x \approx -300$ or $x \approx 300$. Thus the distance between the two intercepts is approximately 600.

6.5 The Inverse Trigonometric Functions

1. Since $\sin\frac{\pi}{3} = \frac{\sqrt{3}}{2}$ and $-\frac{\pi}{2} \le \frac{\pi}{3} \le \frac{\pi}{2}$, it follows that $\sin^{-1}\frac{\sqrt{3}}{2} = \frac{\pi}{3}$.

2. Since $\sin\frac{\pi}{2} = 1$ and $-\frac{\pi}{2} \le \frac{\pi}{2} \le \frac{\pi}{2}$, it follows that $\sin^{-1} 1 = \frac{\pi}{2}$.

3. Since $\cos\frac{\pi}{4} = \frac{\sqrt{2}}{2}$ and $0 \le \frac{\pi}{4} \le \pi$, it follows that $\cos^{-1}\frac{\sqrt{2}}{2} = \frac{\pi}{4}$.

4. Since $\cos\frac{2\pi}{3} = -\frac{1}{2}$ and $0 \le \frac{2\pi}{3} \le \pi$, it follows that $\cos^{-1}\left(-\frac{1}{2}\right) = \frac{2\pi}{3}$.

5. Since $\tan\left(-\frac{\pi}{6}\right) = -\frac{1}{\sqrt{3}}$ and $-\frac{\pi}{2} < -\frac{\pi}{6} < \frac{\pi}{2}$, it follows that $\tan^{-1}\left(-\frac{1}{\sqrt{3}}\right) = -\frac{\pi}{6}$.

6. Since $\tan\frac{\pi}{3} = \sqrt{3}$ and $-\frac{\pi}{2} < \frac{\pi}{3} < \frac{\pi}{2}$, it follows that $\tan^{-1}\sqrt{3} = \frac{\pi}{3}$.

7. Since $\cot\frac{\pi}{6} = \sqrt{3}$ and $0 < \frac{\pi}{6} < \pi$, it follows that $\cot^{-1}\sqrt{3} = \frac{\pi}{6}$.

8. Since $\cot\frac{3\pi}{4} = -1$ and $0 < \frac{3\pi}{4} < \pi$, it follows that $\cot^{-1}(-1) = \frac{3\pi}{4}$.

9. Since $\sec\frac{5\pi}{4} = -\sqrt{2}$ and $\pi \le \frac{5\pi}{4} < \frac{3\pi}{2}$, it follows that $\sec^{-1}(-\sqrt{2}) = \frac{5\pi}{4}$.

10. Since $\csc\frac{\pi}{3} = \frac{2\sqrt{3}}{3}$ and $0 < \frac{\pi}{3} < \frac{\pi}{2}$, it follows that $\csc^{-1}\frac{2\sqrt{3}}{3} = \frac{\pi}{3}$.

11. $\sin\left(\sin^{-1}\left(-\frac{1}{2}\right)\right) = \sin\left(-\frac{\pi}{6}\right) = -\frac{1}{2}$

12. $\sin\left(\cos^{-1}\frac{\sqrt{2}}{2}\right) = \sin\frac{\pi}{4} = \frac{\sqrt{2}}{2}$

13. $\tan(\sec^{-1}\sqrt{2}) = \tan\frac{\pi}{4} = 1$

14. $\sec\left(\cos^{-1}\dfrac{\sqrt{3}}{2}\right) = \sec\dfrac{\pi}{6} = \dfrac{2\sqrt{3}}{3}$

15. $\csc(\cot^{-1}(-\sqrt{3})) = \csc\dfrac{5\pi}{6} = 2$

16. $\tan^{-1}(\tan 0) = \tan^{-1} 0 = 0$

17. $\sin^{-1}\left(\cos\dfrac{\pi}{6}\right) = \sin^{-1}\dfrac{1}{2}\sqrt{3} = \dfrac{\pi}{3}$

18. $\cot^{-1}\left(\tan\dfrac{\pi}{3}\right) = \cot^{-1}\sqrt{3} = \dfrac{\pi}{6}$

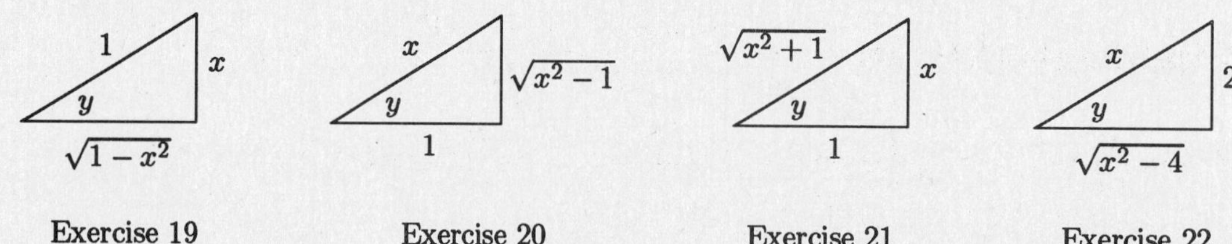

Exercise 19 Exercise 20 Exercise 21 Exercise 22

19. We will evaluate $\cos(\sin^{-1} x)$ by evaluating $\cos y$ for the value of y in $[-\pi/2, \pi/2]$ such that $\sin^{-1} x = y$, that is, $\sin y = x$. From the diagram we have $\cos(\sin^{-1} x) = \cos y = \sqrt{1-x^2}$.

20. We will evaluate $\sin(\sec^{-1} x)$ by evaluating $\sin y$ for the value of y in $[0, \pi/2)$ or $[\pi, 3\pi/2)$ such that $\sec^{-1} x = y$, that is, $\sec y = x$. From the figure we have $\sin(\sec^{-1} x) = \sin y = \sqrt{x^2-1}/x$.

21. We will evaluate $\sec(\tan^{-1} x)$ by evaluating $\sec y$ for the value of y in $(-\pi/2, \pi/2)$ such that $\tan^{-1} x = y$, that is, $\tan y = x$. From the diagram we have $\sec(\tan^{-1} x) = \sec y = \sqrt{x^2+1}$.

22. We will evaluate $\tan(\csc^{-1}(x/2))$ by evaluating $\tan y$ for the value of y in $[0, \pi/2)$ or $[\pi, 3\pi/2)$ such that $\csc^{-1}(x/2) = y$, that is, $\csc y = x/2$. From the figure we have $\tan(\csc^{-1}(x/2)) = \tan y = 2/\sqrt{x^2-4}$.

23. We will evaluate $\cos(\cot^{-1} x^2)$ by evaluating $\cos y$ for the value of y in $(0, \pi)$ such that $\cot^{-1} x^2 = y$, that is, $\cot y = x^2$. Since $x^2 \geq 0$, we have $0 < y \leq \pi/2$. We find from the diagram that $\cos(\cot^{-1} x^2) = \cos y = x^2/\sqrt{x^4+1}$.

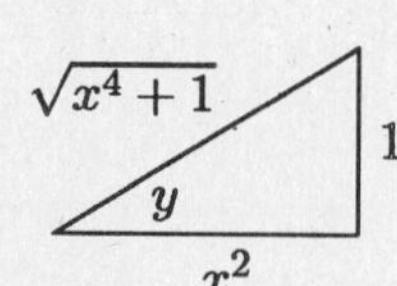

24. We will evaluate $\tan(\cos^{-1}\sqrt{1-x})$ by evaluating $\tan y$ for the value of y in $[0, \pi/2)$ or $(\pi/2, \pi]$ such that $\cos^{-1}\sqrt{1-x} = y$, that is, $\cos y = \sqrt{1-x}$. Since $\sqrt{1-x} \geq 0$, we have $0 < y < \pi/2$, and since $\cos y \leq 1$, we have $x \geq 0$. From the diagram we find that $\tan(\cos^{-1}\sqrt{1-x}) = \tan y = \sqrt{x}/\sqrt{1-x}$.

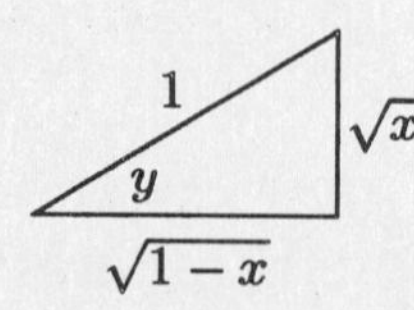

25. Using a trigonometric identity for $\cos 2a$ and the fact that $\cos(\sin^{-1} x) = \sqrt{1-x^2}$ (see Exercise 19), we find that $\cos(2\sin^{-1} x) = \cos^2(\sin^{-1} x) - \sin^2(\sin^{-1} x) = (\sqrt{1-x^2})^2 - x^2 = (1-x^2) - x^2 = 1 - 2x^2$.

26. Using a trigonometric identity for $\sin 2a$ and the fact that $\cos(\sin^{-1}x) = \sqrt{1-x^2}$ (see Exercise 19), we find that $\sin(2\sin^{-1}x) = 2\sin(\sin^{-1}x)\cos(\sin^{-1}x) = 2x\sqrt{1-x^2}$.

27. Using (7), we find that $\dfrac{d}{dx}\cos^{-1}x = \dfrac{-1}{\sqrt{1-x^2}}$, so that by the Chain Rule,

$$f'(x) = \frac{-1}{\sqrt{1-(-3x)^2}}(-3) = \frac{3}{\sqrt{1-9x^2}}.$$

28. Using (1), we find that $f'(x) = \sin^{-1}x^2 + \dfrac{x}{\sqrt{1-(x^2)^2}}(2x) = \sin^{-1}x^2 + \dfrac{2x^2}{\sqrt{1-x^4}}$.

29. Using (4), we find that $f'(t) = \dfrac{1}{(\sqrt{t})^2+1}\left(\dfrac{1}{2\sqrt{t}}\right) = \dfrac{1}{2(t+1)\sqrt{t}}$.

30. Using (4), we find that $f'(x) = \dfrac{1}{((x+1)/(x-1))^2+1}\left[\dfrac{-2}{(x-1)^2}\right] = \dfrac{-1}{x^2+1}$.

31. By (8), $\dfrac{d}{dx}\cot^{-1}x = \dfrac{-1}{x^2+1}$, so that if $f(x) = \cot^{-1}\sqrt{1-x^2}$, then

$$f'(x) = \frac{-1}{(\sqrt{1-x^2})^2+1}\left(\frac{-x}{\sqrt{1-x^2}}\right) = \frac{x}{(2-x^2)\sqrt{1-x^2}}.$$

32. By (9), $\dfrac{d}{dx}\sec^{-1}x = \dfrac{1}{x\sqrt{x^2-1}}$, so that $f'(u) = \dfrac{1}{u\sqrt{(-u)^2-1}} = \dfrac{-1}{u\sqrt{u^2-1}}$.

33. $\displaystyle\int \frac{1}{x^2+16}\,dx = \frac{1}{4}\tan^{-1}\frac{x}{4} + C$

34. $\displaystyle\int \frac{1}{t^2+6}\,dt = \frac{1}{\sqrt{6}}\tan^{-1}\frac{t}{\sqrt{6}} + C$

35. $\displaystyle\int \frac{1}{9x^2+16}\,dx = \frac{1}{9}\int \frac{1}{x^2+\frac{16}{9}}\,dx = \frac{1}{9}\cdot\frac{3}{4}\tan^{-1}\frac{3x}{4} + C = \frac{1}{12}\tan^{-1}\frac{3x}{4} + C$

36. $$\int \frac{1}{x^2+4x+7}\,dx = \int \frac{1}{(x+2)^2+3}\,dx \overset{u=x+2}{=} \int \frac{1}{u^2+3}\,du$$
$$= \frac{1}{\sqrt{3}}\tan^{-1}\frac{u}{\sqrt{3}} + C = \frac{1}{\sqrt{3}}\tan^{-1}\frac{x+2}{\sqrt{3}} + C$$

37. $$\int \frac{1}{2x^2+4x+6}\,dx = \frac{1}{2}\int \frac{1}{(x+1)^2+2}\,dx \overset{u=x+1}{=} \frac{1}{2}\int \frac{1}{u^2+2}\,du$$
$$= \frac{1}{2}\left(\frac{1}{\sqrt{2}}\tan^{-1}\frac{u}{\sqrt{2}}\right) + C = \frac{\sqrt{2}}{4}\tan^{-1}\frac{x+1}{\sqrt{2}} + C$$

38. $$\int \frac{1}{t^2-3t+3}\,dt = \int \frac{1}{(t-\frac{3}{2})^2+\frac{3}{4}}\,dt \overset{u=t-3/2}{=} \int \frac{1}{u^2+\frac{3}{4}}\,du$$
$$= \frac{2}{\sqrt{3}}\tan^{-1}\frac{2}{\sqrt{3}}u + C = \frac{2}{\sqrt{3}}\tan^{-1}\left[\frac{2}{\sqrt{3}}\left(t-\frac{3}{2}\right)\right] + C$$

39. $\int \frac{1}{\sqrt{9-4x^2}}\,dx = \frac{1}{2}\int \frac{1}{\sqrt{\frac{9}{4}-x^2}}\,dx = \frac{1}{2}\sin^{-1}\frac{2x}{3} + C$

40. $\int \frac{1}{\sqrt{4-9x^2}}\,dx = \frac{1}{3}\int \frac{1}{\sqrt{\frac{4}{9}-x^2}}\,dx = \frac{1}{3}\sin^{-1}\frac{3x}{2} + C$

41. $\int \frac{1}{x\sqrt{x^2-25}}\,dx = \frac{1}{5}\sec^{-1}\frac{x}{5} + C$

42. $\int \frac{1}{x\sqrt{4x^4-25}}\,dx = \int \frac{1}{x^2\sqrt{4x^4-25}}\,x\,dx \overset{u=2x^2}{=} \int \frac{1}{(u/2)\sqrt{u^2-25}}\left(\frac{1}{4}\right)du$

$= \frac{1}{2}\int \frac{1}{u\sqrt{u^2-25}}\,du = \frac{1}{10}\sec^{-1}\frac{u}{5} + C = \frac{1}{10}\sec^{-1}\frac{2x^2}{5} + C$

43. $\int \frac{x^3}{\sqrt{1-x^8}}\,dx \overset{u=x^4}{=} \frac{1}{4}\int \frac{1}{\sqrt{1-u^2}}\,du = \frac{1}{4}\sin^{-1}u + C = \frac{1}{4}\sin^{-1}x^4 + C$

44. $\int \frac{1}{x\ln x\,\sqrt{(\ln x)^2-1}}\,dx \overset{u=\ln x}{=} \int \frac{1}{u\sqrt{u^2-1}}\,du = \sec^{-1}u + C = \sec^{-1}(\ln x) + C$

45. $\int \frac{e^{-x}}{1+e^{-2x}}\,dx \overset{u=e^{-x}}{=} \int \frac{-1}{1+u^2}\,du = -\tan^{-1}u + C = -\tan^{-1}e^{-x} + C$

46. $\int \frac{e^{3x}}{\sqrt{1-e^{6x}}}\,dx \overset{u=e^{3x}}{=} \int \frac{1}{\sqrt{1-u^2}}\frac{1}{3}\,du = \frac{1}{3}\sin^{-1}u + C = \frac{1}{3}\sin^{-1}e^{3x} + C$

47. $\int \frac{\tan^{-1}2x}{1+4x^2}\,dx \overset{u=\tan^{-1}2x}{=} \frac{1}{2}\int u\,du = \frac{1}{4}u^2 + C = \frac{1}{4}(\tan^{-1}2x)^2 + C$

48. $\int \frac{1}{x[1+(\ln x)^2]}\,dx \overset{u=\ln x}{=} \int \frac{1}{1+u^2}\,du = \tan^{-1}u + C = \tan^{-1}(\ln x) + C$

49. $\int \frac{\cos t}{9+\sin^2 t}\,dt \overset{u=\sin t}{=} \int \frac{1}{9+u^2}\,du = \frac{1}{3}\tan^{-1}\frac{u}{3} + C = \frac{1}{3}\tan^{-1}\left(\frac{1}{3}\sin t\right) + C$

50. $\int \frac{\sec^2 x}{\sqrt{4-\tan^2 x}}\,dx \overset{u=\tan x}{=} \int \frac{1}{\sqrt{4-u^2}}\,du = \sin^{-1}\frac{u}{2} + C = \sin^{-1}\left(\frac{1}{2}\tan x\right) + C$

51. $\int \frac{\cos 4x}{(\sin 4x)\sqrt{16\sin^2 4x-4}}\,dx \overset{u=4\sin 4x}{=} \int \frac{1}{\frac{1}{4}u\sqrt{u^2-4}}\left(\frac{1}{16}\right)du = \frac{1}{4}\int \frac{1}{u\sqrt{u^2-4}}\,du$

$= \frac{1}{8}\sec^{-1}\frac{u}{2} + C = \frac{1}{8}\sec^{-1}(2\sin 4x) + C$

52. $\int \frac{x^{n-1}}{1+x^{2n}}\,dx \overset{u=x^n}{=} \frac{1}{n}\int \frac{1}{1+u^2}\,du = \frac{1}{n}\tan^{-1}u + C = \frac{1}{n}\tan^{-1}x^n + C$

53. $\int_0^2 \frac{1}{\sqrt{16-x^2}}\,dx = \sin^{-1}\frac{x}{4}\Big|_0^2 = \sin^{-1}\frac{1}{2} - \sin^{-1}0 = \frac{1}{6}\pi$

54. $\displaystyle\int_{-2}^{2\sqrt{3}-2} \frac{1}{u^2+4u+8}\,du = \int_{-2}^{2\sqrt{3}-2} \frac{1}{(u+2)^2+4}\,du = \frac{1}{2}\tan^{-1}\left(\frac{u+2}{2}\right)\Big|_{-2}^{2\sqrt{3}-2}$

$$= \frac{1}{2}(\tan^{-1}\sqrt{3} - \tan^{-1}0) = \frac{1}{6}\pi$$

55. $\displaystyle\int_{4\sqrt{3}/3}^{4} \frac{1}{x\sqrt{x^2-4}}\,dx = \frac{1}{2}\sec^{-1}\frac{x}{2}\Big|_{4\sqrt{3}/3}^{4} = \frac{1}{2}\left(\sec^{-1}2 - \sec^{-1}\frac{2\sqrt{3}}{3}\right) = \frac{1}{2}\left(\frac{\pi}{3}-\frac{\pi}{6}\right) = \frac{1}{12}\pi$

56. We have $y = \sin^{-1}(\sin x) = x$ for $-\pi/2 \le x \le \pi/2$, so the part of the graph corresponding to the interval $[-\pi/2, \pi/2]$ is part of the line $y = x$. For $\pi/2 \le x \le 3\pi/2$, $\sin x = -\sin(x-\pi)$, so $y = \sin^{-1}(\sin x) = \sin^{-1}(-\sin(x-\pi)) = -\sin^{-1}(\sin(x-\pi)) = -(x-\pi) = \pi - x$ since $-\pi/2 \le \pi - x \le \pi/2$. Thus the part of the graph corresponding to the interval $[\pi/2, 3\pi/2]$ is part of the line $y = \pi - x$. Finally, since $\sin x$ has period 2π, so does $\sin^{-1}(\sin x)$, which means the graph is repeated every 2π units.

57. The graphs intersect at (x, y) if $1/(x^2-2x+4) = y = \frac{1}{3}$, or $3 = x^2 - 2x + 4$, or $x^2 - 2x + 1 = 0$, or $x = 1$. Since $\frac{1}{3} \ge 1/(x^2-2x+4)$ on $[0, 1]$, we have

$$A = \int_0^1 \left(\frac{1}{3} - \frac{1}{x^2-2x+4}\right)dx = \int_0^1 \left(\frac{1}{3} - \frac{1}{(x-1)^2+3}\right)dx = \left(\frac{x}{3} - \frac{1}{\sqrt{3}}\tan^{-1}\frac{x-1}{\sqrt{3}}\right)\Big|_0^1$$

$$= \left(\frac{1}{3} - 0\right) - \left(0 - \frac{1}{\sqrt{3}}\tan^{-1}\frac{-1}{\sqrt{3}}\right) = \frac{1}{3} - \frac{1}{18}\pi\sqrt{3}.$$

58. The graphs intersect at (x, y) if $1/x = 1/\sqrt{1-x^2}$, or $\sqrt{1-x^2} = x$. Then $x \ge 0$ and $1 - x^2 = x^2$, so that $x = \frac{1}{2}\sqrt{2}$. Also $1/x \ge 1/\sqrt{1-x^2}$ on $[\frac{1}{2}, \frac{1}{2}\sqrt{2}]$ and $1/\sqrt{1-x^2} \ge 1/x$ on $[\frac{1}{2}\sqrt{2}, \frac{1}{2}\sqrt{3}]$. Thus

$$A = \int_{1/2}^{\sqrt{2}/2} \left(\frac{1}{x} - \frac{1}{\sqrt{1-x^2}}\right)dx + \int_{\sqrt{2}/2}^{\sqrt{3}/2} \left(\frac{1}{\sqrt{1-x^2}} - \frac{1}{x}\right)dx$$

$$= (\ln x - \sin^{-1}x)\Big|_{1/2}^{\sqrt{2}/2} + (\sin^{-1}x - \ln x)\Big|_{\sqrt{2}/2}^{\sqrt{3}/2}$$

$$= \left[\left(\ln\frac{\sqrt{2}}{2} - \frac{\pi}{4}\right) - \left(\ln\frac{1}{2} - \frac{\pi}{6}\right)\right] + \left[\left(\frac{\pi}{3} - \ln\frac{\sqrt{3}}{2}\right) - \left(\frac{\pi}{4} - \ln\frac{\sqrt{2}}{2}\right)\right] = \ln 2 - \frac{1}{2}\ln 3.$$

59. Let $f(x) = \sin^{-1}x$, so that $f^{-1}(y) = \sin y$. Also let $a = 0$ and $b = 1$, so that $f(a) = \sin^{-1}0 = 0$ and $f(b) = \sin^{-1}1 = \pi/2$. Therefore by the formula,

$$\int_0^1 \sin^{-1}x\,dx = 1\sin^{-1}1 - 0\sin^{-1}0 - \int_0^{\pi/2} \sin y\,dy = \frac{\pi}{2} + \cos y\Big|_0^{\pi/2} = \frac{\pi}{2} - 1.$$

60. $\displaystyle\int \frac{1}{a^2\sin^2 x + b^2\cos^2 x}\,dx = \int \frac{1}{a^2\tan^2 x + b^2}\cdot\frac{1}{\cos^2 x}\,dx = \int \frac{1}{a^2\tan^2 x + b^2}\sec^2 x\,dx$

$$\overset{u=\tan x}{=} \int \frac{1}{a^2u^2+b^2}\,du = \frac{1}{a^2}\int \frac{1}{u^2+(b/a)^2}\,du$$

$$= \frac{1}{a^2}\cdot\frac{a}{b}\tan^{-1}\frac{a}{b}u + C = \frac{1}{ab}\tan^{-1}\left(\frac{a}{b}\tan x\right) + C$$

61. Let $f(x) = \tan^{-1} x$. Then $f'(x) = 1/(1+x^2)$ and $f''(x) = -2x/(1+x^2)^2$. Since $f'(0)$ exists, $f''(x) > 0$ for $x < 0$, and $f''(x) < 0$ for $x > 0$, there is an inflection point at $x = 0$.

62. By the trigonometric identity for $\sin(a+b)$ and the fact that $\cos(\sin^{-1} x) = \sqrt{1-x^2}$ (see Exercise 19), we find that

$$\sin(\sin^{-1} x + \sin^{-1} y) = \sin(\sin^{-1} x)\cos(\sin^{-1} y) + \cos(\sin^{-1} x)\sin(\sin^{-1} y)$$
$$= x\cos(\sin^{-1} y) + y\cos(\sin^{-1} x) = x\sqrt{1-y^2} + y\sqrt{1-x^2}.$$

Thus if $\sin^{-1} x + \sin^{-1} y$ lies in $[-\pi/2, \pi/2]$, then by definition of the inverse sine function we have $\sin^{-1} x + \sin^{-1} y = \sin^{-1}(x\sqrt{1-y^2} + y\sqrt{1-x^2})$.

63. $$\frac{d}{dx}\left(\tan^{-1}\frac{x}{\sqrt{1-x^2}}\right) = \frac{1}{1+[x/\sqrt{1-x^2}]^2}\cdot\frac{\sqrt{1-x^2}+(x^2/\sqrt{1-x^2})}{1-x^2}$$
$$= (1+x^2)\cdot\frac{1}{(1-x^2)^{3/2}} = \frac{1}{\sqrt{1-x^2}} = \frac{d}{dx}(\sin^{-1} x)$$

Thus by Theorem 4.6 there is a constant C such that $\tan^{-1}\left(x/\sqrt{1-x^2}\right) = \sin^{-1} x + C$. For $x = 0$ we obtain $0 = \tan^{-1} 0 = \sin^{-1} 0 + C = C$, so that $C = 0$ and thus

$$\tan^{-1}\frac{x}{\sqrt{1-x^2}} = \sin^{-1} x.$$

64. By the trigonometric identity for $\tan(a+b)$,

$$\tan(\tan^{-1} x + \tan^{-1} y) = \frac{\tan(\tan^{-1} x) + \tan(\tan^{-1} y)}{1 - \tan(\tan^{-1} x)\tan(\tan^{-1} y)} = \frac{x+y}{1-xy}.$$

Thus if $\tan^{-1} x + \tan^{-1} y$ lies in $(-\pi/2, \pi/2)$, then by definition of the inverse tangent function we have

$$\tan^{-1} x + \tan^{-1} y = \tan^{-1}\frac{x+y}{1-xy} \quad \text{for } xy \neq 1.$$

65. a. $$\tan^{-1}\frac{1}{2} + \tan^{-1}\frac{1}{3} = \tan^{-1}\frac{\frac{1}{2}+\frac{1}{3}}{1-(\frac{1}{2})(\frac{1}{3})} = \tan^{-1} 1 = \frac{\pi}{4}$$

b. $$2\tan^{-1}\frac{1}{3} + \tan^{-1}\frac{1}{7} = \tan^{-1}\frac{\frac{1}{3}+\frac{1}{3}}{1-(\frac{1}{3})(\frac{1}{3})} + \tan^{-1}\frac{1}{7} = \tan^{-1}\frac{3}{4} + \tan^{-1}\frac{1}{7}$$
$$= \tan^{-1}\frac{\frac{3}{4}+\frac{1}{7}}{1-(\frac{3}{4})(\frac{1}{7})} = \tan^{-1} 1 = \frac{\pi}{4}$$

c. $$\tan^{-1}\frac{120}{119} - \tan^{-1}\frac{1}{239} = \tan^{-1}\frac{\frac{120}{119}-\frac{1}{239}}{1+(\frac{120}{119})(\frac{1}{239})} = \tan^{-1} 1 = \frac{\pi}{4}$$

d. Using Exercise 64 twice, we find that

$$4\tan^{-1}\frac{1}{5} = 2\tan^{-1}\frac{\frac{1}{5}+\frac{1}{5}}{1-(\frac{1}{5})(\frac{1}{5})} = 2\tan^{-1}\frac{5}{12} = \tan^{-1}\frac{\frac{5}{12}+\frac{5}{12}}{1-(\frac{5}{12})(\frac{5}{12})} = \tan^{-1}\frac{120}{119}.$$

Now by (c) we obtain $4\tan^{-1}\frac{1}{5} - \tan^{-1}\frac{1}{239} = \tan^{-1}\frac{120}{119} - \tan^{-1}\frac{1}{239} = \pi/4$.

66. By Exercise 64,

$$\tan^{-1}\frac{1}{4}+\tan^{-1}c=\tan^{-1}\frac{1/4+c}{1-c/4}=\tan^{-1}\frac{1+4c}{4-c}.$$

If there is a number c such that $\tan^{-1}\frac{1}{4}+\tan^{-1}c=\pi/4$, then $\pi/4=\tan^{-1}(1+4c)/(4-c)$, so that $1=\tan(\pi/4)=(1+4c)/(4-c)$ and thus $4-c=1+4c$, which means that $c=\frac{3}{5}$. You can check that this value of c satisfies the given equation.

67. $f'(x)=\dfrac{1}{1+x^2}+\dfrac{1}{1+1/x^2}\left(-\dfrac{1}{x^2}\right)=\dfrac{1}{1+x^2}-\dfrac{1}{1+x^2}=0$

on $(-\infty,0)$ and on $(0,\infty)$. Thus on $(-\infty,0)$ there is a constant c_1 such that $f(x)=c_1$; since $f(-1)=\tan^{-1}(-1)+\tan^{-1}(-1)=-\pi/4-\pi/4=-\pi/2$, it follows that on $(-\infty,0)$, $f(x)=-\pi/2$. Similarly, on $(0,\infty)$ there is a constant c_2 such that $f(x)=c_2$; since $f(1)=\tan^{-1}1+\tan^{-1}1=\pi/4+\pi/4=\pi/2$, it follows that on $(0,\infty)$, $f(x)=\pi/2$.

68. From Exercise 64 and the hypothesis that $bc=1+a^2$, we have

$$\tan^{-1}\frac{1}{a+b}+\tan^{-1}\frac{1}{a+c}=\tan^{-1}\frac{\dfrac{1}{a+b}+\dfrac{1}{a+c}}{1-\left(\dfrac{1}{a+b}\right)\left(\dfrac{1}{a+c}\right)}=\tan^{-1}\frac{2a+b+c}{(a+b)(a+c)-1}$$

$$=\tan^{-1}\frac{2a+b+c}{a^2+ab+ac+bc-1}=\tan^{-1}\frac{2a+b+c}{a^2+ab+ac+a^2}=\tan^{-1}\frac{2a+b+c}{a(2a+b+c)}=\tan^{-1}\frac{1}{a}.$$

69. We will use trigonometric identities for $\cos 2a$ and $\sin(\pi/2-a)$, along with the fact that $\cos(\sin^{-1}x)=\sqrt{1-x^2}$ (see Exercise 19).

a. Notice that

$$\sin\left(\frac{\pi}{2}-2\sin^{-1}\sqrt{1-\frac{x}{6}}\right)=\cos\left(2\sin^{-1}\sqrt{1-\frac{x}{6}}\right)$$

$$=\cos^2\left(\sin^{-1}\sqrt{1-\frac{x}{6}}\right)-\sin^2\left(\sin^{-1}\sqrt{1-\frac{x}{6}}\right)$$

$$=\left[\sqrt{1-\left(\sqrt{1-\frac{x}{6}}\right)^2}\right]^2-\left(\sqrt{1-\frac{x}{6}}\right)^2=\left[1-\left(1-\frac{x}{6}\right)\right]-\left(1-\frac{x}{6}\right)=\frac{x}{3}-1.$$

Since $-\pi/2\le\pi/2-2\sin^{-1}\sqrt{1-x/6}\le\pi/2$, it follows that

$$\sin^{-1}\left(\frac{x}{3}-1\right)=\frac{\pi}{2}-2\sin^{-1}\sqrt{1-\frac{x}{6}}.$$

b. Notice that

$$\sin\left(2\sin^{-1}\frac{\sqrt{x}}{\sqrt{6}}-\frac{\pi}{2}\right)=-\sin\left(\frac{\pi}{2}-2\sin^{-1}\frac{\sqrt{x}}{\sqrt{6}}\right)=-\cos\left(2\sin^{-1}\frac{\sqrt{x}}{\sqrt{6}}\right)$$

$$=\sin^2\left(\sin^{-1}\frac{\sqrt{x}}{\sqrt{6}}\right)-\cos^2\left(\sin^{-1}\frac{\sqrt{x}}{\sqrt{6}}\right)$$

$$= \left(\frac{\sqrt{x}}{\sqrt{6}}\right)^2 - \left[\sqrt{1-\left(\frac{\sqrt{x}}{\sqrt{6}}\right)^2}\right]^2 = \frac{x}{6} - \left(1-\frac{x}{6}\right) = \frac{x}{3} - 1.$$

Since $-\pi/2 \le 2\sin^{-1}(\sqrt{x}/\sqrt{6}) - \pi/2 \le \pi/2$, it follows that $\sin^{-1}(x/3-1) = 2\sin^{-1}(\sqrt{x}/\sqrt{6}) - \pi/2$.

70. a. $f'(x) = \dfrac{1}{1+[(x+1)/(x-1)]^2}\left[\dfrac{x-1-(x+1)}{(x-1)^2}\right] = \left[\dfrac{(x-1)^2}{(x-1)^2+(x+1)^2}\right]\left[\dfrac{-2}{(x-1)^2}\right]$

$= \dfrac{-2}{2x^2+2} = \dfrac{-1}{x^2+1}$ for $x \ne 1$.

b. $f''(x) = \dfrac{2x}{(x^2+1)^2}$ for $x \ne 1$.

c. Since $\displaystyle\lim_{x\to 1^+} \frac{x+1}{x-1} = \infty$, we have $\displaystyle\lim_{x\to 1^+} f(x) = \lim_{x\to 1^+} \tan^{-1}\frac{x+1}{x-1} = \frac{\pi}{2}$.

Since $\displaystyle\lim_{x\to 1^-} \frac{x+1}{x-1} = -\infty$, we have $\displaystyle\lim_{x\to 1^-} f(x) = \lim_{x\to 1^-} \tan^{-1}\frac{x+1}{x-1} = -\frac{\pi}{2}$.

d.

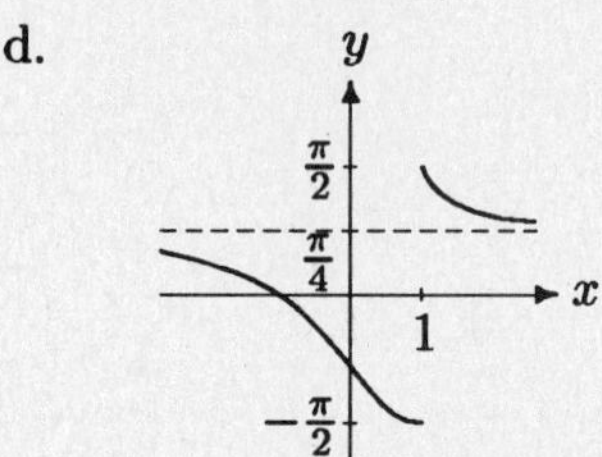

e. Since $\tan^{-1} x$ is continuous at 1, it follows that $\lim_{x\to 1^+}(-\tan^{-1} x + C) = \lim_{x\to 1^-}(-\tan^{-1} x + C)$ for any value of C. But by (c), $\lim_{x\to 1^+} f(x) \ne \lim_{x\to 1^-} f(x)$. Thus the conclusion of the exercise is valid.

f. Since f and $-\tan^{-1} x$ have the same derivative on $(-\infty, 1)$, we know by Theorem 4.6 that there is a constant C_1 such that $f(x) = -\tan^{-1} x + C_1$ for $x < 1$. For $x = 0$ we obtain $-\pi/4 = 0 + C_1$, so that $C_1 = -\pi/4$. Similarly, since f and $-\tan^{-1} x$ have the same derivative on $(1, \infty)$, we know by Theorem 4.6 that there is a constant C_2 such that $f(x) = -\tan^{-1} x + C_2$ for $x > 1$. Since

$$\lim_{x\to 1^+} f(x) = \lim_{x\to 1^+} \tan^{-1}\frac{x+1}{x-1} = \frac{\pi}{2} \quad \text{and} \quad \lim_{x\to 1^+} -\tan^{-1} x = \frac{-\pi}{4}$$

we have $\pi/2 = -\pi/4 + C_2$, so that $C_2 = 3\pi/4$.

71. a. Let $f(x) = \sin^{-1} x + \cos^{-1} x$. Then $f'(x) = 1/\sqrt{1-x^2} - 1/\sqrt{1-x^2} = 0$, so by part (a) of Theorem 4.6, there is a constant c such that $f(x) = c$ for $-1 \le x \le 1$.

b. If $x = 0$ in part (a), we have $c = f(0) = \sin^{-1} 0 + \cos^{-1} 0 = 0 + \pi/2 = \pi/2$.

72. We seek the maximum value of θ, regarded as a function of x. If φ is as in Figure 6.31, then we have

$$\tan(\theta(x) + \varphi(x)) = \frac{7}{x}, \quad \text{so that} \quad \theta(x) + \varphi(x) = \tan^{-1}\frac{7}{x}$$

and

$$\tan\varphi(x) = \frac{2}{x}, \quad \text{so that} \quad \varphi(x) = \tan^{-1}\frac{2}{x}.$$

Therefore

$$\theta(x) = [\theta(x) + \varphi(x)] - \varphi(x) = \tan^{-1}\frac{7}{x} - \tan^{-1}\frac{2}{x} \quad \text{for } x > 0.$$

Consequently by the Chain Rule,

$$\theta'(x) = \frac{-7/x^2}{1+(7/x)^2} - \frac{-2/x^2}{1+(2/x)^2} = \frac{-7}{x^2+49} + \frac{2}{x^2+4} = \frac{-5(x^2-14)}{(x^2+49)(x^2+4)}.$$

Since $x > 0$, this implies that $\theta'(x) = 0$ only for $x = \sqrt{14}$. Since $\theta'(x) > 0$ for $0 < x < \sqrt{14}$ and $\theta'(x) < 0$ for $x > \sqrt{14}$, it follows from the First Derivative Test that θ achieves its maximum value for $x = \sqrt{14}$. Therefore the spectator has the best view when standing $\sqrt{14} \approx 3.74$ feet from the wall.

73. Let x denote the distance in feet from the floor to the bottom of the painting, and let V denote the viewing angle. We are to maximize V. If the bottom of the painting is below eye level, as in the first figure, then

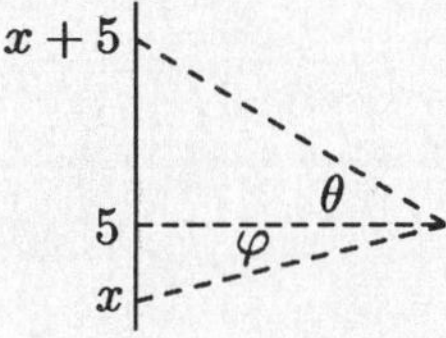

$$V = \theta + \varphi = \tan^{-1}\frac{x}{10} + \tan^{-1}\frac{5-x}{10}$$
$$= \tan^{-1}\frac{x}{10} - \tan^{-1}\frac{x-5}{10} \quad \text{for } x > 5.$$

If the bottom of the painting is above eye level, as in the second figure, then

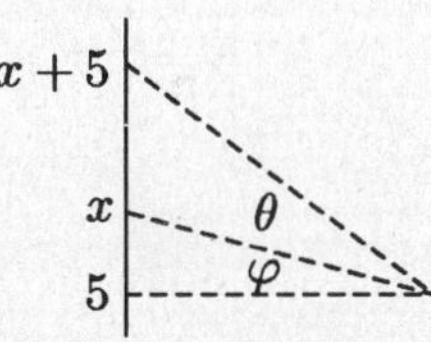

$$V = \theta = (\theta+\varphi) - \varphi = \tan^{-1}\frac{x}{10} - \tan^{-1}\frac{x-5}{10} \quad \text{for } 0 \le x \le 5.$$

Therefore we are to maximize V with respect to x, where

$$V(x) = \tan^{-1}\frac{x}{10} - \tan^{-1}\frac{x-5}{10} \quad \text{with } 0 \le x.$$

Now

$$V'(x) = \frac{1}{1+(x/10)^2}\cdot\frac{1}{10} - \frac{1}{1+[(x-5)/10]^2}\cdot\frac{1}{10}$$

so that $V'(x) = 0$ if

$$1 + \frac{x^2}{10^2} = 1 + \frac{(x-5)^2}{10^2}$$

or $x^2 = (x-5)^2$, or $x^2 = x^2 - 10x + 25$, or $x = 2.5$. Since $V'(x) > 0$ for $0 \le x < 2.5$ and $V'(x) < 0$ for $x > 2.5$, (1) of Section 4.6 and the First Derivative Test implies that V is maximum for $x = 2.5$. Consequently the bottom of the painting should be 2.5 feet above the floor. If 10 is replaced by 15 (or any positive value), a similar analysis would lead again to the equation $x^2 = (x-5)^2$, so the answer would be the same.

74. Let x be the height of the rocket above the ground. Then

$$\tan\theta = \frac{x}{20{,}000}, \quad \text{or} \quad \theta = \tan^{-1}\frac{x}{20{,}000}$$

so that

$$\frac{\pi}{60} = \frac{d\theta}{dt} = \frac{1}{(x/20{,}000)^2+1}\frac{1}{20{,}000}\frac{dx}{dt}.$$

When $\theta = \pi/4$, we have $x = 20{,}000$, so that

$$\frac{\pi}{60} = \frac{1}{2}\frac{1}{20{,}000}\frac{dx}{dt}, \quad \text{or} \quad \frac{dx}{dt} = \frac{2000\pi}{3} \text{ (feet per second).}$$

75. a. Using the notation in the diagram, we wish to maximize the angle θ and we have

$$\alpha+\theta+\beta = \pi, \quad \tan\alpha = \frac{15}{30-x}, \quad \text{and} \quad \tan\beta = \frac{20}{x}.$$

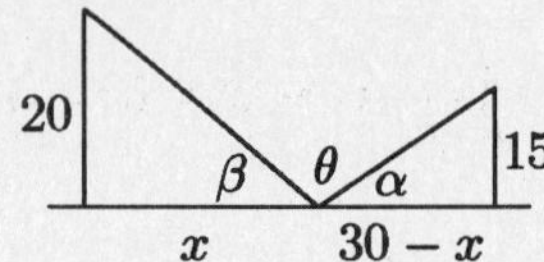

Thus $\theta = \pi - \tan^{-1}(20/x) - \tan^{-1}[15/(30-x)]$, so that

$$\frac{d\theta}{dx} = \frac{-1}{1+(20/x)^2}\left(-\frac{20}{x^2}\right) - \frac{1}{1+\left(15/(30-x)\right)^2}\cdot\frac{15}{(30-x)^2} = \frac{20}{x^2+400} - \frac{15}{(30-x)^2+225}.$$

Thus $d\theta/dx = 0$ if $20[(30-x)^2+225] = 15(x^2+400)$, or $4(30-x)^2+900 = 3x^2+1200$, or $x^2-240x+3300 = 0$. Since $0 \le x \le 30$, it follows from the quadratic formula that $x = \frac{1}{2}(240-\sqrt{(240)^2-4(1)(3300)}) \approx 14.64346247$. We have

$$\frac{d^2\theta}{dx^2} = \frac{-20}{(x^2+400)^2}(2x) - \frac{15\cdot 2(30-x)}{\left((30-x)^2+225\right)^2}$$

so that $d^2\theta/dx^2 < 0$ for $0 < x < 30$. Therefore the value of x for which $d\theta/dx = 0$ yields the maximum value of θ. Thus the tomatoes should be planted approximately $30-14.6 = 15.4$ meters from the smaller building.

b. Using the formula in (a) for θ along with the value of x that maximizes θ, we find by calculator that the maximum value of θ is approximately 1.43 radians. Since an angle of 2π radians corresponds to 24 hours, an angle of 1.43 radians corresponds to $(1.43/2\pi)24 \approx 5.46$ hours. Thus the plants will be in sunlight for approximately 5 hours and 28 minutes.

76. a. Since $v^2 = \rho g\tan\theta$, we have $\theta = \tan^{-1}(v^2/\rho g)$.

b. Using the formula in (a) with $v = 18$, $\rho = 60$, and $g = 9.8$, we find by calculator that $\theta \approx 0.5036262961$ (radians). Thus the curve should be banked at approximately 28.9°.

c. By the formula in (a) with $\rho = 100$ and $g = 9.8$, $\theta = \tan^{-1}(v^2/980)$. Thus

$$\frac{d\theta}{dt} = \frac{1}{1+(v^2/980)^2}\frac{2v}{980}\frac{dv}{dt}.$$

If $v = 18$ and $dv/dt = -1$, this becomes

$$\frac{d\theta}{dt} = \frac{1}{1+(18^2/980)^2}\frac{36}{980}(-1) \approx -0.0331150692 \text{ radians per second.}$$

Thus the banking angle is decreasing at the rate of approximately 1.9 degrees per second.

6.6 L'Hôpital's Rule

1. $\lim_{x\to a}(x^{16}-a^{16})=0=\lim_{x\to a}(x-a)$; $\lim_{x\to a}\dfrac{x^{16}-a^{16}}{x-a}=\lim_{x\to a}\dfrac{16x^{15}}{1}=16a^{15}$

2. $\lim_{x\to 0}\sin x=0=\lim_{x\to 0}x$; $\lim_{x\to 0}\dfrac{\sin x}{x}=\lim_{x\to 0}\dfrac{\cos x}{1}=1$

3. $\lim_{x\to 0}(\cos x-1)=0=\lim_{x\to 0}x$; $\lim_{x\to 0}\dfrac{\cos x-1}{x}=\lim_{x\to 0}\dfrac{-\sin x}{1}=0$

4. $\lim_{x\to\pi/2^-}\cos x=0=\lim_{x\to\pi/2^-}(\sin x-1)$; $\lim_{x\to\pi/2^-}\dfrac{\cos x}{\sin x-1}=\lim_{x\to\pi/2^-}\dfrac{-\sin x}{\cos x}=-\infty$

5. $\lim_{x\to 0^+}\sin 8\sqrt{x}=0=\lim_{x\to 0^+}\sin 5\sqrt{x}$; $\lim_{x\to 0^+}\dfrac{\sin 8\sqrt{x}}{\sin 5\sqrt{x}}=\lim_{x\to 0^+}\dfrac{(\cos 8\sqrt{x})(4/\sqrt{x})}{(\cos 5\sqrt{x})[5/(2\sqrt{x})]}=\lim_{x\to 0^+}\dfrac{8\cos 8\sqrt{x}}{5\cos 5\sqrt{x}}=\dfrac{8}{5}$

6. $\lim_{x\to 1}\ln x=0=\lim_{x\to 1}(x-1)$; $\lim_{x\to 1}\dfrac{\ln x}{x-1}=\lim_{x\to 1}\dfrac{1/x}{1}=\lim_{x\to 1}\dfrac{1}{x}=1$

7. $\lim_{x\to\infty}(e^{1/x}-1)=0=\lim_{x\to\infty}\dfrac{1}{x}$; $\lim_{x\to\infty}\dfrac{e^{1/x}-1}{1/x}=\lim_{x\to\infty}\dfrac{e^{1/x}(-1/x^2)}{-1/x^2}=\lim_{x\to\infty}e^{1/x}=1$

8. $\lim_{x\to\infty}\tan\dfrac{1}{x}=0=\lim_{x\to\infty}\dfrac{1}{x}$; $\lim_{x\to\infty}\dfrac{\tan(1/x)}{1/x}=\lim_{x\to\infty}\dfrac{(-1/x^2)\sec^2(1/x)}{-1/x^2}=\lim_{x\to\infty}\sec^2\dfrac{1}{x}=1$

9. $\lim_{x\to\pi/2^-}\tan x=\infty=\lim_{x\to\pi/2^-}(\sec x+1)$;

$$\lim_{x\to\pi/2^-}\frac{\tan x}{\sec x+1}=\lim_{x\to\pi/2^-}\frac{\sec^2 x}{\sec x\,\tan x}=\lim_{x\to\pi/2^-}\frac{\sec x}{\tan x}=\lim_{x\to\pi/2^-}\frac{1}{\sin x}=1$$

10. $\lim_{x\to 0^+}x^{-1/2}=\infty$ and $\lim_{x\to 0^+}\ln x=-\infty$;

$$\lim_{x\to 0^+}\frac{x^{-1/2}}{\ln x}=\lim_{x\to 0^+}\frac{(-1/2)x^{-3/2}}{1/x}=\lim_{x\to 0^+}\left(-\frac{1}{2}x^{-1/2}\right)=-\infty$$

11. $\lim_{x\to\infty}x=\infty=\lim_{x\to\infty}\ln x$; $\lim_{x\to\infty}\dfrac{x}{\ln x}=\lim_{x\to\infty}\dfrac{1}{1/x}=\lim_{x\to\infty}x=\infty$

12. $\lim_{x\to\infty}x=\infty=\lim_{x\to\infty}e^{2x}$; $\lim_{x\to\infty}\dfrac{x}{e^{2x}}=\lim_{x\to\infty}\dfrac{1}{2e^{2x}}=0$

13. $\lim_{x\to\infty}\ln(1+x)=\infty=\lim_{x\to\infty}\ln x$;

$$\lim_{x\to\infty}\frac{\ln(1+x)}{\ln x}=\lim_{x\to\infty}\frac{1/(1+x)}{1/x}=\lim_{x\to\infty}\frac{x}{1+x}=\lim_{x\to\infty}\frac{1}{(1/x)+1}=1$$

14. $\lim_{x\to\infty}\ln x=\infty=\lim_{x\to\infty}\ln(\ln x)$; $\lim_{x\to\infty}\dfrac{\ln x}{\ln(\ln x)}=\lim_{x\to\infty}\dfrac{1/x}{(1/\ln x)(1/x)}=\lim_{x\to\infty}\ln x=\infty$

15. $\lim_{x\to 0}(1-\cos x)=0=\lim_{x\to 0}\sin x$; $\lim_{x\to 0}\dfrac{1-\cos x}{\sin x}=\lim_{x\to 0}\dfrac{\sin x}{\cos x}=0$

16. $\lim_{x\to 0}\tan 4x=0=\lim_{x\to 0}\tan 2x$; $\lim_{x\to 0}\dfrac{\tan 4x}{\tan 2x}=\lim_{x\to 0}\dfrac{4\sec^2 4x}{2\sec^2 2x}=2$

17. $\lim_{x\to\pi/2^-} \tan 4x = 0 = \lim_{x\to\pi/2^-} \tan 2x$; $\lim_{x\to\pi/2^-} \dfrac{\tan 4x}{\tan 2x} = \lim_{x\to\pi/2^-} \dfrac{4\sec^2 4x}{2\sec^2 2x} = 2$

18. $\lim_{x\to 0^-} \tan x = 0 = \lim_{x\to 0^-} x^2$; $\lim_{x\to 0^-} \dfrac{\tan x}{x^2} = \lim_{x\to 0^-} \dfrac{\sec^2 x}{2x} = -\infty$

19. The conditions for applying l'Hôpital's Rule twice are met;

$$\lim_{x\to 0} \frac{1-\cos 2x}{1-\cos 3x} = \lim_{x\to 0} \frac{2\sin 2x}{3\sin 3x} = \lim_{x\to 0} \frac{4\cos 2x}{9\cos 3x} = \frac{4}{9}.$$

20. The conditions for applying l'Hôpital's Rule twice are met;

$$\lim_{x\to 0^+} \frac{1-\cos\sqrt{x}}{\sin x} = \lim_{x\to 0^+} \frac{(1/(2\sqrt{x}))\sin\sqrt{x}}{\cos x} = \frac{1}{2}\lim_{x\to 0^+} \frac{\sin\sqrt{x}}{\sqrt{x}} \lim_{x\to 0^+} \frac{1}{\cos x}$$

$$= \frac{1}{2}\left(\lim_{x\to 0^+} \frac{(1/(2\sqrt{x}))\cos\sqrt{x}}{1/(2\sqrt{x})}\right) 1 = \frac{1}{2}\lim_{x\to 0^+} \cos\sqrt{x} = \frac{1}{2}.$$

21. $\lim_{x\to 0} \left(\sqrt{1+x} - \sqrt{1-x}\right) = 0 = \lim_{x\to 0} x$;

$$\lim_{x\to 0} \frac{\sqrt{1+x}-\sqrt{1-x}}{x} = \lim_{x\to 0} \frac{1/(2\sqrt{1+x}) + 1/(2\sqrt{1-x})}{1} = 1$$

22. $\lim_{x\to 0^+} e^{1/x} = \infty$ and $\lim_{x\to 0^+} \ln x = -\infty$; $\lim_{x\to 0^+} \dfrac{e^{1/x}}{\ln x} = \lim_{x\to 0^+} \dfrac{e^{1/x}(-1/x^2)}{1/x} = \lim_{x\to 0^+} \dfrac{-e^{1/x}}{x} = -\infty$

23. $\lim_{x\to 0^+} \sin x = 0 = \lim_{x\to 0^+} (e^{\sqrt{x}} - 1)$; $\lim_{x\to 0^+} \dfrac{\sin x}{e^{\sqrt{x}} - 1} = \lim_{x\to 0^+} \dfrac{\cos x}{(1/2\sqrt{x})e^{\sqrt{x}}} = \lim_{x\to 0^+} \dfrac{2\sqrt{x}\cos x}{e^{\sqrt{x}}} = 0$

24. $\lim_{x\to 0} (e^{(x^2)} - 1) = 0 = \lim_{x\to 0} (e^x - 1)$; $\lim_{x\to 0} \dfrac{e^{(x^2)} - 1}{e^x - 1} = \lim_{x\to 0} \dfrac{2xe^{(x^2)}}{e^x} = 0$

25. $\lim_{x\to 0} (5^x - 3^x) = 1 - 1 = 0 = \lim_{x\to 0} x$; $\lim_{x\to 0} \dfrac{5^x - 3^x}{x} = \lim_{x\to 0} \dfrac{(\ln 5)5^x - (\ln 3)3^x}{1} = \ln 5 - \ln 3$

26. $\lim_{x\to 1} (4^x - 3^x - 1) = 0 = \lim_{x\to 1} (x - 1)$; $\lim_{x\to 1} \dfrac{4^x - 3^x - 1}{x - 1} = \lim_{x\to 1} \dfrac{(\ln 4)4^x - (\ln 3)3^x}{1} = 4\ln 4 - 3\ln 3$

27. $\lim_{x\to 0} \sin^{-1} x = 0 = \lim_{x\to 0} x$; $\lim_{x\to 0} \dfrac{\sin^{-1} x}{x} = \lim_{x\to 0} \dfrac{1/\sqrt{1-x^2}}{1} = 1$

28. $\lim_{x\to 1^-} \left(\dfrac{\pi}{2} - \sin^{-1} x\right) = 0 = \lim_{x\to 1^-} \sqrt{1-x^2}$; $\lim_{x\to 1^-} \dfrac{\pi/2 - \sin^{-1} x}{\sqrt{1-x^2}} = \lim_{x\to 1^-} \dfrac{-1/\sqrt{1-x^2}}{-x/\sqrt{1-x^2}} = \lim_{x\to 1^-} \dfrac{1}{x} = 1$

29. The conditions for applying l'Hôpital's Rule three times are met;

$$\lim_{x\to 0} \frac{x^3}{x - \sin x} = \lim_{x\to 0} \frac{3x^2}{1-\cos x} = \lim_{x\to 0} \frac{6x}{\sin x} = \lim_{x\to 0} \frac{6}{\cos x} = 6.$$

30. $\lim_{x\to 1} (\ln x - x + 1) = 0 = \lim_{x\to 1} (x^3 - 3x + 2)$;

$$\lim_{x\to 1} \frac{\ln x - x + 1}{x^3 - 3x + 2} = \lim_{x\to 1} \frac{1/x - 1}{3x^2 - 3} = \lim_{x\to 1} \frac{1-x}{3x(x-1)(x+1)} = \lim_{x\to 1} \frac{-1}{3x(x+1)} = \frac{-1}{6}$$

31. The conditions for applying l'Hôpital's Rule twice are met;

$$\lim_{x\to 0}\frac{\tanh x-\sinh x}{x^2}=\lim_{x\to 0}\frac{\operatorname{sech}^2 x-\cosh x}{2x}=\lim_{x\to 0}\frac{-2\operatorname{sech}^2 x\tanh x-\sinh x}{2}=0.$$

32. $\lim_{x\to\pi/2}(2x-\pi)\sec x=\lim_{x\to\pi/2}\frac{2x-\pi}{\cos x}$; $\lim_{x\to\pi/2}(2x-\pi)=0=\lim_{x\to\pi/2}\cos x$;

$\lim_{x\to\pi/2}(2x-\pi)\sec x=\lim_{x\to\pi/2}\frac{2x-\pi}{\cos x}=\lim_{x\to\pi/2}\frac{2}{\sin x}=\frac{2}{1}=2$

33. $\lim_{x\to 0}(\csc x-\cot x)=\lim_{x\to 0}\frac{1-\cos x}{\sin x}=0$ by Exercise 15

34. $\lim_{x\to\pi/2}(\pi^2-4x^2)\tan x=\lim_{x\to\pi/2}\frac{\pi^2-4x^2}{\cot x}$; $\lim_{x\to\pi/2}(\pi^2-4x^2)=0=\lim_{x\to\pi/2}\cot x$;

$\lim_{x\to\pi/2}(\pi^2-4x^2)\tan x=\lim_{x\to\pi/2}\frac{\pi^2-4x^2}{\cot x}=\lim_{x\to\pi/2}\frac{-8x}{-\csc^2 x}=\frac{-4\pi}{-1}=4\pi$

35. $\lim_{x\to 0^+}\ln(\sin x)=-\infty$; $\lim_{x\to 0^+}\csc x=\infty$

$\lim_{x\to 0^+}\sin x\ln(\sin x)=\lim_{x\to 0^+}\frac{\ln(\sin x)}{\csc x}=\lim_{x\to 0^+}\frac{\cos x/\sin x}{-\csc x\cot x}=\lim_{x\to 0^+}(-\sin x)=0$

36. $\lim_{x\to 0^+}x^{\sin x}=\lim_{x\to 0^+}e^{\sin x\ln x}=e^{\lim_{x\to 0^+}\sin x\ln x}=e^{\lim_{x\to 0^+}(\ln x/\csc x)}$;
the conditions for applying l'Hôpital's Rule twice are met;

$$\lim_{x\to 0^+}\frac{\ln x}{\csc x}=\lim_{x\to 0^+}\frac{1/x}{-\csc x\cot x}=\lim_{x\to 0^+}\frac{-\sin^2 x}{x\cos x}=\lim_{x\to 0^+}\frac{-2\sin x\cos x}{\cos x-x\sin x}=0.$$

Thus $\lim_{x\to 0^+}x^{\sin x}=e^0=1$.

37. $\lim_{x\to 0^+}\left(\ln\frac{1}{x}\right)^x=\lim_{x\to 0^+}e^{x\ln(\ln(1/x))}=e^{\lim_{x\to 0^+}x\ln(\ln(1/x))}=e^{\lim_{x\to 0^+}[\ln(\ln(1/x))/(1/x)]}$;

$\lim_{x\to 0^+}\ln\left(\ln\frac{1}{x}\right)=\infty=\lim_{x\to 0^+}\frac{1}{x}$; $\lim_{x\to 0^+}\frac{\ln(\ln(1/x))}{1/x}=\lim_{x\to 0^+}\frac{\frac{1}{\ln(1/x)}\frac{1}{1/x}\left(\frac{-1}{x^2}\right)}{-1/x^2}=\lim_{x\to 0^+}\frac{x}{\ln(1/x)}=0$
Thus $\lim_{x\to 0^+}(\ln(1/x))^x=e^0=1$.

38. $\lim_{x\to 1/2^-}(\tan\pi x)^{1-2x}=\lim_{x\to 1/2^-}e^{(1-2x)\ln(\tan\pi x)}=e^{\lim_{x\to 1/2^-}(1-2x)\ln(\tan\pi x)}$

$=e^{\lim_{x\to 1/2^-}[\ln(\tan\pi x)]/[1/(1-2x)]}$

The conditions for applying l'Hôpital's Rule twice are met;

$$\lim_{x\to 1/2^-}\frac{\ln(\tan\pi x)}{1/(1-2x)}=\lim_{x\to 1/2^-}\frac{(\pi\sec^2\pi x)/(\tan\pi x)}{2/(1-2x)^2}=\lim_{x\to 1/2^-}\frac{\pi(1-2x)^2}{2\sin\pi x\cos\pi x}$$

$$=\lim_{x\to 1/2^-}\frac{\pi(1-2x)^2}{\sin 2\pi x}=\lim_{x\to 1/2^-}\frac{-4\pi(1-2x)}{2\pi\cos 2\pi x}=0.$$

Thus $\lim_{x\to 1/2^-}(\tan\pi x)^{1-2x}=e^0=1$.

39. $\lim_{x\to\pi/2^-} \ln(\cos x) = -\infty$, $\lim_{x\to\pi/2^-} \tan x = \infty$;

$$\lim_{x\to\pi/2^-} \frac{\ln\cos x}{\tan x} = \lim_{x\to\pi/2^-} \frac{(-\sin x)/(\cos x)}{\sec^2 x} = \lim_{x\to\pi/2^-} (-\sin x \cos x) = 0$$

40. The conditions for applying l'Hôpital's Rule three times are met;

$$\lim_{x\to\infty} \frac{e^x}{x^3} = \lim_{x\to\infty} \frac{e^x}{3x^2} = \lim_{x\to\infty} \frac{e^x}{6x} = \lim_{x\to\infty} \frac{e^x}{6} = \infty.$$

41. $\lim_{x\to\infty} x \sin\frac{1}{x} = \lim_{x\to\infty} \frac{\sin(1/x)}{1/x}$; $\lim_{x\to\infty} \sin\frac{1}{x} = 0 = \lim_{x\to\infty} \frac{1}{x}$;

$$\lim_{x\to\infty} x \sin\frac{1}{x} = \lim_{x\to\infty} \frac{\sin(1/x)}{1/x} = \lim_{x\to\infty} \frac{(-1/x^2)\cos(1/x)}{-1/x^2} = \lim_{x\to\infty} \cos\frac{1}{x} = 1$$

42. $\lim_{x\to\infty} \ln x = \infty = \lim_{x\to\infty} x^2$; $\lim_{x\to\infty} \frac{\ln x}{x^2} = \lim_{x\to\infty} \frac{1/x}{2x} = \lim_{x\to\infty} \frac{1}{2x^2} = 0$

43. $\lim_{x\to\infty} \ln(x^2+1) = \infty = \lim_{x\to\infty} x$; $\lim_{x\to\infty} \frac{\ln(x^2+1)}{\ln x} = \lim_{x\to\infty} \frac{2x/(x^2+1)}{1/x} = \lim_{x\to\infty} \frac{2x^2}{x^2+1} = \lim_{x\to\infty} \frac{2}{1+1/x^2} = 2$

44. $\lim_{x\to\infty} \log_4 x = \lim_{x\to\infty} \frac{\ln x}{\ln 4} = \infty = \lim_{x\to\infty} x$; $\lim_{x\to\infty} \frac{\log_4 x}{x} = \lim_{x\to\infty} \frac{1/(x\ln 4)}{1} = \lim_{x\to\infty} 1/(x\ln 4) = 0$

45. $\lim_{x\to\infty} e^{(e^x)} = \infty = \lim_{x\to\infty} e^x$; $\lim_{x\to\infty} \frac{e^{(e^x)}}{e^x} = \lim_{x\to\infty} \frac{e^x e^{(e^x)}}{e^x} = \lim_{x\to\infty} e^{(e^x)} = \infty$

46. $\lim_{x\to\infty} \left(1 - \frac{1}{x}\right)^x = \lim_{x\to\infty} e^{x\ln(1-1/x)} = e^{\lim_{x\to\infty} x\ln(1-1/x)} = e^{\lim_{x\to\infty}[\ln(1-1/x)]/(1/x)}$;

$$\lim_{x\to\infty} \ln\left(1 - \frac{1}{x}\right) = 0 = \lim_{x\to\infty} \frac{1}{x};\ \lim_{x\to\infty} \frac{\ln(1-1/x)}{1/x} = \lim_{x\to\infty} \frac{[1/(1-1/x)](1/x^2)}{-1/x^2} = \lim_{x\to\infty} \frac{-1}{1-1/x} = -1$$

Thus $\lim_{x\to\infty}(1-1/x)^x = e^{-1}$.

47. $\lim_{x\to\infty} \left(1 + \frac{1}{x^2}\right)^x = \lim_{x\to\infty} e^{x\ln(1+1/x^2)} = e^{\lim_{x\to\infty} x\ln(1+1/x^2)} = e^{\lim_{x\to\infty}[\ln(1+1/x^2)]/(1/x)}$;

$$\lim_{x\to\infty} \frac{\ln(1+1/x^2)}{1/x} = \lim_{x\to\infty} \frac{[x^2/(x^2+1)](-2/x^3)}{-1/x^2} = \lim_{x\to\infty} \frac{2x}{x^2+1} = \lim_{x\to\infty} \frac{2/x}{1+1/x^2} = 0$$

Thus $\lim_{x\to\infty}(1+1/x^2)^x = e^0 = 1$.

48. $\lim_{x\to\infty} \frac{1}{x(\pi/2 - \tan^{-1} x)} = \lim_{x\to\infty} \frac{1/x}{\pi/2 - \tan^{-1} x}$; $\lim_{x\to\infty} \frac{1}{x} = 0 = \lim_{x\to\infty} \left(\frac{\pi}{2} - \tan^{-1} x\right)$;

$$\lim_{x\to\infty} \frac{1}{x(\pi/2 - \tan^{-1} x)} = \lim_{x\to\infty} \frac{1/x}{\pi/2 - \tan^{-1} x} = \lim_{x\to\infty} \frac{-1/x^2}{-1/(x^2+1)} = \lim_{x\to\infty} \frac{x^2+1}{x^2} = \lim_{x\to\infty} \left(1 + \frac{1}{x^2}\right) = 1$$

49. $\lim_{x\to\infty} \ln(\ln x) = \infty = \lim_{x\to\infty} \sqrt{x}$;

$$\lim_{x\to\infty} x^{-1/2} \ln(\ln x) = \lim_{x\to\infty} \frac{\ln(\ln x)}{\sqrt{x}} = \lim_{x\to\infty} \frac{[1/(\ln x)](1/x)}{1/(2\sqrt{x})} = \lim_{x\to\infty} \frac{2}{\sqrt{x}\ln x} = 0$$

50. $\lim_{x\to\infty} x^2\left(1 - x\sin\frac{1}{x}\right) = \lim_{x\to\infty} \frac{1 - x\sin(1/x)}{1/x^2}$

The conditions for applying l'Hôpital's Rule twice are met. In particular, by Exercise 41,

$$\lim_{x\to\infty} x\sin\frac{1}{x} = 1, \quad \text{so that} \quad \lim_{x\to\infty}\left(1 - x\sin\frac{1}{x}\right) = 0 = \lim_{x\to\infty}\frac{1}{x^2};$$

$$\lim_{x\to\infty} x^2\left(1 - x\sin\frac{1}{x}\right) = \lim_{x\to\infty}\frac{1 - x\sin\frac{1}{x}}{1/x^2} = \lim_{x\to\infty}\frac{-\sin\frac{1}{x} + \frac{1}{x}\cos\frac{1}{x}}{-2/x^3}$$

$$= \lim_{x\to\infty}\frac{\frac{1}{x^2}\cos\frac{1}{x} - \frac{1}{x^2}\cos\frac{1}{x} + \frac{1}{x^3}\sin\frac{1}{x}}{6/x^4} = \frac{1}{6}\lim_{x\to\infty}\frac{\sin(1/x)}{1/x} = \frac{1}{6}.$$

51. $\lim_{x\to a}(a^2 - ax) = 0 = \lim_{x\to a}(a - \sqrt{ax})$; $\lim_{x\to a}\frac{a^2 - ax}{a - \sqrt{ax}} = \lim_{x\to a}\frac{-a}{-a/(2\sqrt{ax})} = \lim_{x\to a} 2\sqrt{ax} = 2a$

52. $\lim_{x\to a}(\sqrt{2a^3x - x^4} - a\sqrt[3]{a^2x}) = 0 = \lim_{x\to a}(a - \sqrt[4]{ax^3})$;

$$\lim_{x\to a}\frac{\sqrt{2a^3x - x^4} - a\sqrt[3]{a^2x}}{a - \sqrt[4]{ax^3}} = \lim_{x\to a}\frac{\dfrac{2a^3 - 4x^3}{2\sqrt{2a^3x - x^4}} - \dfrac{a^{5/3}}{3x^{2/3}}}{-\frac{3}{4}a^{1/4}x^{-1/4}} = \frac{16}{9}a$$

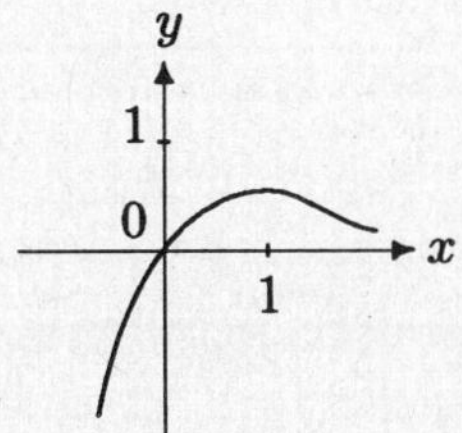

Exercise 53

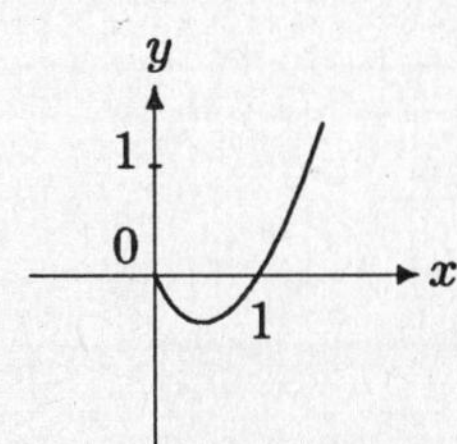

Exercise 54

53. $f'(x) = e^{-x} - xe^{-x}$; $f''(x) = -2e^{-x} + xe^{-x}$; relative maximum value is $f(1) = e^{-1}$; concave downward on $(-\infty, 2)$; concave upward on $(2, \infty)$; inflection point: $(2, 2e^{-2})$; $\lim_{x\to\infty} xe^{-x} = \lim_{x\to\infty}(x/e^x) = \lim_{x\to\infty}(1/e^x) = 0$, so $y = 0$ is a horizontal asymptote. Also $\lim_{x\to-\infty} xe^{-x} = -\infty$.

54. $f'(x) = \ln x + 1$; $f''(x) = 1/x$; relative minimum value is $f(e^{-1}) = -e^{-1}$; concave upward on $(0, \infty)$; $\lim_{x\to0^+} x\ln x = 0$ by the solution of Example 7. Also $\lim_{x\to\infty} x\ln x = \infty$.

55. The conditions for applying l'Hôpital's Rule twice are met;

$$\lim_{x\to0^+} f(x) = \lim_{x\to0^+} x(\ln x)^2 = \lim_{x\to0^+}\frac{(\ln x)^2}{1/x} = \lim_{x\to0^+}\frac{(2\ln x)(1/x)}{-1/x^2}$$

$$= \lim_{x\to0^+}\frac{2\ln x}{-1/x} = \lim_{x\to0^+}\frac{2/x}{1/x^2} = \lim_{x\to0^+} 2x = 0 = f(0).$$

56. a. The conditions for applying l'Hôpital's Rule are met for $\lim_{x\to-\pi/2} f(x)$ and $\lim_{x\to\pi/2} f(x)$;

$$\lim_{x\to-\pi/2} f(x) = \lim_{x\to-\pi/2} \frac{\cos x}{x^2-\pi^2/4} = \lim_{x\to-\pi/2} \frac{-\sin x}{2x} = \frac{-(-1)}{2(-\pi/2)} = -\frac{1}{\pi} = f\left(-\frac{\pi}{2}\right);$$

similarly,

$$\lim_{x\to\pi/2} f(x) = \lim_{x\to\pi/2} \frac{\cos x}{x^2-\pi^2/4} = \lim_{x\to\pi/2} \frac{-\sin x}{2x} = \frac{-(1)}{2(\pi/2)} = -\frac{1}{\pi} = f\left(\frac{\pi}{2}\right).$$

Thus f is continuous at $-\pi/2$ and $\pi/2$.

b. The conditions for applying l'Hôpital's Rule twice are met in each case;

$$\lim_{x\to-\pi/2} \frac{f(x)-f(-\pi/2)}{x-(-\pi/2)} = \lim_{x\to-\pi/2} \frac{(\cos x)/(x^2-\pi^2/4)-(-1/\pi)}{x+\pi/2}$$

$$= \lim_{x\to-\pi/2} \frac{\pi\cos x + x^2 - \pi^2/4}{\pi(x^2-\pi^2/4)(x+\pi/2)} = \lim_{x\to-\pi/2} \frac{-\pi\sin x + 2x}{\pi[2x(x+\pi/2)+x^2-\pi^2/4]}$$

$$= \lim_{x\to-\pi/2} \frac{-\pi\cos x + 2}{\pi[2(x+\pi/2)+2x+2x]} = \frac{0+2}{\pi(0-\pi-\pi)} = -\frac{1}{\pi^2};$$

similarly,

$$\lim_{x\to\pi/2} \frac{f(x)-f(\pi/2)}{x-\pi/2} = \lim_{x\to\pi/2} \frac{-\pi\cos x + 2}{\pi[2(x-\pi/2)+2x+2x]} = \frac{0+2}{\pi(0+\pi+\pi)} = \frac{1}{\pi^2}.$$

Thus f is differentiable at $-\pi/2$ and $\pi/2$.

57. a. $\lim_{x\to\pi/2} \sin x \neq 0$ and $\lim_{x\to\pi/2} x \neq 0$. Thus l'Hôpital's Rule does not apply.

b. By the Quotient Rule for Limits,

$$\lim_{x\to\pi/2} \frac{\sin x}{x} = \frac{\lim_{x\to\pi/2} \sin x}{\lim_{x\to\pi/2} x} = \frac{\sin \pi/2}{\pi/2} = \frac{2}{\pi}.$$

58. If we use l'Hôpital's Rule twice, we find that

$$\lim_{x\to\infty} \frac{x}{\sqrt{x^2+1}} = \lim_{x\to\infty} \frac{1}{\dfrac{x}{\sqrt{x^2+1}}} = \lim_{x\to\infty} \frac{\sqrt{x^2+1}}{x} = \lim_{x\to\infty} \frac{\dfrac{x}{\sqrt{x^2+1}}}{1} = \lim_{x\to\infty} \frac{x}{\sqrt{x^2+1}}.$$

Thus we return to the original limit, so l'Hôpital's Rule does not yield the value of the limit. However, for $x > 0$,

$$\frac{x}{\sqrt{x^2+1}} = \frac{1}{\sqrt{1+1/x^2}}, \quad \text{so} \quad \lim_{x\to\infty} \frac{x}{\sqrt{x^2+1}} = \lim_{x\to\infty} \frac{1}{\sqrt{1+1/x^2}} = \frac{1}{\sqrt{1+0}} = 1.$$

59. Applying l'Hôpital's Rule several times, we find that

$$\lim_{x\to0} \frac{e^{-1/x^2}}{x} = \lim_{x\to0} \frac{e^{-1/x^2}(2/x^3)}{1} = \lim_{x\to0} \frac{2e^{-1/x^2}}{x^3} = \lim_{x\to0} \frac{2e^{-1/x^2}(2/x^3)}{3x^2}$$

$$= \lim_{x\to0} \frac{4e^{-1/x^2}}{3x^5} = \lim_{x\to0} \frac{4e^{-1/x^2}(2/x^3)}{15x^4} = \lim_{x\to0} \frac{8e^{-1/x^2}}{15x^7}.$$

Thus each time we apply l'Hôpital's Rule we obtain a fraction with a higher power of x in the denominator, so that we are unable to evaluate the limit in this manner.

60. By (9) of Section 6.3, $x^{(x^x)} = e^{x^x \ln x}$. Since $\lim_{x\to 0^+} x^x = 1$ by Example 8 and since $\lim_{x\to 0^+} \ln x = -\infty$, it follows that $\lim_{x\to 0^+} x^x \ln x = -\infty$ and hence that $\lim_{x\to 0^+} e^{x^x \ln x} = 0$. Thus $\lim_{x\to 0^+} x^{(x^x)} = \lim_{x\to 0^+} e^{x^x \ln x} = 0$.

61. $\lim_{x\to 0^+} (x^x)^x = \lim_{x\to 0^+} e^{x \ln(x^x)} = \lim_{x\to 0^+} e^{x^2 \ln x} = e^{\lim_{x\to 0^+} x^2 \ln x}$

Since $\lim_{x\to 0^+} x^2 \ln x = \lim_{x\to 0^+} (\ln x)/(1/x^2)$, and since $\lim_{x\to 0^+} \ln x = -\infty$ and $\lim_{x\to 0^+} 1/x^2 = \infty$, l'Hôpital's Rule implies that

$$\lim_{x\to 0^+} \frac{\ln x}{1/x^2} = \lim_{x\to 0^+} \frac{1/x}{-2/x^3} = \lim_{x\to 0^+} \left(-\frac{x^2}{2}\right) = 0.$$

Thus $\lim_{x\to 0^+} (x^x)^x = e^0 = 1$.

62. $\lim_{x\to\infty} \left(\frac{x}{x+c}\right)^x = \lim_{x\to\infty} e^{x \ln[x/(x+c)]} = e^{\lim_{x\to\infty} x \ln[x/(x+c)]}$;

$$\lim_{x\to\infty} x \ln\left(\frac{x}{x+c}\right) = \lim_{x\to\infty} \frac{\ln[x/(x+c)]}{1/x} = \lim_{x\to\infty} \frac{\dfrac{1}{x/(x+c)} \cdot \dfrac{x+c-x}{(x+c)^2}}{-1/x^2} = \lim_{x\to\infty} \frac{\dfrac{c}{x(x+c)}}{-1/x^2}$$

$$= \lim_{x\to\infty} \frac{-cx^2}{x(x+c)} = \lim_{x\to\infty} \frac{-c}{1+c/x} = -c$$

Therefore $\lim_{x\to\infty} (x/(x+c))^x = e^{\lim_{x\to\infty} x \ln(x/(x+c))} = e^{-c}$. Thus $e^{-c} = e^3$, so $c = -3$.

63.
$$\begin{aligned}
\lim_{x\to 0} \frac{\int_0^x (x-t)\sin(t^2)\,dt}{\ln(1+x^4)} &= \lim_{x\to 0} \frac{x\int_0^x \sin(t^2)\,dt - \int_0^x t\sin(t^2)\,dt}{\ln(1+x^4)} \\
&\overset{\text{l'Hôpital's Rule}}{=} \lim_{x\to 0} \frac{\int_0^x \sin(t^2)\,dt + x\cdot\sin(x^2) - x\sin(x^2)}{[1/(1+x^4)]4x^3} \\
&= \lim_{x\to 0} \frac{(1+x^4)\int_0^x \sin(t^2)\,dt}{4x^3} \\
&\overset{\text{l'Hôpital's Rule}}{=} \lim_{x\to 0} \frac{4x^3\int_0^x \sin(t^2)\,dt + (1+x^4)\sin(x^2)}{12x^2} \\
&= \lim_{x\to 0} \frac{x}{3}\int_0^x \sin(t^2)\,dt + \lim_{x\to 0}(1+x^4)\frac{\sin x^2}{12x^2} \\
&= 0 + \lim_{x\to 0}(1+x^4)\lim_{x\to 0}\frac{\sin x^2}{12x^2} = \frac{1}{12}
\end{aligned}$$

64. By Exercise 44(b) of Section 6.4, we have

$$\frac{f^{-1}(x)}{c\ln 2x} = \frac{\ln[(x+\sqrt{x^2-c^2})/c]}{\ln 2x}.$$

The conditions for applying l'Hôpital's Rule twice are met;

$$\lim_{x\to\infty} \frac{f^{-1}(x)}{c\ln 2x} = \lim_{x\to\infty} \frac{\ln[(x+\sqrt{x^2-c^2})/c]}{\ln 2x} = \lim_{x\to\infty} \frac{[c/(x+\sqrt{x^2-c^2})]\cdot(1+x/\sqrt{x^2-c^2})\cdot(1/c)}{(1/2x)\cdot 2}$$

$$= \lim_{x\to\infty}\left[\frac{x}{x+\sqrt{x^2-c^2}}\cdot\frac{\sqrt{x^2-c^2}+x}{\sqrt{x^2-c^2}}\right] = \lim_{x\to\infty}\frac{x}{\sqrt{x^2-c^2}} = \lim_{x\to\infty}\frac{1}{\sqrt{1-c^2/x^2}} = 1.$$

65. a. Since the hypotenuse l of T is tangent to the graph of e^{-x} at (z, e^{-z}), a point-slope equation of l is $y - e^{-z} = -e^{-z}(x-z)$. If $x = 0$ then $y = e^{-z} - e^{-z}(-z) = (1+z)e^{-z}$, so the y intercept of l is $(1+z)e^{-z}$. If $y = 0$ then $-e^{-z} = -e^{-z}(x-z)$, so $1 = x - z$ and hence $x = 1+z$; thus the x intercept of l is $1+z$. Therefore the area A of T is given by $A = \frac{1}{2}[(1+z)e^{-z}](1+z) = \frac{1}{2}(1+z)^2e^{-z}$. By l'Hôpital's Rule,

$$\lim_{z\to\infty}\frac{1}{2}(1+z)^2e^{-z} = \lim_{z\to\infty}\frac{1}{2}\frac{(1+z)^2}{e^z} = \lim_{z\to\infty}\frac{1+z}{e^z} = \lim_{z\to\infty}\frac{1}{e^z} = 0.$$

Consequently for any given $\varepsilon > 0$ the area A of T is less than ε if z is large enough.

b. By part (a) the area A of T is given by $A = \frac{1}{2}(1+z)^2e^{-z}$. Thus $dA/dz = (1+z)e^{-z} - \frac{1}{2}(1+z)^2e^{-z} = (1+z)[1-\frac{1}{2}(1+z)]e^{-z} = \frac{1}{2}(1+z)(1-z)e^{-z}$. Since $dA/dz > 0$ if $0 < z < 1$ and $dA/dz < 0$ if $z > 1$, it follows that A is maximum if $z = 1$. Since by part (a) the x intercept of l is $1+z$, the area of T is maximal if the base of T has length $1+1=2$.

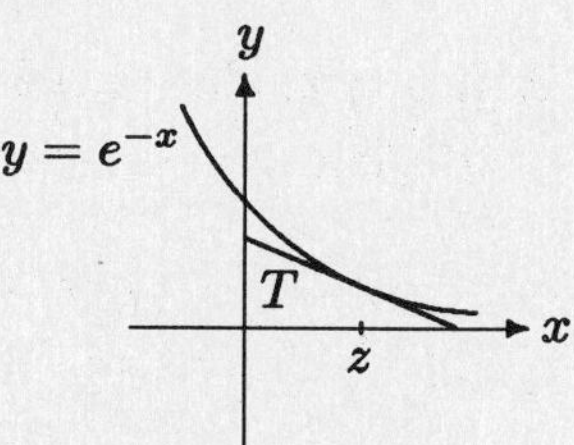

66. a. By (4), $\lim_{\lambda\to\infty} I_0(\lambda) = \lim_{\lambda\to\infty}(2\pi ckT)/\lambda^4 = 0$. By Example 10 this means that

$$\lim_{\lambda\to\infty} I_1(\lambda) = \lim_{\lambda\to\infty}\left[\frac{I_1(\lambda)}{I_0(\lambda)}I_0(\lambda)\right] = \lim_{\lambda\to\infty}\frac{I_1(\lambda)}{I_0(\lambda)}\lim_{\lambda\to\infty} I_0(\lambda) = 1\cdot 0 = 0.$$

b. By l'Hôpital's Rule,

$$\lim_{\lambda\to\infty}\frac{e^{a\lambda}}{\lambda^5} = \lim_{\lambda\to\infty}\frac{ae^{a\lambda}}{5\lambda^4} = \lim_{\lambda\to\infty}\frac{a^2e^{a\lambda}}{20\lambda^3} = \lim_{\lambda\to\infty}\frac{a^3e^{a\lambda}}{60\lambda^2} = \lim_{\lambda\to\infty}\frac{a^4e^{a\lambda}}{120\lambda} = \lim_{\lambda\to\infty}\frac{a^5e^{a\lambda}}{120} = \infty.$$

c. Let $y = 1/\lambda$, so $\lim_{y\to\infty} y = \lim_{\lambda\to 0^+} 1/\lambda = \infty$. Then by the Substitution Rule and by (b),

$$\lim_{\lambda\to 0^+}\lambda(e^{a/\lambda}-1) = \lim_{y\to\infty}\left(\frac{e^{ay}}{y^5}-\frac{1}{y^5}\right) = \lim_{y\to\infty}\frac{e^{ay}}{y^5} = \infty.$$

d. By (c), $\lim_{\lambda\to 0^+} 1/[\lambda^5(e^{a/\lambda}-1)] = 0$. If $a = hc/kT$, then this means that

$$\lim_{\lambda\to 0^+}\frac{1}{\lambda^5(e^{hc/\lambda kT}-1)} = 0.$$

Thus

$$\lim_{\lambda\to 0^+} I_1(\lambda) = \lim_{\lambda\to 0^+}\frac{2\pi hc^2}{\lambda^5(e^{hc/\lambda kT}-1)} = 0.$$

(Since $\lim_{\lambda\to 0^+} I_1(\lambda) = 0 = \lim_{\lambda\to\infty} I_1(\lambda)$, and since I_1 is continuous on $(0,\infty)$, it can be proved that I_1 is bounded on $(0,\infty)$.)

6.7 Introduction to Differential Equations

1. If $y = \frac{1}{3}e^{3t}$, then $dy/dt = 3(\frac{1}{3}e^{3t}) = e^{3t}$, so that $dy/dt = e^{3t}$.

2. If $y = 5e^{3t} - \frac{2}{3}t - \frac{2}{9}$, then $dy/dt = 15e^{3t} - \frac{2}{3}$; since $2t + 3y = 2t + 3(5e^{3t} - \frac{2}{3}t - \frac{2}{9}) = 15e^{3t} - \frac{2}{3}$, we have $dy/dt = 2t + 3y$.

3. If $y = \tan t + \sec t$ for $0 < t < \pi/2$, then $dy/dt = \sec^2 t + \sec t \tan t$, so that $2(dy/dt) - y^2 = 2(\sec^2 t + \sec t\ \tan t) - (\tan t + \sec t)^2 = 2\sec^2 t + 2\sec t\ \tan t - (\tan^2 t + 2\sec t\ \tan t + \sec^2 t) = \sec^2 t - \tan^2 t = 1$. Thus $2(dy/dt) - y^2 = 1$.

4. If $y = 3 + t/3$ then $dy/dt = \frac{1}{3}$, so that $t(dy/dt)^2 - y(dy/dt) + 1 = t(\frac{1}{9}) - (3 + t/3)(\frac{1}{3}) + 1 = 0$. Thus $t(dy/dt)^2 - y(dy/dt) + 1 = 0$.

5. If $y = \sin 2x - \cos 2x$, then $dy/dx = 2\cos 2x + 2\sin 2x$, and $d^2y/dx^2 = -4\sin 2x + 4\cos 2x$. Thus $d^2y/dx^2 + 4y = -4\sin 2x + 4\cos 2x + 4(\sin 2x - \cos 2x) = 0$, so that $d^2y/dx^2 + 4y = 0$.

6. If $y = e^{-x} + \sin x$, then $dy/dx = -e^{-x} + \cos x$ and $d^2y/dx^2 = e^{-x} - \sin x$. Thus $d^2y/dx^2 + y = (e^{-x} - \sin x) + (e^{-x} + \sin x) = 2e^{-x}$, so that $d^2y/dx^2 + y = 2e^{-x}$.

7. If $y = xe^{-2x}$, then $dy/dx = e^{-2x} - 2xe^{-2x}$ and $d^2y/dx^2 = -2e^{-2x} - 2e^{-2x} + 4xe^{-2x}$. Thus $d^2y/dx^2 + 4(dy/dx) + 4y = (-2e^{-2x} - 2e^{-2x} + 4xe^{-2x}) + 4(e^{-2x} - 2xe^{-2x}) + 4xe^{-2x} = 0$, so that $d^2y/dx^2 + 4(dy/dx) + 4y = 0$.

8. If $y = e^{-4x}$, then $dy/dx = -4e^{-4x}$, $d^2y/dx^2 = 16e^{-4x}$,and $d^3y/dx^3 = -64e^{-4x}$. Thus $d^3y/dx^3 + 64y = -64e^{-4x} + 64e^{-4x} = 0$, so that $d^3y/dx^3 + 64y = 0$.

9. If $y = -2e^{-3x}$, then $dy/dx = 6e^{-3x}$, so that $dy/dx + 5y = 6e^{-3x} + 5(-2e^{-3x}) = --4e^{-3x}$. Thus y satisfies the differential equation. Since $y(0) = -2e^{-3(0)} = -2$, y also satisfies the initial condition.

10. If $y = x^2 - 2x$, then $dy/dx = 2x - 2$. Thus $(dy/dx)^2 = (2x-2)^2 = 4x^2 - 8x + 4$ and $4(y+1) = 4(x^2 - 2x + 1) = 4x^2 - 8x + 4$, so that $(dy/dx)^2 = 4(y+1)$. Thus y satisfies the differential equation. Since $y(0) = 0^2 - 2\cdot 0 = 0$ and $y(2) = 2^2 - 2\cdot 2 = 0$, y also satisfies the initial conditions.

11. If $y = x\int_0^x \sqrt{1+t^4}\,dt$, then $dy/dx = \int_0^x \sqrt{1+t^4}\,dt + x\sqrt{1+x^4}$. Thus

$$x\frac{dy}{dx} - y = x\left(\int_0^x \sqrt{1+t^4}\,dt + x\sqrt{1+x^4}\right) - x\int_0^x \sqrt{1+t^4}\,dt = x^2\sqrt{1+x^4}$$

so that y satisfies the differential equation. Since $y(0) = 0\int_0^0 \sqrt{1+t^4}\,dt = 0$ and $y'(0) = \int_0^0 \sqrt{1+t^4}\,dt + 0\sqrt{1+0^4} = 0$, y also satisfies the initial conditions.

12. If $y = e^x \sin x$, then $dy/dx = e^x \sin x + e^x \cos x$, and $d^2y/dx^2 = e^x \sin x + 2e^x \cos x - e^x \sin x = 2e^x \cos x$. Thus $d^2y/dx^2 - 2(dy/dx) + 2y = 2e^x \cos x - 2(e^x \sin x + e^x \cos x) + 2e^x \sin x = 0$, so that y satisfies the differential equation. Since $y(0) = e^0 \sin 0 = 0$ and $y'(0) = e^0 \sin 0 + e^0 \cos 0 = 1$, y also satisfies the initial conditions.

13. Part of the slope field of the differential equation $dy/dx = 2x$.

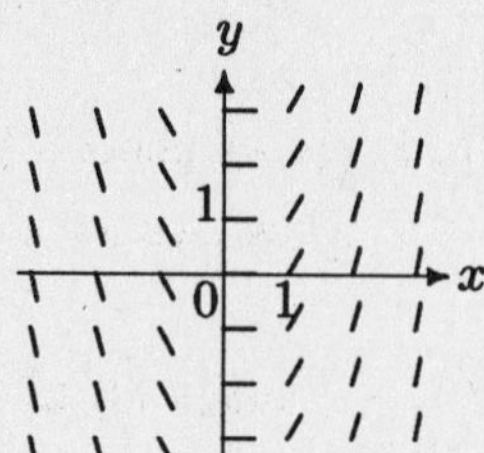

14. Part of the slope field of the differential equation $dy/dx = 1/x$.

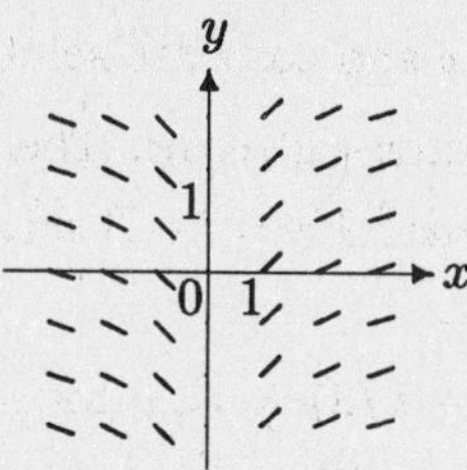

15. Part of the slope field of the differential equation $dy/dx = -x/y$.

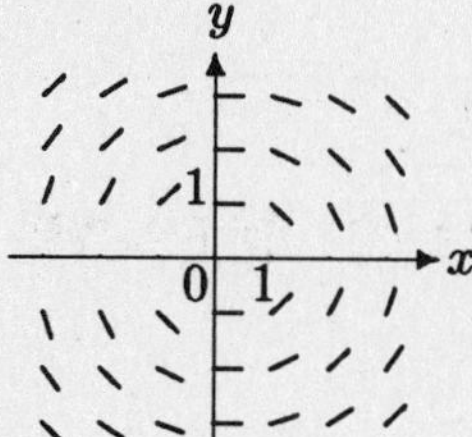

16. Part of the slope field of the differential equation $dy/dx = -4xy$.

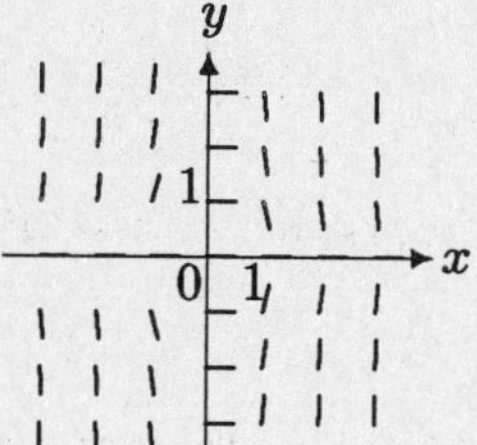

17. Part of the slope field of the differential equation $dy/dx = x/y$.

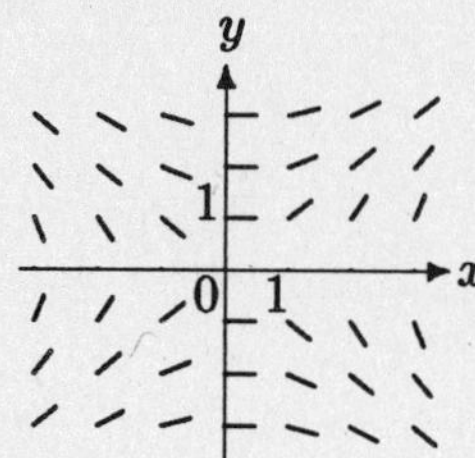

18. Part of the slope field of the differential equation $dy/dt = x - y$.

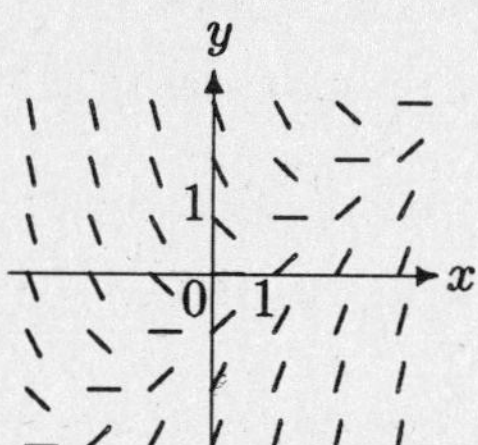

19. If $y = \sqrt{r^2 - x^2}$, then $dy/dx = -x/\sqrt{r^2 - x^2} = -x/y$, so that $y(dy/dx) + x = y(-x/y) + x = 0$. Thus y satisfies the differential equation.

20. If $y = c\cosh x/c$, then $dy/dx = \sinh x/c$, and $d^2y/dx^2 = (1/c)\cosh x/c$. Thus

$$\frac{1}{c}\sqrt{1 + \left(\frac{dy}{dx}\right)^2} = \frac{1}{c}\sqrt{1 + (\sinh x/c)^2} = \frac{1}{c}\cosh x/c = \frac{d^2y}{dx^2}$$

so that y satisfies the differential equation.

21. Let $y = x^2$. Then $dy/dx = 2x$. Substituting into the differential equation, we obtain $c(2x)^2 - x(2x) + x^2 = 0$, or $(4c - 1)x^2 = 0$. Thus $c = \frac{1}{4}$.

22. a. First let $y = \sin x$. Then $dy/dx = \cos x$ and $d^2y/dx^2 = -\sin x$, so $d^2y/dx^2 + y = -\sin x + \sin x = 0$. Now let $y = \cos x$. Then $dy/dx = -\sin x$ and $d^2y/dx^2 = -\cos x$, so $d^2y/dx^2 + y = -\cos x + \cos x = 0$. Thus $\sin x$ and $\cos x$ are solutions.

b. Let $y = C_1 \sin x + C_2 \cos x$. Then $dy/dx = C_1 \cos x - C_2 \sin x$ and $d^2y/dx^2 = -C_1 \sin x - C_2 \cos x$, so that $d^2y/dx^2 + y = (-C_1 \sin x - C_2 \cos x) + (C_1 \sin x + C_2 \cos x) = 0$. Thus $C_1 \sin x + C_2 \cos x$ is a solution.

c. Since $\sin(x + \pi/3) = \sin x \cos(\pi/3) + \cos x \sin(\pi/3) = C_1 \sin x + C_2 \cos x$, where $C_1 = \cos(\pi/3)$ and $C_2 = \sin(\pi/3)$, it follows from (b) that $\sin(x + \pi/3)$ is a solution.

23. a. We have $dy/dx = g(y) > 0$ for all y, so that y is an increasing function. Thus the graph of any solution will rise from left to right.

b. By the Chain Rule, we have

$$\frac{d^2y}{dx^2} = \frac{d}{dx}(g(y)) = \frac{d}{dy}(g(y))\frac{dy}{dx} = g'(y)g(y) > 0.$$

Therefore the graph of any solution will be concave upward (in addition to the property obtained in (a)).

24. a. $\left(\frac{dy}{dx}\right)^2 = -1$ has no solution.

b. $\left(\frac{dy}{dx}\right)^2 = -y^2$ has only the solution $y = 0$.

25. Since $dy/dx)^2 \geq 0$, c must be nonnegative. If $c \geq 0$ and $y = \sqrt{c}\,x$, then $dy/dx = \sqrt{c}$, so y is a solution of $(dy/dx)^2 = c$.

26. If $W = ((c/3)t + 1)^k$, then

$$\frac{dW}{dt} = k\left(\frac{c}{3}t + 1\right)^{k-1} \cdot \frac{c}{3} = \frac{ck}{3}\left(\frac{c}{3}t + 1\right)^{k-1}.$$

Thus W is a solution of $dW/dt = cW^{2/3}$ if and only if

$$\frac{ck}{3}\left(\frac{c}{3}t + 1\right)^{k-1} = c\left(\frac{c}{3}t + 1\right)^{2k/3}, \quad \text{or} \quad \frac{k}{3}\left(\frac{c}{3}t + 1\right)^{(k/3)-1} = 1.$$

The last equation is satisfied if and only if $k = 3$.

27. If $C = c(1 - e^{-at})$, then $dC/dt = ace^{-at}$. Thus C is a solution of $dC/dt + aC = b$ if and only if $ace^{-at} + ac(1 - e^{-at}) = b$, or $ac = b$. Thus $c(1 - e^{-at})$ is a solution if and only if $c = b/a$.

28. If $y = (mgt)/p + C_1 + C_2e^{pt/m}$, then

$$\frac{dy}{dt} = \frac{mg}{p} + \frac{pC_2}{m}e^{pt/m} \quad \text{and} \quad \frac{d^2y}{dt^2} = \frac{p^2C_2}{m^2}e^{pt/m}.$$

Therefore

$$\frac{d^2y}{dt^2} - \frac{p}{m}\frac{dy}{dt} = \frac{p^2C_2}{m^2}e^{pt/m} - \frac{p}{m}\left(\frac{mg}{p} + \frac{pC_2}{m}e^{pt/m}\right) = -g,$$

so y is a solution of the differential equation.

6.8 Methods of Solving Differential Equations

1. $\dfrac{dy}{dx} = \dfrac{x}{y}$, so $y\,dy = x\,dx$; thus $\frac{1}{2}y^2 = \frac{1}{2}x^2 + C_1$, or $y^2 - x^2 = C$.

2. $\dfrac{2y}{y^2+1}\dfrac{dy}{dx} = \dfrac{1}{x^2}$, so $\dfrac{2y}{y^2+1}\,dy = \dfrac{1}{x^2}\,dx$; thus $\ln(y^2+1) = -1/x + C_1$, so that $y^2 + 1 = e^{-(1/x)+C_1}$, which means that $y^2 = -1 + Ce^{-1/x}$, with $C > 0$.

3. $(1+x^2)\,dy = (1+y^2)\,dx$, so $\dfrac{1}{1+y^2}\,dy = \dfrac{1}{1+x^2}\,dx$; thus $\tan^{-1} y = \tan^{-1} x + C$.

4. $dy = \dfrac{y}{1+y}dx$, so $\left(\dfrac{1+y}{y}\right)dy = dx$, or $\left(1+\dfrac{1}{y}\right)dy = dx$; thus $y + \ln y = x + C$.

5. $\dfrac{1+e^x}{1-e^{-y}}\,dy + e^{x+y}\,dx = 0$, so $\dfrac{e^{-y}}{1+e^x}\left(\dfrac{1+e^x}{1-e^{-y}}\,dy + e^{x+y}\,dx\right) = 0$, or $\dfrac{e^{-y}}{1-e^{-y}}\,dy + \dfrac{e^x}{1+e^x}\,dx = 0$; thus $\ln|1-e^{-y}| + \ln(1+e^x) = C_1$, so that if $C_1 = \ln C$, then $\ln|1-e^{-y}| + \ln(1+e^x) = \ln C$, or $\ln[|1-e^{-y}|(1+e^x)] = \ln C$. Therefore $|1-e^{-y}|(1+e^x) = C$, or $|1-e^{-y}| = C/(1+e^x)$.

6. $e^{x+y^2}\,dy = (x/y)\,dx$, so $ye^{y^2}\,dy = xe^{-x}\,dx$. Since $\int xe^{-x}\,dx \overset{\text{parts}}{=} -xe^{-x} + \int e^{-x}\,dx = -xe^{-x} - e^{-x} + C$, we conclude that $\frac{1}{2}e^{y^2} = -xe^{-x} - e^{-x} + C$.

7. $e^{-2y}\,dy = (x-2)\,dx$, and thus $-\frac{1}{2}e^{-2y} = \frac{1}{2}x^2 - 2x + C$. If $y(0) = 0$, then $-\frac{1}{2}e^0 = 0 - 0 + C$, so that $C = -\frac{1}{2}$. Therefore the particular solution with $y(0) = 0$ is $-\frac{1}{2}e^{-2y} = \frac{1}{2}x^2 - 2x - \frac{1}{2}$, or $y = -\frac{1}{2}\ln(-x^2 + 4x + 1)$.

8. $(\ln y)^2\dfrac{dy}{dx} = x^2 y$, so $\dfrac{1}{y}(\ln y)^2\,dy = x^2\,dx$; thus $\frac{1}{3}(\ln y)^3 = \frac{1}{3}x^3 + C_1$, or $y = e^{(x^3+C)^{1/3}}$. If $y(2) = 1$, then $1 = e^{(x^3+C)^{1/3}}$, so that $0 = 2^3 + C$ and thus $C = -8$. Therefore the particular solution with $y(2) = 1$ is $y = e^{(x^3-8)^{1/3}}$

9. $y^2 x\dfrac{dy}{dx} - x + 1 = 0$, so $y^2\,dy = \dfrac{1}{x}\,(x-1)\,dx = \left(1 - \dfrac{1}{x}\right)dx$; thus $\frac{1}{3}y^3 = x - \ln|x| + C$. If $y(1) = 3$, then $\frac{1}{3}(3)^3 = 1 - \ln 1 + C$, so that $C = 8$. Therefore the particular solution with $y(1) = 3$ is $\frac{1}{3}y^3 = x - \ln|x| + 8$.

10. $\sqrt{x^2+1}\,\dfrac{dy}{dx} = \dfrac{x}{y}$, so $y\,dy = \dfrac{x}{\sqrt{x^2+1}}\,dx$; thus $\frac{1}{2}y^2 = \sqrt{x^2+1} + C$. If $y(\sqrt{3}) = 2$, then $\frac{1}{2}(2)^2 = \sqrt{(\sqrt{3})^2 + 1} + C$, so that $C = 0$. Therefore the particular solution with $y(\sqrt{3}) = 2$ is $\frac{1}{2}y^2 = \sqrt{x^2+1}$, or $y = \sqrt{2\sqrt{x^2+1}}$.

11. $P(x) = 1/x^2$ and $Q(x) = 0$. Since $-1/x$ is an antiderivative of P, $S(x) = -1/x$, so (12) implies that $y = e^{1/x}\int e^{-1/x}0\,dx = e^{1/x}(C) = Ce^{1/x}$.

12. $P(x) = -\sinh x$ and $Q(x) = 0$. Since $-\cosh x$ is an antiderivative of P, $S(x) = -\cosh x$, so (12) implies that $y = e^{\cosh x}\int e^{-\cosh x}0\,dx = e^{\cosh x}(C) = Ce^{\cosh x}$.

13. $P(x) = 2$ and $Q(x) = 4$. Since $2x$ is an antiderivative of P, $S(x) = 2x$, so (12) implies that $y = e^{-2x}\int e^{2x}4\,dx = 4e^{-2x}\int e^{2x}\,dx = 4e^{-2x}(\frac{1}{2}e^{2x} + C_1) = 2 + Ce^{-2x}$.

14. $P(x) = -a$ and $Q(x) = f(x)$. Since $-ax$ is an antiderivative of P, $S(x) = -ax$, so (12) implies that $y = e^a x \int e^{-ax} f(x)\,dx$.

15. $P(x) = -1$ and $Q(x) = 1/(1-e^{-x})$. Since $-x$ is an antiderivative of P, $S(x) = -x$, so (12) implies that

$$y = e^x \int e^{-x}\frac{1}{1-e^{-x}}\,dx = e^x(\ln|1-e^{-x}| + C).$$

16. $P(x) = \cos x$ and $Q(x) = \cos x$. Since $\sin x$ is an antiderivative of P, $S(x) = \sin x$, so (12) implies that $y = e^{-\sin x}\int e^{\sin x}\cos x\,dx = e^{-\sin x}(e^{\sin x} + C) = 1 + Ce^{-\sin x}$.

17. $P(x) = \tan x$ and $Q(x) = \tan x$. Since $-\ln\cos x$ is an antiderivative of P for $-\pi/2 < x < \pi/2$ (since $\cos x > 0$ for such x), we have that $S(x) = -\ln\cos x$. Then (12) implies that

$$y = e^{\ln\cos x}\int e^{-\ln\cos x}\tan x\,dx = \cos x\int \sec x\tan x\,dx = \cos x\,(\sec x + C) = 1 + C\cos x.$$

18. $P(x) = -\tan x$ and $Q(x) = e^{\sin x}$. Since $\ln\cos x$ is an antiderivative of P for $-\pi/2 < x < \pi/2$ (since $\cos x > 0$ for such x), we have $S(x) = \ln\cos x$. Then (12) implies that

$$y = e^{-\ln\cos x}\int e^{\ln\cos x}e^{\sin x}\,dx = \sec x\int(\cos x)e^{\sin x}\,dx = (\sec x)(e^{\sin x} + C).$$

19. $P(x) = 5$ and $Q(x) = -4e^{-3x}$. Since $5x$ is an antiderivative of P, $S(x) = 5x$, so (12) implies that $y = e^{-5x}\int e^{5x}(-4e^{-3x})\,dx = -4e^{-5x}\int e^{2x}\,dx = -4e^{-5x}(\frac{1}{2}e^{2x} + C)$. If $y(0) = -4$, then $-4 = -4e^{-5(0)}(\frac{1}{2}e^{2(0)} + C)$, so that $C = \frac{1}{2}$. Therefore the particular solution with $y(0) = -4$ is $y = -4e^{-5x}(\frac{1}{2}e^{2x} + \frac{1}{2}) = -2e^{-3x} - 2e^{-5x}$.

20. The equation is equivalent to $dy/dx - (4/x)y = 1$, so that $P(x) = -4/x$ and $Q(x) = 1$. Since $-4\ln|x|$ is an antiderivative of P, $S(x) = -4\ln|x|$, so (12) implies that $y = e^{4\ln|x|}\int e^{-4\ln|x|}\,dx = x^4\int x^{-4}\,dx = x^4(-\frac{1}{3}x^{-3} + C) = -\frac{1}{3}x + Cx^4$. If $y(1) = 1$, then $1 = -\frac{1}{3} + C$, so that $C = \frac{4}{3}$. Therefore the particular solution with $y(1) = 1$ is $y = -\frac{1}{3}x + \frac{4}{3}x^4$.

21. The equation is equivalent to $dy/dx + (1/\cos x)y = 1/\cos x$, so that $P(x) = 1/\cos x = \sec x = Q(x)$. Since $\ln(\sec x + \tan x)$ is an antiderivative of P for $0 < x < \pi/2$, $S(x) = \ln(\sec x + \tan x)$, so (12) implies that

$$y = e^{-\ln(\sec x + \tan x)}\int e^{\ln(\sec x + \tan x)}\sec x\,dx = \frac{1}{\sec x + \tan x}\int(\sec x + \tan x)\sec x\,dx$$

$$= \frac{1}{\sec x + \tan x}\int(\sec^2 x + \tan x\sec x)\,dx = \frac{1}{\sec x + \tan x}(\tan x + \sec x + C) = 1 + \frac{C}{\sec x + \tan x}.$$

If $y(\pi/4) = 2$, then $2 = 1 + C/(\sqrt{2} + 1)$, so that $C = \sqrt{2} + 1$. Therefore the particular solution with $y(\pi/4) = 2$ is $y = 1 + (\sqrt{2} + 1)/(\sec x + \tan x)$.

22. $P(x) = -2x$ and $Q(x) = x$. Since $-x^2$ is an antiderivative of P, $S(x) = -x^2$, so (12) implies that $y = e^{x^2}\int e^{-x^2}x\,dx = e^{x^2}(-\frac{1}{2}e^{-x^2} + C) = -\frac{1}{2} + Ce^{x^2}$. If $y(0) = 0$, then $0 = -\frac{1}{2} + Ce^{0^2}$, so that $C = \frac{1}{2}$. Therefore the particular solution with $y(0) = 0$ is $y = -\frac{1}{2} + \frac{1}{2}e^{x^2}$.

23. a. Since $v = y/x$, we have $y = xv$, so that $dy/dx = x(dv/dx) + v$.

b. By (15), $f(v) = f(y/x) = dy/dx \overset{(15)}{=} x(dv/dx) + v$, so that $f(v) - v = x(dv/dx)$ and thus $[1/(f(v) - v)]\, dv = (1/x)\, dx$.

24. $\dfrac{x+y}{x} = 1 + \dfrac{y}{x} = f(y/x)$, where $f(v) = 1 + v$. By (16), $1/((1+v) - v)\, dv = (1/x)\, dx$, so that $dv = (1/x)\, dx$, and thus $v = \ln|x| + C_1$. If $\ln C = C_1$, then since $v = y/x$, we conclude that $y/x = \ln|x| + \ln C = \ln C|x|$, so that $y = x \ln C|x|$, with $C > 0$.

25. If we multiply both sides of the differential equation by $(x^2 + y^2)/y$, we obtain $y + 2x(dy/dx) = 0$, and can be rewritten as $(2/y)\, dy = -(1/x)\, dx$. The solution is given by $2 \ln y = -\ln x + C_1$, or $\ln y^2 + \ln x = C_1$, or $\ln(xy^2) = C_1$, or $xy^2 = C$, where $C = e^{C_1}$.

26. The differential equation is equivalent to $dI/dt + (R/L)I = 2/L$, which conforms to (10) if $P(t) = R/L$ and $Q(t) = 2/L$. Since Rt/L is an antiderivative of P, $S(t) = Rt/L$, so we conclude from (12) that

$$I = e^{-(R/L)t} \int e^{(R/L)t} \frac{2}{L}\, dt = e^{-(R/L)t}\left(\frac{2}{R} e^{(R/L)t} + C\right) = \frac{2}{R} + Ce^{-(R/L)t}.$$

27. a. Letting $v = mg/b$ in (13), we obtain $-mg + b(mg/b) = m(dv/dt)$, so $dv/dt = 0$.

b. When the velocity reaches the limiting velocity, it no longer changes, so $dv/dt = 0$.

28. The differential equation $dT/dL = T/2L$ is separable. Separating the variables, we obtain $(1/T)\, dT = (1/2L)\, dL$. Thus $\ln T = \frac{1}{2} \ln L + C_1$, so that $T = e^{(1/2)\ln L + C_1} = e^{C_1} L^{1/2} = CL^{1/2}$, where $C = e^{C_1}$. Therefore T is proportional to the square root of L.

29. a. Separating the variables in (18), we obtain $(1/\sqrt{s})\, ds = \sqrt{2g}\, dt$, so that $2\sqrt{s} = \sqrt{2g}\, t + C$. Since $s(0) = 0$, we have $C = 0$. Thus $2\sqrt{s} = \sqrt{2g}\, t$, or $s = \frac{1}{2} g t^2$.

b. Since $s(0) = 0$, the initial height h_0 of the object is 0, and since the object is dropped, the initial velocity v_0 is 0. Thus (1) of Section 1.3, which applies when height is measured in meters and time in seconds, becomes $h(t) = -4.9t^2 = \frac{1}{2}(-9.8)t^2 = \frac{1}{2} g t^2$. (Similarly, (2) of Section 1.3, which applies when height is measured in feet and time in seconds, becomes $h(t) = -16t^2 = \frac{1}{2}(-32)t^2 = \frac{1}{2} g t^2$. This also agrees with the result in part (a).)

30. $\dfrac{1}{V}\dfrac{dV}{dt} = \dfrac{1}{(4\pi/3)r^3} \cdot \dfrac{4\pi}{3}\left(3r^2 \dfrac{dr}{dt}\right) = 3 \cdot \dfrac{1}{r}\dfrac{dr}{dt}$

Thus the specific rate of growth $(1/V)dV/dt$ of the volume equals 3 times the specific rate of growth $(1/r)dr/dt$ of the radius.

31. Suppose $y = Cx^k$, as in (7). Substituting first $x = 25$ and $y = .44$, and then $x = 110$ and $y = 3$, we obtain $.44 = C\, 25^k$ and $3 = C\, 110^k$. Dividing these two equations to eliminate C, we find that $.44/3 = (25/110)^k = (5/22)^k$. Taking natural logarithms, we find that $\ln(.44/3) = k \ln(5/22)$. Using a calculator, we obtain $k \approx 1.2956$. Then $C = 3/110^k \approx .0068$. If we substitute the values 460, 1400, and 6000 of x in the table into the equation $y = Cx^k$, we obtain approximately 19, 81, and 534, respectively, for the corresponding values of y. These values are reasonably close to the values of y given in the table, so the data seems to (nearly) satisfy an allometric relation.

32. By the discussion of Newton's Law of Cooling, the body temperature y is given by $y = y_0 + Ce^{kt}$, where y_0 is the temperature of the surrounding medium, and C and k are constants. Let $t = 0$ at noon. We wish to find the time t at which $y = 98.6$. We are given that $y(0) = 87$, $y(\frac{1}{2}) = 83$, and $y_0 = 75$. Therefore $87 = 75 + Ce^0$ and $83 = 75 + Ce^{k/2}$. From the first of these two equations, it follows that $C = 12$, so that the second equation becomes $83 = 75 + 12e^{k/2}$, or $e^{k/2} = 8/12 = 2/3$, so that $k = 2\ln\frac{2}{3}$. Therefore $y = 75 + 12e^{2t\ln(2/3)}$. Thus $y = 98.6$ if

$$e^{2t\ln(2/3)} = \frac{98.6 - 75}{12} = \frac{23.6}{12}, \quad \text{or} \quad 2t\ln\frac{2}{3} = \ln\frac{23.6}{12}.$$

By calculator we find that $t \approx -0.834$. Thus the time of death was approximately 50 minutes before noon, or 11:10 A.M.

33. a. Separating the variables in $dy/dx = c(1 + y^2)^{1/2}$, we obtain $[1/(1 + y^2)^{1/2}]\,dy = c\,dx$. By (9) in Section 6.4, this implies $\sinh^{-1} y = cx + C$, where C is a constant. Therefore $y = \sinh(cx + C)$.

b. By (a), $f'(x) = y = \sinh(cx + C)$. Therefore since

$$\frac{d}{dx}\left(\frac{1}{c}\cosh(cx + C)\right) = \sinh(cx + C),$$

Theorem 4.6 implies that

$$f(x) = \frac{1}{c}\cosh(cx + C) + D, \quad \text{where } D \text{ is a constant.}$$

34. Separating the variables in $M(dv/dM) = -v_e$, we obtain $dv = -(v_e/M)\,dM$, so that $v = -v_e \ln M + C$, where C is a constant. Substituting $v = v_0$ and $M = M_0$, we find that $C = v_0 + v_e \ln M_0$. Therefore $v = -v_e \ln M + v_0 + v_e \ln M_0 = v_0 + v_e \ln(M_0/M)$.

Chapter 6 Review

1. $f'(x) = 9x^2 + 25x^4 \geq 0$ for all x, and $f'(x) = 0$ only for $x = 0$, so f has an inverse.

2. $f(-x) = f(x)$ for all x, so f does not have an inverse.

3. $f'(x) = 1/x^2 > 0$ for x in $(-\infty, 0)$ and $(0, \infty)$, and $f(x) > 1$ for $x < 0$, whereas $f(x) < 1$ for $x > 0$. Thus f has an inverse.

4. $f(1) = 0 = f(-1)$, so f does not have an inverse even though $f'(x) = 1 + 1/x^2 > 0$ for $x \neq 0$.

5. $g(x + 2\pi) = g(x)$ for all x, so g does not have an inverse.

6. $g'(x) = 1 - \sin x \geq 0$ for all x, and $g'(x) = 0$ only if $x = \pi/2 + 2n\pi$ for some integer n. Thus f is increasing on every bounded interval and hence on $(-\infty, \infty)$, so f has an inverse.

7. $y = \dfrac{3x - 2}{-x + 1}$; $(-x + 1)y = 3x - 2$; $x(y + 3) = y + 2$; $x = \dfrac{y + 2}{y + 3}$; $f^{-1}(x) = \dfrac{x + 2}{x + 3}$

8. $y = \dfrac{x^3}{4-x^3}$; $(4-x^3)y = x^3$; $x^3(y+1) = 4y$; $x = \left(\dfrac{4y}{y+1}\right)^{1/3}$; $f^{-1}(x) = \left(\dfrac{4x}{x+1}\right)^{1/3}$

9. Since $f(-x) = f(x)$ for every x in $(-a, a)$, f cannot have an inverse by (3) of Section 6.1.

10. a. $f'(x) = \dfrac{e^x(e^x+1) - (e^x)^2}{(1+e^x)^2} = \dfrac{e^x}{(1+e^x)^2} > 0$ for all x, so f has an inverse.

b. $f(0) = \dfrac{1}{2}$; $(f^{-1})'\left(\dfrac{1}{2}\right) = \dfrac{1}{f'(0)} = \dfrac{1}{1/4} = 4$

11. $\dfrac{dy}{dx} = \dfrac{1}{1+2^x}(\ln 2)\, 2^x = \dfrac{(\ln 2)\, 2^x}{1+2^x}$

12. $y = x^{\cos x} = e^{\ln x \cos x}$, so $\dfrac{dy}{dx} = e^{\ln x \cos x}\left(\dfrac{1}{x}\cos x - \ln x \sin x\right) = x^{\cos x}\left(\dfrac{1}{x}\cos x - \ln x \sin x\right)$.

13. $\dfrac{dy}{dx} = \dfrac{1}{1+\sinh^2 x}\cosh x = \dfrac{\cosh x}{\cosh^2 x} = \dfrac{1}{\cosh x}$

14. $y = x^{(2^x)} = e^{(e^{x\ln 2})\ln x}$, so $\dfrac{dy}{dx} = x^{(2^x)}\left(e^{x\ln 2}\ln 2 \ln x + e^{x \ln 2}\dfrac{1}{x}\right) = x^{(2^x)}\, 2^x\left(\ln 2 \ln x + \dfrac{1}{x}\right)$.

15. $\dfrac{dy}{dx} = \dfrac{1}{\sqrt{1-(1-x^2)^{2/3}}}\,\dfrac{1}{3}(1-x^2)^{-2/3}(-2x) = \dfrac{-2x}{3(1-x^2)^{2/3}\sqrt{1-(1-x^2)^{2/3}}}$

16. $\dfrac{dy}{dx} = \dfrac{x\cosh x - \sinh x}{x^2}$

17. Since $y = \dfrac{\ln(\tan^{-1} x^2)}{\ln 4}$, it follows that $\dfrac{dy}{dx} = \dfrac{1}{(\ln 4)(\tan^{-1} x^2)} \cdot \dfrac{2x}{1+x^4} = \dfrac{2x}{(\ln 4)(1+x^4)\tan^{-1} x^2}$.

18. $\dfrac{dy}{dx}\sinh^{-1} x + \dfrac{y}{\sqrt{1+x^2}} + e^y\dfrac{dy}{dx} = 5y^4\dfrac{dy}{dx}$; $\dfrac{dy}{dx} = \dfrac{-y}{\sqrt{1+x^2}}\left(\dfrac{1}{\sinh^{-1} x + e^y - 5y^4}\right)$

19. $\displaystyle\int \frac{e^x}{\sqrt{1+e^x}}\,dx \overset{u=1+e^x}{=} \int \frac{1}{\sqrt{u}}\,du = 2\sqrt{u} + C = 2\sqrt{1+e^x} + C$

20. $\displaystyle\int \frac{e^x}{\sqrt{1-e^{2x}}}\,dx \overset{u=e^x}{=} \int \frac{1}{\sqrt{1-u^2}}\,du = \sin^{-1} u + C = \sin^{-1} e^x + C$

21. $\displaystyle\int \frac{e^x}{\sqrt{1+e^{2x}}}\,dx \overset{u=e^x}{=} \int \frac{1}{\sqrt{1+u^2}}\,du = \sinh^{-1} u + C = \sinh^{-1}(e^x) + C$

22. $\displaystyle\int \frac{1}{\sqrt{e^{2x}-1}}\,dx = \int \frac{e^x}{e^x\sqrt{e^{2x}-1}}\,dx \overset{u=e^x}{=} \int \frac{1}{u\sqrt{u^2-1}}\,du = \sec^{-1} u + C = \sec^{-1} e^x + C$

23. $\displaystyle\int \frac{e^x}{e^x+e^{-x}}\,dx \overset{u=e^x}{=} \int \frac{1}{u+1/u}\,du = \int \frac{u}{u^2+1}\,du \overset{v=u^2}{=} \int \frac{1}{v+1}\,\frac{1}{2}\,dv = \frac{1}{2}\int \frac{1}{v+1}\,dv$

$\displaystyle = \frac{1}{2}\ln|v+1| + C = \frac{1}{2}\ln(u^2+1) + C = \frac{1}{2}\ln(e^{2x}+1) + C$

24. $\displaystyle\int e^x \cosh x\,dx = \int e^x\left(\frac{e^x+e^{-x}}{2}\right)dx = \frac{1}{2}\int (e^{2x}+1)\,dx = \frac{1}{2}\left(\frac{1}{2}e^{2x} + x\right) + C = \frac{e^{2x}}{4} + \frac{x}{2} + C$

25. $\displaystyle\int_0^1 x^2 5^{-x^3}\,dx \overset{u=x^3}{=} \int_0^1 5^{-u}\frac{1}{3}\,du = \left.\frac{-5^{-u}}{3\ln 5}\right|_0^1 = \frac{1}{3\ln 5}\left(1-\frac{1}{5}\right) = \frac{4}{15\ln 5}$

26. $\displaystyle\int \frac{\sin x}{\sqrt{1-4\cos^2 x}}\,dx \overset{u=2\cos x}{=} \frac{-1}{2}\int \frac{1}{\sqrt{1-u^2}}\,du = -\frac{1}{2}\sin^{-1}u + C = -\frac{1}{2}\sin^{-1}(2\cos x) + C$

27. $\displaystyle\int \frac{3}{1+4t^2}\,dt \overset{u=2t}{=} \int \frac{3}{1+u^2}\frac{1}{2}\,du = \frac{3}{2}\tan^{-1}u + C = \frac{3}{2}\tan^{-1}2t + C$

28. $\displaystyle\int \frac{t^4}{t^{10}+1}\,dt \overset{u=t^5}{=} \frac{1}{5}\int \frac{1}{u^2+1}\,du = \frac{1}{5}\tan^{-1}u + C = \frac{1}{5}\tan^{-1}t^5 + C$

29. $\displaystyle\int_{-5/4}^{5/4} \frac{1}{\sqrt{25-4t^2}}\,dt = \frac{1}{2}\int_{-5/4}^{5/4} \frac{1}{\sqrt{25/4-t^2}}\,dt = \left.\frac{1}{2}\sin^{-1}\frac{2t}{5}\right|_{-5/4}^{5/4} = \frac{1}{2}\left[\sin^{-1}\frac{1}{2} - \sin^{-1}\left(\frac{-1}{2}\right)\right] = \frac{\pi}{6}$

30. $\displaystyle\int \frac{e^{1+\ln x}}{\sqrt{1+x^2}}\,dx = \int \frac{(e)e^{\ln x}}{\sqrt{1+x^2}}\,dx = \int \frac{ex}{\sqrt{1+x^2}}\,dx \overset{u=1+x^2}{=} \int \frac{e}{\sqrt{u}}\frac{1}{2}\,du = e\sqrt{u} + C = e\sqrt{1+x^2} + C$

31. $$\begin{aligned}\int \operatorname{sech} x\,dx &= \int \frac{1}{\cosh x}\,dx = \int \frac{2}{e^x+e^{-x}}\,dx = \int \frac{2e^x}{e^{2x}+1}\,dx \\ &\overset{u=e^x}{=} \int \frac{2}{u^2+1}\,du = 2\tan^{-1}u + C = 2\tan^{-1}e^x + C\end{aligned}$$

32. $\displaystyle\int \frac{\sqrt{x}}{\sqrt{1+x^3}}\,dx \overset{u=x^{3/2}}{=} \int \frac{1}{\sqrt{1+u^2}}\cdot\frac{2}{3}\,du = \frac{2}{3}\int \frac{1}{\sqrt{1+u^2}}\,du = \frac{2}{3}\sinh^{-1}u + C = \frac{2}{3}\sinh^{-1}(x^{3/2}) + C$

33. $$\begin{aligned}\int \frac{x}{x^4+4x^2+10}\,dx &= \int \frac{x}{(x^2+2)^2+6}\,dx \overset{u=x^2+2}{=} \int \frac{1}{u^2+6}\frac{1}{2}\,du \\ &= \frac{1}{2}\frac{1}{\sqrt{6}}\tan^{-1}\frac{u}{\sqrt{6}} + C = \frac{\sqrt{6}}{12}\tan^{-1}\left(\frac{x^2+2}{\sqrt{6}}\right) + C\end{aligned}$$

34. $\displaystyle\int \frac{1}{x\sqrt{1-(\ln x)^2}}\,dx \overset{u=\ln x}{=} \int \frac{1}{\sqrt{1-u^2}}\,du = \sin^{-1}u + C = \sin^{-1}(\ln x) + C$

35. $\displaystyle\lim_{t\to 0}\sinh at = 0 = \lim_{t\to 0} t;\ \lim_{t\to 0}\frac{\sinh at}{t} = \lim_{t\to 0}\frac{a\cosh at}{1} = a$

36. The conditions for applying l'Hôpital's Rule twice are met;

$$\lim_{x\to 0}\frac{\tan x - x}{\sin x - x} = \lim_{x\to 0}\frac{\sec^2 x - 1}{\cos x - 1} = \lim_{x\to 0}\frac{2\sec^2 x\,\tan x}{-\sin x} = \lim_{x\to 0}\frac{-2}{\cos^3 x} = -2.$$

37. The conditions for applying l'Hôpital's Rule twice are met;

$$\lim_{x\to 0+}\frac{\ln x}{\ln(\sin x)} = \lim_{x\to 0+}\frac{1/x}{(\cos x)/(\sin x)} = \lim_{x\to 0+}\frac{\tan x}{x} = \lim_{x\to 0+}\frac{\sec^2 x}{1} = 1.$$

38. $\displaystyle\lim_{x\to 0+} e^{1/x} = \infty$ and $\displaystyle\lim_{x\to 0+}(1-\cot x) = -\infty$;

$$\lim_{x\to 0+}\frac{e^{1/x}}{1-\cot x} = \lim_{x\to 0+}\frac{e^{1/x}(-1/x^2)}{\csc^2 x} = -\lim_{x\to 0+}\left(\frac{\sin x}{x}\right)^2 e^{1/x} = -\infty$$

39. $\lim_{x\to 0^+}\left(\frac{1}{x}-\frac{1}{\tan^{-1}x}\right)=\lim_{x\to 0^+}\frac{\tan^{-1}x-x}{x\tan^{-1}x}$;
the conditions for applying l'Hôpital's Rule twice are met;

$$\lim_{x\to 0^+}\left(\frac{1}{x}-\frac{1}{\tan^{-1}x}\right)=\lim_{x\to 0^+}\frac{\tan^{-1}x-x}{x\tan^{-1}x}=\lim_{x\to 0^+}\frac{\dfrac{1}{x^2+1}-1}{\tan^{-1}x+\dfrac{x}{x^2+1}}$$

$$=\lim_{x\to 0^+}\frac{\dfrac{-2x}{(x^2+1)^2}}{\dfrac{1}{x^2+1}+\dfrac{1-x^2}{(x^2+1)^2}}=\lim_{x\to 0^+}(-x)=0.$$

40. $\lim_{x\to\infty}x^{1/2}\sin\frac{1}{x}=\lim_{x\to\infty}\frac{\sin(1/x)}{x^{-1/2}};\ \lim_{x\to\infty}\sin\frac{1}{x}=0=\lim_{x\to\infty}x^{-1/2}$;

$\lim_{x\to\infty}x^{1/2}\sin\frac{1}{x}=\lim_{x\to\infty}\frac{\sin(1/x)}{x^{-1/2}}=\lim_{x\to\infty}\frac{(-1/x^2)\cos(1/x)}{(-1/2)x^{-3/2}}=\lim_{x\to\infty}\frac{2}{x^{1/2}}\cos\frac{1}{x}=0$

41. $\lim_{x\to\infty}\left(\frac{x+1}{x-1}\right)^x=\lim_{x\to\infty}e^{x\ln[(x+1)/(x-1)]}=e^{\lim_{x\to\infty}x\ln[(x+1)/(x-1)]}$;

$\lim_{x\to\infty}\left[x\ln\frac{x+1}{x-1}\right]=\lim_{x\to\infty}\frac{\ln[(x+1)/(x-1)]}{1/x}$, and $\lim_{x\to\infty}\ln\frac{x+1}{x-1}=0=\lim_{x\to\infty}\frac{1}{x}$;
thus

$$\lim_{x\to\infty}x\ln\frac{x+1}{x-1}=\lim_{x\to\infty}\frac{\ln\dfrac{x+1}{x-1}}{1/x}=\lim_{x\to\infty}\frac{\dfrac{1}{x+1}-\dfrac{1}{x-1}}{-1/x^2}=\lim_{x\to\infty}\frac{2x^2}{x^2-1}=2$$

so that $\lim_{x\to\infty}\left(\frac{x+1}{x-1}\right)^x=e^2$.

42. $\lim_{x\to 1^+}(\ln x)^{x-1}=\lim_{x\to 1^+}e^{(x-1)\ln(\ln x)}=e^{\lim_{x\to 1^+}(x-1)\ln(\ln x)}$;

$\lim_{x\to 1^+}(x-1)\ln(\ln x)=\lim_{x\to 1^+}\frac{\ln(\ln x)}{1/(x-1)}$;
the conditions for applying l'Hôpital's Rule twice are met. Thus

$$\lim_{x\to 1^+}\frac{\ln(\ln x)}{1/(x-1)}=\lim_{x\to 1^+}\frac{1/(x\ln x)}{-1/(x-1)^2}=\lim_{x\to 1^+}\frac{-(x-1)^2}{x\ln x}=\lim_{x\to 1^+}\frac{-2(x-1)}{\ln x+x(1/x)}=\lim_{x\to 1^+}\frac{-2(x-1)}{1+\ln x}=0$$

so that $\lim_{x\to 1^+}(\ln x)^{x-1}=e^0=1$.

43. $e^{(y^2)}\,dx+x^2y\,dy=0$, so $(1/x^2)\,dx+ye^{-(y^2)}\,dy=0$, which is a separable differential equation. By integration we obtain the general solution $-1/x-(1/2)e^{-(y^2)}=C$.

44. $x\sqrt{1-y^2}+y\sqrt{1-x^2}\,(dy/dx)=0$, so $(x/\sqrt{1-x^2})\,dx-(y/\sqrt{1-y^2})\,dy$, which is a separable differential equation. By integration we obtain the general solution $-\sqrt{1-x^2}=\sqrt{1-y^2}+C$.

45. $P(x) = 2/x$ and $Q(x) = x^2 + 6$. Since $2\ln x$ is an antiderivative of P for $x > 0$, $S(x) = 2\ln x$, so by (12) in Section 6.8, the general solution is

$$y = e^{-2\ln x}\int e^{2\ln x}(x^2+6)\,dx = \frac{1}{x^2}\int x^2(x^2+6)\,dx = \frac{1}{x^2}\int (x^4+6x^2)\,dx$$

$$= \frac{1}{x^2}\left(\frac{1}{5}x^5 + 2x^3 + C\right) = \frac{1}{5}x^3 + 2x + \frac{C}{x^2}.$$

46. $P(x) = -\cot x$ and $Q(x) = \csc x$. Since $-\ln\sin x$ is an antiderivative of P on $(0,\pi)$, $S(x) = -\ln\sin x$, so by (12) in Section 6.8, the general solution is

$$y = e^{\ln\sin x}\int e^{-\ln\sin x}\csc x\,dx = \sin x\int \frac{\csc x}{\sin x}\,dx = \sin x\int \csc^2 x\,dx$$

$$= \sin x(-\cot x + C) = -\cos x + C\sin x.$$

47. $2xy\,dx = (y+1)\,dy$, so $2x\,dx = (1+1/y)\,dy$, which is a separable differential equation. By integration we obtain the general solution $x^2 = y + \ln y + C$. If $y(0) = 1$, then $0^2 = 1 + \ln 1 + C$, so $C = -1$. Consequently the particular solution is $x^2 = y + \ln y - 1$.

48. $y(1+x^2)\,dy + (y^2+1)\,dx = 0$, so $[y/(y^2+1)]\,dy = -[1/(1+x^2)]\,dx$, which is a separable differential equation. By integration we obtain the general solution $\frac{1}{2}\ln(y^2+1) = -\tan^{-1}x + C$. If $y(0) = \sqrt{3}$ then $\frac{1}{2}\ln(3+1) = 0 + C = C$, so $C = \frac{1}{2}\ln 4 = \frac{1}{2}\ln 2^2 = \ln 2$, and thus the particular solution is $\frac{1}{2}\ln(y^2+1) + \tan^{-1}x = \ln 2$.

49. $P(x) = -2$ and $Q(x) = 3$. Since $-2x$ is an antiderivative of P, $S(x) = -2x$, so by (12) of Section 6.8, the general solution is $y = e^{2x}\int e^{-2x}3\,dx = e^{2x}\left(-\frac{3}{2}e^{-2x} + C\right) = -\frac{3}{2} + Ce^{2x}$. If $y(0) = 2$, then $2 = -\frac{3}{2} + C$, so $C = \frac{7}{2}$. Consequently the particular solution is $y = -\frac{3}{2} + \frac{7}{2}e^{2x} = \frac{1}{2}(7e^{2x} - 3)$.

50. $P(x) = \tan x$, and $Q(x) = \sec x$. Since $-\ln\cos x$ is an antiderivative of P on $(-\pi/2, \pi/2)$, $S(x) = -\ln\cos x$, so by (12) in Section 6.8, the general solution is

$$y = e^{\ln\cos x}\int e^{-\ln\cos x}\sec x\,dx = \cos x\int \frac{1}{\cos x}\sec x\,dx = \cos x\int \sec^2 x\,dx$$

$$= \cos x(\tan x + C) = \sin x + C\cos x.$$

If $y(0) = \pi/4$, then $\pi/4 = \sin 0 + C\cos 0 = C$, so the particular solution is $y = \sin x + (\pi/4)\cos x$.

51. $f'(x) = (2x)^x(\ln 2x + 1)$, $f''(x) = (2x)^x[(\ln 2x+1)^2 + 1/x]$; relative minimum value is $f(\frac{1}{2}e^{-1}) = 1/e^{1/(2e)} \approx 0.83$; concave upward on $(0,\infty)$. Finally

$$\lim_{x\to 0^+} f(x) = \lim_{x\to 0^+}(2x)^x = \lim_{x\to 0^+} 2^x \lim_{x\to 0^+} x^x.$$

Since $\lim_{x\to 0^+} 2^x = 2^0 = 1$, and since $\lim_{x\to 0^+} x^x = 1$ by Example 8 of Section 6.6, it follows that $\lim_{x\to 0^+}(2x)^x = 1\cdot 1 = 1$. Also $\lim_{x\to\infty}(2x)^x = \infty$.

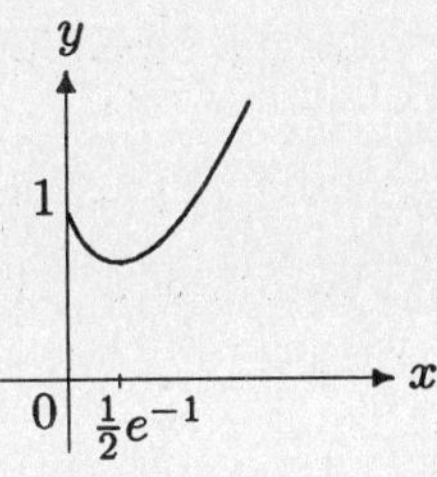

52. Let $y = (x+a)/(x+b)$. Then $xy + by = x + a$, so $xy - x = a - by$ and hence $x = (a - by)/(y-1)$. Thus $f^{-1}(y) = (a - by)/(y-1)$. Converting to the variable x, we have $f^{-1}(x) = (a - bx)/(x-1)$. In order that $f(x) = f^{-1}(x)$, we need

$$\frac{x+a}{x+b} = \frac{a-bx}{x-1} \quad \text{for all } x \neq 1.$$

This holds if $b = -1$.

53. Let $y = \sinh^{-1} x$, so $x = \sinh y$. Note that $\cosh y = \sqrt{1+\sinh^2 y} = \sqrt{1+x^2}$. Then

$$\frac{d}{dx}\sinh^{-1} x = \frac{1}{\dfrac{d}{dy}\sinh y} = \frac{1}{\cosh y} = \frac{1}{\sqrt{1+x^2}}.$$

54. $\cosh 2u - 1 = \dfrac{e^{2u} + e^{-2u}}{2} - 1 = \dfrac{e^{2u} - 2 + e^{-2u}}{2} = \dfrac{1}{2}(e^u - e^{-u})^2$

$\cosh 2u + 1 = \dfrac{e^{2u} + e^{-2u}}{2} + 1 = \dfrac{e^{2u} + 2 + e^{-2u}}{2} = \dfrac{1}{2}(e^u + e^{-u})^2$

55. a. Replacing x by $-x$ in the inequality $e^x > 1 + x$ for $x \neq 0$, we see that $e^{-x} > 1 - x$ for $x \neq 0$. If $x < 1$, then $1 - x > 0$, so it follows that

$$\frac{1}{e^{-x}} < \frac{1}{1-x}, \quad \text{or} \quad e^x < \frac{1}{1-x} \quad \text{for } x < 1.$$

b. Replacing x by $1/x$ in the inequalities $e^x > 1 + x$ and $e^x < 1/(1-x)$ in (a) yields

$$e^{1/x} > 1 + \frac{1}{x} = \frac{x+1}{x} \quad \text{and} \quad e^{1/x} < \frac{1}{1 - 1/x} = \frac{x}{x-1}.$$

These hold in particular for $x > 1$. Taking natural logarithms, we obtain

$$\frac{1}{x} > \ln\frac{x+1}{x} \quad \text{and} \quad \frac{1}{x} < \ln\frac{x}{x-1}, \quad \text{so that} \quad \ln\frac{x+1}{x} < \frac{1}{x} < \ln\frac{x}{x-1} \quad \text{for } x > 1.$$

56. Since $\ln f(x) = x\ln(1 + 1/x)$, we have

$$\frac{d}{dx}\ln f(x) = \ln\left(1 + \frac{1}{x}\right) + x\frac{1}{1+1/x}\left(-\frac{1}{x^2}\right) = \ln\left(1+\frac{1}{x}\right) - \frac{1}{x+1}.$$

By Exercise 55(b), with x replaced by $x + 1$, we deduce that

$$\ln\left(1+\frac{1}{x}\right) - \frac{1}{x+1} = \ln\frac{x+1}{x} - \frac{1}{x+1} > 0 \quad \text{for } x > 0.$$

Thus $(d/dx)\ln f(x) > 0$ for all $x > 0$, so $\ln f(x)$ and hence f are increasing on $(0, \infty)$.

57. a. From the graphs we conjecture that $\lim_{x\to 0^+}[f(x)/g(x)] = 1$.

b. $\lim_{x\to 0+} \frac{f(x)}{g(x)} = \lim_{x\to 0+} \frac{(\sin x)^x}{(\sin x)^{\sin x}} = \lim_{x\to 0+} (\sin x)^{x-\sin x}$

$= \lim_{x\to 0+} e^{(x-\sin x)\ln \sin x} = e^{\lim_{x\to 0+}(x-\sin x)\ln \sin x}$;

$\lim_{x\to 0+}(x-\sin x)\ln \sin x = \lim_{x\to 0+}(\ln \sin x)/[1/(x-\sin x)]$.

The conditions for applying l'Hôpital's Rule are met;

$$\lim_{x\to 0+} \frac{\ln \sin x}{\dfrac{1}{x-\sin x}} = \lim_{x\to 0+} \frac{\dfrac{\cos x}{\sin x}}{-\dfrac{1-\cos x}{(x-\sin x)^2}} = \lim_{x\to 0+} \frac{(x-\sin x)^2 \cos x}{-(\sin x)(1-\cos x)}$$

$$= \lim_{x\to 0+} \frac{(x-\sin x)^2(\cos x)(1+\cos x)}{-(\sin x)(1-\cos x)(1+\cos x)} = \lim_{x\to 0+} \frac{(x-\sin x)^2}{-\sin^3 x} \lim_{x\to 0+} (\cos x)(1+\cos x)$$

provided both of the latter two limits exist. Now $\lim_{x\to 0+}(\cos x)(1+\cos x) = 1(1+1) = 2$ and by l'Hôpital's Rule,

$$\lim_{x\to 0+} \frac{(x-\sin x)^2}{-\sin^3 x} = \lim_{x\to 0+} \frac{2(x-\sin x)(1-\cos x)}{-3(\sin^2 x)(\cos x)} \lim_{x\to 0+} \frac{2(x-\sin x)(1-\cos x)}{-3(1+\cos x)(1-\cos x)(\cos x)}$$

$$= \lim_{x\to 0+} \frac{2(x-\sin x)}{-3(1+\cos x)(\cos x)} = \frac{2(0-0)}{-3(1+1)(1)} = 0.$$

Therefore $\lim_{x\to 0+}(x-\sin x)\ln \sin x = \lim_{x\to 0+}(\ln \sin x)/[1/(x-\sin x)] = 0\cdot 1 = 0$. Consequently $\lim_{x\to 0+} f(x)/g(x) = e^0 = 1$.

58. a. $f(x) = 2^x$, $f'(x) = (\ln 2)2^x$, and $f''(x) = (\ln 2)^2\, 2^x$, so $f(0) = 1$, $f'(0) = \ln 2$, and $f''(0) = (\ln 2)^2$. Therefore $g(x) = 1 + (\ln 2)x + \frac{1}{2}(\ln 2)x^2$.

b. The conditions for applying l'Hôpital's Rule repeatedly are met;

$$\lim_{x\to 0} \frac{f(x)-g(x)}{x^2} = \lim_{x\to 0} \frac{2^x - 1 - (\ln 2)x - \frac{1}{2}(\ln 2)^2 x^2}{x^2} = \lim_{x\to 0} \frac{(\ln 2)2^x - \ln 2 - (\ln 2)^2 x}{2x}$$

$$= \lim_{x\to 0} \frac{(\ln 2)^2 2^x - (\ln 2)^2}{2} = \frac{(\ln 2)^2 - (\ln 2)^2}{2} = 0;$$

$$\lim_{x\to 0} \frac{f(x)-g(x)}{x^3} = \lim_{x\to 0} \frac{2^x - 1 - (\ln 2)x - \frac{1}{2}(\ln 2)^2 x^2}{x^3} = \lim_{x\to 0} \frac{(\ln 2)2^x - (\ln 2) - (\ln 2)^2 x}{3x^2}$$

$$= \lim_{x\to 0} \frac{(\ln 2)^2 2^x - (\ln 2)^2}{6x} = \lim_{x\to 0} \frac{(\ln 2)^3}{6} = \frac{(\ln 2)^3}{6}.$$

Therefore 2 is the largest positive integer such that $\lim_{x\to 0}(f(x)-g(x))/x^n = 0$.

59. $\lim_{x\to\infty} \frac{f(x)}{g(x)} = \lim_{x\to\infty} \frac{x+\sin x}{x} = \lim_{x\to\infty}\left(1+\frac{\sin x}{x}\right) = 1 + 0 = 1$; $\frac{f'(x)}{g'(x)} = \frac{1+\cos x}{1} = 1+\cos x$, but since $\lim_{x\to\infty} 1 = 1$ and $\lim_{x\to\infty} \cos x$ does not exist, it follows that $\lim_{x\to\infty}[f'(x)/g'(x)]$ does not exist.

60. $\lim_{x\to\infty}\left(\frac{2x+1}{2x-1}\right)^x = \lim_{x\to\infty} e^{x\ln[(2x+1)/(2x-1)]} = e^{\lim_{x\to\infty} x\ln[(2x+1)/(2x-1)]}$;

$$\lim_{x\to\infty} x\ln\frac{2x+1}{2x-1} = \lim_{x\to\infty}\frac{\ln\frac{2x+1}{2x-1}}{1/x}, \text{ and } \lim_{x\to\infty}\ln\frac{2x+1}{2x-1} = 0 = \lim_{x\to\infty}\frac{1}{x};$$

Thus

$$\lim_{x\to\infty} x\ln\frac{2x+1}{2x-1} = \lim_{x\to\infty}\frac{\ln\frac{2x+1}{2x-1}}{1/x} = \lim_{x\to\infty}\frac{\frac{2}{2x+1}-\frac{2}{2x-1}}{-1/x^2} = \lim_{x\to\infty}\frac{4x^2}{4x^2-1} = 1$$

so that $\lim_{x\to\infty}[(2x+1)/(2x-1)]^x = e^1 = e$. If $x = 2$, then $[(2x+1)/(2x-1)]^x = (\frac{5}{3})^2 \approx 2.77778$, compared to $\lim_{x\to\infty}[(2x+1)/(2x-1)]^x = e \approx 2.71828$.

61. Since $\sqrt{x} \geq 1/\sqrt{x}$ on $[4, 9]$, it follows that $f(x) \geq g(x)$ on $[4, 9]$. Thus

$$A = \int_4^9 \left(\frac{\sqrt{x}}{x-1}e^{\sqrt{x}} - \frac{1}{\sqrt{x}\,(x-1)}e^{\sqrt{x}}\right) dx = \int_4^9 \frac{x-1}{\sqrt{x}\,(x-1)}e^{\sqrt{x}}\, dx$$

$$= \int_4^9 \frac{e^{\sqrt{x}}}{\sqrt{x}}\, dx \overset{u=\sqrt{x}}{=} \int_2^3 e^u(2)\, du = 2e^u\Big|_2^3 = 2(e^3 - e^2).$$

62. Since $x^2 \geq x^2 - 1$ on $[\sqrt{2}, 2]$, it follows that $f(x) \geq g(x)$ on $[\sqrt{2}, 2]$. Thus

$$A = \int_{\sqrt{2}}^2 \left(\frac{x}{\sqrt{x^2-1}} - \frac{\sqrt{x^2-1}}{x}\right) dx = \int_{\sqrt{2}}^2 \frac{x^2-(x^2-1)}{x\sqrt{x^2-1}}\, dx = \int_{\sqrt{2}}^2 \frac{1}{x\sqrt{x^2-1}}\, dx$$

$$= \sec^{-1} x\Big|_{\sqrt{2}}^2 = \sec^{-1} 2 - \sec^{-1}\sqrt{2} = \frac{\pi}{3} - \frac{\pi}{4} = \frac{\pi}{12}.$$

63. Let R be the rectangle with base $[-x, x]$ on the x axis, with $x > 0$. Also let A be the area of R. Then $A = 2xe^{-x^2}$. Now $dA/dx = 2e^{-x^2} - 4x^2e^{-x^2}$, so $dA/dx = 0$ if $4x^2 = 2$. Therefore $x = 1/\sqrt{2}$. Since $dA/dx > 0$ for $0 < x < 1/\sqrt{2}$ and $dA/dx < 0$ for $1/\sqrt{2} < x$, it follows from (1) of Section 4.6 and the First Derivative Test that A is maximum for $x = 1/\sqrt{2}$. Since $(d/dx)e^{-x^2} = -2xe^{-x^2}$ and $(d^2/dx^2)e^{-x^2} = -2e^{-x^2} + 4x^2e^{-x^2}$, it follows that $(1/\sqrt{2}, e^{-1/2})$ is an inflection point of the graph of e^{-x^2}.

64. Let s denote the distance the boulder has fallen in t seconds, and let θ be the corresponding angle of depression. By (2) of Section 1.3, $s = 16t^2$. Since $\tan\theta = s/800$, we have $\theta = \tan^{-1}(s/800) = \tan^{-1}(16t^2/800) = \tan^{-1}(t^2/50)$. Thus

$$\frac{d\theta}{dt} = \frac{1}{1+(t^2/50)^2}\cdot\frac{t}{25} = \frac{100t}{2500+t^4}$$

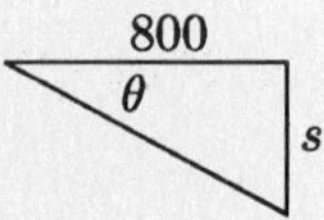

and hence

$$\frac{d^2\theta}{dt^2} = \frac{100(2500+t^4)-(4t^3)(100t)}{(2500+t^4)^2} = \frac{100(2500-3t^4)}{(2500+t^4)^2}.$$

Since we wish to find the positive value of t that maximizes $d\theta/dt$, we determine where its derivative $d^2\theta/dt^2$ equals 0. This yields $2500 - 3t^4 = 0$, or $t = \sqrt[4]{2500/3}$. Since $2500 - 3t^4$ changes from positive to negative at $\sqrt[4]{2500/3}$, $d\theta/dt$ is maximum for $t = \sqrt[4]{2500/3}$. The corresponding angle θ is

$$\tan^{-1}\frac{t^2}{50} = \tan^{-1}\frac{1}{50}\sqrt{\frac{2500}{3}} = \tan^{-1}\frac{1}{\sqrt{3}} = \frac{\pi}{6}.$$

Thus the boulder appears to be falling fastest when $\theta = \pi/6$.

65. If $0 < y < b/a$, then $dy/dt = ay^2 - by = y(ay - b) < y[a(b/a) - b] = 0$. Since $dy/dt < 0$, y is a decreasing function of t.

66. a. By (6) in Section 6.5,

$$\int_{-L/2}^{L/2} \frac{1}{x^2+R^2}\,dx = \frac{1}{R}\tan^{-1}\frac{x}{R}\Big|_{-L/2}^{L/2} = \frac{1}{R}\tan^{-1}\frac{L}{2R} - \frac{1}{R}\tan^{-1}\left(-\frac{L}{2R}\right) = \frac{2}{R}\tan^{-1}\frac{L}{2R}.$$

Therefore

$$F = \frac{GmM}{L}\int_{-L/2}^{L/2}\frac{1}{x^2+R^2}\,dx = \frac{2GmM}{RL}\tan^{-1}\frac{L}{2R}.$$

b. By l'Hôpital's Rule,

$$\lim_{L\to 0^+} F = \lim_{L\to 0^+}\frac{2GmM}{RL}\tan^{-1}\frac{L}{2R} = \frac{2GmM}{R}\lim_{L\to 0^+}\frac{\tan^{-1}(L/2R)}{L}$$

$$\overset{\text{l'Hôpital's Rule}}{=} \frac{2GmM}{R}\lim_{L\to 0^+}\frac{\dfrac{1}{1+(L/2R)^2}\dfrac{1}{2R}}{1} = \frac{2GmM}{R}\frac{1}{2R} = \frac{GmM}{R^2}.$$

67. a. If s is the side length of the cube, and S and V are the surface area and volume of the cube, then $S = 6s^2$ and $V = s^3$. By hypothesis there is a constant c such that $dV/dt = cS$. Thus $dV/dt = cS = c(6s^2) = c(6V^{2/3}) = kV^r$, where $k = 6c$ and $r = \frac{2}{3}$.

b. By (a), $dV/dt = kV^{2/3}$, so $V^{-2/3}\,dV = k\,dt$, which is a separable differential equation. By integration we obtain $3V^{1/3} = kt + C_1$, so that $V^{1/3} = \frac{1}{3}kt + \frac{1}{3}C_1$, and thus $V = \left(\frac{1}{3}kt + C\right)^3$, where $C = \frac{1}{3}C_1$.

c. If $t = 0$, then $V = \left(\frac{1}{3}k\cdot 0 + C\right)^3 = C^3$, so C is the side length of the cube when it begins to melt.

d. The ice cube is completely melted when $V = 0$, that is, $\left(\frac{1}{3}kt + C\right)^3 = 0$, or $t = -3C/k$.

e. Since $dV/dt = 6cs^2$ and $V = s^3$, we have by the Chain Rule that

$$6cs^2 = \frac{dV}{dt} = \frac{dV}{ds}\frac{ds}{dt} = 3s^2\frac{ds}{dt}.$$

Therefore $ds/dt = 2c$.

Cumulative Review(Chapters 1–5)

1. $\lim_{x\to 3^+} \dfrac{\sqrt{x^2-9}}{x-3} = \lim_{x\to 3^+} \dfrac{\sqrt{x-3}\,\sqrt{x+3}}{(\sqrt{x-3})^2} = \lim_{x\to 3^+} \dfrac{\sqrt{x+3}}{\sqrt{x-3}} = \infty$

2. Let $f(x) = \sec x$, so that $f'(x) = \sec x \tan x$. Then

$$\lim_{x\to 0} \frac{\sec x - 1}{x} = \lim_{x\to 0} \frac{f(x)-f(0)}{x-0} = f'(0) = \sec 0 \tan 0 = 0.$$

Alternatively,

$$\lim_{x\to 0} \frac{\sec x - 1}{x} = \lim_{x\to 0} \left(\frac{\sec x - 1}{x} \cdot \frac{\sec x + 1}{\sec x + 1}\right) = \lim_{x\to 0} \frac{\sec^2 x - 1}{x(\sec x + 1)}$$

$$= \lim_{x\to 0} \frac{\tan^2 x}{x(\sec x + 1)} = \lim_{x\to 0} \frac{\sin x}{x} \lim_{x\to 0} \frac{\tan x}{\cos x\,(\sec x + 1)} = 1 \cdot 0 = 0.$$

3. Since

$$-|\sin x| \le \sin x \sin \frac{1}{x} \le |\sin x| \quad \text{and} \quad \lim_{x\to 0} |\sin x| = 0 = \lim_{x\to 0}(-|\sin x|)$$

the Squeezing Theorem implies that $\lim_{x\to 0} \sin x \sin(1/x) = 0$.

4. Since

$$-\frac{1}{x^2} \le \frac{\sin x}{x^2} \le \frac{1}{x^2} \quad \text{and} \quad \lim_{x\to\infty} \frac{1}{x^2} = 0 = \lim_{x\to\infty}\left(-\frac{1}{x^2}\right)$$

the Squeezing Theorem implies that $\lim_{x\to\infty} (\sin x)/x^2 = 0$. Thus

$$\lim_{x\to\infty} \frac{2x^2 - \sin x}{4 - 3x^2} = \lim_{x\to\infty} \frac{2 - (\sin x)/x^2}{(4/x^2) - 3} = \frac{2-0}{0-3} = -\frac{2}{3}.$$

5. a. Since division by 0 is undefined and 0 is not in the domain of the natural logarithm, the domain consists of all x such that $1 + x \ne 0$ and $1 - x \ne 0$, that is, all numbers except -1 and 1.

b. Since $\ln(1/b) = -\ln b$, we have

$$f(-x) = \ln\left|\frac{1-(-x)}{1-x}\right| = \ln\left|\frac{1+x}{1-x}\right| = -\ln\left|\frac{1-x}{1+x}\right| = -f(x).$$

Therefore f is an odd function.

c. Since f is continuous at every number in its domain, the only possible vertical asymptotes are $x = -1$ and $x = 1$. By the version of the Substitution Rule for infinite limits (with $y = 1 - x$).

$$\lim_{x\to 1} \ln\left|\frac{1-x}{1+x}\right| = \lim_{y\to 0} \ln\left|\frac{y}{2-y}\right| = -\infty.$$

Therefore the line $x = 1$ is a vertical asymptote. Since the graph of f is symmetric with respect to the origin (because f is odd), the line $x = -1$ is also a vertical asymptote.

6. $$f'(x) = \frac{1}{2}\left(\frac{1+\cos x}{1-\cos x}\right) \frac{(\sin x)(1+\cos x) - (1-\cos x)(-\sin x)}{(1+\cos x)^2}$$
$$= \frac{1}{2} \frac{2\sin x}{(1-\cos x)(1+\cos x)} = \frac{\sin x}{\sin^2 x} = \csc x$$

7. $f'(x) = \cos x - (x-1)\sin x$

   $f''(x) = -\sin x - \sin x - (x-1)\cos x = -2\sin x - (x-1)\cos x$

   $f^{(3)}(x) = -2\cos x - \cos x + (x-1)\sin x = -3\cos x + (x-1)\sin x$

   $f^{(4)}(x) = 3\sin x + \sin x + (x-1)\cos x = 4\sin x + (x-1)\cos x$

   In general, $f^{(2n)}(x) = (-1)^n[2n\sin x + (x-1)\cos x]$. Thus $f^{(24)}(x) = 24\sin x + (x-1)\cos x$.

8. Differentiating implicitly, we have $y^3 + 3x^2(dy/dx) - 2x = 2y(dy/dx) + y + x(dy/dx)$. For $x = 3$ and $y = 2$, this becomes $8 + 27(dy/dx) - 6 = 4(dy/dx) + 2 + 3(dy/dx)$, which means that $dy/dx = 0$. Therefore an equation of the line tangent at $(3, 2)$ is $y = 2$.

9. If h denotes the height of the equilateral triangle, then the area A is given by $A = (\frac{1}{2}h)(2h/\sqrt{3}) = h^2/\sqrt{3}$. Since the area is by hypothesis growing at the rate of 9 square inches per minute, $9 = dA/dt = (2h/\sqrt{3})(dh/dt)$, so $dh/dt = (9\sqrt{3})/2h$. When $A = \sqrt{3}$, we have $\sqrt{3} = h^2/\sqrt{3}$, so $h = \sqrt{3}$, and thus $dh/dt = (9\sqrt{3})/(2\sqrt{3}) = \frac{9}{2}$ (inches per minute).

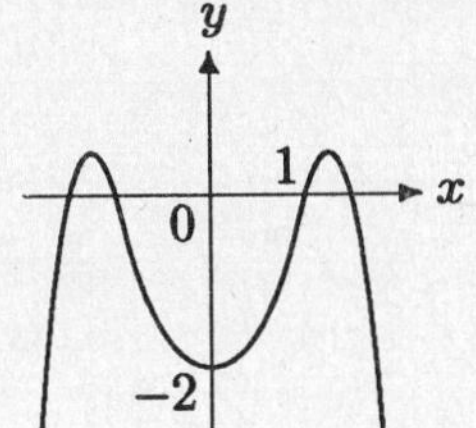

Exercise 10

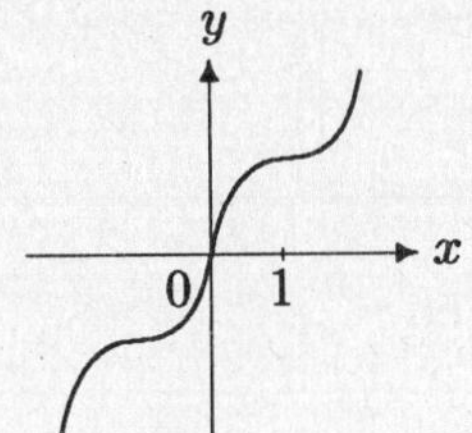

Exercise 11

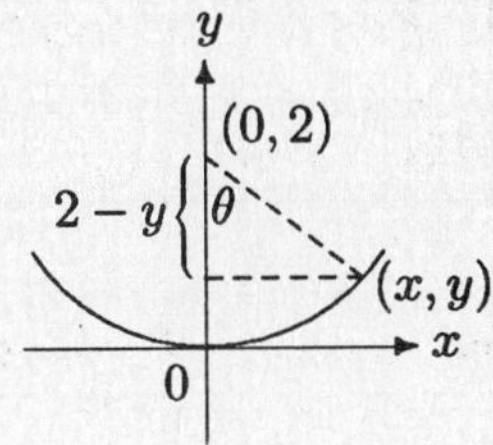

Exercise 12

10. $f'(x) = -4x^3 + 6x = -2x(2x^2 - 3)$; $f''(x) = -12x^2 + 6 = -6(2x^2 - 1)$;

    relative maximum value is $f\left(-\sqrt{\frac{3}{2}}\right) = f\left(\sqrt{\frac{3}{2}}\right) = \frac{1}{4}$; relative minimum value is $f(0) = -2$; increasing on $\left(-\infty, -\sqrt{\frac{3}{2}}\right]$ and $\left[0, \sqrt{\frac{3}{2}}\right]$; decreasing on $\left[-\sqrt{\frac{3}{2}}, 0\right]$ and $\left[\sqrt{\frac{3}{2}}, \infty\right)$; concave upward on $\left(-\sqrt{\frac{1}{2}}, \sqrt{\frac{1}{2}}\right)$, and concave downward on $\left(-\infty, -\sqrt{\frac{1}{2}}\right)$ and $\left(\sqrt{\frac{1}{2}}, \infty\right)$; inflection points are $\left(-\sqrt{\frac{1}{2}}, -\frac{3}{4}\right)$ and $\left(\sqrt{\frac{1}{2}}, -\frac{3}{4}\right)$; symmetry with respect to the y axis.

11. $f'(x) = 5x^4 - 10x^2 + 5 = 5(x^2 - 1)^2$; $f''(x) = 20x^3 - 20x = 20x(x^2 - 1)$;

    increasing on $(-\infty, \infty)$; concave upward on $(-1, 0)$ and $(1, \infty)$, and concave downward on $(-\infty, -1)$ and $(0, 1)$; inflection points are $(-1, -\frac{8}{3})$, $(0, 0)$, and $(1, \frac{8}{3})$; symmetry with respect to origin.

12. Let θ be the angle in the figure. We are to determine $(dx/dt)\big|_{t=t_0}$ at the instant t_0 when $x = 1$ and $y = \frac{1}{5}$. From the figure,

$$\cot\theta = \frac{2-y}{x} = \frac{2}{x} - \frac{x^2/5}{x} = \frac{2}{x} - \frac{x}{5}$$

so

$$(-\csc^2\theta)\frac{d\theta}{dt} = -\frac{2}{x^2}\frac{dx}{dt} - \frac{1}{5}\frac{dx}{dt} = -\left(\frac{2}{x^2} + \frac{1}{5}\right)\frac{dx}{dt}.$$

When $x = 1$, we have $\cot\theta = 2 - \frac{1}{5} = \frac{9}{5}$, so that $\csc^2\theta = 1 + \cot^2\theta = 1 + (\frac{9}{5})^2 = \frac{106}{25}$. Then, since the light rotates at the rate of $\frac{1}{2}$ radian per second, it follows that

$$-\frac{106}{25}\left(\frac{1}{2}\right) = -\left(\frac{2}{1} + \frac{1}{5}\right)\bigg|_{t=t_0} = -\frac{11}{5}\frac{dx}{dt}\bigg|_{t=t_0}$$

and consequently

$$\frac{dx}{dt}\bigg|_{t=t_0} = \frac{53}{25}\frac{5}{11} = \frac{53}{55} \text{ (miles per second).}$$

13. $a(t) = \frac{1}{2}t + \cos t$, and we are to find the maximum value of a on $[0, \pi/2]$. Now $a'(t) = \frac{1}{2} - \sin t$, so that $a'(t) = 0$ if $\sin t = \frac{1}{2}$. Since t must lie in $[0, \pi/2]$, it follows that $t = \pi/6$. Since $a''(t) = -\cos t < 0$ for t in $(0, \pi/2)$, we conclude from (1) in Section 4.6 and the Second Derivative Test that $a(\pi/6)$ is the maximum value, so that the acceleration is maximum in $[0, \pi/2]$ for $t = \pi/6$.

14. Let C be the cost, r the radius, h the height, and V the volume of the tank. We are to minimize C. Since $V = 40\pi$, we have $\pi r^2 h = 40\pi$, so that $h = 40/r^2$, and thus $C = 10(2\pi rh) + 25(2\pi r^2) = 800\pi/r + 50\pi r^2$. Then $C'(r) = -800\pi/r^2 + 100\pi r$, so that $C'(r) = 0$ if $800\pi/r^2 = 100\pi r$, or $r^3 = 8$, or $r = 2$. Since $C''(r) = 1600\pi/r^3 + 100\pi > 0$, it follows from (1) in Section 4.6 and the Second Derivative Test that C is minimized for $r = 2$. The corresponding value of h is $40/2^2 = 10$. Thus the cost is minimized if the radius is 2 meters and the height is 10 meters.

15. It suffices to find the points on the graph of $y = 2/(1 + x^2)$ for which the square S of the distance to the origin is minimized. For (x, y) on the graph, S is given by

$$S = (x - 0)^2 + (y - 0)^2 = x^2 + \left(\frac{2}{1 + x^2}\right)^2 = x^2 + \frac{4}{(1 + x^2)^2}.$$

Thus

$$S'(x) = 2x - \frac{16x}{(1 + x^2)^3} = 2x\left(1 - \frac{8}{(1 + x^2)^3}\right)$$

so that $S'(x) = 0$ if $x = -1$, $x = 0$, or $x = 1$. Since S' changes from negative to positive at -1 and 1, and from positive to negative at 0, it follows that S assumes its minimum value at -1 and 1 (at which points S takes on the same value, namely 2). Thus the points $(-1, 1)$ and $(1, 1)$ are the points on the graph that are closest to the origin.

16. $v(e) = v(1) + \displaystyle\int_1^e v'(t)\,dt = v(1) + \int_1^e a(t)\,dt = 5 + \int_1^e \frac{1}{t(\ln t + 2)}\,dt$

Let $u = \ln t + 2$, so that $du = (1/t)\,dt$. If $t = 1$, then $u = 2$; if $t = e$, then $u = 3$. Thus

$$\int_1^e \frac{1}{t(\ln t + 2)}\,dt = \int_2^3 \frac{1}{u}\,du = \ln u\big|_2^3 = \ln 3 - \ln 2 = \ln\frac{3}{2}.$$

Thus $v(e) = 5 + \ln\frac{3}{2}$.

17. Since $g(x) = \displaystyle\int_x^{x+\pi} \sin^{2/3} t\,dt = \int_0^{x+\pi} \sin^{2/3} t\,dt - \int_0^x \sin^{2/3} t\,dt$, we have

$$g'(x) = \sin^{2/3}(x + \pi) - \sin^{2/3} x = (-\sin x)^{2/3} - \sin^{2/3} x = 0.$$

Thus g is a constant function, by Theorem 4.6(a).

18. Let $u = 2x - 3$, so that $du = 2\,dx$;

$$\int \frac{1}{\sqrt{2x-3}}\,dx = \int \frac{1}{\sqrt{u}}\left(\frac{1}{2}\right)du = \sqrt{u} + C = \sqrt{2x-3} + C.$$

19. Let $u = 2 + \cos x$, so that $du = -\sin x\,dx$; if $x = 0$, then $u = 3$, and if $x = \pi$, then $u = 1$;

$$\int_0^\pi \frac{\sin x}{2+\cos x}\,dx = \int_3^1 \frac{1}{u}(-1)\,du = -\ln u\Big|_3^1 = \ln 3.$$

20. Let $u = 1 + \sqrt{x}$, so that $du = 1/(2\sqrt{x})\,dx$ and $\sqrt{x} = u - 1$;

$$\int x(1+\sqrt{x})^{1/3}\,dx = \int x\sqrt{x}\,(1+\sqrt{x})^{1/3}\frac{1}{\sqrt{x}}\,dx = \int (u-1)^3\,u^{1/3}\,2\,du$$

$$= 2\int (u^{10/3} - 3u^{7/3} + 3u^{4/3} - u^{1/3})\,du = 2\left(\frac{3}{13}u^{13/3} - \frac{9}{10}u^{10/3} + \frac{9}{7}u^{7/3} - \frac{3}{4}u^{4/3}\right) + C$$

$$= \frac{6}{13}(1+\sqrt{x})^{13/3} - \frac{9}{5}(1+\sqrt{x})^{10/3} + \frac{18}{7}(1+\sqrt{x})^{7/3} - \frac{3}{2}(1+\sqrt{x})^{4/3} + C.$$

21. Let $u = \ln t$, so that $du = (1/t)\,dt$;

$$\int \frac{1}{t}(\ln t)^{5/3}\,dt = \int u^{5/3}\,du = \frac{3}{8}u^{8/3} + C = \frac{3}{8}(\ln t)^{8/3} + C.$$

22. a. $\displaystyle\int_1^n \frac{1}{x^{.9}}\,dx = \frac{x^{.1}}{.1}\Big|_1^n = 10(n^{1/10} - 1)$, so that $\displaystyle\int_1^n \frac{1}{x^{.9}}\,dx > 1000$ if $n^{1/10} - 1 > 100$, or $n > (101)^{10}$.

Thus

$$\int_1^n \frac{1}{x^{.9}}\,dx > 1000 \quad \text{for } n = (101)^{10} + 1.$$

b. $\displaystyle\int_1^n \frac{1}{x^{1.1}}\,dx = \frac{-10}{x^{.1}}\Big|_1^n = 10\left(1 - \frac{1}{n^{1/10}}\right) < 10$ for every positive integer n.

Thus there is no positive integer n such that

$$\int_1^n \frac{1}{x^{1.1}}\,dx > 1000.$$

Chapter 7

Techniques of Integration

7.1 Integration by Parts

1. $u = x$, $dv = \sin x\,dx$; $du = dx$, $v = -\cos x$; $\int x \sin x\,dx = x(-\cos x) - \int(-\cos x)\,dx = -x\cos x + \sin x + C$.

2. $u = x$, $dv = \sec^2 x\,dx$; $du = dx$, $v = \tan x$; $\int x \sec^2 x\,dx = x\tan x - \int \tan x\,dx = x\tan x - (-\ln|\cos x|) + C = x\tan x + \ln|\cos x| + C$.

3. $u = \ln x$, $dv = x\,dx$; $du = (1/x)\,dx$, $v = \frac{1}{2}x^2$; $\int x\ln x\,dx = \frac{1}{2}x^2\ln x - \int(\frac{1}{2}x^2)(1/x)\,dx = \frac{1}{2}x^2\ln x - \frac{1}{2}\int x\,dx = \frac{1}{2}x^2\ln x - \frac{1}{4}x^2 + C$.

4. $u = \ln x^2$, $dv = x\,dx$; $du = (2/x)\,dx$, $v = x^2/2$; $\int x\ln x^2\,dx = (\ln x^2)(\frac{1}{2}x^2) - \int(x^2/2)(2/x)\,dx = (2\ln x)(\frac{1}{2}x^2) - \int x\,dx = x^2\ln x - \frac{1}{2}x^2 + C$. (Alternatively, note that $\ln x^2 = 2\ln x$.)

5. $u = (\ln x)^2$, $dv = dx$; $du = [(2\ln x)/x]\,dx$, $v = x$; $\int(\ln x)^2\,dx = (\ln x)^2 x - \int x[(2\ln x)/x]\,dx = x(\ln x)^2 - 2\int \ln x\,dx$. By Example 3, $-2\int \ln x\,dx = -2x\ln x + 2x + C$. Thus $\int(\ln x)^2\,dx = x(\ln x)^2 - 2x\ln x + 2x + C$.

6. $u = \ln x$, $dv = x^2\,dx$; $du = (1/x)\,dx$, $v = \frac{1}{3}x^3$; $\int x^2\ln x\,dx = (\ln x)(\frac{1}{3}x^3) - \int(\frac{1}{3}x^3)(1/x)\,dx = \frac{1}{3}x^3\ln x - \frac{1}{3}\int x^2\,dx = \frac{1}{3}x^3\ln x - \frac{1}{9}x^3 + C$.

7. $u = \ln x$, $dv = x^3\,dx$; $du = (1/x)\,dx$, $v = \frac{1}{4}x^4$; $\int x^3\ln x\,dx = (\ln x)(\frac{1}{4}x^4) - \int(\frac{1}{4}x^4)(1/x)\,dx = \frac{1}{4}x^4\ln x - \frac{1}{4}\int x^3\,dx = \frac{1}{4}x^4\ln x - \frac{1}{16}x^4 + C$.

8. $u = x$, $dv = e^{-x}\,dx$; $du = dx$, $v = -e^{-x}$; $\int xe^{-x}\,dx = -xe^{-x} + \int e^{-x}\,dx = -xe^{-x} - e^{-x} + C$.

9. $u = x^2$, $dv = e^{4x}\,dx$; $du = 2x\,dx$, $v = \frac{1}{4}e^{4x}$; $\int x^2e^{4x}\,dx = \frac{1}{4}x^2e^{4x} - \int\frac{1}{2}xe^{4x}\,dx = \frac{1}{4}x^2e^{4x} - \frac{1}{2}\int xe^{4x}\,dx$. For $\int xe^{4x}\,dx$, let $u = x$, $dv = e^{4x}\,dx$; $du = dx$, $v = \frac{1}{4}e^{4x}$; $\int xe^{4x}\,dx = \frac{1}{4}xe^{4x} - \int\frac{1}{4}e^{4x}\,dx = \frac{1}{4}xe^{4x} - \frac{1}{16}e^{4x} + C_1$. Thus $\int x^2e^{4x}\,dx = \frac{1}{4}x^2e^{4x} - \frac{1}{8}xe^{4x} + \frac{1}{32}e^{4x} + C$.

10. $u = x^2$, $dv = \sin x\,dx$; $du = 2x\,dx$, $v = -\cos x$; $\int x^2\sin x\,dx = x^2(-\cos x) - \int 2x(-\cos x)\,dx = -x^2\cos x + 2\int x\cos x\,dx$. For $\int x\cos x\,dx$, let $u = x$, $dv = \cos x\,dx$; $du = dx$, $v = \sin x$; $2\int x\cos x\,dx = 2x\sin x - 2\int\sin x\,dx = 2x\sin x + 2\cos x + C$. Thus $\int x^2\sin x\,dx = -x^2\cos x + 2x\sin x + 2\cos x + C$.

11. $u = x^3$, $dv = \cos x\,dx$; $du = 3x^2\,dx$, $v = \sin x$; $\int x^3 \cos x\,dx = x^3 \sin x - \int 3x^2 \sin x\,dx = x^3 \sin x - 3\int x^2 \sin x\,dx$. Since $\int x^2 \sin x\,dx = -x^2 \cos x + 2x \sin x + 2\cos x + C_1$ by the solution of Exercise 10, it follows that $\int x^3 \cos x\,dx = x^3 \sin x + 3x^2 \cos x - 6x \sin x - 6\cos x + C$.

12. $u = \sin x$, $dv = e^x\,dx$; $du = \cos x\,dx$, $v = e^x$; $\int e^x \sin x\,dx = e^x \sin x - \int e^x \cos x\,dx$. For $\int e^x \cos x\,dx$, let $u = \cos x$, $dv = e^x\,dx$; $du = -\sin x\,dx$, $v = e^x$; $\int e^x \cos x\,dx = e^x \cos x + \int e^x \sin x\,dx$. Thus $\int e^x \sin x\,dx = e^x \sin x - e^x \cos x - \int e^x \sin x\,dx$, so that $2\int e^x \sin x\,dx = e^x \sin x - e^x \cos x + C_1$. Therefore $\int e^x \sin x\,dx = \frac{1}{2}e^x \sin x - \frac{1}{2}e^x \cos x + C$.

13. $u = \cos 3x$, $dv = e^{3x}\,dx$; $du = -3\sin 3x\,dx$, $v = \frac{1}{3}e^{3x}$; $\int e^{3x} \cos 3x\,dx = \frac{1}{3}e^{3x} \cos 3x + \int e^{3x} \sin 3x\,dx$. For $\int e^{3x} \sin 3x\,dx$, let $u = \sin 3x$, $dv = e^{3x}\,dx$; $du = 3\cos 3x\,dx$, $v = \frac{1}{3}e^{3x}$; $\int e^{3x} \sin 3x\,dx = \frac{1}{3}e^{3x} \sin 3x - \int e^{3x} \cos 3x\,dx$. Thus $\int e^{3x} \cos 3x\,dx = \frac{1}{3}e^{3x} \cos 3x + \frac{1}{3}e^{3x} \sin 3x - \int e^{3x} \cos 3x\,dx$, so $2\int e^{3x} \cos 3x\,dx = \frac{1}{3}e^{3x} \cos 3x + \frac{1}{3}e^{3x} \sin 3x + C_1$ and therefore $\int e^{3x} \cos 3x\,dx = \frac{1}{6}e^{3x} \cos 3x + \frac{1}{6}e^{3x} \sin 3x + C$.

14. Since $\int [(\sin x)/e^x]\,dx = \int e^{-x} \sin x\,dx$, we let $u = \sin x$, $dv = e^{-x}\,dx$; $du = \cos x\,dx$, $v = -e^{-x}$. Then $\int e^{-x} \sin x\,dx = -e^{-x} \sin x + \int e^{-x} \cos x\,dx$. For $\int e^{-x} \cos x\,dx$, let $u = \cos x$, $dv = e^{-x}\,dx$; $du = -\sin x\,dx$, $v = -e^{-x}$; $\int e^{-x} \cos x\,dx = -e^{-x} \cos x - \int e^{-x} \sin x\,dx$. Thus $\int e^{-x} \sin x\,dx = -e^{-x} \sin x - e^{-x} \cos x - \int e^{-x} \sin x\,dx$, so $2\int e^{-x} \sin x\,dx = -e^{-x} \sin x - e^{-x} \cos x + C_1$. Thus $\int [(\sin x)/e^x]\,dx = \int e^{-x} \sin x\,dx = -\frac{1}{2}e^{-x}(\sin x + \cos x) + C$.

15. $u = t$, $dv = 2^t\,dt$; $du = dt$, $v = (1/\ln 2)2^t$;

$$\int t \cdot 2^t\,dt = \frac{t}{\ln 2}2^t - \int \frac{1}{\ln 2}2^t\,dt = \frac{t}{\ln 2}2^t - \frac{1}{(\ln 2)^2}2^t + C.$$

16. $u = t$, $dv = 3^{-t}\,dt$; $du = dt$, $v = (-1/\ln 3)3^{-t}$;

$$\int t \cdot 3^{-t}\,dt = \frac{-t}{\ln 3}3^{-t} + \int \frac{3^{-t}}{\ln 3}\,dt = -\frac{t}{\ln 3}3^{-t} - \frac{1}{(\ln 3)^2}3^{-t} + C.$$

17. $u = t^2$, $dv = 4^t\,dt$; $du = 2t\,dt$, $v = (1/\ln 4)4^t$;

$$\int t^2 4^t\,dt = \frac{t^2}{\ln 4}4^t - \int \frac{2t}{\ln 4}4^t\,dt = \frac{t^2}{\ln 4}4^t - \frac{2}{\ln 4}\int t \cdot 4^t\,dt.$$

For $\int t \cdot 4^t\,dt$, let $u = t$, $dv = 4^t\,dt$; $du = dt$, $v = (1/\ln 4)4^t$;

$$\int t \cdot 4^t\,dt = \frac{t}{\ln 4}4^t - \int \frac{1}{\ln 4}4^t\,dt = \frac{t}{\ln 4}4^t - \frac{1}{(\ln 4)^2}4^t + C_1.$$

Thus

$$\int t^2\,4^t\,dt = \left(\frac{t^2}{\ln 4} - \frac{2t}{(\ln 4)^2} + \frac{2}{(\ln 4)^3}\right)4^t + C.$$

18. Since $\log_6 x = (\ln x)/(\ln 6)$, it follows from Example 3 that

$$\int \log_6 x\,dx = \int \frac{\ln x}{\ln 6}\,dx = \frac{1}{\ln 6}\int \ln x\,dx = \frac{1}{\ln 6}(x \ln x - x + C_1) = \frac{1}{\ln 6}(x \ln x - x) + C.$$

19. $u = t$, $dv = \sinh t\,dt$; $du = dt$, $v = \cosh t$; $\int t \sinh t\,dt = t\cosh t - \int \cosh t\,dt = t\cosh t - \sinh t + C$.

20. $u = t^2$, $dv = \cosh t\,dt$; $du = 2t\,dt$, $v = \sinh t$; $\int t^2 \cosh t\,dt = t^2 \sinh t - \int 2t \sinh t\,dt = t^2 \sinh t - 2\int t \sinh t\,dt$. Since $\int t\sinh t\,dt = t\cosh t - \sinh t + C_1$ by the solution of Exercise 19, it follows that $\int t^2 \cosh t\,dt = t^2 \sinh t - 2t\cosh t + 2\sinh t + C$.

21. $u = \tan^{-1} x$, $dv = dx$; $du = 1/(1+x^2)\,dx$, $v = x$;

$$\int \tan^{-1} x\,dx = x\tan^{-1} x - \int \frac{x}{1+x^2}\,dx.$$

For $\int [x/(1+x^2)]\,dx$ substitute $u = 1 + x^2$, so that $du = 2x\,dx$. Then

$$\int \frac{x}{1+x^2}\,dx = \int \frac{1}{u}\frac{1}{2}\,du = \frac{1}{2}\int \frac{1}{u}\,du = \frac{1}{2}\ln|u| + C = \frac{1}{2}\ln(1+x^2) + C.$$

Thus $\int \tan^{-1} x\,dx = x\tan^{-1} x - \frac{1}{2}\ln(1+x^2) + C$.

22. $u = \sin^{-1} 3x$, $dv = dx$; $du = (3/\sqrt{1-(3x)^2}\,)\,dx = (3/\sqrt{1-9x^2}\,)\,dx$, $v = x$;

$$\int \sin^{-1} 3x\,dx = x\sin^{-1} 3x - \int \frac{3x}{\sqrt{1-9x^2}}\,dx = x\sin^{-1} 3x - 3\int \frac{x}{\sqrt{1-9x^2}}\,dx.$$

For $\int (x/\sqrt{1-9x^2}\,)\,dx$ substitute $u = 1 - 9x^2$, so that $du = -18x\,dx$. Then

$$\int \frac{x}{\sqrt{1-9x^2}}\,dx = \int \frac{1}{\sqrt{u}}\left(-\frac{1}{18}\right)du = -\frac{1}{18}\int \frac{1}{\sqrt{u}}\,du = -\frac{1}{9}\sqrt{u} + C_1 = -\frac{1}{9}\sqrt{1-9x^2} + C_1.$$

Thus $\int \sin^{-1} 3x\,dx = x\sin^{-1} 3x + \frac{1}{3}\sqrt{1-9x^2} + C$.

23. $u = \cos^{-1}(-7x)$, $dv = dx$; $du = -(-7/\sqrt{1-(-7x)^2}\,)dx = (7/\sqrt{1-49x^2}\,)\,dx$, $v = x$;

$$\int \cos^{-1}(-7x)\,dx = x\cos^{-1}(-7x) - \int \frac{7x}{\sqrt{1-49x^2}}\,dx = x\cos^{-1}(-7x) - 7\int \frac{x}{\sqrt{1-49x^2}}\,dx.$$

For $\int (x/\sqrt{1-49x^2}\,)\,dx$ substitute $u = 1 - 49x^2$, so that $du = -98x\,dx$. Then

$$\int \frac{x}{\sqrt{1-49x^2}}\,dx = \int \frac{1}{\sqrt{u}}\left(-\frac{1}{98}\right)du = -\frac{1}{49}\sqrt{u} + C_1 = -\frac{1}{49}\sqrt{1-49x^2} + C_1.$$

Thus $\int \cos^{-1}(-7x)\,dx = x\cos^{-1}(-7x) + \frac{1}{7}\sqrt{1-49x^2} + C$.

24. $u = \ln x$, $dv = x^n\,dx$; $du = (1/x)\,dx$, $v = [1/(n+1)]x^{n+1}\,dx$;

$$\int x^n \ln x\,dx = (\ln x)\left(\frac{1}{n+1}x^{n+1}\right) - \int \left(\frac{1}{n+1}x^{n+1}\right)\frac{1}{x}\,dx$$

$$= \frac{1}{n+1}x^{n+1}\ln x - \frac{1}{n+1}\int x^n\,dx = \frac{1}{n+1}x^{n+1}\ln x - \frac{1}{(n+1)^2}x^{n+1} + C.$$

25. By Exercise 24,

$$x^n \ln x \, dx = \frac{1}{n+1} x^{n+1} \ln x - \frac{1}{(n+1)^2} x^{n+1} + C_1.$$

Thus

$$\int x^n \ln x^m \, dx = m \int x^n \ln x \, dx = \frac{m}{n+1} x^{n+1} \ln x - \frac{m}{(n+1)^2} x^{n+1} + C.$$

26. $u = \sin(\ln x)$, $dv = dx$; $du = (1/x) \cos(\ln x) \, dx$, $v = x$;

$$\int \sin(\ln x) \, dx = x \sin(\ln x) - \int x \left(\frac{1}{x} \cos(\ln x) \right) dx = x \sin(\ln x) - \int \cos(\ln x) \, dx.$$

For $\int \cos(\ln x) \, dx$, let $u = \cos(\ln x)$, $dv = dx$; $du = (-1/x) \sin(\ln x) \, dx$, $v = x$;

$$\int \cos(\ln x) \, dx = [\cos(\ln x)]x - \int x((-1/x) \sin(\ln x)) \, dx = x \cos(\ln x) + \int \sin(\ln x) \, dx.$$

Thus

$$\int \sin(\ln x) \, dx = x \sin(\ln x) - x \cos(\ln x) - \int \sin(\ln x) \, dx,$$

so that $\int \sin(\ln x) \, dx = \frac{1}{2}[x \sin(\ln x) - x \cos(\ln x)] + C$.

27. By the solution of Exercise 26, we have $\int \cos(\ln x) \, dx = x \cos(\ln x) + \int \sin(\ln x) \, dx$ and $\int \sin(\ln x) \, dx = x \sin(\ln x) - \int \cos(\ln x) \, dx$, so that $\int \cos(\ln x) \, dx = \frac{1}{2}[x \cos(\ln x) + x \sin(\ln x)] + C$.

28. $u = \ln(x+1)$, $dv = x \, dx$; $du = [1/(x+1)] \, dx$, $v = (x^2 - 1)/2$;

$$\int x \ln(x+1) \, dx = (\ln(x+1)) \left(\frac{x^2-1}{2} \right) - \int \frac{x^2-1}{2} \frac{1}{x+1} \, dx$$

$$= \left(\frac{x^2-1}{2} \right) \ln(x+1) - \int \frac{x-1}{2} \, dx = \left(\frac{x^2-1}{2} \right) \ln(x+1) - \frac{x^2}{4} + \frac{x}{2} + C.$$

29. $u = x$, $dv = e^{5x} \, dx$; $du = dx$, $v = \frac{1}{5} e^{5x}$;

$$\int_0^1 x e^{5x} \, dx = \frac{1}{5} x e^{5x} \Big|_0^1 - \int_0^1 \frac{1}{5} e^{5x} \, dx = \frac{1}{5} e^5 - \frac{1}{5} \int_0^1 e^{5x} \, dx$$

$$= \frac{1}{5} e^{5x} - \left(\frac{1}{25} e^{5x} \right) \Big|_0^1 = \frac{1}{5} e^5 - \frac{1}{25} e^5 + \frac{1}{25} e^0 = \frac{4}{25} e^5 + \frac{1}{25}.$$

30. $u = x$, $dv = \sin x \, dx$; $du = dx$, $v = -\cos x$;

$$\int_0^{\pi/2} (x + x \sin x) \, dx = \int_0^{\pi/2} x \, dx + \int_0^{\pi/2} x \sin x \, dx$$

$$= \frac{x^2}{2} \Big|_0^{\pi/2} - x \cos x \Big|_0^{\pi/2} + \int_0^{\pi/2} \cos x \, dx = \frac{\pi^2}{8} - 0 + \sin x \Big|_0^{\pi/2} = \frac{\pi^2}{8} + 1.$$

31. $u = t^2$, $dv = \cos t \, dt$; $du = 2t \, dt$, $v = \sin t$; $\int_0^\pi t^2 \cos t \, dt = t^2 \sin t \Big|_0^\pi - \int_0^\pi 2t \sin t \, dt = -2 \int_0^\pi t \sin t \, dt$. By the solution of Exercise 1, $-2 \int_0^\pi t \sin t \, dt = -2(-t \cos t + \sin t) \Big|_0^\pi = -2(-\pi \cos \pi + \sin \pi) + 2 \cdot 0 = -2\pi$. Thus $\int_0^\pi t^2 \cos t \, dt = -2\pi$.

32. $u = \ln x$, $dv = x^{3/2}\,dx$; $du = (1/x)\,dx$, $v = \frac{2}{5}x^{5/2}\,dx$;

$$\int_1^4 x^{3/2}\ln x\,dx = (\ln x)\left(\frac{2}{5}x^{5/2}\right)\Big|_1^4 - \int_1^4\left(\frac{2}{5}x^{5/2}\right)\frac{1}{x}\,dx$$

$$= \frac{2}{5}x^{5/2}\ln x\Big|_1^4 - \frac{2}{5}\int_1^4 x^{3/2}\,dx = \frac{128}{5}\ln 2 - \frac{4}{25}x^{5/2}\Big|_1^4 = \frac{128}{5}\ln 2 - \frac{124}{25}.$$

33. $u = x$, $dv = \sec^2 x\,dx$; $du = dx$, $v = \tan x$;

$$\int_{-\pi/3}^{\pi/4} x\sec^2 x\,dx = x\tan x\big|_{-\pi/3}^{\pi/4} - \int_{-\pi/3}^{\pi/4}\tan x\,dx = \frac{\pi}{4} - \frac{\pi\sqrt{3}}{3} + (\ln|\cos x|)\big|_{-\pi/3}^{\pi/4}$$

$$= \frac{\pi}{4} - \frac{\pi\sqrt{3}}{3} + \ln\frac{1}{\sqrt{2}} - \ln\frac{1}{2} = \frac{\pi}{4} - \frac{\pi\sqrt{3}}{3} + \frac{1}{2}\ln 2.$$

34. $u = (\ln x)^2$, $dv = x^2\,dx$; $du = (2/x)\ln x\,dx$, $v = \frac{1}{3}x^3$;

$$\int x^2(\ln x)^2\,dx = (\ln x)^2\left(\frac{1}{3}x^3\right) - \int\left(\frac{1}{3}x^3\right)\left(\frac{2}{x}\ln x\right)dx = \frac{1}{3}x^3(\ln x)^2 - \frac{2}{3}\int x^2\ln x\,dx.$$

For $\int x^2\ln x\,dx$, let $u = \ln x$, $dv = x^2\,dx$; $du = (1/x)\,dx$, $v = \frac{1}{3}x^3$. Then

$$\frac{-2}{3}\int x^2\ln x\,dx = \frac{-2}{3}(\ln x)\left(\frac{1}{3}x^3\right) + \frac{2}{3}\int\left(\frac{1}{3}x^3\right)\frac{1}{x}\,dx$$

$$= \frac{-2}{9}x^3\ln x + \frac{2}{9}\int x^2\,dx = \frac{-2}{9}x^3\ln x + \frac{2}{27}x^3 + C.$$

Thus

$$\int_1^b x^2(\ln x)^2\,dx = \frac{1}{3}x^3(\ln x)^2\Big|_1^b - \frac{2}{9}x^3\ln x\Big|_1^b + \frac{2}{27}x^3\Big|_1^b = \frac{1}{3}b^3(\ln b)^2 - \frac{2}{9}b^3\ln b + \frac{2}{27}(b^3 - 1).$$

35. Substitute $u = x + 1$, so that $du = dx$. If $x = 0$ then $u = 1$, and if $x = 1$ then $u = 2$. Thus by the solution of Example 3,

$$\int_0^1 \ln(x+1)\,dx = \int_1^2 \ln u\,du = (u\ln u - u)\big|_1^2 = (2\ln 2 - 2) + 1 = 2\ln 2 - 1.$$

36. Substitute $u = 1 + e^x$, so that $du = e^x\,dx$. Then $\int e^x\ln(1+e^x)\,dx = \int \ln u\,du$, and by the solution of Example 3, $\int \ln u\,du = u\ln u - u + C$. Thus $\int e^x\ln(1+e^x)\,dx = (1+e^x)\ln(1+e^x) - (1+e^x) + C$.

37. Substitute $u = ax$, so that $du = a\,dx$ and $x = u/a$. Then

$$\int x\sin ax\,dx = \int\frac{u}{a}(\sin u)\frac{1}{a}\,du = \frac{1}{a^2}\int u\sin u\,du.$$

By the solution of Exercise 1, $\int u\sin u\,du = -u\cos u + \sin u + C_1$. Thus

$$\int x\sin ax\,dx = \frac{1}{a^2}(-ax\cos ax + \sin ax + C_1) = -\frac{x}{a}\cos ax + \frac{1}{a^2}\sin ax + C.$$

38. Substitute $u = e^{3x}$, so that $du = 3e^{3x}\,dx$. Then

$$\int e^{6x}\cos e^{3x}\,dx = \int e^{3x}(\cos e^{3x})e^{3x}\,dx = \int u(\cos u)\frac{1}{3}\,du = \frac{1}{3}\int u\cos u\,du.$$

By the solution of Example 1, $\int u\cos u\,du = u\sin u + \cos u + C_1$. Thus $\int e^{6x}\cos e^{3x}\,dx = \frac{1}{3}e^{3x}\sin e^{3x} + \frac{1}{3}\cos e^{3x} + C$.

39. Substitute $u = \cos x$, so that $du = -\sin x\,dx$. Then $\int \sin x\,\tan^{-1}(\cos x)\,dx = -\int \tan^{-1}u\,du$. By the solution of Exercise 21, $\int \tan^{-1}u\,du = u\tan^{-1}u - \frac{1}{2}\ln(1+u^2) + C_1$. Thus $\int \sin x\,\tan^{-1}(\cos x)\,dx = -\cos x\,\tan^{-1}(\cos x) + \frac{1}{2}\ln(1+\cos^2 x) + C$.

40. Substitute $t = \ln x$, so that $dt = (1/x)\,dx$. Then $\int (1/x)\sin^{-1}(\ln x)\,dx = \int \sin^{-1}t\,dt$. For $\int \sin^{-1}t\,dt$ we integrate by parts, with $u = \sin^{-1}t$, $dv = dt$;

$$du = \frac{1}{\sqrt{1-t^2}}\,dt, v = t; \qquad \int \sin^{-1}t\,dt = t\sin^{-1}t - \int \frac{t}{\sqrt{1-t^2}}\,dt.$$

For $\int \left(t/\sqrt{1-t^2}\right)dt$ substitute $s = 1-t^2$, so that $ds = -2t\,dt$. Then

$$\int \frac{t}{\sqrt{1-t^2}}\,dt = \int \frac{1}{\sqrt{s}}\left(-\frac{1}{2}\right)ds = -\sqrt{s} + C = -\sqrt{1-t^2} + C_1.$$

Thus

$$\int \frac{1}{x}\sin^{-1}(\ln x)\,dx = \int \sin^{-1}t\,dt = t\sin^{-1}t + \sqrt{1-t^2} + C = (\ln x)\sin^{-1}(\ln x) + \sqrt{1-(\ln x)^2} + C.$$

41. Substitute $s = \sqrt{t}$, so that $ds = [1/2\sqrt{t}]\,dt$. Then $\int \cos\sqrt{t}\,dt = \int (\cos s)(2s)\,ds = 2\int s\cos s\,ds$. By the solution of Example 1, $\int s\cos s\,ds = s\sin s + \cos s + C_1$. Thus $\int \cos\sqrt{t}\,dt = 2\int s\cos s\,ds = 2s\sin s + 2\cos s + C = 2\sqrt{t}\sin\sqrt{t} + 2\cos\sqrt{t} + C$.

42. Let $u = \ln t$, so that $du = (1/t)\,dt$ and $t = e^u$. Then

$$\int \frac{(\ln t)^2}{t^2}\,dt = \int \frac{(\ln t)^2}{t}\frac{1}{t}\,dt = \int \frac{u^2}{e^u}\,du = \int u^2 e^{-u}\,du.$$

By the solution of Example 4, $\int u^2 e^{-u}\,du = -u^2e^{-u} + \int 2ue^{-u}\,du = -u^2e^{-u} - 2ue^{-u} + 2\int e^{-u}\,du = -u^2e^{-u} - 2ue^{-u} - 2e^{-u}$. Thus

$$\int \frac{(\ln t)^2}{t^2}\,dt = -(\ln t)^2 e^{-\ln t} - 2(\ln t)e^{-\ln t} - 2e^{-\ln t} + C = \frac{-(\ln t)^2}{t} - 2\frac{\ln t}{t} - \frac{2}{t} + C.$$

43. Substitute $u = x/2$, so that $du = \frac{1}{2}\,dx$. If $x = 0$ then $u = 0$, and if $x = \pi/2$ then $u = \pi/4$. Thus $\int_0^{\pi/2}\cos^3(x/2)\,dx = 2\int_0^{\pi/4}\cos^3 u\,du$. By (11) with $n = 3$ we have

$$\int_0^{\pi/4}\cos^3 u\,du = \frac{1}{3}\cos^2 u\,\sin u\Big|_0^{\pi/4} + \frac{2}{3}\int_0^{\pi/4}\cos u\,du$$

$$= \left(\frac{1}{3}\left(\frac{\sqrt{2}}{2}\right)^3 - 0\right) + \left(\frac{2}{3}\sin u\right)\Big|_0^{\pi/4} = \frac{\sqrt{2}}{12} + \frac{\sqrt{2}}{3} = \frac{5}{12}\sqrt{2}.$$

Therefore
$$\int_0^{\pi/2} \cos^3 \frac{x}{2}\, dx = 2\int_0^{\pi/4} \cos^3 u\, du = 2\left(\frac{5}{12}\sqrt{2}\right) = \frac{5\sqrt{2}}{6}.$$

44. By (10), $\int \sin^5 x\, dx = -\frac{1}{5}\sin^4 x \cos x + \frac{4}{5}\int \sin^3 x\, dx$, and again by (10),
$$\frac{4}{5}\int \sin^3 x\, dx = \frac{4}{5}\left(-\frac{1}{3}\sin^2 x \cos x + \frac{2}{3}\int \sin x\, dx\right) = -\frac{4}{15}\sin^2 x \cos x - \frac{8}{15}\cos x + C.$$
Thus $\int \sin^5 x\, dx = -\frac{1}{5}\sin^4 x \cos x - \frac{4}{15}\sin^2 x \cos x - \frac{8}{15}\cos x + C$.

45. Using the formula for $\int \sin^n x\, dx$ in (10) and then the one for $\int \sin^2 x\, dx$, we have
$$\int \sin^4 x\, dx = \frac{-1}{4}\sin^3 x \cos x + \frac{3}{4}\int \sin^2 x\, dx = \frac{-1}{4}\sin^3 x \cos x - \frac{3}{16}\sin 2x + \frac{3}{8}x + C$$
$$= \frac{-1}{4}\sin^3 x \cos x - \frac{3}{8}\sin x \cos x + \frac{3}{8}x + C.$$

46. Using the formula for $\int \cos^n x\, dx$ in (11) and then the one for $\int \cos^2 x\, dx$, we have
$$\int \cos^4 x\, dx = \frac{1}{4}\cos^3 x \sin x + \frac{3}{4}\int \cos^2 x\, dx$$
$$= \frac{1}{4}\cos^3 x \sin x + \frac{3}{16}\sin 2x + \frac{3}{8}x + C = \frac{1}{4}\cos^3 x \sin x + \frac{3}{8}\cos x \sin x + \frac{3}{8}x + C.$$

47. $u = \cos^{n-1} x$, $dv = \cos x\, dx$; $du = -(n-1)\cos^{n-2} x \sin x\, dx$, $v = \sin x$;
$$\int \cos^n\, dx = \int \cos^{n-1} x \cos x\, dx = (\cos^{n-1} x)(\sin x) - \int [\sin x][-(n-1)\cos^{n-2} x \sin x]\, dx$$
$$= \cos^{n-1} x \sin x + (n-1)\int \cos^{n-2} x \sin^2 x\, dx = \cos^{n-1} x \sin x + (n-1)\int (\cos^{n-2} x - \cos^n x)\, dx.$$
Thus $n\int \cos^n x\, dx = \cos^{n-1} x \sin x + (n-1)\int \cos^{n-2} x\, dx$, so that
$$\int \cos^n x\, dx = \frac{1}{n}\cos^{n-1} x \sin x + \frac{n-1}{n}\int \cos^{n-2} x\, dx.$$

48. $u = (\ln x)^n$, $dv = dx$; $du = (n/x)(\ln x)^{n-1}\, dx$, $v = x$; $\int (\ln x)^n\, dx = (\ln x)^n x - \int x[(n/x)(\ln x)^{n-1}]\, dx = x(\ln x)^n - n\int (\ln x)^{n-1}\, dx$.

49. $u = \dfrac{1}{(x^2+a^2)^n}$, $dv = dx$; $du = \dfrac{-2nx}{(x^2+a^2)^{n+1}}\, dx$, $v = x$;
$$\int \frac{1}{(x^2+a^2)^n}\, dx = \frac{x}{(x^2+a^2)^n} + \int \frac{2nx^2}{(x^2+a^2)^{n+1}}\, dx = \frac{x}{(x^2+a^2)^n} + \int \frac{2n(x^2+a^2-a^2)}{(x^2+a^2)^{n+1}}\, dx$$
$$= \frac{x}{(x^2+a^2)^n} + \int \frac{2n}{(x^2+a^2)^n}\, dx - \int \frac{2na^2}{(x^2+a^2)^{n+1}}\, dx.$$
Thus
$$(1-2n)\int \frac{1}{(x^2+a^2)^n}\, dx = \frac{x}{(x^2+a^2)^n} - \int \frac{2na^2}{(x^2+a^2)^{n+1}}\, dx$$
so
$$\int \frac{1}{(x^2+a^2)^{n+1}}\, dx = \frac{x}{2na^2(x^2+a^2)^n} + \frac{2n-1}{2na^2}\int \frac{1}{(x^2+a^2)^n}\, dx.$$

50. $u = \sec^{n-2} x$, $dv = \sec^2 x\,dx$;

$du = (n-2)\sec^{n-3} x\,(\sec x\,\tan x)\,dx = (n-2)\sec^{n-2} x\,\tan x\,dx$, $v = \tan x$;

$$\int \sec^n x\,dx = \int \sec^{n-2} x\,\sec^2 x\,dx = \sec^{n-2} x\,\tan x - \int \tan x\,[(n-2)\sec^{n-2} x\,\tan x]\,dx$$

$$= \sec^{n-2} x\,\tan x - (n-2)\int \sec^{n-2} x\,\tan^2 x\,dx$$

$$= \sec^{n-2} x\,\tan x - (n-2)\int \sec^n x\,dx + (n-2)\int \sec^{n-2} x\,dx.$$

Thus $(n-1)\int \sec^n x\,dx = \sec^{n-2} x\,\tan x + (n-2)\int \sec^{n-2} x\,dx$, so that

$$\int \sec^n x\,dx = \frac{1}{n-1}\sec^{n-2} x\,\tan x + \frac{n-2}{n-1}\int \sec^{n-2} x\,dx.$$

51. By Exercise 48 with $n = 3$, $\int (\ln x)^3\,dx = x(\ln x)^3 - 3\int (\ln x)^2\,dx$.

By Exercise 48 with $n = 2$, $\int (\ln x)^2\,dx = x(\ln x)^2 - 2\int \ln x\,dx$.

By Example 3, $\int \ln x\,dx = x\ln x - x + C_1$. Thus

$$\int (\ln x)^3\,dx = x(\ln x)^3 - 3x(\ln x)^2 + 6x\ln x - 6x + C.$$

52. By Exercise 50 with $n = 5$ and then with $n = 3$, we find that

$$\int_{\pi/3}^{\pi/4} \sec^5 x\,dx = \left.\frac{\sec^3 x\,\tan x}{4}\right|_{\pi/3}^{\pi/4} + \frac{3}{4}\int_{\pi/3}^{\pi/4} \sec^3 x\,dx$$

$$= \frac{1}{2}\sqrt{2} - 2\sqrt{3} + \frac{3}{4}\left(\left.\frac{\sec x\,\tan x}{2}\right|_{\pi/3}^{\pi/4} + \frac{1}{2}\int_{\pi/3}^{\pi/4} \sec x\,dx\right)$$

$$= \frac{1}{2}\sqrt{2} - 2\sqrt{3} + \frac{3}{8}\sqrt{2} - \frac{3}{4}\sqrt{3} + \left.\frac{3}{8}\ln|\sec x + \tan x|\right|_{\pi/3}^{\pi/4}$$

$$= \frac{7}{8}\sqrt{2} - \frac{11}{4}\sqrt{3} + \frac{3}{8}\ln(\sqrt{2}+1) - \frac{3}{8}\ln(2+\sqrt{3}).$$

53. For the integral $\int e^{-x}\sin x\,dx$ let $u = \sin x$ and $dv = e^{-x}\,dx$. Then $du = \cos x\,dx$ and $v = -e^{-x}$. Therefore $\int e^{-x}\sin x\,dx = (\sin x)(-e^{-x}) - \int(-e^{-x})\cos x\,dx = -e^{-x}\sin x + \int e^{-x}\cos x\,dx$. Together with the information from the first integration by parts, this yields $\int e^{-x}\cos x\,dx = e^{-x}\sin x + (-e^{-x}\sin x + \int e^{-x}\cos x\,dx) = \int e^{-x}\cos x\,dx$.

54. a. $u = \sin bx$, $dv = e^{ax}\,dx$; $du = b\cos bx\,dx$, $v = (1/a)e^{ax}$;

$$\int e^{ax}\sin bx\,dx = \frac{1}{a}e^{ax}\sin bx - \int \frac{b}{a}e^{ax}\cos bx\,dx = \frac{1}{a}e^{ax}\sin bx - \frac{b}{a}\int e^{ax}\cos bx\,dx.$$

For $\int e^{ax}\cos bx\,dx$, let $u = \cos bx$, $dv = e^{ax}\,dx$; $du = -b\sin bx\,dx$, $v = (1/a)e^{ax}$; $\int e^{ax}\cos bx\,dx = (1/a)e^{ax}\cos bx + \int (b/a)e^{ax}\sin bx\,dx$. Thus

$$\int e^{ax}\sin bx\,dx = \frac{1}{a}e^{ax}\sin bx - \frac{b}{a^2}e^{ax}\cos bx - \frac{b^2}{a^2}\int e^{ax}\sin bx\,dx$$

so that $(1+b^2/a^2)\int e^{ax}\sin bx\,dx = (1/a)e^{ax}\sin bx - (b/a^2)e^{ax}\cos bx + C_1$. Since $1+b^2/a^2 = (a^2+b^2)/a^2$, we find that

$$\int e^{ax}\sin bx\,dx = \frac{a^2}{a^2+b^2}\left(\frac{1}{a}e^{ax}\sin bx - \frac{b}{a^2}e^{ax}\cos bx\right) + C = \frac{e^{ax}}{a^2+b^2}(a\sin bx - b\cos bx) + C.$$

b. $u = \cos bx$, $dv = e^{ax}\,dx$; $du = -b\sin bx\,dx$, $v = (1/a)e^{ax}$;

$$\int e^{ax}\cos bx\,dx = \frac{1}{a}e^{ax}\cos bx - \int -\frac{b}{a}e^{ax}\sin bx\,dx = \frac{1}{a}e^{ax}\cos bx + \frac{b}{a}\int e^{ax}\sin bx\,dx.$$

Therefore by part (a),

$$\int e^{ax}\cos bx\,dx = \frac{1}{a}e^{ax}\cos bx + \frac{b}{a}\frac{e^{ax}}{a^2+b^2}(a\sin bx - b\cos bx) + C$$

$$= \frac{e^{ax}}{a^2+b^2}\left[\frac{a^2+b^2}{a}\cos bx + b\sin bx - \frac{b^2}{a}\cos bx\right] + C = \frac{e^{ax}}{a^2+b^2}[a\cos bx + b\sin bx] + C.$$

55. Using the solution of Example 3, we find that the area A is given by

$$A = \int_1^2 \ln x\,dx = (x\ln x - x)\Big|_1^2 = (2\ln 2 - 2) + 1 = 2\ln 2 - 1.$$

56. For $1/e \le x \le 1$, $f(x) \le 0$; for $1 \le x \le e$, $f(x) \ge 0$. Using the solution of Exercise 3, we find that the area A is given by

$$A = -\int_{1/e}^1 x\ln x\,dx + \int_1^e x\ln x\,dx = -\left(\frac{1}{2}x^2\ln x - \frac{1}{4}x^2\right)\Big|_{1/e}^1 + \left(\frac{1}{2}x^2\ln x - \frac{1}{4}x^2\right)\Big|_1^e$$

$$= -\left[-\frac{1}{4} - \left(-\frac{1}{2e^2} - \frac{1}{4e^2}\right)\right] + \left[\frac{1}{2}e^2 - \frac{1}{4}e^2 + \frac{1}{4}\right] = \frac{1}{2} + \frac{1}{4}e^2 - \frac{3}{4e^2}.$$

57. Using the solution of Exercise 1, we find that the area A is given by

$$A = \int_0^{\pi/2} x\sin x\,dx = (-x\cos x + \sin x)\Big|_0^{\pi/2} = (0+1) - (0+0) = 1.$$

58. Using the solution of Exercise 21, we find that the area A is given by

$$A = \int_0^1 \tan^{-1}x\,dx = \left(x\tan^{-1}x - \frac{1}{2}\ln(1+x^2)\right)\Big|_0^1 = \left(\tan^{-1}1 - \frac{1}{2}\ln 2\right) - 0 = \frac{\pi}{4} - \frac{1}{2}\ln 2.$$

59. The graphs intersect at (x,y) if $3x\ln x = y = x^2\ln x$, or $x = 1$ or 3. Since $3x\ln x \ge x^2\ln x$ on $[1,3]$, we have $A = \int_1^3(3x\ln x - x^2\ln x)\,dx = \int_1^3(3x - x^2)\ln x\,dx$. Let $u = \ln x$, $dv = (3x - x^2)\,dx$, $du = (1/x)\,dx$, $v = \frac{3}{2}x^2 - \frac{1}{3}x^3$. Then

$$\int_1^3 (3x - x^2)\ln x\,dx = \left(\frac{3}{2}x^2 - \frac{1}{3}x^3\right)\ln x\Big|_1^3 - \int_1^3\left(\frac{3}{2}x - \frac{1}{3}x^2\right)dx$$

$$= \left(\frac{27}{2} - 9\right)\ln 3 - \left(\frac{3}{4}x^2 - \frac{1}{9}x^3\right)\Big|_1^3 = \frac{9}{2}\ln 3 - \left(\frac{27}{4} - 3\right) + \left(\frac{3}{4} - \frac{1}{9}\right) = \frac{9}{2}\ln 3 - \frac{28}{9}.$$

Thus $A = \frac{9}{2}\ln 3 - \frac{28}{9}$.

60. a. By Example 1, the moment M is given by

$$M = \int_0^{\pi/2} x\cos x\,dx = (x\sin x + \cos x)\Big|_0^{\pi/2} = \frac{\pi}{2} - 1.$$

b. By Example 1, the moment M is given by

$$M = \int_{-\pi/2}^{\pi/2} x\cos x\,dx = (x\sin x + \cos x)\Big|_{-\pi/2}^{\pi/2} = 0.$$

c. By Exercise 3, the moment M is given by

$$M = \int_1^2 x\ln x\,dx = \left(\frac{1}{2}x^2\ln x - \frac{x^2}{4}\right)\Big|_1^2 = 2\ln 2 - \frac{3}{4}.$$

61. By (12), $c = \int_0^{\pi/2}\sin^4 x\,dx = (-\frac{1}{4}\sin^3 x\,\cos x - \frac{3}{8}\sin x\,\cos x + \frac{3}{8}x)\Big|_0^{\pi/2} = \frac{3}{16}\pi$.

62. a. Notice that f is linear on $[-L/2, 0]$ and passes through the points $(-L/2, 0)$ and $(0, H)$. Similarly, f is linear on $[0, L/2]$ and passes through the points $(0, H)$ and $(L/2, 0)$. Thus

$$f(x) = \begin{cases} 2Hx/L + H & \text{for } -L/2 \le x \le 0 \\ -2Hx/L + H & \text{for } 0 < x \le L/2 \end{cases}$$

b. Since f and $\cos x$ are even functions, it follows that $f(x)\cos(\pi x/L)$ is also an even function. Thus

$$\int_{-L/2}^{L/2} f(x)\cos\frac{\pi}{L}x\,dx = 2\int_0^{L/2}\left(-\frac{2H}{L}x + H\right)\cos\frac{\pi}{L}x\,dx$$

$$= -\frac{4H}{L}\int_0^{L/2} x\cos\frac{\pi}{L}x\,dx + 2H\int_0^{L/2}\cos\frac{\pi}{L}x\,dx.$$

To evaluate the first integral, let $u = \pi x/L$, so $du = (\pi/L)\,dx$. If $x = 0$, then $u = 0$; if $x = L/2$, then $u = \pi/2$. Thus by Example 1,

$$\int_0^{L/2} x\cos\frac{\pi}{L}x\,dx = \int_0^{\pi/2}\frac{L}{\pi}u\cos u\,\frac{L}{\pi}\,du = \frac{L^2}{\pi^2}(u\sin u + \cos u)\Big|_0^{\pi/2} = \frac{L^2}{\pi^2}\left(\frac{\pi}{2} - 1\right).$$

For the second integral we have

$$\int_0^{L/2}\left(\cos\frac{\pi}{L}x\right)dx = \int_0^{\pi/2}(\cos u)\,\frac{L}{\pi}\,du = \frac{L}{\pi}\sin u\Big|_0^{\pi/2} = \frac{L}{\pi}.$$

Therefore

$$\int_{-L/2}^{L/2} f(x)\cos\frac{\pi}{L}x\,dx = -\frac{4HL^2}{L\pi^2}\left(\frac{\pi}{2} - 1\right) + 2H\left(\frac{L}{\pi}\right) = \frac{4HL}{\pi^2}.$$

63. The differential equation is

$$L\frac{dI}{dt}+RI=\sin t,\quad \text{or equivalently,}\quad \frac{dI}{dt}+\frac{R}{L}I=\frac{1}{L}\sin t.$$

This differential equation has the form of (10) in Section 6.8, where $P(t)=R/L$ and $Q(t)=(\sin t)/L$. Since Rt/L is an antiderivative of P, we conclude from (12) in Section 6.8 that

$$I=e^{-Rt/L}\int e^{Rt/L}\frac{1}{L}\sin t\,dt=\frac{1}{L}e^{-Rt/L}\int e^{Rt/L}\sin t\,dt.$$

By Exercise 54(a) with $a=R/L$, $b=1$, and $x=t$, we conclude that

$$\int e^{Rt/L}\sin t\,dt=\frac{e^{Rt/L}}{(R/L)^2+1}\left(\frac{R}{L}\sin t-\cos t\right)+C=\frac{Le^{Rt/L}}{R^2+L^2}(R\sin t-L\cos t)+C.$$

Therefore

$$I=\frac{1}{L}e^{-Rt/L}\left[\frac{Le^{Rt/L}}{R^2+L^2}(R\sin t-L\cos t)+C\right]=\frac{1}{R^2+L^2}(R\sin t-L\cos t)+\frac{C}{L}e^{-Rt/L}.$$

7.2 Trigonometric Integrals

1. $u=\cos x$, $du=-\sin x\,dx$; $\int\sin^3 x\cos^2 x\,dx=-\int(-\sin x)(1-\cos^2 x)\cos^2 x\,dx=-\int(1-u^2)u^2\,du=$ $\int(-u^2+u^4)\,du=\frac{-1}{3}u^3+\frac{1}{5}u^5+C=\frac{-1}{3}\cos^3 x+\frac{1}{5}\cos^5 x+C$.

2. $u=\cos x$, $du=-\sin x\,dx$; $\int\sin^3 x\cos^3 x\,dx=-\int(-\sin x)(1-\cos^2 x)\cos^3 x\,dx=-\int(1-u^2)u^3\,du=$ $\int(-u^3+u^5)\,du=\frac{-1}{4}u^4+\frac{1}{6}u^6+C=\frac{-1}{4}\cos^4 x+\frac{1}{6}\cos^6 x+C$.

3. $u=\sin 3x$, $du=3\cos 3x\,dx$; $\int\sin^3 3x\cos 3x\,dx=\frac{1}{3}\int u^3\,du=\frac{1}{12}u^4+C=\frac{1}{12}\sin^4 3x+C$.

4. $u=\sin t$, $du=\cos t\,dt$; if $t=0$, then $u=0$, and if $t=\pi/2$, then $u=1$; $\int_0^{\pi/2}\sin^2 t\cos^5 t\,dt=$ $\int_0^{\pi/2}\sin^2 t\,(1-\sin^2 t)^2\cos t\,dt=\int_0^1 u^2(1-u^2)^2\,du=\int_0^1(u^2-2u^4+u^6)\,du=\left(\frac{1}{3}u^3-\frac{2}{5}u^5+\frac{1}{7}u^7\right)\Big|_0^1=\frac{8}{105}$.

5. First let $u=1/x$, so that $du=-(1/x^2)\,dx$. Then

$$\int\frac{1}{x^2}\sin^5\frac{1}{x}\cos^2\frac{1}{x}\,dx=\int-\sin^5 u\cos^2 u\,du=-\int\sin^5 u\cos^2 u\,du.$$

For $\int\sin^5 u\cos^2 u\,du$, let $v=\cos u$, so that $dv=-\sin u\,du$. Then

$$\int\sin^5 u\cos^2 u\,du=\int(1-\cos^2 u)^2(\sin u)\cos^2 u\,du=\int-(1-v^2)^2v^2\,dv=-\int(v^2-2v^4+v^6)\,dv$$

$$=-\left(\frac{1}{3}v^3-\frac{2}{5}v^5+\frac{1}{7}v^7\right)+C_1=-\frac{1}{3}\cos^3 u+\frac{2}{5}\cos^5 u-\frac{1}{7}\cos^7 u+C_1.$$

Thus

$$\int\frac{1}{x^2}\sin^5\frac{1}{x}\cos^2\frac{1}{x}\,dx=\frac{1}{3}\cos^3\frac{1}{x}-\frac{2}{5}\cos^5\frac{1}{x}+\frac{1}{7}\cos^7\frac{1}{x}+C.$$

6. First let $u = 6x$, so that $du = 6\,dx$. Then $\int \sin^8 6x \cos^3 6x\,dx = \int \frac{1}{6}\sin^8 u \cos^3 u\,du = \frac{1}{6}\int \sin^8 u \cos^3 u\,du$. For $\int \sin^8 u \cos^3 u\,du$, let $v = \sin u$, so that $dv = \cos u\,du$. Then

$$\int \sin^8 u \cos^3 u\,du = \int \sin^8 u\,(1 - \sin^2 u) \cos u\,du = \int v^8(1 - v^2)\,dv$$

$$= \int (v^8 - v^{10})\,dv = \frac{1}{9}v^9 - \frac{1}{11}v^{11} + C_1 = \frac{1}{9}\sin^9 u - \frac{1}{11}\sin^{11} u + C_1.$$

Thus $\int \sin^8 6x \cos^3 6x\,dx = \frac{1}{54}\sin^9 6x - \frac{1}{66}\sin^{11} 6x + C$.

7. By (1), $\int \sin^2 y \cos^2 y\,dy = \int (\sin y \cos y)^2\,dy = \int (\frac{1}{2}\sin 2y)^2\,dy = \frac{1}{4}\int \sin^2 2y\,dy$. Next, let $u = 2y$, so that $du = 2\,dy$. Then $\int \sin^2 2y\,dy = \int (\sin^2 u)\frac{1}{2}\,du = \frac{1}{2}\int \sin^2 u\,du$. By (4), $\int \sin^2 u\,du = \frac{1}{2}u - \frac{1}{4}\sin 2u + C_1$. Thus $\int \sin^2 y \cos^2 y\,dy = \frac{1}{4}\int \sin^2 2y\,dy = \frac{1}{8}\int \sin^2 u\,du = \frac{1}{8}(\frac{1}{2}u - \frac{1}{4}\sin 2u) + C = \frac{1}{8}y - \frac{1}{32}\sin 4y + C$.

8. By (1) and (2),

$$\int_0^{\pi/2} \sin^4 x \cos^2 x\,dx = \int_0^{\pi/2} \sin^2 x\,(\sin^2 x \cos^2 x)\,dx = \int_0^{\pi/2} \sin^2 x\,(\sin x \cos x)^2\,dx$$

$$= \int_0^{\pi/2} \left(\frac{1 - \cos 2x}{2}\right)\left(\frac{1}{2}\sin 2x\right)^2 dx = \frac{1}{8}\int_0^{\pi/2} (\sin^2 2x - \sin^2 2x \cos 2x)\,dx$$

$$= \frac{1}{8}\int_0^{\pi/2} \sin^2 2x\,dx - \frac{1}{8}\int_0^{\pi/2} \sin^2 2x \cos 2x\,dx.$$

Now let $u = 2x$, so that $du = 2\,dx$. If $x = 0$ then $u = 0$, and if $x = \pi/2$ then $u = \pi$. Thus

$$\frac{1}{8}\int_0^{\pi/2} \sin^2 2x\,dx - \frac{1}{8}\int_0^{\pi/2} \sin^2 2x \cos 2x\,dx = \frac{1}{16}\int_0^{\pi} \sin^2 u\,du - \frac{1}{16}\int_0^{\pi} \sin^2 u \cos u\,du.$$

By (4), $\frac{1}{16}\int_0^{\pi} \sin^2 u\,du = \frac{1}{16}(\frac{1}{2}u - \frac{1}{4}\sin 2u)\Big|_0^{\pi} = \frac{1}{32}\pi$. Next, let $v = \sin u$; then $dv = \cos u\,du$. If $u = 0$, then $v = 0$, and if $u = \pi$ then $v = 0$ also. Thus $-\frac{1}{16}\int_0^{\pi} \sin^2 u \cos u\,du = -\frac{1}{16}\int_0^0 v^2\,dv = 0$. Consequently $\int_0^{\pi/2} \sin^4 x \cos^2 x\,dx = \frac{1}{16}\int_0^{\pi} \sin^2 u\,du - \frac{1}{16}\int_0^{\pi} \sin^2 u \cos u\,du = \frac{1}{32}\pi - 0 = \frac{1}{32}\pi$.

9. By (1), $\int \sin^4 x \cos^4 x\,dx = \int \frac{1}{16}(2\sin x \cos x)^4\,dx = \frac{1}{16}\int \sin^4 2x\,dx$. Next, let $u = 2x$, so that $du = 2\,dx$. Then $\frac{1}{16}\int \sin^4 2x\,dx = \frac{1}{16}\int (\sin^4 u)\frac{1}{2}\,du = \frac{1}{32}\int \sin^4 u\,du$. By (12) of Section 7.1, $\frac{1}{32}\int \sin^4 u\,du = \frac{1}{32}(-\frac{1}{4}\sin^3 u \cos u - \frac{3}{8}\sin u \cos u + \frac{3}{8}u) + C = -\frac{1}{128}\sin^3 2x \cos 2x - \frac{3}{256}\sin 2x \cos 2x + \frac{3}{128}x + C$.

10. $$\int \sin^6 w \cos^4 w\,dw = \int \left(\frac{1 - \cos 2w}{2}\right)^3 \left(\frac{1 + \cos 2w}{2}\right)^2 dw$$

$$= \frac{1}{32}\int (1 - \cos 2w)(1 - \cos 2w)^2(1 + \cos 2w)^2\,dw$$

$$= \frac{1}{32}\int (1 - \cos 2w)(1 - \cos^2 2w)^2\,dw = \frac{1}{32}\int (1 - \cos 2w)\sin^4 2w\,dw$$

$$= \frac{1}{32}\int \sin^4 2w\,dw = \frac{1}{32}\int \cos 2w \sin^4 2w\,dw.$$

Let $u = 2w$; then by (12) in Section 7.1,

$$\frac{1}{32}\int \sin^4 2w\,dw = \frac{1}{64}\int \sin^4 u\,du = \frac{1}{64}\left(-\frac{1}{4}\sin^3 u\,\cos u - \frac{3}{8}\sin u\,\cos u + \frac{3}{8}u\right) + C_1$$

$$= \frac{1}{64}\left(-\frac{1}{4}\sin^3 2w\,\cos 2w - \frac{3}{8}\sin 2w\,\cos 2w + \frac{3}{4}w\right) + C_1.$$

Also

$$\frac{1}{32}\int \cos 2w\,\sin^4 2w\,dw = \frac{1}{64}\int \cos u\,\sin^4 u\,du = \frac{1}{320}\sin^5 u + C_2 = \frac{1}{320}\sin^5 2w + C_2.$$

Thus

$$\int \sin^6 w\,\cos^4 w\,dw = -\frac{1}{256}\sin^3 2w\,\cos 2w - \frac{3}{512}\sin 2w\,\cos 2w + \frac{3}{256}w - \frac{1}{320}\sin^5 2w + C.$$

11. $u = \sin x$, $du = \cos x\,dx$; $\int \sin^{-10} x\,\cos^3 x\,dx = \int \sin^{-10} x\,(1-\sin^2 x)\,\cos x\,dx = \int (u^{-10} - u^{-8})\,du = -\frac{1}{9}u^{-9} + \frac{1}{7}u^{-7} + C = -\frac{1}{9}\sin^{-9} x + \frac{1}{7}\sin^{-7} x + C.$

12. $u = \sin x$, $du = \cos x\,dx$; $\int \sin^{-17} x\,\cos^5 x\,dx = \int \sin^{-17} x\,(1-\sin^2 x)^2\,\cos x\,dx = \int u^{-17}(1-u^2)^2\,du = \int (u^{-17} - 2u^{-15} + u^{-13})\,du = -\frac{1}{16}u^{-16} + \frac{2}{14}u^{-14} - \frac{1}{12}u^{-12} + C = -\frac{1}{16}\sin^{-16} x + \frac{1}{7}\sin^{-14} x - \frac{1}{12}\sin^{-12} x + C.$

13. $$\int (1+\sin^2 x)(1+\cos^2 x)\,dx = \int \left(1 + \frac{1-\cos 2x}{2}\right)\left(1 + \frac{1+\cos 2x}{2}\right)dx$$

$$= \int \left(\frac{3-\cos 2x}{2}\right)\left(\frac{3+\cos 2x}{2}\right)dx = \frac{1}{4}\int (9 - \cos^2 2x)\,dx$$

Using (5) we find that $\frac{1}{4}\int (9-\cos^2 2x)\,dx = \frac{9}{4}x - \frac{1}{8}x - \frac{1}{32}\sin 4x + C = \frac{17}{8}x - \frac{1}{32}\sin 4x + C.$

14. $u = \cos x\,dx$, $du = -\sin x\,dx$;

$$\int \sin^5 x\,\cos^{1/2} x\,dx = \int (1-\cos^2 x)^2 \sin x\,\cos^{1/2} x\,dx = \int (1-u^2)^2 u^{1/2}(-1)\,du$$

$$= -\int (u^{1/2} - 2u^{5/2} + u^{9/2})\,du = -\frac{2}{3}u^{3/2} + \frac{4}{7}u^{7/2} - \frac{2}{11}u^{11/2} + C$$

$$= -\frac{2}{3}\cos^{3/2} x + \frac{4}{7}\cos^{7/2} x - \frac{2}{11}\cos^{11/2} x + C.$$

15. $u = \cos x$, $du = -\sin x\,dx$; if $x = 0$ then $u = 1$, and if $x = \pi/4$ then $u = \sqrt{2}/2$;

$$\int_0^{\pi/4} \frac{\sin^3 x}{\cos^2 x}\,dx = \int_0^{\pi/4} \frac{(1-\cos^2 x)}{\cos^2 x}\,\sin x\,dx = \int_1^{\sqrt{2}/2} \frac{-(1-u^2)}{u^2}\,du$$

$$= \int_1^{\sqrt{2}/2}\left(1 - \frac{1}{u^2}\right)du = \left(u + \frac{1}{u}\right)\Big|_1^{\sqrt{2}/2} = \left(\frac{\sqrt{2}}{2} + \sqrt{2}\right) - (1+1) = \frac{3}{2}\sqrt{2} - 2.$$

16. $u = \sin x$, $du = \cos x\,dx$;

$$\int \frac{\cos^3 x}{\sin^{5/2} x}\,dx = \int \frac{(1-\sin^2 x)}{\sin^{5/2} x}\cos x\,dx = \int \frac{1-u^2}{u^{5/2}}\,du = \int (u^{-5/2} - u^{-1/2})\,du$$

$$= -\frac{2}{3}u^{-3/2} - 2u^{1/2} + C = -\frac{2}{3}\sin^{-3/2} x - 2\sin^{1/2} x + C.$$

17. $u = \tan x$, $du = \sec^2 x\,dx$; $\int \tan^5 x \sec^2 x\,dx = \int u^5\,du = \frac{1}{6}u^6 + C = \frac{1}{6}\tan^6 x + C$.

18. $u = \tan 5x$, $du = 5\sec^2 5x\,dx$; $\int \tan^3 5x \sec^2 5x\,dx = \frac{1}{5}\int u^3\,du = \frac{1}{20}u^4 + C = \frac{1}{20}\tan^4 5x + C$.

19. $u = \tan t$, $du = \sec^2 t\,dt$; if $t = 0$ then $u = 0$, and if $t = \pi/4$ then $u = 1$; $\int_0^{\pi/4} \tan^5 t \sec^4 t\,dt = \int_0^{\pi/4} \tan^5 t\,(\tan^2 t + 1)\sec^2 t\,dt = \int_0^1 u^5(u^2+1)\,du = \int_0^1 (u^7 + u^5)\,du = (\frac{1}{8}u^8 + \frac{1}{6}u^6)\big|_0^1 = \frac{7}{24}$.

20. $u = \tan x^2$, $du = 2x\sec^2 x^2\,dx$;

$$\int x\tan^3 x^2 \sec^4 x^2\,dx = \int x\tan^3 x^2\,(\tan^2 x^2 + 1)\sec^2 x^2\,dx = \int u^3(u^2+1)\frac{1}{2}\,du$$

$$= \frac{1}{2}\int (u^5 + u^3)\,du = \frac{1}{12}u^6 + \frac{1}{8}u^4 + C = \frac{1}{12}\tan^6 x^2 + \frac{1}{8}\tan^4 x^2 + C.$$

21. $u = \sec x$, $du = \sec x \tan x\,dx$; if $x = 5\pi/4$ then $u = -\sqrt{2}$, and if $x = 4\pi/3$ then $u = -2$;

$$\int_{5\pi/4}^{4\pi/3} \tan^3 x \sec x\,dx = \int_{5\pi/4}^{4\pi/3} (\sec^2 x - 1)(\sec x \tan x)\,dx$$

$$= \int_{-\sqrt{2}}^{-2} (u^2 - 1)\,du = \left(\frac{1}{3}u^3 - u\right)\Big|_{-\sqrt{2}}^{-2} = -\frac{2}{3} - \frac{1}{3}\sqrt{2}.$$

22. $u = \sec x$, $du = \sec x \tan x\,dx$;

$$\int \tan x \sec^3 x\,dx = \int \sec^2 x\,(\sec x \tan x)\,dx = \int u^2\,du = \frac{1}{3}u^3 + C = \frac{1}{3}\sec^3 x + C.$$

23. $u = \sec\sqrt{x}$, $du = [1/(2\sqrt{x})]\sec\sqrt{x}\tan\sqrt{x}\,dx$;

$$\int \frac{1}{\sqrt{x}}\tan^3\sqrt{x}\sec^3\sqrt{x}\,dx = \int (\tan^2\sqrt{x})(\sec^2\sqrt{x})\left(\frac{1}{\sqrt{x}}\sec\sqrt{x}\tan\sqrt{x}\right)dx$$

$$= \int \left[(\sec^2\sqrt{x} - 1)\sec^2\sqrt{x}\right]\frac{1}{\sqrt{x}}\sec\sqrt{x}\tan\sqrt{x}\,dx = \int (u^2-1)u^2(2)\,du$$

$$= 2\int (u^4 - u^2)\,du = \frac{2}{5}u^5 - \frac{2}{3}u^3 + C = \frac{2}{5}\sec^5\sqrt{x} - \frac{2}{3}\sec^3\sqrt{x} + C.$$

24. $u = \tan(1-y)$, $du = -\sec^2(1-y)\,dy$;

$$\int \tan^4(1-y)\sec^4(1-y)\,dy = \int \tan^4(1-y)\,[\tan^2(1-y) + 1]\sec^2(1-y)\,dy = -\int u^4(u^2+1)\,du$$

$$= -\int (u^6 + u^4)\,du = -\frac{1}{7}u^7 - \frac{1}{5}u^5 + C = -\frac{1}{7}\tan^7(1-y) - \frac{1}{5}\tan^5(1-y) + C.$$

25. $u = \tan x$, $du = \sec^2 x\,dx$; $\int \tan^3 x \sec^4 x\,dx = \int \tan^3 x\,(\tan^2 x + 1)\sec^2 x\,dx = \int u^3(u^2+1)\,du = \int (u^5+u^3)\,du = \frac{1}{6}u^6 + \frac{1}{4}u^4 + C = \frac{1}{6}\tan^6 x + \frac{1}{4}\tan^4 x + C.$

26. $u = \sec x$, $du = \sec x \tan x\,dx$; $\int_0^{\pi/3} \tan x \sec^{3/2} x\,dx = \int_1^2 u^{1/2}\,du = \frac{2}{3}u^{3/2}\Big|_1^2 = \frac{4}{3}\sqrt{2} - \frac{2}{3}.$

27. $u = \sec x$, $du = \sec x \tan x\,dx$; $\int \tan x \sec^5 x\,dx = \int u^4\,du = \frac{1}{5}u^5 + C = \frac{1}{5}\sec^5 x + C.$

28. $u = \csc x$, $dv = \csc^2 x\,dx$; $du = -\csc x \cot x\,dx$, $v = -\cot x$;

$$\int \csc^3 x\,dx = -\csc x \cot x - \int \csc x \cot^2 x\,dx$$

$$= -\csc x \cot x - \int \csc x\,(\csc^2 x - 1)\,dx = -\csc x \cot x - \int \csc^3 x\,dx + \int \csc x\,dx.$$

Thus $2\int \csc^3 x\,dx = -\csc x \cot x + \int \csc x\,dx = -\csc x \cot x - \ln|\csc x + \cot x| + C_1$ by Exercise 36 of Section 5.7. Therefore $\int \csc^3 x\,dx = -\frac{1}{2}\csc x \cot x - \frac{1}{2}\ln|\csc x + \cot x| + C.$

29. $u = \cot x$, $du = -\csc^2 x\,dx$; $\int \cot^3 x \csc^2 x\,dx = -\int u^3\,du = -\frac{1}{4}u^4 + C = -\frac{1}{4}\cot^4 x + C.$

30. $u = \cot s$, $du = -\csc^2 s\,ds$; $\int \cot^3 s \csc^4 s\,ds = \int \cot^3 s\,(\cot^2 s + 1)\csc^2 s\,ds = \int u^3(u^2+1)(-1)\,du = -\int (u^5+u^3)\,du = -\frac{1}{6}u^6 - \frac{1}{4}u^4 + C = -\frac{1}{6}\cot^6 s - \frac{1}{4}\cot^4 s + C.$

31. $u = \csc x$, $du = -\csc x \cot x\,dx$; if $x = \pi/4$ then $u = \sqrt{2}$, and if $x = \pi/2$ then $u = 1$;

$$\int_{\pi/4}^{\pi/2} \cot^3 x \csc^3 x\,dx = \int_{\pi/4}^{\pi/2} (\csc^2 x - 1)\csc^2 x\,(\cot x \csc x)\,dx$$

$$= \int_{\sqrt{2}}^{1} (u^2-1)u^2(-1)\,du = -\int_{\sqrt{2}}^{1}(u^4 - u^2)\,du = \left(\frac{-1}{5}u^5 + \frac{1}{3}u^3\right)\Big|_{\sqrt{2}}^{1} = \frac{2}{15}(\sqrt{2}+1).$$

32. $u = \csc x$, $du = -\csc x \cot x\,dx$; if $x = \pi/3$ then $u = 2\sqrt{3}/3$, and if $x = \pi/4$ then $u = \sqrt{2}$;

$$\int_{\pi/3}^{\pi/4} \cot x \csc^3 x\,dx = -\int_{2\sqrt{3}/3}^{\sqrt{2}} u^2\,du = \frac{-1}{3}u^3\Big|_{2\sqrt{3}/3}^{\sqrt{2}} = \frac{8}{27}\sqrt{3} - \frac{2}{3}\sqrt{2}.$$

33. $\displaystyle\int \cot x \csc^{-2} x\,dx = \int \frac{\cos x}{\sin x}\sin^2 x\,dx = \int \cos x \sin x\,dx = \frac{1}{2}\sin^2 x + C$

34. $\displaystyle\int \frac{\cot t}{\csc^3 t}\,dt = \int \frac{\cos t}{\sin t}\sin^3 t\,dt = \int \cos t \sin^2 t\,dt = \frac{1}{3}\sin^3 t + C$

35. $u = \cos x$, $du = -\sin x\,dx$;

$$\int \frac{\tan x}{\cos^3 x}\,dx = \int \frac{\sin x}{\cos^4 x}\,dx = \int \frac{1}{u^4}(-1)\,du = \frac{1}{3u^3} + C = \frac{1}{3\cos^3 x} + C.$$

36. $u = \cos x$, $du = -\sin x\,dx$;

$$\int \tan^3 x \csc^2 x\,dx = \int \frac{\sin^3 x}{\cos^3 x}\frac{1}{\sin^2 x}\,dx = \int \frac{\sin x}{\cos^3 x}\,dx$$

$$= -\int \frac{1}{u^3}\,du = \frac{1}{2u^2} + C = \frac{1}{2\cos^2 x} + C = \frac{1}{2}\sec^2 x + C.$$

37. $\displaystyle\int \frac{\tan^2 x}{\sec^5 x}\,dx = \int \frac{\sin^2 x}{\cos^2 x}\cos^5 x\,dx = \int \sin^2 x\cos^3 x\,dx = \int \sin^2 x\,(1-\sin^2 x)\,\cos x\,dx$

$$= \int (\sin^2 x - \sin^4 x)\,\cos x\,dx$$

If $u = \sin x$ then $du = \cos x\,dx$, so

$$\int \frac{\tan^2 x}{\sec^5 x}\,dx = \int (\sin^2 x - \sin^4 x)\,\cos x\,dx = \int (u^2 - u^4)\,du = \frac{1}{3}u^3 - \frac{1}{5}u^5 + C = \frac{1}{3}\sin^3 x - \frac{1}{5}\sin^5 x + C.$$

38. $u = \sin w$, $du = \cos w\,dw$;

$$\int \sin^5 w\cot^3 w\,dw = \int \sin^5 w\left(\frac{\cos^3 w}{\sin^3 w}\right)dw = \int \sin^2 w\cos^3 w\,dw$$

$$= \int \sin^2 w\,(1-\sin^2 w)\,\cos w\,dw = \int (u^2 - u^4)\,du = \frac{1}{3}u^3 - \frac{1}{5}u^5 + C = \frac{1}{3}\sin^3 w - \frac{1}{5}\sin^5 w + C.$$

39. $\displaystyle\int \frac{\tan x}{\sec^2 x}\,dx = \int \frac{\sin x}{\cos x}\cos^2 x\,dx = \int \sin x\cos x\,dx = \frac{1}{2}\sin^2 x + C$

40. $u = \sec x$, $du = \sec x\tan x\,dx$;

$$\int \frac{\tan^5 x}{\sec^4 x}\,dx = \int \frac{\tan^4 x\sec x\tan x}{\sec^5 x}\,dx = \int \frac{(\sec^2 x - 1)^2\sec x\tan x}{\sec^5 x}\,dx = \int \frac{(u^2-1)^2}{u^5}\,du$$

$$= \int \frac{u^4 - 2u^2 + 1}{u^5}\,du = \int \left(\frac{1}{u} - \frac{2}{u^3} + \frac{1}{u^5}\right)du = \ln|u| + \frac{1}{u^2} - \frac{1}{4u^4} + C$$

$$= \ln|\sec x| + \frac{1}{\sec^2 x} - \frac{1}{4\sec^4 x} + C = \ln|\sec x| + \cos^2 x - \frac{1}{4}\cos^4 x + C.$$

41. $\int \tan^2 x\,dx = \int (\sec^2 x - 1)\,dx = \tan x - x + C$

42. $\int \tan^3 x\,dx = \int \tan x\,(\sec^2 x - 1)\,dx = \int \tan x\sec^2 x\,dx - \int \tan x\,dx = \frac{1}{2}\tan^2 x + \ln|\cos x| + C$

43. $\int \tan^4 x\,dx = \int \tan^2 x\,(\sec^2 x - 1)\,dx = \int \tan^2 x\sec^2 x\,dx - \int \tan^2 x\,dx$. For $\int \tan^2 x\sec^2 x\,dx$, let $u = \tan x$, so that $du = \sec^2 x\,dx$. Then $\int \tan^2 x\sec^2 x\,dx = \int u^2\,du = \frac{1}{3}u^3 + C_1 = \frac{1}{3}\tan^3 x + C_1$. By Exercise 41, $\int \tan^2 x\,dx = \tan x - x + C_2$. Thus $\int \tan^4 x\,dx = \frac{1}{3}\tan^3 x - \tan x + x + C$.

44. $\displaystyle\int \cot^5 x\,dx = \int \cot^3 x\,(\csc^2 x - 1)\,dx = \int \cot^3 x\csc^2 x\,dx - \int \cot^3 x\,dx$

$$= \int \cot^3 x\csc^2 x\,dx - \int \cot x\,(\csc^2 x - 1)\,dx$$

$$= \int \cot^3 x\csc^2 x\,dx - \int \cot x\csc^2 x\,dx + \int \cot x\,dx$$

Let $u = \cot x$, so that $du = -\csc^2 x\,dx$. Then

$$\int \cot^5 x\,dx = \int \cot^3 x\csc^2 x\,dx - \int \cot x\csc^2 x\,dx + \int \cot x\,dx = -\int u^3\,du + \int u\,du + \int \cot x\,dx$$

$$= -\frac{1}{4}u^4 + \frac{1}{2}u^2 + \ln|\sin x| + C = -\frac{1}{4}\cot^4 x + \frac{1}{2}\cot^2 x + \ln|\sin x| + C.$$

45. By (8) with $a = 2$ and $b = 3$, $\int \sin 2x \cos 3x\, dx = \frac{1}{2}\int(\sin(-x)+\sin 5x)\, dx = \frac{1}{2}\cos(-x) - \frac{1}{10}\cos 5x + C = \frac{1}{2}\cos x - \frac{1}{10}\cos 5x + C$.

46. By (8) with $a = 1$ and $b = 2$, $\int_0^{2\pi/3} \sin x \cos 2x\, dx = \frac{1}{2}\int_0^{2\pi/3}(\sin(-x) + \sin 3x)\, dx = \left(\frac{1}{2}\cos(-x) - \frac{1}{6}\cos 3x\right)\Big|_0^{2\pi/3} = -\frac{3}{4}$.

47. By (8) with $a = -4$ and $b = -2$, $\int \sin(-4x)\cos(-2x)\, dx = \frac{1}{2}\int(\sin(-2x)+\sin(-6x))\, dx = \frac{1}{4}\cos(-2x) + \frac{1}{12}\cos(-6x) + C = \frac{1}{4}\cos 2x + \frac{1}{12}\cos 6x + C$.

48. By (8) with $a = 3$ and $b = \frac{1}{2}$, $\int \sin 3x \cos \frac{1}{2}x\, dx = \frac{1}{2}\int(\sin\frac{5}{2}x + \sin\frac{7}{2}x)\, dx = -\frac{1}{5}\cos\frac{5}{2}x - \frac{1}{7}\cos\frac{7}{2}x + C$.

49. By (8) with $a = \frac{1}{2}$ and $b = \frac{2}{3}$, $\int \sin\frac{1}{2}x \cos\frac{2}{3}x\, dx = \frac{1}{2}\int(\sin(-\frac{1}{6}x)+\sin\frac{7}{6}x)\, dx = 3\cos(-\frac{1}{6}x) - \frac{3}{7}\cos\frac{7}{6}x + C = 3\cos\frac{1}{6}x - \frac{3}{7}\cos\frac{7}{6}x + C$.

50.
$$\int \sin ax \sin bx\, dx = \int \left[\frac{-1}{2}\cos(a+b)x + \frac{1}{2}\cos(a-b)x\right] dx$$
$$= \frac{-1}{2(a+b)}\sin(a+b)x + \frac{1}{2(a-b)}\sin(a-b)x + C$$

51. $\int \sin 2x \sin 3x\, dx = \int[-\frac{1}{2}\cos(2+3)x + \frac{1}{2}\cos(2-3)x]\, dx = -\frac{1}{10}\sin 5x - \frac{1}{2}\sin(-x) + C = -\frac{1}{10}\sin 5x + \frac{1}{2}\sin x + C$

52.
$$\int \cos ax \cos bx\, dx = \int \left[\frac{1}{2}\cos(a+b)x + \frac{1}{2}\cos(a-b)x\right] dx$$
$$= \frac{1}{2(a+b)}\sin(a+b)x + \frac{1}{2(a-b)}\sin(a-b)x + C$$

53. $\int \cos 5x \cos(-3x)\, dx = \int[\frac{1}{2}\cos(5-3)x + \frac{1}{2}\cos(5+3)x]\, dx = \frac{1}{4}\sin 2x + \frac{1}{16}\sin 8x + C$

54.
$$\int \frac{1}{1+\sin x}\, dx = \int \frac{1}{1+\sin x}\,\frac{1-\sin x}{1-\sin x}\, dx = \int \frac{1-\sin x}{\cos^2 x}\, dx$$
$$= \int (\sec^2 x - \sec x \tan x)\, dx = \tan x - \sec x + C$$

55.
$$\int_{\pi/4}^{\pi/2} \frac{1}{1+\cos x}\, dx = \int_{\pi/4}^{\pi/2} \frac{1}{1+\cos x}\,\frac{1-\cos x}{1-\cos x}\, dx = \int_{\pi/4}^{\pi/2} \frac{1-\cos x}{\sin^2 x}\, dx$$
$$= \int_{\pi/4}^{\pi/2} (\csc^2 x - \csc x \cot x)\, dx = (-\cot x + \csc x)\Big|_{\pi/4}^{\pi/2} = 2 - \sqrt{2}$$

56.
$$\int \frac{1}{(1+\sin x)^2}\, dx = \int \frac{1}{(1+\sin x)^2}\,\frac{(1-\sin x)^2}{(1-\sin x)^2}\, dx = \int \frac{(1-\sin x)^2}{(1-\sin^2 x)^2}\, dx$$
$$= \int \frac{1 - 2\sin x + \sin^2 x}{\cos^4 x}\, dx = \int \left(\sec^4 x - \frac{2\sin x}{\cos^4 x} + \tan^2 x \sec^2 x\right) dx$$

Now if $u = \tan x$, then $du = \sec^2 x\,dx$, and $\int \sec^4 x\,dx = \int (\tan^2 x + 1)\sec^2 x\,dx = \int (u^2+1)\,du = \frac{1}{3}u^3 + u + C_1 = \frac{1}{3}\tan^3 x + \tan x + C_1$. If $u = \cos x$, then $du = -\sin x\,dx$, and

$$-2\int \frac{\sin x}{\cos^4 x}\,dx = -2\int \frac{1}{u^4}(-1)\,du = \frac{-2}{3}\frac{1}{u^3} + C_2 = \frac{-2}{3}\sec^3 x + C_2.$$

If $u = \tan x$, then $du = \sec^2 x\,dx$, and $\int \tan^2 x \sec^2 x\,dx = \int u^2\,du = \frac{1}{3}u^3 + C_3 = \frac{1}{3}\tan^3 x + C_3$. Thus

$$\int \frac{1}{(1+\sin x)^2}\,dx = \frac{1}{3}\tan^3 x + \tan x - \frac{2}{3}\sec^3 x + \frac{1}{3}\tan^3 x + C = \frac{2}{3}\tan^3 x + \tan x - \frac{2}{3}\sec^3 x + C.$$

57. $\displaystyle\int \frac{1+\cos x}{\sin x}\,dx = \int \frac{1+\cos x}{\sin x}\,\frac{1-\cos x}{1-\cos x}\,dx = \int \frac{\sin x}{1-\cos x}\,dx = \ln|1-\cos x| + C$

58. $\displaystyle\int \frac{1+\sin x}{\cos x}\,dx = \int \frac{1+\sin x}{\cos x}\,\frac{1-\sin x}{1-\sin x}\,dx = \int \frac{\cos x}{1-\sin x}\,dx = -\ln|1-\sin x| + C$

59. $$\int \tan^n x\,dx = \int \tan^{n-2} x \tan^2 x\,dx = \int \tan^{n-2} x\,(\sec^2 x - 1)\,dx$$
$$= \int \tan^{n-2} x \sec^2 x\,dx - \int \tan^{n-2} x\,dx = \frac{1}{n-1}\tan^{n-1} x - \int \tan^{n-2} x\,dx$$

60. a. If $m \neq n$, then by (8) with $a = m$ and $b = n$,

$$\int_{-\pi}^{\pi} \sin mx \cos nx\,dx = \int_{-\pi}^{\pi} \left\{\frac{1}{2}\sin[(m-n)x] + \frac{1}{2}\sin[(m+n)x]\right\} dx$$
$$= \left\{-\frac{1}{2}\frac{1}{m-n}\cos[(m-n)x] - \frac{1}{2}\frac{1}{m+n}\cos[(m+n)x]\right\}\Big|_{-\pi}^{\pi} = 0$$

since $\cos[(m-n)\pi] = \cos[(m-n)(-\pi)]$ and $\cos[(m+n)\pi] = \cos[(m+n)(-\pi)]$ for all integers m and n. If $m = n$, then $\int_{-\pi}^{\pi} \sin mx \cos nx\,dx = \int_{-\pi}^{\pi} \sin mx \cos mx\,dx = \int_{-\pi}^{\pi} \frac{1}{2}\sin 2mx\,dx = [-1/(4m)]\cos 2mx\big|_{-\pi}^{\pi} = 0$, since $\cos 2m\pi = \cos[2m(-\pi)]$ for all integers m.

b. If $m \neq n$, then by the solution to Exercise 52,

$$\int_{-\pi}^{\pi} \cos mx \cos nx\,dx = \left[\frac{1}{2(m+n)}\sin(m+n)x + \frac{1}{2(m-n)}\sin(m-n)x\right]\Big|_{-\pi}^{\pi} = 0$$

since $\sin k\pi = 0$ for all integers k. If $m = n$, then by (3),

$$\int_{-\pi}^{\pi} \cos mx \cos nx\,dx = \int_{-\pi}^{\pi} \cos^2 mx\,dx = \int_{-\pi}^{\pi} \left(\frac{1}{2} + \frac{1}{2}\cos 2mx\right) dx$$
$$= \left(\frac{1}{2}x + \frac{1}{4m}\sin 2mx\right)\Big|_{-\pi}^{\pi} = \left(\frac{1}{2}\pi + 0\right) - \left(-\frac{1}{2}\pi + 0\right) = \pi$$

since $\sin k\pi = 0$ for all integers k.

c. If $m \neq n$, then by the solution to Exercise 50,

$$\int_{-\pi}^{\pi} \sin mx \sin nx\,dx = \left[\frac{-1}{2(m+n)}\sin(m+n)x + \frac{1}{2(m-n)}\sin(m-n)x\right]\Big|_{-\pi}^{\pi} = 0$$

since $\sin k\pi = 0$ for all integers k. If $m = n$, then by (2),

$$\int_{-\pi}^{\pi} \sin mx \sin nx\, dx = \int_{-\pi}^{\pi} \sin^2 mx\, dx = \int_{-\pi}^{\pi} \left(\frac{1}{2} - \frac{1}{2}\cos 2mx\right) dx$$

$$= \left(\frac{1}{2}x - \frac{1}{4m}\sin 2mx\right)\Big|_{-\pi}^{\pi} = \left(\frac{1}{2}\pi - 0\right) - \left(-\frac{1}{2}\pi - 0\right) = \pi$$

since $\sin k\pi = 0$ for all integers k.

61. From the hint, $\sin x - 5\cos x = a(\sin x + \cos x) + b(\cos x - \sin x) = (a-b)\sin x + (a+b)\cos x$. Equating coefficients, we obtain $a - b = 1$ and $a + b = -5$, so that $a = -2$ and $b = -3$. Therefore

$$\int \frac{\sin x - 5\cos x}{\sin x + \cos x}\, dx = \int \frac{-2(\sin x + \cos x) - 3(\cos x - \sin x)}{\sin x + \cos x}\, dx$$

$$= \int \left(-2 - 3\frac{\cos x - \sin x}{\sin x + \cos x}\right) dx = -2x - 3\int \frac{\cos x - \sin x}{\sin x + \cos x}\, dx.$$

If $u = \sin x + \cos x$ then $du = (\cos x - \sin x)\, dx$, so that

$$\int \frac{\cos x - \sin x}{\sin x + \cos x}\, dx = \int \frac{1}{u}\, du = \ln|u| + C = \ln|\sin x + \cos x| + C.$$

Thus

$$\int \frac{\sin x - 5\cos x}{\sin x + \cos x}\, dx = -2x - 3\ln|\sin x + \cos x| + C.$$

62. The area is given by $A = \int_0^{\pi/2} \sin^2 x \cos^3 x\, dx$, so by the solution of Example 1, $A = (\frac{1}{3}\sin^3 x - \frac{1}{5}\sin^5 x)\big|_0^{\pi/2} = \frac{1}{3} - \frac{1}{5} = \frac{2}{15}$.

63. The area is given by $A = \int_{-\pi/3}^{\pi/4} \sec^4 x\, dx = \int_{-\pi/3}^{\pi/4} \sec^2 x \sec^2 x\, dx = \int_{-\pi/3}^{\pi/4} (\tan^2 x + 1)\sec^2 x\, dx$. Let $u = \tan x$, so that $du = \sec^2 x\, dx$; if $x = -\pi/3$, then $u = -\sqrt{3}$, and if $x = \pi/4$, then $u = 1$. Thus $A = \int_{-\pi/3}^{\pi/4} (\tan^2 x + 1)\sec^2 x\, dx = \int_{-\sqrt{3}}^{1} (u^2 + 1)\, du = (\frac{1}{3}u^3 + u)\big|_{-\sqrt{3}}^{1} = (\frac{1}{3} + 1) - (-\sqrt{3} - \sqrt{3}) = \frac{4}{3} + 2\sqrt{3}$.

64. The area A is given by

$$A = \int_{\pi/4}^{\pi/3} \tan^3 x \sec x\, dx = \int_{\pi/4}^{\pi/3} \tan^2 x\,(\tan x \sec x)\, dx = \int_{\pi/4}^{\pi/3} (\sec^2 x - 1)(\tan x \sec x)\, dx.$$

Let $u = \sec x$, so that $du = \tan x \sec x\, dx$; if $x = \pi/4$, then $u = \sqrt{2}$; if $x = \pi/3$, then $u = 2$. Thus

$$A = \int_{\pi/4}^{\pi/3} \tan^3 x \sec x\, dx = \int_{\sqrt{2}}^{2} (u^2 - 1)\, du = \left(\frac{1}{3}u^3 - u\right)\Big|_{\sqrt{2}}^{2}$$

$$= \left(\frac{8}{3} - 2\right) - \left(\frac{2\sqrt{2}}{3} - \sqrt{2}\right) = \frac{2}{3} + \frac{\sqrt{2}}{3} = \frac{1}{3}(2 + \sqrt{2}).$$

65. Since $\frac{1}{4}\tan x\sec^4 x - \tan^3 x = \tan x\left(\frac{1}{4}\sec^4 x - (\sec^2 x - 1)\right) = \frac{1}{4}\tan x(\sec^4 x - 4\sec^2 x + 4) = \frac{1}{4}\tan x(\sec^2 x - 2)^2 \geq 0$ on $[0, \pi/3]$, we have

$$A = \int_0^{\pi/3}\left(\frac{1}{4}\tan x\sec^4 x - \tan^3 x\right)dx = \int_0^{\pi/3}\left[\frac{1}{4}\tan x(\tan^2 x + 1)\sec^2 x - \tan x(\sec^2 x - 1)\right]dx$$

$$= \int_0^{\pi/3}\left(\frac{1}{4}\tan^3 x\sec^2 x - \frac{3}{4}\tan x\sec^2 x + \tan x\right)dx = \left(\frac{1}{16}\tan^4 x - \frac{3}{8}\tan^2 x - \ln|\cos x|\right)\Big|_0^{\pi/3}$$

$$= \left(\frac{9}{16} - \frac{9}{8} - \ln\frac{1}{2}\right) - \ln 1 = \ln 2 - \frac{9}{16}.$$

7.3 Trigonometric Substitutions

1. $x = \frac{1}{2}\sin u$, $dx = \frac{1}{2}\cos u\,du$; if $x = 0$ then $u = 0$, and if $x = \frac{1}{2}$ then $u = \pi/2$;

$$\int_0^{1/2}\sqrt{1 - 4x^2}\,dx = \int_0^{\pi/2}\sqrt{1 - \sin^2 u}\left(\frac{1}{2}\cos u\right)du = \frac{1}{2}\int_0^{\pi/2}\cos^2 u\,du$$

$$= \frac{1}{4}\int_0^{\pi/2}(1 + \cos 2u)\,du = \frac{1}{4}\left(u + \frac{1}{2}\sin 2u\right)\Big|_0^{\pi/2} = \frac{\pi}{8}.$$

2. $x = 4\sin u$, $dx = 4\cos u\,du$; if $x = 0$ then $u = 0$, and if $x = 4$ then $u = \pi/2$;

$$\int_0^4\sqrt{16 - x^2}\,dx = \int_0^{\pi/2}\sqrt{16(1 - \sin^2 u)}\,(4\cos u)\,du = 16\int_0^{\pi/2}\cos^2 u\,du$$

$$= 8\int_0^{\pi/2}(1 + \cos 2u)\,du = 8\left(u + \frac{1}{2}\sin 2u\right)\Big|_0^{\pi/2} = 4\pi.$$

3. $x = 2\sin u$, $dx = 2\cos u\,du$; if $x = -2$ then $u = -\pi/2$, and if $x = 2$ then $u = \pi/2$;

$$\int_{-2}^{2}\sqrt{1 - \frac{x^2}{4}}\,dx = \int_{-\pi/2}^{\pi/2}\sqrt{1 - \sin^2 u}\,(2\cos u)\,du = 2\int_{-\pi/2}^{\pi/2}\cos^2 u\,du$$

$$= \int_{-\pi/2}^{\pi/2}(1 + \cos 2u)\,du = \left(u + \frac{1}{2}\sin 2u\right)\Big|_{-\pi/2}^{\pi/2} = \pi.$$

4. $2x - 1 = \tan u$, $dx = \frac{1}{2}\sec^2 u\,du$, $\sqrt{1 + (2x - 1)^2} = \sec u$; by (7) in Section 7.2,

$$\int\sqrt{1 + (2x - 1)^2}\,dx = \int\sqrt{1 + \tan^2 u}\left(\frac{1}{2}\sec^2 u\right)du = \frac{1}{2}\int\sec^3 u\,du$$

$$= \frac{1}{4}\sec u\tan u + \frac{1}{4}\ln|\sec u + \tan u| + C = \frac{1}{4}\sqrt{1 + (2x - 1)^2}\,(2x - 1) + \frac{1}{4}\ln\left|\sqrt{1 + (2x - 1)^2} + (2x - 1)\right| + C.$$

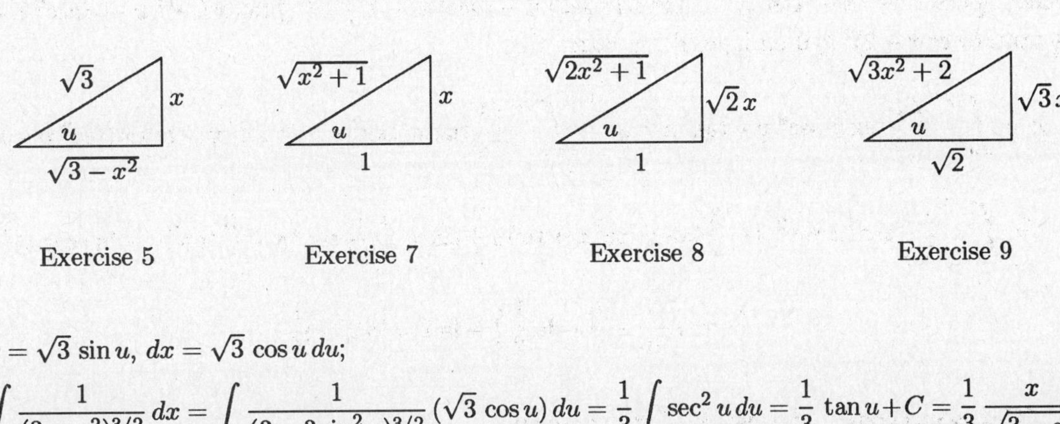

5. $x = \sqrt{3}\sin u,\ dx = \sqrt{3}\cos u\,du;$

$$\int \frac{1}{(3-x^2)^{3/2}}\,dx = \int \frac{1}{(3-3\sin^2 u)^{3/2}}(\sqrt{3}\cos u)\,du = \frac{1}{3}\int \sec^2 u\,du = \frac{1}{3}\tan u + C = \frac{1}{3}\frac{x}{\sqrt{3-x^2}} + C.$$

6. $t = 4\sec u,\ dt = 4\sec u\tan u\,du$; if $t = 4\sqrt{2}$ then $u = \pi/4$, and if $t = 8$ then $u = \pi/3$;

$$\int_{4\sqrt{2}}^{8} \frac{1}{(t^2-16)^{3/2}}\,dt = \int_{\pi/4}^{\pi/3} \frac{1}{(16\sec^2 u - 16)^{3/2}}\,4\sec u\tan u\,du = \frac{1}{16}\int_{\pi/4}^{\pi/3} \frac{\sec u\tan u}{\tan^3 u}\,du$$

$$= \frac{1}{16}\int_{\pi/4}^{\pi/3} \sec u\cot^2 u\,du = \frac{1}{16}\int_{\pi/4}^{\pi/3} \frac{1}{\cos u}\frac{\cos^2 u}{\sin^2 u}\,du = \frac{1}{16}\int_{\pi/4}^{\pi/3} \frac{\cos u}{\sin^2 u}\,du$$

$$= \frac{1}{16}\left(-\frac{1}{\sin u}\right)\bigg|_{\pi/4}^{\pi/3} = -\frac{1}{16}\left(\frac{1}{\sqrt{3}/2} - \frac{1}{\sqrt{2}/2}\right) = \frac{1}{8}\left(\frac{1}{\sqrt{2}} - \frac{1}{\sqrt{3}}\right).$$

7. $x = \tan u,\ dx = \sec^2 u\,du;\ \sin u = x/\sqrt{x^2+1};$

$$\int \frac{1}{(x^2+1)^{3/2}}\,dx = \int \frac{1}{(\tan^2 u+1)^{3/2}}\sec^2 u\,du = \int \frac{\sec^2 u}{\sec^3 u}\,du = \int \cos u\,du = \sin u + C = \frac{x}{\sqrt{x^2+1}} + C.$$

8. $x = (1/\sqrt{2})\tan u,\ dx = (1/\sqrt{2})\sec^2 u\,du;\ \sin u = (\sqrt{2}\,x)/\sqrt{2x^2+1};$

$$\int \frac{1}{(2x^2+1)^{3/2}}\,dx = \int \frac{1}{(\tan^2 u+1)^{3/2}}\left(\frac{1}{\sqrt{2}}\sec^2 u\right)du$$

$$= \frac{1}{\sqrt{2}}\int \cos u\,du = \frac{1}{\sqrt{2}}\sin u + C = \frac{1}{\sqrt{2}}\frac{\sqrt{2}\,x}{\sqrt{2x^2+1}} + C = \frac{x}{\sqrt{2x^2+1}} + C.$$

9. $x = \sqrt{\frac{2}{3}}\tan u,\ dx = \sqrt{\frac{2}{3}}\sec^2 u\,du;\ \sin u = (\sqrt{3}\,x)/\sqrt{3x^2+2};$

$$\int \frac{1}{(3x^2+2)^{5/2}}\,dx = \int \frac{1}{(2\tan^2 u+2)^{5/2}}\left(\sqrt{\frac{2}{3}}\sec^2 u\right)du$$

$$= \frac{1}{4\sqrt{3}}\int \frac{1}{\sec^5 u}\sec^2 u\,du = \frac{1}{4\sqrt{3}}\int \cos^3 u\,du = \frac{1}{4\sqrt{3}}\int (1-\sin^2 u)\cos u\,du$$

$$= \frac{1}{4\sqrt{3}}\left(\sin u - \frac{1}{3}\sin^3 u\right) + C = \frac{x}{4\sqrt{3x^2+2}} - \frac{x^3}{4(3x^2+2)^{3/2}} + C.$$

Thus

$$\int_0^1 \frac{1}{(3x^2+2)^{5/2}}\,dx = \left(\frac{x}{4\sqrt{3x^2+2}} - \frac{x^3}{4(3x^2+2)^{3/2}}\right)\bigg|_0^1 = \frac{\sqrt{5}}{25}.$$

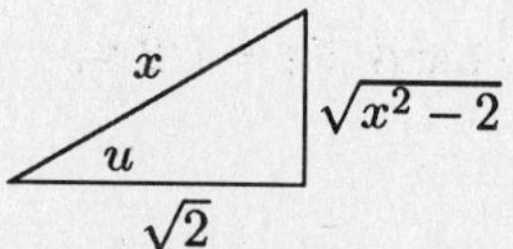

Exercise 10

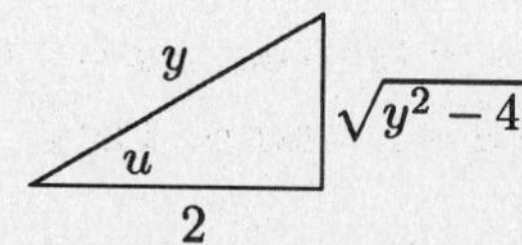

Exercise 12

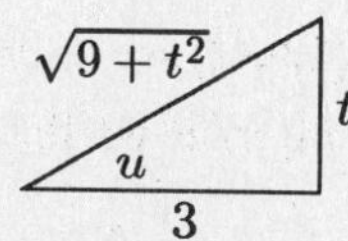

Exercise 13

10. $x = \sqrt{2}\sec u$, $dx = \sqrt{2}\sec u \tan u\, du$;

$$\int \frac{x^2}{(x^2-2)^{5/2}}\,dx = \int \frac{2\sec^2 u}{(2\sec^2 u - 2)^{5/2}}\sqrt{2}\sec u \tan u\, du$$

$$= \int \frac{2\sqrt{2}\sec^3 u}{2^{5/2}\tan^5 u}\tan u\, du = \frac{1}{2}\int \frac{\sec^3 u}{\tan^4 u}\,du = \frac{1}{2}\int \frac{\cos u}{\sin^4 u}\,du = -\frac{1}{6\sin^3 u} + C.$$

Now $x = \sqrt{2}\sec u$ implies that $\sin u = \sqrt{x^2-2}/x$. Thus

$$\int \frac{x^2}{(x^2-2)^{5/2}}\,dx = -\frac{1}{6\sin^3 u} + C = \frac{-x^3}{6(x^2-2)^{3/2}} + C.$$

11. $x = 2\sec u$, $dx = 2\sec u \tan u\, du$; if $x = 2$ then $u = 0$, and if $x = 2\sqrt{2}$ then $u = \pi/4$;

$$\int_2^{2\sqrt{2}} \frac{\sqrt{x^2-4}}{x}\,dx = \int_0^{\pi/4} \frac{\sqrt{4\sec^2 u - 4}}{2\sec u}(2\sec u \tan u)\,du$$

$$= 2\int_0^{\pi/4} \tan^2 u\, du = 2\int_0^{\pi/4} (\sec^2 u - 1)\,du = 2(\tan u - u)\Big|_0^{\pi/4} = 2 - \frac{\pi}{2}.$$

12. $y = 2\sec u$, $dy = 2\sec u \tan u\, du$;

$$\int \frac{1}{(y^2-4)^{3/2}}\,dy = \int \frac{1}{(4\sec^2 u - 4)^{3/2}}2\sec u \tan u\, du$$

$$= \int \frac{1}{4}\frac{\sec u}{\tan^2 u}\,du = \frac{1}{4}\int \frac{\cos u}{\sin^2 u}\,du = \frac{-1}{4\sin u} + C.$$

Now $y = 2\sec u$ implies that $\sin u = \sqrt{y^2-4}/y$. Thus

$$\int \frac{1}{(y^2-4)^{3/2}}\,dy = \frac{-1}{4\sin u} + C = \frac{-y}{4\sqrt{y^2-4}} + C.$$

13. $t = 3\tan u$, $dt = 3\sec^2 u\, du$;

$$\int \frac{1}{(9+t^2)^2}\,dt = \int \frac{1}{(9+9\tan^2 u)^2}3\sec^2 u\, du = \frac{1}{27}\int \frac{\sec^2 u}{\sec^4 u}\,du$$

$$= \frac{1}{27}\int \cos^2 u\, du = \frac{1}{54}\int (1+\cos 2u)\,du = \frac{1}{54}\left(u + \frac{1}{2}\sin 2u\right) + C.$$

Now $t = 3\tan u$ implies that $u = \tan^{-1} t/3$, and from the figure, $\sin u = t/\sqrt{9+t^2}$ and $\cos u = 3/\sqrt{9+t^2}$, so that $\sin 2u = 2\sin u \cos u = 6t/(9+t^2)$. Then

$$\int \frac{1}{(9+t^2)^2}\,dt = \frac{1}{54}u + \frac{1}{108}\sin 2u + C = \frac{1}{54}\tan^{-1}\frac{t}{3} + \frac{t}{18(9+t^2)} + C.$$

14. $x = (1/\sqrt{2})\sec u$, $dx = (1/\sqrt{2})\sec u \tan u\, du$; if $x = 1$ then $u = \pi/4$ and if $x = \sqrt{2}$ then $u = \pi/3$; for u in $[\pi/4, \pi/3]$ we find that $\sqrt{\sec^2 u - 1} = \tan u$. Thus

$$\int_1^{\sqrt{2}} \frac{1}{\sqrt{2x^2-1}}\, dx = \int_{\pi/4}^{\pi/3} \frac{1}{\sqrt{\sec^2 u - 1}} \left(\frac{1}{\sqrt{2}} \sec u \tan u\right) du = \frac{1}{\sqrt{2}} \int_{\pi/4}^{\pi/3} \sec u\, du$$

$$= \frac{1}{\sqrt{2}} \ln|\sec u + \tan u|\Big|_{\pi/4}^{\pi/3} = \frac{1}{\sqrt{2}} \ln \frac{2+\sqrt{3}}{\sqrt{2}+1}.$$

15. $x = \frac{5}{2}\sin u$, $dx = \frac{5}{2}\cos u\, du$; if $x = 0$ then $u = 0$, and if $x = \frac{5}{4}$ then $u = \pi/6$;

$$\int_0^{5/4} \frac{1}{\sqrt{25-4x^2}}\, dx = \int_0^{\pi/6} \frac{1}{\sqrt{25 - 25\sin^2 u}} \left(\frac{5}{2}\cos u\right) du = \frac{1}{2}\int_0^{\pi/6} 1\, du = \frac{1}{2}u\Big|_0^{\pi/6} = \frac{1}{12}\pi.$$

16. $x = \sin u$, $dx = \cos u\, du$;

$$\int \frac{x^2}{\sqrt{1-x^2}}\, dx = \int \frac{\sin^2 u}{\sqrt{1-\sin^2 u}} \cos u\, du$$

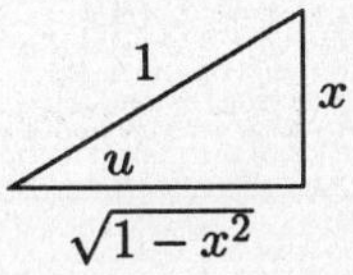

$$= \int \sin^2 u\, du = \frac{1}{2}\int (1 - \cos 2u)\, du = \frac{1}{2}\left(u - \frac{1}{2}\sin 2u\right) + C.$$

Now $x = \sin u$ implies that $u = \sin^{-1} x$. Next, from the figure we see that $\cos u = \sqrt{1-x^2}$, so that $\sin 2u = 2\sin u \cos u = 2x\sqrt{1-x^2}$. Thus

$$\int \frac{x^2}{\sqrt{1-x^2}}\, dx = \frac{1}{2}u - \frac{1}{4}\sin 2u + C = \frac{1}{2}\sin^{-1} x - \frac{1}{4}\left(2x\sqrt{1-x^2}\right) + C = \frac{1}{2}\sin^{-1} x - \frac{1}{2}x\sqrt{1-x^2} + C.$$

17. $$\int \frac{1}{\sqrt{4x^2+4x+2}}\, dx = \int \frac{1}{\sqrt{(4x^2+4x+1)+1}}\, dx = \int \frac{1}{\sqrt{(2x+1)^2+1}}\, dx$$

Let $2x + 1 = \tan u$, so that $2\, dx = \sec^2 u\, du$. Then

$$\int \frac{1}{\sqrt{(2x+1)^2+1}}\, dx = \int \frac{1}{\sqrt{\tan^2 u + 1}} \frac{1}{2} \sec^2 u\, du = \frac{1}{2}\int \sec u\, du = \frac{1}{2}\ln|\sec u + \tan u| + C.$$

Since $\sec u = \sqrt{\tan^2 u + 1} = \sqrt{(2x+1)^2+1} = \sqrt{4x^2+4x+2}$, we have

$$\int \frac{1}{\sqrt{4x^2+4x+2}}\, dx = \frac{1}{2}\ln\left|\sqrt{4x^2+4x+2} + (2x+1)\right| + C.$$

18. $x = \tan u$, $dx = \sec^2 u\, du$; if $x = 1$ then $u = \pi/4$, and if $x = \sqrt{3}$ then $u = \pi/3$;

$$\int_1^{\sqrt{3}} \frac{1}{\sqrt{1+x^2}}\, dx = \int_{\pi/4}^{\pi/3} \frac{1}{\sqrt{1+\tan^2 u}} \sec^2 u\, du = \int_{\pi/4}^{\pi/3} \sec u\, du = \ln|\sec u + \tan u|\Big|_{\pi/4}^{\pi/3} = \ln \frac{2+\sqrt{3}}{\sqrt{2}+1}.$$

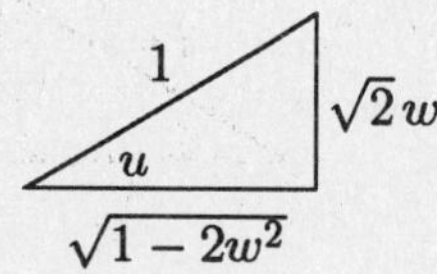

Exercise 19

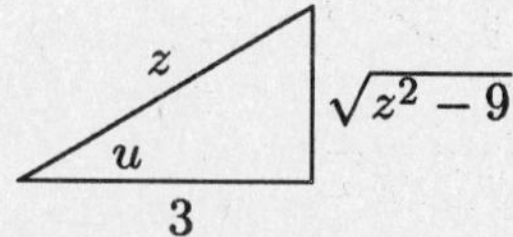

Exercise 22

19. $w = (1/\sqrt{2})\sin u$, $dw = (1/\sqrt{2})\cos u\, du$;

$$\int \frac{1}{(1-2w^2)^{5/2}}\,dw = \int \frac{1}{(1-\sin^2 u)^{5/2}}\left(\frac{1}{\sqrt{2}}\cos u\right)du = \frac{1}{\sqrt{2}}\int \sec^4 u\, du$$

$$= \frac{1}{\sqrt{2}}\int (\tan^2 u + 1)\sec^2 u\, du = \frac{1}{\sqrt{2}}\left(\frac{1}{3}\tan^3 u + \tan u\right) + C$$

$$= \frac{1}{\sqrt{2}}\left(\frac{1}{3}\frac{2\sqrt{2}\,w^3}{(1-2w^2)^{3/2}} + \frac{\sqrt{2}\,w}{(1-2w^2)^{1/2}}\right) + C = \frac{2w^3}{3(1-2w^2)^{3/2}} + \frac{w}{(1-2w^2)^{1/2}} + C.$$

20. $\displaystyle\int_{\sqrt{2}-2}^{(2\sqrt{3}/3)-2} \frac{1}{(t^2+4t+3)^{3/2}}\,dt = \int_{\sqrt{2}-2}^{(2\sqrt{3}/3)-2} \frac{1}{[(t+2)^2-1]^{3/2}}\,dt$

Let $t+2 = \sec u$, so that $dt = \sec u\,\tan u\, du$ and $1/[(t+2)^2-1]^{3/2} = 1/(\sec^2 u - 1)^{3/2} = 1/(\tan^3 u)$. If $t = (2\sqrt{3}/3) - 2$ then $\sec u = 2\sqrt{3}/3$, so $u = \pi/6$, and if $t = \sqrt{2}-2$ then $\sec u = \sqrt{2}$, so $u = \pi/4$.Thus

$$\int_{\sqrt{2}-2}^{(2\sqrt{3}/3)-2} \frac{1}{(t^2+4t+3)^{3/2}}\,dt = \int_{\pi/4}^{\pi/6} \frac{1}{\tan^3 u}(\sec u\,\tan u)\,du = \int_{\pi/4}^{\pi/6} \frac{\cos u}{\sin^2 u}\,du = -\frac{1}{\sin u}\bigg|_{\pi/4}^{\pi/6} = -2+\sqrt{2}.$$

21. $\displaystyle\int_0^1 \frac{1}{2x^2-2x+1}\,dx = \int_0^1 \frac{1}{2(x-\frac{1}{2})^2+\frac{1}{2}}\,dx$

Let $x - \frac{1}{2} = \frac{1}{2}\tan u$, so that $dx = \frac{1}{2}\sec^2 u\, du$; if $x = 0$ then $u = -\pi/4$, and if $x = 1$ then $u = \pi/4$. Then

$$\int_0^1 \frac{1}{2x^2-2x+1}\,dx = \int_0^1 \frac{1}{2(x-\frac{1}{2})^2+\frac{1}{2}}\,dx = \int_{-\pi/4}^{\pi/4} \frac{1}{\frac{1}{2}\tan^2 u + \frac{1}{2}}\left(\frac{1}{2}\sec^2 u\right)du = \int_{-\pi/4}^{\pi/4} 1\, du = \frac{\pi}{2}.$$

22. $z = 3\sec u$, $dz = 3\sec u\,\tan u\, du$;

$$\int \sqrt{z^2-9}\,dz = \int \sqrt{9\sec^2 u - 9}\,(3\sec u\,\tan u)\,du = \int 9\tan^2 u\,\sec u\, du$$

$$= 9\int (\sec^2 u - 1)\sec u\, du = 9\int \sec^3 u\, du - 9\int \sec u\, du.$$

By (6) and (7) of Section 7.2, $9\int \sec^3 u\, du - 9\int \sec u\, du = \frac{9}{2}\sec u\,\tan u + \frac{9}{2}\ln|\sec u + \tan u| - 9\ln|\sec u + \tan u| + C = \frac{9}{2}\sec u\,\tan u - \frac{9}{2}\ln|\sec u + \tan u| + C$. Now $z = 3\sec u$ implies that $\sec u = z/3$ and $\tan u = \sqrt{z^2-9}/3$. Thus

$$\int \sqrt{z^2-9}\,dz = \frac{9}{2}\sec u\,\tan u - \frac{9}{2}\ln|\sec u + \tan u| + C = \frac{z}{2}\sqrt{z^2-9} - \frac{9}{2}\ln\left|\frac{z}{3} + \frac{1}{3}\sqrt{z^2-9}\right| + C.$$

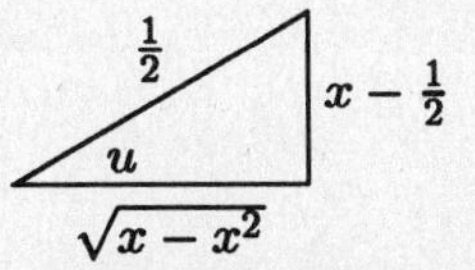

Exercise 23

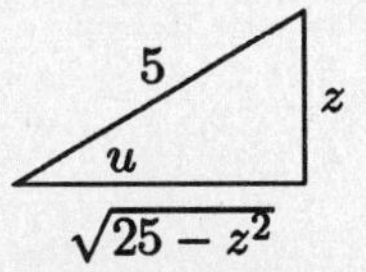

Exercise 24

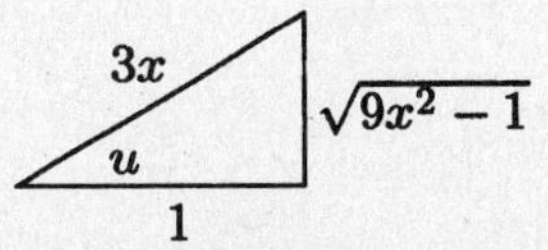

Exercise 25

23. $\int \sqrt{x-x^2}\,dx = \int \sqrt{\frac{1}{4}-\left(x-\frac{1}{2}\right)^2}\,dx.$

Let $x - \frac{1}{2} = \frac{1}{2}\sin u$, so that $dx = \frac{1}{2}\cos u\,du$. Then

$$\int \sqrt{\frac{1}{4}-\left(x-\frac{1}{2}\right)^2}\,dx = \int \sqrt{\frac{1}{4}-\frac{1}{4}\sin^2 u}\left(\frac{1}{2}\cos u\right)du$$

$$= \frac{1}{4}\int \cos^2 u\,du = \frac{1}{4}\int\left(\frac{1}{2}+\frac{1}{2}\cos 2u\right)du = \frac{1}{4}\left(\frac{1}{2}u+\frac{1}{4}\sin 2u\right)+C.$$

Now $x-\frac{1}{2} = \frac{1}{2}\sin u$ implies that $2x-1=\sin u$, so that $u = \sin^{-1}(2x-1)$. From the figure, we see that $\cos u = (\sqrt{x-x^2})/\frac{1}{2} = 2\sqrt{x-x^2}$, so that $\sin 2u = 2\sin u\cos u = [2(2x-1)][2\sqrt{x-x^2}] = 4(2x-1)\sqrt{x-x^2}$. Thus

$$\int \sqrt{x-x^2}\,dx = \int \sqrt{\frac{1}{4}-\left(x-\frac{1}{2}\right)^2}\,dx = \frac{1}{4}\left\{\frac{1}{2}\sin^{-1}(2x-1)+\frac{1}{4}\left[4(2x-1)(\sqrt{x-x^2})\right]\right\}+C$$

$$= \frac{1}{8}\sin^{-1}(2x-1)+\frac{1}{4}(2x-1)\sqrt{x-x^2}+C.$$

24. $z = 5\sin u$, $dz = 5\cos u\,du$;

$$\int \frac{\sqrt{25-z^2}}{z^2}\,dz = \int \frac{\sqrt{25-25\sin^2 u}}{25\sin^2 u}\,5\cos u\,du = \int \frac{\cos^2 u}{\sin^2 u}\,du$$

$$= \int \cot^2 u\,du = \int(\csc^2 -1)\,du = -\cot u - u + C.$$

Now $u = \sin^{-1} z/5$, and by the figure, $\cot u = (1/z)\sqrt{25-z^2}$. Thus

$$\int \frac{\sqrt{25-z^2}}{z^2}\,dz = -\frac{1}{z}\sqrt{25-z^2} - \sin^{-1}\frac{z}{5}+C.$$

25. $x = \frac{1}{3}\sec u$, $dx = \frac{1}{3}\sec u\tan u\,du$;

$$\int \frac{x^2}{\sqrt{9x^2-1}}\,dx = \int \frac{\frac{1}{9}\sec^2 u}{\sqrt{\sec^2 u - 1}}\frac{1}{3}\sec u\tan u\,du = \int \frac{1}{27}\sec^3 u\,du.$$

By (7) of Section 7.2, $\int \frac{1}{27}\sec^3 u\,du = \frac{1}{54}\sec u\tan u + \frac{1}{54}\ln|\sec u+\tan u|+C$. Now $x = \frac{1}{3}\sec u$ implies that $\sec u = 3x$ and $\tan u = \sqrt{9x^2-1}$. Thus

$$\int \frac{x^2}{\sqrt{9x^2-1}}\,dx = \frac{1}{54}\sec u\tan u + \frac{1}{54}\ln|\sec u+\tan u|+C = \frac{1}{18}x\sqrt{9x^2-1}+\frac{1}{54}\ln\left|3x+\sqrt{9x^2-1}\right|+C.$$

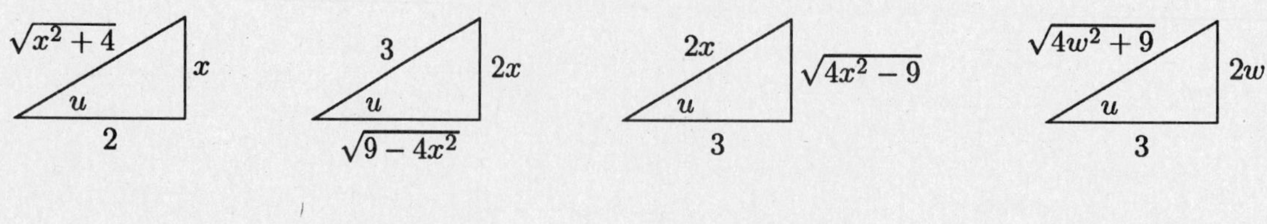

Exercise 27 Exercise 28 Exercise 29 Exercise 30

26. $x = 2\sec u$, $dx = 2\sec u\,\tan u\,du$; if $x = -4/\sqrt{3}$, then $\sec u = -2/\sqrt{3}$, so $u = 7\pi/6$, and if $x = -2\sqrt{2}$, then $\sec u = -\sqrt{2}$ so $u = 5\pi/4$;

$$\int_{-4/\sqrt{3}}^{-2\sqrt{2}} \frac{1}{x\sqrt{x^2-4}}\,dx = \int_{7\pi/6}^{5\pi/4} \frac{1}{2\sec u\sqrt{4\sec^2 u-4}}\,2\sec u\,\tan u\,du = \int_{7\pi/6}^{5\pi/4} \frac{1}{2}\,du = \frac{\pi}{24}.$$

27. $x = 2\tan u$, $dx = 2\sec^2 u\,du$, $\csc u = \sqrt{x^2+4}/x$, $\cot u = 2/x$;

$$\int \frac{1}{x\sqrt{x^2+4}}\,dx = \int \frac{1}{2\tan u\sqrt{4\tan^2 u+4}}(2\sec^2 u)\,du = \frac{1}{2}\int \frac{\sec u}{\tan u}\,du$$

$$= \frac{1}{2}\int \csc u\,du = \frac{-1}{2}\ln|\csc u + \cot u| + C = \frac{-1}{2}\ln\left|\frac{\sqrt{x^2+4}}{x} + \frac{2}{x}\right| + C.$$

28. $x = \frac{3}{2}\sin u$, $dx = \frac{3}{2}\cos u\,du$, $\cot u = \sqrt{9-4x^2}/(2x)$;

$$\int \frac{1}{x^2\sqrt{9-4x^2}}\,dx = \frac{4}{9}\int \frac{1}{\sin^2 u\sqrt{9-9\sin^2 u}}\left(\frac{3}{2}\cos u\right)du$$

$$= \frac{2}{9}\int \csc^2 u\,du = \frac{-2}{9}\cot u + C = \frac{-\sqrt{9-4x^2}}{9x} + C.$$

29. $x = \frac{3}{2}\sec u$, $dx = \frac{3}{2}\sec u\,\tan u\,du$;

$$\int \frac{1}{x^2\sqrt{4x^2-9}}\,dx = \int \frac{1}{\frac{9}{4}\sec^2 u\sqrt{9\sec^2 u-9}}\,\frac{3}{2}\sec u\,\tan u\,du$$

$$= \int \frac{2}{9\sec u}\,du = \frac{2}{9}\int \cos u\,du = \frac{2}{9}\sin u + C.$$

Now $x = \frac{3}{2}\sec u$ implies that $\sin u = \sqrt{4x^2-9}/(2x)$. Thus

$$\int \frac{1}{x^2\sqrt{4x^2-9}}\,dx = \frac{2}{9}\sin u + C = \frac{\sqrt{4x^2-9}}{9x} + C.$$

30. $w = \frac{3}{2}\tan u$, $dw = \frac{3}{2}\sec^2 u\,du$; $\csc u = \sqrt{4w^2+9}/(2w)$;

$$\int \frac{1}{w^2\sqrt{4w^2+9}}\,dw = \frac{4}{9}\int \frac{1}{\tan^2 u\sqrt{9\tan^2 u+9}}\left(\frac{3}{2}\sec^2 u\right)du$$

$$= \frac{2}{9}\int \frac{\cos u}{\sin^2 u}\,du = \frac{-2}{9}\,\frac{1}{\sin u} + C = \frac{-2}{9}\csc u + C = \frac{-\sqrt{4w^2+9}}{9w} + C.$$

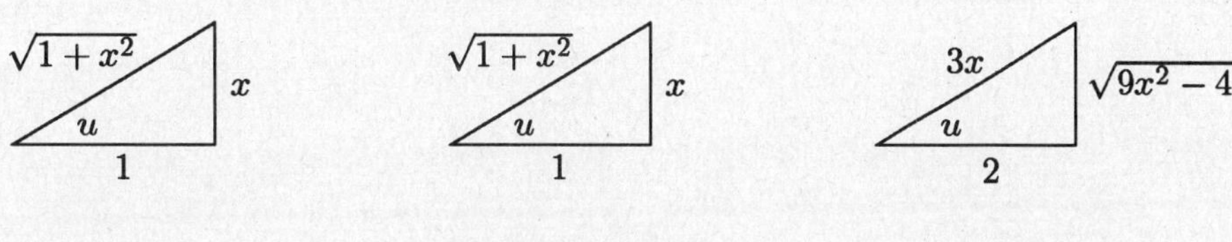

Exercise 31 Exercise 32 Exercise 33

31. $x = \tan u$, $dx = \sec^2 u\,du$, $\sec u = \sqrt{1+x^2}$; from (7) in Section 7.2 we find that

$$\int \frac{x^2}{\sqrt{1+x^2}}\,dx = \int \frac{\tan^2 u}{\sqrt{1+\tan^2 u}}\sec^2 u\,du = \int \tan^2 u \sec u\,du$$

$$= \int (\sec^2 u - 1)\sec u\,du = \int (\sec^3 u - \sec u)\,du$$

$$= \left(\frac{1}{2}\sec u \tan u + \frac{1}{2}\ln|\sec u + \tan u|\right) - \ln|\sec u + \tan u| + C$$

$$= \frac{1}{2}\sec u \tan u - \frac{1}{2}\ln|\sec u + \tan u| + C = \frac{1}{2}x\sqrt{1+x^2} - \frac{1}{2}\ln\left|\sqrt{1+x^2}+x\right| + C.$$

32. $x = \tan u$, $dx = \sec^2 u\,du$, $\sec u = \sqrt{1+x^2}$, $\sin u = x/\sqrt{1+x^2}$;

$$\int \frac{x^2}{(1+x^2)^{3/2}}\,dx = \int \frac{\tan^2 u}{(1+\tan^2 u)^{3/2}}\sec^2 u\,du = \int \frac{\tan^2 u}{\sec u}\,du$$

$$= \int \frac{\sec^2 u - 1}{\sec u}\,du = \int (\sec u - \cos u)\,du = \ln|\sec u + \tan u| - \sin u + C$$

$$= \ln\left|\sqrt{1+x^2}+x\right| - \frac{x}{\sqrt{1+x^2}} + C.$$

33. $x = \frac{2}{3}\sec u$, $dx = \frac{2}{3}\sec u \tan u\,du$;

$$\int \frac{1}{(9x^2-4)^{5/2}}\,dx = \int \frac{1}{(4\sec^2 u - 4)^{5/2}}\frac{2}{3}\sec u \tan u\,du = \int \frac{\sec u \tan u}{48\tan^5 u}\,du$$

$$= \frac{1}{48}\int \frac{\sec u}{\tan^4 u}\,du = \frac{1}{48}\int \frac{\cos^3 u}{\sin^4 u}\,du = \frac{1}{48}\int \frac{1-\sin^2 u}{\sin^4 u}\cos u\,du$$

$$= \frac{1}{48}\int \left(\frac{1}{\sin^4 u} - \frac{1}{\sin^2 u}\right)\cos u\,du = \frac{1}{48}\left(\frac{-1}{3\sin^3 u} + \frac{1}{\sin u}\right) + C.$$

Now $x = \frac{2}{3}\sec u$ implies that $\sin u = \sqrt{9x^2-4}/(3x)$. Thus

$$\int \frac{1}{(9x^2-4)^{5/2}}\,dx = \frac{1}{48}\left(\frac{-1}{3\sin^2 u} + \frac{1}{\sin u}\right) + C = \frac{-3x^3}{16(9x^2-4)^{3/2}} + \frac{x}{16(9x^2-4)^{1/2}} + C.$$

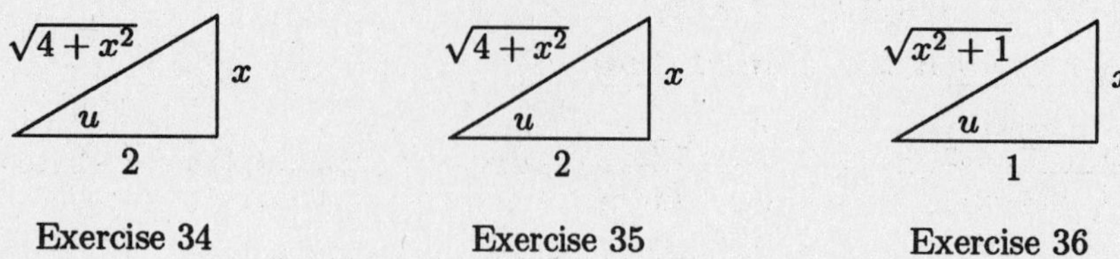

Exercise 34 Exercise 35 Exercise 36

34. $x = 2\tan u$, $dx = 2\sec^2 u\,du$, $\csc u = \sqrt{4+x^2}/x$, $\cot u = 2/x$; by Exercise 28 of Section 7.2, $\int \csc^3 x\,dx = -\frac{1}{2}\csc x\cot x - \frac{1}{2}\ln|\csc x + \cot x| + C$; thus

$$\int \frac{\sqrt{4+x^2}}{x}\,dx = \int \frac{\sqrt{4+4\tan^2 u}}{8\tan^3 u}(2\sec^2 u)\,du = \frac{1}{2}\int \frac{\cos^3 u}{\sin^3 u}\frac{1}{\cos^3 u}\,du$$

$$= \frac{1}{2}\int \csc^3 u\,du = \frac{-1}{4}\csc u\cot u - \frac{1}{4}\ln|\csc u + \cot u| + C$$

$$= \frac{-1}{4}\frac{\sqrt{4+x^2}}{x}\frac{2}{x} - \frac{1}{4}\ln\left|\frac{\sqrt{4+x^2}}{x} + \frac{2}{x}\right| + C = \frac{-\sqrt{4+x^2}}{2x^2} - \frac{1}{4}\ln\left|\frac{\sqrt{4+x^2}+2}{x}\right| + C.$$

35. $x = 2\tan u$, $dx = 2\sec^2 u\,du$; $\sec u = \sqrt{4+x^2}/2$; from (7) in Section 7.2 we have

$$\int \sqrt{4+x^2}\,dx = \int \sqrt{4+4\tan^2 u}\,(2\sec^2 u)\,du = 4\int \sec^3 u\,du$$

$$= 2\sec u\tan u + 2\ln|\sec u + \tan u| + C = \frac{x\sqrt{4+x^2}}{2} + 2\ln\left|\frac{\sqrt{4+x^2}}{2} + \frac{x}{2}\right| + C.$$

36. $x = \tan u$, $dx = \sec^2 u\,du$; $\sin u = x/\sqrt{x^2+1}$;

$$\int \frac{\sqrt{x^2+1}}{x^4}\,dx = \int \frac{\sec u}{\tan^4 u}\sec^2 u\,du = \int \frac{\cos u}{\sin^4 u}\,du.$$

Let $v = \sin u$, so that $dv = \cos u\,du$. Then

$$\int \frac{\cos u}{\sin^4 u}\,du = \int \frac{1}{v^4}\,dv = -\frac{1}{3v^3} + C = -\frac{1}{3\sin^3 u} + C = -\frac{(x^2+1)^{3/2}}{3x^3} + C.$$

37. $x = 3\sec u$, $dx = 3\sec u\tan u\,du$; if $x = 3\sqrt{2}$ then $u = \pi/4$, and if $x = 6$ then $u = \pi/3$. Thus

$$\int_{3\sqrt{2}}^{6} \frac{1}{x^4\sqrt{x^2-9}}\,dx = \int_{\pi/4}^{\pi/3} \frac{1}{(3\sec u)^4\sqrt{9\sec^2 u - 9}}3\sec u\tan u\,du = \int_{\pi/4}^{\pi/3} \frac{1}{81\sec^3 u}\,du$$

$$= \int_{\pi/4}^{\pi/3} \frac{1}{81}\cos^3 u\,du = \frac{1}{81}\int_{\pi/4}^{\pi/3} \cos u\,(1-\sin^2 u)\,du.$$

Let $v = \sin u$, so that $dv = \cos u\,du$. If $u = \pi/4$ then $v = \sqrt{2}/2$, and if $u = \pi/3$ then $v = \sqrt{3}/2$. Thus

$$\frac{1}{81}\int_{\pi/4}^{\pi/3} \cos u\,(1-\sin^2 u)\,du = \frac{1}{81}\int_{\sqrt{2}/2}^{\sqrt{3}/2} (1-v^2)\,dv = \frac{1}{81}\left(v - \frac{1}{3}v^3\right)\Bigg|_{\sqrt{2}/2}^{\sqrt{3}/2}$$

$$= \frac{1}{81}\left[\left(\frac{\sqrt{3}}{2} - \frac{1}{3}\frac{3\sqrt{3}}{8}\right) - \left(\frac{\sqrt{2}}{2} - \frac{1}{3}\frac{\sqrt{2}}{4}\right)\right] = \frac{1}{81}\left(\frac{3\sqrt{3}}{8} - \frac{5\sqrt{2}}{12}\right).$$

38. $\displaystyle\int \frac{2x-3}{\sqrt{4x-x^2-3}}\,dx = \int \frac{2(x-2)+1}{\sqrt{1-(x-2)^2}}\,dx$

Let $x-2=\sin u$, so that $dx = \cos u\,du$. Then

$$\int \frac{2(x-2)+1}{\sqrt{1-(x-2)^2}}\,dx = \int \frac{2\sin u+1}{\sqrt{1-\sin^2 u}}\cos u\,du = \int (2\sin u+1)\,du = -2\cos u + u + C.$$

Since $x-2=\sin u$, we have $\cos u = \sqrt{1-(x-2)^2} = \sqrt{4x-x^2-3}$, and also $u = \sin^{-1}(x-2)$. Thus

$$\int \frac{2x-3}{\sqrt{4x-x^2-3}}\,dx = -2\cos u + u + C = -2\sqrt{4x-x^2-3} + \sin^{-1}(x-2) + C.$$

39. $\displaystyle\int \frac{x}{\sqrt{2x^2+12x+19}}\,dx = \int \frac{x}{\sqrt{2(x^2+6x+9)+1}}\,dx = \int \frac{x}{\sqrt{2(x+3)^2+1}}\,dx$

Let $\sqrt{2}\,(x+3)=\tan u$, so that $\sqrt{2}\,dx = \sec^2 u\,du$ and $x = (1/\sqrt{2})\tan u - 3$. Then

$$\int \frac{x}{\sqrt{2(x+3)^2+1}}\,dx = \int \frac{(1/\sqrt{2})\tan u - 3}{\sqrt{\tan^2 u+1}}\,\frac{1}{\sqrt{2}}\sec^2 u\,du = \frac{1}{2}\int (\tan u - 3\sqrt{2})\sec u\,du$$

$$= \frac{1}{2}\int \tan u\sec u\,du - \frac{3}{2}\sqrt{2}\int \sec u\,du = \frac{1}{2}\sec u - \frac{3}{2}\sqrt{2}\ln|\sec u + \tan u| + C.$$

Since $\sqrt{2}\,(x+3)=\tan u$, we have $\sec u = \sqrt{[\sqrt{2}\,(x+3)]^2+1} = \sqrt{2x^2+12x+19}$, and thus

$$\int \frac{x}{\sqrt{2x^2+12x+19}}\,dx = \frac{1}{2}\sqrt{2x^2+12x+19} - \frac{3}{2}\sqrt{2}\ln\left|\sqrt{2x^2+12x+19} + \sqrt{2}\,(x+3)\right| + C.$$

40. $\displaystyle\int \frac{1}{(w^2+2w+5)^{3/2}}\,dw = \int \frac{1}{(w^2+2w+1+4)^{3/2}}\,dw = \int \frac{1}{[(w+1)^2+4]^{3/2}}\,dw$

Let $w+1 = 2\tan u$, so that $dw = 2\sec^2 u\,du$. Then

$$\int \frac{1}{[(w+1)^2+4]^{3/2}}\,dw = \int \frac{1}{[4\tan^2 u+4]^{3/2}}\,2\sec^2 u\,du = \int \frac{2\sec^2 u}{8\sec^3 u}\,du = \frac{1}{4}\int \cos u\,du = \frac{1}{4}\sin u + C.$$

From the figure, $\sin u = (w+1)/\sqrt{w^2+2w+5}$. Thus

$$\int \frac{1}{(w^2+2w+5)^{3/2}}\,dw = \frac{1}{4}\,\frac{w+1}{\sqrt{w^2+2w+5}} + C.$$

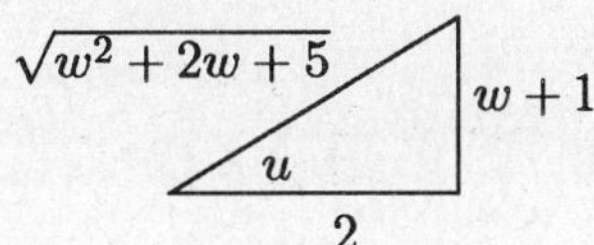

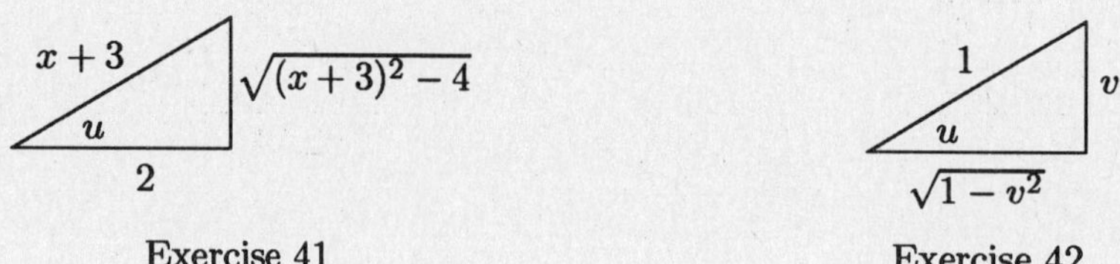

Exercise 41 Exercise 42

41. $\displaystyle\int \sqrt{x^2+6x+5}\,dx = \int \sqrt{(x+3)^2-4}\,dx$

Let $x+3 = 2\sec u$, so that $dx = 2\sec u\,\tan u\,du$;

$$\int \sqrt{(x+3)^2-4}\,dx = \int \sqrt{4\sec^2 u - 4}\,(2\sec u\,\tan u)\,du$$

$$= \int 4\tan^2 u\,\sec u\,du = 4\int(\sec^2 u - 1)\,\sec u\,du = 4\int \sec^3 u\,du - 4\int \sec u\,du.$$

By (6) and (7) of Section 7.2,

$$4\int \sec^3 u\,du - 4\int \sec u\,du = 2\sec u\,\tan u + 2\ln|\sec u + \tan u| - 4\ln|\sec u + \tan u| + C$$

$$= 2\sec u\,\tan u - 2\ln|\sec u + \tan u| + C.$$

Now $x+3 = 2\sec u$ implies that $\sec u = (x+3)/2$ and $\tan u = \sqrt{x^2+6x+5}/2$. Thus

$$\int \sqrt{x^2+6x+5}\,dx = 2\sec u\,\tan u - 2\ln|\sec u + \tan u| + C$$

$$= \frac{x+3}{2}\sqrt{x^2+6x+5} - 2\ln\left|\frac{x+3}{2} + \frac{1}{2}\sqrt{x^2+6x+5}\right| + C.$$

42. Let $v = e^w$, so that $dv = e^w\,dw$. Then

$$\int \frac{e^{3w}}{\sqrt{1-e^{2w}}}\,dw = \int \frac{v^2}{\sqrt{1-v^2}}\,dv.$$

Let $v = \sin u$, so that $dv = \cos u\,du$. Then

$$\int \frac{v^2}{\sqrt{1-v^2}}\,dv = \int \frac{\sin^2 u}{\sqrt{1-\sin^2 u}}\cos u\,du = \int \sin^2 u\,du$$

$$= \int\left(\frac{1}{2} - \frac{1}{2}\cos 2u\right)du = \frac{1}{2}u - \frac{1}{4}\sin 2u + C = \frac{1}{2}u - \frac{1}{2}\sin u\,\cos u + C.$$

Since $v = \sin u$, we have $u = \sin^{-1} v$. From the figure, $\cos u = \sqrt{1-v^2}$. Thus

$$\int \frac{e^{3w}}{\sqrt{1-e^{2w}}}\,dw = \frac{1}{2}u - \frac{1}{2}\sin u\,\cos u + C = \frac{1}{2}\sin^{-1} v - \frac{1}{2}v\sqrt{1-v^2} + C = \frac{1}{2}\sin^{-1} e^w - \frac{1}{2}e^w\sqrt{1-e^{2w}} + C.$$

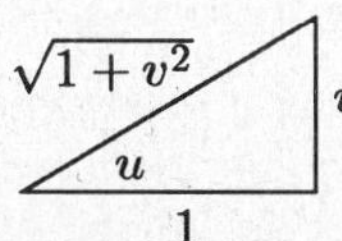

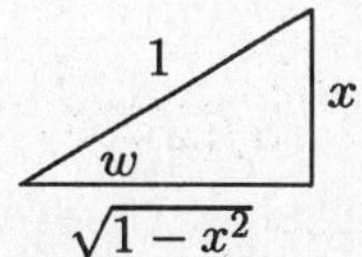

Exercise 43

Exercise 45

43. Let $v = e^w$, so that $dv = e^w\,dw$. Then $\int e^w\sqrt{1+e^{2w}}\,dw = \int \sqrt{1+v^2}\,dv$. Let $v = \tan u$, so that $dv = \sec^2 u\,du$. Then $\int \sqrt{1+v^2}\,dv = \int \sqrt{1+\tan^2 u}\,(\sec^2 u)\,du = \int \sec^3 u\,du$, and by (7) of Section 7.2, $\int \sec^3 u\,du = \frac{1}{2}\sec u\,\tan u + \frac{1}{2}\ln|\sec u + \tan u| + C$. By the figure, $\sec u = \sqrt{1+v^2}$, so that

$$\int e^w\sqrt{1+e^{2w}}\,dw = \int \sqrt{1+v^2}\,dv = \frac{v}{2}\sqrt{1+v^2} + \frac{1}{2}\ln\left|\sqrt{1+v^2}+v\right| + C$$

$$= \frac{1}{2}e^w\sqrt{1+e^{2w}} + \frac{1}{2}\ln\left|\sqrt{1+e^{2w}}+e^w\right| + C.$$

44. For integration by parts, let $u = \sec^{-1} x$, $dv = dx$, so that $du = [1/(x\sqrt{x^2-1})]\,dx$ and $v = x$. Then

$$\int_{\sqrt{2}}^{2} \sec^{-1} x\,dx = x\sec^{-1} x\Big|_{\sqrt{2}}^{2} - \int_{\sqrt{2}}^{2}\frac{x}{x\sqrt{x^2-1}}\,dx = 2\sec^{-1}2 - \sqrt{2}\sec^{-1}\sqrt{2} - \int_{\sqrt{2}}^{2}\frac{1}{\sqrt{x^2-1}}\,dx.$$

For $\int_{\sqrt{2}}^{2}(1/\sqrt{x^2-1})\,dx$ let $x = \sec u$, so that $dx = \sec u\,\tan u\,du$. If $x = \sqrt{2}$ then $\sec u = \sqrt{2}$, so $u = \pi/4$, and if $x = 2$ then $\sec u = 2$, so $u = \pi/3$. Thus

$$\int_{\sqrt{2}}^{2}\frac{1}{\sqrt{x^2-1}}\,dx = \int_{\pi/4}^{\pi/3}\frac{1}{\sqrt{\sec^2 u - 1}}\sec u\,\tan u\,du = \int_{\pi/4}^{\pi/3}\sec u\,du$$

$$= \ln|\sec u + \tan u|\Big|_{\pi/4}^{\pi/3} = \ln|2+\sqrt{3}| - \ln|\sqrt{2}+1| = \ln\frac{2+\sqrt{3}}{\sqrt{2}+1}.$$

Therefore

$$\int_{\sqrt{2}}^{2}\sec^{-1} x\,dx = 2\sec^{-1}2 - \sqrt{2}\sec^{-1}\sqrt{2} - \ln\frac{2+\sqrt{3}}{\sqrt{2}+1} = \frac{2}{3}\pi - \sqrt{2}\frac{\pi}{4} - \ln\frac{2+\sqrt{3}}{\sqrt{2}+1}.$$

45. For integration by parts, let $u = \sin^{-1} x$, $dv = x\,dx$, so that $du = (1/\sqrt{1-x^2})\,dx$, $v = \frac{1}{2}x^2$. Then

$$\int x\sin^{-1} x\,dx = \frac{1}{2}x^2\sin^{-1} x - \int\frac{x^2/2}{\sqrt{1-x^2}}\,dx = \frac{1}{2}x^2\sin^{-1} x - \frac{1}{2}\int\frac{x^2}{\sqrt{1-x^2}}\,dx.$$

For $\int(x^2/\sqrt{1-x^2})\,dx$ let $x = \sin w$, so that $dx = \cos w\,dw$. Then

$$\int\frac{x^2}{\sqrt{1-x^2}}\,dx = \int\frac{\sin^2 w}{\sqrt{1-\sin^2 w}}\cos w\,dw = \int\sin^2 w\,dw$$

$$= \int\left(\frac{1}{2} - \frac{1}{2}\cos 2w\right)dw = \frac{1}{2}w - \frac{1}{4}\sin 2w + C_1 = \frac{1}{2}w - \frac{1}{2}\sin w\,\cos w + C_1.$$

Now $x = \sin w$, so from the figure, $\cos w = \sqrt{1-x^2}$, and thus $\int(x^2/\sqrt{1-x^2})\,dx = \frac{1}{2}w - \frac{1}{2}\sin w\,\cos w + C_1 = \frac{1}{2}\sin^{-1} x - \frac{1}{2}x\sqrt{1-x^2} + C_1$. Consequently $\int x\sin^{-1} x\,dx = \frac{1}{2}x^2\sin^{-1} x - \frac{1}{4}\sin^{-1} x + \frac{1}{4}x\sqrt{1-x^2} + C$.

46. a. $x = \cos 2u$, $dx = -2\sin 2u\,du$;

$$\int \left(\frac{1-x}{1+x}\right)^{1/2} dx = \int \left(\frac{1-\cos 2u}{1+\cos 2u}\right)^{1/2} (-2\sin 2u)\,du = \int \left(\frac{2\sin^2 u}{2\cos^2 u}\right)^{1/2} (-2\sin 2u)\,du$$

$$= \int \frac{\sin u}{\cos u}(-2\sin 2u)\,du = -2\int \frac{\sin u}{\cos u}(2\sin u\,\cos u)\,du = -4\int \sin^2 u\,du$$

$$= -4\int \left(\frac{1}{2} - \frac{1}{2}\cos 2u\right) du = -2u + \sin 2u + C.$$

1

$\sqrt{1-x^2}$

$2u$

x

Since $x = \cos 2u$ we have $2u = \cos^{-1} x$. From the figure, $\sin 2u = \sqrt{1-x^2}$. Thus

$$\int \left(\frac{1-x}{1+x}\right)^{1/2} dx = -\cos^{-1} x + \sqrt{1-x^2} + C.$$

b. Let $x = \cosh 2u$, so that $dx = 2\sinh 2u\,du$. If $x = 1$ then $1 = \cosh 2u$, so $u = 0$, and if $x = \cosh 2$ then $\cosh 2 = \cosh 2u$, so $u = 1$. Thus

$$\int_1^{\cosh 2} \left(\frac{x-1}{x+1}\right)^{1/2} dx = \int_0^1 \left(\frac{\cosh 2u - 1}{\cosh 2u + 1}\right)^{1/2} 2\sinh 2u\,du.$$

Since $\cosh 2u - 1 = 2\sinh^2 u$ (see Exercise 40(b) of Section 6.4), and similarly, $\cosh 2u + 1 = 2\sinh^2 u + 2 = 2(\sinh^2 u + 1) = 2\cosh^2 u$, and since $\sinh 2u = 2\sinh u\,\cosh u$ (see Exercise 40(a) of Section 6.4), we have

$$\int_0^1 \left(\frac{\cosh 2u - 1}{\cosh 2u + 1}\right)^{1/2} 2\sinh 2u\,du = \int_0^1 \left(\frac{2\sinh^2 u}{2\cosh^2 u}\right)^{1/2} 2\sinh 2u\,du$$

$$= \int_0^1 \frac{\sinh u}{\cosh u} 2(2\sinh u\,\cosh u)\,du = 4\int_0^1 \sinh^2 u\,du = 4\int_0^1 \frac{1}{2}(\cosh 2u - 1)\,du$$

$$= 2\left(\frac{1}{2}\sinh 2u - u\right)\Big|_0^1 = 2\left(\frac{1}{2}\sinh 2 - 1\right) = \sinh 2 - 2 = \frac{1}{2}(e^2 - e^{-2}) - 2$$

47. The area A is given by $A = \int_0^1 \sqrt{1-x^2}\,dx$. Let $x = \sin u$, so that $dx = \cos u\,du$. If $x = 0$ then $u = 0$, and if $x = 1$ then $u = \pi/2$. Thus

$$A = \int_0^1 \sqrt{1-x^2}\,dx = \int_0^{\pi/2} \sqrt{1-\sin^2 u}\,\cos u\,du = \int_0^{\pi/2} \cos^2 u\,du$$

$$= \int_0^{\pi/2} \left(\frac{1}{2} + \frac{1}{2}\cos 2u\right) du = \left(\frac{1}{2}u + \frac{1}{4}\sin 2u\right)\Big|_0^{\pi/2} = \frac{\pi}{4}.$$

48. The area A is given by $A = \int_{-1/2}^{1/2} (x^2/\sqrt{1-x^2})\,dx$. By the solution of Exercise 16, $\int (x^2/\sqrt{1-x^2})\,dx = \frac{1}{2}\sin^{-1} x - \frac{1}{2}x\sqrt{1-x^2} + C$, so that

$$A = \left(\frac{1}{2}\sin^{-1} x - \frac{1}{2}x\sqrt{1-x^2}\right)\Big|_{-1/2}^{1/2} = \left(\frac{1}{2}\frac{\pi}{6} - \frac{1}{2}\cdot\frac{1}{2}\sqrt{\frac{3}{4}}\right) - \left(-\frac{1}{2}\frac{\pi}{6} + \frac{1}{2}\cdot\frac{1}{2}\sqrt{\frac{3}{4}}\right) = \frac{\pi}{6} - \frac{1}{4}\sqrt{3}.$$

49. The area A is given by $A = \int_0^3 \sqrt{9+x^2}\,dx$. Let $x = 3\tan u$, so that $dx = 3\sec^2 u\,du$. If $x = 0$ then $u = 0$, and if $x = 3$ then $u = \pi/4$. By (7) of Section 7.2,

$$A = \int_0^3 \sqrt{9+x^2}\,dx = \int_0^{\pi/4} \sqrt{9+9\tan^2 u}\,(3\sec^2 u)\,du = 9\int_0^{\pi/4} \sqrt{1+\tan^2 u}\,\sec^2 u\,du$$

$$= 9\int_0^{\pi/4} \sec^3 u\,du = \left(\frac{9}{2}\sec u\,\tan u + \frac{9}{2}\ln|\sec u + \tan u|\right)\Big|_0^{\pi/4} = \frac{9}{2}\sqrt{2} + \frac{9}{2}\ln(\sqrt{2}+1).$$

50. a. Since the ellipse is symmetric with respect to both axes, the area A is given by

$$A = 4\int_0^a \left(b\sqrt{1-x^2/a^2}\right)dx.$$

Let $x = a\sin u$, $dx = a\cos u\,du$. Then

$$A = 4\int_0^{\pi/2} b\sqrt{1-\sin^2 u}\,a\cos u\,du = 4ab\int_0^{\pi/2} \cos^2 u\,du = 4ab\int_0^{\pi/2}\left(\frac{1}{2}+\frac{1}{2}\cos 2u\right)du$$

$$= 4ab\left(\frac{1}{2}u + \frac{1}{4}\sin 2u\right)\Big|_0^{\pi/2} = 4ab\frac{\pi}{4} = \pi ab.$$

b. By part (a), the amount would be $\pi(750)(640) = 480{,}000\pi$ (square feet).

51. a. Let $x = R + r\sin\theta$, $dx = r\cos\theta\,d\theta$. Then

$$\int_{R-r}^{R+r} 4\pi x\sqrt{r^2-(x-R)^2}\,dx = 4\pi\int_{-\pi/2}^{\pi/2} (R+r\sin\theta)\sqrt{r^2-r^2\sin^2\theta}\,(r\cos\theta)\,d\theta$$

$$= 4\pi\int_{-\pi/2}^{\pi/2} Rr^2\cos^2\theta\,d\theta + 4\pi\int_{-\pi/2}^{\pi/2} r^3\sin\theta\cos^2\theta\,d\theta$$

$$= 4\pi Rr^2\int_{-\pi/2}^{\pi/2}\left(\frac{1}{2}+\frac{1}{2}\cos 2\theta\right)d\theta - \frac{4\pi r^3}{3}\cos^3\theta\Big|_{-\pi/2}^{\pi/2}$$

$$= 4\pi Rr^2\left(\frac{\theta}{2}+\frac{1}{4}\sin 2\theta\right)\Big|_{-\pi/2}^{\pi/2} - 0 = 2\pi^2 Rr^2.$$

b. Since $2\pi^2(4)(2)^2 > 2\pi^2(6)(1)^2$, the doughnut having $R = 4$ and $r = 2$ should cost more.

7.4 Partial Fractions

1. $\displaystyle\int \frac{x}{x+1}\,dx = \int\left(1 - \frac{1}{x+1}\right)dx = x - \ln|x+1| + C$

2. $\displaystyle\int \frac{x^2}{x^2+1}\,dx = \int\left(1 - \frac{1}{x^2+1}\right)dx = x - \tan^{-1}x + C$

3. $\displaystyle\int \frac{x^2}{x^2-1}\,dx = \int\left(1+\frac{1}{(x+1)(x-1)}\right)dx;\ \frac{1}{(x+1)(x-1)} = \frac{A}{x+1}+\frac{B}{x-1};$
$A(x-1)+B(x+1)=1;\ A+B=0,\ -A+B=1;\ A=-\frac{1}{2},\ B=\frac{1}{2};$

$$\int \frac{x^2}{x^2-1}\,dx = \int\left(1-\frac{1}{2(x+1)}+\frac{1}{2(x-1)}\right)dx = x-\frac{1}{2}\ln|x+1|+\frac{1}{2}\ln|x-1|+C = x+\frac{1}{2}\ln\left|\frac{x-1}{x+1}\right|+C$$

4. $\displaystyle\int \frac{t^2-1}{t^2+1}\,dt = \int\left(1-\frac{2}{t^2+1}\right)dt = t-2\tan^{-1}t+C$

5. $\displaystyle\frac{x^2+4}{x(x-1)^2} = \frac{A}{x}+\frac{B}{x-1}+\frac{C}{(x-1)^2};\ A(x-1)^2+Bx(x-1)+Cx = x^2+4;$
$A+B=1,\ -2A-B+C=0,\ A=4;\ A=4,\ B=-3,\ C=5;$

$$\int \frac{x^2+4}{x(x-1)^2}\,dx = \int\left(\frac{4}{x}-\frac{3}{x-1}+\frac{5}{(x-1)^2}\right)dx$$

$$= 4\ln|x|-3\ln|x-1|-\frac{5}{x-1}+C_1 = \ln\left|\frac{x^4}{(x-1)^3}\right|-\frac{5}{x-1}+C_1$$

6. $\displaystyle\int \frac{2x^3+x^2+12}{x^2-4}\,dx = \int\left(2x+1+\frac{8}{x-2}\right)dx = x^2+x+8\ln|x-2|+C$

7. $\displaystyle\frac{5}{(x-2)(x+3)} = \frac{A}{x-2}+\frac{B}{x+3}$; $A(x+3)+B(x-2)=5;\ A+B=0,\ 3A-2B=5;\ A=1,\ B=-1;$

$$\int_3^4 \frac{5}{(x-2)(x+3)}\,dx = \int_3^4\left(\frac{1}{x-2}-\frac{1}{x+3}\right)dx = (\ln|x-2|-\ln|x+3|)\Big]_3^4 = \ln 2-\ln 7+\ln 6 = \ln\frac{12}{7}$$

8. $\displaystyle\frac{5x}{(x-2)(x+3)} = \frac{A}{x-2}+\frac{B}{x+3};\ A(x+3)+B(x-2)=5x;\ A+B=5,\ 3A-2B=0;\ A=2,\ B=3;$

$$\int \frac{5x}{(x-2)(x+3)}\,dx = \int\left(\frac{2}{x-2}+\frac{3}{x+3}\right)dx = 2\ln|x-2|+3\ln|x+3|+C$$

9. $\displaystyle\frac{3t}{t^2-8t+15} = \frac{A}{t-5}+\frac{B}{t-3};\ A(t-3)+B(t-5)=3t;\ A+B=3,\ -3A-5B=0;\ A=\frac{15}{2},\ B=-\frac{9}{2};$

$$\int \frac{3t}{t^2-8t+15}\,dt = \int\left(\frac{15}{2(t-5)}-\frac{9}{2(t-3)}\right)dt = \frac{15}{2}\ln|t-5|-\frac{9}{2}\ln|t-3|+C$$

10. $\displaystyle\frac{2}{x^2-x-6} = \frac{A}{x-3}+\frac{B}{x+2};\ A(x+2)+B(x-3)=2;\ A+B=0,\ 2A-3B=2;\ A=\frac{2}{5},\ B=-\frac{2}{5};$

$$\int \frac{2}{x^2-x-6}\,dx = \int\left(\frac{2}{5(x-3)}-\frac{2}{5(x+2)}\right)dx = \frac{2}{5}\ln|x-3|-\frac{2}{5}\ln|x+2|+C = \frac{2}{5}\ln\left|\frac{x-3}{x+2}\right|+C$$

11. $\displaystyle\int_{-1}^0 \frac{x^2+x+1}{x^2+1}\,dx = \int_{-1}^0\left(1+\frac{x}{x^2+1}\right)dx = \left[x+\frac{1}{2}\ln(x^2+1)\right]\Big]_{-1}^0 = -\left[(-1)+\frac{1}{2}\ln 2\right] = 1-\frac{1}{2}\ln 2$

12. $\dfrac{2x+5}{x^2+3x+2} = \dfrac{A}{x+2} + \dfrac{B}{x+1}$; $A(x+1)+B(x+2) = 2x+5$; $A+B=2$, $A+2B=5$;
if $x=-1$, then $B(1) = 2(-1)+5 = 3$, so $B=3$; if $x=-2$, then $A(-1) = 2(-2)+5 = 1$, so $A=-1$. Therefore

$$\int \frac{2x+5}{x^2+3x+2}\,dx = \int \left(\frac{-1}{x+2} + \frac{3}{x+1}\right) dx = -\ln|x+2| + 3\ln|x+1| + C = \ln\frac{|x+1|^3}{|x+2|} + C.$$

13. $\displaystyle\int \frac{x^2+x+1}{x^2-1}\,dx = \int\left(1+\frac{x+2}{x^2-1}\right)dx$; $\dfrac{x+2}{x^2-1} = \dfrac{A}{x+1}+\dfrac{B}{x-1}$; $A(x-1)+B(x+1) = x+2$; $A+B=1$, $-A+B=2$; $A=-\frac{1}{2}$, $B=\frac{3}{2}$;

$$\int \frac{x^2+x+1}{x^2-1}\,dx = \int\left(1 - \frac{1}{2(x+1)} + \frac{3}{2(x-1)}\right)dx = x - \frac{1}{2}\ln|x+1| + \frac{3}{2}\ln|x-1| + C$$

14. $\displaystyle\int \frac{x^2+2x+1}{x^2-1}\,dx = \int \frac{(x+1)^2}{(x+1)(x-1)}\,dx = \int \frac{x+1}{x-1}\,dx = \int\left(1+\frac{2}{x-1}\right)dx = x + 2\ln|x-1| + C$

15. $\displaystyle\int_0^1 \frac{u-1}{u^2+u+1}\,du = \frac{1}{2}\int_0^1 \frac{2u+1}{u^2+u+1}\,du - \frac{3}{2}\int_0^1 \frac{1}{(u+\frac{1}{2})^2+\frac{3}{4}}\,du$;

$\displaystyle\frac{1}{2}\int_0^1 \frac{2u+1}{u^2+u+1}\,du = \frac{1}{2}\ln(u^2+u+1)\Big|_0^1 = \frac{1}{2}\ln 3$;

$\displaystyle-\frac{3}{2}\int_0^1 \frac{1}{(u+\frac{1}{2})^2+\frac{3}{4}}\,du \overset{v=u+1/2}{=} -\frac{3}{2}\int_{1/2}^{3/2} \frac{1}{v^2+\frac{3}{4}}\,dv = -\frac{3}{2}\left(\frac{2}{\sqrt{3}}\right)\tan^{-1}\frac{2v}{\sqrt{3}}\Big|_{1/2}^{3/2} = -\frac{\sqrt{3}\,\pi}{6}$

Thus

$$\int_0^1 \frac{u-1}{u^2+u+1}\,du = \frac{1}{2}\ln 3 - \frac{\sqrt{3}\,\pi}{6}.$$

16. $\dfrac{2x}{(x+1)^2} = \dfrac{A}{x+1} + \dfrac{B}{(x+1)^2}$; $A(x+1)+B = 2x$; $A=2$, $A+B=0$; $A=2$, $B=-2$;

$$\int \frac{2x}{(x+1)^2}\,dx = \int\left(\frac{2}{x+1} - \frac{2}{(x+1)^2}\right)dx = 2\ln|x+1| + \frac{2}{x+1} + C$$

17. $\dfrac{3x}{x^2-4x+4} = \dfrac{3x}{(x-2)^2} = \dfrac{A}{x-2} + \dfrac{B}{(x-2)^2}$; $A(x-2)+B = 3x$; $A=3$, $-2A+B=0$; $A=3$, $B=6$;

$$\int \frac{3x}{x^2-4x+4}\,dx = \int\left(\frac{3}{x-2} + \frac{6}{(x-2)^2}\right)dx = 3\ln|x-2| - \frac{6}{x-2} + C$$

18. $\dfrac{4x}{x^3+6x^2+11x+6} = \dfrac{4x}{(x+1)(x+2)(x+3)} = \dfrac{A}{x+1} + \dfrac{B}{x+2} + \dfrac{C}{x+3}$;
$A(x+2)(x+3) + B(x+1)(x+3) + C(x+1)(x+2) = 4x$; $A+B+C=0$, $5A+4B+3C=4$, $6A+3B+2C=0$; $A=-2$, $B=8$, $C=-6$;

$$\int \frac{4x}{x^3+6x^2+11x+6}\,dx = \int\left(\frac{-2}{x+1} + \frac{8}{x+2} - \frac{6}{x+3}\right)dx = -2\ln|x+1| + 8\ln|x+2| - 6\ln|x+3| + C_1$$

19. $\dfrac{-x}{x^3-3x^2+2x}=\dfrac{-1}{(x-1)(x-2)}=\dfrac{A}{x-1}+\dfrac{B}{x-2}$;
$A(x-2)+B(x-1)=-1$; $A+B=0$, $-2A-B=-1$; $A=1$, $B=-1$;

$$\int\frac{-x}{x^3-3x^2+2x}\,dx=\int\left(\frac{1}{x-1}-\frac{1}{x-2}\right)dx=\ln|x-1|-\ln|x-2|+C=\ln\left|\frac{x-1}{x-2}\right|+C$$

20. $\dfrac{x+1}{x^3-2x^2+x}=\dfrac{x+1}{x(x-1)^2}=\dfrac{A}{x}+\dfrac{B}{x-1}+\dfrac{C}{(x-1)^2}$;
$A(x-1)^2+Bx(x-1)+Cx=x+1$; $A+B=0$, $-2A-B+C=1$, $A=1$; $A=1$, $B=-1$, $C=2$;

$$\int\frac{x+1}{x^3-2x^2+x}\,dx=\int\left(\frac{1}{x}-\frac{1}{x-1}+\frac{2}{(x-1)^2}\right)dx$$

$$=\ln|x|-\ln|x-1|-\frac{2}{x-1}+C_1=\ln\left|\frac{x}{x-1}\right|-\frac{2}{x-1}+C_1$$

21. $\displaystyle\int\frac{u^3}{(u+1)^2}\,du=\int\left(u-2+\frac{3u+2}{(u+1)^2}\right)du$
$\dfrac{3u+2}{(u+1)^2}=\dfrac{A}{u+1}+\dfrac{B}{(u+1)^2}$; $A(u+1)+B=3u+2$; $A=3$, $A+B=2$; $A=3$, $B=-1$;

$$\int\frac{u^3}{(u+1)^2}\,du=\int\left(u-2+\frac{3}{u+1}-\frac{1}{(u+1)^2}\right)du=\frac{1}{2}u^2-2u+3\ln|u+1|+\frac{1}{u+1}+C$$

22. $\displaystyle\int_0^1\frac{x^3}{(x+1)^3}\,dx=\int_0^1\left(1-\frac{1}{x+1}\right)^3dx=\int_0^1\left(1-\frac{3}{x+1}+\frac{3}{(x+1)^2}-\frac{1}{(x+1)^3}\right)dx$

$$=\left(x-3\ln|x+1|-\frac{3}{x+1}+\frac{1}{2(x+1)^2}\right)\Bigg|_0^1=\frac{17}{8}-3\ln 2$$

23. $\displaystyle\int\frac{1}{(1-x^2)^2}\,dx=\int\left(\frac{1}{2(x+1)}-\frac{1}{2(x-1)}\right)^2dx=\int\left(\frac{1}{4(x+1)^2}-\frac{1}{2(x+1)(x-1)}+\frac{1}{4(x-1)^2}\right)dx$

$$=\int\left[\frac{1}{4(x+1)^2}+\frac{1}{2}\left(\frac{1}{2(x+1)}-\frac{1}{2(x-1)}\right)+\frac{1}{4(x-1)^2}\right]dx$$

$$=\frac{-1}{4(x+1)}+\frac{1}{4}\ln\left|\frac{x+1}{x-1}\right|-\frac{1}{4(x-1)}+C$$

24. $\dfrac{1}{x^4+1}=\dfrac{Ax+B}{x^2+\sqrt{2}\,x+1}+\dfrac{Cx+D}{x^2-\sqrt{2}\,x+1}$;
$(Ax+B)(x^2-\sqrt{2}\,x+1)+(Cx+D)(x^2+\sqrt{2}\,x+1)=1$; $A+C=0$, $-\sqrt{2}\,A+B+\sqrt{2}\,C+D=0$,
$A-\sqrt{2}\,B+C+\sqrt{2}\,D=0$, $B+D=1$; $A=\sqrt{2}/4$, $B=\frac{1}{2}$, $C=-\sqrt{2}/4$, $D=\frac{1}{2}$;

$$\int \frac{1}{x^4+1}\,dx = \frac{1}{4}\int\left(\frac{\sqrt{2}x+2}{x^2+\sqrt{2}x+1}+\frac{-\sqrt{2}x+2}{x^2-\sqrt{2}x+1}\right)dx$$

$$= \frac{1}{4}\int\left(\frac{2x+\sqrt{2}}{\sqrt{2}\,(x^2+\sqrt{2}x+1)}+\frac{1}{x^2+\sqrt{2}x+1}\right.$$

$$\left.-\frac{2x-\sqrt{2}}{\sqrt{2}\,(x^2-\sqrt{2}x+1)}+\frac{1}{x^2-\sqrt{2}x+1}\right)dx$$

$$= \frac{1}{4\sqrt{2}}\ln\left|x^2+\sqrt{2}x+1\right|+\frac{1}{4}\int\frac{1}{(x+\sqrt{2}/2)^2+1/2}\,dx$$

$$-\frac{1}{4\sqrt{2}}\ln\left|x^2-\sqrt{2}x+1\right|+\frac{1}{4}\int\frac{1}{(x-\sqrt{2}/2)^2+1/2}\,dx$$

$$= \frac{\sqrt{2}}{8}\ln\left|\frac{x^2+\sqrt{2}x+1}{x^2-\sqrt{2}x+1}\right|+\frac{\sqrt{2}}{4}\tan^{-1}(\sqrt{2}x+1)+\frac{\sqrt{2}}{4}\tan^{-1}(\sqrt{2}x-1)+C_1$$

25. $\dfrac{x}{(x+1)^2(x-2)} = \dfrac{A}{x+1}+\dfrac{B}{(x+1)^2}+\dfrac{C}{x-2}$;
$A(x+1)(x-2)+B(x-2)+C(x+1)^2 = x$; $A+C=0$, $-A+B+2C=1$, $-2A-2B+C=0$;
$A=-\frac{2}{9}$, $B=\frac{1}{3}$, $C=\frac{2}{9}$;

$$\int\frac{x}{(x+1)^2(x-2)}\,dx = \int\left(\frac{-2}{9(x+1)}+\frac{1}{3(x+1)^2}+\frac{2}{9(x-2)}\right)dx$$

$$= \frac{-2}{9}\ln|x+1|-\frac{1}{3(x+1)}+\frac{2}{9}\ln|x-2|+C_1 = \frac{2}{9}\ln\left|\frac{x-2}{x+1}\right|-\frac{1}{3(x+1)}+C_1$$

26. $\dfrac{1}{(x-1)(x^2+1)^2} = \dfrac{A}{x-1}+\dfrac{Bx+C}{x^2+1}+\dfrac{Dx+E}{(x^2+1)^2}$;
$A(x^2+1)^2+(Bx+C)(x^2+1)(x-1)+(Dx+E)(x-1)=1$;
$A+B=0$, $-B+C=0$, $2A+B-C+D=0$, $-B+C-D+E=0$, $A-C-E=1$;
$A=\frac{1}{4}$, $B=-\frac{1}{4}$, $C=-\frac{1}{4}$, $D=-\frac{1}{2}$, $E=-\frac{1}{2}$;

$$\int\frac{1}{(x-1)(x^2+1)^2}\,dx = \int\left(\frac{1}{4(x-1)}-\frac{x+1}{4(x^2+1)}-\frac{x+1}{2(x^2+1)^2}\right)dx$$

$$= \frac{1}{4}\ln|x-1|-\frac{1}{4}\int\left(\frac{x}{x^2+1}+\frac{1}{x^2+1}\right)dx-\frac{1}{2}\int\left(\frac{2x}{2(x^2+1)^2}+\frac{1}{(x^2+1)^2}\right)dx$$

$$= \frac{1}{4}\ln|x-1|-\frac{1}{8}\ln(x^2+1)-\frac{1}{4}\tan^{-1}x+\frac{1}{4(x^2+1)}-\frac{1}{2}\int\frac{1}{(x^2+1)^2}\,dx$$

To evaluate $\int [1/(x^2+1)^2]\,dx$, let $x = \tan u$, so that $dx = \sec^2 u\,du$, and note from the figure that $\sin u = x/\sqrt{x^2+1}$ and $\cos u = 1/\sqrt{x^2+1}$. We have

$$\int \frac{1}{(x^2+1)^2}\,dx = \int \frac{1}{(\tan^2 u+1)^2}\sec^2 u\,du = \int \frac{1}{\sec^2 u}\,du = \int \cos^2 u\,du$$

$\sqrt{x^2+1}$ x u 1

$$= \frac{1}{2}u + \frac{1}{4}\sin 2u + C_1 = \frac{1}{2}u + \frac{1}{2}\sin u\,\cos u + C_1 = \frac{1}{2}\tan^{-1}x + \frac{1}{2}\left(\frac{x}{\sqrt{x^2+1}}\right)\left(\frac{1}{\sqrt{x^2+1}}\right) + C_1$$

$$= \frac{1}{2}\tan^{-1}x + \frac{1}{2}\frac{x}{x^2+1} + C_1.$$

Therefore

$$\int \frac{1}{(x-1)(x^2+1)^2}\,dx = \frac{1}{4}\ln|x-1| - \frac{1}{8}\ln(x^2+1) - \frac{1}{4}\tan^{-1}x + \frac{1}{4(x^2+1)}$$

$$-\frac{1}{2}\left(\frac{1}{2}\tan^{-1}x + \frac{1}{2}\frac{x}{x^2+1}\right) + C_2$$

$$= \frac{1}{4}\ln|x-1| - \frac{1}{8}\ln(x^2+1) - \frac{1}{2}\tan^{-1}x + \frac{1-x}{4(x^2+1)} + C_2.$$

27. $\dfrac{-x^3+x^2+x+3}{(x+1)(x^2+1)^2} = \dfrac{A}{x+1} + \dfrac{Bx+C}{x^2+1} + \dfrac{Dx+E}{(x^2+1)^2}$;

$A(x^2+1)^2 + (Bx+C)(x+1)(x^2+1) + (Dx+E)(x+1) = -x^3+x^2+x+3$;

$A+B=0$, $B+C=-1$, $2A+B+C+D=1$, $B+C+D+E=1$, $A+C+E=3$;

$A=1$, $B=-1$, $C=0$, $D=0$, $E=2$.

With the help of the evaluation of $\int [1/(x^2+1)^2]\,dx$ in Exercise 26, we find that

$$\int \frac{-x^3+x^2+x+3}{(x+1)(x^2+1)^2}\,dx = \int\left(\frac{1}{x+1} - \frac{x}{x^2+1} + \frac{2}{(x^2+1)^2}\right)dx$$

$$= \ln|x+1| - \frac{1}{2}\ln(x^2+1) + 2\left(\frac{1}{2}\tan^{-1}x + \frac{1}{2}\frac{x}{x^2+1}\right) + C_1 = \ln|x+1| - \frac{1}{2}\ln(x^2+1) + \tan^{-1}x + \frac{x}{x^2+1} + C_1.$$

28. $\dfrac{1}{(x^2+1)(x-2)} = \dfrac{Ax+B}{x^2+1} + \dfrac{C}{x-2}$;

$(Ax+B)(x-2) + C(x^2+1) = 1$; $A+C=0$, $-2A+B=0$, $-2B+C=1$; $A=-\frac{1}{5}$, $B=-\frac{2}{5}$, $C=\frac{1}{5}$;

$$\int \frac{1}{(x^2+1)(x-2)}\,dx = \int\left(\frac{-x-2}{5(x^2+1)} + \frac{1}{5(x-2)}\right)dx = \frac{1}{5}\int\left(\frac{-x}{x^2+1} - \frac{2}{x^2+1} + \frac{1}{x-2}\right)dx$$

$$= \frac{1}{5}\left(\frac{-1}{2}\ln(x^2+1) - 2\tan^{-1}x + \ln|x-2|\right) + C_1 = \frac{-1}{10}\ln(x^2+1) - \frac{2}{5}\tan^{-1}x + \frac{1}{5}\ln|x-2| + C_1.$$

29. $\dfrac{x^2-1}{x^3+3x+4} = \dfrac{(x+1)(x-1)}{(x+1)(x^2-x+4)} = \dfrac{x-1}{x^2-x+4}$;

$$\int \frac{x^2-1}{x^3+3x+4}\,dx = \int\left(\frac{2x-1}{2(x^2-x+4)} - \frac{1}{2(x^2-x+4)}\right)dx = \frac{1}{2}\ln|x^2-x+4| - \frac{1}{2}\int\frac{1}{(x-\frac{1}{2})^2+\frac{15}{4}}\,dx$$

$$= \frac{1}{2}\ln|x^2-x+4| - \frac{1}{2}\left(\frac{2}{\sqrt{15}}\tan^{-1}\frac{x-\frac{1}{2}}{\sqrt{15}/2}\right) + C = \frac{1}{2}\ln|x^2-x+4| - \frac{1}{\sqrt{15}}\tan^{-1}\frac{\sqrt{15}\,(2x-1)}{15} + C.$$

30. Let $u=\sqrt{x}$, so $du = 1/(2\sqrt{x})\,dx$ and $dx = 2u\,du$;

$$\int\frac{\sqrt{x}+1}{x+1}\,dx = \int\frac{u+1}{u^2+1}\,2u\,du = \int\frac{2u^2+2u}{u^2+1}\,du.$$

Now

$$\int\frac{2u^2+2u}{u^2+1}\,du = \int\left(2+\frac{2u}{u^2+1}-\frac{2}{u^2+1}\right)du = 2u+\ln(u^2+1)-2\tan^{-1}u+C.$$

Thus

$$\int\frac{\sqrt{x}+1}{x+1}\,dx = 2\sqrt{x}+\ln(x+1)-2\tan^{-1}\sqrt{x}+C.$$

31. Let $u=\sqrt{x+1}$, so $du = [1/(2\sqrt{x+1})]\,dx$ and $dx = 2u\,du$;

$$\int\frac{1}{x\sqrt{x+1}}\,dx = \int\frac{2u}{(u^2-1)u}\,du = \int\frac{2}{(u+1)(u-1)}\,du = \int\left(\frac{-1}{u+1}+\frac{1}{u-1}\right)du$$

$$= -\ln|u+1|+\ln|u-1|+C = \ln\left|\frac{\sqrt{x+1}-1}{\sqrt{x+1}+1}\right|+C.$$

32. Let $u=\tan x$, so $du = \sec^2 x\,dx$ and $dx = [1/(\tan^2 x+1)]\,du = [1/(u^2+1)]\,du$;

$$\int_0^{\pi/4}\tan^3 x\,dx = \int_0^1\frac{u^3}{u^2+1}\,du = \int_0^1\left(u-\frac{u}{u^2+1}\right)du = \left[\frac{1}{2}u^2-\frac{1}{2}\ln(u^2+1)\right]\Big|_0^1 = \frac{1}{2}-\frac{1}{2}\ln 2.$$

33. Let $u=\sqrt[6]{x}$, so $du = \frac{1}{6}x^{-5/6}\,dx$ and $dx = 6u^5\,du$;

$$\int\frac{\sqrt{x}}{1+\sqrt[3]{x}}\,dx = \int\frac{u^3}{1+u^2}(6u^5)\,du = 6\int\frac{u^8}{1+u^2}\,du = 6\int\left(u^6-u^4+u^2-1+\frac{1}{u^2+1}\right)du$$

$$= 6\left(\frac{1}{7}u^7-\frac{1}{5}u^5+\frac{1}{3}u^3-u+\tan^{-1}u\right)+C = \frac{6}{7}x^{7/6}-\frac{6}{5}x^{5/6}+2x^{1/2}-6x^{1/6}+6\tan^{-1}x^{1/6}+C.$$

34. Let $u=\sqrt[4]{x}$, so $du = \frac{1}{4}x^{-3/4}\,dx$ and $dx = 4u^3\,du$;

$$\int\frac{1}{\sqrt[4]{x}\,(1+\sqrt{x})}\,dx = \int\frac{1}{u(1+u^2)}(4u^3)\,du = 4\int\frac{u^2}{1+u^2}\,du = 4\int\left(1-\frac{1}{1+u^2}\right)du$$

$$= 4u-4\tan^{-1}u+C = 4\sqrt[4]{x}-4\tan^{-1}\sqrt[4]{x}+C.$$

35. Let $u = \sqrt{\dfrac{x+1}{x-1}}$, so $dx = \dfrac{-4u}{(u^2-1)^2}\,du$ and $x = \dfrac{u^2+1}{u^2-1}$;

$$\int_{-5/3}^{-1} \sqrt{\frac{x+1}{x-1}}\,dx = \int_{1/2}^{0} \frac{-4u^2}{(u^2-1)^2}\,du = -4\int_{1/2}^{0}\left(\frac{u}{u^2-1}\right)^2 du = -4\int_{1/2}^{0}\left(\frac{1}{2(u+1)} + \frac{1}{2(u-1)}\right)^2 du$$

$$= -\int_{1/2}^{0}\left(\frac{1}{(u+1)^2} + \frac{2}{(u+1)(u-1)} + \frac{1}{(u-1)^2}\right) du$$

$$= -\int_{1/2}^{0}\left(\frac{1}{(u+1)^2} - \frac{1}{u+1} + \frac{1}{u-1} + \frac{1}{(u-1)^2}\right) du$$

$$= \left(\frac{1}{u+1} + \ln|u+1| - \ln|u-1| + \frac{1}{u-1}\right)\Bigg|_{1/2}^{0} = \frac{4}{3} - \ln 3.$$

36. Let $u = \left(\dfrac{x}{x+1}\right)^{1/3}$, so $dx = \dfrac{3u^2}{(1-u^3)^2}\,du$ and $x = \dfrac{u^3}{1-u^3}$;

$$\int \frac{1}{x}\left(\frac{x}{x+1}\right)^{1/3} dx = \int \left(\frac{1-u^3}{u^3}\right) u \left(\frac{3u^2}{(1-u^3)^2}\right) du = 3\int \frac{1}{1-u^3}\,du = 3\int \frac{1}{(1-u)(1+u+u^2)}\,du.$$

$\dfrac{1}{(1-u)(1+u+u^2)} = \dfrac{A}{1-u} + \dfrac{Bu+C}{1+u+u^2}$; $A(1+u+u^2) + (Bu+C)(1-u) = 1$;
$A - B = 0$, $A + B - C = 0$, $A + C = 1$; $A = \frac{1}{3}$, $B = \frac{1}{3}$, $C = \frac{2}{3}$;

$$\int_{-1/9}^{-1/2} \frac{1}{x}\left(\frac{x}{x+1}\right)^{1/3} dx = 3\int_{-1/2}^{-1}\left[\frac{1}{3(1-u)} + \frac{u+2}{3(1+u+u^2)}\right] du$$

$$= \int_{-1/2}^{-1}\left\{\frac{1}{1-u} + \frac{2u+1}{2(u^2+u+1)} + \frac{3}{2[(u+\frac{1}{2})^2 + \frac{3}{4}]}\right\} du$$

$$= \left[-\ln|1-u| + \frac{1}{2}\ln|u^2+u+1| + \frac{3}{2}\left(\frac{2}{\sqrt{3}}\right)\tan^{-1}\frac{2(u+\frac{1}{2})}{\sqrt{3}}\right]\Bigg|_{-1/2}^{-1}$$

$$= \left[-\ln 2 + \frac{1}{2}\ln 1 + \sqrt{3}\tan^{-1}\left(\frac{-1}{\sqrt{3}}\right)\right] - \left[-\ln\frac{3}{2} + \frac{1}{2}\ln\frac{3}{4} + \sqrt{3}\tan^{-1}0\right]$$

$$= -\ln 2 + \sqrt{3}\left(-\frac{\pi}{6}\right) + \ln 3 - \ln 2 - \frac{1}{2}\ln 3 + \ln 2 = -\ln 2 - \frac{\sqrt{3}\,\pi}{6} + \frac{1}{2}\ln 3.$$

37. Let $u = \sin x$, so that $du = \cos x\,dx$. Then

$$\int \frac{\sin^2 x\cos x}{\sin^2 x + 1}\,dx = \int \frac{u^2}{u^2+1}\,du = \int\left(1 - \frac{1}{u^2+1}\right) du = u - \tan^{-1}u + C = \sin x - \tan^{-1}(\sin x) + C.$$

38. Let $u = e^x$, so that $du = e^x\,dx$. Then

$$\int \frac{e^x}{1-e^{2x}}\,dx = \int \frac{1}{1-u^2}\,du.$$

$$\frac{1}{1-u^2} = \frac{A}{1-u} + \frac{B}{1+u};\ A(1+u) + B(1-u) = 1;\ A + B = 1,\ A - B = 0;\ A = \tfrac{1}{2},\ B = \tfrac{1}{2};$$

$$\int \frac{e^x}{1-e^{2x}}\,dx = \int \frac{1}{1-u^2}\,du = \int \left(\frac{1}{2(1-u)} + \frac{1}{2(1+u)}\right) du$$

$$= -\frac{1}{2}\ln|1-u| + \frac{1}{2}\ln|1+u| + C = \frac{1}{2}\ln\left|\frac{1+u}{1-u}\right| + C = \frac{1}{2}\ln\left|\frac{1+e^x}{1-e^x}\right| + C.$$

39. Let $u = e^x$, so that $du = e^x\,dx$;

$$\int \frac{e^x}{1-e^{3x}}\,dx = \int \frac{1}{1-u^3}\,du = \int \frac{1}{(1-u)(1+u+u^2)}\,du = \int \left(\frac{A}{1-u} + \frac{Bu+C}{1+u+u^2}\right) du;$$

$A(1+u+u^2) + (Bu+C)(1-u) = 1$; $A - B = 0$, $A + B - C = 0$, $A + C = 1$; $A = \frac{1}{3}$, $B = \frac{1}{3}$, $C = \frac{2}{3}$. Therefore

$$\int \frac{1}{(1-u)(1+u+u^2)}\,du = \int \left[\frac{1}{3(1-u)} + \frac{u+2}{3(1+u+u^2)}\right] du$$

$$= \frac{1}{3}\int \frac{1}{1-u}\,du + \frac{1}{6}\int \frac{2u+1}{1+u+u^2}\,du + \frac{1}{2}\int \frac{1}{(u+\frac{1}{2})^2 + \frac{3}{4}}\,du$$

$$= -\frac{1}{3}\ln|1-u| + \frac{1}{6}\ln(1+u+u^2) + \frac{1}{2}\frac{2}{\sqrt{3}}\tan^{-1}\frac{u+\frac{1}{2}}{\sqrt{3}/2} + C$$

$$= -\frac{1}{3}\ln|1-e^x| + \frac{1}{6}\ln(1+e^x+e^{2x}) + \frac{1}{\sqrt{3}}\tan^{-1}\frac{2e^x+1}{\sqrt{3}} + C.$$

40. Let $u = e^x$, so that $du = e^x\,dx$;

$$\int \frac{e^x}{e^{2x}+3e^x+2}\,dx = \int \frac{1}{u^2+3u+2}\,du = \int \frac{1}{(u+2)(u+1)}\,du$$

$$\frac{1}{(u+2)(u+1)} = \frac{A}{u+2} + \frac{B}{u+1};\ A(u+1) + B(u+2) = 1;\ A + B = 0,\ A + 2B = 1;\ A = -1,\ B = 1;$$

$$\int \frac{e^x}{e^{2x}+3e^x+2}\,dx = \int \left(\frac{-1}{u+2} + \frac{1}{u+1}\right) du = -\ln|u+2| + \ln|u+1| + C = \ln\frac{e^x+1}{e^x+2} + C.$$

41. To integrate by parts, let $u = \tan^{-1} x$, $dv = x\,dx$, so that $du = [1/(1+x^2)]\,dx$, $v = \frac{1}{2}x^2$. Then

$$\int x\tan^{-1} x\,dx = \frac{1}{2}x^2\tan^{-1} x - \int \frac{1}{2}x^2\frac{1}{1+x^2}\,dx = \frac{1}{2}x^2\tan^{-1} x - \frac{1}{2}\int \frac{x^2}{1+x^2}\,dx.$$

Now

$$\int \frac{x^2}{1+x^2}\,dx = \int \left(1 - \frac{1}{1+x^2}\right) dx.$$

Thus

$$\int x\tan^{-1} x\,dx = \frac{1}{2}x^2\tan^{-1} x - \frac{1}{2}\int \left(1 - \frac{1}{1+x^2}\right) dx = \frac{1}{2}x^2\tan^{-1} x - \frac{1}{2}x + \frac{1}{2}\tan^{-1} x + C.$$

42. To integrate by parts, let $u = \tan^{-1} x$, $dv = x^3\,dx$, so that $du = [1/(1+x^2)]\,dx$, $v = \frac{1}{4}x^4$. Then

$$\int x^3 \tan^{-1} x\,dx = \frac{1}{4}x^4 \tan^{-1} x - \int \frac{1}{4}x^4 \frac{1}{1+x^2}\,dx = \frac{1}{4}x^4 \tan^{-1} x - \frac{1}{4}\int \frac{x^4}{1+x^2}\,dx.$$

Now

$$\int \frac{x^4}{1+x^2}\,dx = \int \left(x^2 - 1 + \frac{1}{1+x^2}\right) dx = \frac{1}{3}x^3 - x + \tan^{-1} x + C_1.$$

Thus

$$\int x^3 \tan^{-1} x\,dx = \frac{1}{4}x^4 \tan^{-1} x - \frac{1}{12}x^3 + \frac{1}{4}x - \frac{1}{4}\tan^{-1} x + C.$$

43. To integrate by parts, let $u = \ln(x^2+1)$, $dv = dx$, so that $du = [2x/(x^2+1)]\,dx$, $v = x$. Then

$$\int \ln(x^2+1)\,dx = x\ln(x^2+1) - \int x\frac{2x}{x^2+1}\,dx = x\ln(x^2+1) - 2\int \frac{x^2}{x^2+1}\,dx.$$

Now

$$\int \frac{x^2}{x^2+1}\,dx = \int \left(1 - \frac{1}{x^2+1}\right) dx = x - \tan^{-1} x + C_1.$$

Thus

$$\int \ln(x^2+1)\,dx = x\ln(x^2+1) - 2x + 2\tan^{-1} x + C.$$

44. a. $$\int \frac{x^2}{(x^2-4)^2}\,dx = \frac{1}{4}\int \left(\frac{1}{x-2} + \frac{1}{x+2}\right)^2 dx = \frac{1}{4}\int \left(\frac{1}{(x-2)^2} + \frac{2}{(x-2)(x+2)} + \frac{1}{(x+2)^2}\right) dx$$

$$= \frac{1}{4}\int \left(\frac{1}{(x-2)^2} + \frac{1}{2(x-2)} - \frac{1}{2(x+2)} + \frac{1}{(x+2)^2}\right) dx$$

$$= \frac{1}{4}\left(\frac{-1}{x-2} + \frac{1}{2}\ln|x-2| - \frac{1}{2}\ln|x+2| - \frac{1}{x+2}\right) + C$$

$$= \frac{1}{4}\left(\frac{-2x}{x^2-4} + \frac{1}{2}\ln\left|\frac{x-2}{x+2}\right|\right) + C$$

b. Using part (a) and letting $u = \sqrt{x+4}$, so that $u^2 = x+4$ and $dx = 2u\,du$, we have

$$\int \frac{\sqrt{x+4}}{x^2}\,dx = \int \frac{u}{(u^2-4)^2}(2u)\,du = 2\int \frac{u^2}{(u^2-4)^2}\,du$$

$$= \frac{1}{2}\left(\frac{-2u}{u^2-4} + \frac{1}{2}\ln\left|\frac{u-2}{u+2}\right|\right) + C = \frac{-\sqrt{x+4}}{x} + \frac{1}{4}\ln\left|\frac{\sqrt{x+4}-2}{\sqrt{x+4}+2}\right| + C.$$

45. $$\int \frac{1}{2+\sin x}\,dx = \int \frac{1}{2+2u/(1+u^2)}\left(\frac{2}{1+u^2}\right) du = \int \frac{1}{1+u+u^2}\,du$$

$$= \int \frac{1}{(u+\frac{1}{2})^2 + \frac{3}{4}}\,du = \frac{2}{\sqrt{3}}\tan^{-1}\frac{2(u+\frac{1}{2})}{\sqrt{3}} + C = \frac{2}{\sqrt{3}}\tan^{-1}\frac{1}{\sqrt{3}}\left(2\tan\frac{x}{2}+1\right) + C$$

46. $$\int \frac{1}{3-\cos x}\,dx = \int \frac{1}{3-(1-u^2)/(1+u^2)}\left(\frac{2}{1+u^2}\right) du = \int \frac{1}{1+2u^2}\,du$$

$$= \frac{1}{2}\int \frac{1}{u^2+\frac{1}{2}}\,du = \frac{\sqrt{2}}{2}\tan^{-1}\sqrt{2}u + C = \frac{\sqrt{2}}{2}\tan^{-1}\left(\sqrt{2}\tan\frac{x}{2}\right) + C$$

47. $$\int \frac{1}{2\cos x + \sin x}\,dx = \int \frac{1}{\dfrac{2(1-u^2)}{1+u^2} + \dfrac{2u}{1+u^2}}\left(\frac{2}{1+u^2}\right) du$$

$$= \int \frac{1}{1+u-u^2}\,du = \int \frac{1}{\frac{5}{4} - (u-\frac{1}{2})^2}\,du \overset{v=u-1/2}{=} \int \frac{1}{\frac{5}{4} - v^2}\,dv$$

$$= \int \frac{1}{(\sqrt{5}/2 - v)(\sqrt{5}/2 + v)}\,dv = \frac{1}{\sqrt{5}}\int \left(\frac{1}{\sqrt{5}/2 - v} + \frac{1}{\sqrt{5}/2 + v}\right) dv$$

$$= \frac{-1}{\sqrt{5}}\ln\left|\frac{\sqrt{5}}{2} - v\right| + \frac{1}{\sqrt{5}}\ln\left|\frac{\sqrt{5}}{2} + v\right| + C = \frac{\sqrt{5}}{5}\ln\left|\frac{\sqrt{5} - 1 + 2\tan(x/2)}{\sqrt{5} + 1 - 2\tan(x/2)}\right| + C$$

48. Let $u = x^r$, so that $du = rx^{r-1}\,dx$. Then

$$\int \frac{1}{x - x^{r+1}}\,dx = \int \frac{1}{x}\frac{1}{1-x^r}\,dx = \int \frac{1}{1-x^r}\frac{1}{x^r}x^{r-1}\,dx = \int \frac{1}{1-u}\frac{1}{u}\frac{1}{r}\,du.$$

Now

$$\frac{1}{1-u}\frac{1}{u} = \frac{1}{(1-u)u} = \frac{A}{1-u} + \frac{B}{u};$$

$Au + B(1-u) = 1$; $A - B = 0$, $B = 1$; $A = B = 1$;

$$\int \frac{1}{x - x^{r+1}}\,dx = \frac{1}{r}\int \left(\frac{1}{1-u} + \frac{1}{u}\right) du$$

$$= \frac{1}{r}(-\ln|1-u| + \ln|u|) + C = \frac{1}{r}\ln\left|\frac{u}{1-u}\right| + C = \frac{1}{r}\ln\left|\frac{x^r}{1-x^r}\right| + C.$$

49. By Exercise 48 with $r = 10$,

$$\int \frac{1}{x - x^{11}}\,dx = \frac{1}{10}\ln\left|\frac{x^{10}}{1-x^{10}}\right| + C.$$

50. $$\frac{x^2 - x + 1}{x(x^2+1)^2} = \frac{A}{x} + \frac{Bx + C}{x^2+1} + \frac{Dx + E}{(x^2+1)^2};$$

$$x^2 - x + 1 = A(x^2+1)^2 + (Bx + C)x(x^2+1) + (Dx + E)x$$
$$= (A+B)x^4 + Cx^3 + (2A + B + D)x^2 + (C + E)x + A;$$

$A + B = 0$, $C = 0$, $2A + B + D = 1$, $C + E = -1$, $A = 1$; $B = -1$, $D = 0$, $E = -1$;

$$\int \frac{x^2 - x + 1}{x(x^2+1)^2}\,dx = \int \left(\frac{1}{x} - \frac{x}{x^2+1} - \frac{1}{(x^2+1)^2}\right) dx = \ln|x| - \frac{1}{2}\ln(x^2+1) - \int \frac{1}{(x^2+1)^2}\,dx.$$

Letting $n = 1$ and $a = 1$ in the reduction formula, we find that

$$\int \frac{1}{(x^2+1)^2}\,dx = \frac{x}{2(x^2+1)} + \frac{1}{2}\int \frac{1}{x^2+1}\,dx = \frac{x}{2(x^2+1)} + \frac{1}{2}\tan^{-1}x + C_1.$$

Thus

$$\int \frac{x^2 - x + 1}{x(x^2+1)^2}\,dx = \ln|x| - \frac{1}{2}\ln(x^2+1) - \frac{x}{2(x^2+1)} - \frac{1}{2}\tan^{-1}x + C_2.$$

51. $A = \int_0^3 \frac{x^3}{x^2+1}\,dx = \int_0^3 \left(x - \frac{x}{x^2+1}\right) dx = \left[\frac{1}{2}x^2 - \frac{1}{2}\ln(x^2+1)\right]\Big|_0^3$

$= \left(\frac{9}{2} - \frac{1}{2}\ln 10\right) + \frac{1}{2}\ln 1 = \frac{9}{2} - \frac{1}{2}\ln 10$

52. $\frac{4x^2}{(x^2-1)(x^2+1)} = \frac{B}{x-1} + \frac{C}{x+1} + \frac{Dx+E}{x^2+1};$

$4x^2 = B(x+1)(x^2+1) + C(x-1)(x^2+1) + (Dx+E)(x^2-1)$

$= (B+C+D)x^3 + (B-C+E)x^2 + (B+C-D)x + (B-C-E);$

$B+C+D=0,\ B-C+E=4,\ B+C-D=0,\ B-C-E=0;\ D=0,\ E=2,\ B=1,\ C=-1.$

Thus the area is given by

$$A = \int_0^{\sqrt{3}/3} \frac{4x^2}{(x^2-1)(x^2+1)}\,dx = \int_0^{\sqrt{3}/3} \left(\frac{1}{x-1} - \frac{1}{x+1} + \frac{2}{x^2+1}\right) dx$$

$$= \left(\ln|x-1| - \ln|x+1| + 2\tan^{-1}x\right)\Big|_0^{\sqrt{3}/3} = \ln\left|\frac{\sqrt{3}}{3} - 1\right| - \ln\left|\frac{\sqrt{3}}{3} + 1\right| + 2\tan^{-1}\frac{\sqrt{3}}{3}$$

$$= \ln\frac{(3-\sqrt{3})/3}{(\sqrt{3}+3)/3} + \frac{\pi}{3} = \ln\frac{3-\sqrt{3}}{3+\sqrt{3}} + \frac{\pi}{3}.$$

Since $4x^2/[(x^2-1)(x^2+1)] \le 0$ on $[0, \frac{1}{3}\sqrt{3}]$, the area A is given by

$$A = -\left(\ln\frac{3-\sqrt{3}}{3+\sqrt{3}} + \frac{\pi}{3}\right) = \ln\frac{3+\sqrt{3}}{3-\sqrt{3}} - \frac{\pi}{3}.$$

53. The graphs intersect at (x,y) if $x^2/[(x-2)(x^2+1)] = y = 1/(x-3)$, or $x^3 - 3x^2 = x^3 - 2x^2 + x - 2$, or $x^2 + x - 2 = 0$, or $x = 1$ or -2. Since $x^2/[(x-2)(x^2+1)] \ge 1/(x-3)$ on $[-2,1]$, the area is given by

$$A = \int_{-2}^1 \left(\frac{x^2}{(x-2)(x^2+1)} - \frac{1}{x-3}\right) dx.$$

Now

$$\frac{x^2}{(x-2)(x^2+1)} = \frac{B}{x-2} + \frac{Cx+D}{x^2+1};$$

$B(x^2+1) + (Cx+D)(x-2) = x^2;\ B+C=1,\ (-2C+D)=0,\ B-2D=0;\ B=\frac{4}{5},\ C=\frac{1}{5},\ D=\frac{2}{5};$ thus

$$A = \int_{-2}^1 \left(\frac{4}{5(x-2)} + \frac{x+2}{5(x^2+1)} - \frac{1}{x-3}\right) dx$$

$$= \int_{-2}^1 \left(\frac{4}{5}\cdot\frac{1}{x-2} + \frac{1}{10}\cdot\frac{2x}{x^2+1} + \frac{2}{5}\cdot\frac{1}{x^2+1} - \frac{1}{x-3}\right) dx$$

$$= \left(\frac{4}{5}\ln|x-2| + \frac{1}{10}\ln(x^2+1) + \frac{2}{5}\tan^{-1}x - \ln|x-3|\right)\Big|_{-2}^1$$

$$= \left(\frac{1}{10}\ln 2 + \frac{\pi}{10} - \ln 2\right) - \left(\frac{4}{5}\ln 4 + \frac{1}{10}\ln 5 + \frac{2}{5}\tan^{-1}(-2) - \ln 5\right)$$

$$= -\frac{5}{2}\ln 2 + \frac{9}{10}\ln 5 + \frac{\pi}{10} + \frac{2}{5}\tan^{-1}2.$$

54. $\dfrac{1}{y(1-y)} = \dfrac{A}{y} + \dfrac{B}{1-y}$; $A(1-y) + By = 1$; $-A + B = 0$, $A = 1$, so $A = B = 1$. Thus

$$\int \frac{1}{ay(1-y)}\,dy = \frac{1}{a}\int \left(\frac{1}{y} - \frac{1}{1-y}\right) dy = \frac{1}{a}[\ln y - \ln(1-y)] + C = \frac{1}{a}\ln\frac{y}{1-y} + C.$$

55. a. $\dfrac{1}{(a-y)(b-y)} = \dfrac{A}{a-y} + \dfrac{B}{b-y}$; $A(b-y) + B(a-y) = 1$; $Ab + Ba = 1$, $-A - B = 0$; $B = -A$. Thus $A = 1/(b-a)$ and $B = -1/(b-a)$. Therefore

$$t = \int \frac{1}{r(a-y)(b-y)}\,dy = \frac{1}{r}\int \left(\frac{1}{a-b}\frac{1}{y-a} - \frac{1}{a-b}\frac{1}{y-b}\right) dy$$

$$= \frac{1}{r(a-b)}\int \left(\frac{1}{y-a} - \frac{1}{y-b}\right) dy = \frac{1}{r(a-b)}(\ln|y-a| - \ln|y-b|) + C$$

$$= \frac{1}{r(a-b)}\ln\left|\frac{y-a}{y-b}\right| + C \quad \text{for some constant } C.$$

Thus

$$\ln\left|\frac{y-a}{y-b}\right| = r(a-b)t - Cr(a-b), \quad \text{so that} \quad \left|\frac{y-a}{y-b}\right| = e^{r(a-b)t}e^{-Cr(a-b)}.$$

If $C_1 = e^{-Cr(a-b)}$, then

$$\left|\frac{y-a}{y-b}\right| = C_1 e^{(a-b)rt}.$$

b. If the values of y are to lie in (b, a), then $b < y < a$, so that $y - a < 0$ and $y - b > 0$. Thus

$$\left|\frac{y-a}{y-b}\right| = -\left(\frac{y-a}{y-b}\right).$$

Let $C = C_1$ in part (a). Then by part (a),

$$\frac{y-a}{y-b} = -C_1 e^{(a-b)rt} = -Ce^{(a-b)rt}, \quad \text{or} \quad y + yCe^{(a-b)rt} = a + bCe^{(a-b)rt}.$$

Thus

$$y = \frac{a + bCe^{(a-b)rt}}{1 + Ce^{(a-b)rt}}.$$

If the values of y are to lie in $(-\infty, b)$ or (a, ∞), then either $y < b < a$ or $y > a > b$. Thus $y - a$ and $y - b$ have the same sign, so that

$$\left|\frac{y-a}{y-b}\right| = \frac{y-a}{y-b}.$$

Let $C = -C_1$ in part (a). Then by part (a),

$$\frac{y-a}{y-b} = C_1 e^{(a-b)rt} = -Ce^{(a-b)rt}, \quad \text{so once again} \quad y = \frac{a + bCe^{(a-b)rt}}{1 + Ce^{(a-b)rt}}.$$

56. a. $\dfrac{1}{(a-y)(b-y)(c-y)} = \dfrac{A}{a-y} + \dfrac{B}{b-y} + \dfrac{C}{c-y}$; $A(b-y)(c-y)+B(a-y)(c-y)+C(a-y)(b-y) = 1$;
if $y = a$, then $A(b-a)(c-a) = 1$, so $A = 1/[(b-a)(c-a)]$;
if $y = b$, then $B(a-b)(c-b) = 1$, so $B = 1/[(a-b)(c-b)]$;
if $y = c$, then $C(a-c)(b-c) = 1$, so $C = 1/[(a-c)(b-c)]$.
Thus

$$t = \int \frac{1}{r(a-y)(b-y)(c-y)}\, dy$$

$$= \frac{1}{r}\int \left[\frac{1}{(a-b)(a-c)}\frac{1}{a-y} + \frac{1}{(b-c)(b-a)}\frac{1}{b-y} + \frac{1}{(c-a)(c-b)}\frac{1}{c-y}\right] dy$$

$$= \frac{1}{r(a-b)(b-c)(c-a)}\int \left(\frac{c-b}{a-y} + \frac{a-c}{b-y} + \frac{b-a}{c-y}\right) dy$$

$$= \frac{1}{r(a-b)(b-c)(c-a)}\left[-\ln(a-y)^{c-b} - \ln(b-y)^{a-c} - \ln(c-y)^{b-a}\right] + D_1.$$

Therefore

$$(a-c)(b-a)(c-b)r(t-D_1) = \ln\left[(a-y)^{c-b}(b-y)^{a-c}(c-y)^{b-a}\right]$$

so that

$$De^{(a-c)(b-a)(c-b)rt} = e^{(a-c)(b-a)(c-b)r(t-D_1)} = (a-y)^{c-b}(b-y)^{a-c}(c-y)^{b-a}$$

where $D = e^{-(a-c)(b-a)(c-b)rD_1}$.

b. If $y = 0$ when $t = 0$, then $D = a^{c-b}b^{a-c}c^{b-a}$.

7.5 Integration by Tables and Symbolic Integration

1. By Formula 77 in the Table, with $a = 3$, we have $\int \sqrt{x^2+9}\, dx = (x/2)\sqrt{x^2+9} + \frac{9}{2}\ln|x+\sqrt{x^2+9}| + C$.

2. By Formula 75 in the Table, with $a = 4$, we have $\int 1/(16-x^2)^{3/2}\, dx = x/(16\sqrt{16-x^2}) + C$.

3. By Formula 49 in the Table, with $a = 5$ and $b = \frac{1}{2}$, we have

$$\int_0^1 e^{5x}\sin\frac{1}{2}x\, dx = \frac{e^{5x}}{25+\frac{1}{4}}\left(5\sin\frac{1}{2}x - \frac{1}{2}\cos\frac{1}{2}x\right)\Bigg|_0^1 = \frac{4}{101}e^5\left[\left(5\sin\frac{1}{2} - \frac{1}{2}\cos\frac{1}{2}\right)\frac{1}{2}\right].$$

4. By Formula 102 in the Table, with $a = -2$ and $b = 3$, we have

$$\int_1^2 \frac{1}{x(3x-2)}\, dx = \frac{1}{-2}\ln\left|\frac{x}{3x-2}\right|\Bigg|_1^2 = -\frac{1}{2}\ln\frac{1}{2} = \frac{1}{2}\ln 2.$$

5. To use Formula 87 in the Table, we make the substitution $u = 2x$, and note that $a = 3$ in Formula 87:

$$\int \frac{1}{4x^2-9}\, dx \overset{u=2x}{=} \frac{1}{2}\int \frac{1}{u^2-9}\, du = \frac{1}{12}\ln\left|\frac{u-3}{u+3}\right| + C = \frac{1}{12}\ln\left|\frac{2x-3}{2x+3}\right| + C.$$

6. To use Formula 120 in the Table, we make the substitution $u = 2x$, and note that $a = \frac{1}{2}$ in Formula 120:

$$\int \frac{1}{x\sqrt{2x-4x^2}}\,dx \overset{u=2x}{=} \frac{1}{2}\int \frac{1}{\frac{1}{2}u\sqrt{u-u^2}}\,du = \int \frac{1}{u\sqrt{2(\frac{1}{2})u-u^2}}\,du$$

$$= -\frac{\sqrt{2\cdot\frac{1}{2}u-u^2}}{\frac{1}{2}u} + C = \frac{-2\sqrt{u-u^2}}{u} + C = \frac{-\sqrt{2x-4x^2}}{x} + C.$$

7. To use Formula 115 in the Table, we make the substitution $u = \frac{1}{2}x$, and note that $a = 10$ in Formula 115:

$$\int \frac{\sqrt{10x-\frac{1}{4}x^2}}{x}\,dx \overset{u=x/2}{=} 2\int \frac{\sqrt{20u-u^2}}{2u}\,du = \int \frac{\sqrt{2\cdot 10u-u^2}}{u}\,du$$

$$= \sqrt{2\cdot 10u-u^2} + 10\cos^{-1}\left(1-\frac{u}{10}\right) + C = \sqrt{10x-\frac{1}{4}x^2} + 10\cos^{-1}\left(1-\frac{x}{20}\right) + C.$$

8. To use Formula 92 in the Table, we make the substitution $u = \frac{1}{3}x$, and note that $a = \sqrt{5}$ in Formula 92:

$$\int \frac{\sqrt{\frac{1}{9}x^2-5}}{x^2}\,dx \overset{u=x/3}{=} 3\int \frac{\sqrt{u^2-5}}{9u^2}\,du = \frac{1}{3}\int \frac{\sqrt{u^2-5}}{u^2}\,du = -\frac{\sqrt{u^2-5}}{u} + \ln\left|u+\sqrt{u^2-5}\right| + C$$

$$= -\frac{\sqrt{\frac{1}{9}x^2-5}}{\frac{1}{3}x} + \ln\left|\frac{1}{3}x+\sqrt{\frac{1}{9}x^2-5}\right| + C = -\frac{3\sqrt{\frac{1}{9}x^2-5}}{x} + \ln\left|\frac{1}{3}x+\sqrt{\frac{1}{9}x^2-5}\right| + C.$$

9. To use Formula 63 in the Table, we make the substitution $u = \sqrt{x}$, and note that $a = 1$ and $b = 2$ in Formula 63:

$$\int \frac{e^{\sqrt{x}}}{\sqrt{x}}\sinh 2\sqrt{x}\,dx \overset{u=\sqrt{x}}{=} 2\int e^u \sinh 2u\,du = \frac{2e^u}{1^2-2^2}(\sinh 2u - 2\cosh 2u) + C$$

$$= \frac{2}{3}e^{\sqrt{x}}(2\cosh 2\sqrt{x} - \sinh 2\sqrt{x}) + C.$$

10. To use Formula 80 in the Table, we make the substitution $u = \sin x$, and note that $a = 1$ in Formula 80:

$$\int_{\pi/6}^{\pi/2} \frac{\cos x}{\sin^2 x}\sqrt{1+\sin^2 x}\,dx \overset{u=\sin x}{=} \int_{1/2}^{1} \frac{\sqrt{1+u^2}}{u^2}\,du = \left(-\frac{\sqrt{u^2+1}}{u} + \ln\left|u+\sqrt{u^2+1}\right|\right)\Bigg|_{1/2}^{1}$$

$$= \left[-\sqrt{2}+\ln(1+\sqrt{2})\right] - \left[-\sqrt{5}+\ln\left(\frac{1}{2}+\frac{1}{2}\sqrt{5}\right)\right] = \sqrt{5}-\sqrt{2}+\ln(1+\sqrt{2}) - \ln\left(\frac{1}{2}+\frac{1}{2}\sqrt{5}\right).$$

11. To use Formula 27 in the Table, we make the substitution $u = e^x$:

$$\int_0^1 e^{2x}\cos e^x\,dx = \int_0^1 (e^x\cos e^x)e^x\,dx \overset{u=e^x}{=} \int_1^e u\cos u\,du = (u\sin u + \cos u)\Big|_1^e$$

$$= (e\sin e + \cos e) - (\sin 1 + \cos 1) = e\sin e + \cos e - \sin 1 - \cos 1.$$

12. To use Formula 98 in the Table, we make the substitution $u = x^2$, and note that $a = 3$ and $b = -2$ in Formula 98:

$$\int \frac{x}{3-2x^2}\,dx = \int \frac{\frac{1}{2}x^2}{3-2x^2}\,2x\,dx \overset{u=x^2}{=} \frac{1}{2}\int \frac{u}{3-2u}\,du$$

$$= \frac{1}{2}\left[\frac{1}{4}\left(3-2u-3\ln|3-2u|\right)\right] + C = \frac{3}{8} - \frac{1}{4}x^2 - \frac{3}{8}\ln\left|3-2x^2\right| + C.$$

13. To use Formula 49 in the Table, we make the substitution $u = \ln x$, and note that $a = 1$ and $b = 1$ in Formula 49:

$$\int \sin(\ln x)\,dx = \int x[\sin(\ln x)]\,\frac{1}{x}\,dx \overset{u=\ln x}{=} \int e^u \sin u\,du = \frac{e^u}{2}(\sin u - \cos u) + C$$

$$= \frac{e^{\ln x}}{2}\,[\sin(\ln x) - \cos(\ln x)] + C = \frac{1}{2}\,x\,[\sin(\ln x) - \cos(\ln x)] + C.$$

14. To use Formula 101 in the Table, we make the substitution $u = \sqrt{x}$, and note that $a = 2$ and $b = -3$ in Formula 101:

$$\int \frac{\sqrt{x}}{(2-3\sqrt{x})^2}\,dx = \int \frac{2x}{(2-3\sqrt{x})^2}\,\frac{1}{2\sqrt{x}}\,dx \overset{u=\sqrt{x}}{=} 2\int \frac{u^2}{(2-3u)^2}\,du$$

$$= -\frac{2}{27}\left(2-3u-\frac{4}{2-3u}-4\ln|2-3u|\right) + C = \frac{2}{27}\left(-2+3\sqrt{3}+\frac{4}{2-3\sqrt{x}}+4\ln\left|2-3\sqrt{x}\right|\right) + C.$$

15. To use Formula 114 in the Table, we make the substitution $u = \sqrt{x}$, and note that $a = 1$ in Formula 114:

$$\int \sqrt{2\sqrt{x}-x}\,dx \overset{u=\sqrt{x}}{=} 2\int u\sqrt{2u-u^2}\,du = \frac{2u^2-u-3}{3}\sqrt{2u-u^2} + \cos^{-1}(1-u) + C$$

$$= \frac{2x-\sqrt{x}-3}{3}\sqrt{2\sqrt{x}-x} + \cos^{-1}(1-\sqrt{x}) + C.$$

16. To use Formula 109 in the Table, we make the substitution $u = \ln x$, and note that $a = -4$ and $b = 1$ in Formula 109:

$$\int \frac{1}{x\ln x\sqrt{-4+\ln x}}\,dx = \int \frac{1}{\ln x\sqrt{-4+\ln x}}\,\frac{1}{x}\,dx \overset{u=\ln x}{=} \int \frac{1}{u\sqrt{-4+u}}\,du$$

$$= \frac{2}{\sqrt{4}}\tan^{-1}\sqrt{\frac{-4+u}{4}} + C = \tan^{-1}\frac{1}{2}\sqrt{-4+u} + C = \tan^{-1}\frac{1}{2}\sqrt{-4+\ln x} + C.$$

17. By Formula 122 in the Table, with $a = 2$, we have

$$\int x\sqrt{\frac{2+x}{2-x}}\,dx = -\frac{4+x}{2}\sqrt{4-x^2} + 2\sin^{-1}\frac{x}{2} + C.$$

18. By Formula 123 in the Table, with $a = -1$, we have

$$\int \sqrt{\frac{x}{x^3+1}}\,dx = \frac{2}{3}\ln\left(x^{3/2} + \sqrt{x^3+1}\right) + C.$$

19. Mathematica responds that

$$\int x^4\sqrt{a^2+x^2}\,dx = \texttt{Sqrt}\,[\texttt{a}^2+\texttt{x}^2]\;(\frac{-(\texttt{a}^4\,\texttt{x})}{16}+\frac{\texttt{a}^2\,\texttt{x}^3}{24}+\frac{\texttt{x}^5}{6})+\frac{\texttt{a}^6\,\texttt{Log}\,[\texttt{x}+\texttt{Sqrt}\,[\texttt{a}^2+\texttt{x}^2]]}{16}$$

20. Mathematica responds that

$$\int \frac{x^2+a^2}{x^4+a^4}\,dx = \frac{\texttt{ArcTan}\,[\frac{-\texttt{Sqrt}\,[2]+\frac{2\texttt{x}}{\texttt{a}}}{\texttt{Sqrt}\,[2]}]}{\texttt{Sqrt}[2]\,\texttt{a}}+\frac{\texttt{ArcTan}\,[\frac{\texttt{Sqrt}\,[2]+\frac{2\texttt{x}}{\texttt{a}}}{\texttt{Sqrt}\,[2]}]}{\texttt{Sqrt}[2]\,\texttt{a}}$$

21. Mathematica responds that

$$\int \sqrt{x^3+1}\,dx = \frac{2\texttt{xSqrt}\,[1+\texttt{x}^3]}{5}+\frac{3\texttt{Integrate}\,[\frac{1}{\texttt{Sqrt}\,[1+\texttt{x}^3]},\texttt{x}]}{5}$$

meaning that Mathematica tried integration by parts but could not evaluate the integral.

22. Mathematica responds that

$$\int \sin x^3\,dx = \texttt{Integrate}\,[\texttt{Sin}\,[\texttt{x}^3],\texttt{x}]$$

meaning that Mathematica was unable to make any headway in the solution.

7.6 The Trapezoidal Rule and Simpson's Rule

Let T and S be the approximations by the Trapezoidal Rule and Simpson's Rule, respectively.

1. $T=\frac{3-1}{2(6)}\left[1+2(\frac{1}{4/3})+2(\frac{1}{5/3})+\cdots+2(\frac{1}{8/3})+\frac{1}{9/3}\right]\approx 1.106746032$

   $S=\frac{3-1}{3(6)}\left[1+4(\frac{1}{4/3})+2(\frac{1}{5/3})+\cdots+4(\frac{1}{8/3})+\frac{1}{9/3}\right]\approx 1.098941799$

2. $T=\frac{1-0}{2(10)}\left[0+2\sin(0.1)^2+2\sin(0.2)^2+\cdots+2\sin(0.9)^2+\sin 1\right]\approx 0.3111708112$

   $S=\frac{1-0}{3(10)}\left[0+4\sin(0.1)^2+2\sin(0.2)^2+\cdots+4\sin(0.9)^2+\sin 1\right]\approx 0.3102602344$

3. $T=\frac{1-0}{2(10)}\left[1+2e^{-(0.1)^2}+2e^{-(0.2)^2}+\cdots+2e^{-(0.9)^2}+e^{-1}\right]\approx 0.7462107961$

   $S=\frac{1-0}{3(10)}\left[1+4e^{-(0.1)^2}+2e^{-(0.2)^2}+\cdots+4e^{-(0.9)^2}+e^{-1}\right]\approx 0.7468249483$

4. $T=\frac{1-0}{2(40)}\left[1+2e^{-(0.025)^2}+2e^{-(0.05)^2}+\cdots+2e^{-(0.975)^2}+e^{-1}\right]\approx 0.7467858112$

   $S=\frac{1-0}{3(40)}\left[1+4e^{-(0.025)^2}+2e^{-(0.05)^2}+\cdots+4e^{-(0.975)^2}+e^{-1}\right]\approx 0.746824136$

5. Let $f(x)=1/x$. Then $f'(x)=-1/x^2$ and $f''(x)=2/x^3$. For $1\le x\le 3$ we have $|f''(x)|\le 2/1^3=2$, so we can let $K_T=2$. By (3),

$$E_{10}^T\le\frac{2}{12(10)^2}(2^3)=\frac{1}{75}.$$

6. Let $f(x) = \sqrt{1+x^2}$. Then

$$f'(x) = \frac{x}{\sqrt{1+x^2}} \quad \text{and} \quad f''(x) = \frac{\sqrt{1+x^2} - x^2/\sqrt{1+x^2}}{1+x^2} = \frac{1}{(1+x^2)^{3/2}}.$$

For $0 \le x \le 1$ we have $|f''(x)| \le 1$, so we can let $K_T = 1$. By (3),

$$E_{10}^T \le \frac{1}{12(10)^2}(1^3) = \frac{1}{1200}.$$

7. Let $f(x) = 1/(3+x)$. Then

$$f'(x) = \frac{-1}{(3+x)^2}, \quad f''(x) = \frac{2}{(3+x)^3}, \quad f^{(3)}(x) = \frac{-6}{(3+x)^4}, \quad \text{and} \quad f^{(4)}(x) = \frac{24}{(3+x)^5}.$$

For $-1 \le x \le 2$ we have $|f^{(4)}(x)| \le 24/(3-2)^5 = 24$, so we can let $K_S = 24$. By (8),

$$E_{10}^S \le \frac{24}{180(10)^4}\left(2-(-1)\right)^5 = \frac{162}{5 \times 10^4} = 3.24 \times 10^{-3}.$$

8. Let $f(x) = x \ln x$. Then $f'(x) = \ln x + 1$, $f''(x) = 1/x$, $f^{(3)}(x) = -1/x^2$, and $f^{(4)}(x) = 2/x^3$. For $1 \le x \le 4$ we have $|f^{(4)}(x)| \le 2/1^3 = 2$, so we can let $K_S = 2$. By (8),

$$E_{20}^S \le \frac{2}{180(20)^4}(4-1)^5 = \frac{486}{2.88 \times 10^7} \approx 1.6875 \times 10^{-5}.$$

9. Let $f(x) = \sqrt{1+x^2}$ for $1 \le x \le 2$. The computer yields

$$f^{(4)}(x) = \frac{-15x^4}{(1+x^2)^{7/2}} + \frac{18x^2}{(1+x^2)^{5/2}} - \frac{3}{(1+x^2)^{3/2}}.$$

By plotting the graph of $f^{(4)}$ we see that the maximum value of $|f^{(4)}(x)|$ for $1 \le x \le 2$ is $|f^{(4)}(1)|$, and $0.78 < |f^{(4)}(1)| < 0.8$. Thus we can take $K = 0.8$. By (8),

$$E_{10}^S \le \frac{0.8}{180(10)^4}(2-1)^5 = \frac{0.8}{1.8 \times 10^6} \approx 4.444444444 \times 10^{-7}.$$

10. Let $f(x) = 1/(1+x^3)$ for $1 \le x \le 2$. The computer yields

$$f^{(4)}(x) = \frac{1944x^8}{(1+x^3)^5} - \frac{1944x^5}{(1+x^3)^4} + \frac{360x^2}{(1+x^3)^3}.$$

From the plot of $f^{(4)}$ we see that the maximum value of $|f^{(4)}(x)|$ for $2 \le x \le 4$ is $|f^{(4)}(2)|$, and $0.8 < |f^{(4)}(2)| < 0.9$. Thus we can take $K = 0.9$. By (8),

$$E_{10}^S \le \frac{0.9}{180(10^4)}(4-2)^5 = 1.6 \times 10^{-5}.$$

11. By Simpson's Rule with $n = 10$, $A = \int_{-\pi/3}^{\pi/3} 1/(1+\cos x)\,dx \approx 1.154724372$.

12. By Simpson's Rule with $n = 10$, $A = \int_{\pi/2}^{3\pi/2} [(\pi \cos x)/x]\,dx \approx 2.10603484$.

13. a. By Simpson's Rule with $n = 4$, $A \approx \frac{0.9-0.1}{3(4)}[f(0.1)+4f(0.3)+2f(0.5)+4f(0.7)+f(0.9)] \approx \frac{0.8}{12}[1+4(2.4)+2(1.4)+4(1)+2.4] = 1.32$.

b. By Simpson's Rule with $n = 8$, $A \approx \frac{0.9-0.1}{3(8)}[f(0.1)+4f(0.2)+2f(0.3)+\cdots+4f(0.8)+f(0.9)] \approx \frac{0.8}{24}[1+4(2)+2(2.4)+4(2)+2(1.4)+4(1)+2(1)+4(1.4)+2.4] \approx 1.286666667$.

14. a. By Simpson's Rule with $n = 100$,

i. $\int_1^{10}(1/x)\sqrt{1+1/x^4}\,dx \approx 2.415586976$

ii. $\int_1^{100}(1/x)\sqrt{1+1/x^4}\,dx \approx 4.777475167$

iii. $\int_1^{1000}(1/x)\sqrt{1+1/x^4}\,dx \approx 9.945486098$

b. No. Every time b is increased tenfold, the result is nearly doubled. (Note that for large values of x, $(1/x)\sqrt{1+1/x^4} \approx 1/x$, and as b increases without bound, $\int_1^b (1/x)\,dx = \ln b$ increases without bound.)

15. a. *i.* By the Trapezoidal Rule with $n = 10$, $\int_0^1 4/(1+x^2)\,dx \approx 3.139925989$.

ii. By the Simpson's Rule with $n = 10$, $\int_0^1 4/(1+x^2)\,dx \approx 3.141592614$.

b. For the Trapezoidal Rule the error is approximately 0.001666665; for Simpson's Rule the error is approximately 4×10^{-8}.

16. By Simpson's Rule with $n = 2$, $\int_0^{\pi/2}\sqrt{1+\cos x}\,dx \approx 2.00026917$. Letting $u = x/2$, so that $du = \frac{1}{2}\,dx$, we have $\int_0^{\pi/2}\sqrt{1+\cos x}\,dx = \int_0^{\pi/2}\sqrt{2}\cos(x/2)\,dx = 2\sqrt{2}\int_0^{\pi/4}\cos u\,du = 2\sqrt{2}\sin u\big|_0^{\pi/4} = (2\sqrt{2})(\sqrt{2}/2) = 2$. Thus $E_2^S \approx 0.00026917$.

17. a. If $f(x) = 1/x$, then $f'(x) = -1/x^2$, $f''(x) = 2/x^3$, $f^{(3)}(x) = -6/x^4$, $f^{(4)}(x) = 24/x^5$, so $M = \max_{1\le x\le 8}|24/x^5| = 24$. Thus $E_n^S \le [(8-1)^5 24]/(180n^4)$, so $E_n^S \le 10^{-4}$ if $7^5(24)/(180n^4) \le 10^{-4}$, that is, $n^4 \ge 7^5(24)10^4/180$, or $n \ge 68.8$. Therefore, since n must be even, we take $n = 70$.

b. Since $M = \max_{1\le x\le 2} 24/x^5 = 24$, it follows that $E_n^S \le [(2-1)^5 24]/(180n^4) = 2/(15n^4)$ and thus $3E_n^S \le 10^{-4}$ if $6/(15n^4) \le 10^{-4}$, that is, $n^4 \ge (6)10^4/15$, or $n \ge 7.96$. Therefore we take $n = 8$.

18. If $f(x) = mx + c$, then $f''(x) = 0$ for $a \le x \le b$, so that by (3) the error E_n^T by using the Trapezoidal Rule satisfies

$$0 \le E_n^T \le \frac{(b-a)^3 \cdot 0}{12n^2} = 0.$$

19. a. If $f(x) = c_3x^3 + c_2x^2 + c_1x + c_0$, then $f^{(4)}(x) = 0$ for $a \le x \le b$, so that by (8) the error E_n^S by using Simpson's Rule satisfies

$$0 \le E_n^S \le \frac{(b-a)^5 \cdot 0}{180n^4} = 0.$$

b. By Simpson's Rule with $n = 10$, $\int_{-2}^1 (x^3 - 2x^2 + 3x - 1)\,dx = -17.25$. By direct integration, $\int_{-2}^1 (x^3 - 2x^2 + 3x - 1)\,dx = (\frac{1}{4}x^4 - \frac{2}{3}x^3 + \frac{3}{2}x^2 - x)\big|_{-2}^1 = (\frac{1}{4} - \frac{2}{3} + \frac{3}{2} - 1) - (4 + \frac{16}{3} + 6 + 2) = -17.25$. Thus Simpson's Rule gives the exact value.

20. If $f(x) = x^4$, then $\int_0^1 f(x)\,dx = \int_0^1 x^4\,dx = \frac{1}{5}$. The approximation by using Simpson's Rule with $n = 2$ is given by $S = \frac{1}{6}\left(0 + 4(\frac{1}{2})^2 + 1\right) = \frac{5}{24}$, so that the error is $\left|\frac{1}{5} - \frac{5}{24}\right| = \frac{1}{120}$. Since $f^{(4)}(x) = 24$ for $0 \le x \le 1$, we have

$$\frac{(b-a)^5 M}{180n^4} = \frac{1^5(24)}{(180)(2^4)} = \frac{1}{120}$$

which is exactly the error incurred by using Simpson's Rule with $n = 2$. Thus

$$E_n^S = \frac{1}{120} = \frac{(b-a)^5 M}{180n^4}$$

in this case.

21. a. From the figure we see that the trapezoid above $[x_{k-1}, x_k]$ on the x axis contains the region bounded by the graph of f. Adding the corresponding areas, we obtain $T_n \ge \int_a^b f(x)\,dx$.

b. The Trapezoidal Rule approximation will decrease because the trapezoids will more closely approximate the graph of f.

c. If the graph of f is concave downward, then $T_n \le \int_a^b f(x)\,dx$, and the Trapezoidal Rule approximation would increase if n is doubled.

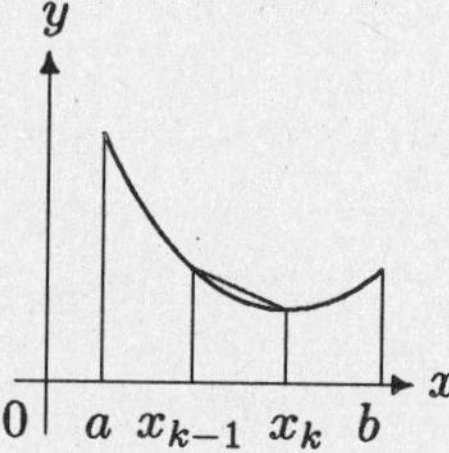

22. Let $P = \{x_0, x_1, \ldots, x_n\}$. Then

$$T_n = \frac{b-a}{2n}[f(x_0) + 2f(x_1) + 2f(x_2) + \cdots + 2f(x_{n-1}) + f(x_n)]$$

$$= \frac{b-a}{2n}[f(x_0) + f(x_1) + \cdots + f(x_{n-1})] + \frac{b-a}{2n}[f(x_1) + f(x_2) + f(x_3) + \cdots + f(x_{n-1}) + f(x_n)]$$

$$= \frac{1}{2}L_n + \frac{1}{2}R_n = \frac{1}{2}(L_n + R_n).$$

23. a. Let $P = \{x_0, x_1, \ldots, x_{2n-1}, x_{2n}\}$ divide $[a, b]$ into $2n$ subintervals of equal length. Then

$$S_{2n} = \frac{b-a}{3(2n)}[f(x_0) + 4f(x_1) + 2f(x_2) + \cdots + 4f(x_{2n-1}) + f(x_{2n})]$$

$$\frac{1}{3}T_n = \frac{b-a}{3(2n)}[f(x_0) + 2f(x_2) + \cdots + 2f(x_{2n-2}) + f(x_{2n})]$$

$$\frac{2}{3}M_n = \frac{2(b-a)}{3n}[f(x_1) + f(x_3) + \cdots + f(x_{2n-1})] = \frac{b-a}{6n}[4f(x_1) + 4f(x_3) + \cdots + 4f(x_{2n-1})].$$

Thus the terms of S_{2n} with even index are covered by $\frac{1}{3}T_n$, and the terms of S_{2n} with odd index are covered by $\frac{2}{3}M_n$. Therefore $S_{2n} = \frac{1}{3}T_n + \frac{2}{3}M_n$.

b. By Exercise 22, $T_n = \frac{1}{2}(L_n + R_n)$. Then part (a) yields $S_{2n} = \frac{1}{3}[\frac{1}{2}(L_n + R_n)] + \frac{2}{3}M_n = \frac{1}{6}L_n + \frac{2}{3}M_n + \frac{1}{6}R_n$. Thus $u = \frac{1}{6}$, $v = \frac{2}{3}$ and $w = \frac{1}{6}$.

24. c, d, and e.

25. Left sum < midpoint sum < Trapezoidal Rule < right sum.

26. Since f is continuous on $[a,b]$ and $[f(x_{k-1})+f(x_k)]/2$ is a number between $f(x_{k-1})$ and $f(x_k)$, the Intermediate Value Theorem says that there is a number c_k in $[x_{k-1},x_k]$ such that $[f(x_{k-1})+f(x_k)]/2 = f(c_k)$. Then

$$\begin{aligned} T &= \frac{b-a}{2n}\left[(f(x_0)+f(x_1))+(f(x_1)+f(x_2))+\cdots+(f(x_{n-1})+f(x_n))\right] \\ &= \frac{b-a}{n}\left[\frac{f(x_0)+f(x_1)}{2}+\frac{f(x_1)+f(x_2)}{2}+\cdots+\frac{f(x_{n-1})+f(x_n)}{2}\right] \\ &= \frac{b-a}{n}[f(c_1)+f(c_2)+\cdots+f(c_n)]. \end{aligned}$$

This is a Riemann sum for f on $[a,b]$.

27. We have $x_1-x_0=x_2-x_1=h$ and $x_2-x_0=2h$. Thus

$$\int_{x_0}^{x_2} f(x_0)\,dx = f(x_0)(x_2-x_0) = 2hf(x_0)$$

$$\int_{x_0}^{x_2}\frac{f(x_1)-f(x_0)}{h}(x-x_0)\,dx = \frac{f(x_1)-f(x_0)}{h}\cdot\frac{1}{2}(x-x_0)^2\Big|_{x_0}^{x_2} = 2h[f(x_1)-f(x_0)].$$

By integration by parts with $u=(x-x_0)$, $dv=(x-x_1)\,dx$, $du=dx$, and $v=\frac{1}{2}(x-x_1)^2$, we have

$$\begin{aligned} &\int_{x_0}^{x_2}\frac{f(x_0)-2f(x_1)+f(x_2)}{2h^2}(x-x_0)(x-x_1)\,dx \\ &= \frac{f(x_0)-2f(x_1)+f(x_2)}{2h^2}\left[(x-x_0)\cdot\frac{1}{2}(x-x_1)^2\Big|_{x_0}^{x_2} - \int_{x_0}^{x_2}\frac{1}{2}(x-x_1)^2\,dx\right] \\ &= \frac{f(x_0)-2f(x_1)+f(x_2)}{2h^2}\left[h^3-\frac{1}{6}(x-x_1)^3\Big|_{x_0}^{x_2}\right] = \frac{h}{3}[f(x_0)-2f(x_1)+f(x_2)]. \end{aligned}$$

Adding these integrals, we find that

$$\int_{x_0}^{x_2} p(x)\,dx = 2hf(x_0)+2h[f(x_1)-f(x_0)]+\frac{h}{3}[f(x_0)-2f(x_1)+f(x_2)] = \frac{h}{3}[f(x_0)+4f(x_1)+f(x_2)].$$

28. Let $v(t)$ denote the velocity of the car at time t. Then the distance D traveled by the car during the two-hour period equals $\int_0^2 v(t)\,dt$. By Simpson's Rule with $n=8$, the distance D is approximately given by $\frac{2-0}{3(8)}[20+4(50)+2(56)+4(54)+2(52)+4(49)+2(54)+4(52)+30]=99.5$ (miles).

29. Let $v(t)$ denote the wind speed at time t, with $t=0$ corresponding to 8 a.m. and $t=12$ corresponding to 8 p.m. By (5) in Section 5.3, the mean speed equals $\frac{1}{12-0}\int_0^{12} v(t)\,dt$. By Simpson's Rule with $n=6$, the mean wind speed during the 12-hour period is approximately $\frac{1}{12}\left\{\frac{12-0}{3(6)}[20+4(24)+2(18)+4(28)+2(21)+4(15)+10]\right\}=\frac{376}{18}\approx 20.9$. Thus the mean wind speed is approximately 20.9 miles per hour.

30. Let $F(t)$ denote the height of the snow at time t, with $t = 0$ corresponding to 1 p.m. and $t = 6$ corresponding to 7 p.m. Then $F'(t)$ is the rate of snow accumulation at time t. By (5) in Section 5.4 the total accumulation of snow between 1 p.m. and 7 p.m. equals $\int_0^6 F'(t)\,dt$.

    a. By the Trapezoidal Rule with $n = 6$, the total accumulation during the 6-hour period is approximately $\frac{6-0}{2(6)}[0.3 + 2(1.3) + 2(2.7) + 2(3.1) + 2(2.9) + 2(1.5) + 0.2] = 11.75$. Thus the total accumulation of snow is approximately 11.75 inches.

    b. By Simpson's Rule with $n = 6$, the total accumulation during the 6-hour period is approximately $\frac{6-0}{3(6)}[0.3 + 4(1.3) + 2(2.7) + 4(3.1) + 2(2.9) + 4(1.5) + 0.2] = \frac{35.3}{3} \approx 11.76666667$. Thus the total accumulation of snow is approximately 11.8 inches.

    c. By (5) in Section 5.3 the mean rate of accumulation during the 6-hour period equals $\frac{1}{6-0}\int_0^6 F'(t)\,dt$. By (b) the mean rate of accumulation is approximately $\frac{1}{6}(\frac{35.3}{3}) \approx 1.961111111$, that is, approximately 1.96 inches per hour.

31. Let $F(t)$ denote the number of flu cases that occur during the epidemic before time t (measured in days), with $t = 0$ corresponding to the outbreak of the epidemic. Then $F'(t)$ equals the rate at which the epidemic is spreading. By (5) in Section 5.4 the total number of flu cases during the 30-day period equals $\int_0^{30} F'(t)\,dt$. By Simpson's Rule with $n = 10$, the total number of cases is approximately $\frac{30-0}{3(10)}[0 + 4(30) + 2(160) + 4(370) + 2(480) + 4(490) + 2(380) + 4(200) + 2(70) + 4(20) + 0] = 6620$.

32. Let $f(x)$ equal the width of the oil spill x miles from the left end of the spill. Then the area of the oil spill equals $\int_0^{10} f(x)\,dx$. By Simpson's Rule with $n = 10$, the area is approximately $\frac{10}{3(10)}[0 + 4(1.1) + 2(1.3) + 4(1.4) + 2(1.6) + 4(1.6) + 2(1.5) + 4(1.4) + 2(1.2) + 4(0.8) + 0] = 12.1$ (square miles).

33. Let the partition points be 20, 70, 120, ..., 320, and assume that the lower boundary of Idaho is 20 miles above the horizontal axis. By Simpson's Rule with $n = 6$, the area of Idaho is approximately $\frac{300}{3(6)}[480 + 4(420) + 2(370) + 4(260) + 2(180) + 4(180) + 190] = \frac{1{,}563{,}000}{18} \approx 86{,}833$. Thus by Simpson's Rule we have calculated the area of Idaho to be approximately 86,833 square miles. (This is less than 5.4% from the true value of the area!)

34. By (6) in Section 5.4 the revenue equals $\int_0^5 m_r(x)\,dx$, where m_r denotes the marginal revenue function. By Simpson's Rule with $n=10$, the revenue is approximately

$$\frac{5-0}{3(10)}(100{,}000)\,[6000 + 4(5000) + 2(4000) + 4(3000) + 2(2000) + 4(1300) + 2(1000)$$

$$+4(1500) + 2(2000) + 4(1700) + 1000] = 1{,}250{,}000{,}000 \text{ (dollars)}.$$

7.7 Improper Integrals

1. converges; $\int_0^1 \frac{1}{x^{0.9}}\,dx = \lim_{c\to0^+}\int_c^1 \frac{1}{x^{0.9}}\,dx = \lim_{c\to0^+} 10x^{0.1}\Big|_c^1 = \lim_{c\to0^+} 10(1 - c^{0.1}) = 10$

2. diverges; $\int_0^1 \frac{1}{x^{1.1}}\,dx = \lim_{c\to 0+} \int_c^1 \frac{1}{x^{1.1}}\,dx = \lim_{c\to 0+} (-10x^{-0.1})\big|_c^1 = \lim_{c\to 0+} \left(-10 + \frac{10}{x^{0.1}}\right) = \infty$

3. diverges; $\int_3^4 \frac{1}{(t-4)^2}\,dt = \lim_{c\to 4-} \int_3^c \frac{1}{(t-4)^2}\,dt = \lim_{c\to 4-} \frac{-1}{t-4}\Big|_3^c = \lim_{c\to 4-} \left(\frac{-1}{c-4} - 1\right) = \infty$

4. diverges; $\int_1^5 \frac{1}{(x-1)^{1.5}}\,dx = \lim_{c\to 1+} \int_c^5 \frac{1}{(x-1)^{1.5}}\,dx = \lim_{c\to 1+} (-2)(x-1)^{-0.5}\big|_c^5$

$$= \lim_{c\to 1+} \left(-1 + 2(c-1)^{-0.5}\right) = \infty$$

5. converges; $\int_3^4 \frac{1}{\sqrt[3]{x-3}}\,dx = \lim_{c\to 3+} \int_c^4 \frac{1}{\sqrt[3]{x-3}}\,dx = \lim_{c\to 3+} \frac{3}{2}(x-3)^{2/3}\Big|_c^4 = \lim_{c\to 3+} \left(\frac{3}{2} - \frac{3}{2}(c-3)^{2/3}\right) = \frac{3}{2}$

6. converges; $\int_0^2 \frac{x}{\sqrt[3]{x^2-2}}\,dx = \lim_{c\to\sqrt{2}-} \int_0^c \frac{x}{\sqrt[3]{x^2-2}}\,dx + \lim_{p\to\sqrt{2}+} \int_p^2 \frac{x}{\sqrt[3]{x^2-2}}\,dx$

$$= \lim_{c\to\sqrt{2}-} \frac{3}{4}(x^2-2)^{2/3}\Big|_0^c + \lim_{p\to\sqrt{2}+} \frac{3}{4}(x^2-2)^{2/3}\Big|_p^2$$

$$= \lim_{c\to\sqrt{2}-} \left[\frac{3}{4}(c^2-2)^{2/3} - \frac{3}{4}(-2)^{2/3}\right] + \lim_{p\to\sqrt{2}+} \left[\frac{3}{4}(2^{2/3}) - \frac{3}{4}(p^2-2)^{2/3}\right]$$

$$= 0$$

7. diverges $\int_0^{\pi/2} \sec^2\theta\,d\theta = \lim_{c\to\pi/2-} \int_0^c \sec^2\theta\,d\theta = \lim_{c\to\pi/2-} \tan\theta\big|_0^c = \lim_{c\to\pi/2-} \tan c = \infty$

8. diverges; $\int_{-\pi/2}^{\pi/4} \tan x\,dx = \lim_{c\to-\pi/2+} \int_c^{\pi/4} \tan x\,dx = \lim_{c\to-\pi/2+} (-\ln|\cos x|)\big|_c^{\pi/4}$

$$= \lim_{c\to-\pi/2+} \left(-\ln\frac{\sqrt{2}}{2} + \ln|\cos c|\right) = -\infty$$

9. converges; let $u = 1 + \cos x$, so that $du = -\sin x\,dx$; then

$$\int_0^{\pi} \frac{\sin x}{\sqrt{1+\cos x}}\,dx = \lim_{c\to\pi-} \int_0^c \frac{\sin x}{\sqrt{1+\cos x}}\,dx = \lim_{c\to\pi-} \int_2^{1+\cos c} \frac{-1}{u^{1/2}}\,du$$

$$= \lim_{c\to\pi-} \left(-2u^{1/2}\right)\Big|_2^{1+\cos c} = \lim_{c\to\pi-} \left[-2(1+\cos c)^{1/2} + 2\sqrt{2}\right] = 2\sqrt{2}.$$

10. diverges; $\int_0^2 \frac{\ln x}{x}\,dx = \lim_{c\to 0+} \int_c^2 \frac{\ln x}{x}\,dx = \lim_{c\to 0+} \frac{1}{2}(\ln x)^2\Big|_c^2 = \lim_{c\to 0+} \left[\frac{1}{2}(\ln 2)^2 - \frac{1}{2}(\ln c)^2\right] = -\infty$

11. diverges; $\int_1^2 \frac{1}{w\ln w}\,dw = \lim_{c\to 1+} \int_c^2 \frac{1}{w\ln w}\,dw = \lim_{c\to 1+} \ln(\ln w)\big|_c^2 = \lim_{c\to 1+} [\ln(\ln 2) - \ln(\ln c)] = \infty$

12. converges; let $u = \ln w$, so that $du = (1/w)\,dw$; then

$$\int_1^2 \frac{1}{w(\ln w)^{1/2}}\,dw = \lim_{c\to 1+} \int_c^2 \frac{1}{w(\ln w)^{1/2}}\,dw = \lim_{c\to 1+} \int_{\ln c}^{\ln 2} \frac{1}{u^{1/2}}\,du$$

$$= \lim_{c\to 1^+} 2u^{1/2}\Big|_{\ln c}^{\ln 2} = \lim_{c\to 1^+} 2\left[(\ln 2)^{1/2} - (\ln c)^{1/2}\right] = 2(\ln 2)^{1/2}$$

13. converges. Let $d = \frac{1}{2}$. Then

$$\int_0^1 \frac{3x^2-1}{\sqrt[3]{x^3-x}}\,dx = \lim_{c\to 0^+}\int_c^{1/2}\frac{3x^2-1}{\sqrt[3]{x^3-x}}\,dx + \lim_{p\to 1^-}\int_{1/2}^{p}\frac{3x^2-1}{\sqrt[3]{x^3-x}}\,dx$$

$$= \lim_{c\to 0^+}\frac{3}{2}(x^3-x)^{2/3}\Big|_c^{1/2} + \lim_{p\to 1^-}\frac{3}{2}(x^3-x)^{2/3}\Big|_{1/2}^{p}$$

$$= \lim_{c\to 0^+}\left[\frac{3}{2}\left(\frac{-3}{8}\right)^{2/3} - \frac{3}{2}(c^3-c)^{2/3}\right] + \lim_{p\to 1^-}\left[\frac{3}{2}(p^3-p)^{2/3} - \frac{3}{2}\left(\frac{-3}{8}\right)^{2/3}\right]$$

$$= \frac{3}{2}\left(\frac{3}{8}\right)^{2/3} - \frac{3}{2}\left(\frac{3}{8}\right)^{2/3} = 0.$$

14. diverges. Let $d = \frac{1}{2}$. Then

$$\int_0^1 \frac{3x^2-1}{x^3-x}\,dx = \lim_{c\to 0^+}\int_c^{1/2}\frac{3x^2-1}{x^3-x}\,dx + \lim_{p\to 1^-}\int_{1/2}^{p}\frac{3x^2-1}{x^3-x}\,dx$$

$$= \lim_{c\to 0^+}\ln|x^3-x|\Big|_c^{1/2} + \lim_{p\to 1^-}\ln|x^3-x|\Big|_{1/2}^{p}$$

$$= \lim_{c\to 0^+}\left(\ln\left|\frac{1}{8}-\frac{1}{2}\right| - \ln|c^3-c|\right) + \lim_{p\to 1^-}\left(\ln|p^3-p| - \ln\left|\frac{1}{8}-\frac{1}{2}\right|\right).$$

Neither one-sided limit exists, so the integral diverges.

15. diverges. Let $d = \pi/2$. Then

$$\int_0^{\pi} \csc^2 x\,dx = \lim_{c\to 0^+}\int_c^{\pi/2}\csc^2 x\,dx + \lim_{p\to \pi^-}\int_{\pi/2}^{p}\csc^2 x\,dx$$

$$= \lim_{c\to 0^+}(-\cot x)\Big|_c^{\pi/2} + \lim_{p\to\pi^-}(-\cot x)\Big|_{\pi/2}^{p} = \lim_{c\to 0^+}(0+\cot c) + \lim_{p\to\pi^-}(-\cot p + 0).$$

Neither one-sided limit exists, so the integral diverges.

16. diverges. Let $d = 0$. Then

$$\int_{-\pi/2}^{\pi/2}\sec\theta\,d\theta = \lim_{c\to -\pi/2^+}\int_c^0 \sec\theta\,d\theta + \lim_{p\to\pi/2^-}\int_0^p \sec\theta\,d\theta$$

$$= \lim_{c\to-\pi/2^+}\ln|\sec\theta+\tan\theta|\Big|_c^0 + \lim_{p\to\pi/2^-}\ln|\sec\theta+\tan\theta|\Big|_0^p$$

$$= \lim_{c\to-\pi/2^+}(0 - \ln|\sec c + \tan c|) + \lim_{p\to\pi/2^-}(\ln|\sec p + \tan p| - 0).$$

Neither one-sided limit exists, so the integral diverges.

17. diverges; let $u = e^t$, so that $du = e^t\,dt$ and $(1/u)\,du = dt$; then

$$\int_0^1 \frac{1}{e^t - e^{-t}}\,dt = \lim_{c\to 0^+} \int_c^1 \frac{1}{e^t - e^{-t}}\,dt = \lim_{c\to 0^+} \int_{e^c}^{e} \frac{1}{u - 1/u}\frac{1}{u}\,du$$

$$= \lim_{c\to 0^+} \int_{e^c}^{e} \frac{1}{u^2-1}\,du = \lim_{c\to 0^+} \int_{e^c}^{e} \left(\frac{1}{2}\frac{1}{u-1} - \frac{1}{2}\frac{1}{u+1}\right) du$$

$$= \lim_{c\to 0^+} \left(\frac{1}{2}\ln|u-1| - \frac{1}{2}\ln|u+1|\right)\Big|_{e^c}^{e} = \lim_{c\to 0^+} \left(\frac{1}{2}\ln\left|\frac{u-1}{u+1}\right|\right)\Big|_{e^c}^{e}$$

$$= \lim_{c\to 0^+} \left(\frac{1}{2}\ln\left|\frac{e-1}{e+1}\right| - \frac{1}{2}\ln\left|\frac{e^c-1}{e^c+1}\right|\right).$$

Since $\lim_{c\to 0^+}(e^c-1)/(e^c+1) = 0$, it follows that

$$\lim_{c\to 0^+} \left(\frac{1}{2}\ln\left|\frac{e-1}{e+1}\right| - \frac{1}{2}\ln\left|\frac{e^c-1}{e^c+1}\right|\right) = \infty$$

so the integral diverges.

18. converges; $\displaystyle\int_{-1}^{2} \frac{1}{x^{1/3}}\,dx = \lim_{c\to 0^-} \int_{-1}^{c} \frac{1}{x^{1/3}}\,dx + \lim_{p\to 0^+} \int_p^2 \frac{1}{x^{1/3}}\,dx = \lim_{c\to 0^-} \frac{3}{2}x^{2/3}\Big|_{-1}^{c} + \lim_{p\to 0^+} \frac{3}{2}x^{2/3}\Big|_p^2$

$$= \lim_{c\to 0^-} \left(\frac{3}{2}c^{2/3} - \frac{3}{2}\right) + \lim_{p\to 0^+} \left(\frac{3}{2}\sqrt[3]{4} - \frac{3}{2}p^{2/3}\right) = \frac{3}{2}\sqrt[3]{4} - \frac{3}{2}$$

19. diverges; $\displaystyle\int_{-1}^{2} \left(\frac{1}{x} + \frac{1}{x^2}\right) dx = \lim_{c\to 0^-} \int_{-1}^{c} \left(\frac{1}{x} + \frac{1}{x^2}\right) dx + \lim_{p\to 0^+} \int_p^2 \left(\frac{1}{x} + \frac{1}{x^2}\right) dx$

$$= \lim_{c\to 0^-} \left(\ln|x| - \frac{1}{x}\right)\Big|_{-1}^{c} + \lim_{p\to 0^+} \left(\ln|x| - \frac{1}{x}\right)\Big|_p^2$$

$$= \lim_{c\to 0^-} \left(\ln|c| - \frac{1}{c} - 1\right) + \lim_{p\to 0^+} \left(\ln 2 - \frac{1}{2} - \ln p + \frac{1}{p}\right)$$

Since $\lim_{p\to 0^+}(\ln 2 - \frac{1}{2} - \ln p + 1/p) = \infty$, the integral diverges.

20. diverges; $\displaystyle\int_0^2 \frac{1}{(x-1)^{4/3}}\,dx = \lim_{c\to 1^-} \int_0^c \frac{1}{(x-1)^{4/3}}\,dx + \lim_{p\to 1^+} \int_p^2 \frac{1}{(x-1)^{4/3}}\,dx$

$$= \lim_{c\to 1^-} (-3)\,(x-1)^{-1/3}\Big|_0^c + \lim_{p\to 1^+} (-3)(x-1)^{-1/3}\Big|_p^2$$

$$= \lim_{c\to 1^-} \left[(-3)(c-1)^{-1/3} - 3\right] + \lim_{p\to 1^+} \left[-3 + 3(p-1)^{-1/3}\right]$$

Neither one-sided limit exists, so the integral diverges.

21. converges; $\displaystyle\int_0^2 \frac{1}{(x-1)^{1/3}}\,dx = \lim_{c\to 1^-} \int_0^c \frac{1}{(x-1)^{1/3}}\,dx + \lim_{p\to 1^+} \int_p^2 \frac{1}{(x-1)^{1/3}}\,dx$

$$= \lim_{c\to 1^-} \frac{3}{2}(x-1)^{2/3}\Big|_0^c + \lim_{p\to 1^+} \frac{3}{2}(x-1)^{2/3}\Big|_p^2$$

$$= \lim_{c\to 1^-} \left(\frac{3}{2}(c-1)^{2/3} - \frac{3}{2}\right) + \lim_{p\to 1^+} \left(\frac{3}{2} - \frac{3}{2}(p-1)^{2/3}\right) = 0$$

22. diverges; $\int_{-\pi/2}^{\pi/2} \frac{1}{x^2} \sin\frac{1}{x}\,dx = \lim_{c\to 0^-} \int_{-\pi/2}^{c} \frac{1}{x^2}\sin\frac{1}{x}\,dx + \lim_{p\to 0^+}\int_p^{\pi/2} \frac{1}{x^2}\sin\frac{1}{x}\,dx$

$$= \lim_{c\to 0^-} \cos\frac{1}{x}\Big|_{-\pi/2}^{c} + \lim_{p\to 0^+} \cos\frac{1}{x}\Big|_p^{\pi/2}$$

$$= \lim_{c\to 0^-}\left[\cos\frac{1}{c} - \cos\left(\frac{-2}{\pi}\right)\right] + \lim_{p\to 0^+}\left(\cos\frac{2}{\pi} - \cos\frac{1}{p}\right)$$

Neither one-sided limit exists, so the integral diverges.

23. converges; $\int_0^1 \frac{1}{\sqrt{1-t^2}}\,dt = \lim_{c\to 1^-}\int_0^c \frac{1}{\sqrt{1-t^2}}\,dt = \lim_{c\to 1^-} \sin^{-1} t\big|_0^c$

$$= \lim_{c\to 1^-}(\sin^{-1} c - \sin^{-1} 0) = \sin^{-1} 1 = \frac{\pi}{2}$$

24. converges; let $u = e^t - 1$, so that $du = e^t\,dt$; then

$$\int_0^1 \frac{e^t}{\sqrt{e^t-1}}\,dt = \lim_{c\to 0^+}\int_c^1 \frac{e^t}{\sqrt{e^t-1}}\,dt = \lim_{c\to 0^+}\int_{e^c-1}^{e-1}\frac{1}{\sqrt{u}}\,du$$

$$= \lim_{c\to 0^+} 2\sqrt{u}\big|_{e^c-1}^{e-1} = \lim_{c\to 0^+}(2\sqrt{e-1} - 2\sqrt{e^c-1}) = 2\sqrt{e-1}$$

25. diverges; $\int_0^\infty \frac{1}{x}\,dx = \lim_{a\to 0^+}\int_a^1 \frac{1}{x}\,dx + \lim_{b\to\infty}\int_1^b \frac{1}{x}\,dx = \lim_{a\to 0^+} \ln|x|\big|_a^1 + \lim_{b\to\infty} \ln|x|\big|_1^b$

$$= \lim_{a\to 0^+}(0 - \ln a) + \lim_{b\to\infty}(\ln b - 0)$$

Since both limits are infinite, the integral diverges.

26. converges; $\int_1^\infty \frac{1}{x^{1.1}}\,dx = \lim_{b\to\infty}\int_1^b \frac{1}{x^{1.1}}\,dx = \lim_{b\to\infty}\left(-10\frac{1}{x^{0.1}}\right)\Big|_1^b = \lim_{b\to\infty}\left(10 - \frac{10}{b^{0.1}}\right) = 10$

27. converges; $\int_0^\infty \frac{1}{(2+x)^\pi}\,dx = \lim_{b\to\infty}\int_0^b (2+x)^{-\pi}\,dx = \lim_{b\to\infty} \frac{1}{-\pi+1}(2+x)^{-\pi+1}\Big|_0^b$

$$= \lim_{b\to\infty}\frac{1}{-\pi+1}\left((2+b)^{-\pi+1} - 2^{-\pi+1}\right) = \frac{1}{\pi-1}2^{-\pi+1}$$

28. diverges; $\int_{-\infty}^0 \sqrt{4-x}\,dx = \lim_{a\to-\infty}\int_a^0 \sqrt{4-x}\,dx = \lim_{a\to-\infty} -\frac{2}{3}(4-x)^{3/2}\Big|_a^0$

$$= \lim_{a\to-\infty}\left[-\frac{2}{3}(8) + \frac{2}{3}(4-a)^{3/2}\right] = \infty$$

29. diverges; $\int_0^\infty \sin y\,dy = \lim_{b\to\infty}\int_0^b \sin y\,dy = \lim_{b\to\infty}(-\cos y)\big|_0^b = \lim_{b\to\infty}(1-\cos b)$

The limit does not exist, so the integral diverges.

30. diverges; $\int_0^\infty \cos x\,dx = \lim_{b\to\infty}\int_0^b \cos x\,dx = \lim_{b\to\infty} \sin x\Big|_0^b = \lim_{b\to\infty} \sin b$

The limit does not exist, so the integral diverges.

31. converges; $\int_0^\infty \frac{1}{(1+x)^3}\,dx = \lim_{b\to\infty}\int_0^b \frac{1}{(1+x)^3}\,dx = \lim_{b\to\infty}\left(\frac{-1}{2}\right)\frac{1}{(1+x)^2}\Big|_0^b$

$$= \lim_{b\to\infty}\left(\frac{-1}{2}\,\frac{1}{(1+b)^2}+\frac{1}{2}\right) = \frac{1}{2}$$

32. diverges; $\int_{-\infty}^0 \frac{1}{1-w}\,dw = \lim_{a\to-\infty}\int_a^0 \frac{1}{1-w}\,dw = \lim_{a\to-\infty} -\ln|1-w|\Big|_a^0 = \lim_{a\to-\infty} \ln|1-a| = \infty$

33. diverges; $\int_0^\infty \frac{x}{1+x^2}\,dx = \lim_{b\to\infty}\int_0^b \frac{x}{1+x^2}\,dx = \lim_{b\to\infty}\frac{1}{2}\ln(1+x^2)\Big|_0^b = \lim_{b\to\infty}\frac{1}{2}\ln(1+b^2) = \infty$

34. converges; $\int_0^\infty \frac{x}{(1+x^2)^4}\,dx = \lim_{b\to\infty}\int_0^b \frac{x}{(1+x^2)^4}\,dx = \lim_{b\to\infty}\frac{-1}{6(1+x^2)^3}\Big|_0^b = \lim_{b\to\infty}\left(\frac{-1}{6(1+b^2)^3}+\frac{1}{6}\right) = \frac{1}{6}$

35. diverges; $\int_3^\infty \ln x\,dx = \lim_{b\to\infty}\int_3^b \ln x\,dx = \lim_{b\to\infty}(x\ln x - x)\Big|_3^b = \lim_{b\to\infty}(b\ln b - b - 3\ln 3 + 3)$

Since $\lim_{b\to\infty}(b\ln b - b) = \lim_{b\to\infty} b(\ln b - 1) = \infty$, the integral diverges.

36. diverges; let $u = -x$, so that $du = -dx$; then

$$\int_{-\infty}^{-1} \ln(-x)\,dx = \lim_{a\to-\infty}\int_a^{-1} \ln(-x)\,dx = \lim_{a\to-\infty}\int_1^{-a} \ln u\,du = \lim_{a\to-\infty}(u\ln u - u)\Big|_1^{-a}$$

$$= \lim_{a\to-\infty}[(-a)\ln(-a)+a+1] = \lim_{a\to-\infty}[(-a)(\ln(-a)-1)+1] = \infty \quad \text{as in Exercise 35.}$$

37. converges; let $u = \ln x$, so that $du = (1/x)\,dx$; then

$$\int_2^\infty \frac{1}{x(\ln x)^3}\,dx = \lim_{b\to\infty}\int_2^b \frac{1}{x(\ln x)^3}\,dx = \lim_{b\to\infty}\int_{\ln 2}^{\ln b}\frac{1}{u^3}\,du$$

$$= \lim_{b\to\infty}\frac{-1}{2u^2}\Big|_{\ln 2}^{\ln b} = \lim_{b\to\infty}\left[-\frac{1}{2(\ln b)^2}+\frac{1}{2(\ln 2)^2}\right] = \frac{1}{2(\ln 2)^2}.$$

38. diverges; let $u = \ln x$, so that $du = (1/x)\,dx$; then

$$\int_2^\infty \frac{1}{x\ln x}\,dx = \lim_{b\to\infty}\int_2^b \frac{1}{x\ln x}\,dx = \lim_{b\to\infty}\int_{\ln 2}^{\ln b}\frac{1}{u}\,du = \lim_{b\to\infty}(\ln|u|)\Big|_{\ln 2}^{\ln b} = \lim_{b\to\infty}[\ln(\ln b) - \ln(\ln 2)] = \infty.$$

39. diverges; let $d = -4$; then

$$\int_{-\infty}^0 \frac{1}{(x+3)^2}\,dx = \lim_{a\to-\infty}\int_a^{-4}\frac{1}{(x+3)^2}\,dx + \lim_{c\to-3^-}\int_{-4}^c \frac{1}{(x+3)^2}\,dx + \lim_{p\to-3^+}\int_p^0 \frac{1}{(x+3)^2}\,dx$$

$$= \lim_{a\to-\infty}\frac{-1}{x+3}\Big|_a^{-4} + \lim_{c\to-3^-}\frac{-1}{x+3}\Big|_{-4}^c + \lim_{p\to-3^+}\frac{-1}{x+3}\Big|_p^0$$

$$= \lim_{a\to-\infty}\left(1+\frac{1}{a+3}\right) + \lim_{c\to-3^-}\left(\frac{-1}{c+3}-1\right) + \lim_{p\to-3^+}\left(-\frac{1}{3}+\frac{1}{p+3}\right).$$

The latter two one-sided limits do not exist, so the integral diverges.

40. converges; let $u = 1/x$, so that $du = -(1/x^2)\,dx$; then

$$\int_{2/\pi}^{\infty} \frac{1}{x^2} \sin\frac{1}{x}\,dx = \lim_{b\to\infty} \int_{2/\pi}^{b} \frac{1}{x^2} \sin\frac{1}{x}\,dx = \lim_{b\to\infty} \int_{\pi/2}^{1/b} -\sin u\,du$$

$$= \lim_{b\to\infty} \cos u \Big|_{\pi/2}^{1/b} = \lim_{b\to\infty} \left(\cos\frac{1}{b} - 0\right) = 1.$$

41. diverges; let $u = \sqrt{x} + 1$, so that $du = 1/(2\sqrt{x})\,dx$; then

$$\int_1^{\infty} \frac{1}{\sqrt{x}\,(\sqrt{x}+1)}\,dx = \lim_{b\to\infty} \int_1^{b} \frac{1}{\sqrt{x}\,(\sqrt{x}+1)}\,dx = \lim_{b\to\infty} 2\int_2^{\sqrt{b}+1} \frac{1}{u}\,du$$

$$= \lim_{b\to\infty} 2\ln|u|\Big|_2^{\sqrt{b}+1} = \lim_{b\to\infty} \left(2\ln(\sqrt{b}+1) - 2\ln 2\right) = \infty.$$

42. converges; $\displaystyle\int_{-\infty}^{0} e^{4x}\,dx = \lim_{a\to-\infty} \int_a^0 e^{4x}\,dx = \lim_{a\to-\infty} \frac{1}{4}e^{4x}\Big|_a^0 = \lim_{a\to-\infty} \left(\frac{1}{4} - \frac{1}{4}e^{4a}\right) = \frac{1}{4}$

43. diverges; $\displaystyle\int_0^{\infty} e^{4x}\,dx = \lim_{b\to\infty} \int_0^b e^{4x}\,dx = \lim_{b\to\infty} \frac{1}{4}e^{4x}\Big|_0^b = \lim_{b\to\infty} \left(\frac{1}{4}e^{4b} - \frac{1}{4}\right) = \infty$

44. converges; $\displaystyle\int_0^{\infty} e^{-ex}\,dx = \lim_{b\to\infty} \int_0^b e^{-ex}\,dx = \lim_{b\to\infty} -\frac{1}{e}e^{-ex}\Big|_0^b = \lim_{b\to\infty} \left(-\frac{1}{e}e^{-eb} + \frac{1}{e}\right) = \frac{1}{e}$

45. converges; let $u = x$, $dv = e^{-x}\,dx$, so $du = dx$, $v = -e^{-x}$;

$$\int_0^{\infty} xe^{-x}\,dx = \lim_{b\to\infty} \int_0^b xe^{-x}\,dx = \lim_{b\to\infty} \left(-xe^{-x}\Big|_0^b + \int_0^b e^{-x}\,dx\right) = \lim_{b\to\infty} \left(-xe^{-x}\Big|_0^b - e^{-x}\Big|_0^b\right)$$

$$= \lim_{b\to\infty} \left[(-be^{-b} + 0) - (e^{-b} - 1)\right] = \left(-\lim_{b\to\infty} be^{-b}\right) - \lim_{b\to\infty} e^{-b} + 1 = \left(-\lim_{b\to\infty} be^{-b}\right) + 1.$$

Since $\lim_{b\to\infty} b = \infty = \lim_{b\to\infty} e^b$, l'Hôpital's Rule implies that

$$\lim_{b\to\infty} be^{-b} = \lim_{b\to\infty} \frac{b}{e^b} = \lim_{b\to\infty} \frac{1}{e^b} = 0.$$

Thus $\int_0^{\infty} xe^{-x}\,dx = 1$.

46. diverges; by Exercise 12 of Section 7.1,

$$\int_0^{\infty} e^x \sin x\,dx = \lim_{b\to\infty} \int_0^b e^x \sin x\,dx = \lim_{b\to\infty} \left(\frac{1}{2}e^x \sin x - \frac{1}{2}e^x \cos x\right)\Big|_0^b = \lim_{b\to\infty} \left[\frac{1}{2}e^b(\sin b - \cos b) + \frac{1}{2}\right]$$

which does not exist because $\lim_{b\to\infty} e^b = \infty$ and $\sin b - \cos b$ assumes the value 1 on each interval of length 2π.

47. diverges; for $\int (1/\sqrt{x^2-1})\,dx$ let $x = \sec u$, so that $dx = \sec u\,\tan u\,du$; thus

$$\int \frac{1}{\sqrt{x^2-1}}\,dx = \int \frac{1}{\sqrt{\sec^2 u - 1}} \sec u\,\tan u\,du = \int \sec u\,du = \ln|\sec u + \tan u| + C.$$

Now $x = \sec u$ implies that $\tan u = \sqrt{x^2 - 1}$. Thus

$$\int \frac{1}{\sqrt{x^2-1}}\,dx = \ln|\sec u + \tan u| + C = \ln|x + \sqrt{x^2-1}| + C.$$

Since

$$\int_1^\infty \frac{1}{\sqrt{x^2-1}}\,dx = \lim_{a\to 1^+}\int_a^2 \frac{1}{\sqrt{x^2-1}}\,dx + \lim_{b\to\infty}\int_2^b \frac{1}{\sqrt{x^2-1}}\,dx$$

and since

$$\lim_{b\to\infty}\int_2^b \frac{1}{\sqrt{x^2-1}}\,dx = \lim_{b\to\infty} \ln|x+\sqrt{x^2-1}|\Big|_2^b = \lim_{b\to\infty}\left[\ln|b+\sqrt{b^2-1}| - \ln(2+\sqrt{3})\right] = \infty$$

it follows that $\int_1^\infty (1/\sqrt{x^2-1})\,dx$ diverges.

48. converges; $\displaystyle\int_{-\infty}^{-2} \frac{1}{x^2+4}\,dx = \lim_{a\to-\infty}\int_a^{-2}\frac{1}{x^2+4}\,dx = \lim_{a\to-\infty}\frac{1}{2}\tan^{-1}\frac{x}{2}\Big|_a^{-2}$

$$= \lim_{a\to-\infty}\left(\frac{1}{2}\tan^{-1}(-1) - \frac{1}{2}\tan^{-1}\frac{a}{2}\right) = \frac{1}{2}\left(-\frac{\pi}{4}\right) - \frac{1}{2}\left(-\frac{\pi}{2}\right) = \frac{\pi}{8}$$

49. converges; $\displaystyle\int_1^\infty \frac{1}{t\sqrt{t^2-1}}\,dt = \lim_{a\to1^+}\int_a^2 \frac{1}{t\sqrt{t^2-1}}\,dt + \lim_{b\to\infty}\int_2^b \frac{1}{t\sqrt{t^2-1}}\,dt$

$$= \lim_{a\to1^+}\sec^{-1}t\Big|_a^2 + \lim_{b\to\infty}\sec^{-1}t\Big|_2^b$$

$$= \lim_{a\to1^+}(\sec^{-1}2 - \sec^{-1}a) + \lim_{b\to\infty}(\sec^{-1}b - \sec^{-1}2)$$

$$= \left(\frac{\pi}{3} - 0\right) + \left(\frac{\pi}{2} - \frac{\pi}{3}\right) = \frac{1}{2}\pi$$

50. diverges; $\displaystyle\int_0^\infty \frac{1}{t^2-2t+1}\,dt = \int_0^\infty \frac{1}{(t-1)^2}\,dt$

$$= \lim_{c\to1^-}\int_0^c \frac{1}{(t-1)^2}\,dt + \lim_{p\to1^+}\int_p^2 \frac{1}{(t-1)^2}\,dt + \lim_{b\to\infty}\int_2^b \frac{1}{(t-1)^2}\,dt$$

$$= \lim_{c\to1^-}\frac{-1}{t-1}\Big|_0^c + \lim_{p\to1^+}\frac{-1}{t-1}\Big|_p^2 + \lim_{b\to\infty}\frac{-1}{t-1}\Big|_2^b$$

$$= \lim_{c\to1^-}\left(\frac{-1}{c-1} - 1\right) + \lim_{p\to1^+}\left(-1 + \frac{1}{p-1}\right) + \lim_{b\to\infty}\left(-\frac{1}{b-1} + 1\right)$$

The first two one-sided limits do not exist, so the integral diverges.

51. converges; since $t^2 + 4t + 8 = (t+2)^2 + 4$, let $u = t + 2$, so that $du = dt$;

$$\int_{-2}^\infty \frac{1}{t^2+4t+8}\,dt = \lim_{b\to\infty}\int_{-2}^b \frac{1}{(t+2)^2+4}\,dt = \lim_{b\to\infty}\int_0^{b+2}\frac{1}{u^2+4}\,dt$$

$$= \lim_{b\to\infty}\frac{1}{2}\tan^{-1}\frac{u}{2}\Big|_0^{b+2} = \lim_{b\to\infty}\frac{1}{2}\tan^{-1}\frac{b+2}{2} = \frac{1}{4}\pi.$$

52. converges; $\displaystyle\int_0^\infty \frac{x\cos x - \sin x}{x^2}\,dx = \lim_{c\to 0^+}\int_c^\pi \frac{x\cos x - \sin x}{x^2}\,dx + \lim_{b\to\infty}\int_\pi^b \frac{x\cos x - \sin x}{x^2}\,dx$

$$= \lim_{c\to 0^+} \left.\frac{\sin x}{x}\right|_c^\pi + \lim_{b\to\infty}\left.\frac{\sin x}{x}\right|_\pi^b$$

$$= \lim_{c\to 0^+}\left(0 - \frac{\sin c}{c}\right) + \lim_{b\to\infty}\left(\frac{\sin b}{b} - 0\right) = -1 + 0 = -1$$

53. diverges; $\displaystyle\int_{-\infty}^\infty x\,dx = \lim_{a\to-\infty}\int_a^0 x\,dx + \lim_{b\to\infty}\int_0^b x\,dx = \lim_{a\to-\infty}\left.\frac{x^2}{2}\right|_a^0 + \lim_{b\to\infty}\left.\frac{x^2}{2}\right|_0^b$

$$= \lim_{a\to-\infty}\frac{-1}{2}a^2 + \lim_{b\to\infty}\frac{1}{2}b^2$$

Neither limit exists, so the integral diverges.

54. diverges; let $u = x^2$, so that $du = 2x\,dx$; then

$$\int_{-\infty}^\infty x\sin x^2\,dx = \lim_{a\to-\infty}\int_a^0 x\sin x^2\,dx + \lim_{b\to\infty}\int_0^b x\sin x^2\,dx = \lim_{a\to-\infty}\frac{1}{2}\int_{a^2}^0 \sin u\,du + \lim_{b\to\infty}\int_0^{b^2}\sin u\,du$$

$$= \lim_{a\to-\infty}\left.\left(-\frac{1}{2}\cos u\right)\right|_{a^2}^0 + \lim_{b\to\infty}\left.\left(-\frac{1}{2}\cos u\right)\right|_0^{b^2} = \lim_{a\to-\infty}\left[-\frac{1}{2} + \frac{1}{2}\cos a^2\right] + \lim_{b\to\infty}\left[-\frac{1}{2}\cos b^2 + \frac{1}{2}\right].$$

Neither limit exists, so the integral diverges.

55. diverges; let $u = x$, $dv = \sin x\,dx$, so $du = dx$, $v = -\cos x$; then

$$\int_{-\infty}^\infty x\sin x\,dx = \lim_{a\to-\infty}\int_a^0 x\sin x\,dx + \lim_{b\to\infty}\int_0^b x\sin x\,dx$$

$$= \lim_{a\to-\infty}\left[-x\cos x\Big|_a^0 + \int_a^0 \cos x\,dx\right] + \lim_{b\to\infty}\left[-x\cos x\Big|_0^b + \int_0^b \cos x\,dx\right]$$

$$= \lim_{a\to-\infty}\left[(0 + a\cos a) + (\sin x)\Big|_a^0\right] + \lim_{b\to\infty}\left[(-b\cos b + 0) + (\sin x)\Big|_0^b\right]$$

$$= \lim_{a\to-\infty}[a\cos a + 0 - \sin a] + \lim_{b\to\infty}[-b\cos b + \sin b - 0].$$

Neither limit exists, so the integral diverges.

56. diverges; let $u = x^4 + 1$, so that $du = 4x^3\,dx$; then

$$\int_{-\infty}^\infty \frac{x^3}{x^4+1}\,dx = \lim_{a\to-\infty}\int_a^0 \frac{x^3}{x^4+1}\,dx + \lim_{b\to\infty}\int_0^b \frac{x^3}{x^4+1}\,dx = \lim_{a\to-\infty}\frac{1}{4}\int_{a^4+1}^1 \frac{1}{u}\,du + \lim_{b\to\infty}\frac{1}{4}\int_1^{b^4+1}\frac{1}{u}\,du$$

$$= \lim_{a\to-\infty}\frac{1}{4}\ln|u|\Big|_{a^4+1}^1 + \lim_{b\to\infty}\frac{1}{4}\ln|u|\Big|_1^{b^4+1} = \lim_{a\to-\infty}\left[0 - \frac{1}{4}\ln(a^4+1)\right] + \lim_{b\to\infty}\left[\frac{1}{4}\ln(b^4+1) - 0\right].$$

Neither limit exists, so the integral diverges.

57. converges; let $u = x^4 + 1$, so that $du = 4x^3\,dx$; then

$$\int_{-\infty}^{\infty} \frac{x^3}{(x^4+1)^2}\,dx = \lim_{a\to-\infty} \int_a^0 \frac{x^3}{(x^4+1)^2}\,dx + \lim_{b\to\infty} \int_0^b \frac{x^3}{(x^4+1)^2}\,dx$$

$$= \lim_{a\to-\infty} \frac{1}{4}\int_{a^4+1}^{1} \frac{1}{u^2}\,du + \lim_{b\to\infty} \frac{1}{4}\int_1^{b^4+1} \frac{1}{u^2}\,du = \lim_{a\to-\infty} \left.\frac{-1}{4u}\right|_{a^4+1}^{1} + \lim_{b\to\infty} \left.\frac{-1}{4u}\right|_1^{b^4+1}$$

$$= \lim_{a\to-\infty} \left[-\frac{1}{4} + \frac{1}{4(a^4+1)}\right] + \lim_{b\to\infty} \left[-\frac{1}{4(b^4+1)} + \frac{1}{4}\right] = 0.$$

58. converges; let $u = x^2$, so that $du = 2x\,dx$;

$$\int_{-\infty}^{\infty} xe^{-(x^2)}\,dx = \lim_{a\to-\infty} \int_a^0 xe^{-(x^2)}\,dx + \lim_{b\to\infty} \int_0^b xe^{-(x^2)}\,dx = \lim_{a\to-\infty} \int_{a^2}^0 \frac{1}{2}e^{-u}\,du + \lim_{b\to\infty} \int_0^{b^2} \frac{1}{2}e^{-u}\,du$$

$$= \lim_{a\to-\infty} \left.-\frac{1}{2}e^{-u}\right|_{a^2}^{0} + \lim_{b\to\infty} \left.-\frac{1}{2}e^{-u}\right|_0^{b^2} = \lim_{a\to-\infty} \left(-\frac{1}{2} + \frac{1}{2}e^{-a^2}\right) + \lim_{b\to\infty} \left(-\frac{1}{2}e^{-b^2} + \frac{1}{2}\right) = -\frac{1}{2} + \frac{1}{2} = 0.$$

59. converges; since $x^2 - 6x + 10 = (x-3)^2 + 1$, let $u = x - 3$, so that $du = dx$; then

$$\int_{-\infty}^{\infty} \frac{1}{x^2 - 6x + 10}\,dx = \lim_{a\to-\infty} \int_a^3 \frac{1}{(x-3)^2+1}\,dx + \lim_{b\to\infty} \int_3^b \frac{1}{(x-3)^2+1}\,dx$$

$$= \lim_{a\to-\infty} \int_{a-3}^0 \frac{1}{u^2+1}\,du + \lim_{b\to\infty} \int_0^{b-3} \frac{1}{u^2+1}\,du = \lim_{a\to-\infty} \tan^{-1} u\Big|_{a-3}^{0} + \lim_{b\to\infty} \tan^{-1} u\Big|_0^{b-3}$$

$$= \lim_{a\to-\infty} -(\tan^{-1}(a-3)) + \lim_{b\to\infty} \tan^{-1}(b-3) = -\left(-\frac{\pi}{2}\right) + \frac{\pi}{2} = \pi.$$

60. converges; $\displaystyle\int_{-\infty}^{\infty} \frac{x\sin x + 2\cos x - 2}{x^3}\,dx = \lim_{a\to-\infty} \int_a^{-2\pi} \frac{x\sin x + 2\cos x - 2}{x^3}\,dx$

$$+ \lim_{c\to0^-} \int_{-2\pi}^{c} \frac{x\sin x + 2\cos x - 2}{x^3}\,dx$$

$$+ \lim_{p\to0^+} \int_p^{2\pi} \frac{x\sin x + 2\cos x - 2}{x^3}\,dx$$

$$+ \lim_{b\to\infty} \int_{2\pi}^{b} \frac{x\sin x + 2\cos x - 2}{x^3}\,dx$$

$$= \lim_{a\to-\infty} \left.\frac{1-\cos x}{x^2}\right|_a^{-2\pi} + \lim_{c\to0^-} \left.\frac{1-\cos x}{x^2}\right|_{-2\pi}^{c}$$

$$+ \lim_{p\to0^+} \left.\frac{1-\cos x}{x^2}\right|_p^{2\pi} + \lim_{b\to\infty} \left.\frac{1-\cos x}{x^2}\right|_{2\pi}^{b}$$

$$= \lim_{a\to-\infty} \frac{\cos a - 1}{a^2} + \lim_{c\to0^-} \frac{1-\cos c}{c^2}$$

$$+ \lim_{p\to0^+} \frac{\cos p - 1}{p^2} + \lim_{b\to\infty} \frac{1-\cos b}{b^2}$$

$$= 0 + \frac{1}{2} - \frac{1}{2} + 0 = 0$$

61. a. $\dfrac{1}{x(x+1)} = \dfrac{A}{x} + \dfrac{B}{x+1} = \dfrac{A(x+1)+Bx}{x(x+1)}$; $A + B = 0$, $A = 1$; thus $B = -1$, so that

$$\frac{1}{x(x+1)} = \frac{1}{x} - \frac{1}{x+1}.$$

b. No, since both $\int_1^\infty (1/x)\,dx$ and $\int_1^\infty [1/(x+1)]\,dx$ diverge, whereas

$$\int_1^\infty \frac{1}{x(x+1)}\,dx = \lim_{b\to\infty}\int_1^b \frac{1}{x(x+1)}\,dx = \lim_{b\to\infty}\int_1^b \left(\frac{1}{x} - \frac{1}{x+1}\right)dx$$

$$= \lim_{b\to\infty}(\ln|x| - \ln|x+1|)\Big|_1^b = \lim_{b\to\infty}[\ln b - \ln(b+1) + \ln 2] = \lim_{b\to\infty}\left(\ln\frac{b}{b+1} + \ln 2\right) = \ln 2.$$

62. a. If $p \neq 1$, then

$$\int_0^1 \frac{1}{x^p}\,dx = \lim_{c\to 0^+}\int_c^1 \frac{1}{x^p}\,dx = \lim_{c\to 0^+}\frac{1}{-p+1}\frac{1}{x^{p-1}}\Big|_c^1 = \lim_{c\to 0^+}\frac{1}{-p+1}\left(1 - \frac{1}{c^{p-1}}\right).$$

The limit exists if $p < 1$ and does not exist if $p > 1$. If $p = 1$, then

$$\int_0^1 \frac{1}{x^p}\,dx = \int_0^1 \frac{1}{x}\,dx = \lim_{c\to 0^+}\int_c^1 \frac{1}{x}\,dx = \lim_{c\to 0^+}\ln|x|\Big|_c^1 = \lim_{c\to 0^+}(-\ln c)$$

and the limit does not exist. Thus $\int_0^1 (1/x)\,dx$ converges if $p < 1$ and diverges if $p \geq 1$.

b. If $p \neq 1$, then

$$\int_1^\infty \frac{1}{x^p}\,dx = \lim_{b\to\infty}\int_1^b \frac{1}{x^p}\,dx = \lim_{b\to\infty}\frac{1}{-p+1}\frac{1}{x^{p-1}}\Big|_1^b = \lim_{b\to\infty}\frac{1}{-p+1}\left(\frac{1}{b^{p-1}} - 1\right)$$

and the limit exists if $p > 1$ and does not exist if $p < 1$. If $p = 1$, then

$$\int_1^\infty \frac{1}{x^p}\,dx = \int_1^\infty \frac{1}{x}\,dx = \lim_{b\to\infty}\int_1^b \frac{1}{x}\,dx = \lim_{b\to\infty}\ln|x|\Big|_1^b = \lim_{b\to\infty}\ln b = \infty.$$

Thus $\int_1^\infty (1/x^p)\,dx$ converges for $p > 1$ and diverges for $p \leq 1$.

c. If $\int_0^\infty (1/x^p)\,dx$ were to converge, then $\int_0^\infty (1/x^p)\,dx = \int_0^1 (1/x^p)\,dx + \int_1^\infty (1/x^p)\,dx$. But $\int_0^1 (1/x^p)\,dx$ diverges if $p \geq 1$ and $\int_1^\infty (1/x^p)\,dx$ diverges if $p \leq 1$. Thus $\int_0^\infty (1/x^p)\,dx$ diverges for all p.

63. $A = \displaystyle\int_{-\infty}^0 \frac{1}{(x-3)^2}\,dx = \lim_{a\to-\infty}\int_a^0 \frac{1}{(x-3)^2}\,dx = \lim_{a\to-\infty}\frac{-1}{x-3}\Big|_a^0 = \lim_{a\to-\infty}\left(\frac{1}{3} + \frac{1}{a-3}\right) = \frac{1}{3}$

so the region has finite area.

64. $A = \displaystyle\int_{-\infty}^3 \frac{1}{(x-3)^2}\,dx = \lim_{a\to-\infty}\int_a^0 \frac{1}{(x-3)^2}\,dx + \lim_{c\to 3^-}\int_0^c \frac{1}{(x-3)^2}\,dx$

$$= \lim_{a\to-\infty}\frac{-1}{x-3}\Big|_a^0 + \lim_{c\to 3^-}\frac{-1}{x-3}\Big|_0^c = \lim_{a\to-\infty}\left(\frac{1}{3} + \frac{1}{a-3}\right) + \lim_{c\to 3^-}\left(\frac{-1}{c-3} - \frac{1}{3}\right) = \infty$$

so the region has infinite area.

65. $A = \int_2^\infty \frac{\ln x}{x}\,dx = \lim_{b\to\infty}\int_2^b \frac{\ln x}{x}\,dx = \lim_{b\to\infty}\frac{1}{2}(\ln x)^2\Big]_2^b = \lim_{b\to\infty}\left[\frac{1}{2}(\ln b)^2 - \frac{1}{2}(\ln 2)^2\right] = \infty$, so the region has infinite area.

66. $A = \int_0^1 \frac{\ln x}{-x}\,dx = \lim_{c\to 0+}\int_c^1 \frac{\ln x}{-x}\,dx = \lim_{c\to 0+} -\frac{1}{2}(\ln x)^2\Big]_c^1 = \lim_{c\to 0+}\frac{1}{2}(\ln c)^2 = \infty$ so the region has infinite area.

67. $A = \int_2^\infty \frac{1}{\sqrt{x+1}}\,dx = \lim_{b\to\infty}\int_2^b \frac{1}{\sqrt{x+1}}\,dx = \lim_{b\to\infty} 2\sqrt{x+1}\Big|_2^b = \lim_{b\to\infty}(2\sqrt{b+1} - 2\sqrt{3}) = \infty$ so the region has infinite area.

68. $A = \int_{-1}^1 \frac{1}{\sqrt{x+1}}\,dx = \lim_{c\to -1^+}\int_c^1 \frac{1}{\sqrt{x+1}}\,dx = \lim_{c\to -1^+} 2\sqrt{x+1}\Big|_c^1 = \lim_{c\to -1^+}(2\sqrt{2} - 2\sqrt{c+1}) = 2\sqrt{2}$ so the region has finite area.

69. Since $1/(1+x^4) \le 1/(1+x^2)$ and since

$$\int_0^\infty \frac{1}{1+x^2}\,dx = \lim_{b\to\infty}\int_0^b \frac{1}{1+x^2}\,dx = \lim_{b\to\infty}\tan^{-1}x\Big|_0^b = \lim_{b\to\infty}\tan^{-1}b = \frac{\pi}{2}$$

it follows from the Comparison Property that $\int_1^\infty 1/(1+x^4)\,dx$ converges.

70. Since $1/\sqrt{2+\sin x} \ge 1/\sqrt{2-1} = 1$ and since $\int_0^\infty 1\,dx$ diverges, it follows from the Comparison Property that $\int_0^\infty (1/\sqrt{2+\sin x})\,dx$ diverges.

71. Since $(\sin^2 x)/\sqrt{1+x^3} \le 1/\sqrt{x^3} = 1/x^{3/2}$, and since $\int_1^\infty (1/x^{3/2})\,dx$ converges by Exercise 62(b), it follows from the Comparison Property that $\int_1^\infty [(\sin^2 x)/\sqrt{1+x^3}]\,dx$ converges.

72. Since $\ln x < x$ for $x \ge 1$, we have $(\ln x)/x^3 < x/x^3 = 1/x^2$. Since $\int_1^\infty (1/x^2)\,dx$ converges by Exercise 62(b), it follows from the Comparison Property that $\int_1^\infty (\ln x)/x^3\,dx$ converges.

73. Since $(1/x)\sqrt{1+1/x^4} \ge 1/x$ and since $\int_1^\infty (1/x)\,dx$ diverges by Exercise 62(b), it follows from the Comparison Property that $\int_1^\infty (1/x)\sqrt{1+1/x^4}\,dx$ diverges.

74. Since $\int_1^\infty (1/x)\,dx = \int_1^\infty [(\sin^2 x + \cos^2 x)/x]\,dx$, and since $\int_1^\infty (1/x)\,dx$ diverges, either $\int_1^\infty [(\sin^2 x)/x]\,dx$ or $\int_1^\infty [(\cos^2 x)/x]\,dx$ must diverge. Suppose that $\int_1^\infty [(\sin^2 x)/x]\,dx$ converged. Then $\int_1^\infty [(\cos^2 x)/x]\,dx$ and hence $\int_{1+\pi/2}^\infty [(\cos^2 x)/x]\,dx$ would need to diverge. Now $\cos x = -\sin(x - \pi/2)$, so $\cos^2 x = \sin^2(x-\pi/2)$. Let $u = x - \pi/2$, so $du = dx$. Then for any $b > 1$,

$$\int_{1+\pi/2}^b \frac{\cos^2 x}{x}\,dx = \int_1^{b-\pi/2} \frac{\sin^2 u}{u+\pi/2}\,dx.$$

It follows that

$$\int_1^\infty \frac{\sin^2 u}{u+\pi/2}\,du \quad \text{and hence} \quad \int_1^\infty \frac{\sin^2 u}{u}\,du$$

must diverge, so that

$$\int_1^\infty \frac{\sin^2 x}{x}\,dx \quad \text{diverges.}$$

This contradicts the assumption that $\int_1^\infty [(\sin^2 x)/x]\,dx$ converges. Consequently $\int_1^\infty [(\sin^2 x)/x]\,dx$ diverges.

75. a. If $\lim_{b\to\infty} \int_a^b f(x)\,dx$ and $\lim_{b\to\infty} \int_a^b g(x)\,dx$ both exist, then $\lim_{b\to\infty} \left(\int_a^b f(x)\,dx + \int_a^b g(x)\,dx\right) = \lim_{b\to\infty} \int_a^b (f(x)+g(x))\,dx$ exists, so $\int_a^\infty (f(x)+g(x))\,dx$ converges.

b. If $\lim_{b\to\infty} \int_a^b f(x)\,dx$ exists, then $\lim_{b\to\infty} c\int_a^b f(x)\,dx = \lim_{b\to\infty} \int_a^b cf(x)\,dx$ exists, so $\int_a^\infty cf(x)\,dx$ converges.

c. If $f(x) = 1/x$ and $g(x) = -1/x$, then $0 = \int_1^\infty (f(x)+g(x))\,dx$, so the integral converges; however, $\int_1^\infty (1/x)\,dx$ and $\int_1^\infty (-1/x)\,dx$ diverge since $\int_1^\infty (1/x)\,dx = \lim_{b\to\infty} \int_1^b (1/x)\,dx = \lim_{b\to\infty} \ln|x|\big|_1^b = \lim_{b\to\infty} \ln b = \infty$.

76. Let $n \geq 1$. For integration by parts, let $u = x^n$, $dv = e^{-x}\,dx$, so that $du = nx^{n-1}\,dx$, $v = -e^{-x}$. Then

$$I_n = \int_0^\infty x^n e^{-x}\,dx = \lim_{b\to\infty} \int_0^b x^n e^{-x}\,dx$$

$$= \lim_{b\to\infty} \left[-x^n e^{-x}\Big|_0^b + \int_0^b nx^{n-1}e^{-x}\,dx\right] = \lim_{b\to\infty} \left(-b^n e^{-b} + n\int_0^b x^{n-1}e^{-x}\,dx\right).$$

Since $\lim_{x\to\infty}(e^x/e^n) = \infty$ by the comment following Example 5 of Section 6.6, it follows that $\lim_{b\to\infty}(-b^n e^{-b}) = -\lim_{b\to\infty}(b^n/e^b) = 0$ for every positive integer n, and thus

$$I_n = \lim_{b\to\infty} n\int_0^b x^{n-1}e^{-x}\,dx = n\int_0^\infty x^{n-1}e^{-x}\,dx = nI_{n-1}.$$

Inductively we have $I_n = nI_{n-1} = n(n-1)I_{n-2} = \cdots = n(n-1)(n-2)\cdots 2I_1$. Now by the above calculation with $n = 1$ we have

$$I_1 = 1\cdot I_0 = \int_0^\infty e^{-x}\,dx = \lim_{b\to\infty} (-e^{-x})\big|_0^b = \lim_{b\to\infty} (1 - e^{-b}) = 1.$$

Therefore $I_n = n(n-1)(n-2)\cdots 2\cdot 1$.

77. a. $$\int_a^\infty f(t)\,dt = \lim_{b\to\infty} \int_a^b f(t)\,dt = \lim_{b\to\infty} \left(\int_a^x f(t)\,dt + \int_x^b f(t)\,dt\right)$$

$$= \int_a^x f(t)\,dt + \lim_{b\to\infty} \int_x^b f(t)\,dt = \int_a^x f(t)\,dt + \int_x^\infty f(t)\,dt$$

b. By part (a),

$$\frac{d}{dx}\int_a^\infty f(t)\,dt = \frac{d}{dx}\int_a^x f(t)\,dt + \frac{d}{dx}\int_x^\infty f(t)\,dt.$$

Now $\int_a^\infty f(t)\,dt$ is independent of x, so $(d/dx)\int_a^\infty f(t)\,dt = 0$. By Theorem 5.12 in Section 5.4, $(d/dx)\int_a^x f(t)\,dt = f(x)$. Thus we obtain

$$0 = f(x) + \frac{d}{dx}\int_x^\infty f(t)\,dt, \quad \text{and thus} \quad \frac{d}{dx}\int_x^\infty f(t)\,dt = -f(x).$$

78. Let $t = 1/x$, so that $dt = (-1/x^2)\,dx$ and $dx = (-1/t^2)\,dt$. If $x = a$, then $t = 1/a$; if $x = b$, then $t = 1/b$. Thus

$$\int_a^b f(x)\,dx = \int_{1/a}^{1/b} f\left(\frac{1}{t}\right)\left(-\frac{1}{t^2}\right)dt = \int_{1/b}^{1/a} \frac{f(1/t)}{t^2}\,dt.$$

Since

$$\lim_{b\to\infty}\int_a^b f(x)\,dx = \int_a^\infty f(x)\,dx \quad\text{and}\quad \lim_{b\to\infty}\int_{1/b}^{1/a} \frac{f(1/t)}{t^2}\,dt = \int_0^{1/a}\frac{f(1/t)}{t^2}\,dt,$$

we conclude that $\int_a^\infty f(x)\,dx$ and $\int_0^{1/a}[f(1/t)/t^2]\,dt$ either both converge or both diverge.

79. a. Since $1/(x^{3/2}+1) \le 1/x^{3/2}$ for $x \ge 1$, and since $\int_1^\infty (1/x^{3/2})\,dx$ converges by Exercise 62(b), it follows from the Comparison Property that $\int_1^\infty [1/(x^{3/2}+1)]\,dx$ converges.

b. If $y = 1/(x^{3/2}+1)$, then $x^{3/2}+1 = 1/y$, so that $x = ((1/y)-1)^{2/3}$. If $1 \le x$, then $0 < y \le \frac{1}{2}$. Thus the area of the red region in Figure 7.29, which is $\int_0^{1/2} ((1/y)-1)^{2/3}\,dy$, equals the area of the blue region, which is $\int_1^\infty [1/(x^{3/2}+1)]\,dx$.

80. a. By Simpson's Rule with $n = 100$, $\int_{-2}^{2}(1/\sqrt{2\pi})\,e^{-x^2/2}\,dx \approx 0.954499733$. Thus approximately 95.4% of the data lies within 2 standard deviations of the mean.

b. By Simpson's Rule with $n = 100$, $\int_{-3}^{3}(1/\sqrt{2\pi})\,e^{-x^2/2}\,dx \approx 0.9973001925$. Thus approximately 99.7% of the data lies within 3 standard deviations of the mean.

81. a. By Simpson's Rule with $n = 100$, $\int_{-5}^{5}(1/\sqrt{2\pi})\,e^{-x^2/2}\,dx \approx 0.9999994265$.

b. If $b = 7$, Simpson's Rule with $n = 100$ yields $\int_{-7}^{7}(1/\sqrt{2\pi})\,e^{-x^2/2}\,dx = 1$.

82. Let $u = (x-\mu)/\sigma$, so that $du = (1/\sigma)\,dx$. If $x = \mu + r\sigma$, then $u = r$; if $x = \mu + s\sigma$, then $u = s$. Therefore

$$\int_{\mu-r\sigma}^{\mu+s\sigma} \frac{1}{\sigma\sqrt{2\pi}}\,e^{-(x-\mu)^2/2\sigma^2}\,dx = \int_r^s \frac{1}{\sqrt{2\pi}}\,e^{-u^2/2}\,du = \int_r^s \frac{1}{\sqrt{2\pi}}\,e^{-x^2/2}\,dx.$$

83. To integrate by parts, let $u = ct$ and $dv = e^{-ct}\,dt$; then $du = c\,dt$ and $v = (-1/c)e^{-ct}$. Therefore

$$\int cte^{-ct}\,dt = ct\left(-\frac{1}{c}e^{-ct}\right) - \int\left(-\frac{1}{c}e^{-ct}\right)c\,dt = -te^{-ct} + \int e^{-ct}\,dt = -te^{-ct} - \frac{1}{c}e^{-ct} + C.$$

Therefore

$$\int_0^\infty cte^{-ct}\,dt = \lim_{b\to\infty}\int_0^b cte^{-ct}\,dt = \lim_{b\to\infty}\left(-te^{-ct} - \frac{1}{c}e^{-ct}\right)\Big|_0^b = \lim_{b\to\infty}\left(-be^{-cb} - \frac{1}{c}e^{-cb} + \frac{1}{c}\right) = \frac{1}{c}$$

where we have used the fact that $\lim_{b\to\infty} be^{-cb} = 0$ by l'Hôpital's Rule.

84. $$P = \int_0^\infty Re^{-rt/100}\,dt = \lim_{b\to\infty}\int_0^b Re^{-rt/100}\,dt = \lim_{b\to\infty} R\left(\frac{-100}{r}\right)e^{-rt/100}\Big|_0^b$$

$$= \lim_{b\to\infty}\frac{100R}{r}\left(1 - e^{-rb/100}\right) = \frac{100R}{r}$$

85. $M = -\frac{1}{A}\int_0^\infty tkf(t)\,dt = -\frac{1}{A}\int_0^\infty tkAe^{kt}\,dt = -\int_0^\infty tke^{kt}\,dt$

For integration by parts, let $u = t$, $dv = ke^{kt}\,dt$, so that $du = dt$, $v = e^{kt}$. Then since $k < 0$,

$$M = \lim_{b\to\infty} -\int_0^b tke^{kt}\,dt = \lim_{b\to\infty} -\left(te^{kt}\Big|_0^b - \int_0^b e^{kt}\,dt\right)$$

$$= \lim_{b\to\infty} -\left(be^{kb} - \frac{1}{k}e^{kt}\Big|_0^b\right) = \lim_{b\to\infty} -\left(be^{kb} - \frac{1}{b}e^{kb} + \frac{1}{k}\right) = -\frac{1}{k}.$$

a. If $k = -1.24\times 10^{-4}$, then $M = 1/1.24\times 10^4 \approx 8060$ years.

b. If $k = -4.36\times 10^{-4}$, then $M = 1/4.36\times 10^4 \approx 2090$ years.

86. To integrate by parts, we let $u = r^2$ and $dv = e^{-2r/a_0}\,dr$; then $du = 2r\,dr$ and $v = -(a_0/2)e^{-2r/a_0}$. Thus

$$\int r^2e^{-2r/a_0}\,dr = r^2\left(-\frac{a_0}{2}e^{-2r/a_0}\right) - \int\left(-\frac{a_0}{2}e^{-2r/a_0}\right)2r\,dr = -\frac{a_0}{2}r^2e^{-2r/a_0} + a_0\int re^{-2r/a_0}\,dr.$$

Next, if $u = r$ and $dv = e^{-2r/a_0}$, then $du = dr$ and $v = (-a_0/2)e^{-2r/a_0}$. Thus

$$\int re^{-2r/a_0}\,dr = r\left(-\frac{a_0}{2}e^{-2r/a_0}\right) - \int\left(-\frac{a_0}{2}e^{-2r/a_0}\right)dr$$

$$= -\frac{a_0}{2}re^{-2r/a_0} + \frac{a_0}{2}\int e^{-2r/a_0}\,dr = -\frac{a_0}{2}re^{-2r/a_0} - \frac{a_0^2}{4}e^{-2r/a_0} + C.$$

Therefore

$$\int_{a_0}^\infty P(r)\,dr = \frac{4}{a_0^3}\lim_{b\to\infty}\int_{a_0}^b r^2e^{-2r/a_0}\,dr$$

$$= \frac{4}{a_0^3}\lim_{b\to\infty}\left[-\frac{a_0}{2}r^2e^{-2r/a_0} + a_0\left(-\frac{a_0}{2}re^{-2r/a_0} - \frac{a_0^2}{4}e^{-2r/a_0}\right)\right]\Bigg|_{a_0}^b$$

$$= \frac{4}{a_0^3}\left[\frac{a_0}{2}a_0^2e^{-2} - a_0\left(-\frac{a_0^2}{2}e^{-2} - \frac{a_0^2}{4}e^{-2}\right)\right] = \frac{4e^{-2}}{a_0^3}\left(\frac{a_0^3}{2} + \frac{a_0^3}{2} + \frac{a_0^3}{4}\right) = 5e^{-2} \approx 0.677$$

where we have used the fact that $\lim_{b\to\infty} b^2e^{-2b/a_0} = 0 = \lim_{b\to\infty} be^{-2b/a_0}$ by l'Hôpital's Rule. Thus the probability that an electron is located outside the first Bohr radius is approximately 0.677.

87. By Exercise 77(b),

$$-g(x) = \frac{d}{dx}\int_x^\infty g(t)\,dt = \frac{d}{dx}cx^{-1.5} = -1.5cx^{-2.5}.$$

Thus $g(x) = 1.5cx^{-2.5}$ for $x \geq s$.

88. a. We have $\mu = 66$ and $\sigma = 3$. Then $70 = \mu + 4\sigma/3$ and $71 = \mu + 5\sigma/3$. Thus we need to approximate

$$\int_{\mu+4\sigma/3}^{\mu+5\sigma/3}\frac{1}{\sigma\sqrt{2\pi}}e^{-(x-\mu)^2/2\sigma^2}\,dx,$$

which by Exercise 82 equals $\int_{4/3}^{5/3}(1/\sqrt{2\pi})e^{-x^2/2}\,dx$. By Simpson's Rule with $n = 100$,

$$\int_{4/3}^{5/3} \frac{1}{\sqrt{2\pi}} e^{-x^2/2}\,dx \approx 0.0434208675.$$

Therefore approximately 4% of the adults in the town are between 70 and 71 inches tall.

b. Using the notation of part (a), we need to approximate

$$\int_{\mu+4\sigma/3}^{\infty} \frac{1}{\sigma\sqrt{2\pi}} e^{-(x-\mu)^2/2\sigma^2}\,dx,$$

which by Exercise 82 equals $\int_{4/3}^{\infty}(1/\sqrt{2\pi})e^{-x^2/2}\,dx$. Notice that

$$\int_{-\infty}^{\infty} \frac{1}{\sqrt{2\pi}} e^{-x^2/2}\,dx = 1 = 2\int_{0}^{\infty} \frac{1}{\sqrt{2\pi}} e^{-x^2/2}\,dx$$

because the graph of $e^{-x^2/2}/\sqrt{2\pi}$ is symmetric with respect to the y axis. Thus

$$\int_{0}^{\infty} \frac{1}{\sqrt{2\pi}} e^{-x^2/2}\,dx = \frac{1}{2}.$$

Then by Exercise 77(a),

$$\int_{4/3}^{\infty} \frac{1}{\sqrt{2\pi}} e^{-x^2/2}\,dx = \int_{0}^{\infty} \frac{1}{\sqrt{2\pi}} e^{-x^2/2}\,dx - \int_{0}^{4/3} \frac{1}{\sqrt{2\pi}} e^{-x^2/2}\,dx = \frac{1}{2} - \int_{0}^{4/3} \frac{1}{\sqrt{2\pi}} e^{-x^2/2}\,dx.$$

By Simpson's Rule with $n = 100$,

$$\int_{0}^{4/3} \frac{1}{\sqrt{2\pi}} e^{-x^2/2}\,dx \approx 0.4087887803.$$

Consequently

$$\int_{4/3}^{\infty} \frac{1}{\sqrt{2\pi}} e^{-x^2/2}\,dx \approx \frac{1}{2} - 0.4087887803 = 0.0912112197$$

so that approximately 9% of adults in the town are taller than 70 inches.

89. a. We have $\mu = 7.5$ and $\sigma = 1$. Then $8 = \mu + 0.5\sigma$ and $12 = \mu + 4.5\sigma$. Thus we need to approximate

$$\int_{\mu+0.5\sigma}^{\mu+4.5\sigma} \frac{1}{\sigma\sqrt{2\pi}} e^{-(x-\mu)^2/2\sigma^2}\,dx,$$

which by Exercise 82 equals $\int_{0.5}^{4.5}(1/\sqrt{2\pi})e^{-x^2/2}\,dx$. By Simpson's Rule with $n = 100$,

$$\int_{0.5}^{4.5} \frac{1}{\sqrt{2\pi}} e^{-x^2/2}\,dx \approx 0.3085341341.$$

Therefore approximately 31% of the babies, that is, approximately 62 babies, born in the Easy-Birth Hospital weigh between 8 and 12 pounds.

b. Here $\mu = 7.5$ and $\sigma = 1$, and thus $6.5 = \mu - \sigma$. We need to approximate

$$\int_{-\infty}^{\mu-\sigma} \frac{1}{\sigma\sqrt{2\pi}} e^{-(x-\mu)^2/2\sigma^2}\, dx,$$

which by Exercise 82 equals $\int_{-\infty}^{-1}(1/\sqrt{2\pi})e^{-x^2/2}\, dx$. Notice that

$$1 = \int_{-\infty}^{\infty} \frac{1}{\sqrt{2\pi}} e^{-x^2/2}\, dx = 2\int_{-\infty}^{0} \frac{1}{\sqrt{2\pi}} e^{-x^2/2}\, dx$$

because the graph of $e^{-x^2/2}/\sqrt{2\pi}$ is symmetric with respect to the y axis. Thus

$$\int_{-\infty}^{0} \frac{1}{\sqrt{2\pi}} e^{-x^2/2}\, dx = \frac{1}{2}.$$

Then by a result analogous to Exercise 77(a),

$$\int_{-\infty}^{-1} \frac{1}{\sqrt{2\pi}} e^{-x^2/2}\, dx = \int_{-\infty}^{0} \frac{1}{\sqrt{2\pi}} e^{-x^2/2}\, dx - \int_{-1}^{0} \frac{1}{\sqrt{2\pi}} e^{-x^2/2}\, dx = \frac{1}{2} - \int_{-1}^{0} \frac{1}{\sqrt{2\pi}} e^{-x^2/2}\, dx.$$

By Simpson's Rule with $n = 100$,

$$\int_{-1}^{0} \frac{1}{\sqrt{2\pi}} e^{-x^2/2}\, dx \approx 0.3413447461.$$

Consequently

$$\int_{-\infty}^{-1} \frac{1}{\sqrt{2\pi}} e^{-x^2/2}\, dx \approx \frac{1}{2} - 0.3413447461 = 0.1586552539.$$

Thus approximately 16% of the babies, that is, approximately 32 babies, born in the hospital weighed under 6.5 pounds at birth.

Chapter 7 Review

1. $u = \ln(x^2+9)$, $dv = dx$; $du = [2x/(x^2+9)]\, dx$, $v = x$;

$$\int \ln(x^2+9)\, dx = x\ln(x^2+9) - \int \frac{2x^2}{x^2+9}\, dx = x\ln(x^2+9) - 2\int \left(1 - \frac{9}{x^2+9}\right) dx$$

$$= x\ln(x^2+9) - 2x + 18\left(\frac{1}{3}\right)\tan^{-1}\frac{x}{3} + C = x\ln(x^2+9) - 2x + 6\tan^{-1}\frac{x}{3} + C.$$

2. By Exercise 48 and Example 3 of Section 7.1, $\int(\ln x)^4\, dx = x(\ln x)^4 - 4\int(\ln x)^3\, dx = x(\ln x)^4 - 4x(\ln x)^3 + 12\int(\ln x)^2\, dx = x(\ln x)^4 - 4x(\ln x)^3 + 12x(\ln x)^2 - 24\int \ln x\, dx = x(\ln x)^4 - 4x(\ln x)^3 + 12x(\ln x)^2 - 24x\ln x + 24x + C$.

3. $u = x$, $dv = \csc^2 x\, dx$; $du = dx$, $v = -\cot x$; $\int x\csc^2 x\, dx = -x\cot x + \int \cot x\, dx = -x\cot x + \ln|\sin x| + C$.

4. $u = x^3$, $dv = e^{3x}\,dx$; $du = 3x^2\,dx$, $v = \frac{1}{3}e^{3x}$; $\int x^3e^{3x}\,dx = \frac{1}{3}x^3e^{3x} - \int x^2e^{3x}\,dx$. For $\int x^2e^{3x}\,dx$, let $u = x^2$, $dv = e^{3x}\,dx$; $du = 2x\,dx$, $v = \frac{1}{3}e^{3x}$; $\int x^2e^{3x}\,dx = \frac{1}{3}x^2e^{3x} - \frac{2}{3}\int xe^{3x}\,dx$. For $\int xe^{3x}\,dx$, let $u = x$, $dv = e^{3x}\,dx$; $du = dx$, $v = \frac{1}{3}e^{3x}$; $\int xe^{3x}\,dx = \frac{1}{3}xe^{3x} - \frac{1}{3}\int e^{3x}\,dx = \frac{1}{3}xe^{3x} - \frac{1}{9}e^{3x} + C_1$. Thus $\int x^3e^{3x}\,dx = \frac{1}{3}x^3e^{3x} - \frac{1}{3}x^2e^{3x} + \frac{2}{3}(\frac{1}{3}xe^{3x} - \frac{1}{9}e^{3x} + C_1) = \frac{1}{3}e^{3x}(x^3 - x^2 + \frac{2}{3}x - \frac{2}{9}) + C$.

5. $u = x$, $dv = \cosh x\,dx$; $du = dx$, $v = \sinh x$; $\int x\cosh x\,dx = x\sinh x - \int \sinh x\,dx = x\sinh x - \cosh x + C$.

6. $u = \sin^{-1} x$, $dv = x^2\,dx$; $du = (1/\sqrt{1-x^2})\,dx$, $v = \frac{1}{3}x^3$;

$$\int x^2 \sin^{-1} x\,dx = \frac{1}{3}x^3 \sin^{-1} x - \frac{1}{3}\int \frac{x^3}{\sqrt{1-x^2}}\,dx.$$

For $\int (x^3/\sqrt{1-x^2})\,dx$ let $w = 1 - x^2$, so that $dw = -2x\,dx$ and $x^2 = 1 - w$. Then

$$\int \frac{x^3}{\sqrt{1-x^2}}\,dx = \int \frac{x^2}{\sqrt{1-x^2}}\,x\,dx = \int \frac{1-w}{\sqrt{w}}\left(-\frac{1}{2}\right)dw = -\frac{1}{2}\int \left(\frac{1}{\sqrt{w}} - \sqrt{w}\right)dw$$

$$= -\frac{1}{2}\left(2\sqrt{w} - \frac{2}{3}w^{3/2}\right) + C_1 = -\sqrt{1-x^2} + \frac{1}{3}(1-x^2)^{3/2} + C_1.$$

Thus $\int x^2 \sin^{-1} x\,dx = \frac{1}{3}x^3 \sin^{-1} x + \frac{1}{3}\sqrt{1-x^2} - \frac{1}{9}(1-x^2)^{3/2} + C$.

7. $\int x\cos^2 x\,dx = \int x(\frac{1}{2} + \frac{1}{2}\cos 2x)\,dx = \frac{1}{2}\int x\,dx + \frac{1}{2}\int x\cos 2x\,dx = \frac{1}{4}x^2 + \frac{1}{2}\int x\cos 2x\,dx$. For $\int x\cos 2x\,dx$, let $u = x$, $dv = \cos 2x\,dx$; $du = dx$, $v = \frac{1}{2}\sin 2x$; $\int x\cos 2x\,dx = \frac{1}{2}x\sin 2x - \frac{1}{2}\int \sin 2x\,dx = \frac{1}{2}x\sin 2x + \frac{1}{4}\cos 2x + C_1$. Thus $\int x\cos^2 x\,dx = \frac{1}{4}x^2 + \frac{1}{4}x\sin 2x + \frac{1}{8}\cos 2x + C$.

8. $$\int \cos^2 x \sin^4 x\,dx = \int \left(\frac{1+\cos 2x}{2}\right)\left(\frac{1-\cos 2x}{2}\right)^2 dx = \frac{1}{8}\int (1 - \cos 2x - \cos^2 2x + \cos^3 2x)\,dx$$

$$= \frac{1}{8}\int \left(1 - \cos^2 2x - (\cos 2x)(1 - \cos^2 2x)\right)\,dx$$

$$= \frac{1}{8}\int \left(\frac{1}{2} - \frac{1}{2}\cos 4x - \cos 2x \sin^2 2x\right)dx$$

$$= \frac{1}{8}\left(\frac{1}{2}x - \frac{1}{8}\sin 4x - \frac{1}{6}\sin^3 2x\right) + C$$

9. $u = \sin x^3$, $du = 3x^2 \cos x^3\,dx$; $\int x^2 \sin x^3 \cos x^3\,dx = \frac{1}{3}\int u\,du = \frac{1}{6}u^2 + C = \frac{1}{6}\sin^2 x^3 + C$.

10. $u = \tan x$, $du = \sec^2 x\,dx$; $\int \sec^4 x\,dx = \int (\tan^2 x + 1)\sec^2 x\,dx = \int (u^2+1)\,du = \frac{1}{3}u^3 + u + C = \frac{1}{3}\tan^3 x + \tan x + C$.

11. $$\int \tan^5 x\,dx = \int \tan^3 x\,(\sec^2 x - 1)\,dx = \int \tan^3 x \sec^2 x\,dx - \int \tan^3 x\,dx$$

$$= \int \tan^3 x \sec^2 x\,dx - \int \tan x\,(\sec^2 x - 1)\,dx$$

$$= \int \tan^3 x \sec^2 x\,dx - \int \tan x \sec^2 x\,dx + \int \tan x\,dx$$

For the first two integrals let $u = \tan x$, so that $du = \sec^2 x\,dx$. Then

$$\int \tan^3 x \sec^2 x\,dx - \int \tan x \sec^2 x\,dx = \int u^3\,du - \int u\,du = \frac{1}{4}u^4 - \frac{1}{2}u^2 + C_1 = \frac{1}{4}\tan^4 x - \frac{1}{2}\tan^2 x + C_1.$$

Thus $\int \tan^5 x\,dx = \frac{1}{4}\tan^4 x - \frac{1}{2}\tan^2 x - \ln|\cos x| + C$.

12. $u = \cos x$, $du = -\sin x\,dx$;

$$\int \frac{\tan^3 x}{\sec^5 x}\,dx = \int \frac{\sin^3 x}{\cos^3 x}\cos^5 x\,dx = \int \sin^3 x\,\cos^2 x\,dx = \int (1-\cos^2 x)\,\sin x\,\cos^2 x\,dx$$

$$= -\int (u^2 - u^4)\,du = -\frac{1}{3}u^3 + \frac{1}{5}u^5 + C = \frac{1}{5}\cos^5 x - \frac{1}{3}\cos^3 x + C.$$

13. $u = x^2$, $dv = x\cos x^2\,dx$; $du = 2x\,dx$, $v = \frac{1}{2}\sin x^2$; $\int x^3\cos x^2\,dx = \frac{1}{2}x^2\sin x^2 - \int \frac{1}{2}(2x)\sin x^2\,dx = \frac{1}{2}x^2\sin x^2 + \frac{1}{2}\cos x^2 + C$.

14. $u = \sqrt{e^t - 1}$, $du = [e^t/(2\sqrt{e^t-1})]\,dt$, so $e^t = u^2 + 1$;

$$\int \sqrt{e^t-1}\,dt = \int u\left(\frac{2u}{u^2+1}\right)du = 2\int \frac{u^2}{u^2+1}\,du = 2\int \left(1 - \frac{1}{u^2+1}\right)du$$

$$= 2u - 2\tan^{-1}u + C = 2\sqrt{e^t-1} - 2\tan^{-1}\sqrt{e^t-1} + C.$$

15. $u = 1 - 3t$, $du = -3\,dt$, so $t = \frac{1}{3}(1-u)$;

$$\int t^2\sqrt{1-3t}\,dt = \int \left[\frac{1}{3}(1-u)\right]^2 \sqrt{u}\left(-\frac{1}{3}\right)du = -\frac{1}{27}\int \left(u^{1/2} - 2u^{3/2} + u^{5/2}\right)du$$

$$= -\frac{1}{27}\left(\frac{2}{3}u^{3/2} - \frac{4}{5}u^{5/2} + \frac{2}{7}u^{7/2}\right) + C = -\frac{2}{81}(1-3t)^{3/2} + \frac{4}{135}(1-3t)^{5/2} - \frac{2}{189}(1-3t)^{7/2} + C.$$

16. $u = 1 - t^4$, $du = -4t^3\,dt$, so $t^4 = 1 - u$;

$$\int \frac{t^7}{(1-t^4)^3}\,dt = \int \frac{1-u}{u^3}\left(-\frac{1}{4}\right)du = -\frac{1}{4}\int \frac{1}{u^3}\,du + \frac{1}{4}\int \frac{1}{u^2}\,du$$

$$= \frac{1}{8u^2} - \frac{1}{4u} + C = \frac{1}{8(1-t^4)^2} - \frac{1}{4(1-t^4)} + C.$$

17. $$\int \frac{\cos x}{1+\cos x}\,dx = \int \frac{\cos x}{1+\cos x}\,\frac{1-\cos x}{1-\cos x}\,dx = \int \frac{\cos x - (1-\sin^2 x)}{\sin^2 x}\,dx$$

$$= \int \left(\frac{\cos x}{\sin^2 x} - \csc^2 x + 1\right)dx = \frac{-1}{\sin x} + \cot x + x + C = -\csc x + \cot x + x + C$$

18. $x^4 = \sec u$, $4x^3\,dx = \sec u\,\tan u\,du$; $\sqrt{\sec^2 u - 1} = \tan u$;

$$\int \frac{x^3}{\sqrt{x^8-1}}\,dx = \frac{1}{4}\int \frac{1}{\sqrt{\sec^2 - 1}}\sec u\,\tan u\,du = \frac{1}{4}\int \sec u\,du$$

$$= \frac{1}{4}\ln|\sec u + \tan u| + C = \frac{1}{4}\ln|x^4 + \sqrt{x^8-1}| + C.$$

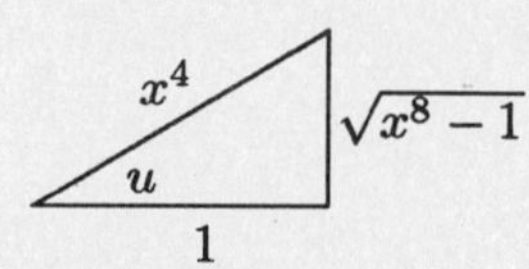

19. $x+1 = 3\tan u,\ dx = 3\sec^2 u\, du;$

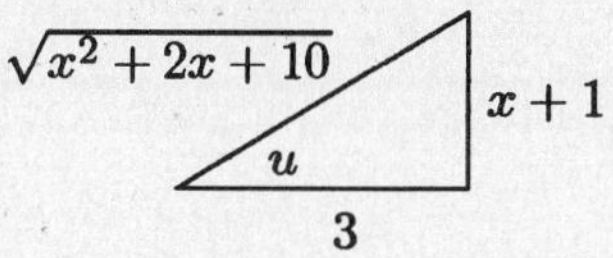

$$\begin{aligned}
\int \frac{x^2}{(x^2+2x+10)^{5/2}}\,dx &= \int \frac{x^2}{\left((x+1)^2+9\right)^{5/2}}\,dx \\
&= \int \frac{(3\tan u - 1)^2}{(9\tan^2 u + 9)^{5/2}}\, 3\sec^2 u\, du \\
&= \frac{1}{81}\int \frac{9\tan^2 u - 6\tan u + 1}{\sec^5 u}\,\sec^2 u\, du \\
&= \frac{1}{9}\int \sin^2 u \cos u\, du - \frac{2}{27}\int \sin u \cos^2 u\, du + \frac{1}{81}\int (1-\sin^2 u)\cos u\, du \\
&= \frac{1}{27}\sin^3 u + \frac{2}{81}\cos^3 u + \frac{1}{81}\sin u - \frac{1}{243}\sin^3 u + C \\
&= \frac{8}{243}\frac{(x+1)^3}{(x^2+2x+10)^{3/2}} + \frac{2}{3}\frac{1}{(x^2+2x+10)^{3/2}} + \frac{1}{81}\frac{x+1}{(x^2+2x+10)^{1/2}} + C.
\end{aligned}$$

20. $\dfrac{1}{x^3-1} = \dfrac{1}{(x-1)(x^2+x+1)} = \dfrac{A}{x-1} + \dfrac{Bx+C}{x^2+x+1};$

$A(x^2+x+1) + (Bx+C)(x-1) = 1;\ A+B=0,\ A-B+C=0,\ A-C=1;$

$A = \frac{1}{3},\ B = -\frac{1}{3},\ C = -\frac{2}{3}$

$$\begin{aligned}
\int \frac{1}{x^3-1}\,dx &= \int \left[\frac{1}{3}\left(\frac{1}{x-1}\right) - \frac{x+2}{3(x^2+x+1)}\right] dx \\
&= \frac{1}{3}\ln|x-1| - \frac{1}{6}\int \left(\frac{2x+1}{x^2+x+1} + \frac{3}{x^2+x+1}\right) dx \\
&= \frac{1}{3}\ln|x-1| - \frac{1}{6}\ln(x^2+x+1) - \frac{1}{2}\int \frac{1}{(x+\frac{1}{2})^2+\frac{3}{4}}\,dx
\end{aligned}$$

For $\int 1/[(x+\frac{1}{2})^2+\frac{3}{4}]\,dx$, let $u = x+\frac{1}{2}$, so $du = dx$. Then

$$\int \frac{1}{(x+\frac{1}{2})^2+\frac{3}{4}}\,dx = \int \frac{1}{u^2+\frac{3}{4}}\,du = \frac{2}{\sqrt{3}}\tan^{-1}\frac{2u}{\sqrt{3}} + C_1 = \frac{2\sqrt{3}}{3}\tan^{-1}\frac{(2x+1)\sqrt{3}}{3} + C_1.$$

Thus

$$\int \frac{1}{x^3-1}\,dx = \frac{1}{3}\ln|x-1| - \frac{1}{6}\ln(x^2+x+1) - \frac{\sqrt{3}}{3}\tan^{-1}\frac{(2x+1)\sqrt{3}}{3} + C_2$$

21. $x = \tan u,\ dx = \sec^2 u\, du;$

$$\begin{aligned}
\int \frac{x^4}{(x^2+1)^2}\,dx &= \int \frac{\tan^4 u}{(\tan^2 u + 1)^2}\sec^2 u\, du = \int \frac{\tan^4 u}{\sec^2 u}\,du = \int \frac{\sin^4 u}{\cos^4 u}\cos^2 u\, du = \int \frac{\sin^4 u}{\cos^2 u}\,du \\
&= \int \frac{(1-\cos^2 u)^2}{\cos^2 u}\,du = \int \frac{1 - 2\cos^2 u + \cos^4 u}{\cos^2 u}\,du = \int (\sec^2 u - 2 + \cos^2 u)\,du \\
&= \tan u - 2u + \int \left(\frac{1}{2} + \frac{1}{2}\cos 2u\right) du = \tan u - 2u + \frac{1}{2}u + \frac{1}{4}\sin 2u + C \\
&= \tan u - \frac{3}{2}u + \frac{1}{2}\sin u \cos u + C
\end{aligned}$$

Now $u = \tan^{-1} x$, and by the figure, $\sin u = x/\sqrt{x^2+1}$ and $\cos u = 1/\sqrt{x^2+1}$, so that

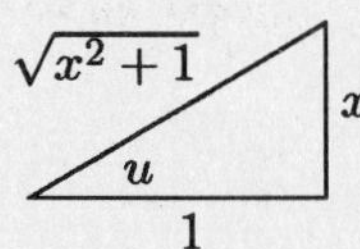

$$\int \frac{x^4}{(x^2+1)^2}\,dx = x - \frac{3}{2}\tan^{-1} x + \frac{1}{2}\,\frac{x}{x^2+1} + C.$$

22. $\dfrac{1}{x(x^2+x+1)} = \dfrac{A}{x} + \dfrac{Bx+C}{x^2+x+1}$; $A(x^2+x+1) + x(Bx+C) = 1$;
$A+B=0$, $A+C=0$, $A=1$; $B=-1$, $C=-1$;

$$\int \frac{1}{x(x^2+x+1)}\,dx = \int \left(\frac{1}{x} - \frac{x+1}{x^2+x+1}\right)dx = \int \frac{1}{x}\,dx - \frac{1}{2}\int \frac{(2x+1)+1}{x^2+x+1}\,dx$$

$$= \ln|x| - \frac{1}{2}\int \frac{2x+1}{x^2+x+1}\,dx - \frac{1}{2}\int \frac{1}{x^2+x+1}\,dx = \ln|x| - \frac{1}{2}\ln(x^2+x+1) - \frac{1}{2}\int \frac{1}{(x+\frac{1}{2})^2+\frac{3}{4}}\,dx$$

For $\int 1/[(x+\frac{1}{2})^2+\frac{3}{4}]\,dx$, let $u = x+\frac{1}{2}$, so $du = dx$. Then

$$\int \frac{1}{(x+\frac{1}{2})^2+\frac{3}{4}}\,dx = \int \frac{1}{u^2+\frac{3}{4}}\,du = \frac{2}{\sqrt{3}}\tan^{-1}\frac{2u}{\sqrt{3}} + C_1 = \frac{2\sqrt{3}}{3}\tan^{-1}\frac{(2x+1)\sqrt{3}}{3} + C_1.$$

Thus

$$\int \frac{1}{x(x^2+x+1)}\,dx = \ln|x| - \frac{1}{2}\ln(x^2+x+1) - \frac{1}{3}\sqrt{3}\tan^{-1}\frac{(2x+1)\sqrt{3}}{3} + C.$$

23. $\displaystyle\int \frac{x}{x^2+3x-18}\,dx = \int \frac{x}{(x+6)(x-3)}\,dx$; $\dfrac{x}{(x+6)(x-3)} = \dfrac{A}{x+6} + \dfrac{B}{x-3}$;
$A(x-3)+B(x+6) = x$; $A+B=1$, $-3A+6B=0$; $A=\frac{2}{3}$, $B=\frac{1}{3}$;

$$\int \frac{x}{x^2+3x-18}\,dx = \int \left(\frac{2}{3}\,\frac{1}{x+6} + \frac{1}{3}\,\frac{1}{x-3}\right)dx$$

$$= \frac{2}{3}\int \frac{1}{x+6}\,dx + \frac{1}{3}\int \frac{1}{x-3}\,dx = \frac{2}{3}\ln|x+6| + \frac{1}{3}\ln|x-3| + C$$

24. $u = \sqrt{2x+1}$, so that $x = (u^2-1)/2$ and $dx = u\,du$;

$$\int \frac{\sqrt{2x+1}}{x+1}\,dx = \int \frac{2u}{u^2+1}\,u\,du = \int \frac{2u^2}{u^2+1}\,du = 2\int \left(1 - \frac{1}{u^2+1}\right)du$$

$$= 2\left(u - \tan^{-1} u\right) + C = 2\left(\sqrt{2x+1} - \tan^{-1}\sqrt{2x+1}\right) + C.$$

25. Improper integral;

$$\int_{-2}^{1} \frac{1}{3x+4}\,dx = \lim_{c\to -4/3^-} \int_{-2}^{c} \frac{1}{3x+4}\,dx + \lim_{p\to -4/3^+} \int_{p}^{1} \frac{1}{3x+4}\,dx$$

$$= \lim_{c\to -4/3^-} \frac{1}{3}\ln|3x+4|\Big|_{-2}^{c} + \lim_{p\to -4/3^+} \frac{1}{3}\ln|3x+4|\Big|_{p}^{1}$$

$$= \lim_{c\to -4/3^-} \left(\frac{1}{3}\ln|3c+4| - \frac{1}{3}\ln 2\right) + \lim_{p\to -4/3^+} \left(\frac{1}{3}\ln 7 - \frac{1}{3}\ln|3p+4|\right).$$

Neither limit exists, so the integral diverges.

26. Improper integral; $u = 1 + \sin x$, $du = \cos x\,dx$;

$$\int_{\pi}^{3\pi/2} \frac{\cos x}{1+\sin x}\,dx = \lim_{c\to 3\pi/2-} \int_{\pi}^{c} \frac{\cos x}{1+\sin x}\,dx = \lim_{c\to 3\pi/2-} \int_{1}^{1+\sin c} \frac{1}{u}\,du$$

$$= \lim_{c\to 3\pi/2-} \ln|u|\Big|_{1}^{1+\sin c} = \lim_{c\to 3\pi/2-} \ln(1+\sin c) = -\infty.$$

Thus the integral diverges.

27. Proper integral; $u = x$, $dv = \sec x \tan x\,dx$, $du = dx$, $v = \sec x$; $\int_0^{\pi/4} x \sec x \tan x\,dx = x\sec x\big|_0^{\pi/4} - \int_0^{\pi/4} \sec x\,dx = x\sec x\big|_0^{\pi/4} - \ln|\sec x + \tan x|\big|_0^{\pi/4} = \frac{\pi\sqrt{2}}{4} - \ln(\sqrt{2}+1)$.

28. Proper integral;

$$\int_0^1 \frac{x}{x+2}\,dx = \int_0^1 \left(1 - \frac{2}{x+2}\right) dx = (x - 2\ln|x+2|)\big|_0^1 = 1 - 2\ln 3 + 2\ln 2 = 1 + \ln\frac{4}{9}.$$

29. Proper integral; $u = 1 + \sqrt{x}$, $du = \frac{1}{2}x^{-1/2}\,dx$, so $dx = 2(u-1)\,du$;

$$\int_1^4 \frac{1}{1+\sqrt{x}}\,dx = \int_2^3 \frac{2(u-1)}{u}\,du = \int_2^3 \left(2 - \frac{2}{u}\right) du$$

$$= (2u - 2\ln|u|)\big|_2^3 = 6 - 2\ln 3 - 4 + 2\ln 2 = 2 + \ln\frac{4}{9}.$$

30. Improper integral; $u = x - 1$, $du = dx$;

$$\int_1^5 \frac{x}{\sqrt{x-1}}\,dx = \lim_{c\to 1+} \int_c^5 \frac{x}{\sqrt{x-1}}\,dx = \lim_{c\to 1+} \int_{c-1}^4 \frac{u+1}{\sqrt{u}}\,du$$

$$= \lim_{c\to 1+} \int_{c-1}^4 \left(\sqrt{u} + \frac{1}{\sqrt{u}}\right) du = \lim_{c\to 1+} \left(\frac{2}{3}u^{3/2} + 2u^{1/2}\right)\Big|_{c-1}^4$$

$$= \lim_{c\to 1+} \left[\frac{16}{3} + 4 - \frac{2}{3}(c-1)^{3/2} - 2(c-1)^{1/2}\right] = \frac{28}{3}.$$

31. Proper integral; $u = \sin x$, $du = \cos x\,dx$;

$$\int_0^{\pi/4} \sin^4 x \cos^3 x\,dx = \int_0^{\pi/4} \sin^4 x\,(1 - \sin^2 x)\cos x\,dx = \int_0^{\sqrt{2}/2} (u^4 - u^6)\,du$$

$$= \left(\frac{1}{5}u^5 - \frac{1}{7}u^7\right)\Big|_0^{\sqrt{2}/2} = \frac{\sqrt{2}}{40} - \frac{\sqrt{2}}{112} = \frac{9\sqrt{2}}{560}.$$

32. Proper integral; $u = \sec x$, $du = \sec x \tan x\,dx$; $\int_0^{\pi/3} \tan^5 x \sec x\,dx = \int_0^{\pi/3} (\sec^2 x - 1)^2 \tan x \sec x\,dx = \int_0^{\pi/3} (\sec^4 x - 2\sec^2 x + 1)\tan x \sec x\,dx = \int_1^2 (u^4 - 2u^2 + 1)\,du = \left(\frac{1}{5}u^5 - \frac{2}{3}u^3 + u\right)\Big|_1^2 = \frac{38}{15}$.

33. Proper integral; $u = \tan x$, $du = \sec^2 x\,dx$; $\int_0^{\pi/4} (\tan^3 x + \tan^5 x)\,dx = \int_0^{\pi/4} \tan^3 x\,(1 + \tan^2 x)\,dx = \int_0^{\pi/4} \tan^3 x \sec^2 x\,dx = \int_0^1 u^3\,du = \frac{u^4}{4}\Big|_0^1 = \frac{1}{4}$.

34. Improper integral; $x = \sin u$, $dx = \cos u\, du$;

$$\int \frac{x^3}{\sqrt{1-x^2}}\,dx = \int \frac{\sin^3 u}{\sqrt{1-\sin^2 u}}\cos u\,du = \int \sin^3 u\,du$$

$$= \int \sin u\,(1-\cos^2 u)\,du = -\cos u + \frac{1}{3}\cos^3 u + C$$

$$= -\sqrt{1-x^2} + \frac{1}{3}\left(1-x^2\right)^{3/2} + C$$

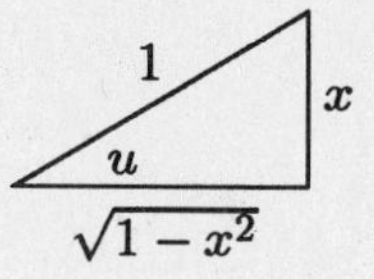

$$\int_0^1 \frac{x^3}{\sqrt{1-x^2}}\,dx = \lim_{c\to 1^-}\int_0^c \frac{x^3}{\sqrt{1-x^2}}\,dx = \lim_{c\to 1^-}\left(-\sqrt{1-x^2}+\frac{1}{3}\left(1-x^2\right)^{3/2}\right)\Bigg|_0^c$$

$$= \lim_{c\to 1^-}\left(-\sqrt{1-c^2}+\frac{1}{3}\left(1-c^2\right)^{3/2}+\frac{2}{3}\right) = \frac{2}{3}$$

35. Proper integral; $x = \sec u$, $dx = \sec u\,\tan u\,du$;

$$\int_1^{\sqrt{2}} \frac{\sqrt{x^2-1}}{x^2}\,dx = \int_0^{\pi/4}\frac{\sqrt{\sec^2 u-1}}{\sec^2 u}\sec u\,\tan u\,du = \int_0^{\pi/4}\frac{\tan^2 u}{\sec u}\,du = \int_0^{\pi/4}\frac{\sec^2 u - 1}{\sec u}\,du$$

$$= \int_0^{\pi/4}(\sec u - \cos u)\,du = \left(\ln|\sec u + \tan u| - \sin u\right)\Big|_0^{\pi/4} = \ln(\sqrt{2}+1) - \frac{\sqrt{2}}{2}$$

36. Proper integral; $x^3 = \tan u$, $3x^2\,dx = \sec^2 u\,du$;

$$\int_0^1 \frac{x^2}{1+x^6}\,dx = \frac{1}{3}\int_0^{\pi/4}\frac{\sec^2 u}{1+\tan^2 u}\,du = \frac{1}{3}\int_0^{\pi/4} 1\,du = \frac{1}{3}u\Big|_0^{\pi/4} = \frac{1}{12}\pi$$

37. Proper integral; $u = x^{3/2}$, $du = \frac{3}{2}x^{1/2}\,dx$; then $u = \sin t$, $du = \cos t\,dt$;

$$\int_0^{\sqrt[3]{2}/2}\frac{\sqrt{x}}{\sqrt{1-x^3}}\,dx = \frac{2}{3}\int_0^{1/2}\frac{1}{\sqrt{1-u^2}}\,du = \frac{2}{3}\int_0^{\pi/6}\frac{1}{\sqrt{1-\sin^2 t}}\cos t\,dt = \frac{2}{3}\int_0^{\pi/6}1\,dt = \frac{2}{3}t\Big|_0^{\pi/6} = \frac{1}{9}\pi$$

38. Proper integral; $x = \sin u$, $dx = \cos u\,du$;

$$\int_0^1 x^5\sqrt{1-x^2}\,dx = \int_0^{\pi/2}\sin^5 u\,\cos^2 u\,du = \int_0^{\pi/2}(1-\cos^2 u)^2\cos^2 u\,\sin u\,du$$

$$= \int_0^{\pi/2}(\cos^2 u - 2\cos^4 u + \cos^6 u)\sin u\,du = \left(\frac{-1}{3}\cos^3 u + \frac{2}{5}\cos^5 u - \frac{1}{7}\cos^7 u\right)\Bigg|_0^{\pi/2} = \frac{1}{3} - \frac{2}{5} + \frac{1}{7} = \frac{8}{105}$$

39. Proper integral; $x = \tan u$, $dx = \sec^2 u\,du$;

$$\int_0^{\sqrt{3}}\sqrt{x^2+1}\,dx = \int_0^{\pi/3}\sqrt{\tan^2 u + 1}\,\sec^2 u\,du = \int_0^{\pi/3}\sec^3 u\,du \overset{\text{(7) of Section 7.2}}{=}$$

$$\left(\frac{1}{2}\sec u\,\tan u + \frac{1}{2}\ln|\sec u + \tan u|\right)\Bigg|_0^{\pi/3} = \frac{1}{2}(2)(\sqrt{3}) + \frac{1}{2}\ln|2+\sqrt{3}| = \sqrt{3} + \frac{1}{2}\ln(2+\sqrt{3})$$

40. Proper integral; $x+1=2\tan u$, $dx=2\sec^2 u\,du$;

$$\int_{-1}^{1}\frac{x}{x^2+2x+5}\,dx=\int_{-1}^{1}\frac{x}{(x^2+2x+1)+4}\,dx=\int_{-1}^{1}\frac{x}{(x+1)^2+4}\,dx=\int_{0}^{\pi/4}\frac{2\tan u-1}{4\tan^2 u+4}2\sec^2 u\,du$$

$$=\frac{1}{2}\int_0^{\pi/4}(2\tan u-1)\,du=\left(-\ln|\cos u|-\frac{1}{2}u\right)\Big|_0^{\pi/4}=-\ln\frac{\sqrt{2}}{2}-\frac{\pi}{8}=\ln\sqrt{2}-\frac{\pi}{8}$$

41. $\displaystyle\int_{-5}^{0}\frac{x}{x^2+4x-5}\,dx=\int_{-5}^{0}\frac{x}{(x+5)(x-1)}\,dx$, so the integral is improper. Next,

$$\frac{x}{(x+5)(x-1)}=\frac{A}{x+5}+\frac{B}{x-1}=\frac{A(x-1)+B(x+5)}{(x+5)(x-1)}$$

$$A(x-1)+B(x+5)=x; A+B=1, -A+5B=0; A=\frac{5}{6}, B=\frac{1}{6}.$$

Thus

$$\int_{-5}^{0}\frac{x}{x^2+4x-5}\,dx=\lim_{c\to-5^+}\int_c^0\left(\frac{5}{6}\frac{1}{x+5}+\frac{1}{6}\frac{1}{x-1}\right)dx=\lim_{c\to-5^+}\left(\frac{5}{6}\int_c^0\frac{1}{x+5}\,dx+\frac{1}{6}\int_c^0\frac{1}{x-1}\,dx\right)$$

$$=\lim_{c\to-5^+}\left(\frac{5}{6}\ln|x+5|\Big|_c^0+\frac{1}{6}\ln|x-1|\Big|_c^0\right)=\lim_{c\to-5^+}\left(\frac{5}{6}\ln 5-\frac{5}{6}\ln(c+5)-\frac{1}{6}\ln|c-1|\right).$$

Since $\lim_{c\to-5^+}\ln(c+5)=-\infty$, the integral diverges.

42. Since

$$\int_{-1}^{1}\frac{5x^3}{x^2+x-6}\,dx=\int_{-1}^{1}\frac{5x^3}{(x+3)(x-2)}\,dx,$$

the integral is proper. Next,

$$\frac{5x^3}{x^2+x-6}=5x-5+\frac{35x-30}{(x+3)(x-2)}$$

and by partial fractions we get

$$\frac{35x-30}{(x+3)(x-2)}=\frac{A}{x+3}+\frac{B}{x-2}=\frac{A(x-2)+B(x+3)}{(x+3)(x-2)}$$

$$A+B=35, -2A+3B=-30; A=27, B=8;$$

thus

$$\int_{-1}^{1}\frac{5x^3}{x^2+x-6}\,dx=\int_{-1}^{1}\left(5x-5+\frac{35x-30}{(x+3)(x-2)}\right)dx=\int_{-1}^{1}\left(5x-5+\frac{27}{x+3}+\frac{8}{x-2}\right)dx$$

$$=\left(\frac{5}{2}x^2-5x+27\ln|x+3|+8\ln|x-2|\right)\Big|_{-1}^{1}=\left(\frac{5}{2}-5+27\ln 4\right)-\left(\frac{5}{2}+5+27\ln 2+8\ln 3\right)$$

$$=-10+27\ln 4-27\ln 2-8\ln 3=-10+27\ln 2-8\ln 3$$

43. Improper integral;

$$\int_0^{\pi/2} \frac{1}{1-\sin x}\,dx = \lim_{c\to\pi/2^-} \int_0^c \frac{1}{1-\sin x}\,dx = \lim_{c\to\pi/2^-} \int_0^c \frac{1}{1-\sin x}\,\frac{1+\sin x}{1+\sin x}\,dx$$

$$= \lim_{c\to\pi/2^-} \int_0^c \frac{1+\sin x}{\cos^2 x}\,dx = \lim_{c\to\pi/2^-} \int_0^c \left(\sec^2 x + \frac{\sin x}{\cos^2 x}\right) dx = \lim_{c\to\pi/2^-} \left(\tan x\Big|_0^c + \int_0^c \frac{\sin x}{\cos^2 x}\,dx\right)$$

For $\int_0^c (\sin x)/(\cos^2 x)\,dx$ let $u = \cos x$, so $du = -\sin x\,dx$. Then

$$\int_0^c \frac{\sin x}{\cos^2 x}\,dx = \int_1^{\cos c} -\frac{1}{u^2}\,du = \frac{1}{u}\Big|_1^{\cos c} = \frac{1}{\cos c} - 1 = \sec c - 1.$$

Thus

$$\int_0^{\pi/2} \frac{1}{1-\sin x}\,dx = \lim_{c\to\pi/2^-} (\tan c + \sec c - 1).$$

Since $\lim_{c\to\pi/2^-} \tan c = \infty = \lim_{c\to\pi/2^-} \sec c$, the integral diverges.

44. Proper integral; $u = 1 + \tan x$, so that $du = \sec^2 x\,dx$ and

$$dx = \frac{1}{\sec^2 x}\,du = \frac{1}{[(u-1)^2+1]}\,du = \frac{1}{u^2-2u+2}\,du.$$

$$\int_0^{\pi/4} \frac{1}{1+\tan x}\,dx = \int_1^2 \frac{1}{u}\left(\frac{1}{u^2-2u+2}\right) du; \quad \frac{1}{u(u^2-2u+2)} = \frac{A}{u} + \frac{Bu+C}{u^2-2u+2}$$

$$A(u^2-2u+2) + (Bu+C)u = 1, A+B=0, -2A+C=0, 2A=1; A=\frac{1}{2}, B=-\frac{1}{2}, C=1;$$

$$\int_0^{\pi/4} \frac{1}{1+\tan x}\,dx = \int_1^2 \frac{1}{u(u^2-2u+2)}\,du = \int_1^2 \left(\frac{1}{2u} + \frac{(-1/2)u+1}{u^2-2u+2}\right) du$$

$$= \frac{1}{2}\ln|u|\Big|_1^2 - \frac{1}{4}\int_1^2 \frac{2u-4}{u^2-2u+2}\,du = \frac{1}{2}\ln 2 - \frac{1}{4}\int_1^2 \left[\frac{2u-2}{u^2-2u+2} - \frac{2}{(u-1)^2+1}\right] du$$

$$= \frac{1}{2}\ln 2 - \frac{1}{4}\ln(u^2-2u+2)\Big|_1^2 + \frac{1}{2}\tan^{-1}(u-1)\Big|_1^2 = \frac{1}{2}\ln 2 - \frac{1}{4}\ln 2 + \frac{1}{2}\left(\frac{\pi}{4}\right) = \frac{1}{4}\ln 2 + \frac{\pi}{8}$$

45. Improper integral; $u = \ln x$, $dv = x\,dx$, $du = (1/x)\,dx$, $v = \frac{1}{2}x^2$; $\int x\ln x\,dx = \frac{1}{2}x^2\ln x - \int \frac{1}{2}x\,dx = \frac{1}{2}x^2\ln x - \frac{1}{4}x^2 + C$. Thus

$$\int_0^1 x\ln x\,dx = \lim_{c\to0^+} \int_c^1 x\ln x\,dx = \lim_{c\to0^+} \left(\frac{1}{2}x^2\ln x - \frac{1}{4}x^2\right)\Big|_c^1 = \lim_{c\to0^+} \left(-\frac{1}{4} - \frac{1}{2}c^2\ln c + \frac{1}{4}c^2\right) = -\frac{1}{4}$$

since $\lim_{c\to0^+} c\ln c = 0$ by Example 7 of Section 6.6.

46. Improper integral; $\int_0^\infty x\ln x\,dx$ converges only if $\int_0^1 x\ln x\,dx$ and $\int_1^\infty x\ln x\,dx$ converge. By Exercise 45, $\int_0^1 x\ln x\,dx = -\frac{1}{4}$. By the solution of Exercise 45, we find that $\int_1^\infty x\ln x\,dx = \lim_{b\to\infty} \int_1^b x\ln x\,dx = \lim_{b\to\infty} \left(\frac{1}{2}x^2\ln x - \frac{1}{4}x^2\right)\Big|_1^b = \lim_{b\to\infty} \left(\frac{1}{2}b^2\ln b - \frac{1}{4}b^2 + \frac{1}{4}\right) = \lim_{b\to\infty} \left(\frac{1}{2}b^2(\ln b - \frac{1}{2}) + \frac{1}{4}\right) = \infty$. Thus $\int_0^\infty x\ln x\,dx$ diverges.

47. Improper integral;

$$\int_1^\infty \frac{1}{x(\ln x)^2}\,dx = \lim_{c\to 1^+}\int_c^2 \frac{1}{x(\ln x)^2}\,dx + \lim_{b\to\infty}\int_2^b \frac{1}{x(\ln x)^2}\,dx$$

$$= \lim_{c\to 1^+} \left.\frac{-1}{\ln x}\right|_c^2 + \lim_{b\to\infty}\left.\frac{-1}{\ln x}\right|_2^b = \lim_{c\to 1^+}\left(\frac{1}{\ln c}-\frac{1}{\ln 2}\right) + \lim_{b\to\infty}\left(\frac{1}{\ln 2}-\frac{1}{\ln b}\right).$$

Since $\lim_{c\to 1^+}(1/(\ln c) - 1/(\ln 2)) = \infty$, the integral diverges.

48. Improper integral; since $\ln x < x$ for all x in $[3, \infty)$, we have $1/(1+\ln x) > 1/(1+x)$. Now

$$\int_3^\infty \frac{1}{1+x}\,dx = \lim_{b\to\infty}\int_3^\infty \frac{1}{1+x}\,dx = \lim_{b\to\infty} \ln(1+x)\Big|_3^b = \lim_{b\to\infty}(\ln(1+b) - \ln 4) = \infty.$$

Thus $\int_3^\infty 1/(1+\ln x)\,dx$ diverges by the Comparison Property.

49. Improper integral; by Exercise 54(b) of Section 7.1, with $a = -1$ and $b = 1$, $\int e^{-x}\cos x\,dx = \frac{1}{2}e^{-x}(-\cos x + \sin x) + C$. Thus

$$\int_0^\infty e^{-x}\cos x\,dx = \lim_{b\to\infty}\int_0^b e^{-x}\cos x\,dx = \lim_{b\to\infty}\left.\frac{1}{2}e^{-x}(\sin x - \cos x)\right|_0^b$$

$$= \lim_{b\to\infty}\left[\frac{1}{2}e^{-b}(\sin b - \cos b) + \frac{1}{2}\right] = \frac{1}{2}.$$

50. Improper integral; $u = x^3$, $du = 3x^2\,dx$;

$$\int_1^\infty x^2 e^{-(x^3)}\,dx = \lim_{b\to\infty}\int_1^b x^2 e^{-(x^3)}\,dx = \lim_{b\to\infty}\int_1^{b^3}\frac{1}{3}e^{-u}\,du$$

$$= \lim_{b\to\infty}\left.-\frac{1}{3}e^{-u}\right|_1^{b^3} = \lim_{b\to\infty}\left(-\frac{1}{3}e^{-(b^3)} + \frac{1}{3}e^{-1}\right) = \frac{1}{3}e^{-1}.$$

51. Improper integral;

$$\int_1^\infty \frac{1}{x(x^2+1)}\,dx = \lim_{b\to\infty}\int_1^b \frac{1}{x(x^2+1)}\,dx \overset{x=\tan u}{=} \lim_{b\to\infty}\int_{\pi/4}^{\tan^{-1} b}\frac{1}{\tan u\,(\sec^2 u)}\sec^2 u\,du$$

$$= \lim_{b\to\infty}\int_{\pi/4}^{\tan^{-1} b}\cot u\,du = \lim_{b\to\infty}\ln|\sin u|\Big|_{\pi/4}^{\tan^{-1} b}.$$

By the figure, if $u = \tan^{-1} b$, then $\sin u = b/\sqrt{b^2+1}$, so that

$$\lim_{b\to\infty}\ln|\sin u|\Big|_{\pi/4}^{\tan^{-1} b} = \lim_{b\to\infty}\left(\ln\frac{b}{\sqrt{b^2+1}} - \ln\left(\sin\frac{\pi}{4}\right)\right)$$

$$= \lim_{b\to\infty}\left(\ln 1 - \ln\frac{\sqrt{2}}{2}\right) = \ln\sqrt{2} = \frac{1}{2}\ln 2.$$

Therefore the integral converges, and $\int_1^\infty 1/[x(x^2+1)]\,dx = \frac{1}{2}\ln 2$.

52. Improper integral;

$$\int_0^\infty \frac{1}{x(x^2+4)}\,dx = \lim_{c\to 0+}\int_c^2 \frac{1}{x(x^2+4)}\,dx + \lim_{b\to\infty}\int_2^b \frac{1}{x(x^2+4)}\,dx.$$

Now

$$\lim_{c\to 0+}\int_c^2 \frac{1}{x(x^2+4)}\,dx \overset{x=2\tan u}{=} \lim_{c\to 0+}\int_{\tan^{-1} c/2}^{\pi/4} \frac{1}{(2\tan u)(4\tan^2 u+4)}\,2\sec^2 u\,du$$

$$= \lim_{c\to 0+}\frac{1}{4}\int_{\tan^{-1} c/2}^{\pi/4} \cot u\,du = \lim_{c\to 0+}\frac{1}{4}\ln|\sin u|\Big|_{\tan^{-1} c/2}^{\pi/4}.$$

By the figure, if $u=\tan^{-1} c/2$ then $\sin u = c/\sqrt{c^2+4}$, so that

$$\lim_{c\to 0+}\int_c^2 \frac{1}{x(x^2+4)}\,dx = \lim_{c\to 0+}\frac{1}{4}\ln|\sin u|\Big|_{\tan^{-1} c/2}^{\pi/4}$$

$$= \lim_{c\to 0+}\frac{1}{4}\left(\ln\sin\frac{\pi}{4} - \ln\frac{c}{\sqrt{c^2+4}}\right) = \infty.$$

$\sqrt{c^2+4}$ c u 2

Thus the integral diverges.

53. $u=\ln x$, $dv=(1/x)\,dx$, $du=(1/x)\,dx$, $v=\ln x$;

$$\int \frac{\ln x}{x}\,dx = (\ln x)^2 - \int\frac{\ln x}{x}\,dx, \quad \text{so that} \quad 2\int\frac{\ln x}{x}\,dx = (\ln x)^2 + C_1$$

and thus $\int(\ln x)/x\,dx = \frac{1}{2}(\ln x)^2 + C$.

54. a. $x=\sin u$, $dx=\cos u\,du$;

$$\int_0^1 x^m(1-x^2)^n\,dx = \int_0^{\pi/2}\sin^m u\,(1-\sin^2 u)^n\cos u\,du$$

$$= \int_0^{\pi/2}\sin^m u\,(\cos^2 u)^n\cos u\,du = \int_0^{\pi/2}\sin^m u\,\cos^{2n+1} u\,du$$

b. $$\int_0^1 x^3(1-x^2)^{10}\,dx = \int_0^{\pi/2}\sin^3 u\cos^{21} u\,du = \int_0^{\pi/2}(1-\cos^2 u)\cos^{21} u\,\sin u\,du$$

$$= \int_0^{\pi/2}(\cos^{21} u - \cos^{23} u)\sin u\,du = -\left(\frac{1}{22}\cos^{22} u - \frac{1}{24}\cos^{24} u\right)\Big|_0^{\pi/2}$$

$$= \frac{1}{22} - \frac{1}{24} = \frac{1}{264}$$

55. a. $x = \dfrac{u}{1-u}$, $dx = \dfrac{1}{(1-u)^2}\,du$, $u=\dfrac{x}{1+x}$ and $1+x = \dfrac{1}{1-u}$;

$$\int_0^b \frac{x^{m-1}}{(1+x)^{m+n}}\,dx = \int_0^b\left(\frac{x}{1+x}\right)^{m-1}\frac{1}{(1+x)^{n+1}}\,dx$$

$$= \int_0^{b/(1+b)} u^{m-1}(1-u)^{n+1}\frac{1}{(1-u)^2}\,du = \int_0^{b/(1+b)} u^{m-1}(1-u)^{n-1}\,du.$$

b. Using (a) with $m = 4$ and $n = 1$, we obtain

$$\int_0^\infty \frac{x^3}{(1+x)^5}\,dx = \lim_{b\to\infty}\int_0^b \frac{x^3}{(1+x)^5}\,dx = \lim_{b\to\infty}\int_0^{b/(1+b)} u^3(1-u)^0\,du$$

$$= \lim_{b\to\infty}\int_0^{b/(1+b)} u^3\,du = \lim_{b\to\infty}\frac{1}{4}u^4\bigg|_0^{b/(1+b)} = \lim_{b\to\infty}\frac{1}{4}\frac{b^4}{(1+b)^4} = \frac{1}{4}.$$

56. a. $I_n = \int_0^1 (1-x^2)^n\,dx = \int_0^1 [(1-x^2)^{n-1} - x^2(1-x^2)^{n-1}\,dx$

$$= \int_0^1 (1-x^2)^{n-1}\,dx - \int_0^1 x^2(1-x^2)^{n-1}\,dx$$

Let $u = x$, $dv = x(1-x^2)^{n-1}\,dx$, $du = dx$, $v = [-1/(2n)](1-x^2)^n$. Then

$$\int_0^1 x^2(1-x^2)^{n-1}\,dx = \frac{-x}{2n}(1-x^2)^n\bigg|_0^1 + \frac{1}{2n}\int_0^1 (1-x^2)^n\,dx = \frac{1}{2n}\int_0^1 (1-x^2)^n\,dx = \frac{1}{2n}I_n.$$

Thus

$$I_n = \int_0^1 (1-x^2)^{n-1}\,dx - \frac{1}{2n}I_n = I_{n-1} - \frac{1}{2n}I_n, \quad \text{so} \quad I_n = \frac{2n}{2n+1}I_{n-1}.$$

b. Using (a),

$$\int_0^1 (1-x^2)^4\,dx = I_4 = \frac{8}{9}I_3 = \frac{8}{9}\frac{6}{7}I_2 = \frac{8}{9}\frac{6}{7}\frac{4}{5}I_1 = \frac{64}{105}\int_0^1 (1-x^2)\,dx = \frac{64}{105}\left(x - \frac{x^3}{3}\right)\bigg|_0^1 = \frac{128}{315}.$$

57. Using the given identities, we have

$$\int \frac{\tan(\pi/4 + x/2)}{\sec^2(x/2)}\,dx = \int \frac{\sin(\pi/2 + x)}{1 + \cos(\pi/2 + x)}\,\frac{1+\cos x}{2}\,dx$$

$$= \int \left(\frac{\cos x}{1-\sin x}\right)\left(\frac{1+\cos x}{2}\right)dx = \frac{1}{2}\int \frac{(\cos x + \cos^2 x)(1+\sin x)}{(1-\sin x)(1+\sin x)}\,dx$$

$$= \frac{1}{2}\int \frac{(\cos x + \cos^2 x)(1+\sin x)}{\cos^2 x}\,dx = \frac{1}{2}\int (\sec x + 1 + \tan x + \sin x)\,dx$$

$$= \frac{1}{2}(\ln|\sec x + \tan x| + \ln|\sec x| - \cos x + x) + C = \frac{1}{2}\ln\left|\sec^2 x + \sec x\,\tan x\right| - \frac{1}{2}\cos x + \frac{x}{2} + C.$$

58. a. With $n = 10$, the Trapezoidal Rule yields $\int_0^1 \sqrt{1-x^2}\,dx \approx 0.7761295816$.

b. With $n = 10$, Simpson's Rule yields $\int_0^1 \sqrt{1-x^2}\,dx \approx 0.7817520397$.

59. a. With $n = 10$, the Trapezoidal Rule yields $\int_0^2 \sqrt{2x-x^2}\,dx \approx 1.518524414$.

b. With $n = 10$, Simpson's Rule yields $\int_0^2 \sqrt{2x-x^2}\,dx \approx 1.55008698$.

60. If $f(x) = \sqrt{x^2-1}$, then $f''(x) = -(x^2-1)^{-3/2}$, and $|f''(x)| \le |f''(2)| = 1/(3\sqrt{3})$ for $2 \le x \le 2.5$. Then for the Trapezoidal Rule,

$$E_n^T \le \frac{(\frac{1}{2})^3[1/(3\sqrt{3})]}{12n^2} = \frac{1}{288\sqrt{3}\,n^2}, \quad \text{and} \quad \frac{1}{288\sqrt{3}\,n^2} < 0.0001 \quad \text{if } n \ge 5.$$

Next

$$f^{(4)}(x) = \frac{-3 - 12x^2}{(x^2-1)^{7/2}}, \quad \text{and} \quad |f^{(4)}(x)| \le \frac{12(2.5)^2 + 3}{3^{7/2}} = \frac{26}{27}\sqrt{3} < 1.668 \quad \text{for } 2 \le x \le 2.5.$$

Then for Simpson's Rule,

$$E_n^S \le \frac{(\frac{1}{2})^5(1.668)}{180n^4}, \quad \text{and} \quad \frac{(\frac{1}{2})^5(1.668)}{180n^4} < 0.001 \quad \text{if } n \ge 2.$$

61. a. By the solution of Exercise 60 it suffices to use the Trapezoidal Rule with $n = 5$. We obtain

$$\int_2^{2.5} \sqrt{x^2-1}\,dx \approx \frac{1}{20}\left(\sqrt{3} + 2\sqrt{3.41} + 2\sqrt{3.84} + 2\sqrt{4.29} + 2\sqrt{4.76} + \sqrt{5.25}\right) \approx 1.007085359.$$

b. By the solution of Exercise 60 it suffices to use Simpson's Rule with $n = 2$. We obtain

$$\int_2^{2.5} \sqrt{x^2-1}\,dx \approx \frac{1}{12}\left(\sqrt{3} + 4\sqrt{4.0625} + \sqrt{5.25}\right) \approx 1.007133034.$$

62. $A = \displaystyle\int_0^{\pi/2} \cos^3 x\,dx = \int_0^{\pi/2} (1 - \sin^2 x)\cos x\,dx = \int_0^{\pi/2} \cos x\,dx - \int_0^{\pi/2} \sin^2 x \cos x\,dx$

$= \sin x\Big|_0^{\pi/2} - \dfrac{1}{3}\sin^3 x\Big|_0^{\pi/2} = 1 - \dfrac{1}{3} = \dfrac{2}{3}$

63. $A = \int_{-3}^0 \sqrt{9-x^2}\,dx$. Let $x = 3\sin u$, so that $dx = 3\cos u\,du$. Then

$$\int_{-3}^0 \sqrt{9-x^2}\,dx = \int_{-\pi/2}^0 \sqrt{9 - 9\sin^2 u}\,3\cos u\,du$$

$$= 9\int_{-\pi/2}^0 \cos^2 u\,du = 9\left(\frac{1}{2}u + \frac{1}{4}\sin 2u\right)\Big|_{-\pi/2}^0 = 0 - 9\left(-\frac{\pi}{4}\right) = \frac{9}{4}\pi.$$

64. $A = \int_0^4 \sqrt{1+x^5}\,dx \approx \frac{1}{3}\left(1 + 4\sqrt{2} + 2\sqrt{33} + 4\sqrt{244} + \sqrt{1025}\right) \approx 37.54786605.$

65. $A = \displaystyle\int_\pi^{3\pi/2} \left|\frac{\cos x}{1+\sin x}\right| dx = \int_\pi^{3\pi/2} \frac{-\cos x}{1+\sin x}\,dx = -\lim_{c\to 3\pi/2^-} \int_\pi^c \frac{\cos x}{1+\sin x}\,dx$

$= -\displaystyle\lim_{c\to 3\pi/2^-} \ln(1+\sin x)\Big|_\pi^c = -\lim_{c\to 3\pi/2^-} \ln(1+\sin c) = \infty$

so the region has infinite area.

66. $A = \displaystyle\int_\pi^{3\pi/2} \left|\frac{\cos x}{\sqrt{1+\sin x}}\right| dx = \int_\pi^{3\pi/2} \frac{-\cos x}{\sqrt{1+\sin x}}\,dx = -\lim_{c\to 3\pi/2^-} \int_\pi^c \frac{\cos x}{\sqrt{1+\sin x}}\,dx$

$= -\displaystyle\lim_{c\to 3\pi/2^-} 2\sqrt{1+\sin x}\Big|_\pi^c = -\lim_{c\to 3\pi/2^-} \left(2\sqrt{1+\sin c} - 2\right) = 2$

67. $A = \int_{-\infty}^{\infty} \left| \frac{x^3}{2+x^4} \right| dx = \lim_{a \to -\infty} \int_a^0 \frac{-x^3}{2+x^4}\, dx + \lim_{b \to \infty} \int_0^b \frac{x^3}{2+x^4}\, dx$

$= \lim_{a \to -\infty} \left(\frac{-1}{4} \ln(2+x^4) \right) \Big|_a^0 + \lim_{b \to \infty} \frac{1}{4} \ln(2+x^4) \Big|_0^b$

$= \lim_{a \to -\infty} \left[\frac{1}{4} \ln(2+a^4) - \frac{1}{4} \ln 2 \right] + \lim_{b \to \infty} \left[\frac{1}{4} \ln(2+b^4) - \frac{1}{4} \ln 2 \right]$

Neither limit exists, so the area is infinite.

68. $A = \int_{-\infty}^{\infty} \left| \frac{x^3}{\sqrt{2+x^4}} \right| dx = \lim_{a \to -\infty} \int_a^0 \frac{-x^3}{\sqrt{2+x^4}}\, dx + \lim_{b \to \infty} \int_0^b \frac{x^3}{\sqrt{2+x^4}}\, dx$

$= \lim_{a \to -\infty} \left(\frac{-1}{2} \sqrt{2+x^4} \right) \Big|_a^0 + \lim_{b \to \infty} \left(\frac{1}{2} \sqrt{2+x^4} \right) \Big|_0^b$

$= \lim_{a \to -\infty} \left(\frac{1}{2} \sqrt{2+a^4} - \frac{\sqrt{2}}{2} \right) + \lim_{b \to \infty} \left(\frac{1}{2} \sqrt{2+b^4} - \frac{\sqrt{2}}{2} \right)$

Neither limit exists, so the area is infinite.

69. $A = \int_{-\infty}^{\infty} \left| \frac{x^3}{(2+x^4)^2} \right| dx = \lim_{a \to -\infty} \int_a^0 \frac{-x^3}{(2+x^4)^2}\, dx + \lim_{b \to \infty} \int_0^b \frac{x^3}{(2+x^4)^2}\, dx$

$= \lim_{a \to -\infty} \frac{1}{4(2+x^4)} \Big|_a^0 + \lim_{b \to \infty} \frac{-1}{4(2+x^4)} \Big|_0^b$

$= \lim_{a \to -\infty} \left[\frac{1}{8} - \frac{1}{4(2+a^4)} \right] + \lim_{b \to \infty} \left[\frac{1}{8} - \frac{1}{4(2+b^4)} \right] = \frac{1}{4}$

70. a. $\int_0^a \frac{k}{r^2}\, dr = \lim_{c \to 0^+} \int_c^a \frac{k}{r^2}\, dr = \lim_{c \to 0^+} -\frac{k}{r} \Big|_c^a = \lim_{c \to 0^+} \left(\frac{k}{c} - \frac{k}{a} \right) = \infty$

Thus the work would be infinite, so it is not possible for the electrons to be brought together.

b. $\int_a^\infty \frac{k}{r^2}\, dr = \lim_{b \to \infty} \int_a^b \frac{k}{r^2}\, dr = \lim_{b \to \infty} -\frac{k}{r} \Big|_a^b = \lim_{b \to \infty} \left(\frac{k}{a} - \frac{k}{b} \right) = \frac{k}{a}$

In theory it is possible for the electron to be taken arbitrarily far from the proton.

71. Let $c = m/(2kT)$. We are to evaluate $\int_0^\infty v^3 e^{-cv^2}\, dv$ and $\int_0^\infty v^2 e^{-cv^2}\, dv$. For the first integral we integrate by parts, letting $t = v^2$ and $du = ve^{-cv^2}\, dv$; then $dt = 2v\, dv$ and $u = -(1/2c)e^{-cv^2}$. Therefore

$$\int_0^b v^3 e^{-cv^2}\, dv = \int_0^b v^2 (ve^{-cv^2})\, dv = v^2 \left(-\frac{1}{2c} e^{-cv^2} \right) \Big|_0^b + \int_0^b \frac{v}{c} e^{-cv^2}\, dv$$

$$= \frac{-b^2}{2c} e^{-cb^2} - \frac{1}{2c^2} e^{-cv^2} \Big|_0^b = -\frac{b^2}{2c} e^{-cb^2} - \frac{1}{2c^2} e^{-cb^2} + \frac{1}{2c^2}.$$

Since $\lim_{b \to \infty} b^2 e^{-cb^2} = 0$ by l'Hôpital's Rule, and also $\lim_{b \to \infty} e^{-cb^2} = 0$, we conclude that

$$A = \int_0^\infty v^3 e^{-cv^2}\, dv = \lim_{b \to \infty} \int_0^b v^3 e^{-cv^2}\, dv = \lim_{b \to \infty} \left[-\frac{b^2}{2c} e^{-cb^2} - \frac{1}{2c^2} e^{-cb^2} + \frac{1}{2c^2} \right] = \frac{1}{2c^2}.$$

For the second integral, we use integration by parts, letting $t = v$ and $du = ve^{-cv^2}\,dv$; thus $dt = dv$ and $u = -(1/2c)e^{-cv^2}$. Therefore

$$\int_0^b v^2 e^{-cv^2}\,dv = \int_0^b v(ve^{-cv^2})\,dv = v\left(-\frac{1}{2c}e^{-cv^2}\right)\Big|_0^b + \int_0^b \frac{1}{2c}e^{-cv^2}\,dv = -\frac{b}{2c}e^{-cb^2} + \int_0^b \frac{1}{2c}e^{-cv^2}\,dv.$$

Since $\lim_{b\to\infty} be^{-cb^2} = 0$ by l'Hôpital's Rule, it follows that

$$B = \int_0^\infty v^2 e^{-cv^2}\,dv = \lim_{b\to\infty}\left(-\frac{b}{2c}e^{-cb^2} + \int_0^b \frac{1}{2c}e^{-cv^2}\,dv\right) = \lim_{b\to\infty}\frac{1}{2c}\int_0^b e^{-cv^2}\,dv = \frac{1}{2c}\int_0^\infty e^{-cv^2}\,dv.$$

Now let $w = \sqrt{2c}\,v$, so that $dw = \sqrt{2c}\,dv$. If $v = 0$, then $w = 0$; if v approaches ∞, then so does w. Therefore by the hint,

$$\frac{1}{2c}\int_0^\infty e^{-cv^2}\,dv = \frac{1}{2c}\int_0^\infty e^{-w^2/2}\frac{1}{\sqrt{2c}}\,dw = \frac{1}{(2c)^{3/2}}\int_0^\infty e^{-w^2/2}\,dw = \frac{1}{(2c)^{3/2}}\sqrt{\frac{\pi}{2}} = \frac{\sqrt{\pi}}{4c^{3/2}}.$$

As a result, $B = \sqrt{\pi}/(4c^{3/2})$, so that

$$\frac{A}{B} = \frac{1/(2c^2)}{\sqrt{\pi}/(4c^{3/2})} = \frac{2}{\sqrt{\pi c}} = \sqrt{\frac{8kT}{\pi m}}.$$

Cumulative Review(Chapters 1–6)

1. $\lim_{x\to\sqrt{2}} \dfrac{2\sqrt{2}-2x}{8-4x^2} = \lim_{x\to\sqrt{2}} \dfrac{2(\sqrt{2}-x)}{4(\sqrt{2}-x)(\sqrt{2}+x)} = \lim_{x\to\sqrt{2}} \dfrac{1}{2(\sqrt{2}+x)} = \dfrac{1}{4\sqrt{2}} = \dfrac{1}{8}\sqrt{2}$

2. Since $0 \le e^{-x}(1+\sin^2(e^x)) \le e^{-x}(1+1) = 2e^{-x}$ and $\lim_{x\to\infty} 2e^{-x} = 0$, it follows from the Squeezing Theorem that $\lim_{x\to\infty} e^{-x}(1+\sin^2(e^x)) = 0$.

3. $f'(x) = \dfrac{-e^{-x}(1+e^x) - (1+e^{-x})e^x}{(1+e^x)^2} = \dfrac{-e^{-x} - 2 - e^x}{(1+e^x)^2}$

4. Since $f(x) = \int_0^{2x+1} e^{(t^2)}\,dt - \int_0^x e^{(t^2)}\,dt$, we have $f'(x) = e^{(2x+1)^2}\cdot 2 - e^{(x^2)} = 2e^{(2x+1)^2} - e^{(x^2)}$.

5. $f'(x) = 1/x - \frac{1}{4}x$, so

$$\sqrt{1+(f'(x))^2} = \sqrt{1+\left(\frac{1}{x}-\frac{1}{4}x\right)^2} = \sqrt{1+\frac{1}{x^2}-\frac{1}{2}+\frac{1}{16}x^2}$$

$$= \sqrt{\frac{1}{x^2}+\frac{1}{2}+\frac{1}{16}x^2} = \sqrt{\left(\frac{1}{x}+\frac{1}{4}x\right)^2} = \frac{1}{x}+\frac{1}{4}x.$$

6. (a) Let (a,b) be on the graph of the equation, so that $2a^{3/2} - 2b^{3/2} = 3ab^{1/2}$. Then $a \ge 0$ and $b \ge 0$ since otherwise $a^{3/2}$ or $b^{32/2}$ would be meaningless. Also $2a^{3/2} = 2b^{3/2} + 3ab^{1/2} \ge 2b^{3/2}$, so that $a \ge b \ge 0$.

(b) Differentiating the given equation implicitly, we find that

$$3x^{1/2} - 3y^{1/2}\frac{dy}{dx} = 3y^{1/2} + \frac{3}{2}xy^{-1/2}\frac{dy}{dx} \quad \text{so that} \quad \frac{dy}{dx} = \frac{3x^{1/2} - 3y^{1/2}}{3y^{1/2} + \frac{3}{2}xy^{-1/2}} = \frac{2(x^{1/2} - y^{1/2})}{2y^{1/2} + xy^{-1/2}}.$$

Notice that there is no tangent line at the point $(0,0)$ on the graph, since there are no points on the graph with a negative coordinate. At any other point (a,b) on the graph, we have $a > b > 0$, so the slope $2(a^{1/2} - b^{1/2})/(2b^{1/2} + ab^{-1/2})$ of the tangent line is positive.

7. a. The inequality $(x-4)/(2x+6) > \frac{3}{20}$ is equivalent to $(x-4)/(2x+6) - \frac{3}{20} > 0$, or $[14(x-7)]/[40(x+3)] > 0$. From the diagram we see that the solution is the union of $(-\infty,-3)$ and $(7,\infty)$. Thus $f(x) > \frac{3}{20}$ for $x > 7$.

$x-7$ — — — — — — — — — 0 + +

$x+3$ — — 0 + + + + + + + +

$\dfrac{14(x-7)}{40(x+3)}$ + + — — — — — 0 + +

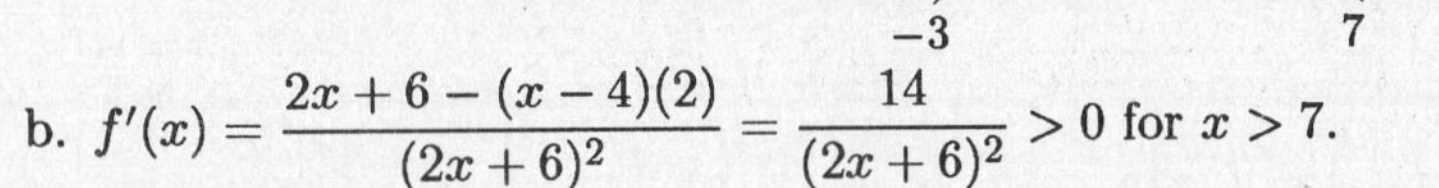

b. $f'(x) = \dfrac{2x+6-(x-4)(2)}{(2x+6)^2} = \dfrac{14}{(2x+6)^2} > 0$ for $x > 7$.

Thus f is increasing on $[7,\infty)$. Since $f(7) = \frac{3}{20}$, it follows that $f(x) > \frac{3}{20}$ for $x > 7$.

8. $f'(x) = \dfrac{-\sin x\,(1-\sin x) - \cos x\,(-\cos x)}{(1-\sin x)^2} = \dfrac{1}{1-\sin x}$; $f''(x) = \dfrac{\cos x}{(1-\sin x)^2}$;

f is increasing on $(\pi/2+2n\pi, 5\pi/2+2n\pi)$ for every integer n; concave upward on $(3\pi/2+2n\pi, 5\pi/2+2n\pi)$ and concave downward on $(\pi/2+2n\pi, 3\pi/2+2n\pi)$ for every integer n; inflection points are $(3\pi/2+2n\pi, 0)$ for every integer n; asymptotes are $x = \pi/2 + 2n\pi$ for every integer n.

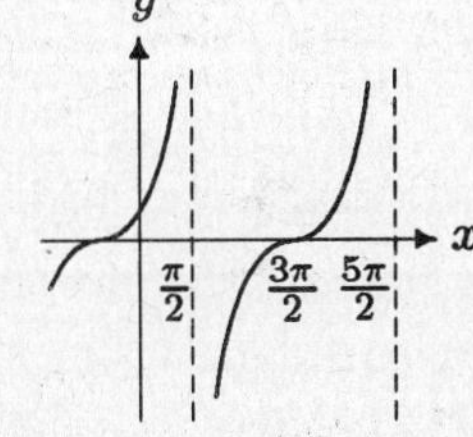

9. $f'(x) = -e^x e^{(1-e^x)}$; $f''(x) = -e^x e^{(1-e^x)} + e^{2x}e^{(1-e^x)} = e^x e^{(1-e^x)}(-1+e^x)$; $f'(x) < 0$ for all x, so f is a decreasing function; $f''(x) > 0$ if $-1 + e^x > 0$, or equivalently, $x > 0$; $f''(x) < 0$ if $x < 0$; concave downward on $(-\infty,0)$ and concave upward on $(0,\infty)$; inflection point is $(0,1)$. Let $y = 1 - e^x$. Then $\lim_{x\to-\infty}(1-e^x) = 1$, so that $\lim_{x\to-\infty} e^{(1-e^x)} = \lim_{y\to1^-} e^y = e$. Similarly, $\lim_{x\to\infty}(1-e^x) = -\infty$, so that $\lim_{x\to\infty} e^{(1-e^x)} = \lim_{y\to-\infty} e^y = 0$. Thus the horizontal asymptotes are $y = 0$ and $y = e$.

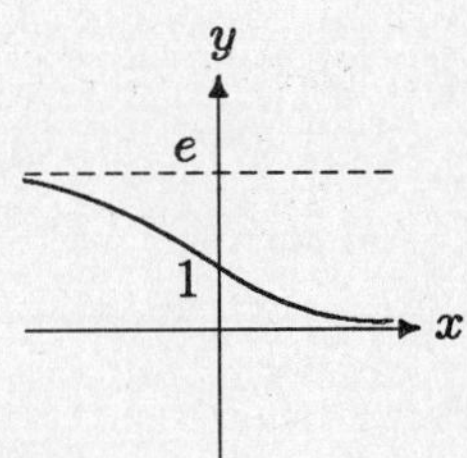

10. For $y = x^2 + 3$, we have $dy/dx = 2x$; for $x = cy^2$, we have $y = \sqrt{x/c}$, so $dy/dx = 1/(2\sqrt{cx})$. If the parabolas have the same tangent line at (x,y), then $2x = 1/(2\sqrt{cx})$, so $\sqrt{c} = 1/(4x^{3/2})$, or $c = 1/(16x^3)$. Also $x^2 + 3 = y = \sqrt{x/c} = \sqrt{16x^4} = 4x^2$, so $3x^2 = 3$ or $x = 1$ (since c and hence x are positive). The corresponding values of y and c are 4 and $\frac{1}{16}$, respectively. Thus if $c = \frac{1}{16}$, then the parabolas have the same tangent line at $(1,4)$.

11. Using the notation in the figure and the Law of Cosines, we have

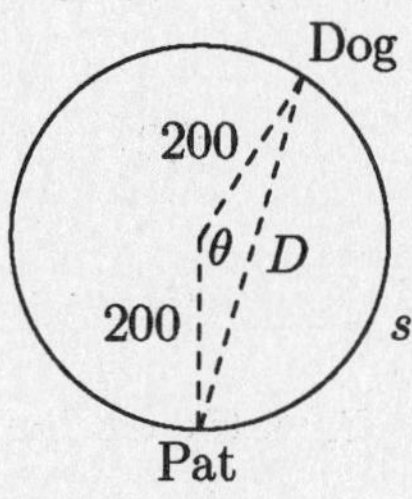

$$D^2 = (200)^2 + (200)^2 - 2(200)(200)\cos\theta = 80{,}000(1-\cos\theta).$$

We are to find dD/dt at the moment that $D = 200$. Differentiating $D^2 = 80{,}000(1-\cos\theta)$ implicitly, we find that

$$2D\frac{dD}{dt} = 80{,}000(\sin\theta)\frac{d\theta}{dt}.$$

To determine $d\theta/dt$, we use the fact that if s is the length of the circular arc corresponding to D, then $s = 200\theta$. Since the dog moves at the rate of 50 feet per second, it follows that $50 = ds/dt = 200(d\theta/dt)$, so that $d\theta/dt = \frac{1}{4}$. At the instant $D = 200$, the triangle in the figure is equilateral, so $\theta = \pi/3$. Therefore at that instant

$$\frac{dD}{dt} = \frac{80{,}000(\sin(\pi/3))\frac{1}{4}}{2(200)} = 25\sqrt{3}\,\text{(feet per second)}.$$

12. If we set up a coordinate system as in the figure, then the arch has an equation of the form $y = a - bx^2$. Since $(0,36)$ and $(18,0)$ are on the arch, it follows that $a = 36$ and $b = 36/18^2 = \frac{1}{9}$. Thus an equation of the arch is $y = 36 - \frac{1}{9}x^2$, so the area A of the window in the figure is given by

$$A = 2xy = 2x\left(36 - \frac{1}{9}x^2\right) = 72x - \frac{2}{9}x^3.$$

We are to maximize A. We find that $A'(x) = 72 - \frac{2}{3}x^2$, so $A'(x) = 0$ for $x = \sqrt{(3\cdot 72)/2} = 6\sqrt{3}$. Since $A''(x) = -\frac{4}{3}x < 0$ for $x > 0$, it follows from (1) in Section 4.6 and the Second Derivative Test that A is maximum for $x = 6\sqrt{3}$, so the maximum area is $A(6\sqrt{3}) = 72(6\sqrt{3}) - \frac{2}{9}(6\sqrt{3})^3 = 288\sqrt{3}$ (square inches).

13. Let $u = 4 + x^2$, so that $du = 2x\,dx$;

$$\int \frac{x}{4+x^2}\,dx = \int \frac{1}{u}\left(\frac{1}{2}\right)du = \frac{1}{2}\ln|u| + C = \frac{1}{2}\ln(4+x^2) + C.$$

14. $$\int_0^2 \frac{1}{4+3x^2}\,dx = \frac{1}{3}\int_0^2 \frac{1}{\frac{4}{3}+x^2}\,dx = \frac{1}{3}\cdot\frac{\sqrt{3}}{2}\tan^{-1}\frac{\sqrt{3}x}{2}\bigg|_0^2$$
$$= \frac{\sqrt{3}}{6}\left(\tan^{-1}\sqrt{3} - \tan^{-1}0\right) = \frac{\sqrt{3}}{6}\left(\frac{\pi}{3} - 0\right) = \frac{\pi\sqrt{3}}{18}$$

15. $\int e^{-3x}(e^{5x}+1)\,dx = \int(e^{-3x}e^{5x}+e^{-3x})\,dx = \int(e^{2x}+e^{-3x})\,dx = \int e^{2x}\,dx + \int e^{-3x}\,dx = \frac{1}{2}e^{2x} - \frac{1}{3}e^{-3x} + C$

16. Let $u = \sin^{-1}x$, so that $du = (1/\sqrt{1-x^2})\,dx$;

$$\int \frac{\sin^{-1}x}{\sqrt{1-x^2}}\,dx = \int u\,du = \frac{1}{2}u^2 + C = \frac{1}{2}\left(\sin^{-1}x\right)^2 + C.$$

17. Let $f(t)$ be the position of the car at time t. Then

$$f(2) - f(0) = \int_0^2 f'(t)\,dt = \int_0^2 v(t)\,dt = \int_0^2 \left(40 + \frac{40}{4+t^2}\right) dt = \left(40t + \frac{40}{2}\tan^{-1}\frac{t}{2}\right)\Big|_0^2$$

$$= (80 + 20\tan^{-1}1) - (0 + 20\tan^{-1}0) = 80 + 20\left(\frac{\pi}{4}\right) = 80 + 5\pi.$$

Thus the car travels $80 + 5\pi \approx 95.7$ (miles) in the two hours.

18. For $x > 0$ and $y \geq 0$, we have $y^2 - x^7 = 8x^4$, so $y = \sqrt{8x^4 + x^7} = x^2\sqrt{8 + x^3}$. Thus $A = \int_1^2 x^2\sqrt{8+x^3}\,dx$. Let $u = 8 + x^3$, so that $du = 3x^2\,dx$. If $x = 1$, then $u = 9$, and if $x = 2$, then $u = 16$. Thus $A = \int_1^2 x^2\sqrt{8+x^3}\,dx = \int_9^{16} \sqrt{u}\,\left(\frac{1}{3}\right)\,du = \frac{2}{9}u^{3/2}\big|_9^{16} = \frac{2}{9}(64 - 27) = \frac{74}{9}$.

19. Let $u = cx$, so that $du = c\,dx$. If $x = a$, then $u = ca$; if $x = b$, then $u = cb$. Therefore

$$\int_a^b f(cx)\,dx = \int_{ca}^{cb} f(u)\frac{1}{c}\,du = \frac{1}{c}\int_{ca}^{cb} f(x)\,dx.$$

20. By Theorem 5.12, $f'(t) = (d/dt)\int_0^t f(s)\,ds = f(t)$. Then Theorem 4.8 implies that $f(t) = f(0)e^t$ for all $t \geq 0$. Since $f(0) = \int_0^0 f(s)\,ds = 0$, this means that $f(t) = 0$ for all $t \geq 0$.

Chapter 8

Applications of the Integral

8.1 Volumes: The Cross-Sectional Method

1. $V = \int_0^1 \pi(x^2)^2\,dx = \frac{\pi}{5}x^5\Big|_0^1 = \frac{\pi}{5}$

2. $V = \int_1^2 \pi(x^2)^2\,dx = \frac{\pi}{5}x^5\Big|_1^2 = \frac{31\pi}{5}$

3. $V = \int_0^{\sqrt{3}} \pi(\sqrt{3-x^2})^2\,dx = \pi\int_0^{\sqrt{3}}(3-x^2)\,dx = \pi\left(3x - \frac{1}{3}x^3\right)\Big|_0^{\sqrt{3}} = 2\sqrt{3}\,\pi$

4. $V = \int_0^{\pi/6} \pi(\sqrt{\cos x})^2\,dx = \pi\int_0^{\pi/6}\cos x\,dx = \pi\sin x\Big|_0^{\pi/6} = \frac{\pi}{2}$

5. $V = \int_{-\pi/4}^{0} \pi\sec^2 x\,dx = \pi\tan x\Big|_{-\pi/4}^{0} = \pi$

6. $V = \int_0^{\pi} \pi(\sqrt{x\sin x})^2\,dx = \pi\int_0^{\pi}\sin x\,dx \overset{\text{parts}}{=} -\pi x\cos x\Big|_0^{\pi} + \pi\int_0^{\pi}\cos x\,dx = \pi^2 + \pi\sin x\Big|_0^{\pi} = \pi^2$

7. $V = \int_0^1 \pi(\sqrt{x}\,e^x)^2\,dx = \pi\int_0^1 xe^{2x}\,dx \overset{\text{parts}}{=} \pi\left(\frac{1}{2}xe^{2x} - \frac{1}{4}e^{2x}\right)\Big|_0^1$

$= \pi\left[\left(\frac{1}{2}e^2 - \frac{1}{4}e^2\right) - \left(0 - \frac{1}{4}\right)\right] = \frac{\pi}{4}(e^2+1)$

8. $V = \int_1^2 \pi(\sqrt{\ln x})^2\,dx = \pi\int_1^2 \ln x\,dx \overset{\text{parts}}{=} \pi x\ln x\Big|_1^2 - \pi\int_1^2 1\,dx$

$= \pi(x\ln x - x)\Big|_1^2 = \pi[(2\ln 2 - 2) - (0-1)] = \pi(2\ln 2 - 1)$

9. $V = \int_1^2 \pi[x(x^3+1)^{1/4}]^2\,dx = \pi\int_1^2 x^2(x^3+1)^{1/2}\,dx \overset{u=x^3+1}{=} \pi\int_2^9 u^{1/2}\cdot\frac{1}{3}\,du$

$= \frac{\pi}{3}\left(\frac{2}{3}u^{3/2}\right)\Big|_2^9 = 6\pi - \frac{4\sqrt{2}}{9}\pi$

10. $V = \int_0^1 \pi[(1+x^2)^{1/4}]^2\,dx = \pi\int_0^1 \sqrt{1+x^2}\,dx$. Let $x = \tan u$, so $dx = \sec^2 u\,du$. Then, by (7) in Section 7.2,

$$\int_0^1 \pi\sqrt{1+x^2}\,dx = \pi\int_0^{\pi/4} \sqrt{1+\tan^2 u}\,\sec^2 u\,du = \pi\int_0^{\pi/4} \sec^3 u\,du$$

$$= \pi\left[\frac{1}{2}\sec u\,\tan u + \frac{1}{2}\ln|\sec u + \tan u|\right]\Bigg|_0^{\pi/4} = \frac{\pi}{2}(\sqrt{2} + \ln(\sqrt{2}+1)).$$

Thus $V = \frac{\pi}{2}(\sqrt{2} + \ln(\sqrt{2}+1))$.

11. Since the solid is the same as the solid obtained if f is replaced by $|f|$, it follows that $V = \int_a^b \pi|f(x)|^2\,dx = \int_a^b \pi[f(x)]^2\,dx$.

12. a. By Exercise 11, $V = \int_{-1}^8 \pi(x^{1/3})^2\,dx = \int_{-1}^8 \pi x^{2/3}\,dx = \frac{3}{5}\pi x^{5/3}\big|_{-1}^8 = \frac{3}{5}\pi(32-(-1)) = \frac{99}{5}\pi$.

b. By Exercise 11 and (3) of Section 5.6,

$$V = \int_{-\pi/2}^{\pi} \pi(\sin x)^2\,dx = \int_{-\pi/2}^{\pi} \pi\sin^2 x\,dx = \pi\left(\frac{1}{2}x - \frac{1}{4}\sin 2x\right)\Bigg|_{-\pi/2}^{\pi} = \pi\left(\frac{\pi}{2} - \left(-\frac{\pi}{4}\right)\right) = \frac{3}{4}\pi^2.$$

13. $V = \displaystyle\int_1^2 \pi(e^y)^2\,dy = \pi\int_1^2 e^{2y}\,dy = \frac{\pi}{2}e^{2y}\Big|_1^2 = \frac{\pi}{2}e^4 - \frac{\pi}{2}e^2 = \frac{\pi}{2}(e^4 - e^2)$

14. $V = \displaystyle\int_0^{\pi/4} \pi\cos^2 y\,dy = \pi\int_0^{\pi/4}\left(\frac{1}{2} + \frac{1}{2}\cos 2y\right)dy = \pi\left(\frac{1}{2}y + \frac{1}{4}\sin 2y\right)\Bigg|_0^{\pi/4} = \pi\left(\frac{\pi}{8} + \frac{1}{4}\right)$

15. $V = \displaystyle\int_1^2 \pi(\sqrt{1+y^3})^2\,dy = \pi\int_1^2 (1+y^3)\,dy = \pi\left(y + \frac{1}{4}y^4\right)\Bigg|_1^2 = \pi\left[(2+4) - \left(1+\frac{1}{4}\right)\right] = \frac{19}{4}\pi$

16. $V = \displaystyle\int_0^{1/2} \pi\left(\frac{1}{(1-y^2)^{1/4}}\right)^2 dy = \pi\int_0^{1/2} \frac{1}{\sqrt{1-y^2}}\,dy = \pi\sin^{-1} y\big|_0^{1/2} = \pi\left(\frac{\pi}{6}\right) = \frac{\pi^2}{6}$

17. $V = \displaystyle\int_1^3 \pi\left[(\sqrt{x}+1)^2 - (\sqrt{x}-1)^2\right]dx = \pi\int_1^3 2\,dx = 2\pi x\big|_1^3 = 4\pi$

18. $V = \displaystyle\int_1^4 \pi[(x+1)^2 - (x-1)^2]\,dx = \pi\int_1^4 4x\,dx = 2\pi x^2\big|_1^4 = 30\pi$

19. $V = \displaystyle\int_0^{\pi/4} \pi[(\cos x + \sin x)^2 - (\cos x - \sin x)^2]\,dx$

$$= \pi\int_0^{\pi/4} (4\cos x\,\sin x)\,dx \overset{u=\sin x}{=} \pi\int_0^{\sqrt{2}/2} 4u\,du = 2\pi u^2\big|_0^{\sqrt{2}/2} = \pi$$

Exercise 17

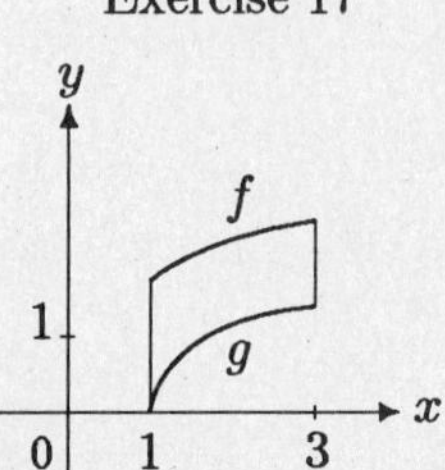

Exercise 18

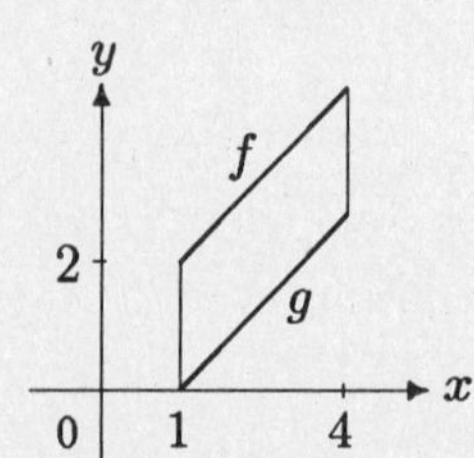

Exercise 19

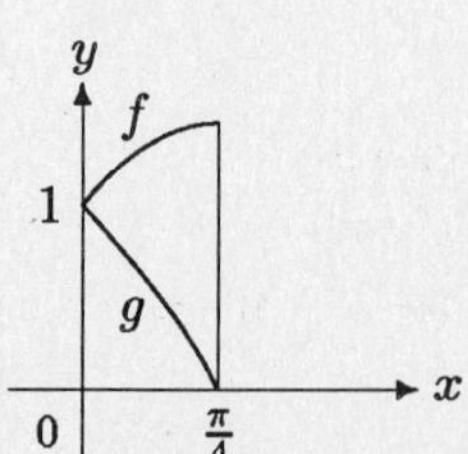

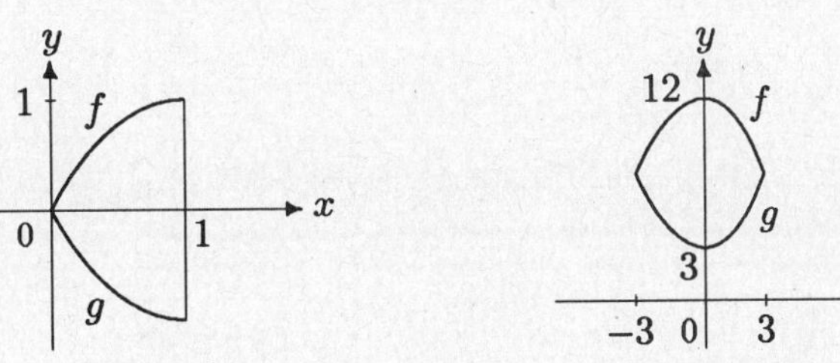

20. The washer method does not work because $g(x) \le 0$ for $0 \le x \le 1$. In fact $g(x) = -f(x)$ for all x. Thus the volume found by revolving R about the x axis is the same as the volume obtained by revolving about the x axis the region between the graph of f and the x axis:

$$V = \int_0^1 \pi(2x - x^2)^2\,dx = \pi\int_0^1 (4x^2 - 4x^3 + x^4)\,dx = \pi\left(\frac{4}{3}x^3 - x^4 + \frac{1}{5}x^5\right)\Big|_0^1 = \frac{8}{15}\pi.$$

21. The graphs of $y = x^2/2 + 3$ and $y = 12 - x^2/2$ intersect for (x, y) such that $x^2/2 + 3 = y = 12 - x^2/2$, or $x^2 = 9$, so that $x = -3$ or $x = 3$. Since $x^2/2 + 3 \le 12 - x^2/2$ for $-3 \le x \le 3$, it follows that

$$V = \int_{-3}^3 \pi\left[\left(12 - \frac{x^2}{2}\right)^2 - \left(\frac{x^2}{2} + 3\right)^2\right]dx = \pi\int_{-3}^3 (135 - 15x^2)\,dx = \pi(135x - 5x^3)\Big|_{-3}^3 = 540\pi.$$

22. The graphs of $y = x^{1/2}$ and $y = 2x^{1/4}$ intersect for (x, y) such that $x^{1/2} = y = x^{1/4}$, so that $x^2 = 16x$, that is, $x = 0$ or $x = 16$. Since $2x^{1/4} \ge x^{1/2}$ for $0 \le x \le 16$, it follows that

$$V = \int_0^{16} \pi[(2x^{1/4})^2 - (x^{1/2})^2]\,dx = \pi\int_0^{16} (4x^{1/2} - x)\,dx = \pi\left(\frac{8}{3}x^{3/2} - \frac{1}{2}x^2\right)\Big|_0^{16} = \frac{128}{3}\pi.$$

23. The graphs of $y = 5x$ and $y = x^2 + 2x + 2$ intersect for (x, y) such that $5x = y = x^2 + 2x + 2$, or $x^2 - 3x + 2 = 0$, so that $x = 1$ or $x = 2$. Since $5x \ge x^2 + 2x + 2$ for $1 \le x \le 2$, it follows that

$$V = \int_1^2 \pi[(5x)^2 - (x^2 + 2x + 2)^2]\,dx = \pi\int_1^2 (-x^4 - 4x^3 + 17x^2 - 8x - 4)\,dx$$

$$= \pi\left(-\frac{1}{5}x^5 - x^4 + \frac{17}{3}x^3 - 4x^2 - 4x\right)\Big|_1^2$$

$$= \pi\left[\left(-\frac{32}{5} - 16 + \frac{136}{3} - 16 - 8\right) - \left(-\frac{1}{5} - 1 + \frac{17}{3} - 4 - 4\right)\right] = \frac{37}{15}\pi.$$

24. The graphs of $y = x^3 + 2$ and $y = x^2 + 2x + 2$ intersect for (x, y) such that $x^3 + 2 = y = x^2 + 2x + 2$, or $x^3 - x^2 - 2x = 0$, or $x(x - 2)(x + 1) = 0$, so that $x = -1$, $x = 0$, or $x = 2$. Since $x^3 + 2 \ge x^2 + 2x + 2$ for $-1 \le x \le 0$ and $x^2 + 2x + 2 \ge x^3 + 2$ for $0 \le x \le 2$, it follows that

$$V = \int_{-1}^0 \pi[(x^3 + 2)^2 - (x^2 + 2x + 2)^2]\,dx + \int_0^2 \pi[(x^2 + 2x + 2)^2 - (x^3 + 2)^2]\,dx$$

$$= \pi \int_{-1}^{0} (x^6 - x^4 - 8x^2 - 8x)\, dx + \pi \int_{0}^{2} (-x^6 + x^4 + 8x^2 + 8x)\, dx$$

$$= \pi \left(\frac{1}{7}x^7 - \frac{1}{5}x^5 - \frac{8}{3}x^3 - 4x^2 \right)\Big|_{-1}^{0} + \pi \left(-\frac{1}{7}x^7 + \frac{1}{5}x^5 + \frac{8}{3}x^3 + 4x^2 \right)\Big|_{0}^{2}$$

$$= \pi \left(\frac{1}{7} - \frac{1}{5} - \frac{8}{3} + 4 \right) + \pi \left(-\frac{128}{7} + \frac{32}{5} + \frac{64}{3} + 16 \right) = \frac{2806}{105}\pi.$$

25. By Simpson's Rule with $n = 10$, $V = \int_{-1}^{1} \pi \left(e^{-x^2/2}\right)^2 dx = \int_{-1}^{1} \pi e^{-x^2}\, dx \approx 4.69251561$.

26. Since $1 \geq \ln x$ for $1 \leq x \leq e$, it follows by Simpson's Rule with $n = 10$ that $V = \int_1^e \pi[1^2 - (\ln x)^2]\, dx \approx 3.141507713$.

27. Since $e^x \cos x \geq e^x \sin x$ for $0 \leq x \leq \pi/4$, it follows by Simpson's Rule with $n = 10$ that $V = \int_0^{\pi/4} \pi \left[(e^x \cos x)^2 - (e^x \sin x)^2\right] dx \approx 2.992701086$.

28. Since $e^x \cos x \geq e^x \sin x$ for $0 \leq x \leq \pi/4$, and $e^x \sin x \geq e^x \cos x$ for $\pi/4 \leq x \leq \pi/2$, it follows by Simpson's Rule with $n = 10$ that

$$V = \int_0^{\pi/4} \pi \left[(e^x \cos x)^2 - (e^x \sin x)^2\right] dx + \int_{\pi/4}^{\pi/2} \pi \left[(e^x \sin x)^2 - (e^x \cos x)^2\right] dx$$

$$\approx 2.992701086 + 21.95250175 = 24.94520283.$$

29. Place the base so that L_1 lies along the positive x axis with the vertex opposite L_2 at the origin. Then the diameter of the semicircle x units from the origin is x and the cross-sectional area is given by $A(x) = \frac{1}{2}\pi(x/2)^2 = \frac{1}{8}\pi x^2$, so $V = \int_0^4 \frac{1}{8}\pi x^2\, dx = \frac{1}{24}\pi x^3\Big|_0^4 = \frac{8}{3}\pi$.

30. $V = \int_{-3}^{3} A(x)\, dx$. The base extends from -3 to 3 on the x axis, and for any x in $[-3, 3]$, the distance from x to the origin is $|x|$, so $A(x) = |x|$. Thus $V = \int_{-3}^{3} |x|\, dx = 2\int_0^3 x\, dx = x^2\Big|_0^3 = 9$.

31. Let a square cross-section x units from the center have a side $s(x)$ units long. The points $(x, -\sqrt{1-x^2})$ and $(x, \sqrt{1-x^2})$ are on the circular base, so $s(x) = 2\sqrt{1-x^2}$. Thus the cross-sectional area of the corresponding square is given by $A(x) = (s(x))^2 = 4(1-x^2)$, so $V = \int_{-1}^{1} 4(1-x^2)\, dx = (4x - \frac{4}{3}x^3)\Big|_{-1}^{1} = \frac{16}{3}$.

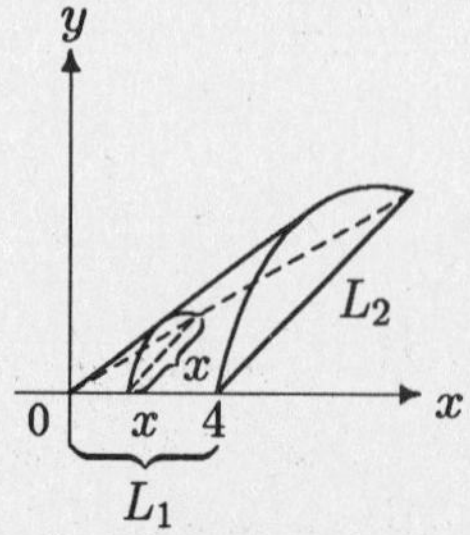

Exercise 29

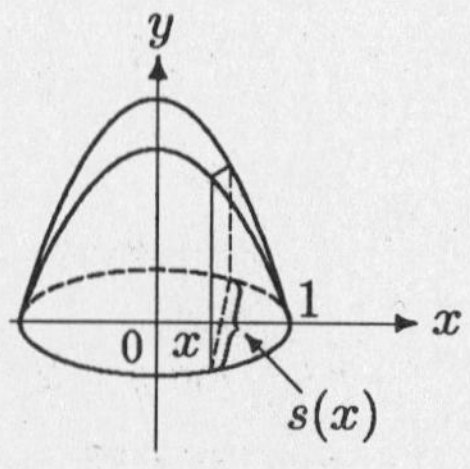

Exercise 31

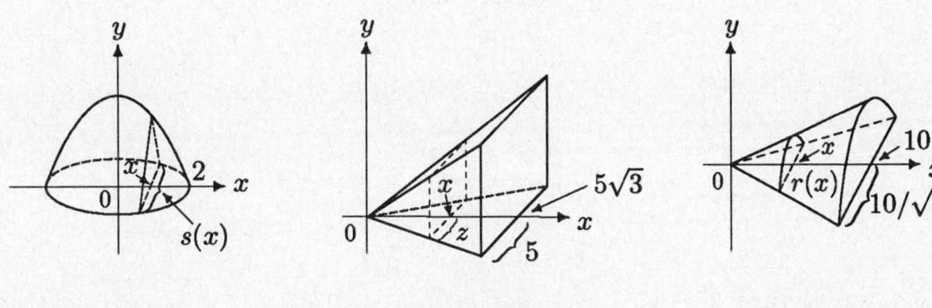

Exercise 32 Exercise 33 Exercise 34

32. Place the center of the circle at the origin. Let a triangular cross-section x units from the center of the circle have a side $s(x)$ units long. The points $(x, -\sqrt{4-x^2})$ and $(x, \sqrt{4-x^2})$ are on the circular base, so $s(x) = 2\sqrt{4-x^2}$. Thus the cross-sectional area is given by $A(x) = \frac{1}{4}\sqrt{3}\,(s(x))^2 = \sqrt{3}\,(4-x^2)$, so $V = \int_{-2}^{2} \sqrt{3}\,(4-x^2)\,dx = (4\sqrt{3}\,x - \frac{1}{3}\sqrt{3}\,x^3)\big|_{-2}^{2} = \frac{32}{3}\sqrt{3}$.

33. Place the base so that the given altitude lies along the positive x axis with the vertex at the origin. Then the length of a side of the square x units from the origin is $2z$, where by similar triangles $z/x = 5/(5\sqrt{3})$, or $z = x/\sqrt{3}$. The area of that square is given by $A(x) = (2z)^2 = \frac{4}{3}x^2$. Thus $V = \int_0^{5\sqrt{3}} \frac{4}{3}x^2\,dx = \frac{4}{9}x^3\big|_0^{5\sqrt{3}} = \frac{4}{9}(125)(3\sqrt{3}) = \frac{500}{3}\sqrt{3}$.

34. Let the radius of the semicircular cross-section x units from the vertex 0 shown in the figure be $r(x)$ units long. Then by similar triangles $r(x)/x = (10/\sqrt{3})/10$, or $r(x) = x/\sqrt{3}$. Thus the cross-sectional area is given by $A(x) = \frac{1}{2}\pi(r(x))^2 = \frac{1}{6}\pi x^2$, so $V = \int_0^{10} \frac{1}{6}\pi x^2\,dx = \frac{1}{18}\pi x^3\big|_0^{10} = \frac{500}{9}\pi$.

35. $V = \displaystyle\int_a^b \pi[f(x) - c]^2\,dx$

36. $$V = \int_0^1 \pi(\sqrt{x+1}+1)^2\,dx = \pi\int_0^1 (x+2+2\sqrt{x+1})\,dx$$
$$= \pi\left[\frac{1}{2}x^2 + 2x + \frac{4}{3}(x+1)^{3/2}\right]\Bigg|_0^1 = \pi\left[\left(\frac{5}{2}+\frac{8}{3}\sqrt{2}\right) - \frac{4}{3}\right] = \left(\frac{7}{6}+\frac{8}{3}\sqrt{2}\right)\pi$$

37. $$V = \int_0^1 \pi(1-e^{-2x})^2\,dx = \pi\int_0^1 (1-2e^{-2x}+e^{-4x})\,dx = \pi\left(x + e^{-2x} - \frac{1}{4}e^{-4x}\right)\Bigg|_0^1$$
$$= \pi\left[\left(1 - e^{-2} - \frac{1}{4}e^{-4}\right) - \left(1 - \frac{1}{4}\right)\right] = \pi\left(\frac{1}{4} - e^{-2} - \frac{1}{4}e^{-4}\right)$$

38. $V = \displaystyle\int_a^b \pi[f(x) - c]^2\,dx - \int_a^b \pi[g(x) - c]^2\,dx$

39. The graphs of $y = x^2-x+1$ and $y = 2x^2-4x+3$ intersect for (x, y) such that $x^2-x+1 = y = 2x^2-4x+3$, or $x^2-3x+2 = 0$, so that $x = 1$ or $x = 2$. Since $x^2-x+1 \ge 2x^2-4x+3$ for $1 \le x \le 2$, it follows from Exercise 38 that $V = \int_1^2 \pi[(x^2-x+1)-1]^2\,dx - \int_1^2 \pi[(2x^2-4x+3)-1]^2\,dx = \pi\int_1^2 (x^4-2x^3+x^2)\,dx - \pi\int_1^2 4(x-1)^4\,dx = \pi\left(\frac{1}{5}x^5 - \frac{1}{2}x^4 + \frac{1}{3}x^3\right)\big|_1^2 - \frac{4}{5}\pi(x-1)^5\big|_1^2 = \pi\left[\left(\frac{32}{5} - 8 + \frac{8}{3}\right) - \left(\frac{1}{5} - \frac{1}{2} + \frac{1}{3}\right)\right] - \frac{4}{5}\pi = \frac{7}{30}\pi$.

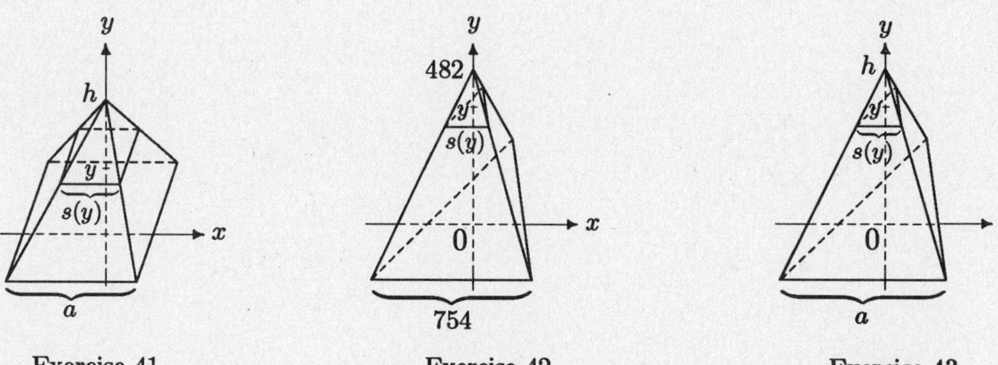

Exercise 41 Exercise 42 Exercise 43

40. The graphs of $y = x + 1$ and $y = x^2 - 2x + 3$ intersect for (x, y) such that $x + 1 = y = x^2 - 2x + 3$, or $x^2 - 3x + 2 = 0$, so that $x = 1$ or $x = 2$. Since $x + 1 \geq x^2 - 2x + 3$ for $1 \leq x \leq 2$, it follows from Exercise 38 that $V = \int_1^2 \pi[(x+1) - 2]^2\,dx - \int_1^2 [(x^2 - 2x + 3) - 2]^2\,dx = \int_1^2 \pi(x-1)^2\,dx - \int_1^2 \pi(x-1)^4\,dx = \frac{1}{3}\pi(x-1)^3\Big|_1^2 - \frac{1}{5}\pi(x-1)^5\Big|_1^2 = \frac{1}{3}\pi - \frac{1}{5}\pi = \frac{2}{15}\pi$.

41. We follow the solution of Example 2, with h replacing 4 and a replacing 3. Then the length $s(y)$ of a side of the cross-section at y satisfies, by similar triangles,

$$\frac{s(y)}{a} = \frac{h-y}{h}, \quad \text{so} \quad s(y) = \frac{a}{h}(h-y)$$

so the cross-sectional area is given by $A(y) = [s(y)]^2 = (a^2/h^2)(h-y)^2$. Then

$$V = \int_0^h \frac{a^2}{h^2}(h-y)^2\,dy = -\frac{a^2}{3h^2}(h-y)^3\Big|_0^h = \frac{a^2h^3}{3h^2} = \frac{1}{3}a^2h.$$

42. Let a triangular cross-section y feet above the base have a side $s(y)$ feet long. By similar triangles, we have $s(y)/(482 - y) = \frac{754}{482}$, so $s(y) = \frac{754}{482}(482 - y)$. Thus the cross-sectional area is given by $A(y) = \frac{1}{2}s(y)((\sqrt{3}/2)s(y)) = (\sqrt{3}/4)(s(y))^2$, which is $\sqrt{3}/4$ of the cross-sectional area of the Cheops pyramid. Since the height is still 482 feet, the volume V is $\sqrt{3}/4$, or approximately 43.3%, of the original volume.

43. Let a triangular cross-section y feet above the base have a side $s(y)$ feet long. By similar triangles, we have $s(y)/(h-y) = a/h$, so $s(y) = (a/h)(h-y)$. Thus the cross-sectional area is given by

$$A(y) = \frac{1}{2}s(y)\left(\frac{\sqrt{3}}{2}s(y)\right) = \frac{\sqrt{3}}{4}\frac{a^2}{h^2}(h-y)^2,$$

so

$$V = \int_0^h A(y)\,dy = \int_0^h \frac{\sqrt{3}}{4}\frac{a^2}{h^2}(h-y)^2\,dy = -\frac{\sqrt{3}}{12}\frac{a^2}{h^2}(h-y)^3\Big|_0^h = \frac{\sqrt{3}}{12}a^2h.$$

44. Let $f(x) = \sqrt{r^2 - x^2}$ for $h \leq x \leq r$. The solid region whose volume we seek is obtained by revolving the graph of f about the x axis. Thus $V = \int_h^r \pi\left(\sqrt{r^2 - x^2}\right)^2 dx = \pi\int_h^r (r^2 - x^2)\,dx = \pi\left(r^2x - \frac{1}{3}x^3\right)\Big|_h^r = \pi\left(\frac{2}{3}r^3 - r^2h + \frac{1}{3}h^3\right) = \frac{1}{3}\pi(r-h)^2(2r+h)$.

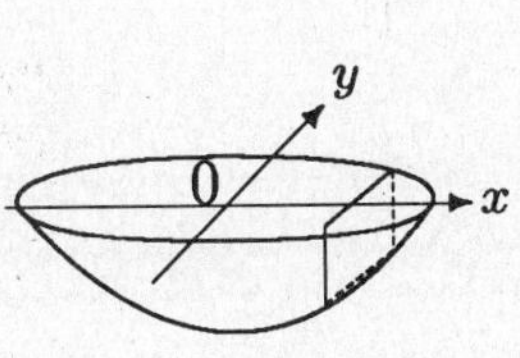

Exercise 47

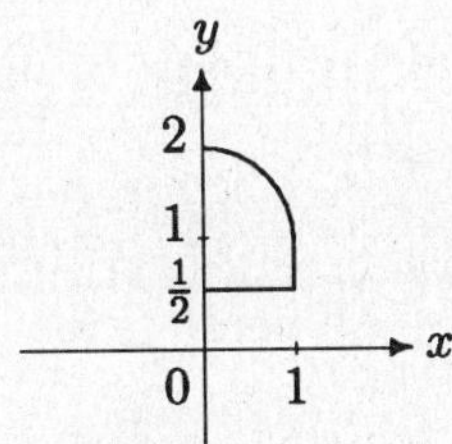

Exercise 50

45. a. $\lim_{b\to\infty}\int_1^b \pi\left(\frac{1}{x}\right)^2 dx = \lim_{b\to\infty}\pi\int_1^b \frac{1}{x^2}\,dx = \lim_{b\to\infty}\pi\left(-\frac{1}{x}\right)\Big|_1^b = \lim_{b\to\infty}\pi\left(-\frac{1}{b}+1\right) = \pi$, so the volume is π.

b. $\lim_{b\to\infty}\int_1^b \pi\left(\frac{1}{x^2}\right)^2 dx = \lim_{b\to\infty}\pi\int_1^b \frac{1}{x^4}\,dx = \lim_{b\to\infty}\frac{-\pi}{3x^3}\Big|_1^b = \lim_{b\to\infty}\left(-\frac{\pi}{3b^3}+\frac{\pi}{3}\right) = \frac{\pi}{3}$, so the volume is $\pi/3$.

46. Let $A_1(x)$ be the cross-sectional area at x for the first solid and $A_2(x)$ the cross-sectional area at x for the second solid. Then $A_1(x) = A_2(x)$ for each x in $[a,b]$. By (1) the volume of the first solid is given by $V_1 = \int_a^b A_1(x)\,dx$, and the volume of the second is given by $V_2 = \int_a^b A_2(x)\,dx$. Since $A_1(x) = A_2(x)$ for all x, we must have $V_1 = V_2$.

47. Let a square cross-section x feet from the center have a side $s(x)$ feet long. Then $s(x) = 20\sqrt{1-x^2/400} = \sqrt{400-x^2}$. Thus the cross-sectional area is given by $A(x) = (s(x))^2 = 400 - x^2$, so that $V = \int_{-20}^{20}(400-x^2)\,dx = (400x - \frac{1}{3}x^3)\big|_{-20}^{20} = \frac{32{,}000}{3}$ (cubic feet).

48. The plane region that is revolved lies between the graph of $y = b\sqrt{1-x^2/a^2}$ and the x axis on $[-a,a]$. Thus

$$V = \int_{-a}^{a}\pi\left(b\sqrt{1-\frac{x^2}{a^2}}\right)^2 dx = \pi b^2\int_{-a}^{a}\left(1-\frac{x^2}{a^2}\right)dx = \pi b^2\left(x - \frac{1}{3}\frac{x^3}{a^2}\right)\Big|_{-a}^{a} = \frac{4}{3}\pi ab^2.$$

49. We can use the result of Exercise 48 with $a = \frac{1}{2}$ and $b = 1$. Then $V = \frac{4}{3}\pi(\frac{1}{2})(1)^2 = 2\pi/3$ (cubic centimeters).

50. The volume is given by

$$V = \int_0^1 \pi\left[(1+\sqrt{1-x^2})^2 - \left(\frac{1}{2}\right)^2\right]dx = \pi\int_0^1\left(\frac{7}{4} - x^2 + 2\sqrt{1-x^2}\right)dx$$

$$= \pi\left(\frac{7}{4}x - \frac{x^3}{3}\right)\Big|_0^1 + 2\pi\int_0^1\sqrt{1-x^2}\,dx \overset{x=\sin u}{=} \frac{17}{12}\pi + 2\pi\int_0^{\pi/2}\sqrt{1-\sin^2 u}\,\cos u\,du$$

$$= \frac{17}{12}\pi + 2\pi\int_0^{\pi/2}\cos^2 u\,du = \frac{17}{12}\pi + 2\pi\left(\frac{1}{2}u + \frac{1}{4}\sin 2u\right)\Big|_0^{\pi/2} = \frac{17\pi}{12} + \frac{\pi^2}{2}.$$

51. The volume is given by

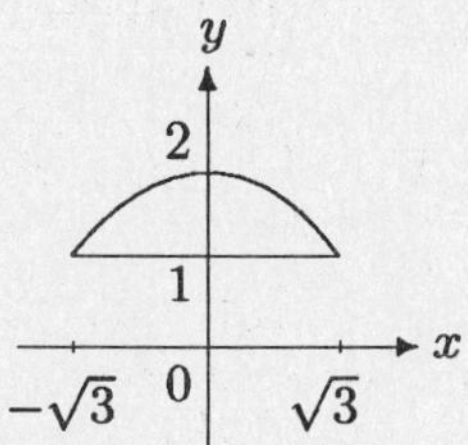

$$V = \int_{-\sqrt{3}}^{\sqrt{3}} \pi[(4-x^2)^2 - 1^2]\,dx = \pi\int_{-\sqrt{3}}^{\sqrt{3}} (15 - 8x^2 + x^4)\,dx$$

$$= \pi\left(15x - \frac{8}{3}x^3 + \frac{x^5}{5}\right)\Bigg|_{-\sqrt{3}}^{\sqrt{3}} = \frac{88\sqrt{3}}{5}\pi.$$

52. In order to integrate along the y axis, we notice that $x = \sqrt{y/6}$ for $0 \le y \le 6$. For any depth h of soda, the volume of the soda is given by

$$V = \int_0^h \pi\left(\sqrt{\frac{y}{6}}\right)^2 dy = \pi\int_0^h \frac{y}{6}\,dy = \pi\frac{h^2}{12}.$$

Therefore $dV/dt = \pi(h/6)(dh/dt)$. Since $dV/dt = -\frac{1}{2}$, it follows that when $h = \frac{3}{2}$ we have $dh/dt = (-\frac{1}{2})[6/\pi(\frac{3}{2})] = -2/\pi$. Thus the depth is decreasing at the rate of $2/\pi$ inches per second.

53. By Exercise 42, the volume of the small pyramid at the top is $\frac{1}{3}(10.5)^2(16.79) = 617.0325$ (cubic meters). To compute the volume of the rest of the monument, we will use the fact that the horizontal cross sections of the monument are squares and use (2). Since the cross-section at the base is a square 16.8 meters on a side and the cross-section at a height of 152.49 meters is a square 10.5 meters on a side, it follows that the cross-section y meters above ground is a square $16.8 + \frac{10.5-16.8}{152.49}y$ meters on a side, for $0 \le y \le 152.49$. By (2), the volume V_1 of that part of the monument is given by

$$V_1 = \int_0^{152.49}\left(16.8 + \frac{10.5-16.8}{152.49}y\right)^2 dy = \frac{1}{3}\left(\frac{152.49}{-6.3}\right)\left(16.8 - \frac{6.3}{152.49}y\right)^3\Bigg|_0^{152.49}$$

$$= \frac{1}{3}\left(\frac{152.49}{-6.3}\right)((10.5)^3 - (16.8)^3) = 28{,}916.6787 \text{ (cubic meters)}.$$

Thus the volume of the Washington Monument is $617.0325 + 28{,}916.6787 = 29{,}533.7112 \approx 29{,}534$ cubic meters.

54. $$V = \int_0^5 \pi\left[(f(x))^2 - (g(x))^2\right] dx$$

$$= \pi\int_0^{1/2} \frac{x^2}{4}\,dx + \pi\int_{1/2}^{7/2} \frac{1}{16}\,dx + \pi\int_{7/2}^{9/2} \frac{1}{16}\left[1 + \left(x - \frac{7}{2}\right)^2\right]^2 dx + \pi\int_{9/2}^{5}\left[\frac{1}{4} - \left(x - \frac{9}{2}\right)^2\right] dx$$

$$= \frac{\pi}{12}x^3\Big|_0^{1/2} + \frac{\pi}{16}x\Big|_{1/2}^{7/2} + \frac{\pi}{16}\int_{7/2}^{9/2}\left[1 + 2\left(x-\frac{7}{2}\right)^2 + \left(x - \frac{7}{2}\right)^4\right] dx + \pi\left(\frac{1}{4}x - \frac{1}{3}\left(x - \frac{9}{2}\right)^3\right)\Bigg|_{9/2}^{5}$$

$$= \frac{\pi}{96} + \frac{3\pi}{16} + \frac{\pi}{16}\left[x + \frac{2}{3}\left(x - \frac{7}{2}\right)^3 + \frac{1}{5}\left(x - \frac{7}{2}\right)^5\right]\Bigg|_{7/2}^{9/2} + \frac{\pi}{12}$$

$$= \frac{\pi}{96} + \frac{3\pi}{16} + \frac{\pi}{16}\left(\frac{28}{15}\right) + \frac{\pi}{12} = \frac{191}{480}\pi \text{ (cubic centimeters)}$$

8.2 Volumes: The Shell Method

1. $V = \int_0^{\sqrt{3}} 2\pi x\sqrt{x^2+1}\,dx \overset{u=x^2+1}{=} \pi\int_1^4 u^{1/2}\,du = \frac{2\pi}{3}u^{3/2}\Big|_1^4 = \frac{14\pi}{3}$

2. $V = \int_{\sqrt{\pi}/2}^{\sqrt{\pi}} 2\pi x\sin x^2\,dx \overset{u=x^2}{=} \pi\int_{\pi/4}^{\pi} \sin u\,du = -\pi\cos u\Big|_{\pi/4}^{\pi} = \pi\left(1+\frac{2}{2}\right)$

3. $V = \int_0^1 2\pi x e^{2x+1}\,dx \overset{\text{parts}}{=} 2\pi\left(\frac{1}{2}xe^{2x+1}\Big|_0^1 - \int_0^1 \frac{1}{2}e^{2x+1}\,dx\right)$
$= 2\pi\left(\frac{1}{2}e^3 - \frac{1}{4}e^{2x+1}\Big|_0^1\right) = 2\pi\left(\frac{1}{4}e^3+\frac{1}{4}e\right) = \frac{1}{2}\pi e(e^2+1)$

4. $V = \int_0^2 2\pi x(x-1)^2\,dx = 2\pi\int_0^2 (x^3-2x^2+x)\,dx = 2\pi\left(\frac{1}{4}x^4 - \frac{2}{3}x^3+\frac{1}{2}x^2\right)\Big|_0^2 = \frac{4\pi}{3}$

5. $V = \int_1^2 2\pi x\sqrt{x-1}\,dx \overset{u=x-1}{=} 2\pi\int_0^1 (u+1)u^{1/2}\,du = 2\pi\int_0^1 (u^{3/2}+u^{1/2})\,du$
$= 2\pi\left(\frac{2}{5}u^{5/2}+\frac{2}{3}u^{3/2}\right)\Big|_0^1 = \frac{32\pi}{15}$

6. $V = \int_{\pi/4}^{\pi/2} 2\pi x\sin x\,dx \overset{\text{parts}}{=} -2\pi x\cos x\Big|_{\pi/4}^{\pi/2} + 2\pi\int_{\pi/4}^{\pi/2}\cos x\,dx$
$= \frac{\pi^2\sqrt{2}}{4} + 2\pi\sin x\Big|_{\pi/4}^{\pi/2} = \pi\left(\frac{\sqrt{2}\pi}{4}+2-\sqrt{2}\right)$

7. $V = \int_1^3 2\pi x\ln x\,dx \overset{\text{parts}}{=} 2\pi\left(\frac{1}{2}x^2\ln x\right)\Big|_1^3 - 2\pi\int_1^3 \frac{1}{2}x\,dx = 9\pi\ln 3 - \frac{\pi}{2}x^2\Big|_1^3 = 9\pi\ln 3 - 4\pi$

8. $V = \int_0^4 2\pi x\sqrt{1+\sqrt{x}}\,dx \overset{u=1+\sqrt{x}}{=} 2\pi\int_1^3 (u-1)^2\sqrt{u}\,[2(u-1)]\,du$
$= 4\pi\int_1^3\left(u^{7/2}-3u^{5/2}+3u^{3/2}-u^{1/2}\right)du = 4\pi\left(\frac{2}{9}u^{9/2}-\frac{6}{7}u^{7/2}+\frac{6}{5}u^{5/2}-\frac{2}{3}u^{3/2}\right)\Big|_1^3$
$= 4\pi\left(\frac{128}{35}\sqrt{3}+\frac{32}{315}\right)$

9. $V = \int_0^1 2\pi y\left(y^2\sqrt{1+y^4}\right)dy \overset{u=1+y^4}{=} 2\pi\int_1^2 \sqrt{u}\cdot\frac{1}{4}\,du = 2\pi\cdot\frac{1}{4}\cdot\frac{2}{3}u^{3/2}\Big|_1^2 = \frac{1}{3}\pi(2\sqrt{2}-1)$

10. $V = \int_1^2 2\pi y\left(\frac{\ln y}{y}\right)dy = 2\pi\int_1^2 \ln y\,dy \overset{\text{parts}}{=} 2\pi\left(y\ln y\Big|_1^2 - \int_1^2 y\cdot\frac{1}{y}\,dy\right)$
$= 2\pi\left(2\ln 2 - y\Big|_1^2\right) = 2\pi(2\ln 2-1)$

11. $V = \int_0^{\sqrt{2}/2} 2\pi \frac{y}{\sqrt{1-y^4}}\,dy \overset{u=y^2}{=} 2\pi \int_0^{1/2} \frac{1}{\sqrt{1-u^2}} \cdot \frac{1}{2}\,du = \pi \sin^{-1} u\big|_0^{1/2} = \frac{\pi^2}{6}$

12. $V = \int_0^\infty 2\pi y e^{-y}\,dy = \lim_{b\to\infty} \int_0^b 2\pi y e^{-y}\,dy$. To integrate by parts, let $u = 2\pi y$, $dv = e^{-y}\,dy$; then $du = 2\pi\,dy$, $v = -e^{-y}$. Therefore $\int 2\pi y e^{-y}\,dy = -2\pi y e^{-y} + \int 2\pi e^{-y}\,dy = -2\pi y e^{-y} - 2\pi e^{-y} + C$. Thus $V = \lim_{b\to\infty} \int_0^b 2\pi y e^{-y}\,dy = \lim_{b\to\infty}(-2\pi y e^{-y} - 2\pi e^{-y})\big|_0^b = \lim_{b\to\infty}(-2\pi b e^{-b} - 2\pi e^{-b} + 2\pi) = 2\pi$, since $\lim_{b\to\infty}(-2\pi b e^{-b}) = 0$ by l'Hôpital's Rule.

13. Since $f(x) = \cos x \geq \sin x = g(x)$ for $0 \leq x \leq \pi/4$,

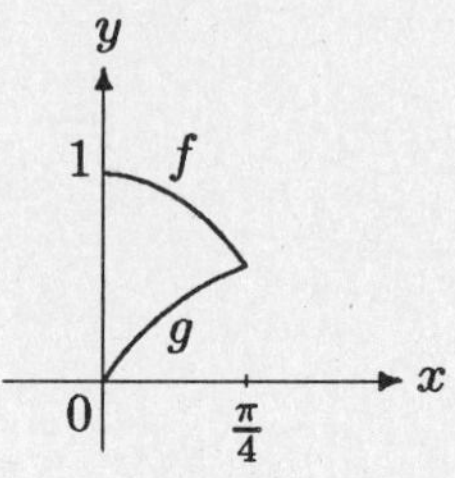

$$\begin{aligned} V &= \int_0^{\pi/4} 2\pi x(\cos x - \sin x)\,dx \\ &\overset{\text{parts}}{=} 2\pi x(\sin x + \cos x)\big|_0^{\pi/4} - 2\pi \int_0^{\pi/4} (\sin x + \cos x)\,dx \\ &= \frac{\pi^2\sqrt{2}}{2} + 2\pi(\cos x - \sin x)\big|_0^{\pi/4} = \frac{1}{2}\sqrt{2}\,\pi^2 - 2\pi. \end{aligned}$$

14. For $\frac{1}{2} \leq x \leq 1$ we have $\ln x \leq 0 < x$, and for $1 < x \leq 2$ we have $\ln x < 1 < x$. Therefore $g(x) = x > \ln x = f(x)$ for $\frac{1}{2} \leq x \leq 2$, so that

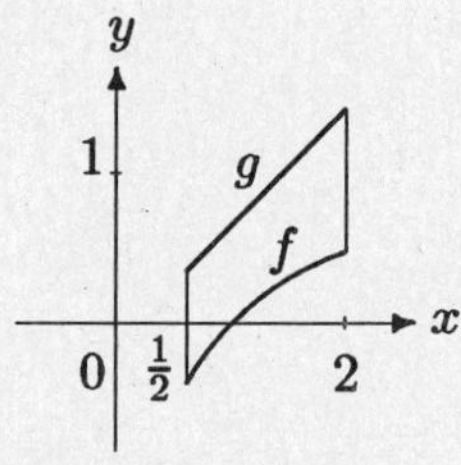

$$\begin{aligned} V &= \int_{1/2}^2 2\pi x(x - \ln x)\,dx = 2\pi \int_{1/2}^2 x^2\,dx - 2\pi \int_{1/2}^2 x \ln x\,dx \\ &\overset{\text{parts}}{=} \frac{2\pi}{3}x^3\Big|_{1/2}^2 - 2\pi\left(\frac{x^2}{2}\ln x\right)\Big|_{1/2}^2 + 2\pi \int_{1/2}^2 \frac{x^2}{2}\frac{1}{x}\,dx \\ &= \left(\frac{16\pi}{3} - \frac{\pi}{12}\right) - \left(4\pi\ln 2 - \frac{\pi}{4}\ln\frac{1}{2}\right) + \frac{\pi x^2}{2}\Big|_{1/2}^2 = \frac{57\pi}{8} - \frac{17\pi}{4}\ln 2. \end{aligned}$$

15. By Simpson's Rule with $n = 10$, $V = \int_0^1 2\pi x^2\sqrt{1+x^4}\,dx \approx 2.489756022$.

16. Note that $\sqrt{x}\cos x \geq \sqrt{x}\sin x$ for $0 \leq x \leq \pi/4$, and $\sqrt{x}\sin x \geq \sqrt{x}\cos x$ for $\pi/4 \leq x \leq \pi/2$. Then by Simpson's Rule with $n = 10$, $V = \int_0^{\pi/4} 2\pi x^{3/2}(\cos x - \sin x)\,dx + \int_{\pi/4}^{\pi/2} 2\pi x^{3/2}(\sin x - \cos x)\,dx \approx 0.42545261 + 3.903220476 \approx 4.328673086$.

17. Let $0 \leq y \leq 1$. Notice that $y^2 + 1 \geq y\sqrt{1+y^3}$ if $y^4 + 2y^2 + 1 = (y^2+1)^2 \geq y^2(1+y^3) = y^2 + y^5$, or equivalently, $y^4 - y^5 + y^2 + 1 \geq 0$, which is valid for $0 \leq y \leq 1$. Thus $f(y) \geq g(y)$ for $0 \leq y \leq 1$, so that

$$\begin{aligned} V &= \int_0^1 2\pi y\left[(y^2+1) - y\sqrt{1+y^3}\right]dy \\ &= 2\pi\left[\left(\frac{1}{4}y^4 + \frac{1}{2}y^2\right)\Big|_0^1 - \int_0^1 y^2\sqrt{1+y^3}\,dy\right] \\ &\overset{u=1+y^3}{=} 2\pi\left(\frac{3}{4} - \int_1^2 \sqrt{u}\cdot\frac{1}{3}\,du\right) = 2\pi\left(\frac{3}{4} - \frac{1}{3}\cdot\frac{2}{3}u^{3/2}\Big|_1^2\right) \\ &= 2\pi\left(\frac{3}{4} - \frac{4}{9}\sqrt{2} + \frac{2}{9}\right) = \frac{\pi}{18}\left(35 - 16\sqrt{2}\right). \end{aligned}$$

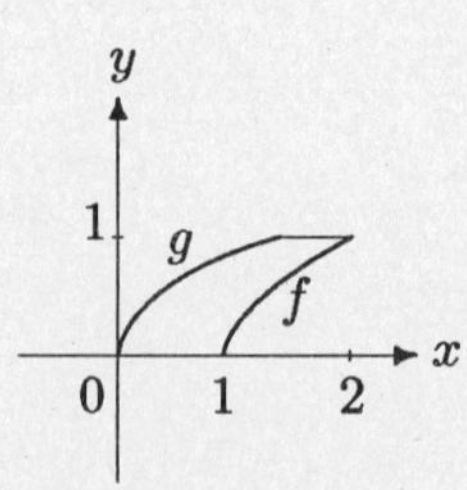

18. Since $g(y) = \dfrac{1}{y+2} \ge \dfrac{1}{(y+2)^2} = f(y)$ for $0 \le y \le 2$,

$$V = \int_0^2 2\pi y\left[\frac{1}{y+1} - \frac{1}{(y+2)^2}\right] dy \overset{u=y+2}{=} 2\pi \int_2^4 (u-2)\left(\frac{1}{u} - \frac{1}{u^2}\right) du$$

$$= 2\pi \int_2^4 \left(1 - \frac{3}{u} + \frac{2}{u^2}\right) du = 2\pi\left(u - 3\ln u - \frac{2}{u}\right)\Big|_2^4$$

$$= 2\pi\left[\left(4 - 3\ln 4 - \frac{1}{2}\right) - (2 - 3\ln 2 - 1)\right] = 2\pi\left(\frac{5}{2} - 3\ln 4 + 3\ln 2\right) = \pi(5 - 6\ln 2).$$

19. The graphs intersect for (x,y) such that $2x = y = x^2$, so that $x = 0$ or $x = 2$. Since $2x \ge x^2$ for $0 \le x \le 2$, we have $V = \int_0^2 2\pi x(2x - x^2)\,dx = 2\pi \int_0^2 (2x^2 - x^3)\,dx = 2\pi\left(\frac{2}{3}x^3 - \frac{1}{4}x^4\right)\Big|_0^2 = 2\pi\left(\frac{16}{3} - 4\right) = \frac{8}{3}\pi$.

20. The graphs intersect for (x,y) such that $\sqrt{x} = y = 3x$, so that $x = 0$ or $x = \frac{1}{9}$. Since $\sqrt{x} \ge 3x$ for $0 \le x \le \frac{1}{9}$, we have $V = \int_0^{1/9} 2\pi x(\sqrt{x} - 3x)\,dx = 2\pi \int_0^{1/9} (x^{3/2} - 3x^2)\,dx = 2\pi\left(\frac{2}{5}x^{5/2} - x^3\right)\Big|_0^{1/9} = 2\pi\left(\frac{2}{5}\cdot\frac{1}{243} - \frac{1}{729}\right) = \frac{2}{3645}\pi$.

21. The graphs intersect for (x,y) such that $|x-2| = y = \frac{1}{2}(x-2)^2 + \frac{1}{2}$. If $x > 2$, then the equations reduce to $x - 2 = \frac{1}{2}(x-2)^2 + \frac{1}{2}$, so that $(x-2)^2 - 2(x-2) + 1 = 0$, or $((x-2)-1)^2 = 0$, so that $x = 3$. If $x < 2$, then the first equations reduce to $-(x-2) = \frac{1}{2}(x-2)^2 + \frac{1}{2}$, so that $(x-2)^2 + 2(x-2) + 1 = 0$, or $((x-2)+1)^2 = 0$, so that $x = 1$. Since $\frac{1}{2}(x-2)^2 + \frac{1}{2} \ge |x-2|$ for $1 \le x \le 3$, we have

$$V = \int_1^2 2\pi x\left[\frac{1}{2}(x-2)^2 + \frac{1}{2} + (x-2)\right] dx + \int_2^3 2\pi x\left[\frac{1}{2}(x-2)^2 + \frac{1}{2} - (x-2)\right] dx$$

$$= 2\pi \int_1^2 \left(\frac{1}{2}x^3 - x^2 + \frac{1}{2}x\right) dx + 2\pi \int_2^3 \left(\frac{1}{2}x^3 - 3x^2 + \frac{9}{2}x\right) dx$$

$$= 2\pi\left(\frac{1}{8}x^4 - \frac{1}{3}x^3 + \frac{1}{4}x^2\right)\Big|_1^2 + 2\pi\left(\frac{1}{8}x^4 - x^3 + \frac{9}{4}x^2\right)\Big|_2^3$$

$$= 2\pi\left[\left(2 - \frac{8}{3} + 1\right) - \left(\frac{1}{8} - \frac{1}{3} + \frac{1}{4}\right)\right] + 2\pi\left[\left(\frac{81}{8} - 27 + \frac{81}{4}\right) - (2 - 8 + 9)\right] = \frac{4}{3}\pi.$$

22. $V = \displaystyle\int_a^b 2\pi(x-c)f(x)\,dx$

23. $V = \displaystyle\int_0^1 2\pi(x+1)x^4\,dx = 2\pi\int_0^1 (x^5 + x^4)\,dx = 2\pi\left(\frac{1}{6}x^6 + \frac{1}{5}x^5\right)\Big|_0^1 = \frac{11}{15}\pi$

24. $V = \displaystyle\int_0^\pi 2\pi(2\pi - x)\sin x\,dx = 2\pi\int_0^\pi 2\pi\sin x\,dx - 2\pi\int_0^\pi x\sin\,dx$

$$\overset{\text{parts}}{=} -4\pi^2\cos x\Big|_0^\pi + \left[(2\pi x\cos x)\Big|_0^\pi - 2\pi\int_0^\pi x\cos x\,dx\right]$$

$$= 8\pi^2 - 2\pi^2 - 2\pi\sin x\Big|_0^\pi = 6\pi^2$$

25. $V = \int_a^b 2\pi(x-c)[f(x)-g(x)]\,dx$

26. The graphs intersect for (x,y) such that $2x = y = -2x^2+4x$, or $2x^2-2x=0$, so that $x=0$ or $x=1$. Since $-2x^2+4x \geq 2x$ for $0 \leq x \leq 1$, we have $V = \int_0^1 2\pi(x+1)[(-2x^2+4x)-2x]\,dx = 2\pi\int_0^1(2x-2x^3)\,dx = 2\pi\left(x^2-\frac{1}{2}x^4\right)\Big|_0^1 = \pi$.

27. The graphs intersect for (x,y) such that $x^2+4 = y = 2x^2+x+2$, or $x^2+x-2=0$, so that $x=-2$ or $x=1$. Since $x^2+4 \geq 2x^2+x+2$ for $-2 \leq x \leq 1$, we have

$$V = \int_{-2}^{1} 2\pi(x+5)[(x^2+4)-(2x^2+x+2)]\,dx = 2\pi\int_{-2}^{1}(-x^3-6x^2-3x+10)\,dx$$

$$= 2\pi\left(-\frac{1}{4}x^4-2x^3-\frac{3}{2}x^2+10x\right)\Big|_{-2}^{1} = 2\pi\left[\left(-\frac{1}{4}-2-\frac{3}{2}+10\right)-(-4+16-6-20)\right] = \frac{81}{2}\pi.$$

28. Let $f(x) = \sqrt{a^2-x^2}$ and $g(x) = -\sqrt{a^2-x^2}$ for $0 \leq x \leq a$. Then a sphere of radius a is obtained by revolving the region between the graphs of f and g about the y axis. By (4) the volume is given by $V = \int_0^a 2\pi x\left[\sqrt{a^2-x^2}-(-\sqrt{a^2-x^2})\right]dx = 4\pi\int_0^a x\sqrt{a^2-x^2}\,dx = 4\pi\left(\frac{-1}{3}(a^2-x^2)^{3/2}\right)\Big|_0^a = \frac{4}{3}\pi a^3$.

29. Let $f(x) = h-(h/a)x$ for $0 \leq x \leq a$. A cone of radius a and height h is obtained by revolving the region between the graph of f and the x axis in $[0,a]$ about the y axis. By (3) the volume is given by

$$V = \int_0^a 2\pi x\left(h-\frac{h}{a}x\right)dx = 2\pi\left(\frac{hx^2}{2}-\frac{hx^3}{3a}\right)\Big|_0^a = \frac{1}{3}\pi a^2 h.$$

30.
$$\begin{aligned}
V &= \int_{b-r}^{b+r} 2\pi x\left[\sqrt{r^2-(x-b)^2}-(-\sqrt{r^2-(x-b)^2})\right]dx = 4\pi\int_{b-r}^{b+r} x\sqrt{r^2-(x-b)^2}\,dx \\
&\overset{x=b+r\sin u}{=} 4\pi\int_{-\pi/2}^{\pi/2}(b+r\sin u)\cdot\sqrt{r^2-r^2\sin^2 u}\,(r\cos u)\,du \\
&= 4\pi r^2\int_{-\pi/2}^{\pi/2}(b\cos^2 u + r\sin u\cos^2 u)\,du \\
&= 4\pi r^2\int_{-\pi/2}^{\pi/2}\left(\frac{b}{2}+\frac{b}{2}\cos 2u + r\sin u\cos^2 u\right)du \\
&= 4\pi r^2\left(\frac{b}{2}u+\frac{b}{4}\sin 2u-\frac{r}{3}\cos^3 u\right)\Big|_{-\pi/2}^{\pi/2} = 2\pi^2 r^2 b
\end{aligned}$$

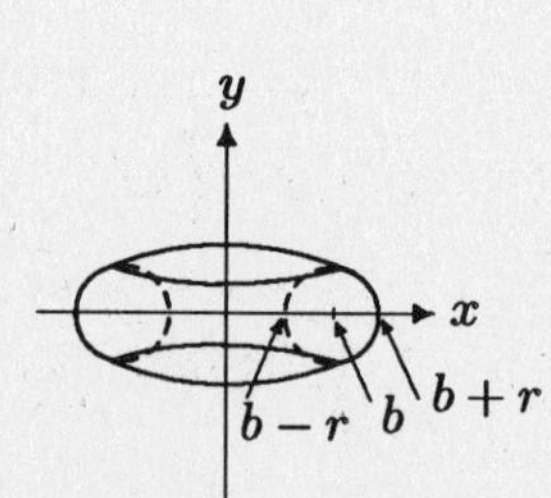

31. Let $f(x) = \sqrt{4-x^2}$ and $g(x) = -\sqrt{4-x^2}$ for $0 \leq x \leq 1$. The solid removed is obtained by revolving the region between the graphs of f and g on $[0,1]$ about the y axis. We obtain

$$V = \int_0^1 2\pi x\left[\sqrt{4-x^2}-(-\sqrt{4-x^2})\right]dx = 4\pi\int_0^1 x\sqrt{4-x^2}\,dx$$

$$= 4\pi\left[\frac{-1}{3}(4-x^2)^{3/2}\right]\Big|_0^1 = \frac{32}{3}\pi - 4\pi\sqrt{3}$$

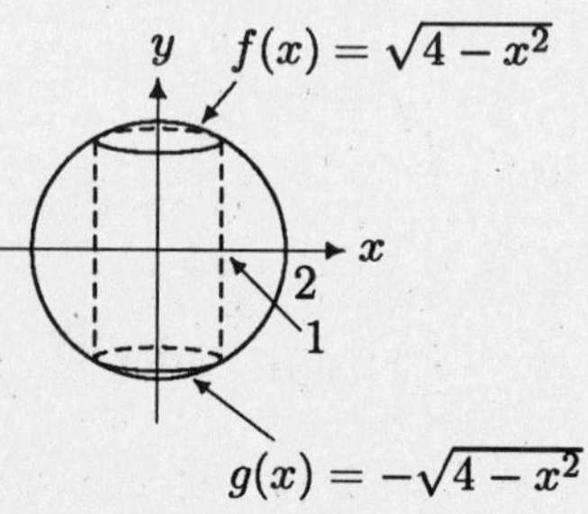

32. If we substitute $x = 20$ into $y = \frac{1}{40}x^2$, we obtain $y = 10$. Thus the wok is 10 centimeters high. By (5), its volume V is given by $V = \int_0^{20} 2\pi x\left(10 - \frac{1}{40}x^2\right) dx = 2\pi \int_0^{20} \left(10x - \frac{1}{40}x^3\right) dx = 2\pi\left(5x^2 - \frac{1}{160}x^4\right)\Big|_0^{20} =$ 2000π (cubic centimeters).

8.3 Length of a Curve

1. $L = \displaystyle\int_1^5 \sqrt{1+(2)^2}\, dx = \int_1^5 \sqrt{5}\, dx = 4\sqrt{5}$

2. $L = \displaystyle\int_1^4 \sqrt{1+(x^{1/2})^2}\, dx = \int_1^4 \sqrt{1+x}\, dx = \frac{2}{3}(1+x)^{3/2}\Big|_1^4 = \frac{2}{3}(5\sqrt{5} - 2\sqrt{2})$

3. $$L = \int_2^3 \sqrt{1+\left(2x - \frac{1}{8x}\right)^2}\, dx = \int_2^3 \sqrt{1+4x^2 - \frac{1}{2} + \frac{1}{64x^2}}\, dx$$
$$= \int_2^3 \sqrt{\left(2x + \frac{1}{8x}\right)^2}\, dx = \int_2^3 \left(2x + \frac{1}{8x}\right) dx = \left(x^2 + \frac{1}{8}\ln|x|\right)\Big|_2^3 = 5 + \frac{1}{8}\ln\frac{3}{2}$$

4. $$L = \int_1^3 \sqrt{1+\left(3x^2 - \frac{1}{12x^2}\right)^2}\, dx = \int_1^3 \sqrt{1+9x^4 - \frac{1}{2} + \frac{1}{144x^4}}\, dx$$
$$= \int_1^3 \sqrt{\left(3x^2 + \frac{1}{12x^2}\right)^2}\, dx = \int_1^3 \left(3x^2 + \frac{1}{12x^2}\right) dx$$
$$= \left(x^3 - \frac{1}{12x}\right)\Big|_1^3 = \left(27 - \frac{1}{36}\right) - \left(1 - \frac{1}{12}\right) = \frac{469}{18}$$

5. $$L = \int_1^2 \sqrt{1+\left(4x^3 - \frac{1}{16x^3}\right)^2}\, dx = \int_1^2 \sqrt{1+16x^6 - \frac{1}{2} + \frac{1}{256x^6}}\, dx$$
$$= \int_1^2 \sqrt{\left(4x^3 + \frac{1}{16x^3}\right)^2}\, dx = \int_1^2 \left(4x^3 + \frac{1}{16x^3}\right) dx = \left(x^4 - \frac{1}{32x^2}\right)\Big|_1^2$$
$$= \left(16 - \frac{1}{128}\right) - \left(1 - \frac{1}{32}\right) = \frac{1923}{128}$$

6. $$L = \int_2^5 \sqrt{1+\left(\frac{2x}{x^2-1}\right)^2}\, dx = \int_2^5 \sqrt{1+\frac{4x^2}{(x^2-1)^2}}\, dx = \int_2^5 \sqrt{\frac{x^4 - 2x^2 + 1 + 4x^2}{(x^2-1)^2}}\, dx$$
$$= \int_2^5 \sqrt{\frac{(x^2+1)^2}{(x^2-1)^2}}\, dx = \int_2^5 \frac{x^2+1}{x^2-1}\, dx = \int_2^5 \left(1 + \frac{1}{x-1} - \frac{1}{x+1}\right) dx$$
$$= (x + \ln|x-1| - \ln|x+1|)\Big|_2^5 = (5 + \ln 4 - \ln 6) - (2 + \ln 1 - \ln 3) = 3 + \ln 2$$

7. $L = \int_1^2 \sqrt{1 + \left[\frac{2x}{1+x^2} - \frac{1}{8}\left(x + \frac{1}{x}\right)\right]^2}\, dx = \int_1^2 \sqrt{1 + \frac{4x^2}{(1+x^2)^2} - \frac{1}{2} + \frac{1}{64}\frac{(1+x^2)^2}{x^2}}\, dx$

$= \int_1^2 \sqrt{\left[\frac{2x}{1+x^2} + \frac{1}{8}\left(\frac{1+x^2}{x}\right)\right]^2}\, dx = \int_1^2 \left[\frac{2x}{1+x^2} + \frac{1}{8}\left(\frac{1}{x} + x\right)\right] dx$

$= \left[\ln(1+x^2) + \frac{1}{8}\left(\ln|x| + \frac{1}{2}x^2\right)\right]\Big|_1^2 = \left(\ln 5 + \frac{1}{8}\ln 2 + \frac{1}{4}\right) - \left(\ln 2 + \frac{1}{16}\right) = \ln 5 - \frac{7}{8}\ln 2 + \frac{3}{16}$

8. $L = \int_1^2 \sqrt{1 + \left[\frac{3x^2}{1+x^3} + \frac{1}{12}\left(\frac{-1}{x^2} - x\right)\right]^2}\, dx$

$= \int_1^2 \sqrt{1 + \frac{9x^4}{(1+x^3)^2} - \frac{1}{2} + \frac{1}{144}\left(\frac{1+x^3}{x^2}\right)^2}\, dx = \int_1^2 \sqrt{\left[\frac{3x^2}{1+x^3} + \frac{1}{12}\left(\frac{1}{x^2} + x\right)\right]^2}\, dx$

$= \int_1^2 \left[\frac{3x^2}{1+x^3} + \frac{1}{12}\left(\frac{1}{x^2} + x\right)\right] dx = \left[\ln(1+x^3) + \frac{1}{12}\left(\frac{-1}{x} + \frac{1}{2}x^2\right)\right]\Big|_1^2$

$= \left(\ln 9 - \frac{1}{24} + \frac{1}{6}\right) - \left(\ln 2 - \frac{1}{12} + \frac{1}{24}\right) = \ln\frac{9}{2} + \frac{1}{6}$

9. $L = \int_{\pi/4}^{\pi/3} \sqrt{1 + \left(\frac{-1}{4}\cos x + \sec x\right)^2}\, dx = \int_{\pi/4}^{\pi/3} \sqrt{1 + \frac{1}{16}\cos^2 x - \frac{1}{2} + \sec^2 x}\, dx$

$= \int_{\pi/4}^{\pi/3} \sqrt{\left(\frac{1}{4}\cos x + \sec x\right)^2}\, dx = \int_{\pi/4}^{\pi/3} \left(\frac{1}{4}\cos x + \sec x\right) dx$

$= \left(\frac{1}{4}\sin x + \ln|\sec x + \tan x|\right)\Big|_{\pi/4}^{\pi/3} = \left[\frac{1}{8}\sqrt{3} + \ln(2+\sqrt{3})\right] - \left[\frac{1}{8}\sqrt{2} + \ln(\sqrt{2}+1)\right]$

$= \frac{1}{8}\left(\sqrt{3} - \sqrt{2}\right) + \ln\frac{2+\sqrt{3}}{\sqrt{2}+1}$

10. $L = \int_0^{\ln 2} \sqrt{1 + \sinh^2 x}\, dx = \int_0^{\ln 2} \cosh x\, dx = \sinh x\big|_0^{\ln 2} = \frac{1}{2}\left(e^{\ln 2} - e^{-\ln 2}\right) = \frac{1}{2}\left(2 - \frac{1}{2}\right) = \frac{3}{4}$

11. $L = \int_0^1 \sqrt{1 + \left[x^2 + 1 - \frac{1}{4(1+x^2)}\right]^2}\, dx = \int_0^1 \sqrt{1 + (x^2+1)^2 - \frac{1}{2} + \left[\frac{1}{4(1+x^2)}\right]^2}\, dx$

$= \int_0^1 \sqrt{(x^2+1)^2 + \frac{1}{2} + \left[\frac{1}{4(1+x^2)}\right]^2}\, dx = \int_0^1 \sqrt{\left[x^2 + 1 + \frac{1}{4(1+x^2)}\right]^2}\, dx$

$= \int_0^1 \left[x^2 + 1 + \frac{1}{4(1+x^2)}\right] dx = \left(\frac{1}{3}x^3 + x + \frac{1}{4}\tan^{-1} x\right)\Big|_0^1 = \frac{4}{3} + \frac{\pi}{16}$

12. $$L = \int_0^{\pi/4} \sqrt{1 + \left[\sec^2 x - \frac{1}{8}(1 + \cos 2x)\right]^2}\, dx = \int_0^{\pi/4} \sqrt{1 + \left[\sec^2 x - \frac{1}{4}\cos^2 x\right]^2}\, dx$$

$$= \int_0^{\pi/4} \sqrt{1 + \sec^4 x - \frac{1}{2} + \frac{1}{16}\cos^4 x\, dx} = \int_0^{\pi/4} \sqrt{\left(\sec^2 x + \frac{1}{4}\cos^2 x\right)^2}\, dx$$

$$= \int_0^{\pi/4} \left(\sec^2 x + \frac{1}{4}\cos^2 x\right) dx = \int_0^{\pi/4} \left[\sec^2 x + \frac{1}{8}(1 + \cos x)\right] dx$$

$$= \left[\tan x + \frac{1}{8}\left(x + \frac{1}{2}\sin 2x\right)\right]\Bigg|_0^{\pi/4} = \frac{17}{16} + \frac{1}{32}\pi$$

13. $$L = \int_{\sqrt{3}}^{\sqrt{8}} \sqrt{1 + \left(\frac{1}{x}\right)^2}\, dx = \int_{\sqrt{3}}^{\sqrt{8}} \sqrt{1 + \frac{1}{x^2}}\, dx$$

$$= \int_{\sqrt{3}}^{\sqrt{8}} \frac{1}{x}\sqrt{x^2 + 1}\, dx \overset{u = \sqrt{x^2+1}}{=} \int_2^3 \frac{u^2}{u^2 - 1}\, du = \int_2^3 \left(1 + \frac{1}{2}\frac{1}{u - 1} - \frac{1}{2}\frac{1}{u + 1}\right) du$$

$$= \left[u + \frac{1}{2}\ln(u - 1) - \frac{1}{2}\ln(u + 1)\right]\Bigg|_2^3 = \left(3 + \frac{1}{2}\ln 2 - \frac{1}{2}\ln 4\right) - \left(2 - \frac{1}{2}\ln 3\right) = 1 - \frac{1}{2}\ln 2 + \frac{1}{2}\ln 3$$

14. For integration by parts, let $u = \sqrt{1 + e^{2x}}$, $e^{2x} = u^2 - 1$, $2e^{2x}\, dx = 2u\, du$, $dx = \dfrac{u}{u^2 - 1}\, du$; then

$$L = \int_{\ln\sqrt{3}}^{\ln\sqrt{8}} \sqrt{1 + (e^x)^2}\, dx = \int_2^3 u\left(\frac{u}{u^2 - 1}\right) du = \int_2^3 \left(1 + \frac{1}{u^2 - 1}\right) du$$

$$= \int_2^3 \left(1 + \frac{1}{2(u - 1)} - \frac{1}{2(u + 1)}\right) du = \left(u + \frac{1}{2}\ln|u - 1| - \frac{1}{2}\ln|u + 1|\right)\Bigg|_2^3$$

$$= \left(3 + \frac{1}{2}\ln 2 - \frac{1}{2}\ln 4\right) - \left(2 - \frac{1}{2}\ln 3\right) = 1 + \frac{1}{2}\ln\frac{3}{2}.$$

15. $L = \int_0^1 \sqrt{1 + (2x)^2}\, dx = \int_0^1 \sqrt{1 + 4x^2}\, dx$. Let $x = \frac{1}{2}\tan u$. Then, by (7) of Section 7.2,

$$\int \sqrt{1 + 4x^2}\, dx = \int \sqrt{1 + \tan^2 u}\left(\frac{1}{2}\sec^2 u\right) du = \frac{1}{2}\int \sec^3 u\, du$$

$$= \frac{1}{4}[\sec u \tan u + \ln|\sec u + \tan u|] + C$$

$$= \frac{1}{4}\left[2x\sqrt{1 + 4x^2} + \ln\left(\sqrt{1 + 4x^2} + 2x\right)\right] + C.$$

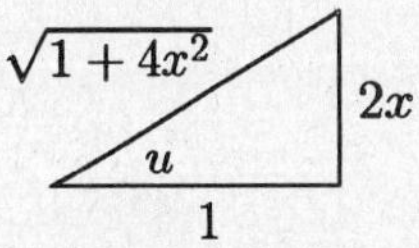

Thus

$$L = \int_0^1 \sqrt{1 + (2x)^2}\, dx = \frac{1}{4}\left[2x\sqrt{1 + 4x^2} + \ln\left(\sqrt{1 + 4x^2} + 2x\right)\right]\Bigg|_0^1 = \frac{1}{2}\sqrt{5} + \frac{1}{4}\ln(\sqrt{5} + 2).$$

16. $L = \int_0^1 \sqrt{1+(2x-1)^2}\,dx$. Let $2x-1 = \tan u$. Then

$$\int_0^1 \sqrt{1+(2x-1)^2}\,dx = \int_{-\pi/4}^{\pi/4} \sqrt{1+\tan^2 u}\left(\frac{1}{2}\sec^2 u\right)du = \frac{1}{2}\int_{-\pi/4}^{\pi/4} \sec^3 u\,du.$$

By (7) of Section 7.2,

$$\frac{1}{2}\int_{-\pi/4}^{\pi/4} \sec^3 u\,du = \frac{1}{4}[\sec u\,\tan u + \ln|\sec u + \tan u|]\Big|_{-\pi/4}^{\pi/4}$$

$$= \frac{1}{4}\left[2\sqrt{2} + \ln(\sqrt{2}+1) - \ln(\sqrt{2}-1)\right]$$

$$= \frac{1}{2}\sqrt{2} + \frac{1}{4}\ln(3+2\sqrt{2}) = \frac{1}{2}\sqrt{2} + \frac{1}{2}\ln(\sqrt{2}+1).$$

$\sqrt{1+(2x-1)^2}$

$2x-1$

u

1

17. $L = \int_2^3 \sqrt{1+(\sqrt{x^2-1})^2}\,dx = \int_2^3 \sqrt{x^2}\,dx = \int_2^3 x\,dx = \frac{1}{2}x^2\Big|_2^3 = \frac{5}{2}$

18. $L = \int_0^{\pi/4} \sqrt{1+\tan^2 x}\,dx = \int_0^{\pi/4} \sec x\,dx = \ln|\sec x + \tan x|\big|_0^{\pi/4} = \ln(\sqrt{2}+1)$

19. $L = \int_{2\pi/3}^{3\pi/4} \sqrt{1+(\sqrt{\tan^2 x - 1})^2}\,dx = \int_{2\pi/3}^{3\pi/4} |\tan x|\,dx$

$$= \int_{2\pi/3}^{3\pi/4} -\tan x\,dx = \ln|\cos x|\big|_{2\pi/3}^{3\pi/4} = \ln\frac{\sqrt{2}}{2} - \ln\frac{1}{2} = \frac{1}{2}\ln 2$$

20. $L = \int_2^4 \sqrt{1+(\sqrt{x^n-1})^2}\,dx = \int_2^4 x^{n/2}\,dx = \frac{1}{(n/2)+1}x^{(n+2)/2}\Big|_2^4 = \frac{2}{n+2}\left(4^{(n+2)/2} - 2^{(n+2)/2}\right)$

21. $L = \int_{25}^{100} \sqrt{1+\left(\sqrt{\sqrt{x}-1}\right)^2}\,dx = \int_{25}^{100} x^{1/4}\,dx = \frac{4}{5}x^{5/4}\Big|_{25}^{100} = \frac{4}{5}\left(10^{5/2} - 5^{5/2}\right)$

22. $L = \int_1^{2^n} \sqrt{1+(\sqrt{x^{1/n}-1})^2}\,dx = \int_1^{2^n} x^{1/(2n)}\,dx = \frac{1}{(1/2n)+1}x^{(1+2n)/(2n)}\Big|_1^{2^n}$

$$= \frac{2n}{2n+1}\left(2^{n[(1+2n)/(2n)]} - 1\right) = \frac{2n}{2n+1}\left(\sqrt{2}\,2^n - 1\right)$$

23. $L = \int_{-1}^1 \sqrt{1+\left(\frac{-3x}{2\sqrt{4-x^2}}\right)^2}\,dx = \int_{-1}^1 \sqrt{1+\frac{9x^2}{4(4-x^2)}}\,dx = \int_{-1}^1 \frac{1}{2}\sqrt{\frac{16+5x^2}{4-x^2}}\,dx \approx 2.202806546$

24. $L = \int_0^\pi \sqrt{1+\cos^2 x}\,dx \approx 3.820187624$

25. a. The length would be given by $L = \int_0^{\ln 2} \sqrt{1+\cosh^2 x}\,dx = \int_0^{\ln 2} \sqrt{1+\frac{1}{4}(e^{2x}+2+e^{-2x})}\,dx$. Neither integrand can be simplified as in Exercise 10, so the integration appears to be impossible.

b. By Simpson's Rule with $n = 10$, the value of the integral in part (a) is approximately 1.021832851.

26. Since $f'(x) = nx^{n-1}$, we have $L = \int_1^2 \sqrt{1+n^2x^{2n-2}}\,dx$. If $n = 1$, then $L = \int_1^2 \sqrt{1+1}\,dx = \sqrt{2}$. If $n = 2$, then $L = \int_1^2 \sqrt{1+4x^2}\,dx$. This integral can be evaluated by trigonometric substitution. If $n = 3$, then $L = \int_1^2 \sqrt{1+9x^4}\,dx$, which cannot be integrated by techniques discussed in the text. If $n > 3$, the same is true. Thus the values of n for which we can perform the integration are 1 and 2.

27. a. $f'(x) = \dfrac{2n+1}{2n}x^{1/(2n)}$, so that $L = \displaystyle\int_a^b \sqrt{1+\frac{(2n+1)^2x^{1/n}}{(2n)^2}}\,dx.$

b. Let $u = \sqrt{1+[(2n+1)/(2n)]^2x^{1/n}}$. Then

$$u^2 = 1 + \left(\frac{2n+1}{2n}\right)^2 x^{1/n}$$

so that

$$2u\,du = \frac{1}{n}\left(\frac{2n+1}{2n}\right)^2 x^{(1/n)-1}\,dx = \frac{1}{n}\left(\frac{2n+1}{2n}\right)^2 x^{(1-n)/n}\,dx$$

and

$$x^{1/n} = \left(\frac{2n}{2n+1}\right)^2 (u^2-1).$$

Thus

$$dx = 2n\left(\frac{2n}{2n+1}\right)^2 ux^{(n-1)/n}\,du$$

$$= 2n\left(\frac{2n}{2n+1}\right)^2 u\left(\frac{2n}{2n+1}\right)^{2(n-1)}(u^2-1)^{n-1}\,du = 2n\left(\frac{2n}{2n+1}\right)^{2n} u(u^2-1)^{n-1}\,du.$$

Thus

$$\int_a^b \sqrt{1+\left(\frac{2n+1}{2n}\right)^2 x^{1/n}}\,dx = \int_c^d 2n\left(\frac{2n}{2n+1}\right)^{2n} u^2(u^2-1)^{n-1}\,du,$$

where c and d are the values of u corresponding to $x = 1$ and $x = b$, respectively. Therefore the integral in (a) becomes the integral of a polynomial in u.

c. For $n = 1$, $u = \sqrt{1+\frac{9}{4}x}$. If $x = 0$, then $u = 1$, and if $x = 1$, then $u = \sqrt{13}/2$. By part (a), the length equals $\int_1^{\sqrt{13}/2} 2\left(\frac{2}{3}\right)^2 u^2\,du = \frac{8}{27}u^3\Big|_1^{\sqrt{13}/2} = \frac{8}{27}\left(\frac{13}{8}\sqrt{13}-1\right)$.

28. a. $y = \left(r^{2/3}-x^{2/3}\right)^{3/2}$ for $0 \le x \le r$.

b. From (a), $y = \left(r^{2/3}-x^{2/3}\right)^{3/2}$. Now if $f(x) = \left(r^{2/3}-x^{2/3}\right)^{3/2}$ then

$$f'(x) = \frac{3}{2}(r^{2/3}-x^{2/3})^{1/2}\left(-\frac{2}{3}x^{-1/3}\right) = -x^{-1/3}\left(r^{2/3}-x^{2/3}\right)^{1/2} \quad \text{for } x > 0,$$

so that if L is the total length of the astroid, then

$$\frac{1}{4}L = \lim_{a\to0^+}\int_a^r \sqrt{1+[f'(x)]^2}\,dx = \lim_{a\to0^+}\int_a^r \sqrt{1+\left[-x^{-1/3}\left(r^{2/3}-x^{2/3}\right)^{1/2}\right]^2}\,dx$$

$$= \lim_{a\to0^+}\int_a^r \sqrt{1+x^{-2/3}\left(r^{2/3}-x^{2/3}\right)}\,dx = \lim_{a\to0^+}\int_a^r \sqrt{x^{-2/3}r^{2/3}}\,dx$$

$$= \lim_{a\to0^+}\int_a^r x^{-1/3}r^{1/3}\,dx = \lim_{a\to0^+}\frac{3}{2}x^{2/3}r^{1/3}\Big|_a^r = \lim_{a\to0^+}\left(\frac{3}{2}r - \frac{3}{2}a^{2/3}r^{1/3}\right) = \frac{3}{2}r.$$

Thus $L = 6r$.

29. The length of the graph of f is the same as the length of the graph of f^{-1}. Now $f^{-1}(x) = x^{3/2}$ for $0 \le x \le 4$, and $(f^{-1})'(x) = \frac{3}{2}x^{1/2}$. Then $L = \int_0^4 \sqrt{1+[(f^{-1})'(x)]^2}\,dx = \int_0^4 \sqrt{1+\frac{9}{4}x}\,dx = \frac{2}{3}\left(1+\frac{9}{4}x\right)^{3/2}\left(\frac{4}{9}\right)\Big|_0^4 = \frac{8}{27}(10)^{3/2} - \frac{8}{27} = \frac{8}{27}(10\sqrt{10}-1)$.

30. To find the point $(c, c^{2/3})$, we seek a number c in $[0,1]$ such that

$$\int_0^c \sqrt{1+\left(\frac{3}{2}y^{1/2}\right)^2}\,dy = \int_c^1 \sqrt{1+(\frac{3}{2}y^{1/2})^2}\,dy.$$

Since $\int \sqrt{1+(\frac{3}{2}y^{1/2})^2}\,dy = \int \sqrt{1+\frac{9}{4}y}\,dy = \frac{8}{27}\left(1+\frac{9}{4}y\right)^{3/2} + C$, it follows that c must satisfy

$$\frac{8}{27}\left(1+\frac{9}{4}y\right)^{3/2}\Bigg|_0^c = \frac{8}{27}\left(1+\frac{9}{4}y\right)^{3/2}\Bigg|_c^1, \quad \text{or} \quad \left(1+\frac{9}{4}c\right)^{3/2} - 1 = \left(\frac{13}{4}\right)^{3/2} - \left(1+\frac{9}{4}\right)^{3/2},$$

or $\left(1+\frac{9}{4}c\right)^{3/2} = \frac{1}{2}+\frac{13}{16}\sqrt{13}$. Thus $c = \frac{4}{9}\left[\left(\frac{1}{2}+\frac{13}{16}\sqrt{13}\right)^{2/3} - 1\right] \approx 0.5662942656$, and the point $(c, c^{2/3})$ is the required point halfway along the curve.

31. $L = \displaystyle\int_0^{26} \sqrt{1+\left(\frac{-4x}{169}+\frac{4}{13}\right)^2}\,dx$. To evaluate the integral we first let $\tan u = \dfrac{4x}{169} - \dfrac{4}{13}$. Then

$$\sec u = \sqrt{1+\left(\frac{4x}{169}-\frac{4}{13}\right)^2},$$

and by (7) of Section 7.2 we obtain

$$\int \sqrt{1+\left(\frac{-4x}{169}+\frac{4}{13}\right)^2}\,dx = \int \sqrt{1+\tan^2 u}\left(\frac{169}{4}\right)\sec^2 u\,du$$

$$= \frac{169}{4}\int \sec^3 u\,du = \frac{169}{8}(\sec u\,\tan u + \ln|\sec u + \tan u|) + C$$

$$= \frac{169}{8}\left[\sqrt{1+\left(\frac{4x}{169}-\frac{4x}{13}\right)^2}\left(\frac{4x}{169}-\frac{4}{13}\right) + \ln\left|\sqrt{1+\left(\frac{4x}{169}-\frac{4}{13}\right)^2} + \left(\frac{4x}{169}-\frac{4}{13}\right)\right|\right] + C.$$

Thus

$$L = \left[\sqrt{1+\left(\frac{4x}{169}-\frac{4}{13}\right)^2}\left(\frac{x}{2}-\frac{13}{2}\right) + \frac{169}{8}\ln\left|\sqrt{1+\left(\frac{4x}{169}-\frac{4}{13}\right)^2} + \left(\frac{4x}{169}-\frac{4}{13}\right)\right|\right]\Bigg|_0^{26}$$

$$= 13\sqrt{1+\frac{16}{169}} + \frac{169}{8}\ln\left|\frac{4}{13}+\sqrt{1+\frac{16}{169}}\right| - \frac{169}{8}\ln\left|-\frac{4}{13}+\sqrt{1+\frac{16}{169}}\right|$$

$$= \sqrt{185} + \frac{169}{8}\left(\ln\frac{4+\sqrt{185}}{13} - \ln\frac{-4+\sqrt{185}}{13}\right) \approx 26.4046\,(\text{feet}).$$

32. If $f(x) = c\cosh(x/c)$, then by Figure 8.28 we find that $20 = f(0) = c\cosh 0 = c$. Thus $f(x) = 20\cosh(x/20)$. Therefore $L = \int_{-10}^{20}\sqrt{1+(\sinh(x/20))^2}\,dx = \int_{-10}^{20}\cosh(x/20)\,dx = 20\sinh(x/20)\Big|_{-10}^{20} = 20\left[\sinh 1 - \sinh\left(\frac{-1}{2}\right)\right] = 20[\frac{1}{2}(e-e^{-1}) - \frac{1}{2}(e^{-1/2}-e^{1/2})] \approx 33.9$ (feet).

33. $L = \displaystyle\int_0^2 \sqrt{1+\left(\frac{4\pi}{16}\cos 4\pi x\right)^2}\,dx = \int_0^2 \sqrt{1+\frac{\pi^2}{16}\cos^2 4\pi x}\,dx \approx 2.54$ (inches).

8.4 Area of a Surface

1. $$S = \int_{-1/2}^{3/2} 2\pi\sqrt{4-x^2}\sqrt{1+\left(\frac{-x}{\sqrt{4-x^2}}\right)^2}\,dx$$
$$= 2\pi\int_{-1/2}^{3/2}\sqrt{4-x^2}\sqrt{1+\frac{x^2}{4-x^2}}\,dx = 2\pi\int_{-1/2}^{3/2} 2\,dx = 4\pi x\Big|_{-1/2}^{3/2} = 8\pi$$

2. $$S = \int_0^{\sqrt{2}} (2\pi)\frac{1}{3}\sqrt{1+(x^2)^2}\,dx = \frac{2}{3}\pi\int_0^{\sqrt{2}} x^3\sqrt{1+x^4}\,dx \overset{u=1+x^4}{=} \frac{2\pi}{3}\int_1^5 \sqrt{u}\cdot\frac{1}{4}\,du$$
$$= \frac{\pi}{6}\left(\frac{2}{3}u^{3/2}\right)\Big|_1^5 = \frac{\pi}{9}\left(5\sqrt{5}-1\right)$$

3. $$S = \int_2^6 2\pi\sqrt{x}\sqrt{1+\left(\frac{1}{2\sqrt{x}}\right)^2}\,dx = 2\pi\int_2^6 \sqrt{x}\sqrt{1+\frac{1}{4x}}\,dx = \pi\int_2^6 \sqrt{4x+1}\,dx$$
$$= \frac{\pi}{6}(4x+1)^{3/2}\Big|_2^6 = \frac{\pi}{6}(125-27) = \frac{49}{3}\pi$$

4. $$S = \int_{-1}^0 (2\pi)2\sqrt{1-x}\sqrt{1+\left(\frac{-1}{\sqrt{1-x}}\right)^2}\,dx = 4\pi\int_{-1}^0 \sqrt{1-x}\sqrt{1+\frac{1}{1-x}}\,dx$$
$$= 4\pi\int_{-1}^0 \sqrt{2-x}\,dx = 4\pi\left(-\frac{2}{3}(2-x)^{3/2}\right)\Big|_{-1}^0 = \frac{8\pi}{3}\left(3\sqrt{3}-2\sqrt{2}\right)$$

5. $$S = \int_1^2 2\pi\left(x^2-\frac{1}{8}\ln x\right)\sqrt{1+\left(2x-\frac{1}{8x}\right)^2}\,dx = 2\pi\int_1^2\left(x^2-\frac{1}{8}\ln x\right)\sqrt{1+\left(4x^2-\frac{1}{2}+\frac{1}{64x^2}\right)}\,dx$$
$$= 2\pi\int_1^2\left(x^2-\frac{1}{8}\ln x\right)\sqrt{\left(2x+\frac{1}{8x}\right)^2}\,dx = 2\pi\int_1^2\left(x^2-\frac{1}{8}\ln x\right)\left(2x+\frac{1}{8x}\right)dx$$
$$= 2\pi\int_1^2\left(2x^3+\frac{1}{8}x\right)dx - 2\pi\int_1^2\frac{1}{4}x\ln x\,dx - 2\pi\int_1^2\frac{1}{64}\frac{\ln x}{x}\,dx$$
$$= 2\pi\left(\frac{1}{2}x^4+\frac{1}{16}x^2\right)\Big|_1^2 - \frac{\pi}{2}\left(\frac{1}{2}x^2\ln x-\frac{1}{4}x^2\right)\Big|_1^2 - \frac{\pi}{64}(\ln x)^2\Big|_1^2$$
$$= 2\pi\left(\frac{33}{4}-\frac{9}{16}\right) - \frac{\pi}{2}\left[(2\ln 2-1)+\frac{1}{4}\right] - \frac{\pi}{64}(\ln 2)^2 = \pi\left[\frac{63}{4}-\ln 2-\frac{1}{64}(\ln 2)^2\right]$$

6. $S = \int_0^1 2\pi \cosh x \sqrt{1+\sinh^2 x}\, dx = 2\pi \int_0^1 \cosh^2 x\, dx = 2\pi \int_0^1 \left(\frac{e^x + e^{-x}}{2}\right)^2 dx$

$= \frac{\pi}{2} \int_0^1 (e^{2x} + 2 + e^{-2x})\, dx = \frac{\pi}{2}\left(\frac{1}{2}e^{2x} + 2x - \frac{1}{2}e^{-2x}\right)\Big|_0^1$

$= \frac{\pi}{2}\left[\left(\frac{1}{2}e^2 + 2 - \frac{1}{2}e^{-2}\right) - 0\right] = \frac{\pi}{4}(e^2 + 4 - e^{-2})$

7. $S = \int_0^\pi 2\pi \sin x \sqrt{1+\cos^2 x}\, dx \overset{u=\cos x}{=} 2\pi \int_0^{-1} \sqrt{1+u^2}\,(-1)\, du \overset{u=\tan v}{=} -2\pi \int_{\pi/4}^{-\pi/4} \sec^3 v\, dv,$

so by (7) of Section 7.2,

$$S = -2\pi\left(\frac{1}{2}\sec v\, \tan v + \frac{1}{2}\ln|\sec v + \tan v|\right)\Big|_{\pi/4}^{-\pi/4}$$

$$= \pi\left[2\sqrt{2} + \ln(\sqrt{2}+1) - \ln(\sqrt{2}-1)\right] = \pi\left[2\sqrt{2} + \ln(3+2\sqrt{2})\right].$$

8. $S = \int_0^{(\ln 3)/2} 2\pi e^{-x}\sqrt{1+(-e^{-x})^2}\, dx = 2\pi \int_0^{(\ln 3)/2} e^{-x}\sqrt{1+e^{-2x}}\, dx \overset{u=e^{-x}}{=} 2\pi \int_1^{1/\sqrt{3}} -\sqrt{1+u^2}\, du$

$\overset{u=\tan v}{=} -2\pi \int_{\pi/4}^{\pi/6} \sqrt{1+\tan^2 v}\, \sec^2 v\, dv = 2\pi \int_{\pi/6}^{\pi/4} \sec^3 v\, dv$

so by (7) of Section 7.2,

$$S = 2\pi\left(\frac{1}{2}\sec v\, \tan v + \frac{1}{2}\ln|\sec v + \tan v|\right)\Big|_{\pi/6}^{\pi/4}$$

$$= \pi\left\{\left[\sqrt{2} + \ln(\sqrt{2}+1)\right] - \left[\frac{2}{\sqrt{3}}\cdot\frac{1}{\sqrt{3}} + \ln\left(\frac{2}{\sqrt{3}} + \frac{1}{\sqrt{3}}\right)\right]\right\} = \pi\left(\sqrt{2} + \ln(\sqrt{2}+1) - \frac{2}{3} - \frac{1}{2}\ln 3\right).$$

9. By Simpson's Rule with $n = 10$, $S = \int_0^1 2\pi x^4\sqrt{1+(4x^3)^2}\, dx = \int_0^1 2\pi x^4\sqrt{1+16x^6}\, dx \approx 3.43941846.$

10. By Simpson's Rule with $n = 10$, $S = \int_0^{\pi/4} 2\pi \tan x\sqrt{1+(\sec^2 x)^2}\, dx = \int_0^{\pi/4} 2\pi \tan x\sqrt{1+\sec^4 x}\, dx \approx$ 3.839390645.

11. By Simpson's Rule with $n = 10$,

$$S = \int_1^2 2\pi\left(\frac{1}{x^2}\right)\sqrt{1+\left(-\frac{2}{x^3}\right)^2}\, dx = \int_1^2 \frac{2\pi}{x^2}\sqrt{1+\frac{4}{x^6}}\, dx = \int_1^2 \frac{2\pi}{x^5}\sqrt{x^6+4}\, dx \approx 4.458002253.$$

12. By Simpson's Rule with $n = 10$,

$$S = \int_1^5 2\pi \ln x\sqrt{1+\left(\frac{1}{x}\right)^2}\, dx = \int_1^5 2\pi \ln x\sqrt{1+\frac{1}{x^2}}\, dx = \int_1^5 \frac{2\pi \ln x}{x}\sqrt{x^2+1}\, dx \approx 26.85376768.$$

13. Let S_b be the surface area of the portion of Gabriel's horn between $x = 1$ and $x = b$. By part (b) of Example 3,

$$S_b = \int_1^b 2\pi \frac{1}{x}\sqrt{1+\frac{1}{x^4}}\,dx = \int_1^b 2\pi\left(\frac{1}{x^3}\right)\sqrt{x^4+1}\,dx.$$

By Simpson's Rule with $n = 50$, we have $S_4 \approx 9.417263863$ and $S_5 \approx 10.82118211$. Thus $b = 5$.

14. By the figure, along with the formula for the area of the surface of a cone, we find that the area S of the frustum of the cone is given by $S = \pi r_2(l_1 + l) - \pi r_1 l_1$. We need to show that $S = \pi(r_1 + r_2)l$. By similar triangles, $(l_1 + l)/r_2 = l_1/r_1$, so that $r_2 l_1 = r_1(l_1 + l) = r_1 l_1 + r_1 l$. Thus $(r_2 - r_1)l_1 = r_1 l$, so that $S = \pi r_2 l + \pi(r_2 - r_1)l_1 = \pi r_2 l + \pi r_1 l = \pi(r_2 + r_1)l$.

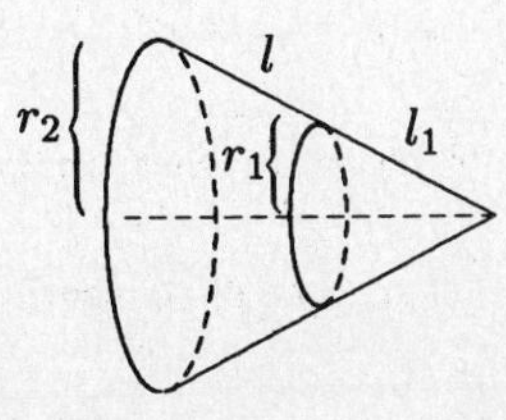

15. a. $$S = \int_{-a}^{a} 2\pi\sqrt{r^2-x^2}\sqrt{1+\left(\frac{-x}{\sqrt{r^2-x^2}}\right)^2}\,dx$$

$$= 2\pi\int_{-a}^{a}\sqrt{r^2-x^2}\sqrt{1+\frac{x^2}{r^2-x^2}}\,dx = 2\pi\int_{-a}^{a} r\,dx = 4\pi ra$$

b. Yes.

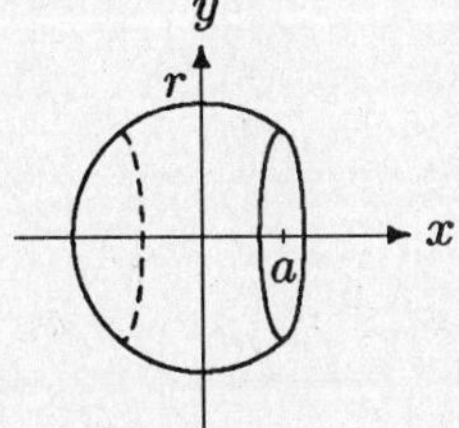

16. $$S = \int_a^b 2\pi\sqrt{1-x^2}\sqrt{1+\left(\frac{-x}{\sqrt{1-x^2}}\right)^2}\,dx = 2\pi\int_a^b\sqrt{1-x^2}\sqrt{1+\frac{x^2}{1-x^2}}\,dx = 2\pi\int_a^b 1\,dx = 2\pi(b-a)$$

17. The surface area S is twice the surface area of the portion between $x = 0$ and $x = 1$. Since $y = (1-x^{2/3})^{3/2}$, we have

$$S = 2\int_0^1 2\pi(1-x^{2/3})^{3/2}\sqrt{1+\left[\frac{3}{2}(1-x^{2/3})^{1/2}\left(-\frac{2}{3}x^{-1/3}\right)\right]^2}\,dx$$

$$= 4\pi\int_0^1 \frac{1}{x^{1/3}}(1-x^{2/3})^{3/2}\,dx \overset{u=1-x^{2/3}}{=} 4\pi\int_1^0\left(-\frac{3}{2}u^{3/2}\right)du = -4\pi\left(\frac{3}{5}u^{5/2}\right)\Big|_1^0 = \frac{12}{5}\pi.$$

18. The surface area S is twice the surface area of the portion for which $x > 0$. Since $y = \sqrt{9-x^2}$ for $\frac{1}{8} \le x \le 2$, this means that the surface area S_1 of the curved portions of the yo-yo is given by

$$S_1 = 2\int_{1/8}^{2} 2\pi\sqrt{9-x^2}\sqrt{1+\left(\frac{-x}{\sqrt{9-x^2}}\right)^2}\,dx$$

$$= 4\pi\int_{1/8}^{2}\sqrt{9-x^2}\sqrt{1+\frac{x^2}{9-x^2}}\,dx = 4\pi\int_{1/8}^{2} 3\,dx = 12\pi\left(2-\frac{1}{8}\right) = \frac{45}{2}\pi.$$

The surface area S_2 of the flat sides is given by $S_2 = 2\pi\left(\sqrt{9-2^2}\right)^2 = 10\pi$. Thus the surface area $S = S_1 + S_2 = \frac{45}{2}\pi + 10\pi = 32.5\pi$ (square centimeters).

19. The wok is obtained by revolving about the y axis the graph of $y = \frac{1}{40}x^2$ for $0 \le x \le 20$. The graph is equivalent to the graph of $x = \sqrt{40y}$ for $0 \le y \le 10$. Thus

$$S = \int_0^{10} 2\pi\sqrt{40y}\sqrt{1+\left(\frac{20}{\sqrt{40y}}\right)^2}\,dy = 2\pi\int_0^{10}\sqrt{40y}\sqrt{1+\frac{400}{40y}}\,dy = 2\pi\sqrt{40}\int_0^{10}\sqrt{y+10}\,dy$$

$$= 2\pi\sqrt{40}\left[\frac{2}{3}(y+10)^{3/2}\right]\Bigg|_0^{10} = \frac{4}{3}\pi\sqrt{40}\left(20^{3/2}-10^{3/2}\right) = \frac{800}{3}\pi(2\sqrt{2}-1)\text{ (square centimeters).}$$

20. The area of the lateral surface of the barrel is given by

$$S = \int_{-\sin^{-1}1/\sqrt{3}}^{\sin^{-1}1/\sqrt{3}} 2\pi\cos x\,\sqrt{1+(-\sin x)^2}\,dx$$

$$= 2\pi\int_{-\sin^{-1}1/\sqrt{3}}^{\sin^{-1}1/\sqrt{3}}\cos x\,\sqrt{1+\sin^2 x}\,dx \overset{u=\sin x}{=} 2\pi\int_{-1/\sqrt{3}}^{1/\sqrt{3}}\sqrt{1+u^2}\,du$$

$$\overset{u=\tan v}{=} 2\pi\int_{-\pi/6}^{\pi/6}\sec^3 v\,dv = 2\pi\left[\frac{1}{2}\sec v\,\tan v + \frac{1}{2}\ln|\sec v+\tan v|\right]\Bigg|_{-\pi/6}^{\pi/6}$$

$$= \pi\left[\frac{2}{\sqrt{3}}\cdot\frac{1}{\sqrt{3}} + \ln\left(\frac{2}{\sqrt{3}}+\frac{1}{\sqrt{3}}\right) - \frac{2}{\sqrt{3}}\left(\frac{-1}{\sqrt{3}}\right) - \ln\left(\frac{2}{\sqrt{3}}-\frac{1}{\sqrt{3}}\right)\right] = \pi\left(\frac{4}{3}+\ln 3\right).$$

$\sin^{-1}\frac{1}{\sqrt{3}}$ $\sqrt{3}$ 1 $\sqrt{2}$

Each end of the barrel is a disk with radius $\cos(\sin^{-1}(1/\sqrt{3})) = \sqrt{2}/\sqrt{3}$, so the area of each end is $\pi\left(\sqrt{2}/\sqrt{3}\right)^2 = \frac{2}{3}\pi$. Therefore the total surface area of the barrel is $\pi\left(\frac{4}{3}+\ln 3\right)+2\left(\frac{2}{3}\pi\right) = \pi\left(\frac{8}{3}+\ln 3\right)$.

8.5 Work

1. $W = \int_0^{60} 60(1-x^2/20{,}000)\,dx = 60(x-x^3/60{,}000)\big|_0^{60} = 3384$ (joules)

2. $f(x) = 1600$; $W = \int_0^{1200} 1600\,dx = 1600(1200) = 1{,}920{,}000$ (foot-pounds)

3. $f(x) = 10$; $W = \int_0^8 10\,dx = 10x\big|_0^8 = 80$ (foot-pounds)

4. $f(x) = 130$; $W = \int_0^8 130\,dx = 130x\big|_0^8 = 1040$ (foot-pounds)

5. $W = \int_0^\pi 10^4\sin x\,dx = -10^4\cos x\big|_0^\pi = 2\times 10^4$ (newton-kilometers). Thus $W = 2\times 10^7$ joules.

6. $W = \int_0^{1/2} 10{,}000(1+2x)^2\,dx = \frac{5{,}000}{3}(1+2x)^3\big|_0^{1/2} = \frac{35{,}000}{3}$ (ergs)

7. $W = \int_0^5 2(10^6)(5-x)\,dx = 2(10^6)\left(5x-\frac{1}{2}x^2\right)\big|_0^5 = 2(10^6)(25-12.5) = 2.5\times 10^7$ (ergs)

8. By hypothesis, $k(10) = 4\times 10^6$, so that $k = 4\times 10^5$. Thus $W = \int_{10}^{20} 4(10^5)x\,dx = 2(10^5)x^2\big|_{10}^{20} = 6\times 10^7$ (ergs).

9. Using the information of Exercise 8, we have $W = \int_{20}^{30} 4(10^5)x\,dx = 2(10^5)x^2\big|_{20}^{30} = 1000(10^5) = 10^8$ (ergs).

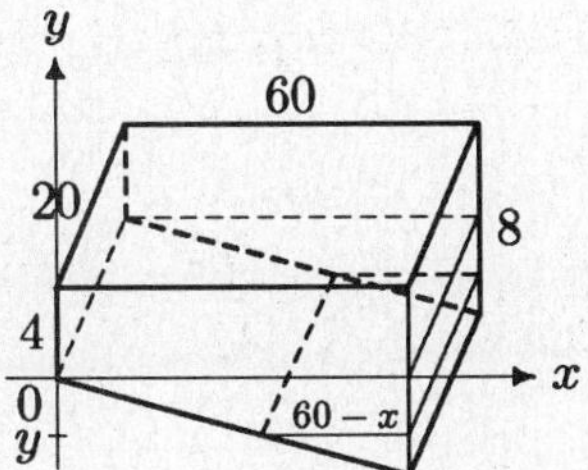

Exercise 13

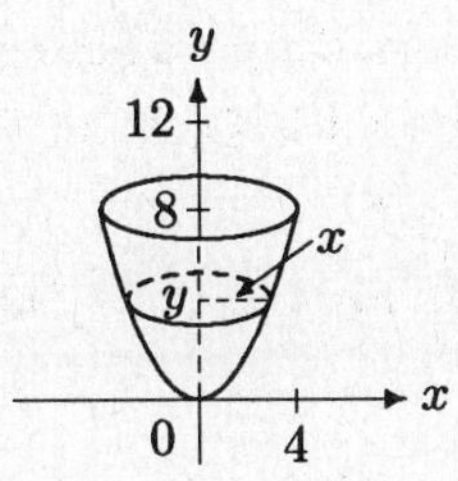

Exercise 14

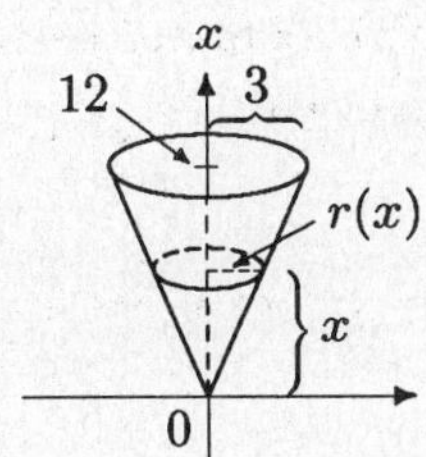

Exercise 15

10. By hypothesis, $6 \times 10^7 = W = \int_0^{-4} kx\,dx$. Since $\int_0^{-4} kx\,dx = \frac{1}{2}kx^2\big|_0^{-4} = 8k$, it follows that $k = \frac{1}{8}(6 \times 10^7)$. Thus the work necessary to compress the spring an additional 4 centimeters is given by $W = \int_{-4}^{-8} \frac{1}{8}(6 \times 10^7)x\,dx = \frac{1}{16}(6 \times 10^7)x^2\big|_{-4}^{-8} = \frac{1}{16}(6 \times 10^7)(48) = 1.8 \times 10^8$ (ergs).

11. By hypothesis, $6 \times 10^7 = W = \int_0^{-5} kx\,dx$. Since $\int_0^{-5} kx\,dx = \frac{1}{2}kx^2\big|_0^{-5} = \frac{25}{2}k$, it follows that $k = \frac{12}{25} \times 10^7$. Thus the work necessary to stretch the spring 2 centimeters is given by $W = \int_0^2 \left(\frac{12}{25} \times 10^7\right) x\,dx = \left(\frac{12}{25} \times 10^7\right)\left(\frac{1}{2}x^2\right)\big|_0^2 = \frac{24}{25} \times 10^7 = 9.6 \times 10^6$ (ergs).

12. We change to 0 the lower limit in the solution of Example 3, obtaining $W = \int_0^5 6250\pi(8 - x)\,dx = 6250\pi\left(8x - \frac{1}{2}x^2\right)\big|_0^5 = 171{,}875\pi$ (foot-pounds).

13. We place the upper edge of the pool floor at the origin, as in the accompanying figure. Then $l = 5$, and a particle of water y feet from the bottom is to be raised $5 - y$ feet. For $0 \le y \le 4$, the cross-sectional area $A(y)$ is given by $A(y) = (60)(20) = 1200$. For $-4 \le y \le 0$ the floor meets the side wall in the line $y = \frac{-4}{60}x = \frac{-1}{15}x$, so that $A(y) = (60 - x)20 = (60 + 15y)20 = 1200 + 300y$. Thus $W = \int_{-4}^0 62.5(5 - y)(1200 + 300y)\,dy + \int_0^4 62.5(5 - y)(1200)\,dy = 18{,}750\int_{-4}^0(-y^2 + y + 20)\,dy + 75{,}000\int_0^4(5 - y)\,dy = 18{,}750\left(-\frac{1}{3}y^3 + \frac{1}{2}y^2 + 20y\right)\big|_{-4}^0 + 75{,}000\left(5y - \frac{1}{2}y^2\right)\big|_0^4 = 18{,}750\left(-\frac{64}{3} - 8 + 80\right) + 75{,}000(20 - 8) = 1{,}850{,}000$ (foot-pounds).

14. We place the bottom of the tank at the origin, as in the figure. Then $l = 12$, and a particle of fluid y feet from the bottom is to be raised $12 - y$ feet. Moreover, the fluid to be pumped extends from 0 to 8 on the y axis, and the cross-sectional area $A(y)$ at y is given by $A(y) = \pi x^2 = 2\pi y$. By (4), with x replaced by y and 62.5 by 80, we have $W = \int_0^8 80(12 - y)2\pi y\,dy = \int_0^8 160\pi(12y - y^2)\,dy = 160\pi\left(6y^2 - \frac{1}{3}y^3\right)\big|_0^8 = 160\pi\left(384 - \frac{512}{3}\right) = \frac{102{,}400\pi}{3}$ (foot-pounds).

15. We position the x axis as in the figure, with the origin at the vertex of the cone. Then $l = 12$, and a particle of water x feet from the vertex is to be raised $12 - x$ feet. Moreover, the water to be pumped extends from 0 to 12 on the x axis. By similar triangles, we have $r(x)/x = \frac{3}{12} = \frac{1}{4}$, so that $r(x) = x/4$ and hence $A(x) = \pi[r(x)]^2 = \pi x^2/16$. Thus by (4),

$$W = \int_0^{12} 62.5(12 - x)\frac{\pi}{16}x^2\,dx = \frac{62.5\pi}{16}\int_0^{12}(12x^2 - x^3)\,dx$$

$$= \frac{62.5\pi}{16}\left(4x^3 - \frac{1}{4}x^4\right)\bigg|_0^{12} = 6750\pi\,\text{(foot-pounds)}.$$

16. Since the volume V of a cone of radius r and height h is given by $V = \frac{1}{3}\pi r^2 h$, the volume of water in the tank is $\frac{1}{3}\pi 3^2 \cdot 12 = 36\pi$ (cubic feet). Thus after half the water has been pumped out, the volume of the remaining water is 18π cubic feet. If h is the height and r the radius of the cone formed by the remaining water, then as in the solution of Exercise 15, we have $r = \frac{1}{4}h$, so that $18\pi = \frac{1}{3}\pi r^2 h = (\pi/48)h^3$, and thus $h = \sqrt[3]{18 \cdot 48} = 6\sqrt[3]{4}$. Thus the water that extends from $6\sqrt[3]{4}$ to 12 on the x axis is pumped to the top of the tank (so that $l = 12$), and the water that extends from 0 to $6\sqrt[3]{4}$ on the x axis is pumped to a level 3 feet above the top (so that $l = 15$). Thus by using (4) twice and the solution of Exercise 15, and adding the results, we find that

$$W = \int_{6\sqrt[3]{4}}^{12} 62.5(12 - x)\frac{\pi}{16}x^2\,dx + \int_0^{6\sqrt[3]{4}} 62.5(15 - x)\frac{\pi}{16}x^2\,dx$$

$$= \frac{62.5\pi}{16}\left(4x^3 - \frac{1}{4}x^4\right)\Bigg|_{6\sqrt[3]{4}}^{12} + \frac{62.5\pi}{16}\left(5x^3 - \frac{1}{4}x^4\right)\Bigg|_0^{6\sqrt[3]{4}}$$

$$= \frac{62.5\pi}{16}\left[1728 - \left(4 \cdot 6^3 \cdot 4 - \frac{1}{4} \cdot 6^4 \cdot 4\sqrt[3]{4}\right)\right] + \frac{62.5\pi}{16}\left(5 \cdot 6^3 \cdot 4 - \frac{1}{4} \cdot 6^4 \cdot 4\sqrt[3]{4}\right)$$

$$= 10{,}125\pi \text{ (foot-pounds)}.$$

17. a. If the tank is positioned with respect to the x axis as in the figure, then $l = 0$ and the gasoline to be pumped extends from -4 to 0 on the x axis. Moreover, the width $w(x)$ of the cross-section at x is given by $w(x) = 2\sqrt{16 - x^2}$, so $A(x) = 10w(x) = 20\sqrt{16 - x^2}$. Thus by (4) with 62.5 replaced by 42, we have

$$W = \int_{-4}^{0} 42(0 - x)20\sqrt{16 - x^2}\,dx \overset{u=16-x^2}{=} 840\int_0^{16} \sqrt{u}\left(\frac{1}{2}\right)du$$

$$= 420\left(\frac{2}{3}u^{3/2}\right)\Bigg|_0^{16} = 17{,}920 \text{ (foot-pounds)}.$$

b. If the tank is positioned with respect to the x axis as in the figure, then $l = 4$ and the gasoline to be pumped extends from 0 to 4 on the x axis. As in the solution of part (a), we have $A(x) = 20\sqrt{16 - x^2}$. Thus $W = \int_0^4 42(4-x)20\sqrt{16 - x^2}\,dx = 3360\int_0^4 \sqrt{16 - x^2}\,dx - 840\int_0^4 x\sqrt{16 - x^2}\,dx$. Now

$$3360\int_0^4 \sqrt{16 - x^2}\,dx \overset{x=4\sin u}{=} 3360\int_0^{\pi/2} \sqrt{16 - 16\sin^2 u}\,(4\cos u)\,du$$

$$= (3360)(16)\int_0^{\pi/2} \cos^2 u\,du$$

$$= (3360)(16)\int_0^{\pi/2}\left(\frac{1}{2} + \frac{1}{2}\cos 2u\right)du$$

$$= (3360)(16)\left(\frac{u}{2} + \frac{1}{4}\sin 2u\right)\Bigg|_0^{\pi/2} = 13{,}440\pi$$

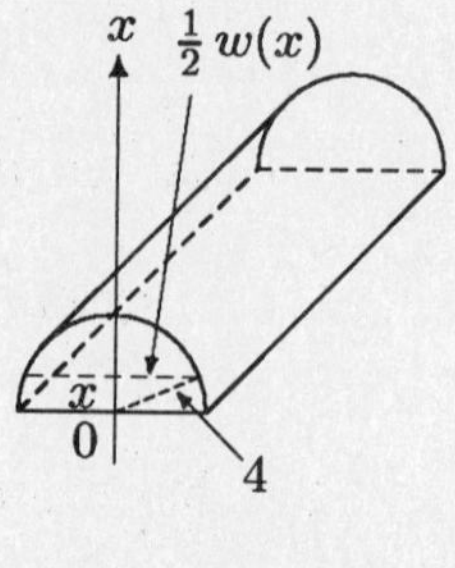

and $840\int_0^4 x\sqrt{16 - x^2}\,dx = -\frac{840}{3}(16 - x^2)^{3/2}\Big|_0^4 = 17{,}920$. Thus $W = 13{,}440\pi - 17{,}920$ (foot-pounds).

18. $W = \int_0^6 F(x)\,dx = \int_0^2 2x\,dx + \int_2^4 4\,dx + \int_4^6 (12-2x)\,dx = x^2\big|_0^2 + 4x\big|_2^4 + (12x - x^2)\big|_4^6 = 4 + (16-8) + (36-32) = 16$.

19. $W = \int_0^8 F(x)\,dx = \int_0^2 4\,dx + \int_2^6 \left(\frac{13}{2} - \frac{5}{4}x\right)dx + \int_6^8 (-1)\,dx = 4x\big|_0^2 + \left(\frac{13}{2}x - \frac{5}{8}x^2\right)\big|_2^6 + (-x)\big|_6^8 = 8 + \left[\left(39 - \frac{45}{2}\right) - \left(13 - \frac{5}{2}\right)\right] + (-8+6) = 12$.

20. Let W_1 denote the work required to extend the spring 6 centimeters from its natural length, and W_2 the work required to compress it to its natural length. Then $W_1 = \int_0^{-6} kx\,dx$ and $W_2 = \int_{-6}^0 kx\,dx$, where k is the spring constant. Then the total work W done in extending and then compressing the spring is given by $W = W_1 + W_2 = \int_0^{-6} kx\,dx + \int_{-6}^0 kx\,dx = \int_0^0 kx\,dx = 0$.

21. By Simpson's Rule with $n = 10$,
$$W = \int_5^7 F(x)\,dx = \int_5^7 \frac{1.3x}{x^2 + 1.3x + 1}\,dx \approx 0.3501250594.$$

22. a. There are approximately 93 full squares, each having an area of 200 square units. Thus $W \approx 93(200) = 18{,}600$ (joules).

 b. $W \approx \frac{200}{3(10)}[0+4(30)+2(130)+4(190)+2(200)+4(180)+2(110)+4(60)+2(30)+4(10)+0] = 18{,}800$ (joules)

23. By Simpson's Rule, $W \approx \frac{20}{3(10)}[1.21+4(2.90)+2(3.01)+4(3.52)+2(3.41)+4(3.19)+2(2.78)+4(2.76)+2(2.83)+4(2.90)+2.84] = 59.46$ (ergs).

24. $$W = \int_{-10^{-9}}^{-10^{-10}} \frac{a}{x^2}\,dx = -\frac{a}{x}\Big|_{-10^{-9}}^{-10^{-10}} = \frac{a}{10^{-10}} - \frac{a}{10^{-9}} = a(10^{10} - 10^9)$$
$$= 9a \times 10^9 = 9(2.3 \times 10^{-28}) \times 10^9 = 2.07 \times 10^{-18} \text{ (joules)}$$

25. a. $h'(t) = 8 - 32t$, so $h'(t) = 0$ for $t = \frac{1}{4}$. The maximum height is $h(\frac{1}{4}) = 7$ (feet). Since $f(h) = -0.2$, we have $W = \int_7^0 -0.2\,dh = (-0.2)h\big|_7^0 = 1.4$ (foot-pounds).

 b. We change to 6 the upper limit on the integral in the solution of part (a). Thus $W = \int_7^6 -0.2\,dh = (-0.2)h\big|_7^6 = 0.2$ (foot-pounds).

26. a. Since the work is done in the direction opposite to gravity,
$$W = \int_{4000}^{5000} \frac{GMm}{x^2}\,dx = \frac{-GMm}{x}\Big|_{4000}^{5000} = \frac{GMm}{20{,}000} \text{ (mile-pounds).}$$

 b. Call the work $W(b)$. Then
$$W(b) = \int_{4000}^{4000+b} \frac{GMm}{x^2}\,dx = \frac{-GMm}{x}\Big|_{4000}^{4000+b} = GMm\left(\frac{1}{4000} - \frac{1}{4000+b}\right) \text{ (mile-pounds).}$$

 c. $\lim_{b\to\infty} W(b) = GMm \lim_{b\to\infty}\left(\frac{1}{4000} - \frac{1}{4000+b}\right) = \frac{GMm}{4000}$ (mile-pounds), so it is possible.

27. a. $f(x) = 200$; $W = \int_0^{80} 200\,dx = 200(80) = 16{,}000$ (foot-pounds).

 b. When the bucket is x feet above the ground, the chain is $80 - x$ feet long, so $f(x) = 200 + (80 - x) = 280 - x$. Thus $W = \int_0^{80} (280 - x)\,dx = \left(280x - \frac{1}{2}x^2\right)\big|_0^{80} = 19{,}200$ (foot-pounds).

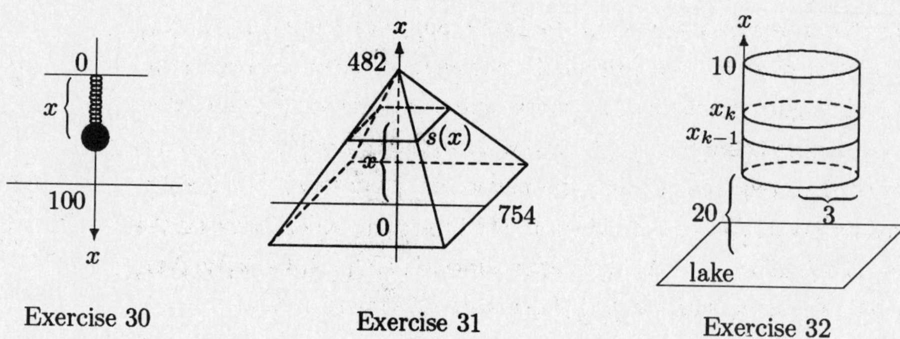

Exercise 30 Exercise 31 Exercise 32

28. When the container has been raised x feet, $x/2$ seconds have elapsed, so that $\frac{1}{2}(x/2)$ pounds of water have leaked out. Therefore the weight is given by $f(x) = 20 - \frac{1}{4}x$ for $0 \leq x \leq 10$. Thus $W = \int_0^{10} (20 - \frac{1}{4}x)\, dx = (20x - \frac{1}{8}x^2)\big|_0^{10} = \frac{375}{2}$ (foot-pounds).

29. When the bucket has been raised x feet, $x/2$ seconds have elapsed, so that $\frac{1}{2}(x/2)$ pounds of water have leaked out. Therefore the total weight of water and bucket is given by $f(x) = 21 - \frac{1}{4}x$. Since the bucket is empty when $\frac{1}{4}x = 20$, or $x = 80$, we have $W = \int_0^{80} (21 - \frac{1}{4}x)\, dx = (21x - \frac{1}{8}x^2)\big|_0^{80} = 880$ (foot-pounds).

30. Since the ball is lowered, we let the positive x axis point downward as in the figure, with the origin at the nighttime position. When the ball has been lowered x feet, the weight of the chain is $3x$ pounds, so the weight of the chain and ball is $2000 + 3x$ pounds. Thus $f(x) = 2000 + 3x$, so $W = \int_0^{100}(2000 + 3x)\, dx = (2000x + \frac{3}{2}x^2)\big|_0^{100} = 215{,}000$ (foot-pounds).

31. Let $s(x)$ denote the length of the side of a cross-section x feet above the ground. Then $s(x)/754 = (482 - x)/482$, so $s(x) = \frac{754}{482}(482 - x)$. The cross-sectional area is given by $A(x) = (s(x))^2 = \left(\frac{754}{482}\right)^2 (482 - x)^2$. Let $P = \{x_0, x_1, \ldots, x_n\}$ be any partition of $[0, 482]$, and for $1 \leq k \leq n$ let t_k be any point in $[x_{k-1}, x_k]$. Then the amount of work ΔW_k required to lift the portion of the pyramid that will reside between the heights x_{k-1} and x_k is approximately $(150A(t_k)\Delta x_k)(t_k)$ (weight × distance). Thus the total work W, which is the sum of $\Delta W_1, \Delta W_2, \ldots, \Delta W_n$, is approximately $\sum_{k=1}^n 150 t_k A(t_k)\Delta x_k$, so that

$$W = \int_0^{482} 150xA(x)\, dx = 150\int_0^{482} x\left(\frac{754}{482}\right)^2 (482 - x)^2\, dx = \frac{150(754)^2}{(482)^2}\int_0^{482} ((482)^2 x - 964x^2 + x^3)\, dx$$

$$= \frac{150(754)^2}{(482)^2}\left[\frac{(482)^2}{2}x^2 - \frac{964}{3}x^3 + \frac{1}{4}x^4\right]\Bigg|_0^{482} = \frac{150(754)^2(482)^2}{12} \approx 1.651 \times 10^{12} \text{ (foot-pounds)}.$$

32. Let $P = \{x_0, x_1, \ldots, x_n\}$ be a partition of $[0, 10]$. The water between the levels $x = x_{k-1}$ and $x = x_k$ has volume $\pi(3)^2\Delta x_k$ and has traveled approximately $x_k + 20$. Thus the work performed in raising that water from the lake is approximately $[62.5\pi(3)^2\Delta x_k]\,(x_k + 20)$. The total work is approximately $\sum_{k=1}^n (62.5)\pi(9)(x_k + 20)\Delta x_k$, which is a Riemann sum for $\int_0^{10} 562.5\pi(x + 20)\, dx$. Thus $W = \int_0^{10} 562.5\pi(x + 20)\, dx$.

33. Set up a coordinate system as in the figure, and let $P = \{x_0, x_1, \ldots, x_n\}$ be a partition of $[0,4]$. The portion of the triangle in the interval $[x_{k-1}, x_k]$ has approximate weight $2y_k\Delta x_k$ units, and must rise approximately x_k feet. By similar triangles, $y_k/(4-x_k) = \frac{3}{4}$, so that $y_k = \frac{3}{4}(4-x_k)$. Thus the work Δx_k required to raise the portion in the interval $[x_{k-1}, x_k]$ is approximately $2\left[\frac{3}{4}(4-x_k)\Delta x_k\right](x_k)$. Then the total work S, which is the sum of ΔW_1, ΔW_2, ..., ΔW_n, is approximately $\sum_{k=1}^{n} \frac{3}{2}(4-x_k)x_k\Delta x_k$, which is a Riemann sum for $\int_0^4 \frac{3}{2}(4-x)x\,dx$. Therefore

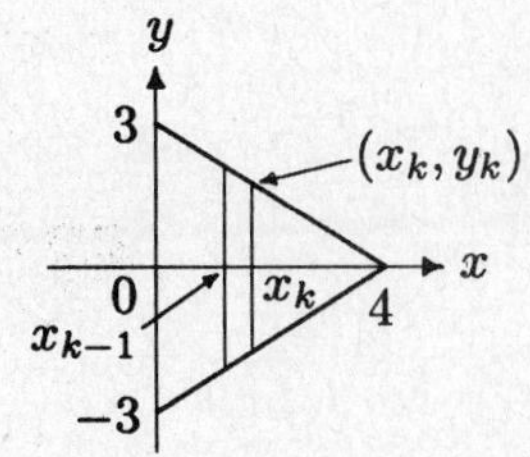

$$W = \int_0^4 \frac{3}{2}(4-x)x\,dx = \frac{3}{2}\int_0^4 (4x - x^2)\,dx = \frac{3}{2}\left(2x^2 - \frac{1}{3}x^3\right)\Bigg|_0^4 = 16 \text{ (foot-pounds).}$$

8.6 Moments and Center of Gravity

1. Take the origin of the x axis at the axis of revolution of the seesaw, with the positive x axis pointing toward the 20-kilogram child. Then the moment of the two children on the seesaw is $15(-2)+20(2) = 10$. For equilibrium the moment of the 10-kilogram child must be -10. Thus that child should sit on the same side as the 15-kilogram child, one meter from the axis of revolution.

2. Take the origin of the x axis at the axis of revolution of the seesaw, with the positive x axis pointing toward the 10-kilogram child. If the 15-kilogram child sits at x and the 20-kilogram child sits at $-x$, then the three children will be in equilibrium if $10(1)+15(x)+20(-x) = 0$, or $10-5x=0$, or $x=2$. Thus the 15-kilogram child should sit 2 meters from the axis of revolution and on the same side as the 10-kilogram child, while the 20-kilogram child should sit on the opposite side, 2 meters from the axis of revolution.

3. Let the origin be the center of mass of the system consisting of the earth and moon, with both earth and moon on the x axis. Let x denote the distance between the center of mass and the earth. Then

moon　　earth
$-3.84 \times 10^5 + x$　　x
7.35×10^{22} kg　　5.98×10^{24} kg
origin
center of mass

$$\underbrace{(7.35 \times 10^{22})}_{\text{moon mass}}\underbrace{(-3.84 \times 10^5 + x)}_{\text{moon coordinate}} + \underbrace{(5.98 \times 10^{24})}_{\text{earth mass}}\underbrace{x}_{\text{earth coordinate}} = 0.$$

Solving for x, we find that

$$x = \frac{(7.35 \times 10^{22})(3.84 \times 10^5)}{(7.35 \times 10^{22}) + (5.98 \times 10^{24})} \approx 4662.426695.$$

Thus the center of the earth is approximately 4662 kilometers from the center of mass. Since the radius of the earth is (approximately) 6.37×10^3 kilometers, the center of mass is inside the earth.

4. $M_y = 50(3)+30(4)+20(-1) = 250$; $M_x = 50(-1)+30(2)+20(1) = 30$; $m = 50+30+20 = 100$;

$$\bar{x} = \frac{M_y}{m} = \frac{250}{100} = \frac{5}{2}; \quad \bar{y} = \frac{M_x}{m} = \frac{30}{100} = \frac{3}{10}$$

Therefore the center of gravity is $(\frac{5}{2}, \frac{3}{10})$.

5. $M_x = \int_0^2 \frac{1}{2}\left[x^2 - (-2)^2\right] dx = \frac{1}{2}\left(\frac{1}{3}x^3 - 4x\right)\Big|_0^2 = -\frac{8}{3};$

$M_y = \int_0^2 x[x - (-2)]\, dx = \int_0^2 (x^2 + 2x)\, dx = \left(\frac{1}{3}x^3 + x^2\right)\Big|_0^2 = \frac{20}{3}$

$A = \int_0^2 ((x - (-2))\, dx = \left(\frac{1}{2}x^2 + 2x\right)\Big|_0^2 = 6$

$\bar{x} = \frac{M_y}{A} = \frac{20/3}{6} = \frac{10}{9};\ \bar{y} = \frac{M_x}{A} = \frac{-8/3}{6} = \frac{-4}{9};\ (\bar{x}, \bar{y}) = \left(\frac{10}{9}, \frac{-4}{9}\right)$

6. $M_x = \int_2^5 \frac{1}{2}\left[(2x-1)^2 - (x-2)^2\right] dx = \int_2^5 \frac{1}{2}\left(3x^2 - 3\right) dx = \frac{1}{2}(x^3 - 3x)\Big|_2^5 = 54$

$M_y = \int_2^5 x[(2x-1) - (x-2)]\, dx = \int_2^5 (x^2 + x)\, dx = \left(\frac{1}{3}x^3 + \frac{1}{2}x^2\right)\Big|_2^5 = \frac{99}{2}$

$A = \int_2^5 [(2x-1) - (x-2)]\, dx = \int_2^5 (x+1)\, dx = \left(\frac{1}{2}x^2 + x\right)\Big|_2^5 = \frac{27}{2}$

$\bar{x} = \frac{M_y}{A} = \frac{99/2}{27/2} = \frac{11}{3};\ \bar{y} = \frac{M_x}{A} = \frac{54}{27/2} = 4;\ (\bar{x}, \bar{y}) = \left(\frac{11}{3}, 4\right)$

7. $M_x = \int_0^2 \frac{1}{2}\left[(2-x)^2 - (-(2-x))^2\right] dx = 0$

$M_y = \int_0^2 x[(2-x) - (-(2-x))]\, dx = \int_0^2 (4x - 2x^2)\, dx = \left(2x^2 - \frac{2}{3}x^3\right)\Big|_0^2 = \frac{8}{3}$

$A = \int_0^2 [(2-x) - (-(2-x))]\, dx = \int_0^2 (4-2x)\, dx = (4x - x^2)\big|_0^2 = 4$

$\bar{x} = \frac{M_y}{A} = \frac{8/3}{4} = \frac{2}{3};\ \bar{y} = \frac{M_x}{A} = \frac{0}{4} = 0;\ (\bar{x}, \bar{y}) = \left(\frac{2}{3}, 0\right)$

8. $M_x = \int_0^1 \frac{1}{2}\left[(3x)^2 - (x^2)^2\right] dx = \int_0^1 \frac{1}{2}\left(9x^2 - x^4\right) dx = \frac{1}{2}\left(3x^3 - \frac{1}{5}x^5\right)\Big|_0^1 = \frac{7}{5}$

$M_y = \int_0^1 x\left(3x - x^2\right) dx = \int_0^1 \left(3x^2 - x^3\right) dx = \left(x^3 - \frac{1}{4}x^4\right)\Big|_0^1 = \frac{3}{4}$

$A = \int_0^1 \left(3x - x^2\right) dx = \left(\frac{3}{2}x^2 - \frac{1}{3}x^3\right)\Big|_0^1 = \frac{7}{6}$

$\bar{x} = \frac{M_y}{A} = \frac{3/4}{7/6} = \frac{9}{14};\ \bar{y} = \frac{M_x}{A} = \frac{7/5}{7/6} = \frac{6}{5};\ (\bar{x}, \bar{y}) = \left(\frac{9}{14}, \frac{6}{5}\right)$

9. $M_x = \int_1^2 \frac{1}{2}\left[(x+1)^4 - (x-1)^4\right] dx = \frac{1}{2}\left[\frac{1}{5}(x+1)^5 - \frac{1}{5}(x-1)^5\right]\Big|_1^2 = 21$

$M_y = \int_1^2 x\left[(x+1)^2 - (x-1)^2\right] dx = \int_1^2 4x^2\, dx = \frac{4}{3}x^3\Big|_1^2 = \frac{28}{3}$

$A = \int_1^2 \left[(x+1)^2 - (x-1)^2\right] dx = \int_1^2 4x\, dx = 2x^2\big|_1^2 = 6$

$$\bar{x} = \frac{M_y}{A} = \frac{28/3}{6} = \frac{14}{9};\ \bar{y} = \frac{M_x}{A} = \frac{21}{6} = \frac{7}{2};\ (\bar{x}, \bar{y}) = \left(\frac{14}{9}, \frac{7}{2}\right)$$

10. $M_x = \int_0^3 \frac{1}{2}\left[(x+1)^2 - (\sqrt{x+1})^2\right] dx = \frac{1}{2}\int_0^3 (x^2+x)\,dx = \frac{1}{2}\left(\frac{1}{3}x^3 + \frac{1}{2}x^2\right)\Big|_0^3 = \frac{27}{4}$

$$M_y = \int_0^3 x\left[(x+1) - \sqrt{x+1}\right] dx = \int_0^3 (x^2+x)\,dx - \int_0^3 x\sqrt{x+1}\,dx$$

$$\stackrel{u=x+1}{=} \left(\frac{1}{3}x^3 + \frac{1}{2}x^2\right)\Big|_0^3 - \int_1^4 (u-1)\sqrt{u}\,du = \frac{27}{2} - \left(\frac{2}{5}u^{5/2} - \frac{2}{3}u^{3/2}\right)\Big|_1^4 = \frac{27}{2} - \frac{116}{15} = \frac{173}{30}$$

$$A = \int_0^3 \left[(x+1) - \sqrt{x+1}\right] dx = \left[\frac{1}{2}x^2 + x - \frac{2}{3}(x+1)^{3/2}\right]\Big|_0^3 = \frac{17}{6}$$

$$\bar{x} = \frac{M_y}{A} = \frac{173/30}{17/6} = \frac{173}{85};\ \bar{y} = \frac{M_x}{A} = \frac{27/4}{17/6} = \frac{81}{34};\ (\bar{x}, \bar{y}) = \left(\frac{173}{85}, \frac{81}{34}\right)$$

11. $M_x = \int_0^1 \frac{1}{2}\left[(\sqrt{1-x^2})^2 - (-(1+x))^2\right] dx = \frac{1}{2}\int_0^1 (-2x - 2x^2)\,dx = \frac{1}{2}\left(-x^2 - \frac{2}{3}x^3\right)\Big|_0^1 = \frac{-5}{6}$

$$M_y = \int_0^1 x\left[\sqrt{1-x^2} - (-(1+x))\right] dx = \int_0^1 \left(x\sqrt{1-x^2} + x + x^2\right) dx$$

$$= \left(\frac{-1}{3}(1-x^2)^{3/2} + \frac{1}{2}x^2 + \frac{1}{3}x^3\right)\Big|_0^1 = \frac{7}{6}$$

$$A = \int_0^1 \left[\sqrt{1-x^2} - (-(1+x))\right] dx = \int_0^1 \sqrt{1-x^2}\,dx + \int_0^1 (1+x)\,dx$$

$$\stackrel{x=\sin u}{=} \int_0^{\pi/2} \sqrt{1-\sin^2 u}\cos u\,du + \left(x + \frac{1}{2}x^2\right)\Big|_0^1 = \int_0^{\pi/2} \cos^2 u\,du + \frac{3}{2}$$

$$= \left(\frac{u}{2} + \frac{1}{4}\sin 2u\right)\Big|_0^{\pi/2} + \frac{3}{2} = \frac{\pi}{4} + \frac{3}{2}$$

$$\bar{x} = \frac{M_y}{A} = \frac{7/6}{\pi/4 + \frac{3}{2}} = \frac{14}{3\pi+18};\ \bar{y} = \frac{M_x}{A} = \frac{-5/6}{\pi/4 + \frac{3}{2}} = \frac{-10}{3\pi+18};\ (\bar{x}, \bar{y}) = \left(\frac{14}{3\pi+18}, \frac{-10}{3\pi+18}\right)$$

12. $M_x = \int_0^{\pi/4} \frac{1}{2}(\cos^2 x - \sin^2 x)\,dx = \frac{1}{2}\int_0^{\pi/4} \cos 2x\,dx = \frac{1}{4}\sin 2x\Big|_0^{\pi/4} = \frac{1}{4}$

$$M_y = \int_0^{\pi/4} x(\cos x - \sin x)\,dx \stackrel{\text{parts}}{=} x(\sin x + \cos x)\big|_0^{\pi/4} - \int_0^{\pi/4} (\sin x + \cos x)\,dx$$

$$= \frac{\pi}{4}\sqrt{2} - (-\cos x + \sin x)\big|_0^{\pi/4} = \frac{\pi\sqrt{2}}{4} - 1$$

$$A = \int_0^{\pi/4} (\cos x - \sin x)\,dx = (\sin x + \cos x)\big|_0^{\pi/4} = \sqrt{2} - 1$$

$$\bar{x} = \frac{M_y}{A} = \frac{\frac{\pi\sqrt{2}}{4} - 1}{\sqrt{2} - 1} = \frac{\pi\sqrt{2} - 4}{4\sqrt{2} - 4};\ \bar{y} = \frac{M_x}{A} = \frac{1/4}{\sqrt{2} - 1} = \frac{1}{4\sqrt{2} - 4};\ (\bar{x}, \bar{y}) = \left(\frac{\pi\sqrt{2} - 4}{4\sqrt{2} - 4}, \frac{1}{4\sqrt{2} - 4}\right)$$

13. $M_x = \int_0^{\pi/2} \frac{1}{2}\left[(\sin x + \cos x)^2 - (\sin x - \cos x)^2\right] dx = \frac{1}{2}\int_0^{\pi/2} 4\sin x \cos x\, dx$

$= \int_0^{\pi/2} \sin 2x\, dx = \frac{-1}{2}\cos 2x\Big|_0^{\pi/2} = 1$

$M_y = \int_0^{\pi/2} x[(\sin x + \cos x) - (\sin x - \cos x)]\, dx = \int_0^{\pi/2} 2x\cos x\, dx$

$\overset{\text{parts}}{=} 2x\sin x\big|_0^{\pi/2} - 2\int_0^{\pi/2} \sin x\, dx = \pi + 2\cos x\big|_0^{\pi/2} = \pi - 2$

$A = \int_0^{\pi/2} [(\sin x + \cos x) - (\sin x - \cos x)]\, dx = \int_0^{\pi/2} 2\cos x\, dx = 2\sin x\big|_0^{\pi/2} = 2$

$\bar{x} = \frac{M_y}{A} = \frac{\pi - 2}{2} = \frac{\pi}{2} - 1$; $\bar{y} = \frac{M_x}{A} = \frac{1}{2}$; $(\bar{x}, \bar{y}) = \left(\frac{\pi}{2} - 1, \frac{1}{2}\right)$

14. $M_x = \int_1^2 \frac{1}{2}\left[(\ln x)^2 - (-4)^2\right] dx \overset{\text{parts}}{=} \frac{1}{2}x(\ln x)^2\Big|_1^2 - \int_1^2 \ln x\, dx - 8x\big|_1^2$

$\overset{\text{parts}}{=} (\ln 2)^2 - (x\ln x - x)\big|_1^2 - 8 = (\ln 2)^2 - 2\ln 2 - 7$

$M_y = \int_1^2 x(\ln x - (-4))\, dx \overset{\text{parts}}{=} \frac{1}{2}x^2 \ln x\Big|_1^2 - \int_1^2 \frac{1}{2}x\, dx + 2x^2\big|_1^2 = 2\ln 2 - \frac{1}{4}x^2\Big|_1^2 + 6 = 2\ln 2 + \frac{21}{4}$

$A = \int_1^2 [\ln x - (-4)]\, dx \overset{\text{parts}}{=} (x\ln x - x)\big|_1^2 + 4x\big|_1^2 = 2\ln 2 + 3$

$\bar{x} = \frac{M_y}{A} = \frac{2\ln 2 + \frac{21}{4}}{2\ln 2 + 3} = \frac{8\ln 2 + 21}{8\ln 2 + 12}$; $\bar{y} = \frac{M_x}{A} = \frac{(\ln 2)^2 - 2\ln 2 - 7}{2\ln 2 + 3}$;

$(\bar{x}, \bar{y}) = \left(\frac{8\ln 2 + 21}{8\ln 2 + 12}, \frac{(\ln 2)^2 - 2\ln 2 - 7}{2\ln 2 + 3}\right)$

15. $M_x = \int_1^2 \frac{1}{2}\left[(1 + \ln x)^2 - (1 - \ln x)^2\right] dx = \frac{1}{2}\int_1^2 4\ln x\, dx \overset{\text{parts}}{=} 2(x\ln x - x)\big|_1^2 = 4\ln 2 - 2$

$M_y = \int_1^2 x[(1 + \ln x) - (1 - \ln x)]\, dx = \int_1^2 2x\ln x\, dx \overset{\text{parts}}{=} x^2 \ln x\big|_1^2 - \int_1^2 x\, dx$

$= 4\ln 2 - \frac{1}{2}x^2\Big|_1^2 = 4\ln 2 - \frac{3}{2}$

$A = \int_1^2 [(1 + \ln x) - (1 - \ln x)]\, dx = \int_1^2 2\ln x\, dx = (2x\ln x - 2x)\big|_1^2 = 4\ln 2 - 2$

$\bar{x} = \frac{M_y}{A} = \frac{4\ln 2 - \frac{3}{2}}{4\ln 2 - 2} = \frac{8\ln 2 - 3}{8\ln 2 - 4}$; $\bar{y} = \frac{M_x}{A} = \frac{4\ln 2 - 2}{4\ln 2 - 2} = 1$; $(\bar{x}, \bar{y}) = \left(\frac{8\ln 2 - 3}{8\ln 2 - 4}, 1\right)$

16. The graphs of f and g intersect for (x, y) such that $11 - x^2 = y = x^2 + 3$, which means that $2x^2 = 8$, and thus $x = -2$ or $x = 2$.

$$M_x = \int_{-2}^2 \frac{1}{2}\left[(11 - x^2)^2 - (x^2 + 3)^2\right] dx = \frac{1}{2}\int_{-2}^2 (112 - 28x^2)\, dx = \frac{1}{2}\left(112x - \frac{28}{3}x^3\right)\Big|_{-2}^2 = \frac{448}{3}$$

$$M_y = \int_{-2}^{2} x\left[(11-x^2)-(x^2+3)\right]dx = \int_{-2}^{2}(8x-2x^3)\,dx = \left(4x^2-\frac{1}{2}x^4\right)\Big|_{-2}^{2} = 0$$

$$A = \int_{-2}^{2}\left[(11-x^2)-(x^2+3)\right]dx = \int_{-2}^{2}(8-2x^2)\,dx = \left(8x-\frac{2}{3}x^3\right)\Big|_{-2}^{2} = \frac{64}{3}$$

$$\bar{x} = \frac{M_y}{A} = 0;\quad \bar{y} = \frac{M_x}{A} = \frac{448/3}{64/3} = 7;\quad (\bar{x},\bar{y}) = (0,7)$$

17. The graphs of f and g intersect for (x,y) such that $2-x^2 = y = |x|$, which means $2-x^2 = x$ for $x \ge 0$ and $2-x^2 = -x$ for $x<0$. Thus $x=-1$ or $x=1$.

$$M_x = \int_{-1}^{1}\frac{1}{2}\left[(2-x^2)^2-|x|^2\right]dx = \frac{1}{2}\int_{-1}^{1}(4-5x^2+x^4)\,dx = \frac{1}{2}\left(4x-\frac{5}{3}x^3+\frac{1}{5}x^5\right)\Big|_{-1}^{1} = \frac{38}{15}$$

$$M_y = \int_{-1}^{1} x\left[(2-x^2)-|x|\right]dx = \int_{-1}^{0}(2x+x^2-x^3)\,dx + \int_{0}^{1}(2x-x^2-x^3)\,dx$$

$$= \left(x^2+\frac{x^3}{3}-\frac{x^4}{4}\right)\Big|_{-1}^{0} + \left(x^2-\frac{x^3}{3}-\frac{x^4}{4}\right)\Big|_{0}^{1} = \frac{-5}{12}+\frac{5}{12} = 0$$

$$A = \int_{-1}^{1}(2-x^2-|x|)\,dx = \int_{-1}^{0}(2+x-x^2)\,dx + \int_{0}^{1}(2-x-x^2)\,dx$$

$$= \left(2x+\frac{x^2}{2}-\frac{x^3}{3}\right)\Big|_{-1}^{0} + \left(2x-\frac{x^2}{2}-\frac{x^3}{3}\right)\Big|_{0}^{1} = \frac{7}{6}+\frac{7}{6} = \frac{7}{3}$$

$$\bar{x} = \frac{M_y}{A} = 0;\quad \bar{y} = \frac{M_x}{A} = \frac{38/15}{7/3} = \frac{38}{35};\quad (\bar{x},\bar{y}) = \left(0,\frac{38}{35}\right)$$

18. The graphs intersect for (x,y) such that $(y^2+5)/2 = x = y+4$, so that $y^2-2y-3=0$, or $y=3$ or $y=-1$. Then $x=7$ or $x=3$. To use Definition 8.5 we let $f(x)=\sqrt{2x-5}$ for $\frac{5}{2}\le x\le 7$ and

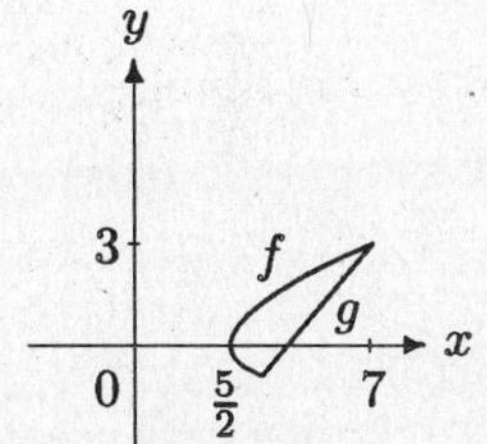

$$g(x) = \begin{cases} -\sqrt{2x-5} & \text{for } \frac{5}{2}\le x\le 3 \\ x-4 & \text{for } 3<x\le 7 \end{cases}$$

$$M_x = \int_{5/2}^{3}\frac{1}{2}\left[(\sqrt{2x-5})^2-(-\sqrt{2x-5})^2\right]dx + \frac{1}{2}\int_{3}^{7}\left[(\sqrt{2x-5})^2-(x-4)^2\right]dx$$

$$= \frac{1}{2}\int_{3}^{7}(-x^2+10x-21)\,dx = \frac{1}{2}\left(\frac{-1}{3}x^3+5x^2-21x\right)\Big|_{3}^{7} = \frac{16}{3}$$

$$M_y = \int_{5/2}^{3} x\left[\sqrt{2x-5}-(-\sqrt{2x-5})\right]dx + \int_{3}^{7} x\left[\sqrt{2x-5}-(x-4)\right]dx$$

$$= 2\int_{5/2}^{3} x\sqrt{2x-5}\,dx + \int_{3}^{7} x\sqrt{2x-5}\,dx - \int_{3}^{7}(x^2-4x)\,dx$$

$$\overset{u=2x-5}{=} \int_{0}^{1}\frac{1}{2}(u+5)u^{1/2}\,du + \frac{1}{4}\int_{1}^{9}(u+5)u^{1/2}\,du - \left(\frac{1}{3}x^3-2x^2\right)\Big|_{3}^{7}$$

$$= \frac{1}{2}\left(\frac{2}{5}u^{5/2} + \frac{10}{3}u^{3/2}\right)\Big|_0^1 + \frac{1}{4}\left(\frac{2}{5}u^{5/2} + \frac{10}{3}u^{3/2}\right)\Big|_1^9 - \frac{76}{3} = \frac{11}{5}$$

$$A = \int_{-1}^{3}\left[(y+4) - \frac{1}{2}(y^2+5)\right] dy = \int_{-1}^{3}\left(y - \frac{1}{2}y^2 + \frac{3}{2}\right) dy = \left(\frac{1}{2}y^2 - \frac{1}{6}y^3 + \frac{3}{2}y\right)\Big|_{-1}^{3} = \frac{16}{3}$$

$$\bar{x} = \frac{M_y}{A} = \frac{112/5}{16/3} = \frac{21}{5}; \quad \bar{y} = \frac{M_x}{A} = \frac{16/3}{16/3} = 1; \quad (\bar{x},\bar{y}) = \left(\frac{21}{5}, 1\right)$$

19. The graphs of the lines $y = x + 2$, $y = -3x + 6$, and $y = (2 - x)/3$ intersect in pairs for (x, y) such that $x + 2 = -3x + 6$, $x + 2 = (2 - x)/3$ or $-3x + 6 = (2 - x)/3$. From these equations we obtain $x = 1$, $x = -1$, and $x = 2$, respectively. To use Definition 8.5 we let

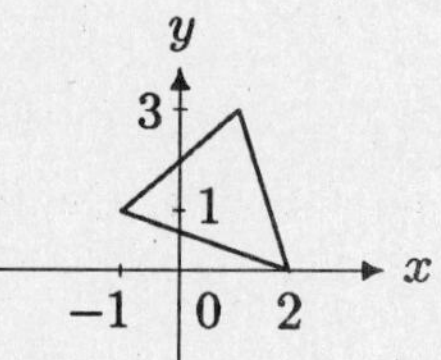

$$f(x) = \begin{cases} x + 2 & \text{for } -1 \le x \le 1 \\ -3x + 6 & \text{for } 1 \le x \le 2 \end{cases}$$

and $g(x) = (2 - x)/3$ for $-1 \le x \le 2$.

$$M_x = \int_{-1}^{1} \frac{1}{2}\left[(x+2)^2 - \left(\frac{2-x}{3}\right)^2\right] dx + \frac{1}{2}\int_1^2 \left[(-3x+6)^2 - \left(\frac{2-x}{3}\right)^2\right] dx$$

$$= \frac{4}{9}\int_{-1}^{1}(x^2 + 5x + 4)\, dx + \frac{49}{9}\int_1^2 (x^2 - 4x + 4)\, dx$$

$$= \frac{4}{9}\left(\frac{1}{3}x^3 + \frac{5}{2}x^2 + 4x\right)\Big|_{-1}^{1} + \frac{40}{9}\left(\frac{1}{3}x^3 - 2x^2 + 4x\right)\Big|_1^2 = \frac{104}{27} + \frac{40}{27} = \frac{16}{3}$$

$$M_y = \int_{-1}^{1} x\left[(x+2) - \left(\frac{2-x}{3}\right)\right] dx + \int_1^2 x\left[(-3x+6) - \left(\frac{2-x}{3}\right)\right] dx$$

$$= \frac{4}{3}\int_{-1}^{1}(x^2 + x)\, dx + \frac{8}{3}\int_1^2(-x^2 + 2x)\, dx = \frac{4}{3}\left(\frac{1}{3}x^3 + \frac{1}{2}x^2\right)\Big|_{-1}^{1} + \frac{8}{3}\left(\frac{-1}{3}x^3 + x^2\right)\Big|_1^2 = \frac{8}{9} + \frac{16}{9} = \frac{8}{3}$$

$$A = \int_{-1}^{1}\left[(x+2) - \left(\frac{2-x}{3}\right)\right] dx + \int_1^2 \left[(-3x+6) - \left(\frac{2-x}{3}\right)\right] dx$$

$$= \frac{4}{3}\int_{-1}^{1}(x+1)\, dx + \frac{8}{3}\int_1^2(-x+2)\, dx = \frac{4}{3}\left(\frac{1}{2}x^2 + x\right)\Big|_{-1}^{1} + \frac{8}{3}\left(\frac{-1}{2}x^2 + 2x\right)\Big|_1^2 = \frac{8}{3} + \frac{4}{3} = 4$$

$$\bar{x} = \frac{M_y}{A} = \frac{8/3}{4} = \frac{2}{3}; \quad \bar{y} = \frac{M_x}{A} = \frac{16/3}{4} = \frac{4}{3}; \quad (\bar{x},\bar{y}) = \left(\frac{2}{3}, \frac{4}{3}\right)$$

20. $(\bar{x},\bar{y}) = (\frac{1}{2}, \frac{3}{2})$

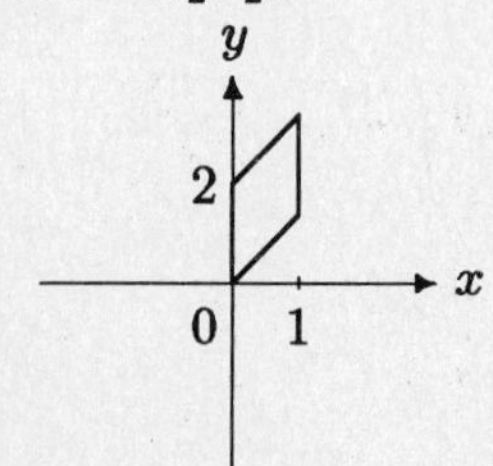

21. $(\bar{x},\bar{y}) = (0, 3)$

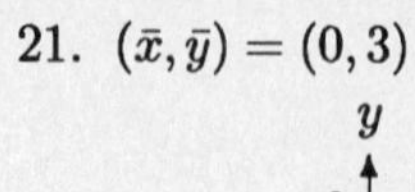

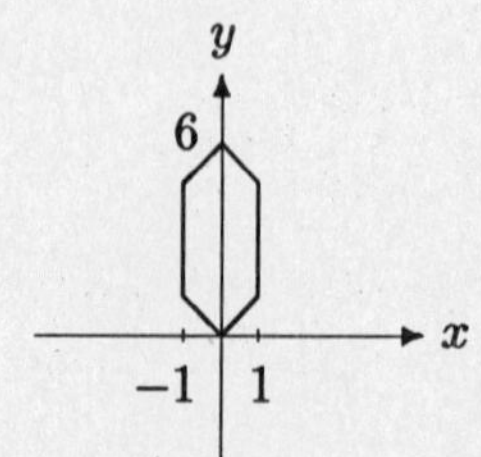

22. $(\bar{x},\bar{y}) = (3, -1)$

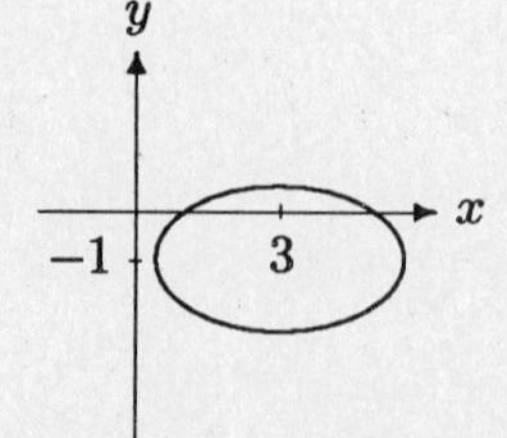

23. $(\bar{x}, \bar{y}) = (0, 0)$

24. $(\bar{x}, \bar{y}) = (0, 0)$

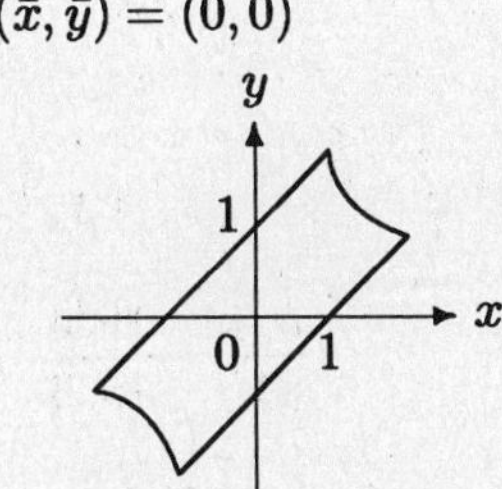

25. The triangle is symmetric with respect to the y axis, so $\bar{x} = 0$. Let

$$f(x) = \begin{cases} h + \dfrac{2h}{b}x & \text{for } \dfrac{-b}{2} \le x \le 0 \\[2mm] h - \dfrac{2h}{b}x & \text{for } 0 \le x \le \dfrac{b}{2} \end{cases}$$

Then

$$M_x = \int_{-b/2}^{0} \frac{1}{2}\left(h + \frac{2h}{b}x\right)^2 dx + \int_{0}^{b/2} \frac{1}{2}\left(h - \frac{2h}{b}x\right)^2 dx$$

$$= \frac{1}{2}\left(\frac{b}{2h}\right)\left(\frac{1}{3}\right)\left(h + \frac{2h}{b}x\right)^3\Bigg|_{-b/2}^{0} + \frac{1}{2}\left(\frac{-b}{2h}\right)\left(\frac{1}{3}\right)\left(h - \frac{2h}{b}x\right)^3\Bigg|_{0}^{b/2} = \frac{bh^2}{6}$$

$$A = \frac{bh}{2}; \quad \bar{y} = \frac{bh^2/6}{bh/2} = \frac{h}{3};$$

$(\bar{x}, \bar{y}) = (0, h/3)$, which is the "centroid" of the triangle.

26. The figure is symmetric with respect to the y axis, so $\bar{x} = 0$. Let $f(x) = h$ and $g(x) = (h/a^2)x^2$.

$$M_x = \int_{-a}^{a} \frac{1}{2}\left[h^2 - \left(\frac{h}{a^2}x^2\right)^2\right] dx = \frac{h^2}{2}\int_{-a}^{a}\left(1 - \frac{x^4}{a^4}\right) dx = \frac{h^2}{2}\left(x - \frac{x^5}{5a^4}\right)\Bigg|_{-a}^{a} = \frac{4}{5}ah^2$$

$$A = \int_{-a}^{a}\left(h - \frac{h}{a^2}x^2\right) dx = h\left(x - \frac{x^3}{3a^2}\right)\Bigg|_{-a}^{a} = \frac{4ah}{3}$$

$$\bar{x} = 0, \quad \bar{y} = \frac{4ah^2/5}{4ah/3} = \frac{3h}{5}; \quad (\bar{x}, \bar{y}) = \left(0, \frac{3h}{5}\right)$$

27. Let $f(x) = (h/a^2)x^2$ and $g(x) = 0$.

$$M_x = \int_{0}^{a} \frac{1}{2}\left(\frac{h}{a^2}x^2\right)^2 dx = \frac{h^2}{2a^4}\left(\frac{1}{5}x^5\right)\Bigg|_{0}^{a} = \frac{ah^2}{10}; \quad M_y = \int_{0}^{a} x\left(\frac{h}{a^2}x^2\right) dx = \frac{hx^4}{4a^2}\Bigg|_{0}^{a} = \frac{a^2h}{4}$$

$$A = \int_{0}^{a} \frac{h}{a^2}x^2\, dx = \frac{hx^3}{3a^2}\Bigg|_{0}^{a} = \frac{ah}{3}; \quad \bar{x} = \frac{a^2h/4}{ah/3} = \frac{3a}{4}; \quad \bar{y} = \frac{ah^2/10}{ah/3} = \frac{3h}{10};$$

thus $(\bar{x}, \bar{y}) = \left(\dfrac{3a}{4}, \dfrac{3h}{10}\right)$.

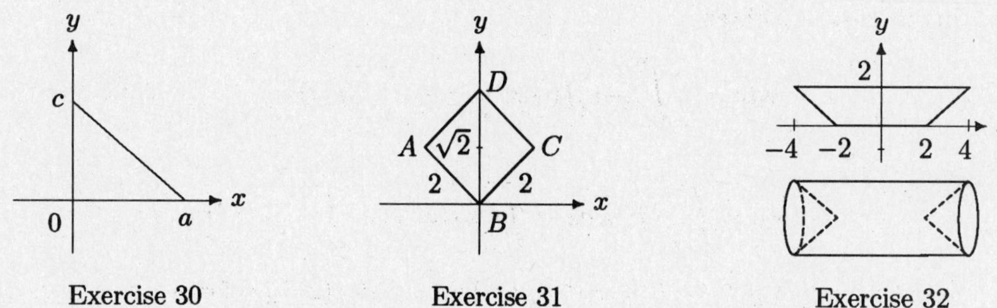

Exercise 30 Exercise 31 Exercise 32

28. The figure is symmetric with respect to the y axis, so $\bar{x} = 0$. Let $f(x) = \sqrt{1 - x^2}$ and $g(x) = -2$ for $-1 \le x \le 1$. Then

$$M_x = \int_{-1}^{1} \frac{1}{2}\left[(\sqrt{1 - x^2})^2 - (-2)^2\right] dx = \frac{1}{2}\int_{-1}^{1} (-x^2 - 3)\, dx = \frac{1}{2}\left(\frac{-1}{3}x^3 - 3x\right)\Big|_{-1}^{1} = \frac{-10}{3}$$

$$A = \frac{\pi}{2} + 4; \quad \bar{y} = \frac{-10/3}{\pi/2 + 4} = \frac{-20}{3(\pi + 8)};$$

thus $(\bar{x}, \bar{y}) = \left(0, \dfrac{-20}{3(\pi + 8)}\right)$.

29. The area A of the semicircular region and the volume V of the sphere generated by revolving the semicircular region R about its diameter are given, respectively, by $A = \frac{1}{2}\pi r^2$ and $V = \frac{4}{3}\pi r^3$. The Theorem of Pappus and Guldin then implies that $\frac{4}{3}\pi r^3 = 2\pi\bar{x}(\frac{1}{2}\pi r^2)$, so that $\bar{x} = 4r/3\pi$. Since $\bar{y} = 0$ by symmetry, the center of gravity of the semicircular region is $(4r/3\pi, 0)$.

30. Set up a coordinate system as in the figure, and revolve the triangle about the side of length c (that is, the y axis). The area A of the triangle is given by $A = \frac{1}{2}ac$, and the volume V of the resulting cone, whose radius is a and height is c, is given by $V = \frac{1}{3}\pi a^2 c$. The Theorem of Pappus and Guldin then yields $\frac{1}{3}\pi a^2 c = 2\pi\bar{x}(\frac{1}{2}ac)$, so that $\bar{x} = a/3$. Revolving the triangle about the x axis merely reverses the roles of a and c, and $\bar{x}$ and $\bar{y}$, so yields $\bar{y} = c/3$. Therefore the center of gravity of the triangle is $(a/3, c/3)$.

31. Set up a coordinate system as in the figure, so that the center of gravity of the square is $(0, \sqrt{2})$ and the square is revolved about the x axis. Since $\bar{y} = \sqrt{2}$ and since the area of the square is 4, the Theorem of Pappus and Guldin says that the volume V of the solid is $V = 2\pi\bar{y}(\text{area}) = 2\pi\sqrt{2}\,(4) = 8\pi\sqrt{2}$.

32. Set up a coordinate system as in the figure. Since the trapezoid is symmetric with respect to the y axis, the center of gravity $(\bar{x}, \bar{y})$ lies on the y axis, so that $\bar{x} = 0$. To find $\bar{y}$, we observe that the solid generated by revolving the trapezoid about the x axis consists of a circular cylinder with a cone removed at each end. Thus the volume V of the revolved trapezoid is the volume $\pi 2^2 \cdot 8$ of the cylinder minus twice the volume $\frac{1}{3}\pi 2^2 \cdot 2$ of either cone, so that $V = 32\pi - 2(\frac{8}{3}\pi) = 80\pi/3$. By the Theorem of Pappus and Guldin, $V = 2\pi\bar{y}A$, where A is the area of the trapezoid. Since $A = \frac{1}{2}(8 + 4)(2) = 12$, we have $80\pi/3 = 2\pi\bar{y}(12)$ so that $\bar{y} = \frac{10}{9}$. Thus the center of gravity lies on the y axis, $\frac{10}{9}$ units above the origin, that is, at the point $(0, \frac{10}{9})$.

33. Substituting $u = -x$, we obtain

$$\int_{-a}^{0} xf(x)\,dx = -\int_{a}^{0} (-u)f(-u)\,du = -\int_{0}^{a} uf(u)\,du = -\int_{0}^{a} xf(x)\,dx.$$

Thus

$$M_y = \int_{-a}^{a} xf(x)\,dx = \int_{-a}^{0} xf(x)\,dx + \int_{0}^{a} xf(x)\,dx = 0.$$

34. Since f is odd and $f(x) \geq 0$ for $0 \leq x \leq a$, we know that $f(x) \leq 0$ for $-a \leq x \leq 0$. Substituting $u = -x$, we obtain

$$\int_{-a}^{0} [f(x)]^2\,dx = -\int_{a}^{0} [f(-u)]^2\,du = \int_{0}^{a} [f(-u)]^2\,du = \int_{0}^{a} [-f(u)]^2\,du = \int_{0}^{a} [f(u)]^2\,du = \int_{0}^{a} [f(x)]^2\,dx$$

so that

$$M_x = \int_{-a}^{0} \left(\frac{1}{2}\right)(-[f(x)]^2)\,dx + \int_{0}^{a} \frac{1}{2}[f(x)]^2\,dx = \frac{-1}{2}\int_{0}^{a} [f(x)]^2\,dx + \frac{1}{2}\int_{0}^{a} [f(x)]^2\,dx = 0.$$

Thus $\bar{y} = 0$. Substituting $u = -x$ again, we obtain

$$\int_{-a}^{0} xf(x)\,dx = -\int_{a}^{0} (-u)f(-u)\,du = -\int_{0}^{a} uf(-u)\,du = \int_{0}^{a} uf(u)\,du = \int_{0}^{a} xf(x)\,dx$$

so that

$$M_y = \int_{-a}^{0} x[0 - f(x)]\,dx + \int_{0}^{a} xf(x)\,dx$$

$$= -\int_{-a}^{0} xf(x)\,dx + \int_{0}^{a} xf(x)\,dx = -\int_{0}^{a} xf(x)\,dx + \int_{0}^{a} xf(x)\,dx = 0.$$

Thus $\bar{x} = 0$. Consequently $(\bar{x}, \bar{y}) = (0, 0)$.

35. If l is any line tangent to the circle which has radius r, and if the area of R is A, then the Theorem of Pappus and Guldin says that the volume V of the solid of revolution is given by $V = (2\pi r)A$.

36. a. Let the centers of gravity of the left-hand triangle, right-hand triangle, and combined region be $(\bar{x}_1, \bar{y}_1)$, $(\bar{x}_2, \bar{y}_2)$, and $(\bar{x}, \bar{y})$, respectively. For the left-hand triangle, let $f(x) = x + 1$ for $-1 \leq x \leq 0$. Then

$$M_x = \int_{-1}^{0} \frac{1}{2}(x+1)^2\,dx = \frac{1}{6}(x+1)^3\Big|_{-1}^{0} = \frac{1}{6}$$

$$M_y = \int_{-1}^{0} x(x+1)\,dx = \left(\frac{x^3}{3} + \frac{x^2}{2}\right)\Big|_{-1}^{0} = \frac{-1}{6}$$

and $A = \frac{1}{2}$. Therefore

$$\bar{x}_1 = \frac{M_y}{A} = \frac{-1/6}{1/2} = \frac{-1}{3}, \quad \bar{y}_1 = \frac{M_x}{A} = \frac{1/6}{1/2} = \frac{1}{3}; \quad \text{thus } (\bar{x}_1, \bar{y}_1) = \left(\frac{-1}{3}, \frac{1}{3}\right).$$

For the right-hand triangle we obtain $\bar{x}_2 = -\frac{1}{3} + 1 = \frac{2}{3}$, $\bar{y}_2 = \frac{1}{3}$. Thus $(\bar{x}_2, \bar{y}_2) = (\frac{2}{3}, \frac{1}{3})$, and $\bar{x}(1) = (-\frac{1}{3})(\frac{1}{2}) + (\frac{2}{3})(\frac{1}{2}) = \frac{1}{6}$, $\bar{y}(1) = (\frac{1}{3})(\frac{1}{2}) + (\frac{1}{3})(\frac{1}{2}) = \frac{1}{3}$, so $(\bar{x}, \bar{y}) = (\frac{1}{6}, \frac{1}{3})$.

b. Let the center of gravity of the triangle be $(\bar{x}_1, \bar{y}_1)$, of the semicircle be $(\bar{x}_2, \bar{y}_2)$, and of the combined region be $(\bar{x}, \bar{y})$. By part (a), $(\bar{x}_1, \bar{y}_1) = (-\frac{1}{3}, \frac{1}{3})$. By reasoning as in Example 3, we find that the center of gravity of the semicircle is $(2/3\pi, \frac{1}{2})$. Thus

$$\bar{x}\left(\frac{1}{2}+\frac{\pi}{8}\right) = \left(\frac{-1}{3}\right)\left(\frac{1}{2}\right) + \left(\frac{2}{3\pi}\right)\left(\frac{\pi}{8}\right) = \frac{-1}{12}$$

$$\bar{y}\left(\frac{1}{2}+\frac{\pi}{8}\right) = \left(\frac{1}{3}\right)\left(\frac{1}{2}\right) + \left(\frac{1}{2}\right)\left(\frac{\pi}{8}\right) = \frac{1}{6}+\frac{\pi}{16}$$

so

$$(\bar{x}, \bar{y}) = \left(\frac{-2}{12+3\pi}, \frac{3\pi+8}{6\pi+24}\right).$$

c. From Example 3 and the similarity of the figures we obtain $(0, 4/3\pi)$ and $(\frac{1}{2}, 2/3\pi)$, respectively, for the centers of gravity of the larger and the smaller circles. If $(\bar{x}, \bar{y})$ is the center of gravity of the given region, then since the large circle is composed of the small circle and the given region, we have

$$\bar{x}\left(\frac{\pi}{2}-\frac{\pi}{8}\right) = 0\left(\frac{\pi}{2}\right) - \left(\frac{1}{2}\right)\left(\frac{\pi}{8}\right) = \frac{-\pi}{16}, \quad \bar{y}\left(\frac{\pi}{2}-\frac{\pi}{8}\right) = \left(\frac{4}{3\pi}\right)\left(\frac{\pi}{2}\right) - \left(\frac{2}{3\pi}\right)\left(\frac{\pi}{8}\right) = \frac{7}{12}$$

so that $(\bar{x}, \bar{y}) = (-1/6, 14/(9\pi))$.

d. If we divide the region into a left-hand and a right-hand region, then the respective centers of gravity are $(\frac{1}{2}, \frac{9}{2})$ and $(\frac{7}{2}, 1)$. Thus $\bar{x}(9+10) = \frac{1}{2}(9) + \frac{7}{2}(10) = \frac{79}{2}$, $\bar{y}(9+10) = \frac{9}{2}(9) + 1(10) = \frac{101}{2}$, so that $(\bar{x}, \bar{y}) = (\frac{79}{38}, \frac{101}{38})$.

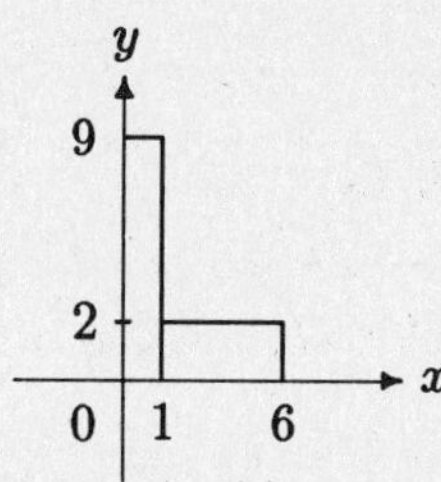

8.7 Hydrostatic Force

1. Following the solution of Example 1, but with $c=3$ instead of 4, we find that $F = \int_0^3 62.5(3-x)(\frac{1}{2}x)\,dx = 31.25\int_0^3 (3x - x^2)\,dx = 31.25\left(\frac{3}{2}x^2 - \frac{1}{3}x^3\right)\Big|_0^3 = (31.25)\frac{9}{2} = 140.625$ (pounds).

2. We place the origin at the bottom of the dam. Then for $0 \le x \le 100$ we have $w(x) = 1000$.

   a. $c = 100$; $F = \int_0^{100} 62.5(10 - x)1000\,dx = (62.5)\left(10^5 x - 500x^2\right)\Big|_0^{100} = (62.5)\left(10^7 - 5\cdot 10^6\right) = (62.5)(5)(10^6) = 3.125 \times 10^8$ (pounds).

   b. $c = 50$; $F = \int_0^{50} 62.5(50 - x)1000\,dx = (62.5)\left(5\cdot 10^4 x - 500x^2\right)\Big|_0^{50} = (62.5)\left(25\cdot 10^5 - 125\cdot 10^4\right) = (62.5)(125)(10^4) \approx 7.813 \times 10^7$ (pounds).

3. We take the origin at water level. Then $c=0$ and $w(x)/2=[x-(-1)]/\sqrt{3}$, so that $w(x)=[(2\sqrt{3})/3](x+1)$;

$$\begin{aligned} F &= \int_{-1}^{0} 62.5(0-x)\frac{2\sqrt{3}}{3}(x+1)\,dx \\ &= \frac{125\sqrt{3}}{3}\left(-\frac{1}{3}x^3-\frac{1}{2}x^2\right)\bigg|_{-1}^{0} \\ &= \frac{125\sqrt{3}}{18} \approx 12.0281 \text{ (pounds).} \end{aligned}$$

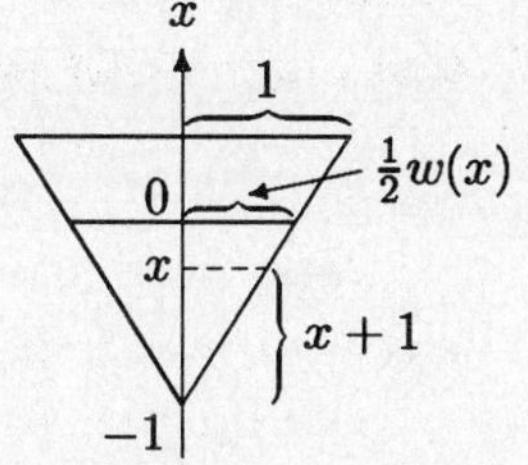

4. We take the origin at the center of the diameter at the top of the floodlight. Then $c = 0$, and $w(x) = 2\sqrt{1-x^2}$;

$$\begin{aligned} F &= \int_{-1}^{0} 62.5(0-x)(2\sqrt{1-x^2})\,dx \\ &= -62.5\int_{-1}^{0} 2x\sqrt{1-x^2}\,dx \\ &\overset{u=1-x^2}{=} 62.5\int_{0}^{1}\sqrt{u}\,du = 62.5\left(\frac{2}{3}u^{3/2}\right)\bigg|_{0}^{1} = \frac{125}{3} \text{ pounds).} \end{aligned}$$

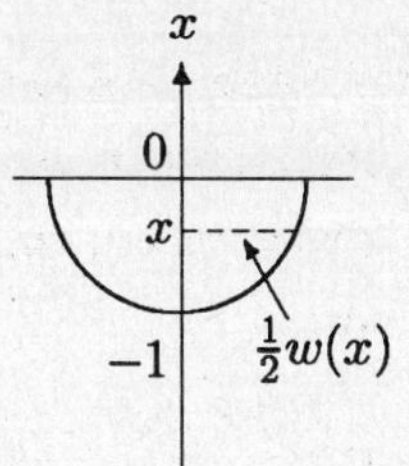

5. For the triangles pointing downward, $c = 0$ and $w(x)/2 = (x+3)/\sqrt{3}$, so that $w(x) = [(2\sqrt{3})/3](x+3)$;

$$\begin{aligned} F &= \int_{-3}^{-3+\sqrt{3}} 62.5(0-x)\frac{2\sqrt{3}}{3}(x+3)\,dx \\ &= \frac{125\sqrt{3}}{3}\left(-\frac{1}{3}x^3-\frac{3}{2}x^2\right)\bigg|_{-3}^{-3+\sqrt{3}} \\ &= \frac{125\sqrt{3}}{3}\left(\frac{9}{2}-\sqrt{3}\right) \approx 199.760 \text{ (pounds).} \end{aligned}$$

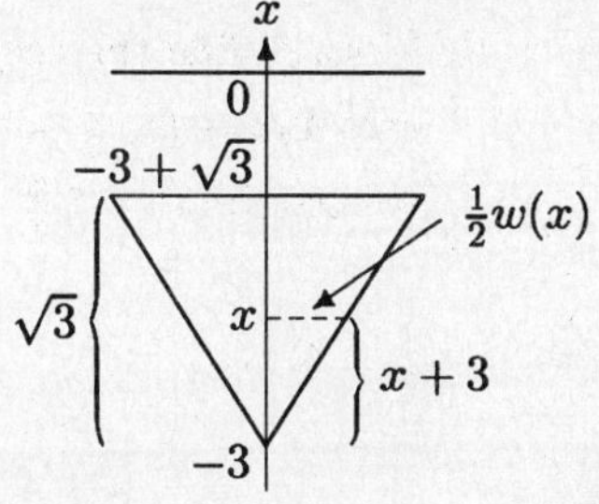

For the triangles pointing upward, $c = 0$ and

$$\frac{w(x)}{2} = \frac{-3+\sqrt{3}-x}{\sqrt{3}}, \quad \text{so that} \quad w(x) = \frac{2\sqrt{3}}{3}\left(-3+\sqrt{3}-x\right);$$

$$\begin{aligned} F &= \int_{-3}^{-3+\sqrt{3}} 62.5(0-x)\frac{2\sqrt{3}}{3}\left(-3+\sqrt{3}-x\right)dx \\ &= \frac{125\sqrt{3}}{3}\left[\frac{(3-\sqrt{3})}{2}x^2+\frac{1}{3}x^3\right]\bigg|_{-3}^{-3+\sqrt{3}} \\ &= \frac{125\sqrt{3}}{3}\left(\frac{9}{2}-\frac{\sqrt{3}}{2}\right) \approx 262.260 \text{ (pounds).} \end{aligned}$$

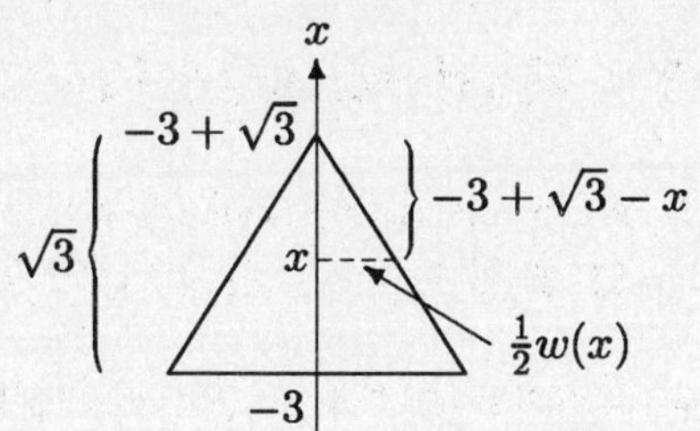

6. We place the x axis so that the origin is at water level. The hydrostatic force on the top of the block is $F = 62.5(5)(1) = 312.5$ (pounds). For each of the sides, we have $c = 0$ and $w(x) = 1$, so that $F = \int_{-6}^{-5} 62.5(0-x)1\,dx = 62.5\left(-\frac{1}{2}x^2\right)\big|_{-6}^{-5} = \frac{1}{2}(62.5)(11) = 343.75$ (pounds). The total hydrostatic force on the five sides is $F = 312.5 + 4(343.75) = 1687.5$ (pounds).

7. If the top of the block is x feet from the surface of the water, the hydrostatic force on the top is $F_t = 62.5(x)(1) = 62.5x$. The hydrostatic force on the bottom is $F_b = 62.5(x+1)(1) = 62.5(x+1)$. The difference between these forces is $F_b - F_t = 62.5(x+1) - 62.5x = 62.5$ (pounds).

8. a. By (2), $F = \int_a^b 62.5(c-x)w(x)\,dx$. Since $c-x$ represents the distance between the line $x=c$ and any point with x coordinate x, it follows from the ideas of Section 8.6 that the moment M about the line $x=c$ of the submerged portion R of the plate is given by $M = \int_a^b (c-x)w(x)\,dx$. But by the Theorem of Pappus and Guldin and the discussion preceding it, if V is the volume of the solid region obtained by revolving R about the line $x=c$ and if h is the distance from the center of gravity of R to the line $x=c$, then $2\pi hA = V = 2\pi M$, so that $hA = M = \int_a^b (c-x)w(x)\,dx$. Since h is by definition the depth of water at the center of gravity of R, it follows that $F = \int_a^b 62.5(c-x)w(x)\,dx = 62.5hA$.

   b. The area of the dam is $\pi 100^2/2$, and by Example 3 of Section 8.6, the center of gravity is $4(100)/3\pi$ feet below the water level. Thus by (a),

$$F = (62.5)\left(\frac{400}{3\pi}\right)\left(\frac{\pi 100^2}{2}\right) = \frac{125}{3} \times 10^6 \text{ (pounds)}.$$

9. The portion of the plate between x_{k-1} and x_k has area approximately equal to $w(t_k)(\Delta x_k \sec\theta)$. Thus the force on that portion of the plate is approximately equal to $(62.5)(c-t_k)(w(t_k)\sec\theta\,\Delta x_k)$. The hydrostatic force F on the plate is approximately equal to $\sum_{k=1}^n (62.5)(c-t_k)(\sec\theta\, w(t_k)\,\Delta x_k)$, which is a Riemann sum for $62.5(c-x)(\sec\theta)w$. It follows that the hydrostatic force is given by $\int_a^b (62.5\sec\theta)(c-x)w(x)\,dx$.

10. We place the x axis so that the origin is at the bottom of the dam. Then $c=50$, $a=0$, $b=50$, $\theta=\pi/3$, and $w(x)=1000$. Thus the result of Exercise 9 implies that $F = \int_0^{50} (62.5\sec(\pi/3))(50-x)1000\,dx = 125{,}000\left(50x - \frac{1}{2}x^2\right)\Big|_0^{50} \approx 1.563 \times 10^8$ (pounds).

11. a. We place the origin at the base of the smaller end of the pool. Then by (2) the hydrostatic force F is given by $F = \int_0^4 62.5(4-x)20\,dx = 1250\left(-\frac{1}{2}\right)(4-x)^2\Big|_0^4 = 10{,}000$ (pounds).

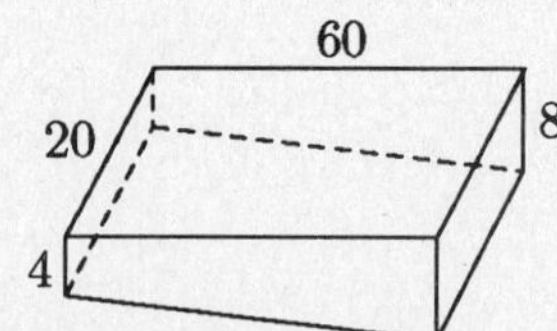

   b. We place the origin at the base of the larger end of the pool. Then by (2) the hydrostatic force F is given by $F = \int_0^8 62.5(8-x)20\,dx = 1250\left(-\frac{1}{2}\right)(8-x)^2\Big|_0^8 = 40{,}000$ (pounds).

   c. We place the origin at the base of the larger end of the pool. For $4 \le x \le 8$, the width $w(x)$ of each side at x is 60 and for $0 \le x \le 4$, the width $w(x)$ of each side at x is $15x$. Thus by (2) the hydrostatic force F on each side of the pool is given by $F = \int_0^8 62.5(8-x)w(x)\,dx = \int_0^4 62.5(8-x)15x\,dx + \int_4^8 62.5(8-x)60\,dx = 937.5\left(4x^2 - \frac{1}{3}x^3\right)\Big|_0^4 + 3750\left(-\frac{1}{2}\right)(8-x)^2\Big|_4^8 = 937.5\left(64 - \frac{64}{3}\right) + 1875(4^2 - 0^2) = 70{,}000$ (pounds).

   d. We place the origin at the base of the larger end of the pool. By Exercise 9 with $\sec\theta = \frac{1}{4}\sqrt{60^2+4^2} = \sqrt{226}$, the hydrostatic force F is given by $F = \int_0^4 62.5\sqrt{226}\,(8-x)20\,dx = 1250\sqrt{226}\left(-\frac{1}{2}\right)(8-x)^2\Big|_0^4 = 625\sqrt{226}\,(8^2 - 4^2) = 30{,}000\sqrt{226} \approx 451{,}000$ (pounds).

12. Let us place the origin at the center of the bottom of the tank, with the x axis pointing upward. Let $P = \{x_0, x_1, \ldots, x_n\}$ be any partition of $[0, 30]$. For each k between 1 and n, let t_k be an arbitrary number in the subinterval $[x_{k-1}, x_k]$. Then the area of the portion S_k of the surface of the tank between x_{k-1} and x_k is $40\pi\Delta x_k$. The pressure at any point on S_k is approximately $(62.5)(30 - t_k)$, and thus the hydrostatic force on S_k is approximately $(62.5)(30 - t_k)(40\pi\Delta x_k)$. The total force F on the sides of the tank is approximately $\sum_{k=1}^{n}(62.5)(30 - t_k)(40\pi\Delta x_k)$, which is a Riemann sum for $(62.5)(30 - x)(40\pi)$. Thus

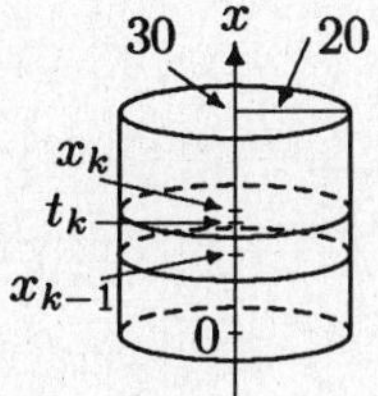

$$F = 62.5\int_0^{30} 40\pi(30 - x)\,dx \overset{u=30-x}{=} 62.5\int_{30}^{0} 40\pi u(-1)\,dx = 62.5\int_0^{30} 40\pi x\,dx.$$

13. Since the diameter is 3 (rather than 40 as in Exercise 12) and the height is 100 (rather than 30 as in Exercise 11), we have $F = 62.5\int_0^{100} 3\pi x\,dx = (62.5)\frac{3}{2}\pi x^2\Big|_0^{100} = 937{,}500\pi \approx 2{,}945{,}000$ (pounds).

Chapter 8 Review

1. Since $1 + \sqrt{x} \ge 1 \ge e^{-x}$ for $0 \le x \le 1$,

$$V = \int_0^1 \pi\left[(1+\sqrt{x})^2 - (e^{-x})^2\right]dx = \pi\int_0^1 \left(1 + 2\sqrt{x} + x - e^{-2x}\right)dx$$

$$= \pi\left(x + \frac{4}{3}x^{3/2} + \frac{1}{2}x^2 + \frac{1}{2}e^{-2x}\right)\Bigg|_0^1 = \pi\left(\frac{7}{3} + \frac{1}{2}e^{-2}\right).$$

2. Since $\sec^2 x \ge 1 \ge \cos x$ for $-\pi/6 \le x \le \pi/4$, and since $\sec^4 x = \sec^2 x \sec^2 x = \sec^2 x\,(1 + \tan^2 x)$, it follows that

$$V = \int_{-\pi/6}^{\pi/4} \pi[(\sec^2 x)^2 - (\cos x)^2]\,dx = \pi\int_{-\pi/6}^{\pi/4} (\sec^4 x - \cos^2 x)\,dx$$

$$= \pi\int_{-\pi/6}^{\pi/4} \sec^2 x\,(1 + \tan^2 x)\,dx - \pi\int_{-\pi/6}^{\pi/4}\left(\frac{1}{2} + \frac{1}{2}\cos 2x\right)dx$$

$$= \pi\left(\tan x + \frac{1}{3}\tan^3 x\right)\Bigg|_{-\pi/6}^{\pi/4} - \pi\left(\frac{1}{2}x + \frac{1}{4}\sin 2x\right)\Bigg|_{-\pi/6}^{\pi/4}$$

$$= \pi\left[1 + \frac{1}{3} + \frac{1}{3}\sqrt{3} + \frac{1}{3}\left(\frac{1}{3}\sqrt{3}\right)^3\right] - \pi\left(\frac{\pi}{8} + \frac{1}{4} + \frac{\pi}{12} + \frac{1}{8}\sqrt{3}\right) = \pi\left(\frac{13}{12} - \frac{5\pi}{24} + \frac{53}{216}\sqrt{3}\right).$$

3. Since $e^{x^2} \ge 1 \ge e^{-x^2}$ for $0 \le x \le 1$,

$$V = \int_0^1 2\pi x(e^{x^2} - e^{-x^2})\,dx \overset{u=x^2}{=} 2\pi\int_0^1 (e^u - e^{-u})\frac{1}{2}\,du = \pi(e^u - e^{-u})\Big|_0^1 = \pi(e + e^{-1} - 2).$$

4. Since $\sqrt{1+x} \geq 1 \geq \dfrac{\ln x}{x^2}$ for $1 \leq x \leq 3$,

$$V = \int_1^3 2\pi x \left(\sqrt{1+x} - \frac{\ln x}{x^2}\right) dx = 2\pi \left[\int_1^3 x\sqrt{1+x}\, dx - \int_1^3 \frac{\ln x}{x}\, dx\right]$$

$$\overset{u=1+x}{\underset{v=\ln x}{=}} 2\pi \left[\int_2^4 (u-1)\sqrt{u}\, du - \int_0^{\ln 3} v\, dv\right] = 2\pi \left[\left(\frac{2}{5}u^{5/2} - \frac{2}{3}u^{3/2}\right)\Big|_2^4 - \frac{1}{2}v^2\Big|_0^{\ln 3}\right]$$

$$= 2\pi \left\{\left[\left(\frac{2}{5}\cdot 32 - \frac{2}{3}\cdot 8\right) - \left(\frac{8}{5}\sqrt{2} - \frac{4}{3}\sqrt{2}\right)\right] - \frac{1}{2}(\ln 3)^2\right\} = 2\pi \left[\frac{112}{15} - \frac{4}{15}\sqrt{2} - \frac{1}{2}(\ln 3)^2\right].$$

5. a. $V = \displaystyle\int_0^2 2\pi x(x^3)\, dx = \frac{2}{5}\pi x^5\Big|_0^2 = \frac{64}{5}\pi$

b. $M_x = \displaystyle\int_0^2 \frac{1}{2}(x^3)^2\, dx = \frac{1}{14}x^7\Big|_0^2 = \frac{64}{7}$; $M_y = \displaystyle\int_0^2 x(x^3)\, dx = \frac{1}{5}x^5\Big|_0^2 = \frac{32}{5}$

$A = \displaystyle\int_0^2 x^3\, dx = \frac{1}{4}x^4\Big|_0^2 = 4$

$\bar{x} = \dfrac{32/5}{4} = \dfrac{8}{5}$; $\bar{y} = \dfrac{64/7}{4} = \dfrac{16}{7}$; $(\bar{x}, \bar{y}) = \left(\dfrac{8}{5}, \dfrac{16}{7}\right)$

c. $A = 4$, $b = \dfrac{8}{5}$; $V = (2\pi)\left(\dfrac{8}{5}\right)(4) = \dfrac{64}{5}\pi$

6. a. $V_A = \displaystyle\int_0^2 \pi(x^2)^2\, dx = \frac{1}{5}\pi x^5\Big|_0^2 = \frac{32}{5}\pi$

$V_B = \displaystyle\int_0^2 \pi\left[4^2 - (x^2)^2\right] dx = \pi\int_0^2 (16 - x^4)\, dx$

$= \pi\left(16x - \dfrac{1}{5}x^5\right)\Big|_0^2 = \dfrac{128}{5}\pi$

$V_B = 4V_A$

b. $V_A = \displaystyle\int_0^2 2\pi x(x^2)\, dx = \frac{\pi}{2}x^4\Big|_0^2 = 8\pi$

$V_B = \displaystyle\int_0^2 2\pi x(4 - x^2)\, dx = 2\pi\left(2x^2 - \frac{1}{4}x^4\right)\Big|_0^2 = 8\pi$

$V_A = V_B$

7. a. $V_1 = \displaystyle\int_1^3 2\pi x\left[\left(x + \frac{c}{x}\right) - x\right] dx = \int_1^3 2\pi c\, dx = 4\pi c$

b. $V_2 = \displaystyle\int_1^3 \pi\left[\left(x + \frac{c}{x}\right)^2 - x^2\right] dx = \pi\int_1^3 \left(2c + \frac{c^2}{x^2}\right) dx = \pi\left(2cx - \frac{c^2}{x}\right)\Big|_1^3$

$= \pi\left[\left(6c - \dfrac{c^2}{3}\right) - (2c - c^2)\right] = 4\pi c + \dfrac{2}{3}\pi c^2$

c. $4\pi c + \frac{2}{3}\pi c^2 = V_2 = V_1 = 4\pi c$ only if $c = 0$.

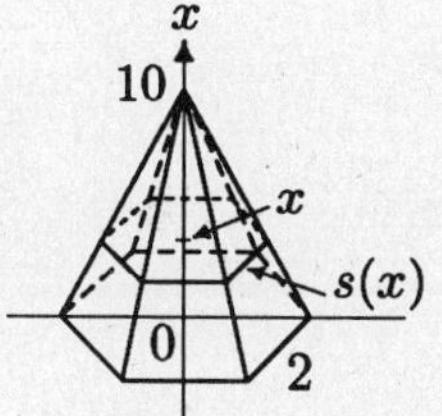

Exercise 9

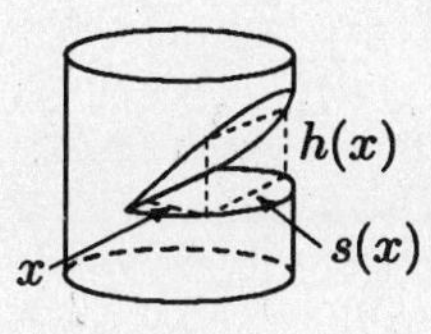

Exercise 10

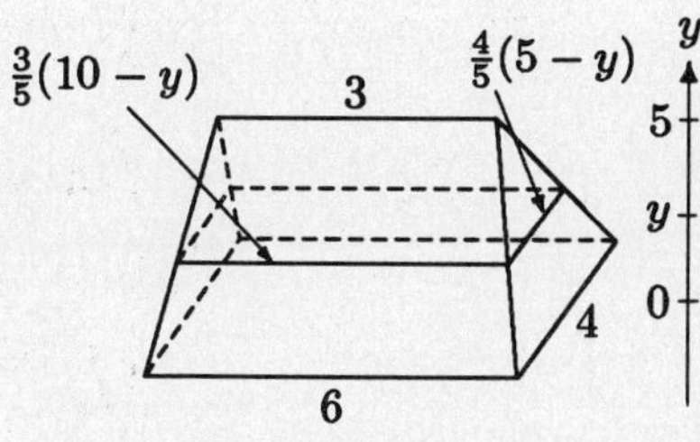

Exercise 11

8. Let $f(x)=\sqrt{r^2-x^2}$ and $g(x)=\sqrt{r^2-\frac{1}{64}}$. Then

$$V=\pi\int_{-1/8}^{1/8}\left[(\sqrt{r^2-x^2})^2-\left(\sqrt{r^2-\frac{1}{64}}\right)^2\right]dx=\pi\int_{-1/8}^{1/8}\left(\frac{1}{64}-x^2\right)dx$$

$$=\pi\left(\frac{1}{64}x-\frac{1}{3}x^3\right)\Big|_{-1/8}^{1/8}=\frac{1}{384}\pi \text{ (cubic inches).}$$

9. Let a hexagonal cross-section x feet from the base have a side $s(x)$ feet long. Then $s(x)/2=(10-x)/10$, so that $s(x)=\frac{1}{5}(10-x)$. The area is $A(x)=6(\sqrt{3}/4)(s(x))^2=[(3\sqrt{3})/50](10-x)^2$. Thus the volume is given by

$$V=\int_0^{10}\frac{3\sqrt{3}}{50}(10-x)^2\,dx=\frac{3\sqrt{3}}{50}\left(\frac{-1}{3}\right)(10-x)^3\Big|_0^{10}=20\sqrt{3}\text{ (cubic feet).}$$

10. Let a rectangular cross-section perpendicular to the first cut be x units from the center and have length $s(x)$ and height $h(x)$. Then $h(x)=x\tan\theta$ and $s(x)=2\sqrt{a^2-x^2}$. The area of the cross-section is $A(x)=(x\tan\theta)(2\sqrt{a^2-x^2})$ and the volume is given by $V=\int_0^a(x\tan\theta)(2\sqrt{a^2-x^2})\,dx=\tan\theta\int_0^a 2x\sqrt{a^2-x^2}\,dx=\tan\theta\left(\frac{-2}{3}\right)(a^2-x^2)^{3/2}\big|_0^a=\frac{2}{3}(\tan\theta)a^3$.

11. We place the origin of the y axis at the base of the solid. As shown in the figure, the cross section at y has length $\frac{3}{5}(10-y)$ and width $\frac{4}{5}(5-y)$. Thus the cross-sectional area at y is given by $A(y)=\frac{3}{5}(10-y)\frac{4}{5}(5-y)=\frac{12}{25}(50-15y+y^2)$. By (2) of Section 8.1, the volume is given by $V=\int_0^5 A(y)\,dy=\int_0^5\frac{12}{25}(50-15y+y^2)\,dy=\frac{12}{25}\left(50y-\frac{15}{2}y^2+\frac{1}{3}y^3\right)\big|_0^5=\frac{12}{25}\left(250-\frac{375}{2}+\frac{125}{3}\right)=50$.

12. $$L=\int_{\pi/6}^{5\pi/6}\sqrt{1+\left(\frac{\cos x}{\sin x}\right)^2}\,dx=\int_{\pi/6}^{5\pi/6}\sqrt{1+\cot^2 x}\,dx=\int_{\pi/6}^{5\pi/6}\csc x\,dx$$

$$=-\ln|\csc x+\cot x|\big|_{\pi/6}^{5\pi/6}=\ln(2+\sqrt{3})-\ln(2-\sqrt{3})=2\ln(2+\sqrt{3})=\ln(7+4\sqrt{3})$$

13. $$L=\int_0^1\sqrt{1+\left(e^x-\frac{1}{4}e^{-x}\right)^2}\,dx=\int_0^1\sqrt{e^{2x}+\frac{1}{2}+\frac{1}{16}e^{-2x}}\,dx=\int_0^1\sqrt{\left(e^x+\frac{1}{4}e^{-x}\right)^2}\,dx$$

$$=\int_0^1\left(e^x+\frac{1}{4}e^{-x}\right)dx=\left(e^x-\frac{1}{4}e^{-x}\right)\Big|_0^1=\left(e-\frac{1}{4}e^{-1}\right)-\left(1-\frac{1}{4}\right)=e-\frac{1}{4}e^{-1}-\frac{3}{4}$$

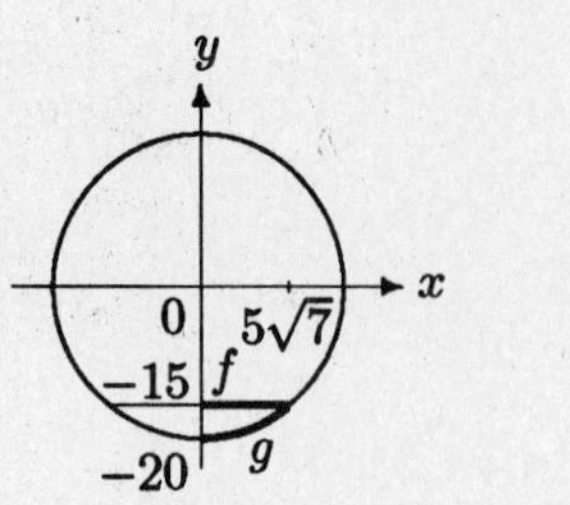

Exercise 17

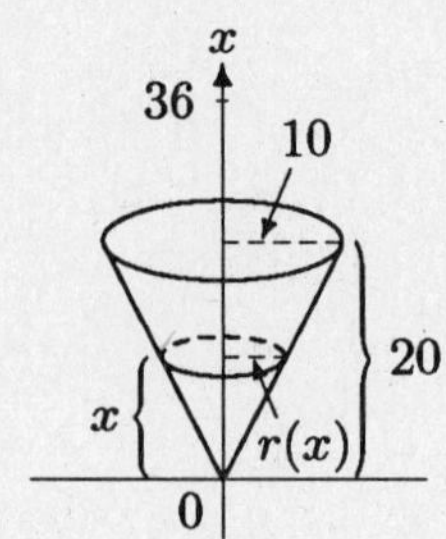

Exercise 20

14. By Simpson's Rule with $n = 10$, $L = \int_1^2 \sqrt{1 + (\frac{1}{2}x^{-1/2})^2}\,dx = \int_1^2 \sqrt{1 + 1/(4x)}\,dx \approx 1.083064587$.

15. $$S = \int_0^1 2\pi \left(e^x + \frac{1}{4}e^{-x}\right)\sqrt{1+\left(e^x - \frac{1}{4}e^{-x}\right)^2}\,dx = 2\pi \int_0^1 \left(e^x + \frac{1}{4}e^{-x}\right)\sqrt{1+\left(e^{2x} - \frac{1}{2} + \frac{1}{16}e^{-2x}\right)}\,dx$$
$$= 2\pi \int_0^1 \left(e^x + \frac{1}{4}e^{-x}\right)\sqrt{e^{2x} + \frac{1}{2} + \frac{1}{16}e^{-2x}}\,dx = 2\pi \int_0^1 \left(e^x + \frac{1}{4}e^{-x}\right)\left(e^x + \frac{1}{4}e^{-x}\right)dx$$
$$= 2\pi \int_0^1 \left(e^{2x} + \frac{1}{2} + \frac{1}{16}e^{-2x}\right)dx = 2\pi \left(\frac{1}{2}e^{2x} + \frac{1}{2}x - \frac{1}{32}e^{-2x}\right)\Big|_0^1 = \pi\left(e^2 - \frac{1}{16}e^{-2} + \frac{1}{16}\right)$$

16. $$S = \int_0^{\pi/2} 2\pi \cos x \sqrt{1 + (-\sin x)^2}\,dx = 2\pi \int_0^{\pi/2} \cos x \sqrt{1 + \sin^2 x}\,dx$$
$$\overset{u=\sin x}{=} 2\pi \int_0^1 \sqrt{1+u^2}\,du \overset{u=\tan v}{=} 2\pi \int_0^{\pi/4} \sqrt{1+\tan^2 v}\,\sec^2 v\,dv = 2\pi \int_0^{\pi/4} \sec^3 v\,dv$$
so by (7) of Section 7.2,
$$S = 2\pi\left(\frac{1}{2}\sec v\,\tan v + \frac{1}{2}\ln|\sec v + \tan v|\right)\Big|_0^{\pi/4} = \pi\left[(\sqrt{2} + \ln(\sqrt{2}+1)) - 0\right] = \pi\left(\sqrt{2} + \ln(\sqrt{2}+1)\right).$$

17. Let $f(x) = -15$, $g(x) = -\sqrt{400 - x^2}$ for $0 \le x \le 5\sqrt{7}$. Then
$$V = \int_0^{5\sqrt{7}} 2\pi x\left[-15 - (-\sqrt{400 - x^2})\right]dx = 2\pi\left[\frac{-15}{2}x^2 - \frac{1}{3}(400 - x^2)^{3/2}\right]\Big|_0^{5\sqrt{7}} = \frac{1375\pi}{3} \text{ (cubic feet).}$$

18. We have $4 = \int_0^{1/2} kx\,dx = (k/2)x^2\big|_0^{1/2} = k/8$, so that $k = 32$. Thus $W = \int_1^{3/2} 32x\,dx = 16x^2\big|_0^{3/2} = 20$ (foot-pounds).

19. $l = 0$, $A(x) = 9\pi$; $W = \int_0^{20} (150)9\pi x\,dx = 675\pi x^2\big|_0^{20} = 270{,}000\pi$ (foot-pounds)

20. If the tank is placed with respect to the axes as in the figure, then $l = 36$, and the radius $r(x)$ of a cross-section x feet from the bottom satisfies $r(x)/10 = x/20$, or $r(x) = \frac{1}{2}x$, so that the cross-sectional area is given by $A(x) = \pi(\frac{1}{2}x)^2 = (\pi/4)x^2$. Next we find the original height of water in the tank. If

r is the corresponding radius, then $h/20 = r/10$, so $h = 2r$. Since originally the tank has 144π cubic feet of water, it follows that $144\pi = \frac{1}{3}\pi r^2 h = \frac{2}{3}\pi r^3$, so $r^3 = 216$, or $r = 6$. Thus $h = 12$, so that

$$W = \int_0^{12} 62.5(36 - x)\frac{\pi}{4}x^2\,dx = 15.625\pi \int_0^{12} (36x^2 - x^3)\,dx$$

$$= 15.625\pi \left(12x^3 - \frac{1}{4}x^4\right)\Big|_0^{12} = (15.625\pi)(12^3 \cdot 9) = 243{,}000\pi \text{ (foot-pounds)}.$$

21. a. If the tank is positioned as in the figure, with the origin in the center of the tank, then $l = 11$, and at a distance x from the center of the tank, the width $w(x)$ of a rectangular cross-section is given by $w(x) = 2\sqrt{25 - x^2}$. Thus the cross-sectional area is given by $A(x) = 40\sqrt{25 - x^2}$. Therefore

$$W = \int_{-5}^{5} 42(11 - x)(40\sqrt{25 - x^2})\,dx = 18{,}480 \int_{-5}^{5} \sqrt{25 - x^2}\,dx - 1680 \int_{-5}^{5} x\sqrt{25 - x^2}\,dx$$

$$\overset{x = 5\sin u}{=} 462{,}000 \int_{-\pi/2}^{\pi/2} \cos^2 u\,du + 1680 \left[-\frac{1}{3}(25 - x^2)^{3/2}\right]\Bigg|_{-5}^{5}$$

$$= 462{,}000 \int_{-\pi/2}^{\pi/2} \left(\frac{1}{2} + \frac{1}{2}\cos 2u\right) du + 0$$

$$= 462{,}000 \left(\frac{1}{2}u + \frac{1}{4}\sin 2u\right)\Big|_{-\pi/2}^{\pi/2}$$

$$= 231{,}000\pi \text{ (foot-pounds)}.$$

b. The figure is the same, except that there are hemispheres at each end of the tank. At a distance x from the center of the tank, the radius $r(x)$ of each hemisphere is given by $r(x) = \sqrt{25 - x^2}$, so the total cross-sectional area is given by $A(x) = \pi(25 - x^2) + 40\sqrt{25 - x^2}$. Using the calculations of part (a), we find that

$$W = \int_{-5}^{5} 42(11 - x)\left[\pi(25 - x^2) + 40\sqrt{25 - x^2}\right] dx$$

$$= 42\pi \int_{-5}^{5} (275 - 25x - 11x^2 + x^3)\,dx$$

$$+42 \int_{-5}^{5} (11 - x)(40\sqrt{25 - x^2})\,dx$$

$$= 42\pi \left(275x - \frac{25}{2}x^2 - \frac{11}{3}x^3 + \frac{1}{4}x^4\right)\Big|_{-5}^{5} + 231{,}000\pi$$

$$= 77{,}000\pi + 231{,}000\pi = 308{,}000\pi \text{ (foot-pounds)}.$$

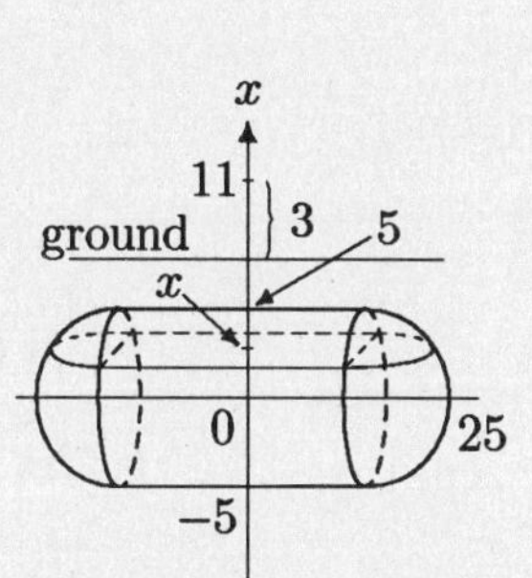

22. a. Since $V = xA$, we have $F = pA = p(V/x) = c/x$.

b. $W = \int_1^2 \frac{c}{x}\,dx = c\ln|x|\Big|_1^2 = c\ln 2$

23. $M_x = \int_0^2 \frac{1}{2}[(1+2x-x^2)^2 - (x^2-2x+1)^2]\,dx = \int_0^2 (4x-2x^2)\,dx = \left(2x^2 - \frac{2}{3}x^3\right)\Big|_0^2 = \frac{8}{3}$

$M_y = \int_0^2 x[(1+2x-x^2)-(x^2-2x+1)]\,dx = \int_0^2 (4x^2-2x^3)\,dx = \left(\frac{4}{3}x^3 - \frac{1}{2}x^4\right)\Big|_0^2 = \frac{32}{3} - 8 = \frac{8}{3}$

$A = \int_0^2 [(1+2x-x^2)-(x^2-2x+1)]\,dx = \int_0^2 (4x-2x^2)\,dx = \left(2x^2 - \frac{2}{3}x^3\right)\Big|_0^2 = \frac{8}{3}$

$\bar{x} = \frac{M_y}{A} = \frac{8/3}{8/3} = 1;\ \bar{y} = \frac{M_x}{A} = \frac{8/3}{8/3} = 1;\ (\bar{x},\bar{y}) = (1,1)$

24. The graphs of f and g intersect for (x,y) such that $x = y = x^2$, which means that $x = 0$ or $x = 1$.

$$M_x = \int_0^1 \frac{1}{2}[x^2 - (x^2)^2]\,dx = \frac{1}{2}\left(\frac{1}{3}x^3 - \frac{1}{5}x^5\right)\Big|_0^1 = \frac{1}{15}$$

$$M_y = \int_0^1 x(x-x^2)\,dx = \left(\frac{1}{3}x^3 - \frac{1}{4}x^4\right)\Big|_0^1 = \frac{1}{12}$$

$$A = \int_0^1 (x-x^2)\,dx = \left(\frac{1}{2}x^2 - \frac{1}{3}x^3\right)\Big|_0^1 = \frac{1}{6}$$

$$\bar{x} = \frac{1/12}{1/6} = \frac{1}{2};\quad \bar{y} = \frac{1/15}{1/6} = \frac{2}{5};\quad (\bar{x},\bar{y}) = \left(\frac{1}{2},\frac{2}{5}\right)$$

25. By the hint, the graphs of $y^2 = 3x$ and $y = x^2 - 2x$ intersect for (x,y) such that $x = 0$ or $x = 3$. To use Definition 8.5 we let $f(x) = \sqrt{3x}$ and $g(x) = x^2 - 2x$ for $0 \le x \le 3$. Then

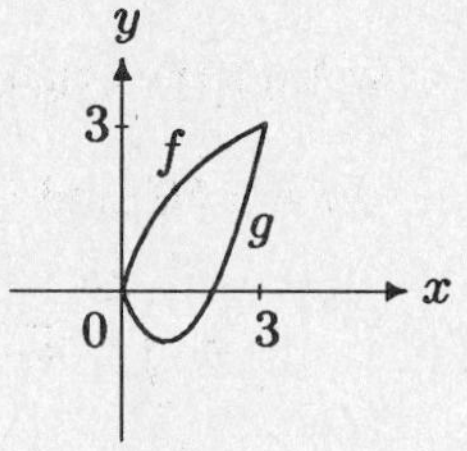

$$M_x = \int_0^3 \frac{1}{2}\left[(\sqrt{3x})^2 - (x^2-2x)^2\right]dx = \frac{1}{2}\int_0^3 (3x - x^4 + 4x^3 - 4x^2)\,dx$$

$$= \frac{1}{2}\left(\frac{3}{2}x^2 - \frac{1}{5}x^5 + x^4 - \frac{4}{3}x^3\right)\Big|_0^3 = \frac{99}{20}$$

$$M_y = \int_0^3 x\left[\sqrt{3x} - (x^2-2x)\right]dx = \int_0^3 \left(\sqrt{3}\,x^{3/2} - x^3 + 2x^2\right)dx$$

$$= \left(\frac{2}{5}\sqrt{3}\,x^{5/2} - \frac{1}{4}x^4 + \frac{2}{3}x^3\right)\Big|_0^3 = \frac{171}{20}$$

$$A = \int_0^3 \left[\sqrt{3x} - (x^2-2x)\right]dx = \left(\frac{2}{3}\sqrt{3}\,x^{3/2} - \frac{1}{3}x^3 + x^2\right)\Big|_0^3 = 6$$

$$\bar{x} = \frac{171/20}{6} = \frac{171}{120} = \frac{57}{40};\quad \bar{y} = \frac{99/20}{6} = \frac{33}{40};\quad (\bar{x},\bar{y}) = \left(\frac{57}{40},\frac{33}{40}\right)$$

26. a. $M_x = \int_1^3 \frac{1}{2}\left[\left(x+\frac{c}{x}\right)^2 - x^2\right]dx = \frac{1}{2}\int_1^3 \left(2c + \frac{c^2}{x^2}\right)dx = \frac{1}{2}\left(2cx - \frac{c^2}{x}\right)\Big|_1^3$

$= \frac{1}{2}\left[\left(6c - \frac{c^2}{3}\right) - (2c - c^2)\right] = 2c + \frac{1}{3}c^2$

$M_y = \int_1^3 x\left[\left(x+\frac{c}{x}\right) - x\right]dx = \int_1^3 c\,dx = 2c$

$$A = \int_1^3 \left[\left(x + \frac{c}{x}\right) - x\right] dx = \int_1^3 \frac{c}{x}\, dx = c \ln x \Big|_1^3 = c \ln 3$$

$$\bar{x} = \frac{M_y}{A} = \frac{2c}{c \ln 3} = \frac{2}{\ln 3}; \; \bar{y} = \frac{M_x}{A} = \frac{2c + c^2/3}{c \ln 3} = \frac{6 + c}{3 \ln 3}$$

Thus the center of gravity is $\left(\dfrac{2}{\ln 3}, \dfrac{6+c}{3\ln 3}\right)$.

b. Using the Theorem of Pappus and Guldin, we find that the volume V_1 of the solid obtained by revolving R about the y axis is given by

$$V_1 = 2\pi \bar{x} A = 2\pi \left(\frac{2}{\ln 3}\right)(c \ln 3) = 4\pi c.$$

Similarly, the volume V_2 of the solid obtained by revolving R about the x axis is given by

$$V_2 = 2\pi \bar{y} A = 2\pi \left(\frac{6+c}{3 \ln 3}\right)(c \ln 3) = 4\pi c + \frac{2}{3}\pi c^2.$$

27. The center of gravity of R is $(1, 1)$ by symmetry. The graphs intersect for (x, y) such that $2-(x-1)^2 = y = (x-1)^2$, or $2 = 2(x-1)^2$, so $x = 0$ or 2. Therefore the area between the graphs is given by $A = \int_0^2 \{[2-(x-1)^2] - (x-1)^2\}\, dx = \int_0^2 [2 - 2(x-1)^2]\, dx = \left[2x - \frac{2}{3}(x-1)^3\right]\Big|_0^2 = \left(4 - \frac{2}{3}\right) - \frac{2}{3} = \frac{8}{3}$. For the volume V_1 of the region obtained by revolving R about the x axis, we have $V_1 = 2\pi \bar{y} A$ by the Theorem of Pappus and Guldin. Since $\bar{y} = 1$, $V_1 = 2\pi(1)\frac{8}{3} = \frac{16}{3}\pi$. For the volume V_2 of the region obtained by revolving R about the y axis, we have $V_2 = 2\pi \bar{x} A$ by the Theorem of Pappus and Guldin. Since $\bar{x} = 1$, $V_2 = 2\pi(1)\frac{8}{3} = \frac{16}{3}\pi$. Thus $V_1 = V_2$.

28. We take the origin at the bottom of the dam.

a. $c = 50$, and from the figure, we see that $\left[\frac{1}{2}w(x) - 50\right]/50 = x/100$, so $w(x) = x + 100$;

$$F = \int_0^{50} 62.5(50 - x)(x + 100)\, dx$$

$$= 62.5 \int_0^{50} (5000 - 50x - x^2)\, dx$$

$$= 62.5 \left(5000x - 25x^2 - \frac{1}{3}x^3\right)\Big|_0^{50} = \frac{27{,}343{,}750}{3} \text{ (pounds).}$$

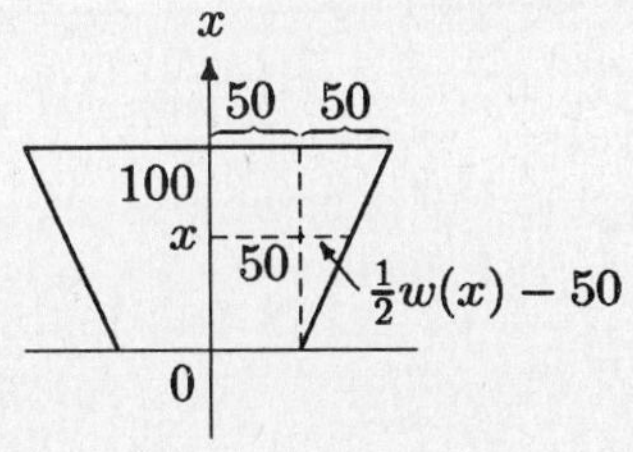

b. $c = 100$, and as in part (a), $w(x) = x + 100$;

$$F = \int_0^{100} 62.5(100 - x)(x + 100)\, dx = 62.5 \int_0^{100} (10{,}000 - x^2)\, dx$$

$$= 62.5 \left(10{,}000x - \frac{1}{3}x^3\right)\Big|_0^{100} = \frac{125{,}000{,}000}{3} \text{ (pounds).}$$

29. a. The force F on the bottom that is due to the olive oil is given by

$$F = (57.3)(\text{depth of barrel})(\text{area of bottom}) = (57.3)(3)[\pi(1)^2] = 171.9\pi \text{ (pounds).}$$

b. We take the origin to be at the center of the end of the barrel, so $c = 1$. Then $w(x) = 2\sqrt{1-x^2}$, so that

$$F = \int_{-1}^{1} (57.3)(1-x)[2\sqrt{1-x^2}]\,dx$$

$$= 114.6\int_{-1}^{1} \sqrt{1-x^2}\,dx - 114.6\int_{-1}^{1} x\sqrt{1-x^2}\,dx.$$

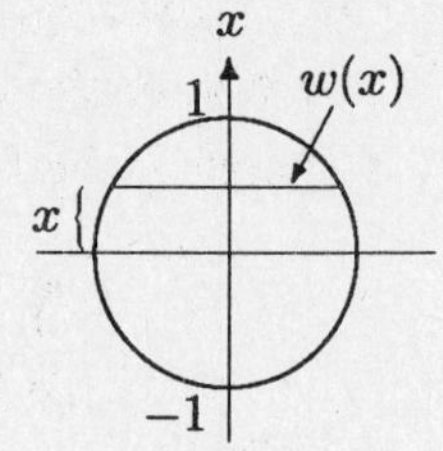

Now $\int_{-1}^{1} \sqrt{1-x^2}\,dx$ = area of semicircle of radius $1 = \pi/2$. Since $x\sqrt{1-x^2}$ is an odd function on $[-1,1]$, $\int_{-1}^{1} x\sqrt{1-x^2}\,dx = 0$. Thus $F = 114.6(\pi/2) + 0 = 57.3\pi$ (pounds).

30. a. By the Chain Rule,

$$F = \frac{d}{dt}(mv) = \left[\frac{d}{dx}(mv)\right]\frac{dx}{dt} = v\,\frac{d}{dx}(mv).$$

b. Since $mv = \dfrac{m_0 v}{\sqrt{1-v^2/c^2}} = \dfrac{m_0 cv}{\sqrt{c^2-v^2}}$, it follows that

$$\frac{d}{dv}(mv) = \frac{m_0 c\sqrt{c^2-v^2} - m_0 cv\dfrac{-v}{\sqrt{c^2-v^2}}}{c^2-v^2} = \frac{m_0 c(c^2-v^2) + m_0 cv^2}{(c^2-v^2)^{3/2}}$$

$$= \frac{m_0 c^3}{(c^2-v^2)^{3/2}} = \frac{m_0}{(1-v^2/c^2)^{3/2}}.$$

c. $$W = \int_{x_0}^{x_1} F(x)\,dx \overset{(a)}{=} \int_{x_0}^{x_1} \left[v\frac{d}{dx}(mv)\right]dx = \int_{x_0}^{x_1} v\left[\frac{d}{dv}(mv)\frac{dv}{dx}\right]dx$$

$$\overset{v=v(x)}{=} \int_{v_0}^{v_1} \left[v\frac{d}{dv}(mv)\right]dv \overset{(b)}{=} \int_{v_0}^{v_1} \frac{m_0 v}{(1-v^2/c^2)^{3/2}}\,dv$$

d. Since

$$\int \frac{m_0 v}{(1-v^2/c^2)^{3/2}}\,dx \overset{u=1-v^2/c^2}{=} \int \frac{m_0(-c^2/2)}{u^{3/2}}\,du = \frac{m_0 c^2}{u^{1/2}} + C = \frac{m_0 c^2}{(1-v^2/c^2)^{1/2}} + C,$$

we conclude that

$$\int_{v_0}^{v_1} \frac{m_0 v}{(1-v^2/c^2)^{3/2}}\,dv = \left.\frac{m_0 c^2}{(1-v^2/c^2)^{1/2}}\right|_{v_0}^{v_1} = \frac{m_0 c^2}{\sqrt{1-v_1^2/c^2}} - \frac{m_0 c^2}{\sqrt{1-v_0^2/c^2}}.$$

31. a. By (3) in Section 8.1 with y replacing x, we have $V = \int_0^h \pi[f(y)]^2\,dy$, so

$$\frac{dV}{dt} = \frac{dV}{dh}\frac{dh}{dt} = \pi[f(h)]^2\frac{dh}{dt}.$$

b. Using the result of part (a), the equation $dV/dt = cA\sqrt{h}$, and the assumption that $dh/dt = k$, we find that $cA\sqrt{h} = dV/dt = \pi[f(h)]^2(dh/dt) = \pi[f(h)]^2 k$. Solving for $f(h)$, we find that

$$f(h) = \left(\frac{cA\sqrt{h}}{\pi k}\right)^{1/2} = \sqrt{\frac{cA}{\pi k}}\,h^{1/4} \quad \text{for } 0 \le h \le b.$$

32. Consider a partition $P = \{x_0, \ldots, x_n\}$ of the interval $[0, L]$. For any k with $1 \le k \le n$, the mass in the subinterval $[x_{k-1}, x_k]$ is $(M/L)\Delta x_k$, since the bar is uniform. Thus the force ΔF_k on that portion of the rod is approximately $[Gm/(x_k + r)^2]((M/L)\Delta x_k)$. Therefore the force F on the whole bar should be approximately

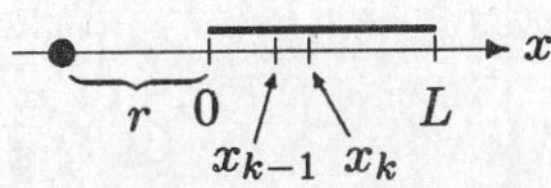

$$\sum_{k=1}^{n} \frac{Gm}{(x_k + r)^2}\left(\frac{M}{L}\Delta x_k\right), \quad \text{which is a Riemann sum for} \quad \int_0^L \frac{GmM}{L(x+r)^2}\,dx.$$

Now

$$\int_0^L \frac{GmM}{L(x+r)^2}\,dx = -\frac{GmM}{L(x+r)}\bigg|_0^L = \frac{GmM}{L}\left(\frac{1}{r} - \frac{1}{r+L}\right) = \frac{GmM}{L}\left(\frac{r+L-r}{r(r+L)}\right) = \frac{GmM}{r(r+L)}.$$

33. Consider the partition $P = \{r_0, \ldots, r_n\}$ of the interval $[0, R]$. For any k with $1 \le k \le n$, the volume ΔV_k of the spherical shell each of whose points lies at a distance r from the center of the star, where $r_{k-1} \le r \le r_k$, is approximately $\frac{4}{3}\pi r_k^3 - \frac{4}{3}\pi r_{k-1}^3 = \frac{4}{3}\pi(r_k^2 + r_k r_{k-1} + r_{k-1}^2)\Delta r_k$. Thus the mass M_k of the shell is approximately $D(r_k)\Delta V_k$. Therefore the mass M of the star is approximately

$$\sum_{k=1}^{n} D(r_k)\Delta V_k = \sum_{k=1}^{n} D(r_k)\left[\frac{4}{3}\pi(r_k^2 + r_k r_{k-1} + r_{k-1}^2)\right]\Delta r_k$$

which is not a Riemann sum, but which approximates the Riemann sum $\sum_{k=1}^{n} D(r_k)\left[\frac{4}{3}\pi(3r_k^2)\right]\Delta r_k$ of $\int_0^R 4\pi r^2 D(r)\,dr$. Consequently $M = \int_0^R 4\pi r^2 D(r)\,dr$.

Cumulative Review(Chapters 1–7)

1. The conditions for applying l'Hôpital's Rule three times are met;

$$\lim_{x\to 0} \frac{\sin x - \sin(\sin x)}{x^3} = \lim_{x\to 0} \frac{\cos x - \cos(\sin x)\cos x}{3x^2} = \lim_{x\to 0} \cos x \lim_{x\to 0} \frac{1 - \cos(\sin x)}{3x^2}$$

$$= \lim_{x\to 0} \frac{1 - \cos(\sin x)}{3x^2} = \lim_{x\to 0} \frac{\sin(\sin x)\cos x}{6x} = \lim_{x\to 0} \frac{\sin(\sin x)}{6x} \lim_{x\to 0} \cos x$$

$$= \lim_{x\to 0} \frac{\sin(\sin x)}{6x} = \lim_{x\to 0} \frac{\cos(\sin x)\cos x}{6}.$$

Let $y = \sin x$, so that y approaches 0 as x approaches 0. Then

$$\lim_{x\to 0} \frac{\cos(\sin x)\cos x}{6} = \lim_{x\to 0} \cos(\sin x) \lim_{x\to 0} \frac{\cos x}{6} = \lim_{y\to 0} \cos y \lim_{x\to 0} \frac{\cos x}{6} = 1 \cdot \frac{1}{6} = \frac{1}{6}.$$

Thus the given limit equals $\frac{1}{6}$.

2. $\lim_{x\to\infty}(1 - 3/x)^x = \lim_{x\to\infty} e^{x\ln(1-3/x)} = e^{\lim_{x\to\infty} x\ln(1-3/x)}$

The conditions for applying l'Hôpital's Rule are met:

$$\lim_{x\to\infty} x\ln\left(1 - \frac{3}{x}\right) = \lim_{x\to\infty} \frac{\ln(1 - 3/x)}{1/x} = \lim_{x\to\infty} \frac{\dfrac{1}{1-3/x}\left(\dfrac{3}{x^2}\right)}{-1/x^2} = \lim_{x\to\infty} \frac{-3}{1 - 3/x} = -3.$$

Thus $\lim_{x\to\infty}(1 - 3/x)^x = e^{-3}$.

3. $\sqrt{cx+1}-\sqrt{x}=\left(\sqrt{cx+1}-\sqrt{x}\right)\dfrac{\left(\sqrt{cx+1}+\sqrt{x}\right)}{\sqrt{cx+1}+\sqrt{x}}=\dfrac{(c-1)x+1}{\sqrt{cx+1}+\sqrt{x}}$

so that if $c=1$, then

$$\lim_{x\to\infty}\left(\sqrt{cx+1}-\sqrt{x}\right)=\lim_{x\to\infty}\frac{1}{\sqrt{x+1}+\sqrt{x}}=0.$$

If $0\le c<1$, then

$$\lim_{x\to\infty}\left(\sqrt{cx+1}-\sqrt{x}\right)=\lim_{x\to\infty}\frac{(c-1)x+1}{\sqrt{cx+1}+\sqrt{x}}=-\infty$$

and if $c>1$, then

$$\lim_{x\to\infty}\left(\sqrt{cx+1}-\sqrt{x}\right)=\lim_{x\to\infty}\frac{(c-1)x+1}{\sqrt{cx+1}+\sqrt{x}}=\infty.$$

Finally, if $c<0$, then $\sqrt{cx+1}$ is not defined for $x>1/|c|$, so $\lim_{x\to\infty}\left(\sqrt{cx+1}-\sqrt{x}\right)$ is meaningless. Thus $\lim_{x\to\infty}\left(\sqrt{cx+1}-\sqrt{x}\right)$ exists only for $c=1$.

4. $f'(x)=\dfrac{1}{2\sqrt{\dfrac{x+1}{3x-2}}}\dfrac{(1)(3x-2)-(x+1)(3)}{(3x-2)^2}=\dfrac{-5}{2(3x-2)^{3/2}(x+1)^{1/2}}$

5. $f'(x)=\dfrac{2e^{2x}(e^x+1)-e^{2x}e^x}{(e^x+1)^2}=\dfrac{e^{3x}+2e^{2x}}{(e^x+1)^2}$

6. $f'(x)=\dfrac{1}{(1-x)^2};\ f''(x)=\dfrac{2}{(1-x)^3};\ f^{(3)}(x)=\dfrac{6}{(1-x)^4};\ f^{(4)}(x)=\dfrac{24}{(1-x)^5};\ f^{(5)}(x)=\dfrac{120}{(1-x)^6}$

7. Differentiating the equation $a^2-a=2v^2-6v$ implicitly, we have

$$2a\frac{da}{dt}-\frac{da}{dt}=4v\frac{dv}{dt}-6\frac{dv}{dt},\quad\text{so that}\quad(2a-1)\frac{da}{dt}=(4v-6)\frac{dv}{dt}.$$

At the instant at which $da/dt=6(dv/dt)$, this becomes

$$(2a-1)6\frac{dv}{dt}=(4v-6)\frac{dv}{dt}.$$

Since $dv/dt=a>0$ by hypothesis, it follows that $(2a-1)6=4v-6$, so that $v=3a$.

8. Let x be the distance and θ the angle shown in the figure. Then $x=10\cot\theta$. Since the difference in the speeds of the cars is 10 feet per second, we have

$$10=\frac{dx}{dt}=-10(\csc^2\theta)\frac{d\theta}{dt}.$$

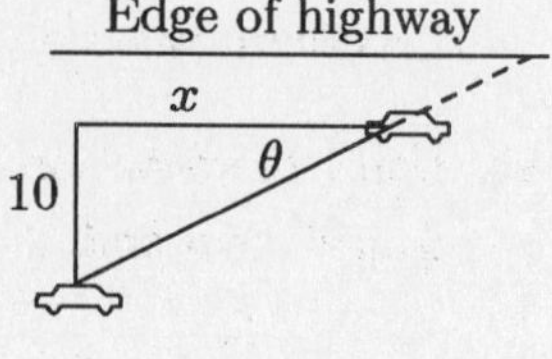

When $\theta=\pi/3$, this becomes $10=-10(\frac{2}{3}\sqrt{3})^2(d\theta/dt)=-\frac{40}{3}(d\theta/dt)$, so that $d\theta/dt=-\frac{3}{4}$. Thus θ is changing at the rate of $\frac{3}{4}$ radian per second when $\theta=\pi/3$.

9. $A(x)=\int_0^x(e^t-1)\,dt=(e^t-t)\big|_0^x=e^x-x-1$. Thus finding the value of $x>0$ for which $A(x)=1$ is equivalent to solving the equation $e^x-x-1=1$, or $e^x-x-2=0$. To that end we let $f(x)=e^x-x-2$, so that $f'(x)=e^x-1$, and apply the Newton-Raphson method with initial value of c equal to 1. By computer we obtain 1.146193221 as the desired approximate zero of f, and hence the approximate value of x for which $A(x)=1$.

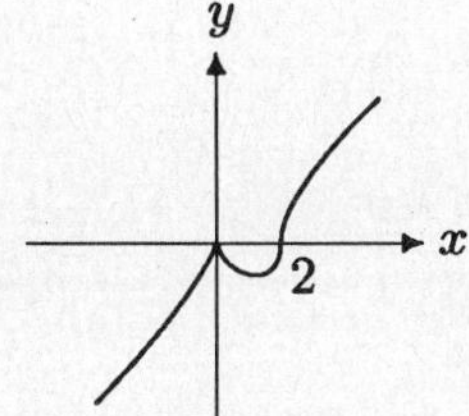

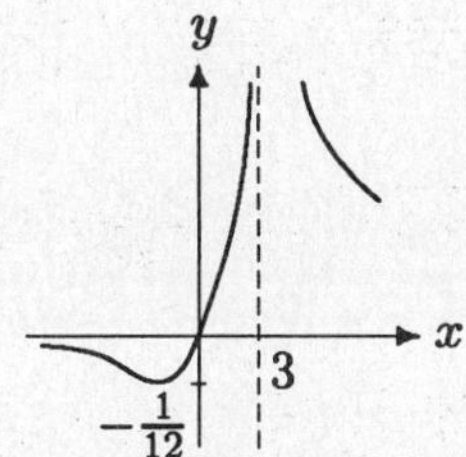

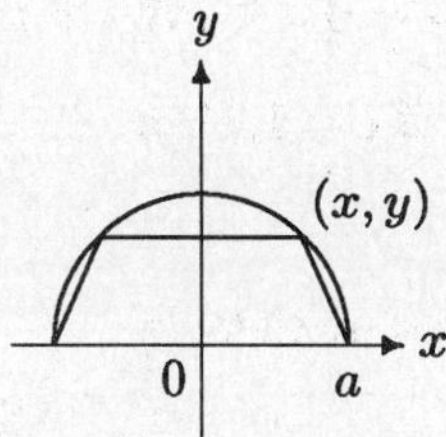

Exercise 10 Exercise 11 Exercise 12

10. $f'(x) = \frac{2}{3}x^{-1/3}(x-2)^{1/3} + \frac{1}{3}x^{2/3}(x-2)^{-2/3} = x^{-1/3}(x-2)^{-2/3}(x-\frac{4}{3})$;

$f''(x) = -\frac{2}{9}x^{-4/3}(x-2)^{1/3} + \frac{2}{9}x^{-1/3}(x-2)^{-2/3} + \frac{2}{9}x^{-1/3}(x-2)^{-2/3} - \frac{2}{9}x^{2/3}(x-2)^{-5/3}$;

$= -\frac{8}{9}x^{-4/3}(x-2)^{-5/3}$

relative maximum value is $f(0) = 0$; relative minimum value is $f(\frac{4}{3}) = (\frac{4}{3})^{2/3}(-\frac{2}{3})^{1/3} = (-\frac{2}{3})2^{2/3} \approx -1.06$; increasing on $(-\infty, 0]$ and $[\frac{4}{3}, \infty)$, and decreasing on $[0, \frac{4}{3}]$; concave upward on $(-\infty, 0)$ and $(0, 2)$, and concave downward on $(2, \infty)$; inflection point is $(2, 0)$.

11. $f'(x) = \dfrac{(1)(x-3)^2 - 2x(x-3)}{(x-3)^4} = -\dfrac{x+3}{(x-3)^3}$; $f''(x) = -\dfrac{(1)(x-3)^3 - 3(x+3)(x-3)^2}{(x-3)^6} = \dfrac{2(x+6)}{(x-3)^4}$;

relative minimum value is $f(-3) = -\frac{1}{12}$; increasing on $[-3, 3)$ and decreasing on $(-\infty, -3]$ and $(3, \infty)$; concave upward on $(-6, 3)$ and $(3, \infty)$, and concave downward on $(-\infty, -6)$; inflection point is $(-6, -\frac{2}{27})$; vertical asymptote is $x = 3$; horizontal asymptote is $y = 0$.

12. Set up a coordinate system as in the figure. Using the notation in the figure, we find that the area is given by $A = y((2x + 2a)/2) = y(x + a)$. We are to maximize A. Notice that (x, y) is on the circle, so that $y = \sqrt{a^2 - x^2}$. Thus $A = (x + a)\sqrt{a^2 - x^2}$. Therefore

$$A'(x) = \sqrt{a^2 - x^2} + (x + a)\left(\frac{-2x}{2\sqrt{a^2 - x^2}}\right) = \frac{a^2 - ax - 2x^2}{\sqrt{a^2 - x^2}}.$$

Since $A'(x) = 0$ for $x = a/2$, and since $A'(x) > 0$ on $(0, a/2)$ and $A'(x) < 0$ on $(a/2, a)$, it follows from (1) of Section 4.6 and the First Derivative Test that $A(a/2) = (a/2 + a)\sqrt{a^2 - (a/2)^2} = \frac{3}{4}\sqrt{3}\,a^2$ is the maximum value of A. Thus the maximum area of such a trapezoid is $\frac{3}{4}\sqrt{3}\,a^2$.

13. Using the notation in the figure, we find that the area A and circumference C are given by $A = \frac{1}{2}xy = \frac{1}{2}\sin\theta\cos\theta$ and $C = 1 + x + y = 1 + \sin\theta + \cos\theta$. Thus the ratio R is given by

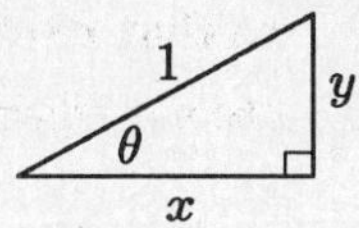

$$R = \frac{C}{A} = \frac{1 + \sin\theta + \cos\theta}{\frac{1}{2}\sin\theta\cos\theta} = 2(\csc\theta\sec\theta + \sec\theta + \csc\theta) \quad \text{for } 0 < \theta < \frac{\pi}{2}.$$

We are to minimize R. Notice that

$$R'(\theta) = 2(-\csc\theta\cot\theta\sec\theta + \csc\theta\sec\theta\tan\theta + \sec\theta\tan\theta - \csc\theta\cot\theta)$$

$$= 2\left(\frac{-1}{\sin^2\theta} + \frac{1}{\cos^2\theta} + \frac{\sin\theta}{\cos^2\theta} - \frac{\cos\theta}{\sin^2\theta}\right) = \frac{2(-\cos^2\theta + \sin^2\theta + \sin^3\theta - \cos^2\theta)}{\sin^2\theta\cos^2\theta}$$

$$= \frac{2(\sin^2\theta + \sin^3\theta - \cos^2\theta - \cos^3\theta)}{\sin^2\theta\cos^2\theta}.$$

If $\theta = \pi/4$, then $R'(\theta) = 0$ since $\sin(\pi/4) = \cos(\pi/4)$. Moreover, since $\sin\theta < \cos\theta$ on $(0, \pi/4)$ and $\sin\theta > \cos\theta$ on $(\pi/4, \pi/2)$, it follows that $R'(\theta) < 0$ for $0 < \theta < \pi/4$ and $R'(\theta) > 0$ for $\pi/4 < \theta < \pi/2$. Consequently (1) of Section 4.6 and the First Derivative Test imply that the ratio R is minimum for $\theta = \pi/4$, that is, when the right triangle is isosceles.

14. Let $f(t)$ be the amount of the radioactive substance present at time t, so that $f(t) = f(0)e^{kt}$ for some k. Since the half-life is 24 hours by hypothesis, we have $\frac{1}{2}f(0) = f(24) = f(0)e^{24k}$, so that $\frac{1}{2} = e^{24k}$, and hence $24k = \ln\frac{1}{2} = -\ln 2$. Consequently $f(t) = f(0)e^{-(t/24)\ln 2}$. When 99% of the substance has disintegrated, we have $f(t) = 0.01f(0)$, so that $f(0)e^{-(t/24)\ln 2} = f(t) = 0.01f(0)$ and thus $e^{-(t/24)\ln 2} = 0.01$. It follows that $-(t/24)\ln 2 = \ln 0.01$, so that $t = (-24\ln 0.01)/(\ln 2) \approx 159.453$. Therefore it takes approximately 159.453 hours for 99% to disintegrate.

15. $\dfrac{2x+3}{x^2+4x-5} = \dfrac{2x+3}{(x+5)(x-1)} = \dfrac{A}{x+5} + \dfrac{B}{x-1}$; $2x+3 = A(x-1) + B(x+5)$;
$A + B = 2$ and $-A + 5B = 3$, so $A = \frac{7}{6}$ and $B = \frac{5}{6}$;

$$\int \frac{2x+3}{x^2+4x-5}\,dx = \int\left(\frac{7}{6}\frac{1}{x+5} + \frac{5}{6}\frac{1}{x-1}\right)dx = \frac{7}{6}\ln|x+5| + \frac{5}{6}\ln|x-1| + C = \frac{1}{6}\ln|x+5|^7|x-1|^5 + C$$

16. $$\int \frac{\sec^4 x}{\tan^5 x}\,dx = \int \frac{1/\cos^4 x}{\sin^5 x/\cos^5 x}\,dx = \int \frac{\cos x}{\sin^5 x}\,dx \overset{u=\sin x}{=} \int \frac{1}{u^5}\,du = \frac{u^{-4}}{-4} + C = \frac{-1}{4\sin^4 x} + C$$

17. $$\int \frac{1}{\sqrt{-x^2+6x-8}}\,dx = \int \frac{1}{\sqrt{1-(x-3)^2}}\,dx = \sin^{-1}(x-3) + C$$

18. Notice that $\sqrt{4+5x^2}$ is an increasing function on $[0,1]$, so that $2 = \sqrt{4+5(0)^2} \le \sqrt{4+5x^2} \le \sqrt{4+5(1)^2} = 3$ for $0 \le x \le 1$. Then $2x^4 \le x^4\sqrt{4+5x^2} \le 3x^4$ for all x in $[0,1]$, so by the Comparison Property, $\int_0^1 2x^4\,dx \le \int_0^1 x^4\sqrt{4+5x^2}\,dx \le \int_0^1 3x^4\,dx$. Since $\int_0^1 2x^4\,dx = \frac{2}{5}x^5\big|_0^1 = \frac{2}{5}$ and $\int_0^1 3x^4\,dx = \frac{3}{5}x^5\big|_0^1 = \frac{3}{5}$ it follows that $\frac{2}{5} \le \int_0^1 x^4\sqrt{4+5x^2}\,dx \le \frac{3}{5}$. Thus we may take $a = \frac{2}{5}$ and $b = \frac{3}{5}$.

19. $$\int_0^{\pi/4} \tan 2x\,dx = \lim_{b\to\pi/4^-}\int_0^b \tan 2x\,dx \overset{u=2x}{=} \lim_{b\to\pi/4^-}\int_0^{2b}\tan u\,du$$
$$= \lim_{b\to\pi/4^-}\left(-\ln|\cos u|\Big|_0^{2b}\right) = \lim_{b\to\pi/4^-}(-\ln|\cos 2b|) = \infty$$

so the given integral diverges.

20. $$\int_1^\infty \frac{1}{x(\ln x)^{3/2}}\,dx = \lim_{c\to1^+}\int_c^2 \frac{1}{x(\ln x)^{3/2}}\,dx + \lim_{b\to\infty}\int_2^b \frac{1}{x(\ln x)^{3/2}}\,dx$$

Since

$$\lim_{c\to1^+}\int_c^2 \frac{1}{x(\ln x)^{3/2}}\,dx \overset{u=\ln x}{=} \lim_{c\to1^+}\int_{\ln c}^{\ln 2}\frac{1}{u^{3/2}}\,du = \lim_{c\to1^+}\frac{-2}{u^{1/2}}\bigg|_{\ln c}^{\ln 2} = \lim_{c\to1^+} 2\left(\frac{1}{(\ln c)^{1/2}} - \frac{1}{(\ln 2)^{1/2}}\right) = \infty,$$

it follows that $\displaystyle\int_1^2 \frac{1}{x(\ln x)^{3/2}}\,dx$ and hence $\displaystyle\int_1^\infty \frac{1}{x(\ln x)^{3/2}}\,dx$ diverge.

21. For $0 \le x \le \pi$, we have $e^x \ge e^{-x}$ and $\sin x \ge 0$, so that $e^x \sin x \ge e^{-x} \sin x$. For $-\pi/2 \le x < 0$,we have $e^x < e^{-x}$ and $\sin x < 0$, so that $e^x \sin x \ge e^{-x} \sin x$. Thus $e^x \sin x \ge e^{-x} \sin x$ for $-\pi/2 \le x \le \pi$, so that $A = \int_{-\pi/2}^{\pi} (e^x \sin x - e^{-x} \sin x)\, dx$. By Exercise 54 of Section 7.1,

$$A = \left[\frac{e^x}{2}(\sin x - \cos x) - \frac{e^{-x}}{2}(-\sin x - \cos x) \right] \Bigg|_{-\pi/2}^{\pi}$$

$$= \frac{1}{2}(e^\pi - e^{-\pi}) - \frac{1}{2}(-e^{-\pi/2} - e^{\pi/2}) = \frac{1}{2}(e^\pi - e^{-\pi} + e^{-\pi/2} + e^{\pi/2}).$$

22. Let $n \ge 1$. We use integration by parts with $u = x^n$ and $dv = e^{-x}\, dx$, so that $du = nx^{n-1}\, dx$ and $v = -e^{-x}$. Thus

$$E_n = \int_0^1 x^n e^{-x}\, dx = -x^n e^{-x} \Big|_0^1 - \int_0^1 (-nx^{n-1} e^{-x})\, dx = -e^{-1} + n \int_0^1 x^{n-1} e^{-x}\, dx = -\frac{1}{e} + nE_{n-1}.$$

Chapter 9

Sequences and Series

9.1 Polynomial Approximation

1. $f(x) = \sin x$, $f'(x) = \cos x$, $f''(x) = -\sin x$, and $f^{(3)}(x) = -\cos x$, so that $f(0) = 0$, $f'(0) = 1$, $f''(0) = 0$, and $f^{(3)}(0) = -1$. Then $p_0(x) = 0$, $p_1(x) = 0 + 1 \cdot x = x$, $p_2(x) = 0 + 1 \cdot x + (0/2!)x^2 = x$, and $p_3(x) = 0 + 1 \cdot x + (0/2!)x^2 - (1/3!)x^3 = x - x^3/3! = x - x^3/6$.

2. $f(x) = \cos x$, $f'(x) = -\sin x$, $f''(x) = -\cos x$, and $f^{(3)}(x) = \sin x$, so that $f(0) = 1$, $f'(0) = 0$, $f''(0) = -1$, and $f^{(3)}(0) = 0$. Then $p_0(x) = 1$, $p_1(x) = 1 + 0 \cdot x = 1$, $p_2(x) = 1 + 0 \cdot x - (1/2!)x^2 = 1 - \frac{1}{2}x^2$, and $p_3(x) = 1 + 0 \cdot x - (1/2!)x^2 + (0/3!)x^3 = 1 - \frac{1}{2}x^2$.

3. $f(x) = e^{-2x}$, $f'(x) = -2e^{-2x}$, $f''(x) = (-2)^2 e^{-2x}$, and $f^{(3)}(x) = (-2)^3 e^{-2x}$, so that $f(0) = 1$, $f'(0) = -2$, $f''(0) = (-2)^2 = 4$, and $f^{(3)}(0) = (-2)^3 = -8$. Then $p_0(x) = 1$, $p_1(x) = 1 - 2x$, $p_2(x) = 1 - 2x + (4/2!)x^2 = 1 - 2x + 2x^2$ and $p_3(x) = 1 - 2x + (4/2!)x^2 - (8/3!)x^3 = 1 - 2x + 2x^2 - \frac{4}{3}x^3$.

4. $f(x) = \ln(2 + x)$, $f'(x) = 1/(2 + x)$, $f''(x) = -1/(2 + x)^2$, and $f^{(3)}(x) = (-2)(-1)/(2 + x)^3$, so that $f(0) = \ln 2$, $f'(0) = \frac{1}{2}$, $f''(0) = -(1/2^2)$, and $f^{(3)}(0) = 2/2^3$. Then $p_0(x) = \ln 2$, $p_1(x) = \ln 2 + \frac{1}{2}x$, $p_2(x) = \ln 2 + (1/2)x - [1/(2^2(2!)]x^2 = \ln 2 + \frac{1}{2}x - \frac{1}{8}x^2$, and $p_3(x) = \ln 2 + (1/2)x - [1/2^2(2!)]x^2 + [2/2^3(3!)]x^3 = \ln 2 + \frac{1}{2}x - \frac{1}{8}x^2 + \frac{1}{24}x^3$.

5. $f(x) = \sin(2x)$, $f'(x) = 2\cos(2x)$, $f''(x) = -(2^2)\sin(2x)$, and $f^{(3)}(x) = -(2^3)\cos(2x)$, so that $f(0) = 0$, $f'(0) = 2$, $f''(0) = 0$, and $f^{(3)}(0) = -2^3$. Then $p_0(x) = 0$, $p_1(x) = 0 + 2x = 2x$, $p_2(x) = 0 + 2x + (0/2!)x^2 = 2x$, and $p_3(x) = 0 + 2x + (0/2!)x^2 - (2^3/3!)x^3 = 2x - \frac{4}{3}x^3$.

6. $f(x) = (1 - x)^{1/2}$, $f'(x) = \dfrac{-1}{2(1 - x)^{1/2}}$, $f''(x) = \dfrac{-1}{2^2(1 - x)^{3/2}}$, and $f^{(3)}(x) = \dfrac{-3}{2^3(1 - x)^{5/2}}$, so that $f(0) = 1$, $f'(0) = -1/2$, $f''(0) = -1/2^2$, and $f^{(3)}(0) = -3/2^3$. Then $p_0(x) = 1$, $p_1(x) = 1 - \frac{1}{2}x$, $p_2(x) = 1 - (1/2)x - (1/2^2 2!)x^2 = 1 - \frac{1}{2}x - \frac{1}{8}x^2$, and $p_3(x) = 1 - (1/2)x - (1/2^2 2!)x^2 - (3/2^3 3!)x^3 = 1 - \frac{1}{2}x - \frac{1}{8}x^2 - \frac{1}{16}x^3$.

7. $f(x) = x^2 - x - 2$, $f'(x) = 2x - 1$, $f''(x) = 2$, and $f^{(n)}(x) = 0$ for $n \geq 3$. Since $f(0) = -2$, $f'(0) = -1$, $f''(0) = 2$, and $f^{(n)}(0) = 0$ for $n \geq 3$, it follows that $p_n(x) = -2 - 1 \cdot x + (2/2!)x^2 = -2 - x + x^2$ for $n \geq 2$.

8. $f(x) = x^5 + x^3 + 4$, $f'(x) = 5x^4 + 3x^2$, $f''(x) = 20x^3 + 6x$, $f^{(3)}(x) = 60x^2 + 6$, $f^{(4)}(x) = 120x$, $f^{(5)}(x) = 120$, and $f^{(n)}(x) = 0$ for $n \geq 6$. Since $f(0) = 4$, $f'(0) = 0$, $f''(0) = 0$, $f^{(3)}(0) = 6$, $f^{(4)}(0) = 0$, $f^{(5)}(0) = 120$, and $f^{(n)}(0) = 0$ for $n \geq 6$, it follows that $p_n(x) = 4 + 0 \cdot x + (0/2!)x^2 + (6/3!)x^3 + (0/4!)x^4 + (120/5!)x^5 = 4 + x^3 + x^5$ for $n \geq 5$.

9. $f(x) = \dfrac{1}{1+x}$, $f'(x) = \dfrac{-1}{(1+x)^2}$, $f''(x) = \dfrac{2}{(1+x)^3}$, $f^{(3)}(x) = \dfrac{-6}{(1+x)^4}$,

$f^{(k)}(x) = \dfrac{(-1)^k k!}{(1+x)^{k+1}}$; $f^{(k)}(0) = (-1)^k k!$;

$$p_n(x) = 1 - x + \frac{2!}{2!}x^2 - \frac{3!}{3!}x^3 + \cdots + \frac{(-1)^n n!}{n!}x^n = 1 - x + x^2 - x^3 + \cdots + (-1)^n x^n$$

10. $f(x) = \dfrac{1}{1+2x}$, $f'(x) = \dfrac{-2}{(1+2x)^2}$, $f''(x) = \dfrac{8}{(1+2x)^3}$, $f^{(3)}(x) = \dfrac{-48}{(1+2x)^4}$,

$f^{(k)}(x) = \dfrac{(-1)^k 2^k k!}{(1+2x)^{k+1}}$; $f^{(k)}(0) = (-1)^k 2^k k!$;

$$p_n(x) = 1 - 2x + \frac{8}{2!}x^2 - \frac{48}{3!}x^3 + \cdots + \frac{(-1)^n 2^n n!}{n!}x^n = 1 - 2x + 4x^2 - 8x^3 + \cdots + (-1)^n 2^n x^n$$

11. $f(x) = e^{-x}$, $f'(x) = -e^{-x}$, $f''(x) = e^{-x}$, $f^{(3)}(x) = -e^{-x}$, $f^{(k)}(x) = (-1)^k e^{-x}$; $f^{(k)}(0) = (-1)^k$

$$p_n(x) = 1 - x + \frac{x^2}{2!} - \frac{x^3}{3!} + \cdots + \frac{(-1)^n}{n!}n!$$

12. $f(x) = e^{3x}$, $f'(x) = 3e^{3x}$, $f''(x) = 9e^{3x}$, $f^{(3)}(x) = 27e^{3x}$, $f^{(k)}(x) = 3^k e^{3x}$; $f^{(k)}(0) = 3^k$;

$$p_n(0) = 1 + 3x + \frac{9}{2!}x^2 + \cdots + \frac{3^n}{n!}x^n$$

13. $f(x) = \cosh x$, $f'(x) = \sinh x$, $f''(x) = \cosh x$, $f^{(2k)}(x) = \cosh x$, $f^{(2k+1)}(x) = \sinh x$;

$f^{(2k)}(0) = 1$, $f^{(2k+1)}(0) = 0$; $p_{2n+1}(x) = p_{2n}(x) = 1 + \dfrac{x^2}{2!} + \dfrac{x^4}{4!} + \cdots + \dfrac{x^{2n}}{(2n)!}$

14. $f(x) = \ln\dfrac{1+x}{1-x} = \ln(1+x) - \ln(1-x)$, $f'(x) = \dfrac{1}{1+x} + \dfrac{1}{1-x}$,

$f''(x) = \dfrac{-1}{(1+x)^2} + \dfrac{1}{(1-x)^2}$, $f^{(3)}(x) = \dfrac{2}{(1+x)^3} + \dfrac{2}{(1-x)^3}$,

$f^{(k)}(x) = \dfrac{(-1)^{k-1}(k-1)!}{(1+x)^k} + \dfrac{(k-1)!}{(1-x)^k}$ for $k \geq 1$; $f^{(2k)}(0) = 0$, $f^{(2k+1)}(0) = 2(2k)!$;

$$p_{2n+2}(x) = p_{2n+1}(x) = 2x + \frac{4}{3!}x^3 + \frac{48}{5!}x^5 + \cdots + \frac{2(2n)!}{(2n+1)!}x^{2n+1} = 2x + \frac{2}{3}x^3 + \frac{2}{5}x^5 + \cdots + \frac{2}{2n+1}x^{2n+1}$$

15. $f(x) = \sin x$, $f'(x) = \cos x$, $f''(x) = -\sin x$, $f^{(3)}(x) = -\cos x$, $f^{(4)}(x) = \sin x$

$f^{(2k)}(x) = (-1)^k \sin x$, $f^{(2k+1)}(x) = (-1)^k \cos x$; $f^{(2k)}(0) = 0$, $f^{(2k+1)}(0) = (-1)^k$;

$$p_{2n+2}(x) = p_{2n+1}(x) = x - \frac{x^3}{3!} + \frac{x^5}{5!} - \frac{x^7}{7!} + \cdots + \frac{(-1)^n}{(2n+1)!}x^{2n+1}$$

16. $f(x)=\cos x$, $f'(x)=-\sin x$, $f''(x)=-\cos x$, $f^{(3)}(x)=\sin x$, $f^{(4)}(x)=\cos x$,

$f^{(2k)}(x)=(-1)^k\cos x$, $f^{(2k+1)}(x)=(-1)^k\sin x$; $f^{(2k)}(0)=(-1)^k$, $f^{(2k+1)}(0)=0$;

$$p_{2n+1}(x)=p_{2n}(x)=1-\frac{x^2}{2!}+\frac{x^4}{4!}-\frac{x^6}{6!}+\cdots+\frac{(-1)^n}{(2n)!}x^{2n}$$

17. $p_2(x)=0$ for all x

18. $f(x)=\sin x^2$, $f'(x)=2x\cos x^2$, $f''(x)=2\cos x^2-4x^2\sin x^2$, $f^{(3)}(x)=-12x\sin x^2-8x^3\cos x^2$;

$f(0)=f'(0)=0$, $f''(0)=2$, $f^{(3)}(0)=0$; $p_3(x)=(2/2!)x^2=x^2$

19. $f(x)=e^{-(x^2)}$, $f'(x)=-2xe^{-(x^2)}$, $f''(x)=-2e^{-(x^2)}+4x^2e^{-(x^2)}$,

$f^{(3)}(x)=12xe^{-(x^2)}-8x^3e^{-(x^2)}$; $f(0)=1$, $f'(0)=0$, $f''(0)=-2$, $f^{(3)}(0)=0$;

$p_3(x)=1+(-2/2!)x^2=1-x^2$

20. $f(x)=\sin^{-1}x$, $f'(x)=1/\sqrt{1-x^2}$, $f''(x)=x/(1-x^2)^{3/2}$; $f(0)=0$, $f'(0)=1$, $f''(0)=0$; $p_2(x)=x$

21. $f(x)=\ln(\cos x)$, $f'(x)=(-\sin x)/(\cos x)=-\tan x$, $f''(x)=-\sec^2 x$;

$f(0)=0$, $f'(0)=0$, $f''(0)=-1$; $p_2(x)=(-1/2!)x^2=-\frac{1}{2}x^2$

22. $f(x)=\tan x$, $f'(x)=\sec^2 x$, $f''(x)=2\sec^2 x\tan x$, $f^{(3)}(x)=4\sec^2 x\tan^2 x+2\sec^4 x$,

$f^{(4)}(x)=8\sec^2 x\tan^3 x+16\sec^4 x\tan x$; $f(0)=0$, $f'(0)=1$, $f''(0)=0$, $f^{(3)}(0)=2$, $f^{(4)}(0)=0$;

$p_4(x)=p_3(x)=x+(2/3!)x^3=x+\frac{1}{3}x^3$

23. $f(x)=\sec x$, $f'(x)=\sec x\tan x$, $f''(x)=\sec x\tan^2 x+\sec^3 x$, $f^{(3)}(x)=\sec x\tan^3 x+5\sec^3 x\tan x$;

$f(0)=1$, $f'(0)=0$, $f''(0)=1$, $f^{(3)}(0)=0$; $p_3(x)=p_2(x)=(1/2!)x^2=1+\frac{1}{2}x^2$

24. $f(x)=(\sin x)/x$ for $x\neq 0$, $f(0)=1$; $f'(x)=(x\cos x-\sin x)/x^2$ for $x\neq 0$; by l'Hôpital's Rule,

$$f'(0)=\lim_{x\to 0}\frac{f(x)-f(0)}{x-0}=\lim_{x\to 0}\frac{(\sin x)/x-1}{x-0}=\lim_{x\to 0}\frac{\sin x-x}{x^2}=\lim_{x\to 0}\frac{\cos x-1}{2x}=\lim_{x\to 0}\frac{-\sin x}{2}=0;$$

by l'Hôpital's Rule,

$$f''(0)=\lim_{x\to 0}\frac{f'(x)-f'(0)}{x-0}=\lim_{x\to 0}\frac{(x\cos x-\sin x)/x^2}{x-0}=\lim_{x\to 0}\frac{x\cos x-\sin x}{x^3}$$

$$=\lim_{x\to 0}\frac{-x\sin x}{3x^2}=\lim_{x\to 0}\frac{-\sin x}{3x}=-\frac{1}{3};$$

$p_2(x)=1+[(-1/3)/2!]x^2=1-\frac{1}{6}x^2$.

25. $f(x) = e^{-1/x^2}$ for $x \neq 0$, $f(0) = 0$; $f'(x) = (2/x^3)e^{-1/x^2}$ for $x \neq 0$; by l'Hôpital's Rule,

$$f'(0) = \lim_{x\to 0} \frac{f(x) - f(0)}{x - 0} = \lim_{x\to 0} \frac{e^{-1/x^2} - 0}{x - 0} = \lim_{x\to 0} \frac{1/x}{e^{1/x^2}} = \lim_{x\to 0} \frac{-1/x^2}{(-2/x^3)e^{1/x^2}} = \lim_{x\to 0} \frac{x}{2} e^{-1/x^2} = 0;$$

by l'Hôpital's Rule,

$$f''(0) = \lim_{x\to 0} \frac{f'(x) - f'(0)}{x - 0} = \lim_{x\to 0} \frac{(2/x^3)e^{-1/x^2} - 0}{x - 0} = \lim_{x\to 0} \frac{2/x^4}{e^{1/x^2}} = \lim_{x\to 0} \frac{-8/x^5}{(-2/x^3)e^{1/x^2}}$$

$$= \lim_{x\to 0} \frac{4/x^2}{e^{1/x^2}} = \lim_{x\to 0} \frac{-8/x^3}{(-2/x^3)e^{1/x^2}} = \lim_{x\to 0} 4e^{-1/x^2} = 0;$$

$p_2(x) = 0$.

26. $f(x) = \tan^{-1} x$, $f'(x) = \dfrac{1}{x^2+1}$, $f''(x) = \dfrac{-2x}{(x^2+1)^2}$, $f^{(3)}(x) = \dfrac{6x^2-2}{(x^2+1)^3}$;

$f(0) = 0$, $f'(0) = 1$, $f''(0) = 0$, $f^{(3)}(0) = -2$; $p_3(x) = x - (2/3!)x^3 = x - \frac{1}{3}x^3$;

$f(1) = \tan^{-1} 1 = \pi/4$, and $p_3(1) = 1 - \frac{1}{3} = \frac{2}{3}$ is the desired approximation to $\pi/4$, whose value is 0.785398 (accurate to 6 digits).

27. a. $f(x) = \sqrt{1+x}$, $f'(x) = \dfrac{1}{2(1+x)^{1/2}}$, $f''(x) = -\dfrac{1}{4(1+x)^{3/2}}$;

$f(0) = 1$, $f'(0) = \frac{1}{2}$, $f''(0) = -\frac{1}{4}$; $p_2(x) = 1 + \frac{1}{2}x - \frac{1}{8}x^2$

b. $f(1) = \sqrt{2}$, and $p_2(1) = 1 + \frac{1}{2} - \frac{1}{8} = 1.375$ is the desired approximation to $\sqrt{2}$, whose value is 1.41421 (accurate to 6 digits).

c. $f(0.1) = \sqrt{1.1}$, and $p_2(0.1) = 1 + \frac{1}{2}(0.1) - \frac{1}{8}(0.01)^2 = 1.04875$ is the desired approximation to $\sqrt{1.1}$, whose value is 1.04881 (accurate to 6 digits).

28. If $f^{(3)}(0)$ exists, then

$$p_3(x) = f(0) + f'(0)x + \frac{f''(0)}{2!}x^2 + \frac{f^{(3)}(0)}{3!}x^3.$$

Thus

$$p_3'(x) = f'(0) + f''(0)x + \frac{f^{(3)}(0)}{2}x^2, \quad p_3''(x) = f''(0) + f^{(3)}(0)x, \quad \text{and} \quad p_3^{(3)}(x) = f^{(3)}(0),$$

so that $p_3(0) = f(0)$, $p_3'(0) = f'(0)$, $p_3''(0) = f''(0)$, and $p_3^{(3)}(0) = f^{(3)}(0)$.

9.2 Sequences

1. $\frac{1}{3}, \frac{1}{4}, \frac{1}{5}, \frac{1}{6}$

2. $1, \frac{1}{3}, \frac{1}{9}, \frac{1}{27}$

3. $0, \frac{1}{3}, \frac{1}{2}, \frac{3}{5}$

4. $5 - \frac{1}{5} = \frac{24}{5}$, $6 - \frac{1}{6} = \frac{35}{6}$, $7 - \frac{1}{7} = \frac{48}{7}$, $8 - \frac{1}{8} = \frac{63}{8}$

5. Let $\varepsilon > 0$, and let N be any integer. If $n \geq N$, then $|(-2) - (-2)| = 0 < \varepsilon$. Thus $\lim_{n\to\infty}(-2) = -2$.

6. Let $\varepsilon > 0$, and let N be any integer greater than $1/\sqrt{\varepsilon}$. If $n \geq N$, then $n^2 \geq N^2$, so that $1/n^2 \leq 1/N^2$, and thus $|1/n^2 - 0| = 1/n^2 \leq 1/N^2 < \varepsilon$. Thus $\lim_{n\to\infty} 1/n^2 = 0$.

7. Let $\varepsilon > 0$, and let N be any integer greater than $1/\varepsilon$. If $n \geq N$, then $1/n \leq 1/N$, so that

$$\left|\frac{3n+1}{n} - 3\right| = \left|3 + \frac{1}{n} - 3\right| = \frac{1}{n} \leq \frac{1}{N} < \varepsilon.$$

Thus $\lim_{n\to\infty}(3n+1)/n = 3$.

8. Let $\varepsilon > 0$, and let N be any integer greater than $3/\varepsilon$. If $n \geq N$, then $1/n \leq 1/N$, so that

$$\left|\frac{2n-1}{n+1} - 2\right| = \left|\frac{2n-1-2n-2}{n+1}\right| = \frac{3}{n+1} < \frac{3}{n} \leq \frac{3}{N} < 3\left(\frac{\varepsilon}{3}\right) = \varepsilon.$$

Thus $\lim_{n\to\infty}(2n-1)/(n+1) = 2$.

9. Let M be any number, and let N be any positive integer such that $N > M^2$. If $n \geq N$, then $\sqrt{n} \geq \sqrt{N} > \sqrt{M^2} = |M| \geq M$. Thus $\lim_{n\to\infty}\sqrt{n} = \infty$.

10. Let M be any number, and let N be any positive integer such that $N > (-M/2)^{1/3}$. If $n \geq N$, then $-2n^3 \leq -2N^3 \leq -2[(-M/2)^{1/3}]^3 = -2(-M/2) = M$. Thus $\lim_{n\to\infty}(-2n^3) = -\infty$.

11. Let M be any number, and let N be any positive integer such that $N > \ln|M|$. If $k \geq N$, then $e^k \geq e^N > e^{\ln|M|} = |M| \geq M$, so that $\lim_{k\to\infty} e^k = \infty$.

12. Let M be any number, and let N be any positive integer such that $N \geq M$. If $k \geq N$, then $(k^2+1)/k = k + 1/k > k \geq N \geq M$, so that $\lim_{k\to\infty}(k^2+1)/k = \infty$.

13. Let $f(x) = \pi + 1/x$ for $x \geq 1$. Then $f(n) = \pi + 1/n$ for $n \geq 1$. Since $\lim_{x\to\infty}(\pi + 1/x) = \pi$, Theorem 9.4 implies that $\lim_{n\to\infty}(\pi + 1/n) = \pi$.

14. Let $f(x) = \pi - x$ for $x \geq 1$. Then $f(n) = \pi - n$ for $n \geq 1$. Since $\lim_{x\to\infty}(\pi - x) = -\infty$, Theorem 9.4 implies that $\lim_{n\to\infty}(\pi - n) = -\infty$.

15. Since $0 < 0.8 < 1$, it follows from (4) with $r = 0.8$ that $\lim_{j\to\infty}(0.8)^j = 0$.

16. Since $3^j/2^j = (\frac{3}{2})^j$ and $\frac{3}{2} > 1$, it follows from (4) with $r = \frac{3}{2}$ that $\lim_{j\to\infty} 3^j/2^j = \infty$.

17. Since $e^{-n} = (1/e)^n$ and $0 < 1/e < 1$, it follows from (4) with $r = 1/e$ that $\lim_{n\to\infty} e^{-n} = 0$.

18. Let $f(x) = e^{1/x}$ for $x \geq 1$. Then $f(n) = e^{1/n}$ for $n \geq 1$. Since e^x is continuous at 0, it follows that $\lim_{x\to\infty} e^{1/x} = e^0 = 1$. Therefore Theorem 9.4 implies that $\lim_{n\to\infty} e^{1/n} = 1$.

19. Let $f(x) = (x+3)/(x^2-2)$ for $x \geq 2$. Then $f(n) = (n+3)/(n^2-2)$ for $n \geq 2$. Since

$$\lim_{x\to\infty} \frac{x+3}{x^2-2} = \lim_{x\to\infty} \frac{1/x + 3/x^2}{1-2/x^2} = \frac{0+0}{1-0} = 0$$

Theorem 9.4 implies that $\lim_{n\to\infty}(n+3)/(n^2-2) = 0$.

20. Let $f(x) = (5x^2+1)/(4-3x^2)$ for $x \geq 2$. Then $f(n) = (5n^2+1)/(4-3n^2)$ for $n \geq 2$. Since

$$\lim_{x\to\infty} \frac{5x^2+1}{4-3x^2} = \lim_{x\to\infty} \frac{5+1/x^2}{4/x^2-3} = -\frac{5}{3}$$

Theorem 9.4 implies that $\lim_{n\to\infty}(5n^2+1)/(4-3n^2) = -\frac{5}{3}$.

21. Let $f(x) = (2x^2-4)/(-x-5)$ for $x \geq 1$. Then $f(n) = (2n^2-4)/(-n-5)$ for $n \geq 1$. Since

$$\lim_{x\to\infty} \frac{2x^2-4}{-x-5} = \lim_{x\to\infty} \frac{2x-4/x}{-1-5/x} = -\infty$$

Theorem 9.4 implies that $\lim_{n\to\infty}(2n^2-4)/(-n-5) = -\infty$.

22. Let $f(x) = \cos \pi/x$ for $x \geq 1$. Then $f(n) = \cos \pi/n$ for $n \geq 1$. Since $\lim_{x\to\infty} \cos \pi/x = \cos 0 = 1$, Theorem 9.4 implies that $\lim_{n\to\infty} \cos \pi/n = 1$.

23. Let $f(x) = x \sin \pi/x$ for $x \geq 1$. Then $f(n) = n \sin \pi/n$ for $n \geq 1$. By l'Hôpital's Rule,

$$\lim_{x\to\infty} x \sin \frac{\pi}{x} = \lim_{x\to\infty} \frac{\sin \pi/x}{1/x} = \lim_{x\to\infty} \frac{(\cos \pi/x)(-\pi/x^2)}{-1/x^2} = \lim_{x\to\infty} \left(\pi \cos \frac{\pi}{x}\right) = \pi$$

so Theorem 9.4 implies that $\lim_{n\to\infty} n \sin \pi/n = \pi$.

24. Notice that $\ln 1/n = -\ln n$, so $\lim_{n\to\infty} \ln 1/n = \lim_{n\to\infty} -\ln n$. Let $f(x) = -\ln x$ for $x \geq 1$. Then $f(n) = -\ln n$ for $n \geq 1$. Since $\lim_{x\to\infty}(-\ln x) = -\lim_{x\to\infty} \ln x = -\infty$, Theorem 9.4 implies that $\lim_{n\to\infty} \ln 1/n = -\infty$.

25. Let $f(x) = (1+0.05/x)^x$ for $x \geq 1$. Then $f(n) = (1+0.05/n)^n$ for $n \geq 1$. Since $\ln f(x) = x \ln(1+0.05/x)$ for $x \geq 1$ and $\lim_{x\to\infty} \ln(1+0.05/x) = 0 = \lim_{x\to\infty} 1/x$, l'Hôpital's Rule implies that

$$\lim_{x\to\infty} \ln f(x) = \lim_{x\to\infty} x \ln\left(1 + \frac{0.05}{x}\right) = \lim_{x\to\infty} \frac{\ln(1+0.05/x)}{1/x}$$

$$= \lim_{x\to\infty} \frac{\dfrac{1}{1+0.05/x}(-0.05/x^2)}{-1/x^2} = \lim_{x\to\infty} \frac{0.05}{1+0.05/x} = 0.05.$$

Therefore $\lim_{x\to\infty} f(x) = e^{0.05}$, so that by Theorem 9.4, $\lim_{n\to\infty}(1+0.05/n)^n = e^{0.05}$.

26. Let $f(x) = [1+1/(3x)]^x$ for $x \geq 1$. Then $f(k) = [1+1/(3k)]^k$ for $k \geq 1$. Since $\ln f(x) = x \ln[1+1/(3x)]$ for $x \geq 1$ and $\lim_{x\to\infty} \ln[1+1/(3x)] = 0 = \lim_{x\to\infty} 1/x$, l'Hôpital's Rule implies that

$$\lim_{x\to\infty} \ln f(x) = \lim_{x\to\infty} \frac{\ln[1+1/(3x)]}{1/x} = \lim_{x\to\infty} \frac{\dfrac{1}{1+1/(3x)}[-1/(3x^2)]}{-1/x^2} = \lim_{x\to\infty} \frac{1}{3[1+1/(3x)]} = \frac{1}{3}.$$

Therefore $\lim_{x\to\infty} f(x) = e^{1/3}$, so that by Theorem 9.4, $\lim_{k\to\infty}[1+1/(3k)]^k = e^{1/3}$.

27. Let $f(x) = (1+x)^{1/(2x)}$ for $x \geq 1$.Then $f(k) = (1+k)^{1/(2k)}$ for $k \geq 1$. Since $\ln f(x) = [1/(2x)]\ln(1+x)$ for $x \geq 1$, and $\lim_{x\to\infty} \ln(1+x) = \infty = \lim_{x\to\infty} 2x$, l'Hôpital's Rule implies that

$$\lim_{x\to\infty} \ln f(x) = \lim_{x\to\infty} \frac{\ln(1+x)}{2x} = \lim_{x\to\infty} \frac{1/(1+x)}{2} = \lim_{x\to\infty} \frac{1}{2(1+x)} = 0.$$

Therefore $\lim_{x\to\infty} f(x) = e^0 = 1$, so that by Theorem 9.4, $\lim_{k\to\infty}(1+k)^{1/(2k)} = 1$.

28. Let $f(x) = \tan^{-1} x$ for $x \geq 0$. Then $f(k) = \tan^{-1} k$ for $k \geq 0$. Since $\lim_{x\to\infty} \tan^{-1} x = \pi/2$, Theorem 9.4 implies that $\lim_{k\to\infty} \tan^{-1} k = \pi/2$.

29. Let $f(x) = (1/\sqrt{2})\cos 1/x$ for $x \geq 1$. Then $f(k) = (1/\sqrt{2})\cos 1/k$ for $k \geq 1$. Since the cosine function is continuous at 0, we have $\lim_{x\to\infty}(1/\sqrt{2})\cos 1/x = (1/\sqrt{2})\cos 0 = 1/\sqrt{2}$. Next, let $g(x) = \sin^{-1} x$. Since the inverse sine function is continuous on $[-1, 1]$, it follows from the Substitution Theorem with $y = (1/\sqrt{2})\cos 1/x$ that $\lim_{x\to\infty} g\big(f(x)\big) = \lim_{x\to\infty} \sin^{-1}[(1/\sqrt{2})\cos 1/x] = \lim_{y\to 1/\sqrt{2}} \sin^{-1} y = \sin^{-1} 1/\sqrt{2} = \pi/4$. Therefore by Theorem 9.4, $\lim_{k\to\infty} \sin^{-1}[(1/\sqrt{2})\cos 1/k] = \pi/4$.

30. Since $\sqrt[k]{2k} = e^{(1/k)\ln 2k}$, we let $f(x) = e^{(1/x)\ln 2k}$ for $x \geq 1$, so that $f(k) = e^{(1/k)\ln 2k}$ for $k \geq 1$. Since $\ln f(x) = (1/x)\ln 2x$ and $\lim_{x\to\infty} \ln 2x = \infty = \lim_{x\to\infty} x$, l'Hôpital's Rule implies that

$$\lim_{x\to\infty} \ln f(x) = \lim_{x\to\infty} \frac{\ln 2x}{x} = \lim_{x\to\infty} \frac{1/x}{1} = 0.$$

Therefore $\lim_{x\to\infty} f(x) = e^0 = 1$, so that by Theorem 9.4, $\lim_{k\to\infty} \sqrt[k]{2k} = 1$.

31. Observe that $\int_{-1/n}^{1/n} e^x\,dx = e^x\big|_{-1/n}^{1/n} = e^{1/n} - e^{-1/n}$. Since $\lim_{n\to\infty} e^{1/n} = 1$ by Exercise 18, we find that

$$\lim_{n\to\infty} \int_{-1/n}^{1/n} e^x\,dx = \lim_{n\to\infty} (e^{1/n} - e^{-1/n}) = \lim_{n\to\infty} \left(e^{1/n} - \frac{1}{e^{1/n}}\right) = 1 - \frac{1}{1} = 0.$$

32. Observe that

$$\int_{1+1/n}^{2-(1/n)} \frac{1}{x}\,dx = \ln\left(2 - \frac{1}{n}\right) - \ln\left(1 + \frac{1}{n}\right) = \ln\frac{2-1/n}{1+1/n} = \ln\frac{2n-1}{n+1}.$$

Let $f(x) = \ln[(2x-1)/(x+1)]$ for $x \geq 1$. Then $f(n) = \ln[(2n-1)/(n+1)]$ for $n \geq 1$. Since

$$\lim_{x\to\infty} f(x) = \lim_{x\to\infty} \ln\frac{2x-1}{x+1} = \lim_{x\to\infty} \frac{2-1/x}{1+1/x} = \ln 2,$$

it follows from Theorem 9.4 that

$$\lim_{n\to\infty} \int_{1+1/n}^{2-(1/n)} \frac{1}{x}\,dx = \lim_{n\to\infty} \ln\frac{2n-1}{n+1} = \ln 2.$$

33. Since $\lim_{n\to\infty}(-4n) = -\infty$, the sequence diverges.

34. Since

$$\lim_{n\to\infty} \frac{n-1}{n} = \lim_{n\to\infty} \frac{1-1/n}{1} = \lim_{n\to\infty} \left(1 - \frac{1}{n}\right) = 1$$

the sequence converges to 1.

35. Since $\lim_{n\to\infty} 1/(n^2-1) = 0$, the sequence converges to 0.

36. Since $\lim_{n\to\infty} 2^n = \infty$, the sequence diverges.

37. Since $\lim_{n\to\infty}(-\frac{1}{3})^n = 0$ by Example 7, the sequence converges to 0.

38. Since $(1/n) - n \le 1 - n$ for $n \ge 2$ and since $\lim_{n\to\infty}(1-n) = -\infty$, it follows that $\lim_{n\to\infty}[(1/n)-n] = -\infty$, so the sequence diverges.

39. $(.25)^n < 10^{-5}$ if $n\log(.25) < -5$, that is, if $n > -5/\log(.25) \approx 8.3$. Thus $n = 9$ is the smallest positive integer such that $(.25)^n < 10^{-5}$.

40. $(.9)^n < 10^{-5}$ if $n\log(.9) < -5$, that is, if $n > -5/\log(.9) \approx 109.27$. Thus $n = 110$ is the smallest positive integer such that $(.9)^n < 10^{-5}$.

41. Since $\sqrt[n]{1.2} > 1$, $|1 - \sqrt[n]{1.2}| < 10^{-3}$ if $1.2^{1/n} < 1.001$, that is, if $(1/n)\ln 1.2 < \ln 1.001$, or $n > (\ln 1.2)/(\ln 1.001) \approx 182.4$. Thus $n = 183$ is the smallest positive integer such that $|1 - \sqrt[n]{1.2}| < 10^{-3}$.

42. Since $\sqrt[n]{n} > 1$, $|1 - \sqrt[n]{n}| < 2 \times 10^{-2}$ if $\sqrt[n]{n} < 1.02$. By trial and error we find that the smallest positive integer n such that this occurs is $n = 286$.

43. $\lim_{n\to\infty} a_n = \lim_{x\to 0^+}(1/x)\sinh(e^{-1/x})$, which appears to be 0.

44. $\lim_{n\to\infty} a_n = \lim_{x\to 0^+}(1/x)^{10}\ln(1+e^{-1/x})$, which appears to be 0.

45. For $n \ge 1$, let $P_n = \{0, 1/n, 2/n, \ldots, (n-1)/n, 1\}$ and for $1 \le k \le n$ let $x_k = k/n$. Then P_n is a partition of $[0,1]$, $\Delta x_k = 1/n$, $\|P_n\| = 1/n$, and x_k is in the kth subinterval $[(k-1)/n, k/n]$. The corresponding Riemann sum for $\int_0^1 x\,dx$ is

$$\frac{1}{n}\Delta x_1 + \frac{2}{n}\Delta x_2 + \frac{3}{n}\Delta x_3 + \cdots + \frac{n-1}{n}\Delta x_{n-1} + \frac{n}{n}\Delta x_n = \frac{1}{n^2} + \frac{2}{n^2} + \frac{3}{n^2} + \cdots + \frac{n}{n^2} = a_n.$$

Thus $\lim_{n\to\infty} a_n = \int_0^1 x\,dx = \frac{1}{2}x^2\big|_0^1 = \frac{1}{2}$.

46. For $n \ge 1$, let $P_n = \{0, 1/n, 2/n, \ldots, (n-1)/n, 1\}$ and for $1 \le k \le n$ let $x_k = k/n$. Then P_n is a partition of $[0,1]$, $\Delta x_k = 1/n$, $\|P_n\| = 1/n$, and x_k is in the kth subinterval $[(k-1)/n, k/n]$. The corresponding Riemann sum for $\int_0^1 x^2\,dx$ is

$$\left(\frac{1}{n}\right)^2\Delta x_1 + \left(\frac{2}{n}\right)^2\Delta x_2 + \cdots + \left(\frac{n-1}{n}\right)^2\Delta x_{n-1} + \left(\frac{n}{n}\right)^2\Delta x_n = \frac{1^2}{n^3} + \frac{2^2}{n^3} + \frac{3^2}{n^3} + \cdots + \frac{n^2}{n^3} = a_n.$$

Thus $\lim_{n\to\infty} a_n = \int_0^1 x^2\,dx = \frac{1}{3}x^3\big|_0^1 = \frac{1}{3}$.

47. Suppose $\lim_{n\to\infty} a_n = L_1$ and $\lim_{n\to\infty} a_n = L_2$. Then for any $\varepsilon > 0$ there are integers N_1 and N_2 such that if $n \ge N_1$, then $|a_n - L_1| < \varepsilon/2$, and if $n \ge N_2$, then $|a_n - L_2| < \varepsilon/2$. Let n be an integer greater than both N_1 and N_2. Then $|L_2 - L_1| = |(a_n - L_1) - (a_n - L_2)| \le |a_n - L_1| + |a_n - L_2| < \varepsilon/2 + \varepsilon/2 = \varepsilon$. Since $|L_2 - L_1| < \varepsilon$ for any $\varepsilon > 0$, we have $L_2 = L_1$. Thus the limit of a convergent sequence is unique.

48. Suppose $\lim_{n\to\infty} a_{2n} = \lim_{n\to\infty} a_{2n+1} = L$. Then for any $\varepsilon > 0$ there are integers N_1 and N_2 such that if $n \geq N_1$, then $|a_{2n} - L| < \varepsilon$, and if $n \geq N_2$, then $|a_{2n+1} - L| < \varepsilon$. Let N be the larger of $2N_1$ and $2N_2 + 1$. If $n \geq N$, then $|a_n - L| < \varepsilon$. Thus $\lim_{n\to\infty} a_n = L = \lim_{n\to\infty} a_{2n} = \lim_{n\to\infty} a_{2n+1}$.

49. By hypothesis, $M > 0$ and $r > 0$. Suppose that $p_n > M$. Then $M - p_n < 0$ and hence

$$\frac{r(M - p_n)}{M} p_n < 0.$$

Therefore (8) implies that

$$p_{n+1} = p_n + \frac{r(M - p_n)}{M} p_n < p_n.$$

Similarly, if $p_n < M$, then $M - p_n > 0$ and hence

$$\frac{r(M - p_n)}{M} p_n > 0.$$

Thus $p_{n+1} > p_n$ by (8).

50. As in the solution of Example 10, we use (7) to find p_{61}. We find that $p_{61} = r^{61}p_0 = (1.2)^{61}100 \approx$ 6,760,000.

51. Let P_0, P_1, and P_2 denote the population in 1900, 1910, and 1920, respectively. Using (6) and the values of P_0 and P_1 given in Example 11, we have

$$r = \frac{P_1}{P_0} \approx \frac{92.2 \times 10^6}{76.2 \times 10^6} \approx 1.21.$$

By (7), $P_2 = r^2 P_0 \approx (1.21)^2(76.2 \times 10^6) \approx 112 \times 10^6$, which means that the population in 1920 would have been approximately 112 million. This is not as close to the actual 1920 census figure of 106,021,537 as the number obtained in the solution of Example 11. Thus the prediction is better when we use a Verhulst sequence.

52. Let P_0, P_1, and P_2 be the populations in 1910, 1920, and 1930, respectively.

a. Using (8) with $M = 197 \times 10^6$, and the value $r = 0.342$ found in Example 11, we obtain

$$P_2 = P_1 + \frac{r(M - P_1)}{M} P_1 \approx 106 \times 10^6 + \frac{(0.342)(197 \times 10^6 - 106 \times 10^6)}{197 \times 10^6}(106 \times 10^6) \approx 123 \times 10^6.$$

b. Using (8) with $n = 0$ and $M = 197 \times 10^6$, we find that

$$r = \frac{M(P_1 - P_0)}{P_0(M - P_0)} \approx \frac{(197 \times 10^6)(106 \times 10^6 - 92 \times 10^6)}{(92 \times 10^6)(197 \times 10^6 - 92 \times 10^6)} \approx 0.286.$$

Using (8) with $n = 1$ and $r = 0.286$, we conclude that

$$P_2 = P_1 + \frac{r(M - P_1)}{M} P_1 \approx 106 \times 10^6 + \frac{(0.286)(197 \times 10^6 - 106 \times 10^6)}{197 \times 10^6}(106 \times 10^6) \approx 120 \times 10^6.$$

Thus the predicted population is 120 million, which is not closer to the actual census figure than the value found in part (a).

53. In general, if the amount of money in the account at the beginning of a year is P, then the interest earned during the year is $(.01)rP$, so that the amount of money in the account at the end of the year is $P + (.01)rP = P(1 + (.01)r)$. Let a_n be the amount of money in the account at the end of the nth year. Then $a_1 = 1000(1 + (.01)r)$ and $a_n = a_{n-1}(1 + (.01)r)$ for $n > 1$. By induction it follows that $a_n = 1000(1 + (.01)r)^n$.

54. a. The interest added at the end of the $(n+1)$st year is $0.05a_n$. Since an additional \$1000 is also added, it follows that

$$a_{n+1} = a_n + 0.05a_n + 1000 = 1.05a_n + 1000 \quad \text{for } n \geq 0.$$

b. We will use induction to verify the formula. Since $a_0 = 1000$, the given formula is valid for $n = 0$. Assuming that the formula is valid for a given positive integer n, we use the result of part (a) to find that

$$a_{n+1} \overset{\text{part (a)}}{=} 1.05a_n + 1000 = 1.05\left\{1000[1 + 1.05 + (1.05)^2 + \cdots + (1.05)^n]\right\} + 1000$$

$$= 1000(1.05 + (1.05)^2 + \cdots + (1.05)^{n+1}) + 1000 = 1000(1 + 1.05 + (1.05)^2 + \cdots + (1.05)^{n+1})$$

so that the formula is valid for $n+1$. By induction, $a_n = 1000[1 + 1.05 + (1.05)^2 + \cdots + (1.05)^n]$ for $n \geq 0$.

c. Since

$$1 + 1.05 + (1.05)^2 + \cdots + (1.05)^n = \frac{(1.05)^{n+1} - 1}{1.05 - 1} = 20[(1.05)^{n+1} - 1]$$

it follows from the formula in part (b) that

$$a_n = 1000(20)[(1.05)^{n+1} - 1] = 20{,}000[(1.05)^{n+1} - 1].$$

55. a. If the interest is compounded n times a year, then each interest period lasts $1/n$ years and the interest rate for each interest period is r/n percent. Thus the amount of money in the account at the end of $1/n$ years is $P(1 + (.01)r/n)$, the amount after $2/n$ years is $P(1 + (.01)r/n)(1 + (.01)r/n) = P(1 + (.01)r/n)^2$, the amount after $3/n$ years is $P(1 + (.01)r/n)^2(1 + (.01)r/n) = P(1 + (.01)r/n)^3$, and by induction the amount at the end of one year (after n interest periods) is $P(1 + (.01)r/n)^n$.

b. By Theorem 9.4,

$$\lim_{n\to\infty} P\left(1 + \frac{(.01)r}{n}\right)^n = \lim_{x\to\infty} P\left(1 + \frac{(.01)r}{x}\right)^x = P \lim_{x\to\infty}\left(1 + \frac{(.01)r}{x}\right)^x.$$

Let $f(x) = (1 + (.01)r/x)^x$. Then $\ln f(x) = x\ln(1 + (.01)r/x)$. By l'Hôpital's Rule,

$$\lim_{x\to\infty} \ln f(x) = \lim_{x\to\infty} \frac{\ln(1 + (.01)(r/x)}{1/x}$$

$$= \lim_{x\to\infty} \frac{\left(\dfrac{1}{1 + (.01)r/x}\right)\left(\dfrac{-(.01)r}{x^2}\right)}{-1/x^2} = \lim_{x\to\infty} \frac{(.01)r}{1 + (.01)r/x} = (.01)r.$$

Thus $\lim_{x\to\infty} f(x) = e^{(.01)r}$, so that $\lim_{n\to\infty} P(1 + (.01)r/n)^n = Pe^{(.01)r}$.

c. If interest is compounded continuously, then by part (b) the amount after 1 year is $1000e^{.05} \approx 1051.27$. If interest is compounded quarterly, then by part (a) the amount after 1 year is $1000(1+(.01)5/4)^4 = 1000(1.0125)^4 \approx 1050.95$. Thus the difference is approximately 32 cents.

56. a. When R_1 is constructed from R_0, the center square is removed; that is, $\frac{1}{9}$ of the total area is removed. Therefore $\frac{8}{9}$ of the original area remains. In each of the subsequent steps $\frac{8}{9}$ of the remaining area is removed. Thus after n steps, $(\frac{8}{9})^n$ of the original area remains, so that $A_n = (\frac{8}{9})^n$ for $n \geq 1$.

b. Using the result of part (a) and Example 7, we have $\lim_{n\to\infty} A_n = \lim_{n\to\infty}(\frac{8}{9})^n = 0$.

9.3 Convergence Properties of Sequences

1. Since $1 \leq 1 + 2/n \leq 1 + 2/1 = 3$ for $n \geq 1$, the sequence is bounded.

2. Since $1 \leq e^{1/n} \leq e^{1/1} = e$ for $n \geq 1$, the sequence is bounded.

3. Since $n + 1/(2n) \geq n$ for $n \geq 1$, the sequence is unbounded.

4. Since $|\cos n^2| \leq 1$ for $n \geq 0$, the sequence is bounded.

5. Since $\cosh k = \frac{1}{2}(e^k + e^{-k}) \geq \frac{1}{2}e^k$ for $k \geq 10$, and since $\lim_{x\to\infty} \frac{1}{2}e^x = \infty$, the sequence is unbounded.

6. Since $\ln(1 + e^x) > \ln e^k = k$ for all k, the sequence is unbounded.

7. By (1), $\lim_{n\to\infty}(2 + 1/n) = \lim_{n\to\infty} 2 + \lim_{n\to\infty} 1/n = 2 + 0 = 2$.

8. By (1) and (2),

$$\lim_{n\to\infty}\left(4 - \frac{2}{n}\right) = \lim_{n\to\infty} 4 + \lim_{n\to\infty}\frac{-2}{n} = \lim_{n\to\infty} 4 - 2\lim_{n\to\infty}\frac{1}{n} = 4 - 2\cdot 0 = 4.$$

9. By (1) and (2),

$$\lim_{n\to\infty}\left(\frac{1}{n} - \frac{1}{n+1}\right) = \lim_{n\to\infty}\frac{1}{n} + \lim_{n\to\infty}\frac{-1}{n+1} = \lim_{n\to\infty}\frac{1}{n} - \lim_{n\to\infty}\frac{1}{n+1} = 0 - 0 = 0.$$

10. By (1), (2) and (3),

$$\lim_{n\to\infty}\left(1 - \frac{1}{n}\right)\left(1 + \frac{1}{n^2}\right) = \lim_{n\to\infty}\left(1 - \frac{1}{n}\right)\lim_{n\to\infty}\left(1 + \frac{1}{n^2}\right)$$
$$= \left[\lim_{n\to\infty} 1 - \lim_{n\to\infty}\frac{1}{n}\right]\left[\lim_{n\to\infty} 1 + \lim_{n\to\infty}\frac{1}{n^2}\right] = (1-0)(1+0) = 1.$$

11. By (2) and Example 7 of Section 9.2,

$$\lim_{n\to\infty}\frac{2^{n+1}}{5^{n+2}} = \lim_{n\to\infty}\frac{2\cdot 2^n}{5^2\,5^n} = \lim_{n\to\infty}\frac{2}{25}\left(\frac{2}{5}\right)^n = \frac{2}{25}\lim_{n\to\infty}\left(\frac{2}{5}\right)^n = \frac{2}{25}\cdot 0 = 0.$$

12. By (1), (2) and Example 7 of Section 9.2,

$$\lim_{n\to\infty}\frac{2^{n-1}+3}{3^{n+2}}=\lim_{n\to\infty}\frac{2^{n-1}}{3^{n+2}}+\lim_{n\to\infty}\frac{3}{3^{n+2}}=\lim_{n\to\infty}\frac{2^{-1}\cdot 2^n}{3^2\cdot 3^n}+\lim_{n\to\infty}\frac{3}{3^2\cdot 3^n}$$

$$=\frac{1}{18}\lim_{n\to\infty}\left(\frac{2}{3}\right)^n+\frac{1}{3}\lim_{n\to\infty}\left(\frac{1}{3}\right)^n=\frac{1}{18}\cdot 0+\frac{1}{3}\cdot 0=0.$$

13. By (1), $\lim_{k\to\infty}(k+1)/k=\lim_{k\to\infty}(1+1/k)=\lim_{k\to\infty}1+\lim_{k\to\infty}1/k=1+0=1.$

14. By (1) – (4),

$$\lim_{k\to\infty}\frac{2k-1}{k^2-7}=\lim_{k\to\infty}\frac{2/k-1/k^2}{1-7/k^2}=\frac{2\cdot 0-0^2}{1-7(0)^2}=0.$$

15. By (1) – (4),

$$\lim_{n\to\infty}\frac{4n^3-5}{6n^3+3}=\lim_{n\to\infty}\frac{4-5/n^3}{6+3/n^3}=\frac{4-5(0)^3}{6+3(0)^3}=\frac{2}{3}.$$

16. By Example 8 of Section 9.2, $\lim_{n\to\infty}\sqrt[n]{5}=1$, and by (1), (2) and (4),

$$\lim_{n\to\infty}\frac{n-1}{n+1}=\lim_{n\to\infty}\frac{1-1/n}{1+1/n}=\frac{1-0}{1+0}=1.$$

Thus it follows from (3) that

$$\lim_{n\to\infty}\sqrt[n]{5}\left(\frac{n-1}{n+1}\right)=\lim_{n\to\infty}\sqrt[n]{5}\lim_{n\to\infty}\frac{n-1}{n+1}=1\cdot 1=1.$$

17. By Examples 8 and 9 of Section 9.2, $\lim_{n\to\infty}\sqrt[n]{3}=1$ and $\lim_{n\to\infty}\sqrt[n]{n}=1$. Thus by (3) we have $\lim_{n\to\infty}\sqrt[n]{3n}=\lim_{n\to\infty}\sqrt[n]{3}\lim_{n\to\infty}\sqrt[n]{n}=1\cdot 1=1.$

18. Observe that

$$\lim_{n\to\infty}\frac{\sqrt{n^2-1}}{2n}=\lim_{n\to\infty}\frac{\sqrt{1-1/n^2}}{2}=\frac{1}{2}\lim_{n\to\infty}\sqrt{1-\frac{1}{n^2}}.$$

Let $f(x)=\sqrt{1-1/x^2}$ for $x\geq 1$, so that $f(n)=\sqrt{1-1/n^2}$. Since $\lim_{x\to\infty}\sqrt{1-1/x^2}=\sqrt{1-0}=1$, Theorem 9.4 implies that $\lim_{n\to\infty}\sqrt{1-1/n^2}=1$, so that

$$\lim_{n\to\infty}\frac{\sqrt{n^2-1}}{2n}=\frac{1}{2}\lim_{n\to\infty}\sqrt{1-\frac{1}{n^2}}=\frac{1}{2}\cdot 1=\frac{1}{2}.$$

19. By (1), (2), and (4),

$$\lim_{n\to\infty}\frac{\sqrt{n}+1}{\sqrt{n}-1}=\lim_{n\to\infty}\frac{1+1/\sqrt{n}}{1-1/\sqrt{n}}=\frac{1+0}{1-0}=1.$$

20. Observe that

$$0\leq\sqrt{n+1}-\sqrt{n}=(\sqrt{n+1}-\sqrt{n})\frac{\sqrt{n+1}+\sqrt{n}}{\sqrt{n+1}+\sqrt{n}}=\frac{(n+1)-n}{\sqrt{n+1}+\sqrt{n}}=\frac{1}{\sqrt{n+1}+\sqrt{n}}\leq\frac{1}{\sqrt{n}}\quad\text{for } n\geq 1.$$

Since $\lim_{n\to\infty}0=0=\lim_{n\to\infty}1/\sqrt{n}$, we conclude from (5) that $\lim_{n\to\infty}(\sqrt{n+1}-\sqrt{n})=0.$

21. By (1) and (4),

$$\lim_{n\to\infty}\sqrt{n}\,(\sqrt{n+1}-\sqrt{n}) = \lim_{n\to\infty}\sqrt{n}\,(\sqrt{n+1}-\sqrt{n})\frac{\sqrt{n+1}+\sqrt{n}}{\sqrt{n+1}+\sqrt{n}}$$

$$= \lim_{n\to\infty}\frac{\sqrt{n}\,[(n+1)-n]}{\sqrt{n+1}+\sqrt{n}} = \lim_{n\to\infty}\frac{\sqrt{n}}{\sqrt{n+1}+\sqrt{n}} = \lim_{n\to\infty}\frac{1}{\sqrt{1+1/n}+1} = \frac{1}{1+1} = \frac{1}{2}.$$

22. By (1),

$$\lim_{n\to\infty}\frac{1-(1+1/n)^2}{1-(1+1/n)} = \lim_{n\to\infty} -n\left[1-\left(1+\frac{1}{n}\right)^2\right] = \lim_{n\to\infty} -n\left[1-\left(1+\frac{2}{n}+\frac{1}{n^2}\right)\right]$$

$$= \lim_{n\to\infty}\left(2+\frac{1}{n}\right) = \lim_{n\to\infty} 2 + \lim_{n\to\infty}\frac{1}{n} = 2+0 = 2.$$

23. Observe that $-1/n \le (-1)^n/n \le 1/n$ for $n \ge 1$. Since $\lim_{n\to\infty} -1/n = 0 = \lim_{n\to\infty} 1/n$, it follows from (5) that $\lim_{n\to\infty}(-1)^n/n = 0$.

24. Since $0 \le 1/[n^2(n^2+1)] \le 1/n^2$ for $n \ge 1$, and since $\lim_{n\to\infty} 0 = 0 = \lim_{n\to\infty} 1/n^2$, it follows from (5) that $\lim_{n\to\infty} 1/[n^2(n^2+1)] = 0$.

25. Since $\lim_{x\to\infty}(x/e^x) = \lim_{x\to\infty}(1/e^x) = 0$ by l'Hôpital's Rule, it follows from Theorem 9.4 that $\lim_{n\to\infty}(n/e^n) = 0$.

26. Since $-1/n \le (\sin n)/n \le 1/n$ for $n \ge 1$, and since $\lim_{n\to\infty}(-1/n) = 0 = \lim_{n\to\infty} 1/n$, it follows from (5) that $\lim_{n\to\infty}(\sin n)/n = 0$.

27. Since $0 \le [\ln(1+1/n)]/n \le (\ln 2)/n$ for $n \ge 1$, and since $\lim_{n\to\infty}(\ln 2)/n = 0$, it follows from (5) that $\lim_{n\to\infty}[\ln(1+1/n)]/n = 0$.

28. Recall that $\lim_{y\to 0^+}(\sin y)/y = 1$. If $y = 1/x$, then

$$\lim_{x\to\infty} x\sin^2\frac{1}{x} = \lim_{y\to 0^+}\frac{1}{y}\sin^2 y = \lim_{y\to 0^+}\left(\frac{\sin y}{y}\sin y\right) = \left(\lim_{y\to 0^+}\frac{\sin y}{y}\right)\left(\lim_{y\to 0^+}\sin y\right) = 1\cdot 0 = 0.$$

It follows from Theorem 9.4 that $\lim_{n\to\infty} n\sin^2 1/n = 0$.

29. Observe that $1 \le (n+1/n)^{1/n} \le (2n)^{1/n}$, $\lim_{n\to\infty} 1 = 1$, and

$$\lim_{n\to\infty}(2n)^{1/n} = \lim_{n\to\infty}\sqrt[n]{2}\,\lim_{n\to\infty}\sqrt[n]{n} = 1.$$

Thus it follows from (5) that $\lim_{n\to\infty}(n+1/n)^{1/n} = 1$.

30. Observe that $1 \le \ln n \le n$ for $n \ge 3$, so that $1 = \sqrt[n]{1} \le \sqrt[n]{\ln n} \le \sqrt[n]{n}$ for $n \ge 3$. Since $\lim_{n\to\infty} 1 = 1 = \lim_{n\to\infty}\sqrt[n]{n}$ by Example 9 in Section 9.2, it follows from (5) with $a_n = 1$, $b_n = \sqrt[n]{n}$ and $c_n = \sqrt[n]{\ln n}$ that $\lim_{n\to\infty}\sqrt[n]{\ln n} = 1$.

31. Since $0 < e^{-2n} < e^{-n}$ for $n \geq 1$, and since $\lim_{n\to\infty} e^{-n} = 0 = \lim_{n\to\infty} 0$ by Exercise 17 of Section 9.2, it follows from (5) that $\lim_{n\to\infty} e^{-2n} = 0$. It follows from (1), (2), and (4) that

$$\lim_{n\to\infty} \tanh n = \lim_{n\to\infty} \frac{1-e^{-2n}}{1+e^{-2n}} = \frac{1-0}{1+0} = 1.$$

32. Conjecture: $L = 0$

33. Conjecture: $L \approx 0.7390851343$

34. a. Since f is continuous at L, $\lim_{n\to\infty} f(x_n) = f(\lim_{n\to\infty} x_n) = f(L)$. Thus $L = \lim_{n\to\infty} x_n = \lim_{n\to\infty} x_{n+1} = \lim_{n\to\infty} f(x_n) = f(L)$. Therefore L is a fixed point of f.

    b. Suppose that $\{a_n\}_{n=1}^{\infty}$ converges to a number L. By (a) this means that $f(L) = L$, so that $L = L^2 + \frac{3}{4}$, or equivalently, $L^2 - L + \frac{3}{4} = 0$. By the quadratic formula, $L = \frac{1}{2}\left(1 \pm \sqrt{-3}\right)$, so that L is not a real number. Therefore $\{a_n\}_{n=1}^{\infty}$ does not converge.

    c. By part (a), if $\lim_{n\to\infty} x_n = L$, then $f(L) = L$. This means that $L = L^2 + \frac{1}{8}$, so that $L^2 - L + \frac{1}{8} = 0$. By the quadratic formula, $L = \frac{1}{2}\left(1 \pm \sqrt{1^2 - \frac{1}{2}}\right) = \frac{1}{2} \pm \frac{1}{2}\sqrt{\frac{1}{2}}$. Notice that if $x_n \leq \frac{1}{4}$, then $x_{n+1} = x_n^2 + \frac{1}{8} \leq \frac{1}{16} + \frac{1}{8} < \frac{1}{4}$. Since $x_0 = 0$, this means that $x_n \leq \frac{1}{4}$ for all n. Since $\frac{1}{2} + \frac{1}{2}\sqrt{2} > \frac{1}{2}$, it follows that $\lim_{n\to\infty} x_n = L = \frac{1}{2} - \frac{1}{2}\sqrt{2}$.

35. We will first show by induction that $1 < a_n \leq 2$ for all n. Since $a_0 = 2$, this is true for $n = 0$. Observe that if $1 < a_n \leq 2$, then

$$\frac{1}{2} \leq \frac{1}{a_n} < 1, \quad \text{so that} \quad -1 < -\frac{1}{a_n} \leq -\frac{1}{2} \quad \text{and hence} \quad 1 < a_{n+1} = 2 - \frac{1}{a_n} \leq \frac{3}{2} \leq 2.$$

Thus the sequence is bounded. Moreover, for any n we have $a_n > 1$, so that $a_n^2 - 2a_n + 1 = (a_n - 1)^2 > 0$, and thus $a_n^2 > 2a_n - 1$. This means that $a_n > 2 - 1/a_n = a_{n+1}$. Consequently the sequence is decreasing. By Theorem 9.6, the given sequence must converge to a limit L. We find that

$$L = \lim_{n\to\infty} a_n = \lim_{n\to\infty} a_{n+1} = \lim_{n\to\infty}\left(2 - \frac{1}{a_n}\right) = 2 - \frac{1}{\lim\limits_{n\to\infty} a_n} = 2 - \frac{1}{L}.$$

This means that $L = 2 - 1/L$, so that $L^2 - 2L + 1 = 0$, and thus $L = 1$. As a result, $\lim_{n\to\infty} a_n = 1$.

36. We will show by induction that $L_n = 2^n/3^n$. In the first place, $L_1 = 1 - \frac{1}{3} = \frac{2}{3}$, $L_2 = \frac{2}{3} - \frac{1}{3}(\frac{2}{3}) = \frac{4}{9} = 2^2/3^2$. In general, if $L = 2^n/3^n$, then

$$L_{n+1} = \frac{2^n}{3^n} - \frac{1}{3}\left(\frac{2^n}{3^n}\right) = \frac{2^n}{3^n} - \frac{2^n}{3^{n+1}} = \frac{3(2^n) - 2^n}{3^{n+1}} = \frac{2(2^n)}{3^{n+1}} = \frac{2^{n+1}}{3^{n+1}}.$$

Thus $\lim_{n\to\infty} L_n = \lim_{n\to\infty} 2^n/3^n = 0$.

37. a. Let $\varepsilon > 0$. Since $\{b_n\}_{n=m}^{\infty}$ is bounded, there is an $M > 0$ such that $|b_n| \leq M$ for all $n \geq m$. Since $\lim_{n\to\infty} a_n = 0$ there is an integer $N \geq m$ such that if $n \geq N$, then $|a_n| < \varepsilon/M$. Thus if $n \geq N$, then $|a_n b_n| = |a_n|\,|b_n| < (\varepsilon/M)M = \varepsilon$. Therefore $\lim_{n\to\infty} a_n b_n = 0$.

b. Let

$$a_n = |c_n| \quad \text{and} \quad b_n = \begin{cases} 1 & \text{if } c_n \geq 0 \\ -1 & \text{if } c_n < 0. \end{cases}$$

Then $\{b_n\}_{n=1}^{\infty}$ is bounded and $c_n = a_n b_n$. If $\lim_{n\to\infty} |c_n| = 0$, then $\lim_{n\to\infty} a_n = 0$, so by part (a), $\lim_{n\to\infty} c_n = \lim_{n\to\infty} a_n b_n = 0$.

c. (i) Let $a_n = 1/n$ and $b_n = \sin n$ for $n \geq 1$. Then $\lim_{n\to\infty} a_n = 0$ and $\{b_n\}_{n=1}^{\infty}$ is bounded. By part(a), $\lim_{n\to\infty}(\sin n)/n = \lim_{n\to\infty} a_n b_n = 0$.

(ii) Let $a_n = 1/n^2$ and $b_n = \ln(1+(-1)^n/n)$ for $n \geq 2$. Then $\lim_{n\to\infty} a_n = 0$ and $\ln \frac{2}{3} \leq b_n \leq \ln \frac{3}{2}$, so that $\{b_n\}_{n=2}^{\infty}$ is bounded. By part (a),

$$\lim_{n\to\infty} \frac{1}{n^2} \ln\left(1 + \frac{(-1)^n}{n}\right) = \lim_{n\to\infty} a_n b_n = 0.$$

(iii) Let $a_n = 1/e^n$ and $b_n = 2 + (-1)^n$ for $n \geq 1$. Then $\lim_{n\to\infty} a_n = 0$ and $1 \leq b_n \leq 3$, so that $\{b_n\}_{n=1}^{\infty}$ is bounded. By part (a), $\lim_{n\to\infty}[2 + (-1)^n]/e^n = \lim_{n\to\infty} a_n b_n = 0$.

(iv) Let $a_n = 1/e^n$ and $b_n = [2n + (-1)^n]/e^n$ for $n \geq 1$. Then $\lim_{n\to\infty} a_n = 0$ and $0 \leq b_n \leq [2n + (-1)^n]/2^n \leq 2$, so that $\{b_n\}_{n=1}^{\infty}$ is bounded. By part (a), $\lim_{n\to\infty}[2n + (-1)^n]/e^{2n} = \lim_{n\to\infty} a_n b_n = 0$.

38. a. $a_1 = \sqrt{2} < 2$, and if $a_n \leq 2$, then $a_{n+1} = \sqrt{2 + a_n} \leq \sqrt{2+2} = 2$. By induction, $a_n \leq 2$ for $n \geq 1$. Since $a_n \leq 2$, then $a_{n+1} = \sqrt{2 + a_n} \geq \sqrt{a_n + a_n} = \sqrt{2a_n} \geq \sqrt{a_n^2} = a_n$, so $\{a_n\}_{n=1}^{\infty}$ is bounded and increasing.

b. The result follows directly from (a) and Theorem 9.6.

c. Since $\lim_{n\to\infty}(2 + a_n) = 2 + r$ by (1), and since $\lim_{n\to\infty} a_{n+1}^2 = r^2$ by (3) and (6), we have $r^2 = \lim_{n\to\infty} a_{n+1}^2 = \lim_{n\to\infty}(2 + a_n) = 2 + r$, so that $0 = r^2 - r - 2 = (r-2)(r+1)$. Since $r > 0$, this means that $r = 2$.

39. a. First, $a_1 = \sqrt{2} < 2$. Next, if $a_n < 2$, then $a_{n+1} = (\sqrt{2})^{a_n} < (\sqrt{2})^2 = 2$, so by induction, $a_n < 2$ for $n \geq 1$. Therefore $\{a_n\}_{n=1}^{\infty}$ is bounded. Next, we will show that $\{a_n\}_{n=1}^{\infty}$ is increasing. Since $a_n < 2$, it follows from Exercise 57(a) of Section 5.7 that $(\ln a_n)/a_n < (\ln 2)/2 = \ln \sqrt{2}$, so that $\ln a_n < a_n \ln \sqrt{2} = \ln((\sqrt{2})^{a_n}) = \ln a_{n+1}$. Since $\ln x$ is increasing, we conclude that $a_n < a_{n+1}$. By Theorem 9.6 the bounded, increasing sequence $\{a_n\}_{n=1}^{\infty}$ converges to a number L, and $L \leq 2$ since $a_n < 2$ for $n \geq 1$.

b. By part (a), $\lim_{n\to\infty} a_n = L$, so that $\lim_{n\to\infty} a_{n+1} = L$. Thus $\ln L = \lim_{n\to\infty} \ln a_{n+1} = \lim_{n\to\infty} \ln((\sqrt{2})^{a_n}) = \lim_{n\to\infty}(a_n \ln \sqrt{2}) = (\ln \sqrt{2}) \lim_{n\to\infty} a_n = (\ln \sqrt{2})L$. Therefore $(\ln L)/L = \ln \sqrt{2} = (\ln 2)/2$. Since $0 < L < e$ and $(\ln x)/x$ is increasing on $(0, e)$ by Exercise 57(a) in Section 5.7, it follows that $L = 2$.

40. a. Since $1/t \geq 1/(n+1)$ for t in $[n, n+1]$, it follows that

$$\ln(n+1) - \ln n = \int_n^{n+1} \frac{1}{t}\, dt \geq \int_n^{n+1} \frac{1}{n+1}\, dt = \frac{1}{n+1}[(n+1) - n] = \frac{1}{n+1}.$$

b. By the definition of the sequence $\{a_n\}_{n=1}^{\infty}$, for $n \geq 1$ we have

$$a_n - a_{n+1} = \left(1 + \frac{1}{2} + \cdots + \frac{1}{n} - \ln n\right) - \left(1 + \frac{1}{2} + \cdots + \frac{1}{n} + \frac{1}{n+1} - \ln(n+1)\right)$$
$$= \ln(n+1) - \ln n - \frac{1}{n+1}.$$

By part (a), $\ln(n+1) - \ln n - 1/(n+1) \geq 0$. Thus $a_n - a_{n+1} \geq 0$ for $n \geq 1$, so that $\{a_n\}_{n=1}^{\infty}$ is a decreasing sequence.

c. $$\ln n = \int_1^n \frac{1}{t}\,dt = \int_1^2 \frac{1}{t}\,dt + \int_2^3 \frac{1}{t}\,dt + \cdots + \int_{n-1}^n \frac{1}{t}\,dt$$
$$\leq \int_1^2 1\,dt + \int_2^3 \frac{1}{2}\,dt + \cdots + \int_{n-1}^n \frac{1}{n-1}\,dt$$
$$= 1(2-1) + \frac{1}{2}(3-2) + \cdots + \frac{1}{n-1}(n-(n-1)) = 1 + \frac{1}{2} + \cdots + \frac{1}{n-1}$$

Thus $a_n = 1 + \frac{1}{2} + \cdots + 1/(n-1) - \ln n \geq 0$ for $n \geq 1$.

d. Since $\{a_n\}_{n=1}^{\infty}$ is decreasing and nonnegative, and hence bounded, Theorem 9.6 implies that it converges.

41. Let $b_n = a_{n+1}/a_n$ and $b = \lim_{n\to\infty} b_n = \lim_{n\to\infty} b_{n-1}$. Since $a_{n+1} = a_n + a_{n-1}$ for $n \geq 2$, we have $a_{n+1}/a_n = 1 + a_{n-1}/a_n$, so that $b_n = 1 + 1/b_{n-1}$. Thus $b = \lim_{n\to\infty} b_n = \lim_{n\to\infty}(1 + 1/b_{n-1}) = 1 + 1/b$, or $b = 1 + 1/b$, or $b^2 - b - 1 = 0$. Since $b \geq 0$, it follows that $b = (1 + \sqrt{1+4})/2 = (1+\sqrt{5})/2$.

9.4 Infinite Series

1. $s_4 = 1 + 1 + 1 + 1 = 4$

2. $s_4 = 1 + 2 + 3 + 4 = 10$

3. $s_4 = 1 + \frac{1}{3} + \frac{1}{9} + \frac{1}{27} = \frac{40}{27}$

4. $s_4 = -1 + 1 - 1 + 1 = 0$

5. $s_4 = \frac{1}{2} - \frac{1}{3} + \frac{1}{4} - \frac{1}{5} = \frac{13}{60}$

6. $\lim_{n\to\infty} \left(\frac{-1}{7}\right)^n = 0$; series could converge.

7. $\lim_{n\to\infty} \left(1 + \frac{1}{n}\right) = 1$; series diverges.

8. $\lim_{n\to\infty} \frac{n^2}{n+1} = \lim_{n\to\infty} \frac{n}{1+1/n} = \infty$; series diverges.

9. $\lim_{n\to\infty} (-1)^n \frac{1}{n^2} = 0$; series could converge.

10. $\lim_{n\to\infty} \sin n\pi = \lim_{n\to\infty} 0 = 0$; series converges.

11. $\lim_{n\to\infty} \sin\left(\frac{\pi}{2} - \frac{1}{n}\right) = \sin\frac{\pi}{2} = 1$; series diverges.

12. $\lim_{n\to\infty} \tan\left(\frac{\pi}{2} - \frac{1}{n}\right) = \infty$; series diverges.

13. $\lim_{n\to\infty} n\sin\frac{1}{n} = \lim_{n\to\infty} \frac{\sin 1/n}{1/n} = 1$; series diverges.

14. $\lim_{n\to\infty} \left(1+\frac{1}{n}\right)\ln\left(1+\frac{1}{n}\right) = (1)\ln 1 = 0$; series could converge.

15. $s_j = j$; $\lim_{j\to\infty} s_j = \infty$; series diverges.

16. $s_j = \frac{1}{4} + \left(\frac{1}{4}\right)^2 + \cdots + \left(\frac{1}{4}\right)^j = \frac{1}{4}\left(\frac{1-(\frac{1}{4})^j}{1-\frac{1}{4}}\right) = \frac{1}{3}\left(1-\left(\frac{1}{4}\right)^j\right)$;

$$\lim_{j\to\infty} s_j = \lim_{j\to\infty} \frac{1}{3}\left(1-\left(\frac{1}{4}\right)^j\right) = \frac{1}{3};\ \sum_{n=1}^{\infty}\left(\frac{1}{4}\right)^n = \frac{1}{3}$$

17. $s_{2j} = 0$ and $s_{2j+1} = 1$ for $j \geq 1$; $\lim_{j\to\infty} s_j$ does not exist; series diverges.

18. $s_j = \frac{1}{3\cdot 2} + \frac{1}{4\cdot 3} + \cdots + \frac{1}{(j+2)(j+1)}$

$$= \left(\frac{1}{2}-\frac{1}{3}\right) + \left(\frac{1}{3}-\frac{1}{4}\right) + \cdots + \left(\frac{1}{j} - \frac{1}{j+1}\right) + \left(\frac{1}{j+1} - \frac{1}{j+2}\right) = \frac{1}{2} - \frac{1}{j+2};$$

$$\lim_{j\to\infty} s_j = \lim_{j\to\infty}\left(\frac{1}{2} - \frac{1}{j+2}\right) = \frac{1}{2};\ \sum_{n=3}^{\infty}\frac{1}{n(n-1)} = \frac{1}{2}$$

19. $s_j = \left(\frac{1}{2}-\frac{1}{3}\right) + \left(\frac{1}{3}-\frac{1}{4}\right) + \cdots + \left(\frac{1}{j+1} - \frac{1}{j+2}\right) = \frac{1}{2} - \frac{1}{j+2}$;

$$\lim_{j\to\infty} s_j = \lim_{j\to\infty}\left(\frac{1}{2} - \frac{1}{j+2}\right) = \frac{1}{2};\ \sum_{n=1}^{\infty}\left(\frac{1}{n+1} - \frac{1}{n+2}\right) = \frac{1}{2}$$

20. $s_j = \left(1-\frac{1}{8}\right) + \left(\frac{1}{8} - \frac{1}{27}\right) + \cdots + \left(\frac{1}{j^3} - \frac{1}{(j+1)^3}\right) = 1 - \frac{1}{(j+1)^3}$;

$$\lim_{j\to\infty} s_j = \lim_{j\to\infty}\left(1 - \frac{1}{(j+1)^3}\right) = 1;\ \sum_{n=1}^{\infty}\left(\frac{1}{n^3} - \frac{1}{(n+1)^3}\right) = 1$$

21. $s_j = (1-8) + (8-27) + \cdots + (j^3 - (j+1)^3) = 1 - (j+1)^3$;

$$\lim_{j\to\infty} s_j = \lim_{j\to\infty}(1-(j+1)^3) = -\infty;\ \text{series diverges}$$

22. $s_j = \frac{1}{1\cdot 2\cdot 3} + \frac{1}{2\cdot 3\cdot 4} + \cdots + \frac{1}{j(j+1)(j+2)}$

$$= \left[\frac{1}{2}\left(1-\frac{1}{2}\right) - \frac{1}{2}\left(\frac{1}{2}-\frac{1}{3}\right)\right] + \left[\frac{1}{2}\left(\frac{1}{2}-\frac{1}{3}\right) - \frac{1}{2}\left(\frac{1}{3}-\frac{1}{4}\right)\right]$$

$$+ \cdots + \left[\frac{1}{2}\left(\frac{1}{j}-\frac{1}{j+1}\right) - \frac{1}{2}\left(\frac{1}{j+1}-\frac{1}{j+2}\right)\right]$$

$$= \frac{1}{2}\left(1-\frac{1}{2}\right) - \frac{1}{2}\left(\frac{1}{j+1}-\frac{1}{j+2}\right) = \frac{1}{4} - \frac{1}{2(j+1)(j+2)};$$

$$\lim_{j\to\infty} s_j = \lim_{j\to\infty}\left(\frac{1}{4} - \frac{1}{2(j+1)(j+2)}\right) = \frac{1}{4}; \sum_{n=1}^{\infty}\frac{1}{n(n+1)(n+2)} = \frac{1}{4}$$

23. $s_n = (a_1 - a_2) + (a_2 - a_3) + \cdots + (a_{n-1} - a_n) + (a_n - a_{n+1}) = a_1 - a_{n+1}$. Thus $\lim_{n\to\infty} s_n$ exists if and only if $\lim_{n\to\infty} a_{n+1}$, or equivalently, $\lim_{n\to\infty} a_n$, exists. If $\lim_{n\to\infty} a_n$ exists, then

$$\lim_{n\to\infty} s_n = \lim_{n\to\infty}(a_1 - a_{n+1}) = a_1 - \lim_{n\to\infty} a_{n+1} = a_1 - \lim_{n\to\infty} a_n.$$

24. Recall that $a_1 = a_2 = 1$ and $a_{n+1} = a_n + a_{n-1}$ for $n \geq 2$. Thus $a_{n-1} = a_{n+1} - a_n$, so that $a_1+a_2+\cdots+a_n = (a_3-a_2)+(a_4-a_3)+(a_5-a_4)+\cdots+(a_{n+1}-a_n)+(a_{n+2}-a_{n+1}) = a_{n+2}-a_2 = a_{n+2}-1$.

25. Since the series is a geometric series with ratio $\frac{4}{7} < 1$, it converges;

$$\sum_{n=1}^{\infty} 5\left(\frac{4}{7}\right)^n = \frac{5(\frac{4}{7})}{1-\frac{4}{7}} = \frac{20}{3}.$$

26. Since the series is a geometric series with ratio $\frac{7}{4} > 1$, it diverges.

27. Since the series is a geometric series with ratio -0.3 and $|-0.3| < 1$, it converges;

$$\sum_{n=0}^{\infty}(-1)^n(0.3)^n = \sum_{n=0}^{\infty}(-0.3)^n = \frac{1}{1-(-0.3)} = \frac{10}{13}.$$

28. Since the series is a geometric series with ratio $0.33 < 1$, it converges:

$$\sum_{n=2}^{\infty}(0.33)^n = \frac{(0.33)^2}{1-(0.33)} = \frac{1089}{6700}.$$

29. Since the series is a geometric series with ratio $\frac{1}{2} < 1$, it converges:

$$\sum_{n=1}^{\infty} 5\left(\frac{1}{2}\right)^{n+1} = \sum_{n=1}^{\infty}\frac{5}{2}\left(\frac{1}{2}\right)^n = \frac{\frac{5}{2}(\frac{1}{2})}{1-\frac{1}{2}} = \frac{5}{2}.$$

30. Since the series is a geometric series with ratio $\frac{5}{7} < 1$, it converges;

$$\sum_{n=0}^{\infty}\frac{5^n}{7^{n+1}} = \sum_{n=0}^{\infty}\frac{1}{7}\left(\frac{5}{7}\right)^n = \frac{\frac{1}{7}}{1-\frac{5}{7}} = \frac{1}{2}.$$

31. Since the series is a geometric series with ratio $\frac{3}{5} < 1$, it converges;

$$\sum_{n=1}^{\infty} \frac{3^{n+3}}{5^{n-1}} = \sum_{n=1}^{\infty} (27)(5)\left(\frac{3}{5}\right)^n = \frac{135(\frac{3}{5})}{1-\frac{3}{5}} = \frac{405}{2}.$$

32. Since $\sum_{n=0}^{\infty}(\frac{1}{5})^n$ and $\sum_{n=0}^{\infty}(\frac{1}{2})^n$ are convergent geometric series and $(2^n+5^n)/(2^n5^n) = (\frac{1}{5})^n + (\frac{1}{2})^n$, the series $\sum_{n=0}^{\infty}(2^n+5^n)/(2^n5^n)$ converges;

$$\sum_{n=0}^{\infty} \frac{2^n+5^n}{2^n5^n} = \sum_{n=0}^{\infty}\left(\frac{1}{5}\right)^n + \sum_{n=0}^{\infty}\left(\frac{1}{2}\right)^n = \frac{1}{1-\frac{1}{5}} + \frac{1}{1-\frac{1}{2}} = \frac{5}{4} + 2 = \frac{13}{4}.$$

33. Since the series is a geometric series with ratio $-3/2$ and $|-3/2| > 1$, it diverges.

34. Since the series is a geometric series with ratio $(\frac{2}{3})^2 = \frac{4}{9} < 1$, it converges;

$$\sum_{n=0}^{\infty}(-3)\left(\frac{2}{3}\right)^{2n} = \sum_{n=0}^{\infty}(-3)\left(\frac{4}{9}\right)^n = \frac{-3}{1-\frac{4}{9}} = \frac{-27}{5}.$$

35. $\frac{1}{7} + \frac{1}{7^2} + \frac{1}{7^3} + \cdots = \frac{1}{7} + \frac{1}{7^2} + \frac{1}{7^3} + \sum_{n=4}^{\infty}\left(\frac{1}{7}\right)^n = \frac{57}{343} + \sum_{n=4}^{\infty}\left(\frac{1}{7}\right)^n$

36. $1 + \frac{2}{3} + \frac{2^2}{3^2} + \frac{2^3}{3^3} + \cdots = 1 + \frac{2}{3} + \frac{2^2}{3^2} + \sum_{n=4}^{\infty}\frac{2^{n-1}}{3^{n-1}} = \frac{19}{9} + \sum_{n=4}^{\infty}\frac{2^{n-1}}{3^{n-1}}$

37. $\sum_{n=1}^{\infty}\frac{1}{n^2+1} = \frac{1}{2} + \frac{1}{5} + \frac{1}{10} + \sum_{n=4}^{\infty}\frac{1}{n^2+1} = \frac{4}{5} + \sum_{n=4}^{\infty}\frac{1}{n^2+1}$

38. $\sum_{n=1}^{\infty}(-1)^n\frac{1}{n} = -1 + \frac{1}{2} - \frac{1}{3} + \sum_{n=4}^{\infty}(-1)^n\frac{1}{n} = \frac{-5}{6} + \sum_{n=4}^{\infty}(-1)^n\frac{1}{n}$

39. $\sum_{n=1}^{\infty}\frac{1}{n^2} = 1 + \frac{1}{4} + \frac{1}{9} + \sum_{n=4}^{\infty}\frac{1}{n^2} = \frac{49}{36} + \sum_{n=4}^{\infty}\frac{1}{n^2}$

40. $0.6666666\ldots = 6\left(\frac{1}{10}\right) + 6\left(\frac{1}{10}\right)^2 + 6\left(\frac{1}{10}\right)^3 + \cdots = \sum_{n=1}^{\infty} 6\left(\frac{1}{10}\right)^n = \frac{6(\frac{1}{10})}{1-\frac{1}{10}} = \frac{2}{3}$

41. $0.72727272\ldots = 72\left(\frac{1}{100}\right) + 72\left(\frac{1}{100}\right)^2 + 72\left(\frac{1}{100}\right)^3 + \cdots = \sum_{n=1}^{\infty} 72\left(\frac{1}{100}\right)^n = \frac{72(\frac{1}{100})}{1-\frac{1}{100}} = \frac{8}{11}$

42. $0.024242424\ldots = 24\left(\frac{1}{10}\right)^3 + 24\left(\frac{1}{10}\right)^5 + 24\left(\frac{1}{10}\right)^7 + \cdots = \sum_{n=1}^{\infty}\frac{24}{10}\left(\frac{1}{100}\right)^n = \frac{\frac{24}{10}(\frac{1}{100})}{1-\frac{1}{100}} = \frac{4}{165}$

43. $0.232232232\ldots = 232\left(\frac{1}{1000}\right) + 232\left(\frac{1}{1000}\right)^2 + 232\left(\frac{1}{1000}\right)^3 + \cdots$

$$= \sum_{n=1}^{\infty} 232\left(\frac{1}{1000}\right)^n = \frac{232(\frac{1}{1000})}{1-\frac{1}{1000}} = \frac{232}{999}$$

44. $0.453232232232\ldots = 0.453 + 232\left(\frac{1}{1000}\right)^2 + 232\left(\frac{1}{1000}\right)^3 + 232\left(\frac{1}{1000}\right)^4 + \cdots$

$$= \frac{453}{1000} + \sum_{n=1}^{\infty} 232\left(\frac{1}{1000}\right)^n = \frac{453}{1000} + \frac{232(\frac{1}{1000})^2}{1 - \frac{1}{1000}}$$

$$= \frac{453}{1000} + \frac{232}{999000} = \frac{452779}{999000}$$

45. $27.56123123123\ldots = 27.56 + 123\left(\frac{1}{10}\right)^5 + 123\left(\frac{1}{10}\right)^8 + 123\left(\frac{1}{10}\right)^{11} + \cdots$

$$= \frac{2756}{100} + \sum_{n=1}^{\infty} \frac{123}{100}\left(\frac{1}{1000}\right)^n = \frac{2756}{100} + \frac{\frac{123}{100}(\frac{1}{1000})}{1 - \frac{1}{1000}}$$

$$= \frac{2756}{100} + \frac{123}{99900} = \frac{917789}{33300}$$

46. $0.00649649649649\ldots = 649\left(\frac{1}{10}\right)^5 + 649\left(\frac{1}{10}\right)^8 + 649\left(\frac{1}{10}\right)^{11} + \cdots$

$$= \sum_{n=1}^{\infty} \frac{649}{100}\left(\frac{1}{1000}\right)^n = \frac{\frac{649}{100}(\frac{1}{1000})}{1 - \frac{1}{1000}} = \frac{649}{99900}$$

47. $0.86400000 = \frac{864}{1000} = \frac{108}{125}$

48. a. $\sum_{n=3}^{\infty} \frac{1}{n^2} = \sum_{n=1}^{\infty} \frac{1}{n^2} - \left(1 + \frac{1}{4}\right) = \frac{\pi^2}{6} - \frac{5}{4}$

b. $\sum_{n=1}^{\infty} \frac{1}{\pi^4(n+1)^4} = \frac{1}{\pi^4}\sum_{n=1}^{\infty} \frac{1}{(n+1)^4} = \frac{1}{\pi^4}\sum_{n=2}^{\infty} \frac{1}{n^4} = \frac{1}{\pi^4}\left(\sum_{n=1}^{\infty} \frac{1}{n^4} - 1\right) = \frac{1}{\pi^4}\left(\frac{\pi^4}{90} - 1\right) = \frac{1}{90} - \frac{1}{\pi^4}$

49. $\sum_{n=4}^{\infty}(-1)^{n+1}\frac{1}{n} = \sum_{n=1}^{\infty}(-1)^{n+1}\frac{1}{n} - \left(1 - \frac{1}{2} + \frac{1}{3}\right) = \ln 2 - \frac{5}{6}$

50. If $-1 < r < 1$, then $0 \le r^2 < 1$, so that by Exercise 50 (with r replaced by r^2), $\sum_{n=0}^{\infty}(-1)^n r^{2n} = 1/(1 + r^2)$.

51. a. 11

b. 31

52. Let s_j and s'_j be the jth partial sums of $\sum_{n=1}^{\infty} ca_n$ and $\sum_{n=1}^{\infty} a_n$, respectively. Then $s_j = ca_1 + ca_2 + ca_3 + \cdots + ca_j = c(a_1 + a_2 + a_3 + \cdots + a_j) = cs'_j$. By hypothesis $\lim_{j\to\infty} s'_j$ exists. Thus $\lim_{j\to\infty} s_j$ exists, and

$$\sum_{n=1}^{\infty} ca_n = \lim_{j\to\infty} s_j = \lim_{j\to\infty} cs'_j = c\lim_{j\to\infty} s'_j = c\sum_{n=1}^{\infty} a_n.$$

53. If $r > 0$, then either $r > 1$ or $1/r \ge 1$, so that either $\sum_{n=0}^{\infty}(1/r)^n$ or $\sum_{n=1}^{\infty} r^n$ diverges.

54. The series $1+2+4+8+\cdots$ diverges, so a is not a number.

55. Let c_j denote the concentration of insulin just after the jth injection, for $j \geq 1$. Then $c_j = c_0 + c_0 e^{-bt_0} + c_0 e^{-2bt_0} + \cdots + c_0 e^{-(j-1)bt_0} = \sum_{n=0}^{j-1} c_0 e^{-nbt_0}$. Since the first term is c_0,

$$\lim_{j\to\infty} c_j = \sum_{n=0}^{\infty} c_0 e^{-nbt_0} = \frac{c_0}{1-e^{-bt_0}}.$$

56. On the first bounce the ball reaches a height of 0.6 meters; on the second bounce it reaches a height of $(0.6)^2$ meters; and in general, on the nth bounce it reaches a height of $(0.6)^n$ meters. Thus the total distance traveled is

$$1+2(0.6)+2(0.6)^2+2(0.6)^3+\cdots = 1+\sum_{n=1}^{\infty} 2(0.6)^n = 1+\frac{2(0.6)}{1-(0.6)} = 4\,(\text{meters}).$$

57. If the height of the ball at its zenith is a, then until it hits the ground, the height is given by $h(t) = -4.9t^2 + a$. Thus $h(t) = 0$ if $0 = -4.9t^2 + a$, so that $t = a^{1/2}/(4.9)^{1/2}$. Therefore it takes $a^{1/2}/(4.9)^{1/2}$ seconds for the ball to hit the ground. Since the ball begins 1 meter above the surface, it takes $1/(4.9)^{1/2}$ seconds for it to drop to the surface. Between the first and second bounces the ball is in the air for $2(0.6)^{1/2}/(4.9)^{1/2}$ and likewise between the nth and $(n+1)$st bounces it takes $2(0.6)^{n/2}/(4.9)^{1/2}$ seconds. Thus the total time the ball is in the air is

$$\frac{1}{(4.9)^{1/2}} + \sum_{n=1}^{\infty} \frac{2(0.6)^{n/2}}{(4.9)^{1/2}} = \frac{1}{(4.9)^{1/2}} + \frac{2}{(4.9)^{1/2}} \sum_{n=1}^{\infty} [(0.6)^{1/2}]^n = \frac{1}{(4.9)^{1/2}} \left[1 + 2\frac{(0.6)^{1/2}}{1-(0.6)^{1/2}}\right] \approx 0.846.$$

Thus the total time the ball is in the air is approximately 0.846 seconds.

58. Let a_n = the fraction of weeds killed during the nth treatment. Then $a_1 = r$, $a_2 = ra_1 = r^2$, $a_3 = ra_2 = r^3$, and in general, $a_n = r^n$. Consequently the total fraction of weeds killed during the infinite number of treatments is $\sum_{n=1}^{\infty} a_n = \sum_{n=1}^{\infty} r^n$.

   a. If $r = \frac{1}{3}$, then since $\sum_{n=1}^{\infty} (\frac{1}{3})^n = \frac{1/3}{1-1/3} = \frac{1}{2}$, the fraction of weeds killed remains less that $\frac{1}{2}$ of the total number of weeds for all time.

   b. If $r = \frac{1}{2}$, then since $\sum_{n=1}^{\infty} (\frac{1}{2})^n = \frac{1/2}{1-1/2} = 1$, the fraction of weeds killed approaches 1. Thus the lawn can be made as nearly weed-free as we wish.

   c. We need to find an r in $(0, 1)$ such that $s = \sum_{n=1}^{\infty} r^n$. Since $\sum_{n=1}^{\infty} r^n = r/(1-r)$, this means that $s = r/(1-r)$. Solving for r, we find that $s - sr = r$, so that $r = s/(1+s)$.

59. During the first month the person earns 2500 and spends $p2500$, so that $w_1 = 2500 - p2500 = 2500(1-p)$. If $n \geq 2$, then during the nth month the person earns 2500 and spends $p(2500 + w_{n-1})$. Thus

$$w_n = 2500 + w_{n-1} - p(2500 + w_{n-1}) = (2500 + w_{n-1})(1-p).$$

We will show by induction that $w_n = 2500(1-p) + 2500(1-p)^2 + \cdots + 2500(1-p)^n$. If

$$w_{n-1} = 2500(1-p) + 2500(1-p)^2 + \cdots + 2500(1-p)^{n-1},$$

then

$$w_n = (2500 + w_{n-1})(1-p) = 2500(1-p) + 2500(1-p)^2 + \cdots + 2500(1-p)^n$$

which is the nth partial sum of the geometric series $\sum_{n=1}^{\infty} 2500(1-p)^n$. Since $0 < p < 1$ by hypothesis, it follows that $0 < 1-p < 1$, so that the series converges, and

$$\lim_{n\to\infty} w_n = \sum_{n=1}^{\infty} 2500(1-p)^n = \frac{2500(1-p)}{1-(1-p)} = \frac{2500(1-p)}{p}.$$

60. The real worth to the company is $100 + 90 + 81 + \cdots = \sum_{n=0}^{\infty} 100(0.9)^n = 100/(1-0.9) = 1000$ (dollars).

61. a. Initially there is one equilateral triangle whose sides have length 1. At each successive step in generating the Koch snowflake, each line segment of the nth step is replaced by 4 line segments, each having 1/3 the length of the line segment being replaced. Consequently after n steps there are $3 \cdot 4^n$ sides of length $1/3^n$. It follows that for the $(n+1)$st step there are $3 \cdot 4^n$ new equilateral triangles (one for each of the sides at the nth step). The side of such a triangle has length $1/3^{n+1}$, and thus the area of the triangle is given by

$$\frac{\sqrt{3}}{4}\left(\frac{1}{3^{n+1}}\right)^2 = \frac{\sqrt{3}}{4} \cdot \frac{1}{3^{2n+2}} = \frac{\sqrt{3}}{36} \cdot \frac{1}{3^{2n}}.$$

Therefore in the $(n+1)$st step the total amount of area of the $3 \cdot 4^n$ new triangles is

$$3 \cdot 4^n \left(\frac{\sqrt{3}}{36} \cdot \frac{1}{3^{2n}}\right) = \frac{\sqrt{3}}{12} \cdot \frac{4^n}{9^n} = \frac{\sqrt{3}}{12}\left(\frac{4}{9}\right)^n.$$

Consequently the area A of the Koch snowflake is given by

$$A = \frac{\sqrt{3}}{4} + \sum_{n=0}^{\infty} \frac{\sqrt{3}}{12}\left(\frac{4}{9}\right)^n = \frac{\sqrt{3}}{4} + \frac{\sqrt{3}}{12} \cdot \frac{1}{1-4/9} = \frac{\sqrt{3}}{4} + \frac{\sqrt{3}}{12} \cdot \frac{9}{5} = \frac{2}{5}\sqrt{3}.$$

b. As we noted in the solution of part (a), there are $3 \cdot 4^n$ sides of length $1/3^n$ after n steps. Thus the length of the boundary after n steps is $(3 \cdot 4^n)(1/3^n) = 3(\frac{4}{3})^n$. Since $\lim_{n\to\infty} 3(\frac{4}{3})^n = \infty$, the boundary of the snowflake has infinite length.

62. Since the bee travels twice as fast as the trains, when the bee flies from train A to train B, the bee will cover $\frac{2}{3}$ of the distance and train B will cover $\frac{1}{3}$ of the distance. Train A will travel exactly as far as train B, so that when the bee arrives at train B, the distance remaining between the trains is $\frac{1}{3}$ the distance between the trains when the bee was at train A. Thus on the first trip between the trains the bee flies $\frac{2}{3}(1)$, on the second flies $\frac{2}{3}(\frac{1}{3})$, on the third it flies $\frac{2}{3}(\frac{1}{9})$. In general, on the nth trip between the trains the bee flies $\frac{2}{3}(\frac{1}{3})^{n-1}$. Thus the total distance traveled by the bee is

$$\sum_{n=1}^{\infty} \frac{2}{3}\left(\frac{1}{3}\right)^{n-1} = \frac{\frac{2}{3}}{1-\frac{1}{3}} = 1\,(\text{mile}).$$

For a simple solution, notice that the two trains collide after 2 minutes. In 2 minutes the bee flies 1 mile.

63. The distance run by Achilles is

$$100 + 10 + 1 + \frac{1}{10} + \cdots = \sum_{n=0}^{\infty} 100\left(\frac{1}{10}\right)^n = \frac{100}{1 - \frac{1}{10}} = \frac{1000}{9} \text{ (yards)}.$$

The distance run by the tortoise during the same time is

$$10 + 1 + \frac{1}{10} + \frac{1}{100} + \cdots = \sum_{n=0}^{\infty} 10\left(\frac{1}{10}\right)^n = \frac{10}{1 - \frac{1}{10}} = \frac{100}{9} \text{ (yards)}.$$

Since $\frac{1000}{9} - \frac{100}{9} = \frac{900}{9} = 100$, Achilles catches up with the tortoise after running $\frac{1000}{9}$ (yards).

64. Let $n \geq 2$. Assume that the center of gravity of the first $n-1$ blocks lies over the right-hand end of the nth block, as in the figure. Set up a coordinate system as shown in the diagram, with the y axis passing through the center of gravity of the first $n-1$ blocks.

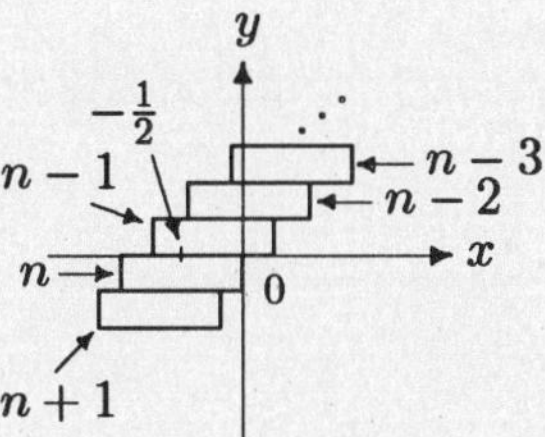

Then the moment of the first $n-1$ blocks about the y axis is 0, and the center of the nth block is $-1/2$, so that the moment of the first n blocks about the y axis is $0 + (-1/2) = -1/2$. Thus the x coordinate of the center of gravity of the first n blocks is given by $\bar{x} = (-1/2)/n = -1/(2n)$. If we place the $(n+1)$st block with the x coordinate of its center being $-1/2 - 1/(2n)$, then the center of gravity of the first n blocks will lie over the right-hand end of the $(n+1)$st block. Thus the nth block can protrude up to $1/(2n)$ from the end of the $(n+1)$st block. This means that the top block can protrude up to $\frac{1}{2} + \frac{1}{4} + \frac{1}{6} + \cdots + 1/(2n) = \frac{1}{2}(1 + \frac{1}{2} + \frac{1}{3} + \cdots + 1/n)$ from the $(n+1)$st block. Since the harmonic series $\sum_{n=1}^{\infty} 1/n$ diverges, it follows that the top block can protrude as far from the bottom block as we wish.

65. a. By the end of the 1st minute the ant has covered 1 foot, which is $\frac{1}{3}$ of the band. The band is then stretched so it is 6 feet long. By the end of the 2nd minute the ant has covered another foot, which is $\frac{1}{6}$ of the stretched band. Thus at the end of 2 minutes the ant has covered altogether $\frac{1}{3} + \frac{1}{6}$ of the band. The band is then stretched so it is 9 feet long. In general, during the jth minute the band is $3j$ feet long, and until the ant reaches the end of the band it covers an additional foot during that minute, which means covering $1/(3j)$ of the stretched band. Thus at the end of the jth minute the ant has covered altogether $\frac{1}{3} + \frac{1}{6} + \frac{1}{9} + \cdots + 1/(3j)$ of the band. So we need to find the smallest positive integer j so that $\frac{1}{3} + \frac{1}{6} + \frac{1}{9} + \cdots + 1/(3j) \geq 1$, that is, $\frac{1}{3}(1 + \frac{1}{2} + \frac{1}{3} + \cdots + 1/j) \geq 1$, or $\sum_{n=1}^{j} 1/n \geq 3$. But by Exercise 51(a), this happens if $j = 11$. Thus the ant reaches the other end of the band, and it takes between 10 and 11 minutes to do so.

b. For $n \geq 1$ let a_n be the distance in feet from the ant to the starting point at the end of n minutes (just after the band has been stretched). During the first minute the ant crawls 1 foot and hence is $\frac{1}{20}$ of the way between the two ends. Thus after the band is stretched an additional 20 feet, the ant is still $\frac{1}{20}$ of the way between the two ends, so that $a_1 = \frac{1}{20}(40) = 2$. By an argument similar to that used in part (a), we have $a_n = [(a_{n-1}+1)/(20n)][20(n+1)]$, so that $a_n/[20(n+1)] = a_{n-1}/(20n) + 1/(20n)$. By induction it follows that $a_n/[20(n+1)] = \frac{1}{20}(1+\frac{1}{2}+\frac{1}{3}+\cdots+1/n)$. The ant will reach the other end of the band during the $(n+1)$st minute if n satisfies $a_n + 1 \geq 20(n+1)$, or $a_n/[20(n+1)] + 1/[20(n+1)] \geq 1$, or $\frac{1}{20}(1+\frac{1}{2}+\frac{1}{3}+\cdots+1/(n+1)) \geq 1$. By the comments following the solution of Example 4 the ant reaches the other end, and it takes between 272,400,599 and 272,400,600 minutes.

9.5 Positive Series: The Integral Test and the Comparison Tests

1. Since $1/(n+1)^2 \leq 1/n^2$ for $n > 1$, and since $\sum_{n=1}^{\infty} 1/n^2$ is a convergent p series (with $p = 2$), $\sum_{n=1}^{\infty} 1/(n+1)^2$ converges by the Comparison Test.

2. $\sum_{n=1}^{\infty} 1/\sqrt{n}$ is a divergent p series (with $p = \frac{1}{2}$).

3. Since $1/\sqrt{n^3+1} \leq 1/n^{3/2}$ for $n \geq 1$, and since $\sum_{n=1}^{\infty} 1/n^{3/2}$ is a convergent p series (with $p = \frac{3}{2}$), $\sum_{n=1}^{\infty} 1/\sqrt{n^3+1}$ converges by the Comparison Test.

4. Since $1/\sqrt{n^2-1} \geq 1/n$ for $n \geq 2$, and since $\sum_{n=2}^{\infty} 1/n$ diverges, so does $\sum_{n=2}^{\infty} 1/\sqrt{n^2-1}$ by the Comparison Test.

5. Since $1/\sqrt{n^2+1} \geq 1/\sqrt{n^2+2n+1} = 1/(n+1)$ for $n \geq 1$, and since $\sum_{n=1}^{\infty} 1/(n+1) = \sum_{n=2}^{\infty} 1/n$ diverges, so does $\sum_{n=1}^{\infty} 1/\sqrt{n^2+1}$ by the Comparison Test.

6. Since $\sqrt{n} \leq n$ and thus $1/(n+\sqrt{n}) \geq 1/(n+n) = 1/(2n)$ for $n \geq 1$, and since $\sum_{n=1}^{\infty} 1/(2n)$ diverges, so does $\sum_{n=1}^{\infty} 1/(n+\sqrt{n})$ by the Comparison Test.

7. Since $1/e^{(n^2)} < 1/e^n = (1/e)^n$ for $n \geq 1$, and since $\sum_{n=1}^{\infty} (1/e)^n$ is a convergent geometric series, $\sum_{n=1}^{\infty} 1/e^{(n^2)}$ converges by the Comparison Test.

8. Let $f(x) = 1/(x\sqrt{\ln x})$. Then f is positive, continuous, and decreasing on $[2, \infty)$, $f(n) = 1/(n\sqrt{\ln n})$ for $n \geq 2$, and

$$\int_2^{\infty} \frac{1}{x\sqrt{\ln x}}\,dx = \lim_{b\to\infty} \int_2^b \frac{1}{x\sqrt{\ln x}}\,dx = \lim_{b\to\infty} 2\sqrt{\ln x}\Big|_2^{\infty} = \lim_{b\to\infty} (2\sqrt{\ln b} - 2\sqrt{\ln 2}) = \infty.$$

By the Integral Test, $\sum_{n=2}^{\infty} 1/(n\sqrt{\ln n})$ diverges.

9. Since $1/(n-1)(n-2) \leq 1/(n-2)^2$ for $n \geq 3$, and since $\sum_{n=3}^{\infty} 1/(n-2)^2 = \sum_{n=1}^{\infty} 1/n^2$ converges, so does $\sum_{n=3}^{\infty} 1/(n-1)(n-2)$ by the Comparison Test.

10. Since

$$\lim_{n\to\infty} \frac{n/(n^3-n-1)}{1/n^2} = \lim_{n\to\infty} \frac{n^3}{n^3-n-1} = \lim_{n\to\infty} \frac{1}{1-1/n^2-1/n^3} = 1$$

and since $\sum_{n=2}^{\infty} 1/n^2$ converges, the Limit Comparison Test implies that $\sum_{n=2}^{\infty} n/(n^3-n-1)$ converges.

11. Since

$$\lim_{n\to\infty} \frac{(n^2-1)/(n^3-n-1)}{1/n} = \lim_{n\to\infty} \frac{n^3-n}{n^3-n-1} = \lim_{n\to\infty} \frac{1-1/n^2}{1-1/n^2-1/n^3} = 1$$

and since $\sum_{n=2}^{\infty} 1/n$ diverges, the Limit Comparison Test implies that $\sum_{n=2}^{\infty}(n^2-1)/(n^3-n-1)$ diverges.

12. Observe that $0 \le (3+\cos n)/(n^2-4) \le 4/(n^2-4)$ for $n \ge 3$ and that

$$\lim_{n\to\infty} \frac{4/(n^2-4)}{1/n^2} = \lim_{n\to\infty} \frac{4n^2}{n^2-4} = \lim_{n\to\infty} \frac{4}{1-4/n^2} = 4.$$

By the Limit Comparison Test, $\sum_{n=3}^{\infty} 4/(n^2-4)$ converges because $\sum_{n=3}^{\infty} 1/n^2$ converges. Thus by the Comparison Test, $\sum_{n=3}^{\infty}(3+\cos n)/(n^2-4)$ converges.

13. Since $n/7^n < n/6^n = (n/2^n)(1/3^n) < (\frac{1}{3})^n$ for $n \ge 1$, and since $\sum_{n=1}^{\infty}(\frac{1}{3})^n$ is a convergent geometric series, the Comparison Test implies that $\sum_{n=1}^{\infty} n/7^n$ converges.

14. Since $\sqrt{n}/(n^2+3) \le 1/n^{3/2}$ for $n \ge 1$, and since $\sum_{n=1}^{\infty} 1/n^{3/2}$ is a convergent p series (with $p = 3/2$), the Comparison Test implies that $\sum_{n=1}^{\infty} \sqrt{n}/(n^2+3)$ converges.

15. Since

$$\lim_{n\to\infty} \frac{\sqrt{n}/(n^2-3)}{1/n^{3/2}} = \lim_{n\to\infty} \frac{n^2}{n^2-3} = \lim_{n\to\infty} \frac{1}{1-3/n^2} = 1$$

and since $\sum_{n=4}^{\infty} 1/n^{3/2}$ is a convergent p series (with $p = \frac{3}{2}$), the Limit Comparison Test implies that $\sum_{n=4}^{\infty} \sqrt{n}/(n^2-3)$ converges.

16. Since $(\cos^2 n)/n^{3/2} \le 1/n^{3/2}$ for $n \ge 1$, and since $\sum_{n=1}^{\infty} 1/n^{3/2}$ is a convergent p series (with $p = \frac{3}{2}$), the Comparison Test implies that $\sum_{n=1}^{\infty}(\cos^2 n)/n^{3/2}$ converges.

17. Since

$$\lim_{n\to\infty} \frac{n/(n^3+1)^{3/7}}{1/n^{2/7}} = \lim_{n\to\infty} \frac{n^{9/7}}{(n^3+1)^{3/7}} = \lim_{n\to\infty} \frac{1}{(1+1/n^3)^{3/7}} = 1$$

and since $\sum_{n=1}^{\infty} 1/n^{2/7}$ is a divergent p series (with $p = \frac{2}{7}$), the Limit Comparison Test implies that $\sum_{n=1}^{\infty} n/(n^3+1)^{3/7}$ diverges.

18. Since

$$\lim_{n\to\infty} \frac{1/\sqrt[3]{n^2+1}}{1/n^{2/3}} = \lim_{n\to\infty} \frac{n^{2/3}}{\sqrt[3]{n^2+1}} = \lim_{n\to\infty} \frac{1}{\sqrt[3]{1+1/n^2}} = 1$$

and since $\sum_{n=1}^{\infty} 1/n^{2/3}$ is a divergent p series (with $p = \frac{2}{3}$), the Limit Comparison Test implies that $\sum_{n=1}^{\infty} 1/\sqrt[3]{n^2+1}$ diverges.

19. Since

$$\lim_{n\to\infty} \frac{1/(n\sqrt{n^2-1})}{1/n^2} = \lim_{n\to\infty} \frac{n}{\sqrt{n^2-1}} = \lim_{n\to\infty} \frac{1}{\sqrt{1-1/n^2}} = 1$$

and since $\sum_{n=2}^{\infty} 1/n^2$ is a convergent p series (with $p = 2$), the Limit Comparison Test implies that $\sum_{n=2}^{\infty} 1/(n\sqrt{n^2-1})$ converges.

20. Let $f(x) = xe^{-x^2}$. Then $f'(x) = e^{-x^2} - 2x^2e^{-x^2} = e^{-x^2}(1-2x^2) < 0$ for $x \geq 1$. Thus f is positive, continuous, and decreasing on $[1, \infty)$, and $f(n) = ne^{-n^2}$. Also

$$\int_1^{\infty} xe^{-x^2}\,dx = \lim_{b\to\infty} \int_1^b xe^{-x^2}\,dx = \lim_{b\to\infty} \left(-\frac{1}{2}e^{-x^2}\right)\Big|_1^b = \lim_{b\to\infty} \left(-\frac{1}{2}e^{-b^2} + \frac{1}{2}e^{-1}\right) = \frac{1}{2e}.$$

By the Integral Test, $\sum_{n=1}^{\infty} ne^{-n^2}$ converges.

21. Since $0 \leq (\tan^{-1} n)/(n^2+1) \leq \pi/2n^2$ for $n \geq 1$, and since $\sum_{n=1}^{\infty} \pi/2n^2$ converges by Example 1, the Comparison Test implies that $\sum_{n=1}^{\infty} (\tan^{-1} n)/(n^2+1)$ converges.

22. Let $f(x) = 1/[x(\ln x)^2]$. Then f is positive, continuous, and decreasing on $[3, \infty)$, and

$$\int_3^{\infty} \frac{1}{x(\ln x)^2}\,dx = \lim_{b\to\infty} \int_3^b \frac{1}{x(\ln x)^2}\,dx = \lim_{b\to\infty} \frac{-1}{\ln x}\Big|_3^b = \lim_{b\to\infty} \left(\frac{-1}{\ln b} + \frac{1}{\ln 3}\right) = \frac{1}{\ln 3}.$$

By the Integral Test, $\sum_{n=3}^{\infty} 1/[n(\ln n)^2]$ converges. Thus $\sum_{n=2}^{\infty} 1/[n(\ln n)^2]$ converges also.

23. Since $(\ln n)/n^2 \leq 2\sqrt{n}/n^2 = 2/n^{3/2}$ for $n \geq 1$, and since $\sum_{n=1}^{\infty} 2/n^{3/2}$ converges by Example 1, the Comparison Test implies that $\sum_{n=1}^{\infty} (\ln n)/n^2$ converges.

24. Since $\ln n \leq 2\sqrt{n}$ for $n \geq 1$, it follows that $1/(\ln n)^2 \geq 1/4n$ for $n \geq 2$. But $\sum_{n=2}^{\infty} 1/4n$ diverges, and consequently $\sum_{n=2}^{\infty} 1/(\ln n)^2$ diverges by the Comparison Test.

25. Since $0 < 1/(\ln n)^n < 1/(\ln 3)^n$ for $n \geq 3$, and since $1/\ln 3 < 1$, which implies that $\sum_{n=3}^{\infty} 1/(\ln 3)^n$ is a convergent geometric series, the Comparison Test implies that $\sum_{n=3}^{\infty} 1/(\ln n)^n$ converges. Thus $\sum_{n=2}^{\infty} 1/(\ln n)^n$ also converges.

26. Since $1+2+3+\cdots+n = n(n+1)/2$, we have

$$\sum_{n=1}^{\infty} \frac{1}{1+2+3+\cdots+n} = \sum_{n=1}^{\infty} \frac{2}{n(n+1)}.$$

Since

$$\frac{2}{n(n+1)} \leq \frac{2}{n^2}$$

and $\sum_{n=1}^{\infty} 2/n^2$ converges (because the p series converges when $p = 2$), the Comparison Test implies that the given series converges.

27. Since

$$\lim_{n\to\infty} \frac{\sin 1/n}{1/n} = \lim_{x\to 0+} \frac{\sin x}{x} = 1$$

and since $\sum_{n=1}^{\infty} 1/n$ diverges, the Limit Comparison Test implies that $\sum_{n=1}^{\infty} \sin 1/n$ diverges.

28. Since

$$\lim_{n\to\infty} \frac{1/(n\sqrt[n]{n})}{1/n} = \lim_{n\to\infty} \frac{1}{\sqrt[n]{n}} = 1$$

and since $\sum_{n=1}^{\infty} 1/n$ diverges, the Limit Comparison Test implies that $\sum_{n=1}^{\infty} 1/(n\sqrt[n]{n})$ diverges.

29. By (9) with $p = 3$, we have $E_j \le 1/(2j^2)$. Since $1/(2j^2) \le 0.02$ if $j^2 \ge 25$, we can let $j = 5$.

30. By (9) with $p = \frac{4}{3}$, we have

$$E_j \le \frac{1}{\frac{1}{3}j^{1/3}} = \frac{3}{j^{1/3}}.$$

Since $3/j^{1/3} \le 0.02 = 2/100$, if $j^{1/3} \ge 150$, or equivalently, $j \ge 150^3 = 3{,}375{,}000$, we can let $j = 3{,}375{,}000$.

31. By (9) with $p = \frac{8}{7}$, we have

$$E_j \le \frac{1}{\frac{1}{7}j^{1/7}} = \frac{7}{j^{1/7}}.$$

Since $7/j^{1/7} \le 0.02 = 2/100$ if $j^{1/7} \ge 350$, or equivalently, $j \ge 350^7 \approx 6.43 \times 10^{17}$, we can let $j = 6.44 \times 10^{17}$.

32. Let $f(x) = \dfrac{1}{x(\ln x)^2}$. Then by (8)

$$E_j \le \int_j^{\infty} \frac{1}{x(\ln x)^2}\,dx = \lim_{b\to\infty} \int_j^b \frac{1}{x(\ln x)^2}\,dx \overset{u=\ln x}{=} \lim_{b\to\infty} \int_{\ln j}^{\ln b} \frac{1}{u^2}\,du$$

$$= \lim_{b\to\infty} -\frac{1}{u}\bigg|_{\ln j}^{\ln b} = \lim_{b\to\infty} \left(\frac{1}{\ln j} - \frac{1}{\ln b}\right) = \frac{1}{\ln j}.$$

Since $1/\ln j \le 0.02$ if $\ln j \ge 50$, or equivalently, $j \ge e^{50} \approx 5.18 \times 10^{21}$, we can let $j = 5.19 \times 10^{21}$.

33. a. By (6) and (7),

$$\sum_{n=1}^{j-1} a_n + \sum_{n=j+1}^{\infty} a_n \overset{(6)}{\le} \sum_{n=1}^{j-1} a_n + \int_j^{\infty} f(x)\,dx \overset{(7)}{\le} \sum_{n=1}^{j-1} a_n + \sum_{n=j}^{\infty} a_n = \sum_{n=1}^{\infty} a_n.$$

b. By part (a) and (6),

$$0 \overset{(a)}{\le} \sum_{n=1}^{\infty} a_n - \left(\sum_{n=1}^{j-1} a_n + \int_j^{\infty} f(x)\,dx\right) = \sum_{n=j}^{\infty} a_n - \int_j^{\infty} f(x)\,dx \le \sum_{n=j}^{\infty} a_n - \sum_{n=j+1}^{\infty} a_n = a_j.$$

34. First notice that if $j = 11$, then $a_j = 1/11^4 < 1/10^4 = 10^{-4}$. By Exercise 33 this means that

$$0 \le \sum_{n=1}^{\infty} \frac{1}{n^4} - \left(\sum_{n=1}^{10} \frac{1}{n^4} + \int_{11}^{\infty} \frac{1}{x^4}\,dx\right) \le 10^{-4}.$$

Since $\sum_{n=1}^{10} 1/n^4 \approx 1.082036583$ and

$$\int_{11}^{\infty} \frac{1}{x^4}\,dx = \lim_{b\to\infty} \int_{11}^{b} \frac{1}{x^4}\,dx = \lim_{b\to\infty} -\frac{1}{3x^3}\bigg|_{11}^{b}$$

$$= \lim_{b\to\infty}\left(\frac{1}{3(11)^3} - \frac{1}{3b^3}\right) = \frac{1}{3(11)^3} \approx 2.50438267\times 10^{-4}$$

it follows that the desired approximation of $\sum_{n=1}^{\infty} 1/n^4$ is

$$1.082036583 + 2.50438267\times 10^{-4} \approx 1.082287021.$$

35. Observe that if $p \neq 1$,

$$\int_2^{\infty} \frac{1}{x(\ln x)^p}\,dx = \lim_{b\to\infty}\int_2^b \frac{1}{x(\ln x)^p}\,dx = \lim_{b\to\infty} \left.\frac{-1}{(p-1)(\ln x)^{p-1}}\right|_2^b$$

$$= \lim_{b\to\infty}\left[\frac{1}{(p-1)(\ln 2)^{p-1}} - \frac{1}{(p-1)(\ln b)^{p-1}}\right].$$

Since

$$\lim_{b\to\infty}\frac{1}{(\ln b)^{p-1}} = \lim_{b\to\infty}(\ln b)^{1-p} = \begin{cases} \infty & \text{if } p<1 \\ 0 & \text{if } p>1 \end{cases}$$

we conclude from the Integral Test that $\sum_{n=2}^{\infty} 1/[n(\ln n)^p]$ converges provided that $p > 1$, and diverges for $p < 1$. For $p = 1$, the series diverges by Example 3.

36. Observe that for any positive value of a,

$$\int_a^{\infty} \frac{1}{x^p}\,dx = \lim_{b\to\infty}\int_a^b \frac{1}{x^p}\,dx = \lim_{b\to\infty} \left.\frac{-1}{(p-1)x^{p-1}}\right|_a^b$$

$$= \lim_{b\to\infty}\left(\frac{1}{(p-1)a^{p-1}} - \frac{1}{(p-1)b^{p-1}}\right) = \frac{1}{(p-1)a^{p-1}}$$

since $p > 1$. Taking first $a = j+1$ and then $a = j$, we conclude from (8) that

$$\frac{1}{(p-1)(j+1)^{p-1}} \le E_j \le \frac{1}{(p-1)j^{p-1}}.$$

37. Since $\sum_{n=1}^{\infty} a_n$ converges, we have $\lim_{n\to\infty} a_n = 0$. Thus there is an integer N such that $a_n < 1$ for $n \ge N$. Then $a_n^2 < a_n$ for $n \ge N$. Since $\sum_{n=N}^{\infty} a_n$ converges, the Comparison Test implies that $\sum_{n=N}^{\infty} a_n^2$ converges. Thus $\sum_{n=1}^{\infty} a_n^2$ converges also.

38. Since $\sum_{n=1}^{\infty} b_n$ converges, we have $\lim_{n\to\infty} b_n = 0$. Since $b_n \ge 0$ this means there is a positive integer N such that $0 \le b_n \le 1$ for $n \ge N$. Then $0 \le a_n b_n \le a_n$ for $n \ge N$. Since $\sum_{n=1}^{\infty} a_n$ converges by hypothesis, the Comparison Test implies that $\sum_{n=N}^{\infty} a_n b_n$ converges. Thus $\sum_{n=1}^{\infty} a_n b_n$ converges.

39. Taking $f(x) = 1/x$ and $a_n = 1/n$ in (2) and (3), we have

$$\frac{1}{2} + \frac{1}{3} + \cdots + \frac{1}{j} \le \int_1^j \frac{1}{x}\,dx \le 1 + \frac{1}{2} + \cdots + \frac{1}{j-1}.$$

Since $\int_1^j (1/x)\,dx = \ln j$, we have

$$\frac{1}{2} + \frac{1}{3} + \cdots + \frac{1}{j} \le \ln j \le 1 + \frac{1}{2} + \cdots + \frac{1}{j-1}$$

so that

$$\frac{1}{j} + \ln j \le 1 + \frac{1}{2} + \cdots + \frac{1}{j} \le 1 + \ln j.$$

Thus

$$\frac{1}{j \ln j} + 1 \le \frac{\sum_{n=1}^{j} 1/n}{\ln j} \le \frac{1}{\ln j} + 1.$$

Since

$$\lim_{j\to\infty} \left(\frac{1}{j \ln j} + 1 \right) = 1 = \lim_{j\to\infty} \left(\frac{1}{\ln j} + 1 \right),$$

(5) of Section 9.3 implies that

$$\lim_{j\to\infty} \frac{\sum_{n=1}^{j} 1/n}{\ln j} = 1.$$

40. The proportion of fuel used during the first j hundred miles is the jth partial sum of the series $\sum_{n=1}^{\infty} 1/(n+1)^2 = \sum_{n=2}^{\infty} 1/n^2$. Since $\sum_{n=1}^{\infty} 1/n^2 = \pi^2/6$, we have $\sum_{n=2}^{\infty} 1/n^2 = \pi^2/6 - 1 < 1$. Thus the rocket never uses up all its fuel.

41. a. Let $n \ge 2$. For the nth floor the circumference is $2\pi[10/(n \ln n)] = 20\pi/(n \ln n)$. Thus the total circumference of all the floors except the first is $\sum_{n=2}^{\infty} 20\pi/(n \ln n) = 20\pi \sum_{n=2}^{\infty} 1/(n \ln n)$. By Example 3, the series diverges. Therefore the total circumference is infinite.

b. For the nth floor the area is $\pi[10/(n \ln n)]^2 = 100\pi/[n^2(\ln n)^2]$. Therefore the total area of all the floors except the first is $\sum_{n=2}^{\infty} 100\pi/[n^2(\ln n)^2]$. Since $1/[n^2(\ln n)^2] \le 1/n^2$ for $n \ge 3$, and since $\sum_{n=2}^{\infty} 1/n^2$ converges, it follows from the Comparison Test that $\sum_{n=3}^{\infty} 1/[n^2(\ln n)^2]$, and hence $\sum_{n=2}^{\infty} 100\pi/[n^2(\ln n)^2]$, converge. Consequently the total area of all the floors is finite.

9.6 Positive Series: The Ratio Test and the Root Test

1. $\displaystyle\lim_{n\to\infty} \frac{(n+1)!/2^{n+1}}{n!/2^n} = \lim_{n\to\infty} \frac{n+1}{2} = \infty$; the series diverges.

2. $\displaystyle\lim_{n\to\infty} \sqrt[n]{\frac{n}{10^n}} = \lim_{n\to\infty} \frac{\sqrt[n]{n}}{10} = \frac{1}{10} < 1$; the series converges.

3. $\displaystyle\lim_{n\to\infty} \frac{(n+1)!\,3^{n+1}/10^{n+1}}{n!\,3^n/10^n} = \lim_{n\to\infty} \frac{3(n+1)}{10} = \infty$; the series diverges.

4. $\displaystyle\lim_{n\to\infty} \frac{(n+1)!/2^{[(n+1)^2]}}{n!/2^{(n^2)}} = \lim_{n\to\infty} \frac{n+1}{2^{2n+1}} = 0$; the series converges.

5. $\displaystyle\lim_{n\to\infty} \sqrt[n]{\left(\frac{n}{2n+5}\right)^n} = \lim_{n\to\infty} \frac{n}{2n+5} = \frac{1}{2} < 1$; the series converges.

6. $\displaystyle\lim_{n\to\infty} \frac{(n+1)!/(2n+2)!}{n!/(2n)!} = \lim_{n\to\infty} \frac{n+1}{(2n+2)(2n+1)} = 0$; the series converges.

7. $\displaystyle\lim_{n\to\infty} \frac{(2n+2)!/[(n+1)!]^2}{(2n)!/(n!)^2} = \lim_{n\to\infty} \frac{(2n+2)(2n+1)}{(n+1)^2} = 4 > 1$; the series diverges.

8. $\displaystyle\lim_{n\to\infty}\frac{2^{2n}/(2n)!}{2^{2n-2}/(2n-2)!}=\lim_{n\to\infty}\frac{4}{(2n)(2n-1)}=0$; the series converges.

9. $\displaystyle\lim_{n\to\infty}\sqrt[n]{n^{100}e^{-n}}=\lim_{n\to\infty}(\sqrt[n]{n})^{100}e^{-1}=e^{-1}<1$; the series converges.

10. $\displaystyle\lim_{n\to\infty}\frac{(1.1)^{n+1}/(n+1)^7}{(1.1)^n/n^7}=\lim_{n\to\infty}(1.1)\frac{n^7}{(n+1)^7}=\lim_{n\to\infty}(1.1)\Big/\left(1+\frac{1}{n}\right)^7=1.1>1$; the series diverges.

11. $\displaystyle\lim_{n\to\infty}\frac{(n+1)^{1.7}/(1.7)^{n+1}}{n^{1.7}/(1.7)^n}=\lim_{n\to\infty}\frac{(n+1)^{1.7}}{(1.7)n^{1.7}}=\lim_{n\to\infty}\frac{1}{(1.7)}\left(1+\frac{1}{n}\right)^{1.7}=\frac{1}{1.7}<1$; the series converges.

12. By l'Hôpital's Rule,

$$\lim_{n\to\infty}\frac{\ln(n+1)}{\ln n}=\lim_{x\to\infty}\frac{\ln(x+1)}{\ln x}=\lim_{x\to\infty}\frac{1/(x+1)}{1/x}=\lim_{x\to\infty}\frac{x}{x+1}=\lim_{x\to\infty}\frac{1}{1+1/x}=1.$$

Thus for the series,

$$\lim_{n\to\infty}\frac{\ln(n+1)/e^{n+1}}{(\ln n)/e}=\lim_{n\to\infty}\frac{1}{e}\frac{\ln(n+1)}{\ln n}=\frac{1}{e}<1;$$

the series converges.

13. $\displaystyle\lim_{n\to\infty}\frac{(n+1)!/e^{n+1}}{n!/e^n}=\lim_{n\to\infty}\frac{n+1}{e}=\infty$; the series diverges.

14. $\displaystyle\lim_{n\to\infty}\sqrt[n]{n\left(\frac{\pi}{4}\right)^n}=\lim_{n\to\infty}n^{1/n}\left(\frac{\pi}{4}\right)=\frac{\pi}{4}<1$; the series converges.

15. $\displaystyle\lim_{n\to\infty}\sqrt[n]{\frac{1}{(\ln n)^n}}=\lim_{n\to\infty}\frac{1}{\ln n}=0$; the series converges.

16. Both the Ratio and the Root Test fail. However, $(n+5)/n^3\le 6n/n^3=6/n^2$ for $n\ge 1$. Since $\sum_{n=1}^{\infty}6/n^2$ converges, the Comparison Test implies that $\sum_{n=1}^{\infty}(n+5)/n^3$ converges.

17. Since

$$\frac{1\cdot 3\cdot 5\cdots(2n-1)}{2\cdot 4\cdot 6\cdots(2n)}=\frac{3}{2}\cdot\frac{5}{4}\cdots\frac{2n-1}{2n-2}\cdot\frac{1}{2n}>\frac{1}{2n}$$

and since $\sum_{n=1}^{\infty}1/2n$ diverges, the given series diverges by the Comparison Test.

18. $\displaystyle\lim_{n\to\infty}\frac{\dfrac{1\cdot 3\cdot 5\cdots(2n+3)}{2\cdot 5\cdot 8\cdots(3n+5)}}{\dfrac{1\cdot 3\cdot 5\cdots(2n+1)}{2\cdot 5\cdot 8\cdots(3n+2)}}=\lim_{n\to\infty}\frac{2n+3}{3n+5}=\lim_{n\to\infty}\frac{2+\dfrac{3}{n}}{3+\dfrac{5}{n}}=\frac{2}{3}$; the series converges.

19. $\displaystyle\lim_{n\to\infty}\frac{\dfrac{(2n+2)!}{(n+1)!\,(2n+2)^{n+1}}}{\dfrac{(2n)!}{n!\,(2n)^n}}=\lim_{n\to\infty}\frac{(2n+2)(2n+1)(2n)^n}{(n+1)(2n+2)^{n+1}}=\lim_{n\to\infty}\left(\frac{2n+1}{n+1}\right)\left(\frac{n}{n+1}\right)^n$

$$=\lim_{n\to\infty}\frac{2+1/n}{(1+1/n)(1+1/n)^n}=\frac{2}{e}<1;$$

the series converges.

20. Since $(n!/n^n)^n \le (\frac{1}{2})^n$ for $n \ge 2$ and since $\sum_{n=2}^{\infty}(\frac{1}{2})^n$ is a convergent geometric series, the Comparison Test implies that $\sum_{n=2}^{\infty}(n!/n^n)^n$ converges.

21. Since $\sin 1/n! \le 1/n!$ and $\cos 1/n! \ge \cos 1$ for $n \ge 1$, we have

$$\frac{\sin 1/n!}{\cos 1/n!} \le \frac{1}{n!\,\cos 1}.$$

It follows from Example 1 that $\sum_{n=1}^{\infty} 1/(n!\,\cos 1)$ converges. By the Comparison Test

$$\sum_{n=1}^{\infty} \frac{\sin(1/n!)}{\cos(1/n!)}$$

converges.

22. $\lim_{n\to\infty} \sqrt[n]{a_n} = \lim_{n\to\infty} \sum_{k=1}^{n} \frac{1}{k} = \infty$; the series diverges.

23. Let $b_n = (n/(2n+1))^n$ for $n \ge 1$. Then

$$\lim_{n\to\infty} \sqrt[n]{b_n} = \lim_{n\to\infty} \frac{n}{2n+1} = \lim_{n\to\infty} \frac{1}{2+1/n} = \frac{1}{2} < 1.$$

Thus $\sum_{n=1}^{\infty} b_n$ converges by the Root Test. Since $0 \le a_n \le b_n$ for $n \ge 1$, it follows from the Comparison Test that $\sum_{n=1}^{\infty} a_n$ converges.

24. $\lim_{n\to\infty} \dfrac{c^{n+1}/(n+1)!}{c^n/n!} = \lim_{n\to\infty} \dfrac{c}{n+1} = 0$, so that $\sum_{n=0}^{\infty} \dfrac{c^n}{n!}$ converges.

25. a. Let n be even. Then

$$\frac{a_{n+1}}{a_n} = \frac{1/(n+1)^{n+1}}{1/(2n)^{2n}} = \frac{(2n)^{2n}}{(n+1)^{n+1}} = \frac{(2n)^{n+1}(2n)^{n-1}}{(n+1)^{n+1}} = \left(\frac{2n}{n+1}\right)^{n+1} (2n)^{n-1} \ge (2n)^{n-1}$$

which grows without bound as n increases. Next, let n be odd. Then

$$\frac{a_{n+1}}{a_n} = \frac{1/(2n+2)^{2n+2}}{1/n^n} = \frac{n^n}{(2n+2)^{2n+2}} = \frac{n^n}{(2n+2)^n(2n+2)^{n+2}}$$

$$= \left(\frac{n}{2n+2}\right)^n \frac{1}{(2n+2)^{n+2}} \le \frac{1}{(2n+2)^{n+2}}$$

which decreases and approaches 0 as n increases. Thus $\lim_{n\to\infty} a_{n+1}/a_n$ does not exist, so the Ratio Test is inconclusive.

b. For odd n, $\sqrt[n]{a_n} = 1/n$; for even n, $\sqrt[n]{a_n} = 1/(2n)^2$. Thus $\lim_{n\to\infty} \sqrt[n]{a_n} = 0$. By the Root Test, the series converges.

26. a. Observe that $n/3^n < 1/2^n$ is equivalent to $n < (\frac{3}{2})^n$, or $\sqrt[n]{n} < \frac{3}{2}$. Notice that if $n = 3$, then $\sqrt[3]{3} < \frac{3}{2}$. To show that $n/3^n < 1/2^n$ for all $n \ge 3$, we will show that if $f(x) = x^{1/x}$ for $x \ge 3$, then f is decreasing. Let $f(x) = x^{1/x} = e^{(\ln x)/x}$ for $x \ge 3$. Then

$$f'(x) = e^{(\ln x)/x}\left(-\frac{1}{x^2}\ln x + \frac{1}{x^2}\right) = e^{(\ln x)/x}\left(\frac{1}{x^2}\right)(1 - \ln x).$$

Since $x \geq 3 > e$, it follows that $f'(x) < 0$, so that f is decreasing. Thus if $n > 3$, then $\sqrt[n]{n} < \sqrt[3]{3} < \frac{3}{2}$, so that $n/3^n < 1/2^n$.

b. By part (a),

$$E_{20} = \sum_{n=21}^{\infty} \frac{n}{3^n} < \sum_{n=21}^{\infty} \frac{1}{2^n} = \frac{(\frac{1}{2})^{21}}{1-\frac{1}{2}} = \frac{1}{2^{20}} \approx 9.536743164 \times 10^{-7}.$$

27. a. Let $n = 20$. Then

$$\frac{2^n}{n!} = \frac{2^{20}}{20!} = \frac{\overbrace{2 \cdot 2 \cdots 2}^{\text{20 of these}}}{(20)(19)\cdots(2)(1)} < 1 = \left(\frac{2}{21}\right)^{n-20}.$$

Let $n > 20$. Then

$$\frac{2^n}{n!} < \left(\frac{2}{21}\right)^{n-20} \quad \text{is equivalent to} \quad \frac{1}{n!} < \frac{2^{n-20}}{2^n(21)^{n-20}} = \frac{1}{2^{20}(21)^{n-20}}.$$

Since $2^{20} < 20!$ and $(21)^{n-20} < n(n-1)(n-2)\cdots(22)(21)$, it follows that

$$\frac{1}{2^{20}(21)^{n-20}} > \frac{1}{(20!)[n(n-1)(n-2)\cdots(22)(21)]} = \frac{1}{n!}.$$

b. By part (a),

$$E_{20} = \sum_{n=21}^{\infty} \frac{2^n}{n!} < \sum_{n=21}^{\infty} \left(\frac{2}{21}\right)^{n-20} = \sum_{n=1}^{\infty} \left(\frac{2}{21}\right)^{n} = \frac{\frac{2}{21}}{1-\frac{2}{21}} = \frac{2}{19}.$$

28. a. If $n = 2k$, then

$$\frac{a_{n+1}}{a_n} = \frac{a_{2k+1}}{2_{2k}} = \frac{1/(2k+1)^2}{1/k^2} = \frac{k^2}{(2k+1)^2}.$$

If $n = 2k+1$, then

$$\frac{a_{n+1}}{a_n} = \frac{a_{2k+2}}{a_{2k+1}} = \frac{1/(k+1)^2}{1/(2k+1)^2} = \frac{(2k+1)^2}{(k+1)^2}.$$

Since

$$\lim_{k\to\infty} \frac{k^2}{(2k+1)^2} = \lim_{k\to\infty} \frac{1}{(2+1/k)^2} = \frac{1}{4} \quad \text{and} \quad \lim_{k\to\infty} \frac{(2k+1)^2}{(k+1)^2} = \lim_{k\to\infty} \frac{(2+1/k)^2}{(1+1/k)^2} = 4$$

it follows that $\lim_{n\to\infty} a_{n+1}/a_n$ does not exist. However, $a_{2n+1} = 1/(2n+1)^2$ and $a_{2n} = 1/n^2 = 4/(2n)^2$, so that $a_n \leq 4/n^2$ for $n \geq 1$. By the Comparison Test, $\sum_{n=1}^{\infty} a_n$ converges.

b. Let $a_n = (n-1)!$ for $n \geq 1$. Then $a_{n+1}/a_n = n!/(n-1)! = n$, so that $\lim_{n\to\infty} a_{n+1}/a_n$ does not exist. Since $\lim_{n\to\infty} a_n = \lim_{n\to\infty}(n-1)! = \infty$, $\sum_{n=1}^{\infty} a_n$ diverges.

29. a. $$\sqrt[n]{a_n} = \begin{cases} 0 & \text{for } n \text{ even} \\ \dfrac{n}{2n+1} & \text{for } n \text{ odd} \end{cases}$$

Since $n/(2n+1) \geq \frac{1}{3}$ for $n \geq 1$, it follows that $\lim_{n\to\infty} \sqrt[n]{a_n}$ does not exist. The solution of Exercise 23 shows that $\sum_{n=1}^{\infty} a_n$ converges.

b. Let $a_n = n^n$ for $n \geq 1$. Then $\sqrt[n]{a_n} = n$, so that $\lim_{n\to\infty} \sqrt[n]{a_n}$ does not exist. Since $\lim_{n\to\infty} a_n = \lim_{n\to\infty} n^n = \infty$, $\sum_{n=1}^{\infty}$ does not converge.

9.7 Alternating Series and Absolute Convergence

1. Since $\{1/(2n+1)\}_{n=1}^{\infty}$ is a decreasing, positive sequence with $\lim_{n\to\infty} 1/(2n+1) = 0$, the series converges.

2. Since $\{1/\ln n\}_{n=2}^{\infty}$ is a decreasing, positive sequence with $\lim_{n\to\infty} 1/\ln n = 0$, the series converges.

3. Since $\lim_{n\to\infty}(2n+1)/(5n+1) = \frac{2}{5} \neq 0$, the nth term $(-1)^n(2n+1)/(5n+1)$ does not converge to 0, so the series diverges.

4. Since $(\cos n\pi)/\sqrt{n} = (-1)^n/\sqrt{n}$ and $\{1/\sqrt{n}\}_{n=3}^{\infty}$ is a positive, decreasing sequence with $\lim_{n\to\infty} 1/\sqrt{n} = 0$, the series converges.

5. Let $f(x) = (x+2)/(x^2+3x+5)$. Then $f'(x) = (-x^2-4x-1)/(x^2+3x+5)^2 < 0$ for $x > 0$, so f is decreasing on $[1,\infty)$. Thus $\{(n+2)/(n^2+3n+5)\}_{n=1}^{\infty}$ is a positive, decreasing sequence, and $\lim_{n\to\infty}(n+2)/(n^2+3n+5) = 0$. Therefore the series converges.

6. Since $\lim_{n\to\infty}(n+1)/4n = \frac{1}{4} \neq 0$, the nth term $(-1)^n(n+1)/4n$ does not converge to 0, so the series diverges.

7. Let $f(x) = (\ln x)/x$. Since $f'(x) = (1-\ln x)/x^2 < 0$ for $x > e$, the function f is decreasing on $[e,\infty)$. Thus $\{(\ln n)/n\}_{n=3}^{\infty}$ is a positive, decreasing sequence, and $\lim_{n\to\infty}(\ln n)/n = 0$. Therefore $\sum_{n=3}^{\infty}(-1)^n[(\ln n)/n]$ converges, and hence $\sum_{n=1}^{\infty}(-1)^n[(\ln n)/n]$ converges.

8. Let $f(x) = (\ln x)^2/x$. Since

$$f'(x) = \frac{2\ln x - (\ln x)^2}{x^2} = \frac{(\ln x)(2-\ln x)}{x^2} < 0 \quad \text{for } x > e^2$$

the function f is decreasing on $[e^2,\infty)$. Thus $\{(\ln n)^2/n\}_{n=9}^{\infty}$ is a positive, decreasing sequence, and $\lim_{n\to\infty}(\ln n)^2/n = 0$. Therefore $\sum_{n=9}^{\infty}(-1)^n[(\ln n)^2/n]$ converges, and hence $\sum_{n=1}^{\infty}(-1)^n[(\ln n)^2/n]$ converges.

9. Let $f(x) = (\ln x)^p/x$. Then

$$f'(x) = \frac{p(\ln x)^{p-1} - (\ln x)^p}{x^2} = \frac{(\ln x)^{p-1}(p-\ln x)}{x^2} < 0 \quad \text{for } x > e^p.$$

Moreover, by l'Hôpital's Rule,

$$\lim_{x\to\infty}\frac{(\ln x)^p}{x} = \lim_{x\to\infty}\frac{p(\ln x)^{p-1}}{x} = \cdots = \lim_{x\to\infty}\frac{p!}{x} = 0.$$

Thus $\{(\ln n)^p/n\}_{n=3^p}^{\infty}$ is a positive, decreasing sequence with $\lim_{n\to\infty}(\ln n)^p/n = 0$. Thus

$$\sum_{n=3^p}^{\infty}(-1)^n\frac{(\ln n)^p}{n}$$

converges, and hence $\sum_{n=1}^{\infty}(-1)^n[(\ln n)^p/n]$ converges.

10. Let $f(x) = \sqrt{x}/(2x+1)$. Then

$$f'(x) = \frac{(2x+1)[1/(2\sqrt{x})] - 2\sqrt{x}}{(2x+1)^2} = \frac{-\sqrt{x} + 1/(2\sqrt{x})}{(2x+1)^2} < 0 \quad \text{if } x \geq 1.$$

Thus $\{\sqrt{n}/(2n+1)\}_{n=1}^{\infty}$ is a positive, decreasing sequence and $\lim_{n\to\infty} \sqrt{n}/(2n+1) = 0$, so the series converges.

11. Since

$$\lim_{n\to\infty} \left| \frac{(-1)^{n+2}(n+1)!/100^{n+1}}{(-1)^{n+1}n!/100^n} \right| = \lim_{n\to\infty} \frac{n+1}{100} = \infty,$$

the series diverges by the Generalized Ratio Test.

12. Since $\pi/2 - 1/n < \pi/2 - 1/(n+1)$ and $\cot x$ is a decreasing function on $(0, \pi/2)$, we have $\cot(\pi/2 - 1/n) > \cot(\pi/2 - 1/(n+1))$. Thus $\{\cot(\pi/2 - 1/n)\}_{n=1}^{\infty}$ is a positive, decreasing sequence, and $\lim_{n\to\infty} \cot(\pi/2 - 1/n) = \cot \pi/2 = 0$, so the series converges.

13. Since $\lim_{n\to\infty} n^2/(2n+1) = \infty$, the nth term $(-1)^{n+1}n^2/(2n+1)$ does not converge to 0, so the series diverges.

14. Since $\{1/n^{1/10}\}_{n=1}^{\infty}$ is a positive, decreasing sequence with $\lim_{n\to\infty} 1/n^{1/10} = 0$, the sequence converges.

15. For any $p > 0$, $\{1/n^p\}_{n=1}^{\infty}$ is a positive, decreasing sequence with $\lim_{n\to\infty} 1/n^p = 0$. Thus

$$\sum_{n=1}^{\infty} (-1)^n \frac{1}{n^p}$$

converges for any $p > 0$.

16. $E_{10} < a_{11} = \dfrac{1}{11}$

17. $E_{10} < a_{11} = \dfrac{1}{121}$

18. $E_{10} < \dfrac{1}{11!}$

19. $E_{11} < \dfrac{1}{\sqrt{15}}$

20. Since $\dfrac{8}{10^n + 1} < \dfrac{1}{1000}$ if $n \geq 4$, it follows from (1) that

$$\sum_{n=1}^{3} (-1)^n \frac{8}{10^n + 1} \approx -0.6560568145$$

approximates the sum of the given series with an error less than 0.001.

21. Since $\frac{1}{n^3} < \frac{1}{1000}$ if $n \geq 11$, it follows from (1) that

$$\sum_{n=1}^{10}(-1)^{n+1}\frac{1}{n^3} \approx 0.9011164764$$

approximates the sum of the series with an error less than 0.001.

22. Since $\frac{1}{1+n+6n^2} < \frac{1}{1000}$ if $n \geq 13$, it follows from (1) that

$$\sum_{n=2}^{12}(-1)^{n+1}\frac{1}{1+n+6n^2} \approx -0.0264097368$$

approximates the sum of the series with an error less than 0.001.

23. $\{1/(3n+4)\}_{n=1}^{\infty}$ is a positive, decreasing sequence and $\lim_{n\to\infty} 1/(3n+4) = 0$. Thus

$$\sum_{n=1}^{\infty}(-1)^{n+1}\frac{1}{3n+4}$$

converges. But notice that $\sum_{n=1}^{\infty} 1/(3n+4)$ diverges because $1/(3n+1) \geq 1/7n$ for $n \geq 1$ and $\sum_{n=1}^{\infty} 1/7n$ diverges. Thus $\sum_{n=1}^{\infty}(-1)^{n+1}[1/(3n+4)]$ converges conditionally.

24. $\lim_{n\to\infty} \sqrt[n]{n(\frac{4}{5})^n} = \lim_{n\to\infty} \sqrt[n]{n}\,(\frac{4}{5}) = \frac{4}{5}$; the series converges absolutely.

25. $\displaystyle\lim_{n\to\infty} \frac{(n+1)^{n+1}/(n+1)!}{n^n/n!} = \lim_{n\to\infty}\left(\frac{n+1}{n}\right)^n = \lim_{n\to\infty}\left(1+\frac{1}{n}\right)^n = e > 1$; the series diverges.

26. Since

$$\frac{1}{n(n-2)} \leq \frac{1}{(n-2)^2} \quad \text{and} \quad \sum_{n=3}^{\infty}\frac{1}{(n-2)^2} = \sum_{n=1}^{\infty}\frac{1}{n^2}$$

converges, the series $\sum_{n=3}^{\infty} 1/[n(n-2)]$ converges. Thus $\sum_{n=3}^{\infty}(-1)^{n+1}\{1/[n(n-2)]\}$ converges absolutely.

27. Since $\lim_{n\to\infty} 1/n^{1/n} = 1$, the nth term $(-1)^{n+1}/n^{1/n}$ does not converge to 0, so the series diverges.

28. The series $\sum_{n=2}^{\infty} 1/(n\ln n)$ diverges by Example 3 of Section 9.5. Since $\{1/(n\ln n)\}_{n=2}^{\infty}$ is a positive, decreasing sequence, with $\lim_{n\to\infty} 1/(n\ln n) = 0$, the series $\sum_{n=2}^{\infty}(-1)^n[1/(n\ln n)]$ converges conditionally.

29. Since

$$\int_2^{\infty}\frac{1}{x(\ln x)^2}\,dx = \lim_{b\to\infty}\int_2^b \frac{1}{x(\ln x)^2}\,dx = \lim_{b\to\infty}\left(\frac{-1}{\ln x}\right)\Big|_2^b = \lim_{b\to\infty}\left(\frac{-1}{\ln b}+\frac{1}{\ln 2}\right) = \frac{1}{\ln 2}$$

the Integral Test implies that $\sum_{n=2}^{\infty} 1/[n(\ln n)^2]$ converges. Thus $\sum_{n=2}^{\infty}(-1)^{n+1}\{1/[n(\ln n)^2]\}$ converges absolutely.

30. $|(\sin n)/(n^2+1)| \le 1/(n^2+1) < 1/n^2$ and $\sum_{n=1}^{\infty} 1/n^2$ converges. Thus $\sum_{n=1}^{\infty}(\sin n)/(n^2+1)$ converges absolutely.

31. $\lim_{n\to\infty} \sqrt[n]{\left(\frac{1}{\ln n}\right)^n} = \lim_{n\to\infty} \frac{1}{\ln n} = 0$ so $\sum_{n=2}^{\infty}(-1)^{n+1}[1/(\ln n)^n]$ converges absolutely.

32. Since $\ln n < n$ for $n \ge 1$, we have $1/(\ln n)^{1/n} \ge 1/n^{1/n}$. But $\lim_{n\to\infty} 1/n^{1/n} = 1$, so it is impossible that $\lim_{n\to\infty}(-1)^{n+1}/(\ln n)^{1/n} = 0$. Thus $\sum_{n=2}^{\infty}(-1)^{n+1}[1/(\ln n)^{1/n}]$ diverges.

33. $$\lim_{n\to\infty} \frac{\dfrac{1\cdot 3\cdot 5\cdots(2n+3)}{2\cdot 5\cdot 8\cdots(3n+5)}}{\dfrac{1\cdot 3\cdot 5\cdots(2n+1)}{2\cdot 5\cdot 8\cdots(3n+2)}} = \lim_{n\to\infty} \frac{2n+3}{3n+5} = \lim_{n\to\infty} \frac{2+\dfrac{3}{n}}{3+\dfrac{5}{n}} = \frac{2}{3}$$
The series converges absolutely.

34. $\lim_{n\to\infty} \frac{(n+1)!/(n+1)^{n+1}}{n!/n^n} = \lim_{n\to\infty} \left(\frac{n}{n+1}\right)^n = \lim_{n\to\infty} \frac{1}{(1+1/n)^n} = \frac{1}{e} < 1$, so $\lim_{n\to\infty} \frac{n!}{n^n} = 0$.

35. $\lim_{n\to\infty} \frac{(n+2)^2/(n+1)!}{(n+1)^2/n!} = \lim_{n\to\infty} \frac{(n+2)^2}{(n+1)^3} = 0$, so $\lim_{n\to\infty} \frac{(n+1)^2}{n!} = 0$.

36. $\lim_{n\to\infty} \sqrt[n]{\frac{x^{2n}}{n^n}} = \lim_{n\to\infty} \frac{x^2}{n} = 0$ for all x, so $\lim_{n\to\infty} \frac{x^{2n}}{n^n} = 0$ for all x.

37. $\lim_{n\to\infty} \sqrt[n]{\frac{x^{2n}}{n}} = \lim_{n\to\infty} \frac{x^2}{\sqrt[n]{n}} = x^2$
If $|x| < 1$, then $x^2 < 1$, so $\lim_{n\to\infty} x^{2n}/n = 0$.

38. $\lim_{n\to\infty} \sqrt[n]{\frac{|x|^n}{2^n}} = \frac{|x|}{2}$, so if $|x| < 2$, then $\lim_{n\to\infty} \frac{x^n}{2^n} = 0$.

39. $\lim_{n\to\infty} \frac{(n+1)!\,|x|^{n+1}/(n+1)^{n+1}}{n!\,|x|^n/n^n} = \lim_{n\to\infty} |x| \left(\frac{n}{n+1}\right)^n = \lim_{n\to\infty} |x| \frac{1}{(1+1/n)^n} = \frac{|x|}{e}$, so that if $|x| < e$, then $\lim_{n\to\infty} n!\,x^n/n^n = 0$.

40. By the Generalized Ratio Test,
$$\lim_{n\to\infty} \frac{(n+1)!\,|x|^{n+1}/(n+1)^{n+1}}{n!\,|x|^n/n^n} = \lim_{n\to\infty} |x| \left(\frac{n}{n+1}\right)^n = \lim_{n\to\infty} |x| \frac{1}{(1+1/n)^n} = \frac{|x|}{e}$$
so that if $|x| < e$, then the given series converges.

41. The series $\sum_{n=1}^{\infty}(-1)^n(1/\sqrt{n})$ converges (conditionally), but $\left((-1)^n(1/\sqrt{n})\right)^2 = 1/n$ and $\sum_{n=1}^{\infty} 1/n$ diverges.

42. The series $\sum_{n=1}^{\infty} a_n$ converges absolutely, so both $\sum_{n=1}^{\infty} |a_n|$ and $\sum_{n=1}^{\infty} |a_{n+1}| = \sum_{n=2}^{\infty} |a_n|$ converge, and hence $\sum_{n=1}^{\infty}(|a_n| + |a_{n+1}|)$ converges. Since $0 \le |a_n + a_{n+1}| \le |a_n| + |a_{n+1}|$, the Comparison Test implies that $\sum_{n=1}^{\infty} |a_n + a_{n+1}|$ converges. Thus $\sum_{n=1}^{\infty}(a_n + a_{n+1})$ converges absolutely.

43. Since $\lim_{n\to\infty} a_n = a \neq 0$, there is an integer N such that if $n \geq N$, then $|a_n - a| < |a|/2$, so that $|a|/2 < |a_n| < 3|a|/2$, and thus $2/(3|a|) < 1/|a_n| < 2/|a|$. Notice that $|1/a_{n+1} - 1/a_n| = |(a_{n+1} - a_n)/a_{n+1}a_n|$, and that for $n \geq N$, we have

$$\frac{4}{9a^2}|a_{n+1} - a_n| < \left|\frac{a_{n+1} - a_n}{a_{n+1}a_n}\right| < \frac{4}{a^2}|a_{n+1} - a_n|.$$

Since $\sum_{n=N}^{\infty}(4/(9a^2))|a_{n+1} - a_n|$, $\sum_{n=N}^{\infty}(4/a^2)|a_{n+1} - a_n|$, and $\sum_{n=N}^{\infty}|a_{n+1} - a_n|$ all converge or all diverge, the same is true of $\sum_{n=1}^{\infty}|a_{n+1} - a_n|$ and $\sum_{n=1}^{\infty}|1/a_{n+1} - 1/a_n|$, and thus both converge or both diverge.

9.8 Power Series

1. $\lim\limits_{n\to\infty} \sqrt[n]{\dfrac{|x|^n}{n^2}} = \lim\limits_{n\to\infty} \dfrac{|x|}{(\sqrt[n]{n})^2} = |x|;$

the series converges for $|x| < 1$ and diverges for $|x| > 1$. Since $\sum_{n=1}^{\infty} 1/n^2$ converges and hence $\sum_{n=1}^{\infty}(-1)^n/n^2$ converges, the interval of convergence is $[-1, 1]$.

2. $\lim_{n\to\infty} \sqrt[n]{2^n|x|^n} = \lim_{n\to\infty} 2|x| = 2|x|;$

the series converges for $|x| < \frac{1}{2}$ and diverges for $|x| > \frac{1}{2}$. Since $\sum_{n=0}^{\infty} 2^n x^n$ diverges for $|x| = \frac{1}{2}$, the interval of convergence is $(-\frac{1}{2}, \frac{1}{2})$.

3. $\lim\limits_{n\to\infty} \sqrt[n]{\dfrac{1}{\sqrt{n}\,3^n}|x|^n} = \lim\limits_{n\to\infty} \dfrac{|x|}{3(\sqrt[n]{n})^{1/2}} = \dfrac{|x|}{3};$

the series converges for $|x| < 3$ and diverges for $|x| > 3$. Since $\sum_{n=1}^{\infty} 1/\sqrt{n}$ diverges and $\sum_{n=1}^{\infty}(-1)^n/\sqrt{n}$ converges, the interval of convergence is $[-3, 3)$.

4. $\lim\limits_{n\to\infty} \sqrt[n]{\dfrac{n}{4^n}|x|^n} = \lim\limits_{n\to\infty} \dfrac{|x|}{4}\sqrt[n]{n} = \dfrac{|x|}{4};$

the series converges for $|x| < 4$ and diverges for $|x| > 4$. Since $\sum_{n=0}^{\infty} n$ and $\sum_{n=0}^{\infty}(-1)^n n$ diverge, the interval of convergence is $(-4, 4)$.

5. $\lim\limits_{n\to\infty} \dfrac{|x|^{2n+2}/(n+2)}{|x|^{2n}/(n+1)} = \lim\limits_{n\to\infty} \dfrac{n+1}{n+2}x^2 = x^2;$

the series converges for $|x| < 1$ and diverges for $|x| > 1$. Since $\sum_{n=0}^{\infty}(-1)^n/(n+1)$ converges, the interval of convergence is $[-1, 1]$.

6. $\lim\limits_{n\to\infty} \dfrac{2|x|^{n+1}/[3^{n+2}(n+1)^2]}{2|x|^n/[3^{n+1}n^2]} = \lim\limits_{n\to\infty} \left(\dfrac{n}{n+1}\right)^2 \dfrac{|x|}{3} = \dfrac{|x|}{3};$

the series converges for $|x| < 3$ and diverges for $|x| > 3$. Since $\sum_{n=1}^{\infty} 2/(3n^2)$ converges and thus $\sum_{n=1}^{\infty}(-1)^n 2/(3n^2)$ converges, the interval of convergence is $[-3, 3]$

7. $\lim\limits_{n\to\infty} \dfrac{|x|^{n+2}/(2n+1)}{|x|^{n+1}/(2n-1)} = \lim\limits_{n\to\infty} \dfrac{2n-1}{2n+1}|x| = |x|;$

the series converges for $|x| < 1$ and diverges for $|x| > 1$. The alternating series

$$\sum_{n=1}^{\infty} \frac{(-1)^n}{2n-1} = \sum_{n=1}^{\infty} \frac{(-1)^n 1^{n+1}}{2n-1}$$

converges, and

$$\sum_{n=1}^{\infty} \frac{-1}{2n-1} = \sum_{n=1}^{\infty} \frac{(-1)^n(-1)^{n+1}}{2n-1}$$

diverges, so the interval of convergence is $(-1, 1]$.

8. $\lim_{n\to\infty} \frac{n|x|^{n+1}/(n+1)^{2n+2}}{(n-1)|x|^n/n^{2n}} = \lim_{n\to\infty} \frac{n^{2n+1}}{(n-1)(n+1)^{2n+2}}|x| = \lim_{n\to\infty} \frac{1}{(n-1)(n+1)(1+1/n)^{2n+1}}|x| = 0;$
the interval of convergence is $(-\infty, \infty)$.

9. $\lim_{n\to\infty} \sqrt[n]{\frac{|x|^n}{n^n}} = \lim_{n\to\infty} \frac{|x|}{n} = 0$; the interval of convergence is $(-\infty, \infty)$.

10. $\lim_{n\to\infty} \sqrt[n]{\frac{2^n|x|^n}{n^n}} = \lim_{n\to\infty} \frac{2|x|}{n} = 0$; the interval of convergence is $(-\infty, \infty)$.

11. $\lim_{n\to\infty} \frac{(n+1)!\,|x|^{n+1}/(2n+2)!}{n!\,|x|^n/(2n)!} = \lim_{n\to\infty} \frac{n+1}{(2n+1)(2n+2)}|x| = 0$; the interval of convergence is $(-\infty, \infty)$.

12. $\lim_{n\to\infty} \frac{4^{n+2}|x|^{n+4}/\pi^{n+3}}{4^{n+1}|x|^{n+3}/\pi^{n+2}} = \lim_{n\to\infty} \frac{4}{\pi}|x| = \frac{4}{\pi}|x|;$
the series converges for $|x| < \pi/4$ and diverges for $|x| > \pi/4$. Since $\sum_{n=0}^{\infty} \pi/16$ and $\sum_{n=0}^{\infty}(-1)^{n+1}(\pi/16)$ both diverge, the interval of convergence is $(-\pi/4, \pi/4)$.

13. $\lim_{n\to\infty} \frac{2^{n+1}|x|^{n+2}/(n+1)3^{n+3}}{2^n|x|^{n+1}/n3^{n+2}} = \lim_{n\to\infty} \frac{2n}{3(n+1)}|x| = \frac{2}{3}|x|;$
the series converges for $|x| < \frac{3}{2}$ and diverges for $|x| > \frac{3}{2}$. Since $\sum_{n=1}^{\infty} 1/(6n)$ diverges and $\sum_{n=1}^{\infty}(-1)^{n+1}/(6n)$ converges, the interval of convergence is $[-\frac{3}{2}, \frac{3}{2})$.

14. $\lim_{n\to\infty} \frac{|x|^{n+1}/[(n+1)^3-4]}{|x|^n/(n^3-4)} = \lim_{n\to\infty} \frac{n^3-4}{(n+1)^3-4}|x| = \lim_{n\to\infty} \frac{1-\frac{4}{n^3}}{\left(1+\frac{1}{n}\right)^3 - \frac{4}{n^3}}|x| = |x|;$
the series converges for $|x| < 1$ and diverges for $|x| > 1$. Since $\sum_{n=3}^{\infty} 1/(n^3-4)$ and $\sum_{n=3}^{\infty}(-1)^n/(n^3-4)$ both converge, the interval of convergence is $[-1, 1]$.

15. By l'Hôpital's Rule,

$$\lim_{x\to\infty} \frac{\ln(x+1)}{\ln x} = \lim_{x\to\infty} \frac{1/(x+1)}{1/x} = \lim_{x\to\infty} \frac{x}{x+1} = 1$$

so we have

$$\lim_{n\to\infty} \frac{|x|^{n+1}\ln(n+1)}{|x|^n \ln n} = \lim_{n\to\infty} \frac{\ln(n+1)}{\ln n}|x| = |x|$$

the series converges for $|x| < 1$ and diverges for $|x| > 1$. Since $\sum_{n=2}^{\infty} \ln n$ and $\sum_{n=2}^{\infty}(-1)^n \ln n$ both diverge, the interval of convergence is $(-1, 1)$.

16. By l'Hôpital's Rule, $\lim_{x\to\infty} \ln(x+1)/\ln x = 1$, so

$$\lim_{n\to\infty} \frac{|x|^{n+1}\ln(n+1)/(n+1)}{|x|^n \ln n/n} = \lim_{n\to\infty} \frac{n}{n+1}\frac{\ln(n+1)}{\ln n}|x| = |x|$$

the series converges for $|x| < 1$ and diverges for $|x| > 1$. Since $(\ln n)/n \geq 1/n$ for $n \geq 3$, the series $\sum_{n=2}^{\infty}(\ln n)/n$ diverges; but by the solution of Exercise 7 of Section 9.7, the alternating series $\sum_{n=2}^{\infty}(-1)^n(\ln n)/n$ converges. Thus the interval of convergence is $[-1,1)$.

17. By l'Hôpital's Rule, $\lim_{x\to\infty} \ln(x+1)/\ln x = 1$, so

$$\lim_{n\to\infty} \frac{|x|^{n+1}\ln(n+1)/(n+1)^2}{|x|^n(\ln n)/n^2} = \lim_{n\to\infty}\left(\frac{n}{n+1}\right)^2 \frac{\ln(n+1)}{\ln n}|x| = |x|$$

the series converges for $|x| < 1$ and diverges for $|x| > 1$. By the solution of Exercise 23 of Section 9.5, $\sum_{n=2}^{\infty}(\ln n)/n^2$ converges and hence $\sum_{n=2}^{\infty}(-1)^n(\ln n)/n^2$ converges. The interval of convergence is $[-1,1]$.

18. The alternating series $\sum_{n=2}^{\infty}(-1)^n(1/\ln n)$ converges; since $1/\ln n > 1/n$ for $n \geq 2$, the series $\sum_{n=2}^{\infty} 1/\ln n$ diverges. Thus the interval of convergence is $[-1,1)$.

19. $\lim_{n\to\infty} \dfrac{|x|^{(n+1)^2}}{|x|^{n^2}} = \lim_{n\to\infty} |x|^{2n+1}$, and $\lim_{n\to\infty} |x|^{2n+1} = 0$ if $|x| < 1$ whereas $\lim_{n\to\infty} |x|^{2n+1} = \infty$ if $|x| > 1$. Thus the series converges for $|x| < 1$ and diverges for $|x| > 1$. Since $\sum_{n=0}^{\infty} 1^{(n^2)}$ and $\sum_{n=0}^{\infty}(-1)^{(n^2)}$ both diverge, the interval of convergence is $(-1,1)$.

20. $\lim_{n\to\infty} \dfrac{|x|^{(n+1)!}}{|x|^{n!}} = \lim_{n\to\infty} |x|^{(n+1)!-n!}$, and $\lim_{n\to\infty} |x|^{(n+1)!-n!} = 0$ if $|x| < 1$ whereas $\lim_{n\to\infty} |x|^{(n+1)!-n!} = \infty$ if $|x| > 1$. Thus the series converges for $|x| < 1$ and diverges for $|x| > 1$. Since $\sum_{n=1}^{\infty} 1^{n!}$ and $\sum_{n=1}^{\infty}(-1)^{n!}$ both diverge, the interval of convergence is $(-1,1)$.

21. $\lim_{n\to\infty} \dfrac{|x|^{n+1}(n+1)!/(n+1)^{n+1}}{|x|^n n!/n^n} = \lim_{n\to\infty} \dfrac{(n+1)!}{n!}\dfrac{n^n}{(n+1)^{n+1}}|x| = \lim_{n\to\infty}\dfrac{1}{(1+1/n)^n}|x| = \dfrac{|x|}{e}$, so $R = e$.

22. $\lim_{n\to\infty} \dfrac{|x|^{n+1}(n+1)^{n+1}/(n+1)!}{|x|^n n^n/n!} = \lim_{n\to\infty} \dfrac{n!}{(n+1)!}\dfrac{(n+1)^{n+1}}{n^n}|x| = \lim_{n\to\infty}\left(1+\dfrac{1}{n}\right)^n|x| = e|x|$, so $R = \dfrac{1}{e}$.

23. $\lim_{n\to\infty} \dfrac{1^2\cdot 3^2\cdot 5^2\cdots(2n+1)^2|x|^{2n+2}/[2^2\cdot 4^2\cdot 6^2\cdots(2n)^2(2n+2)^2]}{1^2\cdot 3^2\cdot 5^2\cdots(2n-1)^2|x|^{2n}/[2^2\cdot 4^2\cdot 6^2\cdots(2n)^2]} = \lim_{n\to\infty}\dfrac{(2n+1)^2}{(2n+2)^2}x^2 = x^2$, so $R = 1$.

24. $\lim_{n\to\infty} \dfrac{1\cdot 3\cdot 5\cdots(2n-3)(2n-1)|x|^{n+1}/[2^{n+1}(n+1)!]}{1\cdot 3\cdot 5\cdots(2n-3)|x|^n/(2^n n!)} = \lim_{n\to\infty}\dfrac{(2n-1)}{2(n+1)}|x| = |x|$, so $R = 1$.

25. $\lim_{n\to\infty} \dfrac{1\cdot 3\cdot 5\cdots(2n-1)(2n+1)|x|^{n+1}/\{2^{n+1}[1\cdot 4\cdot 7\cdots(3n-2)(3n+1)]\}}{1\cdot 3\cdot 5\cdots(2n-1)|x|^n/\{2^n[1\cdot 4\cdot 7\cdots(3n-2)]\}} = \lim_{n\to\infty}\dfrac{2n+1}{2(3n+1)}|x| = \dfrac{|x|}{3}$, so $R = 3$.

26. $f(x) = \sum_{n=0}^{\infty}\dfrac{(-1)^n}{n+1}x^n$ for x in $(-1,1]$; $f'(x) = \sum_{n=1}^{\infty}\dfrac{(-1)^n n}{n+1}x^{n-1}$ for x in $(-1,1)$;

$$\int_0^x f(t)\,dt = \sum_{n=0}^{\infty} \frac{(-1)^n}{(n+1)^2} x^{n+1} \text{ for } x \text{ in } (-1,1).$$

27. $f(x) = \sum_{n=1}^{\infty} (n+1)x^n$ for x in $(-1,1)$; $f'(x) = \sum_{n=1}^{\infty} n(n+1)x^{n-1}$ for x in $(-1,1)$;

$$\int_0^x f(t)\,dt = \sum_{n=1}^{\infty} x^{n+1} \text{ for } x \text{ in } (-1,1).$$

28. $f(x) = \sum_{n=0}^{\infty} \frac{1}{n^2+1} x^{n+1}$ for x in $[-1,1]$; $f'(x) = \sum_{n=0}^{\infty} \frac{n+1}{n^2+1} x^n$ for x in $(-1,1)$;

$$\int_0^x f(t)\,dt = \sum_{n=0}^{\infty} \frac{1}{(n^2+1)(n+2)} x^{n+2} \text{ for } x \text{ in } (-1,1).$$

29. $f(x) = \sum_{n=1}^{\infty} \frac{5}{n} x^{(n^2)}$ for x in $[-1,1)$; $f'(x) = \sum_{n=1}^{\infty} 5nx^{n^2-1}$ for x in $(-1,1)$;

$$\int_0^x f(t)\,dt = \sum_{n=1}^{\infty} \frac{5}{n(n^2+1)} x^{n^2+1} \text{ for } x \text{ in } (-1,1).$$

30. Since $\cos x = \sum_{n=0}^{\infty} (-1)^n x^{2n}/(2n)!$, it follows that

$$\cos\sqrt{x} = \sum_{n=0}^{\infty} \frac{(-1)^n(\sqrt{x})^{2n}}{(2n)!} = \sum_{n=0}^{\infty} \frac{(-1)^n x^n}{(2n)!} \quad \text{for } x \geq 0.$$

By the Integration Theorem,

$$\int_0^1 \cos\sqrt{x}\,dx = \int_0^1 \sum_{n=0}^{\infty} \frac{(-1)^n x^n}{(2n)!}\,dx = \sum_{n=0}^{\infty} \int_0^1 \frac{(-1)^n x^n}{(2n)!}\,dx = \sum_{n=0}^{\infty} \left. \frac{(-1)^n x^{n+1}}{(n+1)(2n)!} \right|_0^1 = \sum_{n=0}^{\infty} \frac{(-1)^n}{(n+1)(2n)!}.$$

By the Alternating Series Test,

$$\left| \sum_{n=m+1}^{\infty} \frac{(-1)^n}{(n+1)(2n)!} \right| < 10^{-3} \quad \text{if} \quad \frac{1}{[(m+1)+1][2(m+1)]!} < 10^{-3}$$

which occurs for $m = 2$. Thus

$$\sum_{n=0}^{2} \frac{(-1)^n}{(n+1)(2n)!} = 1 - \frac{1}{2(2!)} + \frac{1}{3(4!)} \approx 0.738888889$$

is the desired approximation.

31. Since $\sin x = \sum_{n=0}^{\infty} (-1)^n x^{2n+1}/(2n+1)!$, it follows that

$$\sin x^2 = \sum_{n=0}^{\infty} \frac{(-1)^n (x^2)^{2n+1}}{(2n+1)!} = \sum_{n=0}^{\infty} \frac{(-1)^n x^{4n+2}}{(2n+1)!}.$$

By the Integration Theorem,

$$\int_0^2 \sin x^2\,dx = \int_0^2 \sum_{n=0}^{\infty} \frac{(-1)^n x^{4n+2}}{(2n+1)!}\,dx = \sum_{n=0}^{\infty} \int_0^2 \frac{(-1)^n x^{4n+2}}{(2n+1)!}\,dx$$

$$= \sum_{n=0}^{\infty} \left(\frac{(-1)^n x^{4n+3}}{(4n+3)(2n+1)!}\bigg|_0^2 \right) = \sum_{n=0}^{\infty} \frac{(-1)^n 2^{4n+3}}{(4n+3)(2n+1)!}.$$

By the Alternating Series Test,

$$\left| \sum_{n=m+1}^{\infty} \frac{(-1)^n 2^{4n+3}}{(4n+3)(2n+1)!} \right| < 10^{-2} \quad \text{if} \quad \frac{2^{4(m+1)+3}}{[4(m+1)+3][2(m+1)+1]!} < 10^{-2}$$

which occurs for $m = 4$. Thus

$$\sum_{n=0}^{4} \frac{(-1)^n 2^{4n+3}}{(4n+3)(2n+1)!} = \frac{2^3}{3(1!)} - \frac{2^7}{7(3!)} + \frac{2^{11}}{11(5!)} - \frac{2^{15}}{15(7!)} + \frac{2^{19}}{19(9!)} \approx 0.8131655739$$

is the desired approximation.

32. Since $\cos x = \sum_{n=0}^{\infty} (-1)^n x^{2n}/(2n)!$, it follows that

$$\cos x^2 = \sum_{n=0}^{\infty} \frac{(-1)^n (x^2)^{2n}}{(2n)!} = \sum_{n=0}^{\infty} \frac{(-1)^n x^{4n}}{(2n)!}.$$

By the Integration Theorem,

$$\int_0^1 \cos x^2\,dx = \sum_{n=0}^{\infty} \int_0^1 \frac{(-1)^n x^{4n}}{(2n)!}\,dx = \sum_{n=0}^{\infty} \frac{(-1)^n x^{4n+1}}{(4n+1)(2n)!}\bigg|_0^1 = \sum_{n=0}^{\infty} \frac{(-1)^n}{(4n+1)(2n)!}.$$

By the Alternating Series Test,

$$\left| \sum_{n=m+1}^{\infty} \frac{(-1)^n}{(4n+1)(2n)!} \right| < 10^{-7} \quad \text{if} \quad \frac{1}{[4(m+1)+1][2(m+1)]!} < 10^{-7}$$

which occurs for $m = 4$. Thus

$$\sum_{n=0}^{4} \frac{(-1)^n}{(4n+1)(2n)!} = 1 - \frac{1}{5(2!)} + \frac{1}{9(4!)} + \frac{1}{13(6!)} + \frac{1}{17(8!)} \approx 0.9045242509$$

is the desired approximation.

33. Since $e^x = \sum_{n=0}^{\infty} x^n/n!$ by (3), it follows that

$$\frac{1-e^{-x}}{x} = \frac{1 - \sum_{n=0}^{\infty} (-1)^n x^n/n!}{x} = \sum_{n=1}^{\infty} \frac{(-1)^{n+1} x^{n-1}}{n!} \quad \text{for } x \neq 0.$$

By the Integration Theorem,

$$\int_0^1 \frac{1-e^{-x}}{x}\,dx = \lim_{c\to 0+} \int_c^1 \frac{1-e^{-x}}{x}\,dx = \lim_{c\to 0+} \int_c^1 \sum_{n=1}^{\infty} \frac{(-1)^{n+1} x^{n-1}}{n!}\,dx$$

$$= \lim_{c\to 0^+} \sum_{n=1}^{\infty} \int_c^1 \frac{(-1)^{n+1}x^{n-1}}{n!}\,dx = \lim_{c\to 0^+} \sum_{n=1}^{\infty} \left(\frac{(-1)^{n+1}x^n}{n(n!)} \bigg|_c^1 \right)$$

$$= \lim_{c\to 0^+} \left(\sum_{n=1}^{\infty} \frac{(-1)^{n+1}}{n(n!)} - \sum_{n=1}^{\infty} \frac{(-1)^{n+1}c^n}{n(n!)} \right) = \sum_{n=1}^{\infty} \frac{(-1)^{n+1}}{n(n!)}.$$

By the Alternating Series Test,

$$\left| \sum_{n=m+1}^{\infty} \frac{(-1)^{n+1}}{n(n!)} \right| < 10^{-3} \quad \text{if} \quad \frac{1}{(m+1)[(m+1)!]} < 10^{-3}$$

which occurs for for $m = 5$. Thus

$$\sum_{n=1}^{5} \frac{(-1)^{n+1}}{n(n!)} = 1 - \frac{1}{2(2!)} + \frac{1}{3(3!)} - \frac{1}{4(4!)} + \frac{1}{5(5!)} \approx 0.7968055556$$

is the desired approximation.

34. By Example 7, $\tan^{-1} x = \sum_{n=0}^{\infty} (-1)^n x^{2n+1}/(2n+1)$ for $0 \le x \le \frac{1}{5}$. By the Integration Theorem,

$$\int_0^{1/5} \tan^{-1} x\,dx = \int_0^{1/5} \sum_{n=0}^{\infty} \frac{(-1)^n x^{2n+1}}{2n+1}\,dx = \sum_{n=0}^{\infty} \int_0^{1/5} \frac{(-1)^n x^{2n+1}}{2n+1}\,dx$$

$$= \sum_{n=0}^{\infty} \left(\frac{(-1)^n x^{2n+2}}{(2n+2)(2n+1)} \bigg|_0^{1/5} \right) = \sum_{n=0}^{\infty} \frac{(-1)^n}{5^{2n+2}(2n+2)(2n+1)}.$$

By the Alternating Series Test,

$$\left| \sum_{n=m+1}^{\infty} \frac{(-1)^n}{5^{2n+2}(2n+2)(2n+1)} \right| < 10^{-5} \quad \text{if} \quad \frac{1}{5^{2(m+1)+2}[2(m+1)+2][2(m+1)+1]} < 10^{-5}$$

which occurs for $m = 1$. Thus

$$\sum_{n=0}^{1} \frac{(-1)^n}{5^{2n+2}(2n+2)(2n+1)} = \frac{1}{5^2(2)(1)} - \frac{1}{5^4(4)(3)} \approx 0.0198666667$$

is the desired approximation.

35. From (1) we have $1/(1-x) = \sum_{n=0}^{\infty} x^n$ for $|x| < 1$, so that

$$\frac{x^2}{1+x} = \sum_{n=0}^{\infty} x^2(-x)^n = \sum_{n=0}^{\infty} (-1)^n x^{n+2} \quad \text{for } |x| < 1.$$

By the Integration Theorem,

$$\int_0^{1/2} \frac{x^2}{1+x}\,dx = \int_0^{1/2} \sum_{n=0}^{\infty} (-1)^n x^{n+2}\,dx$$

$$= \sum_{n=0}^{\infty} \int_0^{1/2} (-1)^n x^{n+2}\,dx = \sum_{n=0}^{\infty} \left(\frac{(-1)^n x^{n+3}}{n+3} \right) \bigg|_0^{1/2} = \sum_{n=0}^{\infty} \frac{(-1)^n}{2^{n+3}(n+3)}.$$

By the Alternating Series Test,

$$\left|\sum_{n=m+1}^{\infty} \frac{(-1)^n}{2^{n+3}(n+3)}\right| < 10^{-3} \quad \text{if} \quad \frac{1}{2^{(m+1)+3}[(m+1)+3]} < 10^{-3}$$

which occurs for $m = 4$. Thus

$$\sum_{n=0}^{4} \frac{(-1)^n}{2^{n+3}(n+3)} = \frac{1}{2^3(3)} - \frac{1}{2^4(4)} + \frac{1}{2^5(5)} - \frac{1}{2^6(6)} + \frac{1}{2^7(7)} \approx 0.0308035714$$

is the desired approximation.

36. From (1) we have $1/(1-x) = \sum_{n=0}^{\infty} x^n$ for $|x| < 1$, so that

$$\frac{x^3}{2+x} = \frac{\frac{1}{2}x^3}{1+x/2} = \sum_{n=0}^{\infty} \frac{1}{2}x^3\left(-\frac{x}{2}\right)^n = \sum_{n=0}^{\infty} \frac{(-1)^n x^{n+3}}{2^{n+1}} \quad \text{for } |x| < 2.$$

By the Integration Theorem,

$$\int_0^1 \frac{x^3}{2+x}\,dx = \int_0^1 \sum_{n=0}^{\infty} \frac{(-1)^n x^{n+3}}{2^{n+1}}\,dx$$

$$= \sum_{n=0}^{\infty} \int_0^1 \frac{(-1)^n x^{n+3}}{2^{n+1}}\,dx = \sum_{n=0}^{\infty} \left(\frac{(-1)^n x^{n+4}}{(n+4)2^{n+1}}\right)\Bigg|_0^1 = \sum_{n=0}^{\infty} \frac{(-1)^n}{(n+4)2^{n+1}}.$$

By the Alternating Series Test,

$$\left|\sum_{n=m+1}^{\infty} \frac{(-1)^n}{(n+4)2^{n+1}}\right| < 10^{-3} \quad \text{if} \quad \frac{1}{[(m+1)+4]2^{m+1+1}} < 10^{-3}$$

which occurs for $m = 5$. Thus

$$\sum_{n=0}^{5} \frac{(-1)^n}{(n+4)2^{n+1}} = \frac{1}{4(2)} - \frac{1}{5(2^2)} + \frac{1}{6(2^3)} - \frac{1}{7(2^4)} + \frac{1}{8(2^5)} - \frac{1}{9(2^6)} \approx 0.0890749008$$

is the desired approximation.

37. From (3) we have $e^x = \sum_{n=0}^{\infty} x^n/n!$, so that $e^{(x^2)} = \sum_{n=0}^{\infty} (x^2)^n/n! = \sum_{n=0}^{\infty} x^{2n}/n!$. By the Integration Theorem,

$$\int_{-1}^{0} e^{(x^2)}\,dx = \int_{-1}^{0} \sum_{n=0}^{\infty} \frac{x^{2n}}{n!}\,dx = \sum_{n=0}^{\infty} \int_{-1}^{0} \frac{x^{2n}}{n!}\,dx$$

$$= \sum_{n=0}^{\infty} \left(\frac{x^{2n+1}}{(2n+1)n!}\Bigg|_{-1}^{0}\right) = \sum_{n=0}^{\infty} \frac{-(-1)^{2n+1}}{(2n+1)n!} = \sum_{n=0}^{\infty} \frac{1}{(2n+1)n!}.$$

If $a_n = 1/(2n+1)n!$ for $n \geq 0$, then $a_{n+1}/a_n \leq \frac{1}{3}$, so $\sum_{n=m+1}^{\infty} a_n \leq \sum_{n=m+1}^{\infty} 1/3^n$. But

$$\sum_{n=m+1}^{\infty} \frac{1}{3^n} = \frac{(\frac{1}{3})^{m+1}}{1-\frac{1}{3}} = \frac{1}{3^m \cdot 2}$$

by the Geometric Series Theorem, and $1/(3^m \cdot 2) < 10^{-3}$, if $m = 6$. Thus

$$\sum_{n=0}^{6} \frac{1}{(2n+1)n!} = 1 + \frac{1}{3(1)} + \frac{1}{5(2!)} + \frac{1}{7(3!)} + \frac{1}{9(4!)} + \frac{1}{11(5!)} + \frac{1}{13(6!)} \approx 1.4626369$$

is the desired approximation.

38. a. $\cosh x = \frac{1}{2}(e^x + e^{-x}) = \frac{1}{2}\left(\sum_{n=0}^{\infty} \frac{1}{n!}x^n + \sum_{n=0}^{\infty} \frac{(-1)^n}{n!}x^n\right)$

$$= \frac{1}{2}\left(\sum_{n=0}^{\infty} \frac{2}{(2n)!}x^{2n}\right) = \sum_{n=0}^{\infty} \frac{1}{(2n)!}x^{2n} \quad \text{for all } x$$

b. $\sinh x = \frac{1}{2}(e^x - e^{-x}) = \frac{1}{2}\left(\sum_{n=0}^{\infty} \frac{1}{n!}x^n - \sum_{n=0}^{\infty} \frac{(-1)^n}{n!}x^n\right)$

$$= \frac{1}{2}\left(\sum_{n=0}^{\infty} \frac{2}{(2n+1)!}x^{2n+1}\right) = \sum_{n=0}^{\infty} \frac{1}{(2n+1)!}x^{2n+1} \quad \text{for all } x$$

39. Since $\sum_{n=0}^{\infty} x^n = 1/(1-x)$ for $|x| < 1$, the Differentiation Theorem implies that $\sum_{n=1}^{\infty} nx^{n-1} = 1/(1-x)^2$ for $|x| < 1$. Then $\sum_{n=1}^{\infty} nx^n = x\left(\sum_{n=1}^{\infty} nx^{n-1}\right) = x/(1-x)^2$ for $|x| < 1$.

40. If $a_n = ((-1)^n/(2n)!)x^{2n}$ and $b_n = ((-1)^n/(2n+1)!)x^{2n+1}$, then

$$\lim_{n\to\infty} \left|\frac{a_{n+1}}{a_n}\right| = \lim_{n\to\infty} \frac{|x|^{2n+2}/(2n+2)!}{|x|^{2n}/(2n)!} = \lim_{n\to\infty} \frac{1}{(2n+1)(2n+2)}x^2 = 0 \quad \text{for all } x,$$

and

$$\lim_{n\to\infty} \left|\frac{b_{n+1}}{b_n}\right| = \lim_{n\to\infty} \frac{|x|^{2n+3}/(2n+3)!}{|x|^{2n+1}/(2n+1)!} = \lim_{n\to\infty} \frac{1}{(2n+2)(2n+3)}x^2 = 0 \quad \text{for all } x.$$

Thus both series converge for all x.

41. a. By the Differentiation Theorem,

$$f'(x) = \sum_{n=1}^{\infty} \frac{(-1)^n 2n}{(2n)!}x^{2n-1} = \sum_{n=1}^{\infty} \frac{(-1)^n}{(2n-1)!}x^{2n-1} = -\sum_{n=0}^{\infty} \frac{(-1)^n}{(2n+1)!}x^{2n+1} = -g(x)$$

whereas

$$g'(x) = \sum_{n=0}^{\infty} \frac{(-1)^n(2n+1)}{(2n+1)!}x^{2n} = \sum_{n=0}^{\infty} \frac{(-1)^n}{(2n)!}x^{2n} = f(x).$$

b. Since $f'(x) = -g(x)$ and $g'(x) = f(x)$, it follows that $f''(x) = -g'(x) = -f(x)$ and $g''(x) = f'(x) = -g(x)$.

c. The cosine and sine functions have the properties of (a) and (b), respectively.

42. Since $e^x = \sum_{n=0}^{\infty} x^n/n!$, we have

$$\frac{e^x - 1}{x} = \frac{1}{x}\sum_{n=1}^{\infty} \frac{x^n}{n!} = \sum_{n=1}^{\infty} \frac{x^{n-1}}{n!} = \sum_{n=0}^{\infty} \frac{x^n}{(n+1)!} \quad \text{for all } x \neq 0.$$

The latter series converges for all x and defines a continuous function of x, with domain $(-\infty, \infty)$. Thus

$$\lim_{x\to 0} \frac{e^x - 1}{x} = \lim_{x\to 0} \left(\sum_{n=0}^{\infty} \frac{x^n}{(n+1)!} \right) = 1 + \sum_{n=1}^{\infty} \frac{0^n}{(n+1)!} = 1.$$

43. Since $e^x = \sum_{n=0}^{\infty} x^n/n!$, we have

$$e^x - 1 - x = \sum_{n=2}^{\infty} \frac{x^n}{n!} \quad \text{and} \quad \frac{e^x - 1 - x}{x^2} = \sum_{n=2}^{\infty} \frac{x^{n-2}}{n!} = \sum_{n=0}^{\infty} \frac{x^n}{(n+2)!}.$$

The latter series converges for all x and defines a continuous function of x, with domain $(-\infty, \infty)$. Thus

$$\lim_{x\to 0} \frac{e^x - 1 - x}{x^2} = \lim_{x\to 0} \left(\sum_{n=0}^{\infty} \frac{x^n}{(n+2)!} \right) = \frac{1}{2} + \sum_{n=1}^{\infty} \frac{0^n}{(n+2)!} = \frac{1}{2}.$$

44. From (8) we have $\ln(1+x) = \sum_{n=1}^{\infty} ((-1)^{n-1}/n)x^n$ for $|x| < 1$, so that

$$\frac{\ln(1+x)}{x} = \sum_{n=1}^{\infty} \frac{(-1)^{n-1}}{n} x^{n-1} \quad \text{for } |x| < 1.$$

Thus

$$\lim_{x\to 0} \frac{\ln(1+x)}{x} = \lim_{x\to 0} \sum_{n=1}^{\infty} \frac{(-1)^{n-1}}{n} x^{n-1} = 1 + \sum_{n=2}^{\infty} \frac{(-1)^{n-1}}{n} 0^{n-1} = 1.$$

45. From (8) we have $\ln(1+x) = \sum_{n=1}^{\infty} ((-1)^{n-1}/n)x^n$ for $|x| < 1$. Thus $\ln(1+x^2) = \sum_{n=1}^{\infty} ((-1)^{n-1}/n)x^{2n}$ for $|x| < 1$. Since

$$\lim_{n\to\infty} \frac{|x|^{2(n+1)}/(n+1)}{|x|^{2n}/n} = \lim_{n\to\infty} \frac{n}{n+1} |x|^2 = |x|^2$$

the radius of convergence is 1.

46. $$\ln \frac{1+x}{1-x} = \ln(1+x) - \ln(1-x) = \sum_{n=1}^{\infty} \frac{(-1)^{n-1}}{n} x^n - \sum_{n=1}^{\infty} \frac{(-1)^{n-1}}{n} (-x)^n$$

$$= \sum_{n=1}^{\infty} \frac{(-1)^{n-1}}{n} x^n + \sum_{n=1}^{\infty} \frac{1}{n} x^n = \sum_{n=0}^{\infty} \frac{2}{2n+1} x^{2n+1}$$

47. a. $\ln \dfrac{1}{1-x} = -\ln(1-x) = -\displaystyle\sum_{n=1}^{\infty} \frac{(-1)^{n-1}}{n} (-x)^n = \sum_{n=1}^{\infty} \frac{x^n}{n}$ for $|x| < 1$

b. $\ln 2 = \ln \dfrac{1}{1-\frac{1}{2}} = \displaystyle\sum_{n=1}^{\infty} \frac{1}{n} \left(\frac{1}{2}\right)^n = \sum_{n=1}^{\infty} \frac{1}{n2^n}$

c. Since

$$\left| \ln 2 - \sum_{n=1}^{N-1} \frac{1}{n2^n} \right| = \sum_{n=N}^{\infty} \frac{1}{n2^n} \leq \sum_{n=N}^{\infty} \frac{1}{N2^n} = \frac{1}{N} \frac{1/2^N}{1-\frac{1}{2}} = \frac{1}{N2^{N-1}}$$

we need to find N such that $1/(N2^{N-1}) < 0.01$. But if $N = 6$, then $1/N2^{N-1} = 1/(6 \cdot 2^5) < 0.01$, so $\sum_{n=1}^{5} 1/(n2^n) = \frac{1}{2} + \frac{1}{8} + \frac{1}{24} + \frac{1}{64} + \frac{1}{160} \approx 0.6885416667$ is the desired estimate of $\ln 2$.

48. By (10), $\tan^{-1}\frac{1}{2} = \sum_{n=0}^{\infty}(-1)^n/(2n+1)(\frac{1}{2})^{2n+1}$. Since this series is alternating, we need n large enough to ensure that $|((-1)^{n+1}/(2n+3))(\frac{1}{2})^{2n+3}| < .001$. For this it suffices to take $n = 3$. Thus $\frac{1}{2} - \frac{1}{24} + \frac{1}{160} - \frac{1}{896} \approx 0.4634672619$ is the desired estimate of $\tan^{-1}\frac{1}{2}$.

49. $4\left|\frac{(-1)^4(\frac{1}{5})^9}{9}\right| = \frac{4}{9}\left(\frac{1}{5}\right)^9 < 2.276 \times 10^{-7}$ and $\left|\frac{(-1)^1(\frac{1}{239})^3}{3}\right| = \frac{1}{3}\left(\frac{1}{239}\right)^3 < 0.245 \times 10^{-7}$

Thus the error introduced in approximating $\pi/4$ is less that $2.276\times 10^{-7} + 0.245\times 10^{-7} = 2.521\times 10^{-7}$.

50. a. If $|t| < 1$, then $\tan^{-1} t = \sum_{n=0}^{\infty}((-1)^n/(2n+1))t^{2n+1}$, so

$$\frac{\tan^{-1} t}{t} = \sum_{n=0}^{\infty} \frac{(-1)^n}{2n+1} t^{2n} = 1 - \frac{t^2}{3} + \frac{t^4}{5} - \frac{t^6}{7} + \cdots \quad \text{for } 0 < |t| < 1.$$

b. From (a),

$$\lim_{t\to 0} \frac{\tan^{-1} t}{t} = \lim_{t\to 0} \sum_{n=0}^{\infty} \frac{(-1)^n}{2n+1} t^{2n} = 1 + \sum_{n=1}^{\infty} \frac{(-1)^n 0^{2n}}{2n+1} = 1.$$

51. a. From (1),

$$\frac{1}{1+t^4} = \frac{1}{1-(-t^4)} = \sum_{n=0}^{\infty}(-t^4)^n = \sum_{n=0}^{\infty}(-1)^n t^{4n}.$$

Then $t^2/(1+t^4) = \sum_{n=0}^{\infty}(-1)^n t^{4n+2}$ for $|t| < 1$.

b. $$\int_0^{1/2} \frac{t^2}{1+t^4}\,dt = \int_0^{1/2}\left(\sum_{n=0}^{\infty}(-1)^n t^{4n+2}\right)dt = \sum_{n=0}^{\infty}(-1)^n\left(\int_0^{1/2} t^{4n+2}\,dt\right)$$

$$= \sum_{n=0}^{\infty}(-1)^n\left(\left.\frac{t^{4n+3}}{4n+3}\right|_0^{1/2}\right) = \sum_{n=0}^{\infty}\frac{(-1)^n}{4n+3}\left(\frac{1}{2}\right)^{4n+3}$$

52. Since $e^{-t^2} = \sum_{n=0}^{\infty}(1/n!)(-t^2)^n = \sum_{n=0}^{\infty}((-1)^n/n!)t^{2n}$ for all t, we have

$$\text{erf}(1) = \frac{2}{\sqrt{\pi}}\int_0^1 e^{-t^2}\,dt = \frac{2}{\sqrt{\pi}}\int_0^1\left(\sum_{n=0}^{\infty}\frac{(-1)^n}{n!}t^{2n}\right)dt$$

$$= \frac{2}{\sqrt{\pi}}\sum_{n=0}^{\infty}\frac{(-1)^n}{n!}\left(\int_0^1 t^{2n}\,dt\right) = \frac{2}{\sqrt{\pi}}\sum_{n=0}^{\infty}\frac{(-1)^n}{n!}\left(\left.\frac{t^{2n+1}}{2n+1}\right|_0^1\right) = \frac{2}{\sqrt{\pi}}\sum_{n=0}^{\infty}\frac{(-1)^n}{(2n+1)n!}$$

which is an alternating series. Therefore

$$\left|\text{erf}(1) - \frac{2}{\sqrt{\pi}}\sum_{n=0}^{j}\frac{(-1)^n}{(2n+1)n!}\right| < \frac{2}{\sqrt{\pi}}\,\frac{1}{[2(j+1)+1](j+1)!} = \frac{2}{\sqrt{\pi}}\,\frac{1}{(2j+3)(j+1)!}$$

and $(2/\sqrt{\pi})[1/[(2j+3)(j+1)!]] < 0.01$ if $j = 3$. Thus

$$\frac{2}{\sqrt{\pi}}\sum_{n=0}^{3}\frac{(-1)^n}{(2n+1)n!} = \frac{2}{\sqrt{\pi}}\left(1 - \frac{1}{3} + \frac{1}{10} - \frac{1}{42}\right) \approx 0.8382245241$$

is the desired estimate.

53. a. By (3), $e^x = \sum_{n=0}^{\infty} \frac{1}{n!}x^n$, so $xe^x = \sum_{n=0}^{\infty} \frac{1}{n!}x^{n+1}$.

b. On the one hand, by integration by parts with $u = x$, $dv = e^x\,dx$, we obtain

$$\int_0^1 xe^x\,dx = xe^x\Big|_0^1 - \int_0^1 e^x\,dx = e - e^x\Big|_0^1 = e - e + 1 = 1.$$

On the other hand, using the power series expansion of (a), we obtain

$$\int_0^1 xe^x\,dx = \int_0^1 \left(\sum_{n=0}^{\infty} \frac{1}{n!}x^{n+1}\right) dx = \sum_{n=0}^{\infty} \frac{1}{n!}\left(\int_0^1 x^{n+1}\,dx\right) = \sum_{n=0}^{\infty} \frac{1}{n!}\left(\frac{x^{n+2}}{n+2}\Big|_0^1\right) = \sum_{n=0}^{\infty} \frac{1}{n!\,(n+2)}.$$

Thus $\sum_{n=0}^{\infty} 1/n!\,(n+2) = 1$.

54. For $R > 0$, the power series $\sum_{n=0}^{\infty}(1/R^n)x^n$ has radius of convergence R.

55. We will find a positive integer n such that

$$A_n = 4\left|\frac{(-1)^{n+1}}{2(n+1)+1}\left(\frac{1}{5}\right)^{2(n+1)+1}\right| = \frac{4}{2n+3}\left(\frac{1}{5^{2n+3}}\right) < 10^{-11}$$

and a possibly different positive integer m such that

$$B_m = \left|\frac{(-1)^{m+1}}{2(m+1)+1}\left(\frac{1}{239}\right)^{2(m+1)+1}\right| = \frac{1}{2m+3}\left(\frac{1}{239^{2m+3}}\right) < 10^{-11}.$$

We have $A_6 \approx 8.738133333 \times 10^{-12}$ and $B_1 \approx 2.56472314 \times 10^{-13}$. Since $n = 6$, we find that

$$4\tan^{-1}\frac{1}{5} \approx 4\sum_{k=0}^{6} \frac{(-1)^{k+1}}{2k+1}\left(\frac{1}{5}\right)^{2k+1} \approx 4\left(\frac{1}{5} - \frac{1}{3}\frac{1}{5^3} + \frac{1}{5}\frac{1}{5^5} - + \cdots + \frac{1}{13}\frac{1}{5^{13}}\right) \approx 0.7895822394$$

and since $m = 1$, we find that

$$\tan^{-1}\frac{1}{239} = \frac{1}{239} - \frac{1}{3}\left(\frac{1}{239}\right)^3 \approx 0.004184076.$$

Thus

$$\frac{\pi}{4} = 4\tan^{-1}\frac{1}{5} - \tan^{-1}\frac{1}{239} \approx 0.7853981634$$

which is accurate to within $10^{-11} + 10^{-11} = 2 \times 10^{-11}$. Consequently $\pi = 4(\pi/4) \approx 3.1415926536$, with an error at most $4(2 \times 10^{-11}) < 10^{-10}$.

56. $\lim_{n\to\infty}\left|\frac{c_{n+1}x^{n+1}}{c_n x^n}\right| = \lim_{n\to\infty}\left|\frac{c_{n+1}}{c_n}\right| |x| = |x| \lim_{n\to\infty}\left|\frac{c_{n+1}}{c_n}\right|$

so that $\sum_{n=0}^{\infty} c_n x^n$ converges for

$$|x| < \frac{1}{\lim_{n\to\infty}|c_{n+1}/c_n|}$$

and diverges for

$$|x| > \frac{1}{\lim_{n\to\infty}|c_{n+1}/c_n|}.$$

Therefore

$$R = \frac{1}{\lim_{n\to\infty} |c_{n+1}/c_n|},$$

and thus $R = 1/L$.

57. a. $\sum_{n=0}^{\infty} c_n x^n = f(x) = f(-x) = \sum_{n=0}^{\infty} c_n(-x)^n = \sum_{n=0}^{\infty} (-1)^n c_n x^n$
By Corollary 9.27, $c_n = (-1)^n c_n$, so that $c_n = 0$ for n odd.

b. $\sum_{n=0}^{\infty} c_n x^n = f(x) = -f(-x) = -\sum_{n=0}^{\infty} c_n(-x)^n = \sum_{n=0}^{\infty} (-1)^{n+1} c_n x^n$
By Corollary 9.27, $c_n = (-1)^{n+1} c_n$, so that $c_n = 0$ for n even.

58. Since $[(2j-1)/(2j)]^2 < 1$ for $j = 1, 2, \ldots, n$, we have

$$\frac{1^2 \cdot 3^2 \cdot 5^2 \cdots (2n-1)^2}{2^2 \cdot 4^2 \cdot 6^2 \cdots (2n)^2} \le \frac{1^2}{2^2} = \frac{1}{4}.$$

Thus if $x^2 < 0.018$, then

$$\sum_{n=1}^{\infty} \frac{1^2 \cdot 3^2 \cdot 5^2 \cdots (2n-1)^2}{2^2 \cdot 4^2 \cdot 6^2 \cdots (2n)^2} x^{2n} \le \sum_{n=1}^{\infty} \frac{1}{4} x^{2n} \le \sum_{n=1}^{\infty} \frac{1}{4}(0.018)^n = \frac{1}{4}\left(\frac{0.018}{1-0.018}\right) < 0.005.$$

59. Consider $f(x) = \frac{2}{9}[1/(1-x)]$ for $0 < x < 1$, so that $f'(x) = \frac{2}{9}[1/(1-x)^2]$. We also have $f(x) = \frac{2}{9}\sum_{n=0}^{\infty} x^n$, so by the Differentiation Theorem, $f'(x) = \frac{2}{9}\sum_{n=1}^{\infty} nx^{n-1}$. Letting $x = \frac{7}{9}$ we find that

$$\frac{2}{9}\sum_{n=1}^{\infty} n\left(\frac{7}{9}\right)^{n-1} = f'\left(\frac{7}{9}\right) = \frac{2}{9}\frac{1}{(1-\frac{7}{9})^2} = 4.5.$$

Thus the expected value of N is 4.5 (that is, between 4 and 5) rolls.

9.9 Taylor Series

1. $f(x) = 4x^2 - 2x + 1$, $f'(x) = 8x - 2$, $f''(x) = 8$, and $f^{(k)}(x) = 0$ for $k \ge 3$; $f(-3) = 43$, $f'(-3) = -26$, $f''(-3) = 8$, and $f^{(k)}(-3) = 0$ for $k \ge 3$. Thus the Taylor series about -3 is given by

$$43 - 26(x+3) + 8 \cdot \left(\frac{1}{2!}\right)(x+3)^2 = 43 - 26(x+3) + 4(x+3)^2.$$

2. $f(x) = 5x^3 + 4x^2 + 3x + 2$, $f'(x) = 15x^2 + 8x + 3$, $f''(x) = 30x + 8$, $f^{(3)}(x) = 30$, and $f^{(k)}(x) = 0$ for $k \ge 4$; $f(2) = 64$, $f'(2) = 79$, $f''(2) = 68$, $f^{(3)}(2) = 30$, and $f^{(k)}(2) = 0$ for $k \ge 4$. Thus the Taylor series about 2 is given by

$$64 + 79(x-2) + \frac{68}{2!}(x-2)^2 + \frac{30}{3!}(x-2)^3 = 64 + 79(x-2) + 34(x-2)^2 + 5(x-2)^3.$$

3. $f^{(k)}(x) = e^x$ and $f^{(k)}(2) = e^2$ for $k \ge 0$. Thus the Taylor series about 2 is given by

$$e^2 + e^2(x-2) + e^2 \cdot \frac{1}{2!}(x-2)^2 + e^2 \cdot \frac{1}{3!}(x-2)^3 + \cdots = \sum_{n=0}^{\infty} \frac{e^2}{n!}(x-2)^n.$$

4. $f(x) = \frac{1}{x}$, $f^{(k)}(x) = \frac{(-1)^k k!}{x^{k+1}}$, $f^{(k)}(-1) = -(k!)$ for any nonnegative integer k; the Taylor series about -1 is

$$-1 - (x+1) - \frac{2!}{2!}(x+1)^2 - \frac{3!}{3!}(x+1)^3 - \cdots = \sum_{n=0}^{\infty} -(x+1)^n$$

5. $f(x) = \ln x$, $f^{(k)}(x) = \frac{(-1)^{k+1}(k-1)!}{x^k}$, $f^{(k)}(2) = \frac{(-1)^{k+1}(k-1)!}{2^k}$ for any nonnegative integer k; the Taylor series about 2 is

$$\ln 2 + \frac{1}{2}(x-2) - \frac{1}{2^2}\cdot\frac{1}{2!}(x-2)^2 + \frac{2!}{2^3}\cdot\frac{1}{3!}(x-2)^3 - \frac{3!}{2^4}\cdot\frac{1}{4!}(x-2)^4 + \cdots = \ln 2 + \sum_{n=1}^{\infty}\frac{(-1)^{n+1}}{n2^n}(x-2)^n$$

6. $f(x) = \int_0^x \ln(1+t)\,dt$, $f'(x) = \ln(1+x)$, $f''(x) = 1/(1+x)$, $f^{(3)}(x) = -1/(1+x)^2$, $f^{(4)}(x) = (-1)^2 2!/(1+x)^3$, and in general, $f^{(k)}(x) = (-1)^k(k-2)!/(1+x)^{k-1}$ for $k \geq 2$; $f(0) = 0$, $f'(0) = 0$, $f''(0) = 1$, and in general, $f^{(k)}(0) = (-1)^k(k-2)!$ for $k \geq 2$. The Taylor series about 0 is

$$\frac{(-1)^2 0!}{2!}x^2 + \frac{(-1)^3 1!}{3!}x^3 + \frac{(-1)^4 2!}{4!}x^4 + \cdots = \sum_{n=2}^{\infty}\frac{(-1)^n}{n(n-1)}x^n.$$

7. $\sin 2x = \sum_{n=0}^{\infty}\frac{(-1)^n}{(2n+1)!}(2x)^{2n+1} = \sum_{n=0}^{\infty}\frac{(-1)^n 2^{2n+1}}{(2n+1)!}x^{2n+1}$

8. $\cos x^2 = \sum_{n=0}^{\infty}\frac{(-1)^n}{(2n)!}(x^2)^{2n} = \sum_{n=0}^{\infty}\frac{(-1)^n}{(2n)!}x^{4n}$

9. $\ln 3x = \ln 3 + \ln x = \ln 3 + \sum_{n=0}^{\infty}\frac{(-1)^n}{n+1}(x-1)^{n+1}$

10. $\ln\frac{1+x}{1-x} = \ln(1+x) - \ln(1-x) = \sum_{n=0}^{\infty}\frac{(-1)^n}{n+1}x^{n+1} - \sum_{n=0}^{\infty}\frac{(-1)^n}{n+1}(-x)^{n+1}$

$$= \sum_{n=0}^{\infty}\frac{(-1)^n}{n+1}x^{n+1} + \sum_{n=0}^{\infty}\frac{1}{n+1}x^{n+1} = \sum_{n=0}^{\infty}\frac{2}{2n+1}x^{2n+1}$$

11. Since $\ln(1+x) = \sum_{n=0}^{\infty}[(-1)^n/(n+1)]x^{n+1}$, we have

$$x\ln(1+x^2) = x\sum_{n=0}^{\infty}\frac{(1)^n}{n+1}(x^2)^{n+1} = \sum_{n=0}^{\infty}\frac{(-1)^n}{n+1}x^{2n+3}.$$

12. $\sinh x = \frac{1}{2}(e^x - e^{-x}) = \frac{1}{2}\left(\sum_{n=0}^{\infty}\frac{1}{n!}x^n - \sum_{n=0}^{\infty}\frac{(-1)^n}{n!}x^n\right)$

$$= \frac{1}{2}\sum_{n=0}^{\infty}\frac{2}{(2n+1)!}x^{2n+1} = \sum_{n=0}^{\infty}\frac{1}{(2n+1)!}x^{2n+1}$$

13. $2^x = e^{x\ln 2} = \sum_{n=0}^{\infty}\frac{1}{n!}(x\ln 2)^n = \sum_{n=0}^{\infty}\frac{(\ln 2)^n}{n!}x^n$

14. $10^x = e^{x\ln 10} = \sum_{n=0}^{\infty} \frac{1}{n!}(x\ln 10)^n = \sum_{n=0}^{\infty} \frac{(\ln 10)^n}{n!}x^n$

15. $\frac{x-1}{x+1} = 1 - \frac{2}{x+1} = 1 - \frac{2}{2+(x-1)} = 1 - \frac{1}{1+\frac{1}{2}(x-1)} = 1 - \sum_{n=0}^{\infty} \frac{(-1)^n}{2^n}(x-1)^n$

$$= \sum_{n=1}^{\infty} \frac{(-1)^{n+1}}{2^n}(x-1)^n = \sum_{n=0}^{\infty} \frac{(-1)^n}{2^{n+1}}(x-1)^{n+1}$$

16. $\sin^2 x = \frac{1}{2}(1-\cos 2x) = \frac{1}{2}\left(1 - \sum_{n=0}^{\infty} \frac{(-1)^n}{(2n)!}(2x)^{2n}\right) = \sum_{n=1}^{\infty} \frac{(-1)^{n+1}2^{2n-1}}{(2n)!}x^{2n}$

17. $\cos^2 x = \frac{1}{2}(1+\cos 2x) = \frac{1}{2}\left(1 + \sum_{n=0}^{\infty} \frac{(-1)^n}{(2n)!}(2x)^{2n}\right) = 1 + \sum_{n=1}^{\infty} \frac{(-1)^n 2^{2n-1}}{(2n)!}x^{2n}$

18. Since $\frac{1}{1+t} = \sum_{n=0}^{\infty}(-1)^n t^n$ (as a geometric series), it follows that

$$\frac{x}{1+x^3} = x\left(\frac{1}{1+x^3}\right) = x\sum_{n=0}^{\infty}(-1)^n(x^3)^n = \sum_{n=0}^{\infty}(-1)^n x^{3n+1} \quad \text{and} \quad -\frac{1}{1+x^3} = -\sum_{n=0}^{\infty}(-1)^n x^{3n}.$$

Thus

$$\frac{x-1}{1+x^3} = \frac{x}{1+x^3} - \frac{1}{1+x^3} = \sum_{n=0}^{\infty}(-1)^n x^{3n+1} - \sum_{n=0}^{\infty}(-1)^n x^{3n}$$
$$= -1 + x + x^3 - x^4 - x^6 + x^7 + x^9 - x^{10} + - \cdots.$$

19. For $x \neq 0$,

$$\frac{\sin x}{x} = \frac{1}{x}\sum_{n=0}^{\infty} \frac{(-1)^n}{(2n+1)!}x^{2n+1} = \sum_{n=0}^{\infty} \frac{(-1)^n}{(2n+1)!}x^{2n}, \quad \text{so} \quad f(x) = \sum_{n=0}^{\infty} \frac{(-1)^n}{(2n+1)!}x^{2n}.$$

20. Since

$$\sin x - x = \left(\sum_{n=0}^{\infty} \frac{(-1)^n}{(2n+1)!}x^{2n+1}\right) - x = \sum_{n=1}^{\infty} \frac{(-1)^n}{(2n+1)!}x^{2n+1}$$

it follows that for $x \neq 0$,

$$\frac{\sin x - x}{x^3} = \frac{1}{x^3}\sum_{n=1}^{\infty} \frac{(-1)^n}{(2n+1)!}x^{2n+1} = \sum_{n=1}^{\infty} \frac{(-1)^n}{(2n+1)!}x^{2n-2} = \sum_{n=0}^{\infty} \frac{(-1)^{n+1}}{(2n+3)!}x^{2n}.$$

Thus $f(x) = \sum_{n=0}^{\infty} \frac{(-1)^{n+1}}{(2n+3)!}x^{2n}$.

21. $\sin x = \sin\left(x - \frac{\pi}{3} + \frac{\pi}{3}\right) = \sin\left(x - \frac{\pi}{3}\right)\cos\frac{\pi}{3} + \cos\left(x - \frac{\pi}{3}\right)\sin\frac{\pi}{3}$

$$= \frac{1}{2}\sin\left(x - \frac{\pi}{3}\right) + \frac{\sqrt{3}}{2}\cos\left(x - \frac{\pi}{3}\right) = \frac{1}{2}\sum_{n=0}^{\infty}(-1)^n\frac{(x-\pi/3)^{2n+1}}{(2n+1)!} + \frac{\sqrt{3}}{2}\sum_{n=0}^{\infty}(-1)^n\frac{(x-\pi/3)^{2n}}{(2n)!}$$
$$= \frac{1}{2}\sqrt{3} + \frac{1}{2}\left(x - \frac{\pi}{3}\right) - \frac{\sqrt{3}}{2(2!)}\left(x - \frac{\pi}{3}\right)^2 - \frac{1}{2(3!)}\left(x - \frac{\pi}{3}\right)^3 + + - - \cdots$$

22. $\cos x = \cos\left(x - \frac{\pi}{6} + \frac{\pi}{6}\right) = \cos\left(x - \frac{\pi}{6}\right)\cos\frac{\pi}{6} - \sin\left(x - \frac{\pi}{6}\right)\sin\frac{\pi}{6}$

$$= \frac{\sqrt{3}}{2}\cos\left(x - \frac{\pi}{6}\right) - \frac{1}{2}\sin\left(x - \frac{\pi}{6}\right) = \frac{\sqrt{3}}{2}\sum_{n=0}^{\infty}(-1)^n\frac{(x-\pi/6)^{2n}}{(2n)!} - \frac{1}{2}\sum_{n=0}^{\infty}(-1)^n\frac{(x-\pi/6)^{2n+1}}{(2n+1)!}$$

$$= \frac{\sqrt{3}}{2} - \frac{1}{2}\left(x - \frac{\pi}{6}\right) - \frac{\sqrt{3}}{2}\frac{1}{2!}\left(x - \frac{\pi}{6}\right)^2 + \frac{1}{2(3!)}\left(x - \frac{\pi}{6}\right)^3 + - - \cdots$$

23. Let $f(x) = e^x$, so that $f(\frac{1}{2}) = e^{1/2}$. We need to find n such that $\left|r_n(\frac{1}{2})\right| < 0.001$. Then $p_n(\frac{1}{2})$ is the desired approximation of $e^{1/2}$. By (11),

$$r_n\left(\frac{1}{2}\right) = \frac{f^{(n+1)}(t_{1/2})}{(n+1)!}\left(\frac{1}{2}\right)^{n+1} \quad \text{for an appropriate } t_{1/2} \text{ in } (0, \tfrac{1}{2}).$$

Since $f^{(n+1)}(x) = e^x$, we have $f^{(n+1)}(t_{1/2}) = e^{t_{1/2}}$. Since e^x is increasing and $t_{1/2} < \frac{1}{2}$, it follows that $e^{t_{1/2}} < e^{1/2}$. Since $e^{1/2} < 4^{1/2} = 2$, we conclude that

$$\left|r_n\left(\frac{1}{2}\right)\right| = \left|\frac{f^{(n+1)}(t_{1/2})}{(n+1)!}\left(\frac{1}{2}\right)^{n+1}\right| = \frac{e^{t_{1/2}}}{(n+1)!}\left(\frac{1}{2}\right)^{n+1} < \frac{2}{(n+1)!}\left(\frac{1}{2}\right)^{n+1} = \frac{1}{2^n(n+1)!}.$$

Thus $\left|r_n(\frac{1}{2})\right| < 0.001$ if $n \geq 4$. By (2) this means that

$$p_4\left(\frac{1}{2}\right) = \sum_{n=0}^{4}\frac{1}{n!}\left(\frac{1}{2}\right)^n \approx 1.6484375$$

is the desired approximation of $e^{1/2}$.

24. Let $f(x) = e^x$, so that $f(-\frac{1}{2}) = e^{-1/2}$. We need to find n such that $\left|r_n(-\frac{1}{2})\right| < 0.0001$. Then $p_n(-\frac{1}{2})$ is the desired approximation of $e^{-1/2}$. By (11),

$$r_n\left(-\frac{1}{2}\right) = \frac{f^{(n+1)}(t_{-1/2})}{(n+1)!}\left(-\frac{1}{2}\right)^{n+1} \quad \text{for an appropriate } t_{-1/2} \text{ in } (-\tfrac{1}{2}, 0).$$

Since $f^{(n+1)}(x) = e^x$, we have $f^{(n+1)}(t_{-1/2}) = e^{t_{-1/2}}$. Since e^x is increasing and $t_{-1/2} < 0$, it follows that $e^{t_{-1/2}} < e^0 = 1$. Therefore

$$\left|r_n\left(-\frac{1}{2}\right)\right| = \left|\frac{f^{(n+1)}(t_{-1/2})}{(n+1)!}\left(-\frac{1}{2}\right)^{n+1}\right| = \frac{e^{t_{-1/2}}}{(n+1)!}\left(\frac{1}{2}\right)^{n+1} < \frac{1}{(n+1)!\,2^{n+1}}.$$

Thus $\left|r_n(-\frac{1}{2})\right| < 0.0001$ if $n \geq 5$. By (2) this means that

$$p_5\left(-\frac{1}{2}\right) = \sum_{n=0}^{5}\frac{1}{n!}\left(-\frac{1}{2}\right)^n \approx 0.6065104167$$

is the desired approximation of $e^{-1/2}$.

25. Let $f(x) = \ln(1+x)$, so that $f(0.1) = \ln 1.1$. We need to find n such that $|r_n(0.1)| < 0.00001$. Then $p_n(0.1)$ is the desired approximation of $\ln 1.1$. By (11),

$$r_n(0.1) = \frac{f^{(n+1)}(t_{0.1})}{(n+1)!}(0.1)^{n+1} \quad \text{for an appropriate } t_{0.1} \text{ in } (0, 0.1).$$

Since $f^{(n+1)}(x) = (-1)^n n!/(1+x)^{n+1}$, we have $f^{(n+1)}(t_{0.1}) = (-1)^n n!/(1+t_{0.1})^{n+1}$. Since $1/(1+x)^{n+1}$ is decreasing on $[0, 0.1]$, it follows that $1/(1+t_{0.1})^{n+1} < 1$, so that

$$|r_n(0.1)| = \left|\frac{f^{(n+1)}(t_{0.1})}{(n+1)!}(0.1)^{n+1}\right| = \frac{1}{(n+1)(1+t_{0.1})^{n+1}}(0.1)^{n+1} < \frac{1}{n+1}(0.1)^{n+1}.$$

Thus $|r_n(0.1)| < 0.00001$ if $n \geq 4$. By (3) this means that

$$p_4(0.1) = \sum_{n=0}^{4} \frac{(-1)^n}{n+1}(0.1)^{n+1} \approx 0.0953103333$$

is the desired approximation of $\ln 1.1$.

26. Let $f(x) = \sin x$, so that $f(\pi/10) = \sin(\pi/10)$. We need to find n such that $|r_n(\pi/10)| < 0.001$. Then $p_n(\pi/10)$ is the desired approximation of $\sin(\pi/10)$. By (11),

$$r_n\left(\frac{\pi}{10}\right) = \frac{f^{(n+1)}(t_{\pi/10})}{(n+1)!}\left(\frac{\pi}{10}\right)^{n+1} \quad \text{for an appropriate } t_{\pi/10} \text{ in } (0, \pi/10).$$

Since $|f^{(n+1)}(x)| \leq 1$ for all x, it follows that

$$\left|r_n\left(\frac{\pi}{10}\right)\right| = \left|\frac{f^{(n+1)}(t_{\pi/10})}{(n+1)!}\left(\frac{\pi}{10}\right)^{n+1}\right| \leq \frac{1}{(n+1)!}\left(\frac{\pi}{10}\right)^{n+1}.$$

Thus $|r_n(\pi/10)| < 0.001$ if $n \geq 3$. By Example 2, $p_3(\pi/10) = \pi/10 - \frac{1}{6}(\pi/10)^3 \approx 0.3089915526$ is the desired approximation of $\sin(\pi/10)$.

27. Let $f(x) = \cos x$, so that $f(-\pi/7) = \cos(-\pi/7)$. We need to find n such that $|r_n(-\pi/7)| < 0.001$. Then $p_n(-\pi/7)$ is the desired approximation of $\cos(-\pi/7)$. By (11),

$$r_n\left(-\frac{\pi}{7}\right) = \frac{f^{(n+1)}(t_{-\pi/7})}{(n+1)!}\left(-\frac{\pi}{7}\right)^{n+1} \quad \text{for an appropriate } t_{-\pi/7} \text{ in } (-\pi/7, 0).$$

Since $|f^{(n+1)}(x)| \leq 1$ for all x, it follows that

$$\left|r_n\left(-\frac{\pi}{7}\right)\right| = \left|\frac{f^{(n+1)}(t_{-\pi/7})}{(n+1)!}\left(-\frac{\pi}{7}\right)^{n+1}\right| \leq \frac{1}{(n+1)!}\left(\frac{\pi}{7}\right)^{n+1}.$$

Thus $|r_n(-\pi/7)| < 0.001$ if $n \geq 4$. By the Taylor series for $\cos x$ given after Example 1 in the text, $p_4(-\pi/7) = 1 - \frac{1}{2}(-\pi/7)^2 + \frac{1}{24}(-\pi/7)^4 \approx 0.9009801767$ is the desired approximation of $\cos(-\pi/7)$.

28. By (4),

$$\tan^{-1}\frac{1}{2} = \sum_{n=0}^{\infty} \frac{(-1)^n}{2n+1}\left(\frac{1}{2}\right)^{2n+1}.$$

Since this series is alternating and

$$\frac{1}{2n+1}\left(\frac{1}{2}\right)^{2n+1} < 0.001 \quad \text{for } n \geq 4,$$

it follows from (1) of Section 9.7 that

$$\sum_{n=0}^{3} \frac{(-1)^n}{2n+1}\left(\frac{1}{2}\right)^{2n+1} \approx 0.4634672619$$

approximates $\tan^{-1}\frac{1}{2}$ with error less than 0.001.

29. Let $f(x) = \ln[(1+x)/(1-x)] = \ln(1+x) - \ln(1-x)$. Notice that $(1+x)/(1-x) = 2$ if $1+x = 2-2x$, or $x = \frac{1}{3}$. Thus $f(\frac{1}{3}) = \ln 2$. We need to find n such that $|r_n(\frac{1}{3})| < 0.01$. Then $p_n(\frac{1}{3})$ is the desired approximation of $\ln 2$. By (11),

$$r_n\left(\frac{1}{3}\right) = \frac{f^{(n+1)}(t_{1/3})}{(n+1)!}\left(\frac{1}{3}\right)^{n+1} \quad \text{for an appropriate } t_{1/3} \text{ in } (0, \tfrac{1}{3}).$$

Now

$$f^{(n+1)}(x) = \frac{(-1)^n n!}{(1+x)^{n+1}} + \frac{n!}{(1-x)^{n+1}}$$

so that

$$\left|f^{(n+1)}(t_{1/3})\right| = \left|\frac{(-1)^n n!}{(1+t_{1/3})^{n+1}} + \frac{n!}{(1-t_{1/3})^{n+1}}\right| < \frac{n!}{1} + \frac{n!}{(2/3)^{n+1}} = n!\left[1 + \left(\frac{3}{2}\right)^{n+1}\right].$$

Therefore

$$\left|r_n\left(\frac{1}{3}\right)\right| = \left|\frac{f^{(n+1)}(t_{1/3})}{(n+1)!}\left(\frac{1}{3}\right)^{n+1}\right| < \frac{n!\left[1+(\frac{3}{2})^{n+1}\right]}{(n+1)!}\left(\frac{1}{3}\right)^{n+1} = \frac{1+(\frac{3}{2})^{n+1}}{(n+1)3^{n+1}}.$$

Thus $|r_n(\frac{1}{3})| < 0.01$ if $n \geq 4$. By the solution of Exercise 10,

$$\ln\frac{1+x}{1-x} = \sum_{n=0}^{\infty} \frac{2}{2n+1} x^{2n+1},$$

so that $p_4(\frac{1}{3}) = 2(\frac{1}{3}) + \frac{2}{3}(\frac{1}{3})^3 \approx 0.6913580247$ is the desired approximation of $\ln 2$.

30. Let $f(x) = \ln[(1+x)/(1-x)] = \ln(1+x) - \ln(1-x)$. Notice that $(1+x)/(1-x) = \frac{3}{2}$ if $2+2x = 3-3x$ or $x = \frac{1}{5}$. Thus $f(\frac{1}{5}) = \ln\frac{3}{2}$. We need to find n such that $|r_n(\frac{1}{5})| < 0.001$. Then $p_n(\frac{1}{5})$ is the desired approximation of $\ln\frac{3}{2}$. By (11),

$$r_n\left(\frac{1}{5}\right) = \frac{f^{(n+1)}(t_{1/5})}{(n+1)!}\left(\frac{1}{5}\right)^{n+1} \quad \text{for an appropriate } t_{1/5} \text{ in } (0, \tfrac{1}{5}).$$

Now

$$f^{(n+1)}(x) = \frac{(-1)^n n!}{(1+x)^{n+1}} + \frac{n!}{(1-x)^{n+1}}$$

so that

$$\left|f^{(n+1)}(t_{1/5})\right| = \left|\frac{(-1)^n n!}{(1+t_{1/5})^{n+1}} + \frac{n!}{(1-t_{1/5})^{n+1}}\right| < \frac{n!}{1} + \frac{n!}{(4/5)^{n+1}} = n!\left[1 + \left(\frac{5}{4}\right)^{n+1}\right].$$

Therefore

$$\left|r_n\left(\frac{1}{5}\right)\right| = \left|\frac{f^{(n+1)}(t_{1/5})}{(n+1)!}\left(\frac{1}{5}\right)^{n+1}\right| < \frac{n!\,[1+(\frac{5}{4})^{n+1}]}{(n+1)!}\left(\frac{1}{5}\right)^{n+1} = \frac{1+(\frac{5}{4})^{n+1}}{(n+1)5^{n+1}}.$$

Thus $|r_n(\frac{1}{5})| < 0.001$ if $n \geq 4$. By the solution of Exercise 10,

$$\ln\frac{1+x}{1-x} = \sum_{n=0}^{\infty}\frac{2}{2n+1}x^{2n+1},$$

so that $p_4(\frac{1}{5}) = 2(\frac{1}{5}) + \frac{2}{3}(\frac{1}{5})^3 \approx 0.4053333333$ is the desired approximation of $\ln\frac{3}{2}$.

31. If the x window is $[-2,2]$ and the y window is $[-8,8]$, then $n = 4$.

32. If the x window is $[-3,3]$ and the y window is $[-1.5,1.5]$, then $n = 7$.

33. If the x window is $[-4,4]$ and the y window is $[-1.5,1.5]$, then $n = 10$.

34. a. We need to find n such that $|r_n(x)| = |p_n(x) - f(x)| < 0.001$ for all x in $[-\frac{1}{2},\frac{1}{2}]$. Since

$$\tan^{-1}x = \sum_{n=0}^{\infty}\frac{(-1)^n}{2n+1}x^{2n+1},$$

we will use the Alternating Series Test and find a k such that

$$|r_{2k+1}(x)| < \left|\frac{(-1)^{k+1}}{2k+3}x^{2k+3}\right| < 0.001 \quad \text{for all } x \text{ in } [-\tfrac{1}{2},\tfrac{1}{2}].$$

Then we will let $n = 2k+1$. Now

$$\left|\frac{(-1)^{k+1}}{2k+3}x^{2k+3}\right| < 0.001 \quad \text{for all } x \text{ in } [-\tfrac{1}{2},\tfrac{1}{2}] \text{ if } \quad \frac{1}{(2k+3)2^{2k+3}} < \frac{1}{1000}$$

which occurs if $k \geq 3$. Thus if $n = 2(3)+1 = 7$, then $|p_n(x) - f(x)| < 0.001$ for all x in $[-\frac{1}{2},\frac{1}{2}]$.

b. The polynomials converge to $\tan^{-1}x$ for x in $[-1,1]$, but since the radius of convergence of the Taylor series is 1, the polynomials do not converge to $\tan^{-1}x$ for x outside the interval $[-1,1]$.

35. a. As in Example 1 we find that $f(x) = \cos x$, $f'(x) = -\sin x$, $f''(x) = -\cos x$, $f^{(3)}(x) = \sin x$, and in general, $f^{(2k)}(x) = (-1)^k\cos x$ and $f^{(2k+1)}(x) = (-1)^{k+1}\sin x$. Therefore $f^{(2k)}(0) = (-1)^k$ and $f^{(2k+1)}(0) = 0$. Consequently the Taylor series of $\cos x$ is

$$1 - \frac{1}{2!}x^2 + \frac{1}{4!}x^4 - \frac{1}{6!}x^6 + - \cdots = \sum_{n=0}^{\infty}\frac{(-1)^n}{(2n)!}x^{2n}.$$

b. Since $|f^{(n+1)}(x)| \leq 1$ for all x and all $n \geq 0$,

$$|r_n(x)| = \left|\frac{f^{(n+1)}(t_x)}{(n+1)!}x^{n+1}\right| \leq \frac{|x|^{n+1}}{(n+1)!}.$$

By Example 7 of Section 9.7,

$$\lim_{n\to\infty}\frac{|x|^{n+1}}{(n+1)!}=\lim_{n\to\infty}\frac{|x|^n}{n!}=0 \quad \text{for all } x.$$

Therefore $\lim_{n\to\infty} r_n(x)=0$ for all x, so by (12) we conclude that

$$\cos x=\sum_{n=0}^{\infty}\frac{(-1)^n}{(2n)!}x^{2n}.$$

That is, the Taylor series of $\cos x$ converges to $\cos x$ for all x.

36. We need to find an n such that $|r_n(7\pi/36)|<10^{-5}$. Since $|f^{(n+1)}(x)|\le 1$ for all x,

$$\left|r_n\left(\frac{7\pi}{36}\right)\right|=\left|\frac{f^{(n+1)}(t_{7\pi/36})}{(n+1)!}\left(\frac{7\pi}{36}\right)^{n+1}\right|\le\frac{1}{(n+1)!}\left(\frac{7\pi}{36}\right)^{n+1}$$

and

$$\frac{1}{(n+1)!}\left(\frac{7\pi}{36}\right)^{n+1}<10^{-5} \quad \text{if } n\ge 6.$$

37. $$\frac{-3x+2}{2x^2-3x+1}=\frac{-3x+2}{(2x-1)(x-1)}=\frac{A}{2x-1}+\frac{B}{x-1}=\frac{A(x-1)+B(2x-1)}{(2x-1)(x-1)}$$

$A+2B=-3$ and $-A-B=2$ imply that $B=-1$, so $A=-2-B=-1$. Therefore

$$\frac{-3x+2}{2x^2-3x+1}=\frac{-1}{2x-1}+\frac{-1}{x-1}=\frac{1}{1-2x}+\frac{1}{1-x}=\sum_{n=0}^{\infty}(2x)^n+\sum_{n=0}^{\infty}x^n=\sum_{n=0}^{\infty}(2^n+1)x^n$$

38. $f(0)=0$; $f'(x)=1+[f(x)]^2$, so $f'(0)=1+[f(0)]^2=1+\tan^2 0=1$; $f''(x)=2f(x)f'(x)$, so $f''(0)=2f(0)f'(0)=0(1)=0$; $f^{(3)}(x)=2[f'(x)]^2+2f(x)f''(x)$, so $f^{(3)}(0)=2[f'(0)]^2+2f(0)f''(0)=2(1)^2+2(0)(0)=2$; $f^{(4)}(x)=4f'(x)f''(x)+2f'(x)f''(x)+2f(x)f^{(3)}(x)=6f'(x)f''(x)+2f(x)f^{(3)}(x)$, so $f^{(4)}(0)=6(1)(0)+2(0)(2)=0$; $f^{(5)}(x)=6[f''(x)]^2+6f'(x)f^{(3)}(x)+2f'(x)f^{(3)}(x)+2f(x)f^{(4)}(x)=6[f''(x)]^2+8f'(x)f^{(3)}(x)+2f(x)f^{(4)}(x)$, so $f^{(5)}(0)=6(0)^2+8(1)(2)+2(0)(0)=16$; thus the sum of the first six terms of the Taylor series about 0 is

$$0+1\cdot x+\frac{0}{2!}x^2+\frac{2}{3!}x^3+\frac{0}{4!}x^4+\frac{16}{5!}x^5=x+\frac{1}{3}x^3+\frac{2}{15}x^5.$$

39. a. $f(0)=e^{(0^2)}\int_0^0 e^{(-t^2)}\,dt=0$; $f'(x)=2xe^{(x^2)}\int_0^x e^{-(t^2)}\,dt+e^{(x^2)}e^{-(x^2)}=2xf(x)+1$.

b. By part (a), we obtain $f''(x)=2f(x)+2xf'(x)$, $f^{(3)}(x)=2f'(x)+2f'(x)+2xf''(x)=2(2)f'(x)+2xf''(x)$. In general, $f^{(n)}(x)=2(n-1)f^{(n-2)}(x)+2xf^{(n-1)}(x)$ for $n\ge 2$. Therefore $f^{(n)}(0)=2(n-1)f^{(n-2)}(0)$ for $n\ge 2$. By part (a), $f(0)=0$ and $f'(0)=2(0)f(0)+1=1$, so that for $k\ge 0$ we have $f^{(2k)}(0)=2(2k-1)f^{(2k-2)}(0)=\cdots=0$. In addition,

$$f^{(2n+1)}(0)=2(2n)f^{(2n-1)}(0)=2(2n)(2)(2n-2)f^{(2n-3)}(0)$$

$$=2^{2\cdot 2}n(n-1)f^{(2n-3)}(0)=2^{2\cdot 3}n(n-1)(n-2)f^{(2n-5)}(0)=\cdots=2^{2n}n!f'(0)=4^n n!.$$

Consequently $f(x)=\sum_{n=0}^{\infty}[4^n n!/(2n+1)!]x^{2n+1}$.

40. Suppose there is a number M such that $|f^{(n)}(x)| \le M$ for all x and all $n \ge 0$. Then

$$|r_n(x)| = \left|\frac{f^{(n+1)}(t_x)}{(n+1)!}(x-a)^{n+1}\right| \le \frac{M|x-a|^{n+1}}{(n+1)!}$$

and by Example 7 of Section 9.7, $\lim_{n\to\infty} |r_n(x)| = 0$, so that $\lim_{n\to\infty} r_n(x) = 0$ for all x. Thus the Taylor series of f about a converges to $f(x)$ for all x.

41. a. $0 \le a_{n+1} = a_n + a_{n-1} \le 2a_n$. Thus $a_2 \le 2a_1 = 2$, $a_3 \le 2a_2 \le 4$, and, in general,

$$a_n \le 2a_{n-1} \le 4a_{n-2} \le \cdots \le 2^{n-1}a_2 \le 2^n a_1 = 2^n.$$

Since the radius of convergence of $\sum_{n=1}^{\infty} 2^n x^n$ is $\frac{1}{2}$ (by the Ratio Test), it follows that $\sum_{n=1}^{\infty} a_n x^n$ converges for $|x| < \frac{1}{2}$. Thus the radius of convergence of $\sum_{n=1}^{\infty} a_n x^n$ is at least $\frac{1}{2}$.

b.
$$\begin{aligned}\sum_{n=1}^{\infty} a_n x^n - x\sum_{n=1}^{\infty} a_n x^n - x^2\sum_{n=1}^{\infty} a_n x^n &= \left(a_1x + a_2x^2 + \sum_{n=3}^{\infty} a_n x^n\right)\\ &\quad - \left(a_1x^2 + \sum_{n=3}^{\infty} a_{n-1}x^n\right) - \sum_{n=3}^{\infty} a_{n-2}x^n\\ &= (x + x^2 - x^2) + \sum_{n=3}^{\infty}(a_n - a_{n-1} - a_{n-2})x^n\\ &= x \quad \text{for } |x| < \tfrac{1}{2}\end{aligned}$$

since $a_n = a_{n-1} + a_{n-2}$ for $n \ge 3$. Thus $\sum_{n=1}^{\infty} a_n x^n = x/(1 - x - x^2)$ for $|x| < \frac{1}{2}$.

42. If $\sum_{n=0}^{\infty} c_n t^n$ were a power series representation for f on an open interval containing 0, then $c_n = f^{(n)}(0)/n!$ for $n \ge 0$. Since f is stationary for $t \le 0$, it follows that $f^{(n)}(0) = 0$ for $n > 0$, and thus $c_n = 0$ for $n > 0$, so that $f(t) = \sum_{n=0}^{\infty} c_n t^n = c_0$. But $f'(t) > 0$ for $t > 0$ by hypothesis, so $f(t)$ cannot be c_0 for all $t > 0$.This contradiction proves that f has no such power series representation.

43.
$$\begin{aligned}\int_0^1 \sin\frac{\pi x^2}{2}\,dx &= \int_0^1 \sum_{n=0}^{\infty}(-1)^n\frac{(\pi x^2/2)^{2n+1}}{(2n+1)!}\,dx = \sum_{n=0}^{\infty}\frac{(-1)^n\pi^{2n+1}}{2^{2n+1}(2n+1)!}\int_0^1 x^{4n+2}\,dx\\ &= \sum_{n=0}^{\infty}\frac{(-1)^n\pi^{2n+1}}{2^{2n+1}(2n+1)!}\cdot\frac{1}{4n+3}x^{4n+3}\Big|_0^1 = \sum_{n=0}^{\infty}\frac{(-1)^n\pi^{2n+1}}{2^{2n+1}(2n+1)!(4n+3)}\end{aligned}$$

Since

$$\frac{\pi^{2n+1}}{2^{2n+1}(2n+1)!(4n+3)} < 10^{-4} \quad \text{for } n \ge 4$$

it follows from (1) in Section 9.7 that

$$\sum_{n=0}^{3}\frac{(-1)^n\pi^{2n+1}}{2^{2n+1}(2n+1)!(4n+3)} = \frac{\pi}{2(3)} - \frac{\pi^3}{2^3\,3!\,(7)} + \frac{\pi^5}{2^5\,5!\,(11)} - \frac{\pi^7}{2^7\,7!\,(15)} \approx 0.4382508575$$

approximates the given Fresnel integral with an error less than 10^{-4}.

9.10 Binomial Series

1. $\sqrt{1.05} = \sqrt{1 + \frac{1}{20}}$, so by (5) with $s = \frac{1}{2}$ and $x = \frac{1}{20}$, we have

$$\left| r_N\left(\frac{1}{20}\right)\right| \le \frac{1}{2}\frac{1/20^{N+1}}{1 - 1/20} = \frac{1}{38 \cdot 20^N}.$$

Then $|r_N(\frac{1}{20})| < 0.001$ if $N = 2$, so by taking the first 3 terms in (3) we obtain

$$\sqrt{1.05} \approx 1 + \frac{1}{2}\left(\frac{1}{20}\right) - \frac{1}{8}\left(\frac{1}{20}\right)^2 \approx 1.0246875$$

as the desired approximation.

2. $\sqrt[3]{9} = \sqrt[3]{8\left(1 + \frac{1}{8}\right)} = 2\sqrt[3]{1 + \frac{1}{8}}$, so by (5) with $s = \frac{1}{3}$ and $x = \frac{1}{8}$, we have

$$\left| r_N\left(\frac{1}{8}\right)\right| \le \frac{1}{3}\frac{1/8^{N+1}}{1 - \frac{1}{8}} = \frac{1}{21 \cdot 8^N}.$$

Then $|r_N(\frac{1}{8})| < 0.0005$ if $N = 3$, so by taking the first 4 terms in (4) we obtain

$$\sqrt[3]{9} \approx 2\left[1 + \frac{1}{3}\left(\frac{1}{8}\right) + \frac{1}{2!}\left(\frac{1}{3}\right)\left(\frac{-2}{3}\right)\left(\frac{1}{8}\right)^2 + \frac{1}{3!}\left(\frac{1}{3}\right)\left(\frac{-2}{3}\right)\left(\frac{-5}{3}\right)\left(\frac{1}{8}\right)^3\right] \approx 2.080102238$$

as the desired approximation.

3. $\sqrt[4]{83} = \sqrt[4]{81\left(1 + \frac{2}{81}\right)} = 3\sqrt[4]{1 + \frac{2}{81}}$, so by (5) with $s = \frac{1}{4}$ and $x = \frac{2}{81}$, we have

$$\left| r_N\left(\frac{2}{81}\right)\right| \le \frac{1}{4}\frac{(\frac{2}{81})^{N+1}}{1 - \frac{2}{81}} = \frac{2^{N-1}}{79 \cdot 81^N}.$$

Then $|r_N(\frac{2}{81})| < \frac{1}{3000}$ if $N = 1$, so by taking the first two terms in (2) we obtain

$$\sqrt[4]{83} \approx 3\left(1 + \frac{1}{4}\left(\frac{2}{81}\right)\right) \approx 3.018518519$$

as the desired approximation.

4. $\sqrt[5]{35} = \sqrt[5]{32\left(1 + \frac{3}{32}\right)} = 2\sqrt[5]{1 + \frac{3}{32}}$, so by (5) with $s = \frac{1}{5}$ and $x = \frac{3}{32}$, we have

$$\left| r_N\left(\frac{3}{32}\right)\right| \le \frac{1}{5}\frac{(\frac{3}{32})^{N+1}}{1 - \frac{3}{32}} = \frac{3^{N+1}}{145 \cdot 32^N}.$$

Then $|r_N(\frac{3}{32})| < 0.0005$ if $N = 2$, so by taking the first three terms in (2) we obtain

$$\sqrt[5]{35} \approx 2\left[1 + \frac{1}{5}\left(\frac{3}{32}\right) + \frac{1}{2!}\left(\frac{1}{5}\right)\left(\frac{-4}{5}\right)\left(\frac{3}{32}\right)^2\right] \approx 2.03609375$$

as the desired approximation.

5. $\sqrt[6]{65} = \sqrt[6]{64\left(1+\frac{1}{64}\right)} = 2\sqrt[6]{1+\frac{1}{64}}$, so by (5) with $s = \frac{1}{6}$ and $x = \frac{1}{64}$, we have

$$\left|r_N\left(\frac{1}{64}\right)\right| \leq \frac{1}{6}\frac{(\frac{1}{64})^{N+1}}{1-\frac{1}{64}} = \frac{1}{378 \cdot 64^N}.$$

Then $|r_N(\frac{1}{64})| < 0.0005$ if $N = 1$, so by taking the first two terms in (2) we obtain

$$\sqrt[6]{65} \approx 2\left(1+\frac{1}{6}\left(\frac{1}{64}\right)\right) \approx 2.005208333$$

as the desired approximation.

6. $(29)^{2/3} = \left[27\left(1+\frac{2}{27}\right)\right]^{2/3} = 9(1+\frac{2}{27})^{2/3}$, so by (5) with $s = \frac{2}{3}$ and $x = \frac{2}{27}$, we have

$$\left|r_N\left(\frac{2}{27}\right)\right| \leq \frac{2}{3}\frac{(\frac{2}{27})^{N+1}}{1-\frac{2}{27}} = \frac{2^{N+2}}{75 \cdot 27^N}.$$

Then $|r_N(\frac{2}{27})| < \frac{1}{9000}$ if $N = 3$, so by taking the first 4 terms in (2) we obtain

$$(29)^{2/3} \approx 9\left[1+\frac{2}{3}\left(\frac{2}{27}\right)+\frac{1}{2!}\left(\frac{2}{3}\right)\left(\frac{-1}{3}\right)\left(\frac{2}{27}\right)^2+\frac{1}{3!}\left(\frac{2}{3}\right)\left(\frac{-1}{3}\right)\left(\frac{-4}{3}\right)\left(\frac{2}{27}\right)^3\right] \approx 9.439138117$$

as the desired approximation.

7. $\dfrac{1}{\sqrt{1+x}} = \displaystyle\sum_{n=0}^{\infty}\binom{-\frac{1}{2}}{n}x^n = 1-\frac{1}{2}x+\frac{1}{2!}\left(\frac{-1}{2}\right)\left(\frac{-3}{2}\right)x^2+\frac{1}{3!}\left(\frac{-1}{2}\right)\left(\frac{-3}{2}\right)\left(\frac{-5}{2}\right)x^3+\cdots;$

$1-\frac{1}{2}x+\frac{3}{8}x^2-\frac{5}{16}x^3$

8. $(1+x^2)^{1/3} = \displaystyle\sum_{n=0}^{\infty}\binom{\frac{1}{3}}{n}x^{2n} = 1+\frac{1}{3}x^2+\frac{1}{2!}\left(\frac{1}{3}\right)\left(\frac{-2}{3}\right)x^4+\frac{1}{3!}\left(\frac{1}{3}\right)\left(\frac{-2}{3}\right)\left(\frac{-5}{3}\right)x^6+\cdots;$

$1+\frac{1}{3}x^2-\frac{1}{9}x^4+\frac{5}{81}x^6$

9. $(1+x)^{-8/5} = \displaystyle\sum_{n=0}^{\infty}\binom{-\frac{8}{5}}{n}x^n = 1-\frac{8}{5}x+\frac{1}{2!}\left(\frac{-8}{5}\right)\left(\frac{-13}{5}\right)x^2+\frac{1}{3!}\left(\frac{-8}{5}\right)\left(\frac{-13}{5}\right)\left(\frac{-18}{5}\right)x^3+\cdots;$

$1-\frac{8}{5}x+\frac{52}{25}x^2-\frac{312}{125}x^3$

10. $\dfrac{1}{\sqrt{1-x^2}} = \displaystyle\sum_{n=0}^{\infty}\binom{-\frac{1}{2}}{n}(-x^2)^n = \sum_{n=0}^{\infty}(-1)^n\binom{-\frac{1}{2}}{n}x^{2n}$

$$= 1-\left(\frac{-1}{2}\right)x^2+\frac{1}{2!}\left(\frac{-1}{2}\right)\left(\frac{-3}{2}\right)x^4-\frac{1}{3!}\left(\frac{-1}{2}\right)\left(\frac{-3}{2}\right)\left(\frac{-5}{2}\right)x^6+\cdots;$$

$1+\frac{1}{2}x^2+\frac{3}{8}x^4+\frac{5}{16}x^6$

11. $\dfrac{x}{\sqrt{1-x^2}} = x\sum_{n=0}^{\infty}\binom{-\frac{1}{2}}{n}(-x^2)^n = \sum_{n=0}^{\infty}(-1)^n\binom{-\frac{1}{2}}{n}x^{2n+1}$

$$= x - \left(\frac{-1}{2}\right)x^3 + \frac{1}{2!}\left(\frac{-1}{2}\right)\left(\frac{-3}{2}\right)x^5 - \frac{1}{3!}\left(\frac{-1}{2}\right)\left(\frac{-3}{2}\right)\left(\frac{-5}{2}\right)x^7 + \cdots;$$

$x + \dfrac{1}{2}x^3 + \dfrac{3}{8}x^5 + \dfrac{5}{16}x^7$

12. $(1-x^2)^{5/2} = \sum_{n=0}^{\infty}\binom{\frac{5}{2}}{n}(-x^2)^n = \sum_{n=0}^{\infty}(-1)^n\binom{\frac{5}{2}}{n}x^{2n}$

$$= 1 - \frac{5}{2}x^2 + \frac{1}{2!}\left(\frac{5}{2}\right)\left(\frac{3}{2}\right)x^4 - \frac{1}{3!}\left(\frac{5}{2}\right)\left(\frac{3}{2}\right)\left(\frac{1}{2}\right)x^6 + \cdots;$$

$1 - \dfrac{5}{2}x^2 + \dfrac{15}{8}x^4 - \dfrac{5}{16}x^6$

13. $\sqrt{1-(x+1)^2} = \sum_{n=0}^{\infty}\binom{\frac{1}{2}}{n}(-(x+1)^2)^n = \sum_{n=0}^{\infty}(-1)^n\binom{\frac{1}{2}}{n}(x+1)^{2n}$

$$= 1 - \frac{1}{2}(x+1)^2 + \frac{1}{2!}\left(\frac{1}{2}\right)\left(\frac{-1}{2}\right)(x+1)^4 - \frac{1}{3!}\left(\frac{1}{2}\right)\left(\frac{-1}{2}\right)\left(\frac{-3}{2}\right)(x+1)^6 + \cdots;$$

$1 - \dfrac{1}{2}(x+1)^2 - \dfrac{1}{8}(x+1)^4 - \dfrac{1}{16}(x+1)^6$

14. $\sqrt{2x-x^2} = \sqrt{1-(x-1)^2} = \sum_{n=0}^{\infty}\binom{\frac{1}{2}}{n}(-(x-1)^2)^n = \sum_{n=0}^{\infty}(-1)^n\binom{\frac{1}{2}}{n}(x-1)^{2n}$

$$= 1 - \frac{1}{2}(x-1)^2 + \frac{1}{2!}\left(\frac{1}{2}\right)\left(\frac{-1}{2}\right)(x-1)^4 - \frac{1}{3!}\left(\frac{1}{2}\right)\left(\frac{-1}{2}\right)\left(\frac{-3}{2}\right)(x-1)^6 + \cdots;$$

$1 - \dfrac{1}{2}(x-1)^2 - \dfrac{1}{8}(x-1)^4 - \dfrac{1}{16}(x-1)^6$

15. $\displaystyle\int_0^1 \sqrt{1-x^2}\,dx = \int_0^1\left[\sum_{n=0}^{\infty}\binom{\frac{1}{2}}{n}(-1)^n x^{2n}\right]dx = \sum_{n=0}^{\infty}\binom{\frac{1}{2}}{n}\frac{(-1)^n}{2n+1}(1)^{2n} = \sum_{n=0}^{\infty}\binom{\frac{1}{2}}{n}\frac{(-1)^n}{2n+1}$

and by integration by trigonometric substitution with $x = \sin u$, we find that

$$\int_0^1 \sqrt{1-x^2}\,dx = \int_0^{\pi/2}\sqrt{1-\sin^2 u}\cos u\,du$$

$$= \int_0^{\pi/2}\cos^2 u\,du = \frac{1}{2}\int_0^{\pi/2}(1+\cos 2u)\,du = \frac{1}{2}\left(u + \frac{1}{2}\sin 2u\right)\Big|_0^{\pi/2} = \frac{\pi}{4}$$

thus

$$\sum_{n=0}^{\infty}\binom{\frac{1}{2}}{n}\frac{(-1)^n}{2n+1} = \frac{\pi}{4}.$$

16. $$\sin^{-1} x = \int_0^x \frac{1}{\sqrt{1-t^2}}\,dt = \int_0^x \left[\sum_{n=0}^{\infty} \binom{-\frac{1}{2}}{n}(-t^2)^n\right] dt = \sum_{n=0}^{\infty}(-1)^n \binom{-\frac{1}{2}}{n}\left[\int_0^x t^{2n}\,dt\right]$$
$$= \sum_{n=0}^{\infty}(-1)^n \binom{-\frac{1}{2}}{n}\left(\frac{t^{2n+1}}{2n+1}\Big|_0^x\right) = \sum_{n=0}^{\infty}(-1)^n \binom{-\frac{1}{2}}{n}\frac{x^{2n+1}}{2n+1}$$
$$= x + \sum_{n=1}^{\infty} \frac{1\cdot 3\cdot 5\cdots(2n-1)}{[2\cdot 4\cdot 6\cdots(2n)](2n+1)} x^{2n+1}$$

17. Without loss of generality, assume in this problem that $a > 0$.

a. $$\int_0^x \sqrt{a^2+t^2}\,dt = a\int_0^x \sqrt{1+\left(\frac{t}{a}\right)^2}\,dt = a\int_0^x \left(\sum_{n=0}^{\infty}\binom{\frac{1}{2}}{n}\left(\frac{t}{a}\right)^{2n}\right) dt$$
$$= a\sum_{n=0}^{\infty}\binom{\frac{1}{2}}{n}\left(\int_0^x \left(\frac{t}{a}\right)^{2n} dt\right) = a\sum_{n=0}^{\infty}\binom{\frac{1}{2}}{n}\left(\frac{a}{2n+1}\left(\frac{t}{a}\right)^{2n+1}\Big|_0^x\right)$$
$$= a^2\sum_{n=0}^{\infty}\binom{\frac{1}{2}}{n}\frac{1}{2n+1}\left(\frac{x}{a}\right)^{2n+1} = \sum_{n=0}^{\infty}\binom{\frac{1}{2}}{n}\left(\frac{1}{a}\right)^{2n-1}\frac{1}{2n+1}x^{2n+1}$$

Since

$$\lim_{n\to\infty}\left|\frac{\binom{\frac{1}{2}}{n+1}\left(\frac{1}{a}\right)^{2n+1} x^{2n+3}\Big/(2n+3)}{\binom{\frac{1}{2}}{n}\left(\frac{1}{a}\right)^{2n-1} x^{2n+1}\Big/(2n+1)}\right| = \lim_{n\to\infty}\frac{|\frac{1}{2}-n|}{n+1}\,\frac{2n+1}{2n+3}\left|\frac{x}{a}\right|^2 = \left|\frac{x}{a}\right|^2$$

the radius of convergence is a.

b. $$\int_0^x \sqrt{a^2-t^2}\,dt = a\int_0^x \sqrt{1-\left(\frac{t}{a}\right)^2}\,dt = a\int_0^x \left(\sum_{n=0}^{\infty}(-1)^n\binom{\frac{1}{2}}{n}\left(\frac{t}{a}\right)^{2n}\right) dt$$
$$= a\sum_{n=0}^{\infty}(-1)^n\binom{\frac{1}{2}}{n}\left(\int_0^x \left(\frac{t}{a}\right)^{2n} dt\right) = a^2\sum_{n=0}^{\infty}(-1)^n\binom{\frac{1}{2}}{n}\frac{1}{2n+1}\left(\frac{x}{a}\right)^{2n+1}$$
$$= \sum_{n=0}^{\infty}(-1)^n\binom{\frac{1}{2}}{n}\left(\frac{1}{a}\right)^{2n-1}\frac{1}{2n+1}x^{2n+1}$$

As in (a), the radius of convergence is a.

18. a. $\binom{6}{2} = \frac{6\cdot 5}{2!} = 15$; $\binom{\frac{1}{2}}{4} = \frac{1}{4!}\left(\frac{1}{2}\right)\left(\frac{-1}{2}\right)\left(\frac{-3}{2}\right)\left(\frac{-5}{2}\right) = \frac{-5}{128}$.

b. If s is any positive integer, then $\binom{s}{n} = 0$ for $n > s$, and thus by (2),

$$2^s = (1+1)^s = \sum_{n=0}^{\infty}\binom{s}{n}1^n = \sum_{n=0}^{s}\binom{s}{n}.$$

c. If s is any positive integer, then as in (b), $\binom{s}{n} = 0$ for $n > s$, so by (2),

$$0 = (1-1)^s = \sum_{n=0}^{\infty} \binom{s}{n}(-1)^n = \sum_{n=0}^{s} \binom{s}{n}(-1)^n.$$

19. For $s = 0$ we have $\left|\binom{0}{n}\right| = 0 = \left|\binom{0}{n-1}\right|$. For $n = 1$ we have $\left|\binom{s}{1}\right| = |s| \le 1 = \left|\binom{s}{0}\right|$. For $n > 1$ and $0 < |s| \le 1$, we have $|s - n + 1| \le n$, so that

$$\left|\frac{\binom{s}{n-1}}{\binom{s}{n}}\right| = \left|\frac{s(s-1)\cdots(s-n+2)/(n-1)!}{s(s-1)\cdots(s-n+1)/n!}\right| = \frac{n}{|s-n+1|} \ge 1$$

and thus $\left|\binom{s}{n}\right| \le \left|\binom{s}{n-1}\right|$.

20. Let $f(x) = (1+x)^{1/2}$. Then

$$r_1(x) = \frac{f''(t_x)}{2!}x^2 = \frac{-1}{8}\frac{1}{(1+t_x)^{3/2}}x^2$$

where t_x lies between 0 and x. If $|x| < 0.19$, then $|t_x| < 0.19$, so that $0.81 < 1 - |t_x| \le |1 + t_x|$. Thus

$$|r_1(x)| < \frac{1}{8}\frac{1}{(0.81)^{3/2}}x^2 < 0.172x^2.$$

21. a. By (3) with x^4 substituted for x,

$$\int_0^1 \sqrt{1+x^4}\,dx = \int_0^1 (1+x^4)^{1/2}\,dx = \int_0^1 \sum_{n=0}^{\infty}\binom{1/2}{n}x^{4n}\,dx$$

$$= \sum_{n=0}^{\infty}\binom{1/2}{n}\int_0^1 x^{4n}\,dx = \sum_{n=0}^{\infty}\binom{1/2}{n}\frac{1}{4n+1}x^{4n+1}\Big|_0^1 = \sum_{n=0}^{\infty}\binom{1/2}{n}\frac{1}{4n+1}.$$

b. Since

$$\sum_{n=1}^{\infty}\binom{1/2}{n}\frac{1}{4n+1}$$

is an alternating series, we need to find the minimum positive integer j such that

$$\left|\binom{1/2}{n}\frac{1}{4j+3}\right| < 10^{-3}.$$

By calculator we find that if $j = 5$, then we have

$$\left|\binom{1/2}{6}\frac{1}{23}\right| = \frac{(\frac{1}{2})(\frac{1}{2})(\frac{3}{2})(\frac{5}{2})(\frac{7}{2})(\frac{9}{2})}{6!\,(23)} < 10^{-3}.$$

Thus

$$\sum_{n=0}^{5}\binom{1/2}{n}\frac{1}{4n+1} = \binom{1/2}{0} + \binom{1/2}{1}\frac{1}{5} + \binom{1/2}{2}\frac{1}{9} + \binom{1/2}{3}\frac{1}{13} + \binom{1/2}{4}\frac{1}{17} + \binom{1/2}{5}\frac{1}{21}$$

$$= 1 + \frac{1}{2}\frac{1}{5} - \frac{1}{2^2}\frac{1}{2!}\frac{1}{9} + \frac{3}{2^3}\frac{1}{3!}\frac{1}{13} - \frac{(3)(5)}{2^4}\frac{1}{4!}\frac{1}{17} + \frac{(3)(5)(7)}{2^5}\frac{1}{5!}\frac{1}{21} \approx 1.089923093$$

is an approximation of $\int_0^1 \sqrt{1+x^4}\,dx$ that is accurate to within 10^{-3}.

22. By (2) with $s = -\frac{1}{2}$, the Taylor series for $(1 - v^2/c^2)^{-1/2}$ begins

$$\binom{-1/2}{0} + \binom{-1/2}{1}\left(-\frac{v^2}{c^2}\right) + \binom{-1/2}{2}\left(-\frac{v^2}{c^2}\right)^2 + \cdots = 1 - \frac{1}{2}\left(-\frac{v^2}{c^2}\right) + \frac{3}{8}\frac{v^4}{c^4} + \cdots = 1 + \frac{v^2}{2c^2} + \cdots.$$

Thus when v/c is small,

$$K = mc^2\left(\frac{1}{\sqrt{1 - v^2/c^2}} - 1\right) \approx mc^2\left(1 + \frac{v^2}{2c^2} - 1\right) = \frac{mv^2}{2}.$$

23. From the figure, maximum depth is $4000 - x$, where $x = \sqrt{4000^2 - 100^2} = 4000\sqrt{1 - (\frac{100}{4000})^2} = 4000\sqrt{1 - \frac{1}{1600}}$. By Exercise 20,

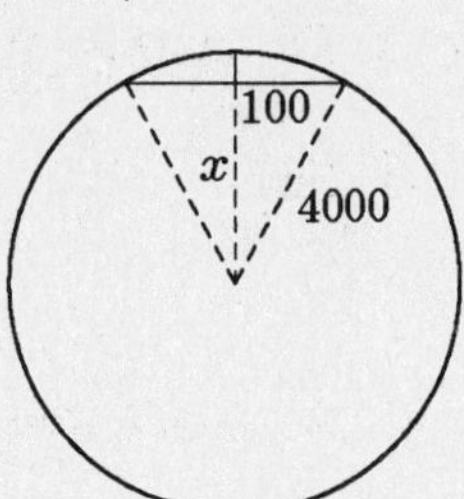

$$\sqrt{1 - \frac{1}{1600}} \approx 1 + \frac{1}{2}\left(-\frac{1}{1600}\right) = \frac{3199}{3200}$$

so that $x \approx 4000(\frac{3199}{3200}) = 3998.75$, and hence the desired approximation of the maximum depth is $4000 - 3998.75 = 1.25$ (miles). (The maximum depth is actually 1.25020, accurate to 6 places.)

24. a. $L = \int_0^x \sqrt{1 + (f'(t))^2}\,dt = \int_0^x \sqrt{1 + \left(\frac{2pt}{2q}\right)^2}\,dt = \int_0^x \sqrt{1 + \frac{p^2t^2}{q^2}}\,dt$

$$= \int_0^x \left(\sum_{n=0}^\infty \binom{\frac{1}{2}}{n}\frac{p^{2n}}{q^{2n}}t^{2n}\,dt\right) = \sum_{n=0}^\infty \binom{\frac{1}{2}}{n}\frac{p^{2n}}{q^{2n}}\left(\int_0^x t^{2n}\,dt\right) = \sum_{n=0}^\infty \binom{\frac{1}{2}}{n}\frac{1}{2n+1}\frac{p^{2n}}{q^{2n}}x^{2n+1}$$

b. As in Exercise 17a, the radius of convergence of

$$\sum_{n=0}^\infty \binom{\frac{1}{2}}{n}\frac{1}{2n+1}x^{2n+1}$$

is 1, so that since

$$\sum_{n=0}^\infty \binom{\frac{1}{2}}{n}\frac{1}{2n+1}\frac{p^{2n}}{q^{2n}}x^{2n+1} = \sum_{n=0}^\infty \binom{\frac{1}{2}}{n}\frac{q}{p}\left(\frac{px}{q}\right)^{2n+1}$$

the radius of convergence is q/p.

25. $L = 2\int_0^{a/2}\left(1 + \frac{64b^2}{a^4}x^2\right)^{1/2}dx = 2\int_0^{a/2}\left[\sum_{n=0}^\infty \binom{\frac{1}{2}}{n}\left(\frac{64b^2}{a^4}\right)^n x^{2n}\right]dx$

$$= 2\sum_{n=0}^\infty \binom{\frac{1}{2}}{n}\left(\frac{8b}{a^2}\right)^{2n}\left(\int_0^{a/2} x^{2n}\,dx\right) = 2\sum_{n=0}^\infty \binom{\frac{1}{2}}{n}\left(\frac{8b}{a^2}\right)^{2n}\frac{1}{2n+1}\left(\frac{a}{2}\right)^{2n+1}$$

$$= \sum_{n=0}^\infty \binom{\frac{1}{2}}{n}\frac{4^{2n}a}{2n+1}\left(\frac{b}{a}\right)^{2n} \approx a\left[1 + \frac{8}{3}\left(\frac{b^2}{a^2}\right) - \frac{32}{5}\left(\frac{b^4}{a^4}\right)\right]$$

If $a = 500$ and $b = 40$, then

$$L \approx 500\left[1 + \frac{8}{3}\left(\frac{40}{500}\right)^2 - \frac{32}{5}\left(\frac{40}{500}\right)^4\right] \approx 508.402 \text{ (feet)}.$$

Chapter 9 Review

1. $\displaystyle\lim_{n\to\infty}\frac{n^2-\sqrt{n}}{4-n^2}=\lim_{n\to\infty}\frac{1-n^{-3/2}}{(4/n^2)-1}=\frac{1-0}{0-1}=-1$

2. Using Theorem 9.4 and l'Hôpital's Rule, we find that

$$\lim_{n\to\infty}\frac{\sqrt{n}}{\ln n}=\lim_{x\to\infty}\frac{\sqrt{x}}{\ln x}=\lim_{x\to\infty}\frac{1/2\sqrt{x}}{1/x}=\lim_{x\to\infty}\frac{\sqrt{x}}{2}=\infty.$$

3. By replacing 0.05 by e in the solution of Exercise 25 in Section 9.2, we obtain $\lim_{n\to\infty}(1+e/n)^n=e^e$.

4. Since

$$\lim_{k\to\infty}\frac{(2k+2)!/2^{k+1}(k+1)^{k+1}}{(2k)!/2^k k^k}=\lim_{k\to\infty}(2k+1)\frac{1}{(1+1/k)^k}=\infty$$

we obtain $\lim_{k\to\infty}(2k)!/2^k k^k=\infty$.

5. $$\begin{aligned}\lim_{n\to\infty}(\sqrt{n^2+n}-\sqrt{n^2-n}) &= \lim_{n\to\infty}(\sqrt{n^2+n}-\sqrt{n^2-n})\left(\frac{\sqrt{n^2+n}+\sqrt{n^2-n}}{\sqrt{n^2+n}+\sqrt{n^2-n}}\right)\\ &= \lim_{n\to\infty}\frac{2n}{\sqrt{n^2+n}+\sqrt{n^2-n}}=\lim_{n\to\infty}\frac{2}{\sqrt{1+1/n}+\sqrt{1-1/n}}\\ &= \frac{2}{2}=1\end{aligned}$$

6. $1^3/n^4+2^3/n^4+\cdots+n^3/n^4=\left[(1/n)^3+(2/n)^3+\cdots+(n/n)^3\right](1/n)$ is a Riemann sum for x^3 on $[0,1]$ with the partition $\{0,1/n,2/n,\ldots,1\}$. Thus

$$\lim_{n\to\infty}\left(\frac{1^3}{n^4}+\frac{2^3}{n^4}+\cdots+\frac{n^3}{n^4}\right)=\int_0^1 x^3\,dx=\left.\frac{1}{4}x^4\right|_0^1=\frac{1}{4}.$$

7. Since $1/(n+n\sqrt{n})<1/n^{3/2}$ for $n\geq 1$, and $\sum_{n=1}^{\infty}1/n^{3/2}$ converges, it follows from the Comparison Test that $\sum_{n=1}^{\infty}1/(n+n\sqrt{n})$ converges.

8. Let $x=1/n$. Then

$$\lim_{n\to\infty}\frac{\sin^2 1/n}{1/n^2}=\lim_{x\to 0+}\frac{\sin^2 x}{x^2}=\left(\lim_{x\to 0+}\frac{\sin x}{x}\right)^2=1^2=1.$$

Since $\sum_{n=1}^{\infty}1/n^2$ converges, the Limit Comparison Test implies that $\sum_{n=1}^{\infty}\sin^2 1/n$ converges.

9. Since $\sqrt{n}/(n^2+n+1)\leq\sqrt{n}/n^2=1/n^{3/2}$ for $n\geq 1$, and $\sum_{n=1}^{\infty}1/n^{3/2}$ converges, it follows from the Comparison Test that $\sum_{n=1}^{\infty}\sqrt{n}/(n^2+n+1)$ converges.

10. $\displaystyle\lim_{n\to\infty}\frac{(n+1)^2e^{-(n+1)/2}}{n^2e^{-n/2}}=\lim_{n\to\infty}\left(\frac{n+1}{n}\right)^2e^{-1/2}=e^{-1/2}<1$, so $\sum_{n=1}^{\infty}n^2e^{-n/2}$ converges (Ratio Test).

11. Since

$$\frac{6^n}{n^2(\ln n)^2} > \frac{6^n}{n^2(2n^{1/2})^2} = \frac{6^n}{4n^3}$$

and since $\lim_{n\to\infty} \sqrt[n]{6^n/4n^3} = \lim_{n\to\infty} 6/\sqrt[n]{4n^3} = 6$, it follows from the Root Test that $\sum_{n=2}^{\infty} 6^n/n^3$ diverges, and hence that $\sum_{n=2}^{\infty} 6^n/[n^2(\ln n)^2]$ diverges by the Comparison Test.

12. Since $(\ln n)^4/n \geq 1/n$ for $n \geq 3$, and $\sum_{n=3}^{\infty} 1/n$ diverges, it follows from the Comparison Test that $\sum_{n=2}^{\infty}(\ln n)^4/n$ diverges. The divergence can also be proved by the Integral Test.

13. Let $f(x) = \sqrt{x}/(x-3)$ for $x \geq 4$. Then

$$f'(x) = \frac{(x-3)/(2\sqrt{x}) - \sqrt{x}}{(x-3)^2} = \frac{-x-3}{2\sqrt{x}\,(x-3)^2} < 0$$

so f is decreasing on $[4, \infty)$. Thus $\{\sqrt{n}/(n-3)\}_{n=4}^{\infty}$ is a nonnegative, decreasing sequence, and

$$\lim_{n\to\infty} \frac{\sqrt{n}}{n-3} = \lim_{n\to\infty} \frac{1}{\sqrt{n} - 3/\sqrt{n}} = 0.$$

Therefore $\sum_{n=4}^{\infty}(-1)^n\sqrt{n}/(n-3)$ converges by the Alternating Series Test.

14. Since $(n^n/n!)^n \geq 1$ for $n \geq 1$, it follows from the nth Term Test that $\sum_{n=1}^{\infty}(n^n/n!)^n$ diverges.

15. Since

$$0 \leq \frac{\sqrt{n^2+1} - \sqrt{n^2-1}}{n} = \frac{\sqrt{n^2+1} - \sqrt{n^2-1}}{n}\,\frac{\sqrt{n^2+1} + \sqrt{n^2-1}}{\sqrt{n^2+1} + \sqrt{n^2-1}}$$

$$= \frac{(n^2+1) - (n^2-1)}{n(\sqrt{n^2+1} + \sqrt{n^2-1})} = \frac{2}{n(\sqrt{n^2+1} + \sqrt{n^2-1})} \leq \frac{2}{n\sqrt{n^2}} = \frac{2}{n^2}$$

and since $\sum_{n=1}^{\infty} 2/n^2$ converges, the given series converges by the Comparison Test.

16. $\displaystyle\lim_{n\to\infty} \frac{(2n+2)!/[2^{n+1}(n+1)!]}{(2n)!/(2^n n!)} = \lim_{n\to\infty}(2n+1) = \infty$, so $\sum_{n=0}^{\infty}(2n)!/(2^n n!)$ diverges.

17. $$27.1318318318\ldots = 27 + \frac{1}{10} + \frac{318}{10^4} + \frac{318}{10^7} + \cdots = 27 + \frac{1}{10} + \sum_{n=1}^{\infty} \frac{318}{10}\left(\frac{1}{1000}\right)^n$$

$$= 27 + \frac{1}{10} + \frac{318}{10}\left(\frac{1/1000}{1 - 1/1000}\right) = 27 + \frac{1}{10} + \frac{318}{10}\left(\frac{1}{999}\right) = \frac{90{,}349}{3330}$$

18. a. Since $\sum_{n=1}^{\infty} a_n$ converges, $\lim_{n\to\infty} a_n = 0$ by Theorem 9.8.

b. $\lim_{n\to\infty} b_n = \lim_{n\to\infty} \sum_{k=1}^{n} a_k = \sum_{k=1}^{\infty} a_k = 5$.

19. a. Since $\lim_{n\to 0} 0 = 0 = \lim_{n\to\infty} 1/n$, the Squeezing Theorem for sequences implies that $\lim_{n\to\infty} a_n = 0$.

b. It is not possible to tell: if $a_n = 1/2n$, then $\sum_{n=1}^{\infty} a_n = \sum_{n=1}^{\infty} 1/2n$ diverges, whereas if $a_n = 1/2n^2$, then $\sum_{n=1}^{\infty} a_n = \sum_{n=1}^{\infty} 1/2n^2$ converges.

20. a. Since $\lim_{n\to\infty} 1 = 1 = \lim_{n\to\infty}(1 + 1/n)$, by the Squeezing Theorem for sequences we have $\lim_{n\to\infty} b_n = 1$.

b. Yes. Since $b_n > 1$ for all n, $\sum_{n=1}^{\infty} b_n$ diverges by the nth Term Test.

21. a. By hypothesis $0 < a_1 < b_1$. To use induction, assume that $0 < a_n < b_n$ for some positive integer n. Then $a_{n+1} < b_{n+1}$ is equivalent to $\sqrt{a_n b_n} < \frac{1}{2}(a_n + b_n)$, that is, $0 < a_n - 2\sqrt{a_n}\sqrt{b_n} + b_n$. Since $a_n - 2\sqrt{a_n}\sqrt{b_n} + b_n = (\sqrt{a_n} - \sqrt{b_n})^2 > 0$, it follows that $a_{n+1} < b_{n+1}$. By induction, $a_n < b_n$ for all n.

b. By (a), $a_n < b_n$, so that $\sqrt{a_n} < \sqrt{b_n}$ and thus $a_n < \sqrt{a_n}\sqrt{b_n} = \sqrt{a_n b_n} = a_{n+1}$. Therefore $\{a_n\}_{n=1}^{\infty}$ is increasing. Likewise, by (a), $b_{n+1} = \frac{1}{2}(a_n + b_n) < \frac{1}{2}(b_n + b_n) = b_n$, so that $\{b_n\}_{n=1}^{\infty}$ is decreasing.

c. Since $0 < a_n < b_n < b_1$ for all n, $\{a_n\}_{n=1}^{\infty}$ is bounded. Since it is also increasing by part (b), Theorem 9.6 implies that $\{a_n\}_{n=1}^{\infty}$ converges to, say, L. Similarly, $b_1 > b_n > a_n > a_1$ for all n, so that $\{b_n\}_{n=1}^{\infty}$ is bounded. Since it is also decreasing by part (b), Theorem 9.6 implies that $\{b_n\}_{n=1}^{\infty}$ converges to, say, M.

d. We have $M = \lim_{n\to\infty} b_n = \lim_{n\to\infty} b_{n+1} = \lim_{n\to\infty} \frac{1}{2}(a_n + b_n) = \frac{1}{2}\left(\lim_{n\to\infty} a_n + \lim_{n\to\infty} b_n\right) = \frac{1}{2}(L + M)$, so that $2M = L + M$, or $L = M$.

e. If $a_1 = 1$ and $b_1 = 2$, then $a_2 = \sqrt{2}$ and $b_2 = 1.5$, so that $a_3 = \sqrt{\sqrt{2}(1.5)} \approx 1.456475315$ and $b_3 = \frac{1}{2}(\sqrt{2} + 1.5) \approx 1.457106781$. Thus since $a_3 < L < b_3$ and $|b_3 - a_3| \approx |1.457106781 - 1.456475315| < 0.01$, it follows that $L \approx 1.45$ to within 0.01.

22. $$\ln 2 = \sum_{n=1}^{\infty}(-1)^{n+1}\frac{1}{n} = 1 - \frac{1}{2} + \frac{1}{3} - \frac{1}{4} + \frac{1}{5} - \frac{1}{6} + \cdots$$
$$= \left(1 - \frac{1}{2}\right) + \left(\frac{1}{3} - \frac{1}{4}\right) + \left(\frac{1}{5} - \frac{1}{6}\right) + \cdots = \frac{1}{1\cdot 2} + \frac{1}{3\cdot 4} + \frac{1}{5\cdot 6} + \cdots$$
$$= \sum_{n=0}^{\infty}\frac{1}{(2n+1)(2n+2)}$$

23. $$\sum_{n=5}^{\infty}(-1)^n\frac{1}{2n+1} = \sum_{n=0}^{\infty}(-1)^n\frac{1}{2n+1} - \sum_{n=0}^{4}(-1)^n\frac{1}{2n+1} = \frac{\pi}{4} - \left(1 - \frac{1}{3} + \frac{1}{5} - \frac{1}{7} + \frac{1}{9}\right)$$
$$= \frac{\pi}{4} - \frac{263}{315} \approx -0.0495224715$$

24. $$\sum_{n=0}^{\infty}(-1)^n\frac{2n+3}{(n+1)(n+2)} = \sum_{n=0}^{\infty}(-1)^n\left(\frac{1}{n+1} + \frac{1}{n+2}\right)$$
$$= \sum_{n=0}^{\infty}(-1)^n\frac{1}{n+1} + \sum_{n=0}^{\infty}(-1)^n\frac{1}{n+2}$$
$$= 1 - \sum_{n=2}^{\infty}(-1)^n\frac{1}{n} + \sum_{n=2}^{\infty}(-1)^n\frac{1}{n} = 1$$

25. Since $\sum_{n=1}^{\infty} x^n = x/(1-x)$ for $|x| < 1$, differentiation yields $\sum_{n=1}^{\infty} nx^{n-1} = 1/(1-x)^2$. Thus

$$(1-x)\sum_{n=1}^{\infty} nx^n = [(1-x)x]\sum_{n=1}^{\infty} nx^{n-1} = (1-x)x\frac{1}{(1-x)^2} = \frac{x}{1-x} \quad \text{for } |x| < 1.$$

26. $\displaystyle\sum_{n=1}^{\infty} x^n = \frac{x}{1-x}$ only for $|x| < 1$ and not for $x = -1$.

27. a. If $\lim_{n\to\infty} a_n = L$ and $\lim_{n\to\infty} b_n = M$, then $\lim_{n\to\infty}(b_n - a_n) = \lim_{n\to\infty} b_n - \lim_{n\to\infty} a_n = M - L$. Let $\varepsilon > 0$. Then there is a positive integer N such that if $n \geq N$, then $|(b_n - a_n) - (M - L)| < \varepsilon$, so that $(M - L) - \varepsilon < b_n - a_n < (M - L) + \varepsilon$. By hypothesis, $a_n \leq b_n$, so that $b_n - a_n \geq 0$, and thus $0 < (M - L) + \varepsilon$, or $-\varepsilon < M - L$. Since ε is arbitrary and positive, $0 \leq M - L$, so that $L \leq M$, which is equivalent to $\lim_{n\to\infty} a_n \leq \lim_{n\to\infty} b_n$.

b. Let $s_j = \sum_{n=1}^{j} a_n$ and $s'_j = \sum_{n=1}^{j} |a_n|$ for $j \geq 1$. Since $a_n \leq |a_n|$ for $n \geq 1$, we have $s_j \leq s'_j$ for $j \geq 1$. Moreover, $\{s_j\}_{j=1}^{\infty}$ and $\{s'_j\}_{j=1}^{\infty}$ converge by hypothesis, and thus by part (a), $\lim_{j\to\infty} s_j \leq \lim_{j\to\infty} s'_j$, so that $\sum_{n=1}^{\infty} a_n \leq \sum_{n=1}^{\infty} |a_n|$. Replacing a_n by $-a_n$, we find that $-\sum_{n=1}^{\infty} a_n = \sum_{n=1}^{\infty}(-a_n) \leq \sum_{n=1}^{\infty} |a_n|$. Thus $|\sum_{n=1}^{\infty} a_n| \leq \sum_{n=1}^{\infty} |a_n|$.

28. $1 \leq (\ln n)^{1/n} \leq 2^{1/n} n^{1/(2n)}$, and $\lim_{n\to\infty} 2^{1/n} = \lim_{n\to\infty} n^{1/(2n)} = 1$, so that $\lim_{n\to\infty}(\ln n)^{1/n} = 1$ by (5) of Section 9.3. Therefore

$$\lim_{n\to\infty} \sqrt[n]{\frac{(\ln n)^2}{n^2}|x|^n} = \lim_{n\to\infty} \frac{[(\ln n)^{1/n}]^2}{(n^{1/n})^2}|x| = |x|.$$

Thus $\sum_{n=2}^{\infty}(-1)^n(\ln n)^2/n^2$ converges for $|x| < 1$ and diverges for $|x| > 1$. Since $\frac{1}{2}\ln x = \ln x^{1/2} \leq 2x^{1/4}$ for $x \geq 2$, we have $(\ln n)^2/n^2 \leq (4n^{1/4})^2/n^2 = 16/n^{3/2}$ for $n \geq 2$. Since $\sum_{n=2}^{\infty} 16/n^{3/2}$ converges, so does $\sum_{n=2}^{\infty}(\ln n)^2/n^2$. Consequently the interval of convergence is $[-1, 1]$.

29. $\displaystyle\lim_{n\to\infty} \sqrt[n]{\frac{3^n}{5^{2n}}|x|^{3n}} = \lim_{n\to\infty} \frac{3}{25}|x|^3 = \frac{3}{25}|x|^3$

so $\sum_{n=0}^{\infty}(3^n/5^{2n})x^{3n}$ converges for $|x| < \sqrt[3]{\frac{25}{3}}$ and diverges for $|x| > \sqrt[3]{\frac{25}{3}}$. Since $\sum_{n=0}^{\infty}(-1)^n$ and $\sum_{n=0}^{\infty} 1$ diverge, the interval of convergence is $(-\sqrt[3]{\frac{25}{3}}, \sqrt[3]{\frac{25}{3}})$

30. $\displaystyle\lim_{n\to\infty} \frac{((n+1)!)^2|x|^{2n+2}/(2n+2)!}{(n!)^2|x|^{2n}/(2n)!} = \lim_{n\to\infty} \frac{(n+1)^2|x|^2}{(2n+2)(2n+1)} = \frac{|x|^2}{4}$

The radius of convergence is 2.

31. $\displaystyle\lim_{n\to\infty} \frac{(n+1)^{2n+2}|x|^{n+1}/(2n+2)!}{n^{2n}|x|^n/(2n)!} = \lim_{n\to\infty} \left[\left(1+\frac{1}{n}\right)^n\right]^2 \frac{n+1}{4n+2}|x| = \frac{e^2|x|}{4}$

The radius of convergence is $4/e^2$.

32. $f(x) = \sec x$, $f'(x) = \sec x \tan x$, $f''(x) = \sec x \tan^2 x + \sec^3 x$, $f^{(3)}(x) = \sec x \tan^3 x + 5\sec^3 x \tan x$;

$f(\pi/6) = \frac{2}{3}\sqrt{3}$, $f'(\pi/6) = \frac{2}{3}$, $f''(\pi/6) = (10\sqrt{3})/9$, $f^{(3)}(\pi/6) = \frac{42}{9}$;

$$p_3(x) = \frac{2}{3}\sqrt{3} + \frac{2}{3}\left(x - \frac{\pi}{6}\right) + \frac{1}{2!}\left(\frac{10\sqrt{3}}{9}\right)\left(x - \frac{\pi}{6}\right)^2 + \frac{1}{3!}\left(\frac{42}{9}\right)\left(x - \frac{\pi}{6}\right)^3$$
$$= \frac{2\sqrt{3}}{3} + \frac{2}{3}\left(x - \frac{\pi}{6}\right) + \frac{5\sqrt{3}}{9}\left(x - \frac{\pi}{6}\right)^2 + \frac{7}{9}\left(x - \frac{\pi}{6}\right)^3$$

33. $f(x) = \sqrt{1+x^4}$, $f'(x) = \dfrac{2x^3}{\sqrt{1+x^4}}$, $f''(x) = \dfrac{6x^2+2x^6}{(1+x^4)^{3/2}}$; $f(0) = 1$, $f'(0) = 0$, $f''(0) = 0$; $p_2(x) = 1$.

34. $f(x) = x^6 - 3x^4 + 2x - 1$, $f'(x) = 6x^5 - 12x^3 + 2$, $f''(x) = 30x^4 - 36x^2$, $f^{(3)}(x) = 120x^3 - 72x$, $f^{(4)}(x) = 360x^2 - 72$, $f^{(5)}(x) = 720x$, $f^{(6)}(x) = 720$, $f^{(n)}(x) = 0$ for $n \geq 7$;

$f(0) = -1$, $f'(0) = 2$, $f''(0) = 0 = f^{(3)}(0)$, $f^{(4)}(0) = -72$, $f^{(5)}(0) = 0$; $f(-1) = -5$, $f'(-1) = 8$, $f''(-1) = -6$, $f^{(3)}(-1) = -48$, $f^{(4)}(-1) = 288$, $f^{(5)}(-1) = -720$, $f^{(6)}(-1) = 720$;

a. $p_5(x) = -1 + 2x - \dfrac{72}{4!}x^4 = -1 + 2x - 3x^4$

b. $$p_4(x) = -5 + 8(x+1) - \frac{6}{2!}(x+1)^2 - \frac{48}{3!}(x+1)^3 + \frac{288}{4!}(x+1)^4$$
$$= -5 + 8(x+1) - 3(x+1)^2 - 8(x+1)^3 + 12(x+1)^4$$

c. $$\sum_{n=0}^{\infty} \frac{f^{(n)}(-1)}{n!}(x+1)^n = -5 + 8(x+1) - 3(x+1)^2 - 8(x+1)^3 + 12(x+1)^4$$
$$-6(x+1)^5 + (x+1)^6$$

35. $f^{(2k)}(x) = (-1)^k \sin x$ and $f^{(2k+1)}(x) = (-1)^k \cos x$, and $f^{(2k)}(\pi/4) = (-1)^k(\sqrt{2}/2)$ and $f^{(2k+1)}(\pi/4) = (-1)^k(\sqrt{2}/2)$ for $k \geq 0$; the Taylor series about $\pi/4$ is

$$\sum_{n=0}^{\infty} \frac{f^{(n)}(\pi/4)}{n!}\left(x - \frac{\pi}{4}\right)^n = \sum_{n=0}^{\infty}(-1)^n \frac{\sqrt{2}}{2}\left[\frac{(x-\pi/4)^{2n}}{(2n)!} + \frac{(x-\pi/4)^{2n+1}}{(2n+1)!}\right]$$

36. We seek to express $\cos 2x$ in a power series in $x - (-\pi/6) = x + \pi/6$. We obtain

$$\cos 2x = \cos\left[2\left(x + \frac{\pi}{6}\right) - \frac{\pi}{3}\right] = \cos 2\left(x + \frac{\pi}{6}\right)\cos\frac{\pi}{3} + \sin 2\left(x + \frac{\pi}{6}\right)\sin\frac{\pi}{3}$$
$$= \frac{1}{2}\cos 2\left(x + \frac{\pi}{6}\right) + \frac{\sqrt{3}}{2}\sin 2\left(x + \frac{\pi}{6}\right)$$
$$= \frac{1}{2}\sum_{n=0}^{\infty}\frac{(-1)^n}{(2n)!}\left[2\left(x + \frac{\pi}{6}\right)\right]^{2n} + \frac{\sqrt{3}}{2}\sum_{n=0}^{\infty}\frac{(-1)^n}{(2n+1)!}\left[2\left(x + \frac{\pi}{6}\right)\right]^{2n+1}$$
$$= \sum_{n=0}^{\infty}\frac{(-1)^n 2^{2n-1}}{(2n)!}\left(x + \frac{\pi}{6}\right)^{2n} + \sum_{n=0}^{\infty}\frac{(-1)^n\sqrt{3}\,2^{2n}}{(2n+1)!}\left(x + \frac{\pi}{6}\right)^{2n+1}.$$

37. $\dfrac{x-1}{x+1} = 1 - \dfrac{2}{x+1} = 1 - \displaystyle\sum_{n=0}^{\infty} 2(-1)^n x^n$

38. $\sqrt{95} = \sqrt{100\left(1 - \frac{1}{20}\right)} = 10\sqrt{1 - \frac{1}{20}}$; by (5) in Section 9.10 with $s = \frac{1}{2}$ and $x = -\frac{1}{20}$,

$$\left|r_N\left(-\frac{1}{20}\right)\right| \leq \frac{1}{2}\frac{(1/20)^{N+1}}{1-(1/20)} = \frac{1}{38 \cdot 20^N} < 0.0001 \quad \text{if } N = 2.$$

By (3) in Section 9.10,

$$\sqrt{95} \approx 10\left[1+\frac{1}{2}\left(\frac{-1}{20}\right)+\frac{1}{2!}\left(\frac{1}{2}\right)\left(\frac{-1}{2}\right)\left(\frac{-1}{20}\right)^2\right] \approx 9.746875$$

is the desired approximation.

39. $\sqrt[4]{17} = \sqrt[4]{16\left(1+\frac{1}{16}\right)} = 2\sqrt[4]{1+\frac{1}{16}}$; by (5) in Section 9.10 with $s = \frac{1}{4}$ and $x = \frac{1}{16}$,

$$\left|r_N\left(\frac{1}{16}\right)\right| \leq \frac{1}{4}\frac{(1/16)^{N+1}}{1-(1/16)} = \frac{1}{60 \cdot 16^N} < 0.0005 \quad \text{if } N = 2.$$

By (2) of Section 9.10,

$$\sqrt[4]{17} \approx 2\left[1+\frac{1}{4}\left(\frac{1}{16}\right)+\frac{1}{2!}\left(\frac{1}{4}\right)\left(\frac{-3}{4}\right)\left(\frac{1}{16}\right)^2\right] \approx 2.030517578$$

is the desired approximation.

40. Let $f(x) = e^x$ and use the Taylor series about 0. Then

$$\left|r_n\left(\frac{-1}{3}\right)\right| = \left|\frac{f^{(n+1)}(t_x)}{(n+1)!}\left(\frac{-1}{3}\right)^{n+1}\right| = \frac{e^{t_x}}{(n+1)!}\left(\frac{1}{3}\right)^{n+1}$$

where $-1/3 < t_x < 0$. Now

$$\frac{e^{t_x}}{(n+1)!}\left(\frac{1}{3}\right)^{n+1} < \frac{1}{(n+1)!}\left(\frac{1}{3}\right)^{n+1} < 0.001 \quad \text{if } n = 3.$$

Thus

$$e^{-1/3} \approx 1+\left(\frac{-1}{3}\right)+\frac{1}{2!}\left(\frac{-1}{3}\right)^2+\frac{1}{3!}\left(\frac{-1}{3}\right)^3 \approx 0.7160493827$$

is the desired approximation.

41. a. By (4) in Section 9.9,

$$\tan^{-1} x = \sum_{n=0}^{\infty} \frac{(-1)^n}{2n+1} x^{2n+1} = x - \frac{x^3}{3} + \frac{x^5}{5} - + \cdots.$$

Thus

$$\tan^{-1} x - x = \sum_{n=1}^{\infty} \frac{(-1)^n}{2n+1} x^{2n+1}$$

and

$$\frac{\tan^{-1} x - x}{x^3} = \sum_{n=1}^{\infty} \frac{(-1)^n}{2n+1} x^{2n-2} = -\frac{1}{3} + \frac{x^2}{5} - \frac{x^4}{7} + - \cdots.$$

Thus

$$\lim_{x \to 0} \frac{\tan^{-1} x - x}{x^3} = -\frac{1}{3}.$$

b. Since $\lim_{x\to 0}(\tan^{-1}x - x) = 0 = \lim_{x\to 0} x^3$, it follows from l'Hôpital's Rule that

$$\lim_{x\to 0}\frac{\tan^{-1}x - x}{x^3} = \lim_{x\to 0}\frac{\dfrac{1}{1+x^2}-1}{3x^2} = \lim_{x\to 0}\frac{1-(1+x^2)}{3x^2(1+x^2)} = \lim_{x\to 0}\frac{-1}{3(1+x^2)} = -\frac{1}{3}.$$

42. In general, if C is a circle of radius r and S is an inscribed square, then the side length of S is $\sqrt{2}\,r$. Thus the region inside C and outside S_1 has area $\pi r^2 - (\sqrt{2}r)^2 = (\pi-2)r^2$. Now if C_1 is the circle of radius 1 and S_1 an inscribed square, then the corresponding area is $\pi - 2$. If C_2 is the circle inscribed in S_1, then C_2 has radius $\sqrt{2}/2$, so the area of the region inside C_2 and outside S_2 is $(\pi-2)(\sqrt{2}/2)^2 = \frac{1}{2}(\pi-2)$. More generally, the radius of the circle C_n inscribed in the square S_{n-1} is $(\sqrt{2}/2)^n$, and the area of the region inside C_n and outside S_n is $(\frac{1}{2})^{n-1}(\pi-2)$. Therefore the area A of the region shaded in Figure 9.27 is given by

$$A = \sum_{n=1}^{\infty}\left(\frac{1}{2}\right)^{n-1}(\pi-2) = (\pi-2)\sum_{n=0}^{\infty}\left(\frac{1}{2}\right)^{n} = (\pi-2)\frac{1}{1-\frac{1}{2}} = 2(\pi-2).$$

43. a. $\displaystyle\sum_{n=1}^{25} a_n = s_{25} = 2 - \frac{2}{25} = \frac{48}{25}$

b. $\lim_{j\to\infty} s_j = \lim_{j\to\infty}(2-2/j) = 2$, so $\sum_{n=1}^{\infty} a_n$ converges and its sum is 2.

c. Since $\sum_{n=1}^{\infty} a_n$ converges, $\lim_{n\to\infty} a_n = 0$

d. $a_n = s_n - s_{n-1} = \left(2-\dfrac{2}{n}\right) - \left(2 - \dfrac{2}{n-1}\right) = \dfrac{2}{n-1} - \dfrac{2}{n} = \dfrac{2}{n(n-1)}$

44. a. $\displaystyle\lim_{n\to\infty}\frac{|x|^{2n+2}/\{4^{n+1}[(n+1)!]^2\}}{|x|^{2n}/\{4^n(n!)^2\}} = \lim_{n\to\infty}\frac{x^2}{4(n+1)^2} = 0$ for all x, so the Generalized Ratio Test implies that the given series converges for all x.

b.
$$\begin{aligned} xJ_0''(x) + J_0'(x) + xJ_0(x) &= x\sum_{n=1}^{\infty}(-1)^n\frac{(2n)(2n-1)}{4^n(n!)^2}x^{2n-2} + \sum_{n=1}^{\infty}(-1)^n\frac{2n}{4^n(n!)^2}x^{2n-1} \\ &\quad + x\sum_{n=0}^{\infty}(-1)^n\frac{1}{4^n(n!)^2}x^{2n} \\ &= \sum_{n=1}^{\infty}(-1)^n\left[\frac{(2n)(2n-1)}{4^n(n!)^2} + \frac{2n}{4^n(n!)^2} - \frac{1}{4^{n-1}[(n-1)!]^2}\right]x^{2n-1} \\ &= \sum_{n=1}^{\infty}(-1)^n\left[\frac{(2n)^2}{4^n(n!)^2} - \frac{1}{4^{n-1}[(n-1)!]^2}\right]x^{2n-1} \\ &= \sum_{n=1}^{\infty}(-1)^n\left[\frac{1}{4^{n-1}[(n-1)!]^2} - \frac{1}{4^{n-1}[(n-1)!]^2}\right]x^{2n-1} = 0 \end{aligned}$$

45. By (1) of Section 9.8 with x replaced by t^2, $\displaystyle\frac{1}{1-t^2} = \sum_{n=0}^{\infty} t^{2n}$, so that

$$\tanh^{-1}x = \int_0^x \frac{1}{1-t^2}\,dt = \int_0^x\left(\sum_{n=0}^{\infty}t^{2n}\right)dt = \sum_{n=0}^{\infty}\left(\int_0^x t^{2n}\,dt\right) = \sum_{n=0}^{\infty}\frac{x^{2n+1}}{2n+1}.$$

46. $\sinh^{-1} x = \int_0^x \frac{1}{\sqrt{1+t^2}}\,dt = \int_0^x \left[\sum_{n=0}^{\infty} \binom{-\frac{1}{2}}{n} t^{2n}\right] dt = \sum_{n=0}^{\infty} \binom{-\frac{1}{2}}{n} \left(\int_0^x t^{2n}\,dt\right) = \sum_{n=0}^{\infty} \binom{-\frac{1}{2}}{n} \frac{x^{2n+1}}{2n+1}$

47. Since $1/(1+x^{3/2}) = \sum_{n=0}^{\infty}(-1)^n(x^{3/2})^n$, which is an alternating series, we know by Theorem 9.17 that for any $N \ge 0$,

$$\left|\frac{1}{1+x^{3/2}} - \sum_{n=0}^{N}(-1)^n x^{3n/2}\right| = \left|\sum_{n=0}^{\infty}(-1)^n x^{3n/2} - \sum_{n=0}^{N}(-1)^n x^{3n/2}\right| \le |x|^{3(N+1)/2}.$$

Thus

$$\left|\int_0^{1/4}\left(\frac{1}{1+x^{3/2}} - \sum_{n=0}^{N}(-1)^n x^{3n/2}\right)dx\right| \le \int_0^{1/4}\left|\frac{1}{1+x^{3/2}} - \sum_{n=0}^{N}(-1)^n x^{3n/2}\right| dx$$

$$\le \int_0^{1/4} x^{3(N+1)/2}\,dx = \left.\frac{2x^{(3N+5)/2}}{3N+5}\right|_0^{1/4} = \frac{2}{3N+5}\left(\frac{1}{2}\right)^{3N+5}$$

Now $2/(3N+5)(\frac{1}{2})^{3N+5} < 0.001$ if $N=1$. Thus

$$\int_0^{1/4}\frac{1}{1+x^{3/2}}\,dx \approx \int_0^{1/4}(1-x^{3/2})\,dx = \left.\left(x-\frac{2}{5}x^{5/2}\right)\right|_0^{1/4} = \frac{1}{4}-\frac{1}{80} = \frac{19}{80} = 0.2375.$$

48. a. $y=\sqrt{4cx}$ implies that $x = y^2/4c$. Thus if $y = d/2$, then $x = d^2/16c$. This implies that the width of the reflecting surface is $d^2/16c$. By (4) in Section 8.4, the area S of the reflecting surface is given by

$$S = \int_0^{d^2/16c} 2\pi\sqrt{4cx}\sqrt{1+\left(\frac{4c}{2\sqrt{4cx}}\right)^2}\,dx = \int_0^{d^2/16c} 4\pi\sqrt{cx}\sqrt{1+\frac{c}{x}}\,dx$$

$$= \int_0^{d^2/16c} 4\pi\sqrt{c}\sqrt{x+c}\,dx = \left.\frac{8}{3}\pi\sqrt{c}(x+c)^{3/2}\right|_0^{d^2/16c}$$

$$= \frac{8\pi}{3}\sqrt{c}\left[\left(\frac{d^2}{16c}+c\right)^{3/2} - c^{3/2}\right] = \frac{8\pi}{3}c^2\left[\left(\frac{d^2}{16c^2}+1\right)^{3/2} - 1\right].$$

b. For $d^2/(16c^2)$ small we use the first two terms of the binomial series (2) in Section 9.10 with $s=\frac{3}{2}$ and x replaced by $d^2/16c^2$. We find that

$$S \approx \frac{8\pi}{3}c^2\left[\left(1+\frac{3}{2}\frac{d^2}{16c^2}\right)-1\right] = \frac{\pi}{4}d^2.$$

Cumulative Review(Chapters 1–8)

1. The conditions for applying l'Hôpital's Rule four times are met;

$$\lim_{x\to 0^-}\frac{\cos x+\frac{1}{2}x^2-1}{x^5} = \lim_{x\to 0^-}\frac{-\sin x + x}{5x^4} = \lim_{x\to 0^-}\frac{-\cos x+1}{20x^3} = \lim_{x\to 0^-}\frac{\sin x}{60x^2} = \lim_{x\to 0^-}\frac{\cos x}{120x} = -\infty.$$

2. Since $0 \le \sin^2(e^x) \le 1$ and the natural logarithm function is increasing, it follows that $0 = \ln 1 \le \ln(1+\sin^2(e^x)) \le \ln 2$, so that

$$0 \le \frac{\ln(1+\sin^2(e^x))}{\sqrt{x}} \le \frac{\ln 2}{\sqrt{x}}.$$

Since $\lim_{x\to\infty}(\ln 2)/\sqrt{x} = 0$, the Squeezing Theorem implies that

$$\lim_{x\to\infty}\frac{\ln(1+\sin^2(e^x))}{\sqrt{x}} = 0.$$

3. $\lim\limits_{x\to 0+} 3^x = \lim\limits_{x\to 0+} e^{x\ln 3} = e^0 = 1$ and $\lim\limits_{x\to 0+}\dfrac{1}{x^3} = \infty$, so $\lim\limits_{x\to 0+}\dfrac{3^x}{x^3} = \infty$.

4. $\dfrac{d}{dx}(\tan^{-1}\sqrt{x-1}) = \dfrac{1}{1+(\sqrt{x-1})^2}\,\dfrac{1}{2\sqrt{x-1}} = \dfrac{1}{2x\sqrt{x-1}}$

5. a. The domain of f consists of all x for which $3x-4>0$ (or $x>\frac{4}{3}$) and $\ln(3x-4)>0$. But $\ln(3x-4)>0$ if and only if $3x-4>1$, or $x>\frac{5}{3}$. Thus the domain is $(\frac{5}{3},\infty)$.

   b. $f'(x) = \dfrac{1}{\ln(3x-4)}\cdot\dfrac{1}{3x-4}\cdot(3) = \dfrac{3}{(3x-4)\ln(3x-4)}$.

6. The slope at $(x, f(x))$ is $f'(x)$, and $f'(x) = 5x^4 - 9x^2$. Since $(d/dx)(f'(x)) = 20x^3 - 18x = 2x(10x^2-9)$, it follows that $(d/dx)(f'(x)) = 0$ for $x = 0$, $-3/\sqrt{10}$, and $3/\sqrt{10}$. Since $f'(0) = 0$, $f'(-3/\sqrt{10}) = f'(3/\sqrt{10}) = -\frac{81}{20}$, and $f'(-1) = f'(1) = -4$, the slope is greatest for $x = 0$.

7. Differentiating the given equation implicitly, we obtain $e^x + 2e^{2x} - y^2(dy/dx) + (dy/dx) = 0$, so that $e^x + 2e^{2x} + (dy/dx)(1-y^2) = 0$. Thus if $(dy/dx)(1-y^2) = -6$ at (a,b), then $e^a + 2e^{2a} - 6 = 0$, or $2e^{2a} + e^a - 6 = 0$, or $(2e^a-3)(e^a+2) = 0$. Since $e^a + 2 > 0$, it follows that $e^a = \frac{3}{2}$, so that $a = \ln\frac{3}{2}$.

8. $f'(x) = e^{-x}(2x - x^2)$; $f''(x) = e^{-x}(2 - 4x + x^2)$; relative maximum value is $f(2) = 4e^{-2}$; relative minimum value is $f(0) = 0$; increasing on $[0,2]$, and decreasing on $(-\infty,0]$ and $[2,\infty)$; concave upward on $(-\infty, 2-\sqrt{2})$ and $(2+\sqrt{2},\infty)$, and concave downward on $(2-\sqrt{2}, 2+\sqrt{2})$; inflection points are $(2-\sqrt{2}, 16-4\sqrt{2}\,e^{\sqrt{2}-2})$ and $(2+\sqrt{2}, 16+4\sqrt{2}\,e^{-2-\sqrt{2}})$.

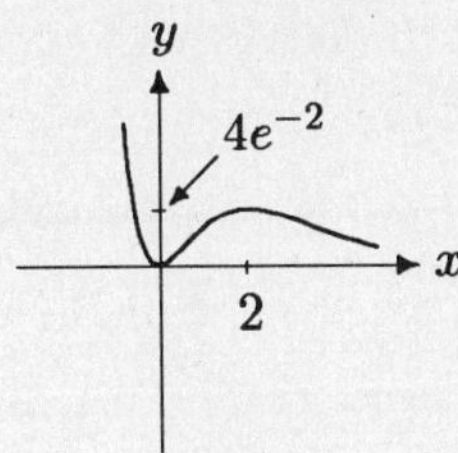

Exercise 8

9. Since $A = \pi r^2$ and $dA/dt = \frac{1}{2}$, we have $\frac{1}{2} = dA/dt = 2\pi r(dr/dt)$, so that $dr/dt = 1/(4\pi r)$. Thus when $r = 1$, the radius is increasing at the rate of $1/(4\pi)$ foot per second.

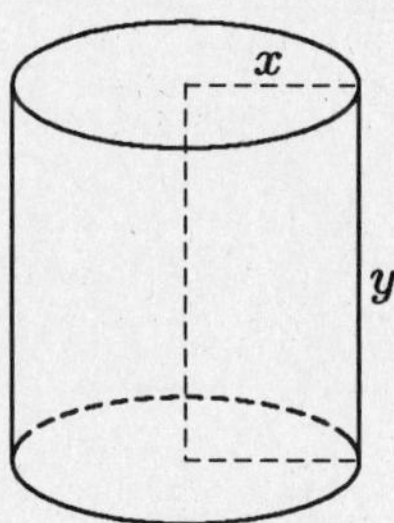

Exercise 10

10. Using the notation in the figure, we find that $2x+2y = p$ and $V = \pi x^2 y = \pi x^2(p/2-x) = (p\pi/2)x^2 - \pi x^3$ for $0 < x < p/2$. Then $V'(x) = p\pi x - 3\pi x^2 = \pi x(p-3x)$, so that $V'(x) = 0$ for $x = p/3$. Since $V'(x) > 0$ for $0 < x < p/3$ and $V'(x) < 0$ for $p/3 < x < p/2$, it follows that V is maximum for $x = p/3$. Thus the maximum volume is $V(p/3) = \pi(p/3)^2(p/2 - p/3) = \pi p^3/54$.

11. By Exercise 54 in Section 7.1,

$$\int \frac{\cos x}{e^{3x}}\,dx = \int e^{-3x}\cos x\,dx = \frac{e^{-3x}}{10}(-3\cos x + \sin x) + C.$$

12. $$\int_{\pi/3}^{\pi/2} \sin x\,\cos^2\frac{x}{2}\,dx = \int_{\pi/3}^{\pi/2} \sin x\,\frac{1+\cos x}{2}\,dx \overset{u=1+\cos x}{=} \int_{3/2}^{1} \frac{u}{2}(-1)\,du = -\frac{1}{4}u^2\Big|_{3/2}^{1} = \frac{5}{16}$$

13. Let $x = 4\sin u$, so that $dx = 4\cos u\,du$. If $x = 2\sqrt{2}$, then $u = \pi/4$, and if $x = 4$, then $u = \pi/2$. Thus

$$\int_{2\sqrt{2}}^{4} \frac{\sqrt{16-x^2}}{x^3}\,dx = \int_{\pi/4}^{\pi/2} \frac{4\cos u}{64\sin^3 u}\,4\cos u\,du$$

$$= \frac{1}{4}\int_{\pi/4}^{\pi/2} \frac{\cos^2 u}{\sin^3 u}\,du = \frac{1}{4}\int_{\pi/4}^{\pi/2} \frac{1-\sin^2 u}{\sin^3 u}\,du = \frac{1}{4}\int_{\pi/4}^{\pi/2} (\csc^3 u - \csc u)\,du.$$

By Exercise 28 of Section 7.2. $\int \csc^3 u\,du = -\frac{1}{2}\csc u\,\cot u - \frac{1}{2}\ln|\csc u + \cot u| + C$, and by Exercise 36 of Section 5.7, $\int \csc u\,du = -\ln|\csc u + \cot u| + C$. Therefore

$$\int_{2\sqrt{2}}^{4} \frac{\sqrt{16-x^2}}{x^3}\,dx = \frac{1}{4}\int_{\pi/4}^{\pi/2} (\csc^3 u - \csc u)\,du = \frac{1}{4}\left(-\frac{1}{2}\csc u\,\cot u + \frac{1}{2}\ln|\csc u + \cot u|\right)\Bigg|_{\pi/4}^{\pi/2}$$

$$= \frac{1}{4}\left(\frac{1}{2}\sqrt{2} - \frac{1}{2}\ln(\sqrt{2}+1)\right) = \frac{1}{8}(\sqrt{2} - \ln(\sqrt{2}+1)).$$

14. $\left(\dfrac{x}{x-1}\right)^2 = \left(\dfrac{x}{x+2}\right)^2$ if $x = 0$ or $(x-1)^2 = (x+2)^2$.

The latter equation is equivalent to $x^2 - 2x + 1 = x^2 + 4x + 4$, or $-6x = 3$, or $x = -\frac{1}{2}$. Since $[x/(x+2)]^2 \le [x/(x-1)]^2$ for x in the given interval $[-\frac{1}{2}, 0]$, it follows that

$$A = \int_{-1/2}^{0} \left[\left(\frac{x}{x-1}\right)^2 - \left(\frac{x}{x+2}\right)^2\right] dx = \int_{-1/2}^{0} \left[\left(1 + \frac{1}{x-1}\right)^2 - \left(1 - \frac{2}{x+2}\right)^2\right] dx$$

$$= \int_{-1/2}^{0} \left(1 + \frac{2}{x-1} + \frac{1}{(x-1)^2} - 1 + \frac{4}{x+2} - \frac{4}{(x+2)^2}\right) dx$$

$$= \left(2\ln|x-1| - \frac{1}{x-1} + 4\ln|x+2| + \frac{4}{x+2}\right)\Big|_{-1/2}^{0}$$

$$= (1 + 4\ln 2 + 2) - \left(2\ln\frac{3}{2} + \frac{2}{3} + 4\ln\frac{3}{2} + \frac{8}{3}\right) = 10\ln 2 - 6\ln 3 - \frac{1}{3}.$$

15. Let $u = 1 + e^x$, so that $du = e^x\,dx$. Then

$$\int \frac{e^x}{(1+e^x)^2}\,dx = \int \frac{1}{u^2}\,du = -\frac{1}{u} + C = \frac{-1}{1+e^x} + C.$$

Thus

$$\int_0^\infty \frac{e^x}{(1+e^x)^2}\,dx = \lim_{b\to\infty}\int_0^b \frac{e^x}{(1+e^x)^2}\,dx = \lim_{b\to\infty}\frac{-1}{1+e^x}\Big|_0^b = \lim_{b\to\infty}\left(\frac{-1}{1+e^b} + \frac{1}{2}\right) = \frac{1}{2}$$

and

$$\int_{-\infty}^0 \frac{e^x}{(1+e^x)^2}\,dx = \lim_{a\to-\infty}\int_a^0 \frac{e^x}{(1+e^x)^2}\,dx$$

$$= \lim_{a\to-\infty}\frac{-1}{1+e^x}\Big|_a^0 = \lim_{a\to-\infty}\left(-\frac{1}{2} + \frac{1}{1+e^a}\right) = -\frac{1}{2} + 1 = \frac{1}{2}.$$

Thus the given integral converges, and

$$\int_{-\infty}^\infty \frac{e^x}{(1+e^x)^2}\,dx = \int_{-\infty}^0 \frac{e^x}{(1+e^x)^2}\,dx + \int_0^\infty \frac{e^x}{(1+e^x)^2}\,dx = \frac{1}{2} + \frac{1}{2} = 1.$$

16. Let $u = \ln x$, so that $du = (1/x)\,dx$. Then

$$\int \frac{1}{x(\ln x)^3}\,dx = \int \frac{1}{u^3}\,du = \frac{-1}{2u^2} + C = \frac{-1}{2(\ln x)^2} + C.$$

Recall that $\ln x = 0$ for $x = 1$ and that $1/e < 1 < e$. Thus

$$\int_{1/e}^1 \frac{1}{x(\ln x)^3}\,dx = \lim_{b\to1^-}\int_{1/e}^b \frac{1}{x(\ln x)^3}\,dx = \lim_{b\to1^-}\frac{-1}{2(\ln x)^2}\Big|_{1/e}^b$$

$$= \lim_{b\to1^-}\left(-\frac{1}{2(\ln b)^2} + \frac{1}{2(\ln 1/e)^2}\right) = \lim_{b\to1^-}\frac{1}{2}\left(1 - \frac{1}{(\ln b)^2}\right) = -\infty.$$

Thus $\int_{1/e}^1 \frac{1}{x(\ln x)^3}\,dx$ and hence $\int_{1/e}^e \frac{1}{x(\ln x)^3}\,dx$ diverge.

17. $M_x = \int_0^{\ln 2} \frac{1}{2}[(1+e^x)^2 - (1-e^{-x})^2]\,dx = \int_0^{\ln 2} \frac{1}{2}[(1+2e^x+e^{2x}) - (1-2e^{-x}+e^{-2x})]\,dx$

$= \int_0^{\ln 2} \left(e^x + \frac{1}{2}e^{2x} + e^{-x} - \frac{1}{2}e^{-2x}\right) dx = \left(e^x + \frac{1}{4}e^{2x} - e^{-x} + \frac{1}{4}e^{-2x}\right)\Big|_0^{\ln 2}$

$= (2 + 1 - \frac{1}{2} + \frac{1}{16}) - (1 + \frac{1}{4} - 1 + \frac{1}{4}) = \frac{33}{16}$

$M_y = \int_0^{\ln 2} x[(1+e^x) - (1-e^{-x})]\,dx = \int_0^{\ln 2} x(e^x + e^{-x})\,dx \overset{\text{parts}}{=} x(e^x - e^{-x})\Big|_0^{\ln 2} - \int_0^{\ln 2} (e^x - e^{-x})\,dx$

$= (\ln 2)(2 - \frac{1}{2}) - (e^x + e^{-x})\Big|_0^{\ln 2} = \frac{3}{2}\ln 2 - (2 + \frac{1}{2}) + (1+1) = \frac{3}{2}\ln 2 - \frac{1}{2}$

$A = \int_0^{\ln 2} [(1+e^x) - (1-e^{-x})]\,dx = \int_0^{\ln 2} (e^x - e^{-x})\,dx = (e^x + e^{-x})\Big|_0^{\ln 2} = (2 + \frac{1}{2}) - (1+1) = \frac{1}{2}$

$\bar{x} = \frac{M_y}{A} = \frac{\frac{3}{2}\ln 2 - \frac{1}{2}}{\frac{1}{2}} = 3\ln 2 - 1; \bar{y} = \frac{M_x}{A} = \frac{33/16}{1/2} = \frac{33}{8}; (\bar{x}, \bar{y}) = (3\ln 2 - 1, \frac{33}{8})$

18. The graphs intersect for (x, y) such that $2x^2 = y = 3 - x^2$, or equivalently, $3x^2 = 3$, so that $x = -1$ or 1. On $[-1, 1]$, $3 - x^2 \geq 2x^2$. Thus $V = \int_{-1}^{1} [(3-x^2) - 2x^2]^2\,dx = \int_{-1}^{1} (3 - 3x^2)^2\,dx = \int_{-1}^{1} (9 - 18x^2 + 9x^4)\,dx = (9x - 6x^3 + \frac{9}{5}x^5)\Big|_{-1}^{1} = \frac{48}{5}$.

19. If $y = x^2$ for $-2 \leq x \leq 2$, then $x = \sqrt{y}$ for $0 \leq y \leq 4$. Thus the width of the cross-section y units above the x axis is $2\sqrt{y}$, so that the cross-sectional area is given by $A(y) = 20\sqrt{y}$ for $0 \leq y \leq 4$. For $0 \leq y \leq 4$ the vertical distance the water must be pumped is $8 - y$. Therefore $W = \int_0^4 62.5(20\sqrt{y})(8 - y)\,dy = 1250 \int_0^4 (8\sqrt{y} - y^{3/2})\,dy = 1250\left(\frac{16}{3}y^{3/2} - \frac{2}{5}y^{5/2}\right)\Big|_0^4 = 1250\left(\frac{128}{3} - \frac{64}{5}\right) = \frac{112{,}000}{3}$ (foot-pounds).

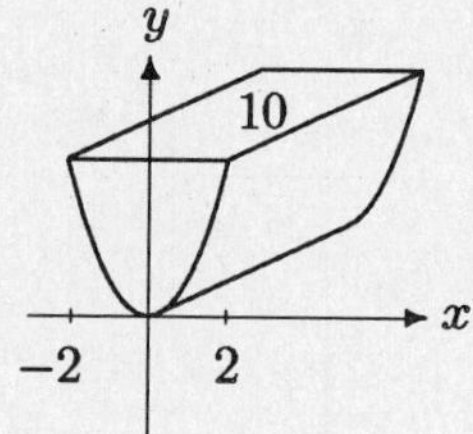

Chapter 10

Curves

10.1 Parametrized Curves

1. $x^2 + y^2 = 4$
   for $0 \le x \le 2$, $0 \le y \le 2$

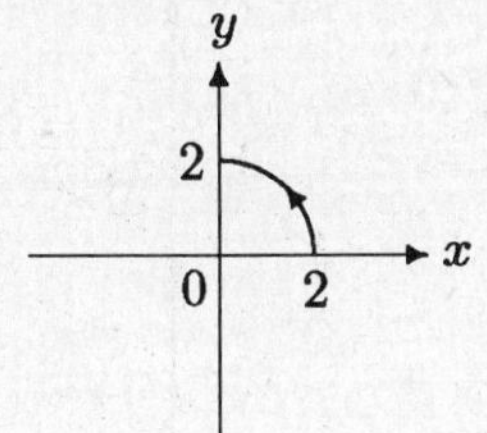

2. $x^2 + y^2 = 9$
   for $-3 \le x \le 3$, $0 \le y \le 3$

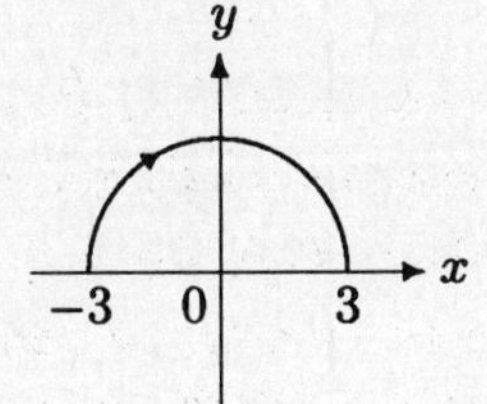

3. $(x-2)^2 + (y+1)^2 = 1$

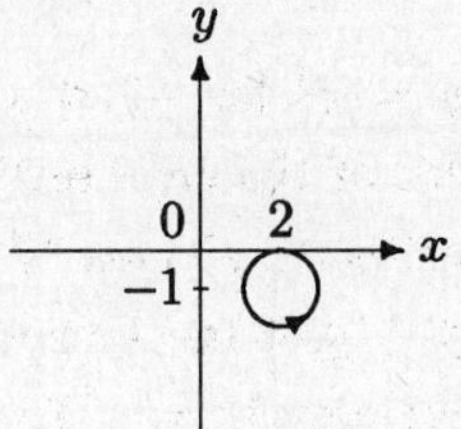

4. $(x+1)^2 + (y - \frac{1}{2})^2 = \frac{9}{4}$

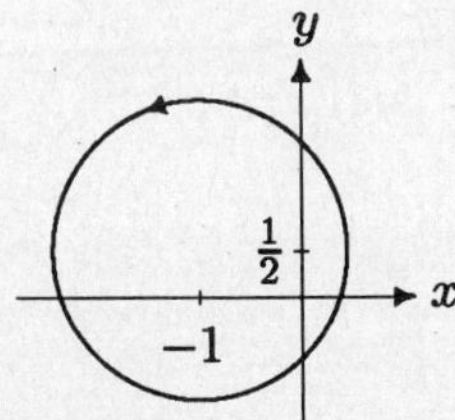

5. $x = -y$

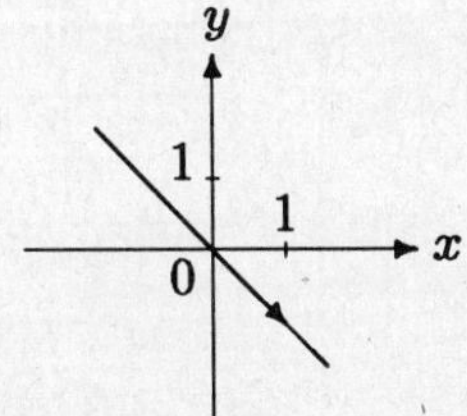

6. $y = -4$ for $x \le 5$

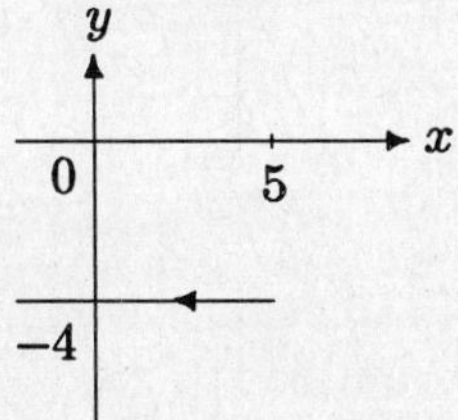

7. $x = 3$ for $-2 \le y \le -1$

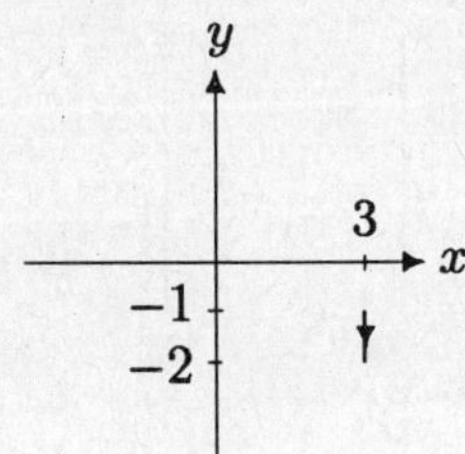

8. $x^2 + y^2 = 1$

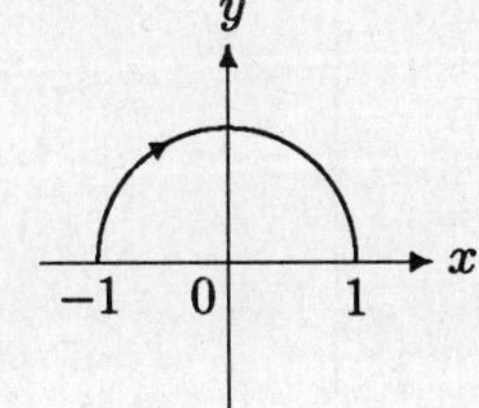

9. $y = x^{2/3}$

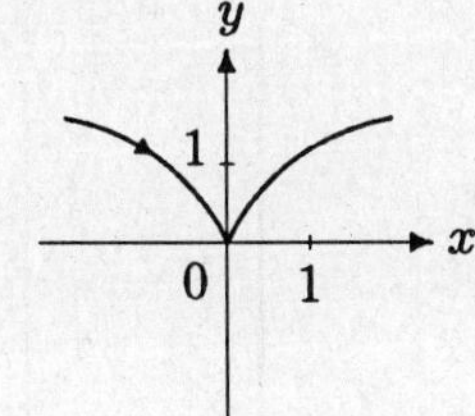

10. $y = 1/x$ for $x > 0$

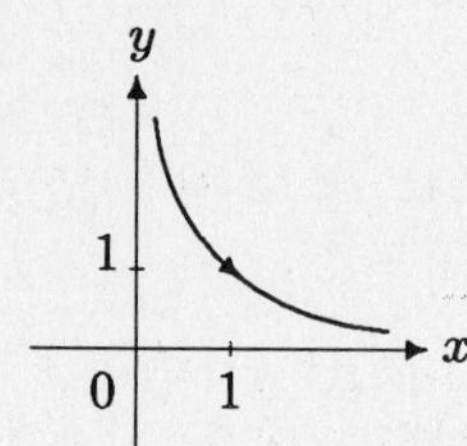

11. $y = 1/x^3$ for $x > 0$

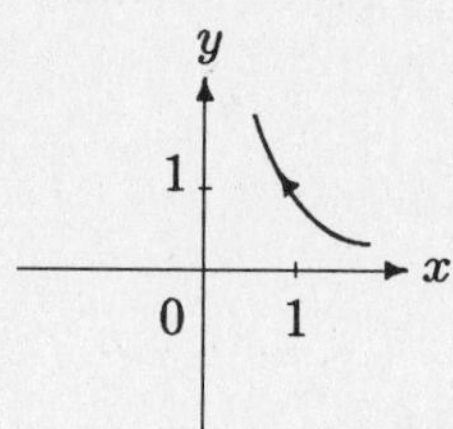

12. $x^2 - y^2 = 1$ for $x > 0$

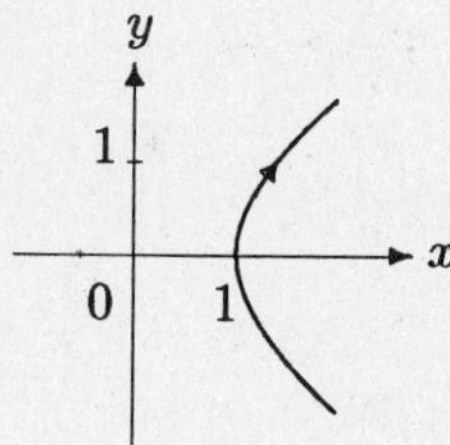

13. a. Notice that for $0 \le t \le 2\pi$, $\sin t$ and $\cos t$ have the same sign only if $0 < t < \pi/2$ or $\pi < t < 3\pi/2$. The points on the two curves coincide if $t = \pi/4$ or $t = 5\pi/4$.

    b. For any value of t for which the corresponding points on the two curves coincide, we have $x = \cos t = -\sin t$ and $y = \sin t = \cos t$. These imply that $\sin t = -\sin t$ and $\cos t = -\cos t$. Thus $\sin t = 0$ and $\cos t = 0$, which is impossible. Thus there is no value of t for which the corresponding points on the two curves coincide.

    c. For any value of t for which the corresponding points on the two curves coincide, we have $x = 1 + \cos t = \sin t$ and $y = \sin t = \cos t$. These imply that $1 + \cos t = \sin t = \cos t$, or $1 = 0$. Thus there is no value of t for which the corresponding points on the two curves coincide.

14. Since $\cos^2 t + \sin^2 t = 1$, $x/a = \cos t$ and $y/b = \sin t$, we have $x^2/a^2 + y^2/b^2 = 1$.

15. a. We have

$$x^3 = \frac{27t^3}{(1+t^3)^3}, \quad y^3 = \frac{27t^6}{(1+t^3)^3} \quad \text{and} \quad xy = \frac{9t^3}{(1+t^3)^2}.$$

Thus

$$x^3 + y^3 = \frac{27t^3}{(1+t^3)^3} + \frac{27t^6}{(1+t^3)^3} = \frac{27t^3(1+t^3)}{(1+t^3)^3} = \frac{27t^3}{(1+t^3)^2} = 3xy,$$

so an equation of the Folium of Descartes in rectangular coordinates is $x^3 + y^3 = 3xy$.

    b. If $t > -1$, then $y > 0$, and if $t < -1$, then $y < 0$. Therefore the part of the folium above the x axis is traced out as t increases without bound, and the part of the folium below the x axis is traced out as t increases toward -1.

16. a. As b increases without bound, the number of loops in the graph increases without bound.

    b. If π is replaced by an integer, then the number of loops in the graph remains fixed as b increases without bound, because x and y are periodic functions of t.

17. a. As n increases, the number of loops increases.

    b. By the Chain Rule, $dy/dt = (dy/dx)(dx/dt)$, so that

$$\frac{dy}{dx} = \frac{dy/dt}{dx/dt} = \frac{n \cos nt}{\cos t}.$$

The outer loops correspond to x near 1 or -1. Since $\sin t = x$ is near 1 or -1, it follows that $\cos t$ is near 0, and because n is even, $\cos nt$ is near -1 or 1. It follows that $dy/dx = (n \cos nt)/(\cos t)$

is large. Thus a small interval of x values is sufficient for y to cycle through its range of values. Therefore the outer loops are thin.

18. a. If r is any even integer, then both x and y will be nonnegative for all t, so the entire graph will lie in the first quadrant.

b. If r is a large positive number, then since $|\sin t| < 1$ except for $t = \pi/2$ and for $t = 3\pi/2$, $y = \sin^r t$ will be small except for $t \approx \pi/2$ and for $t \approx 3\pi/2$. Thus the corresponding point on the graph will be near the x axis. Similarly, x will be small except for $t \approx 0$ and for $t \approx \pi$, and the corresponding point on the graph will be near the y axis. Notice also that the point on the graph corresponding to $t = 0$, $\pi/2$, π, or $3\pi/2$ lies on one of the axes. Thus the graph will be near the axes if r is large and positive.

19. b. Since

$$x^2 = \frac{4t^2}{(1+t^2)^2} \quad \text{and} \quad y^2 = \frac{(1-t^2)^2}{(1+t^2)^2} = \frac{1-2t^2+t^4}{(1+t^2)^2},$$

we have

$$x^2 + y^2 = \frac{4t^2}{(1+t^2)^2} + \frac{1-2t^2+t^4}{(1+t^2)^2} = \frac{1+2t^2+t^4}{(1+t^2)^2} = 1.$$

Thus (x, y) lies on the circle $x^2 + y^2 = 1$. The graph consists of the entire circle except the point $(0, -1)$, since $y = (1-t^2)/(1+t^2)$ cannot equal -1.

20. b. Since

$$x^2 = \frac{(t^2+1)^2}{(t^2-1)^2} = \frac{t^4+2t^2+1}{(t^2-1)^2} \quad \text{and} \quad y^2 = \frac{4t^2}{(t^2-1)^2},$$

we have

$$x^2 - y^2 = \frac{t^4+2t^2+1}{(t^2-1)^2} - \frac{4t^2}{(t^2-1)^2} = \frac{t^4-2t^2+1}{(t^2-1)^2} = 1.$$

Thus (x, y) lies on the hyperbola $x^2 - y^2 = 1$. The graph consists of the entire hyperbola except the point $(1, 0)$, since $x = (t^2+1)/(t^2-1)$ cannot equal 1.

21. $$x = \begin{cases} 0 & \text{for } -\frac{\pi}{2} \le t \le \frac{\pi}{2} \\ -\frac{\pi}{4}\cos t & \text{for } \frac{\pi}{2} < t \le \frac{3\pi}{2} \\ \frac{\pi}{4}\cos t & \text{for } \frac{3\pi}{2} < t \le \frac{5\pi}{2} \end{cases} \qquad y = \begin{cases} t & \text{for } -\frac{\pi}{2} \le t \le \frac{\pi}{2} \\ \frac{\pi}{4}(1+\sin t) & \text{for } \frac{\pi}{2} < t \le \frac{3\pi}{2} \\ -\frac{\pi}{4}(1+\sin t) & \text{for } \frac{3\pi}{2} < t \le \frac{5\pi}{2} \end{cases}$$

10.2 Length and Surface Area for Parametrized Curves

1. $L = \int_0^{\sqrt{3}} \sqrt{(2t)^2 + (2)^2}\, dt = \int_0^{\sqrt{3}} 2\sqrt{t^2+1}\, dt \overset{t=\tan u}{=} \int_0^{\pi/3} 2\sqrt{\tan^2 u + 1}\, \sec^2 u\, du = \int_0^{\pi/3} 2\sec^3 u\, du,$

so by (7) of Section 7.2, $L = (\sec u \tan u + \ln|\sec u + \tan u|)\Big|_0^{\pi/3} = 2\sqrt{3} + \ln(2+\sqrt{3})$.

2. $$L = \int_0^1 \sqrt{(-2t)^2 + (3t^2)^2}\, dt = \int_0^1 t\sqrt{4+9t^2}\, dt \overset{u=4+9t^2}{=} \int_4^{13} \sqrt{u} \cdot \frac{1}{18}\, du$$
$$= \frac{1}{18}\left(\frac{2}{3}u^{3/2}\right)\Big|_4^{13} = \frac{1}{27}(13\sqrt{13} - 8)$$

3. $L = \int_0^{\pi} \sqrt{(e^t \sin t + e^t \cos t)^2 + (e^t \cos t - e^t \sin t)^2}\, dt$

$= \int_0^{\pi} \sqrt{e^{2t}(\sin^2 t + 2\sin t \cos t + 2\cos^2 t - 2\cos t \sin t + \sin^2 t)}\, dt$

$= \int_0^{\pi} e^t\sqrt{2}\, dt = \sqrt{2}\, e^t\Big|_0^{\pi} = \sqrt{2}\,(e^{\pi} - 1)$

4. $L = \int_0^{\pi/2} \sqrt{(\cos t - \cos t + t\sin t)^2 + (\sin t + t\cos t - \sin t)^2}\, dt$

$= \int_0^{\pi/2} \sqrt{t^2(\sin^2 t + \cos^2 t)}\, dt = \int_0^{\pi/2} t\, dt = \frac{1}{2}t^2\Big|_0^{\pi/2} = \frac{1}{8}\pi^2$

5. $L = \int_0^{1/2} \sqrt{\left(\frac{1}{\sqrt{1-t^2}}\right)^2 + \left(\frac{-t}{1-t^2}\right)^2}\, dt = \int_0^{1/2} \sqrt{\frac{1}{1-t^2} + \frac{t^2}{(1-t^2)^2}}\, dt$

$= \int_0^{1/2} \sqrt{\frac{1-t^2+t^2}{(1-t^2)^2}}\, dt = \int_0^{1/2} \frac{1}{1-t^2}\, dt = \int_0^{1/2} \frac{1}{2}\left(\frac{1}{1-t} + \frac{1}{1+t}\right) dt$

$= \left(-\frac{1}{2}\ln|1-t| + \frac{1}{2}\ln|1+t|\right)\Big|_0^{1/2} = \frac{1}{2}\ln\left|\frac{1+t}{1-t}\right|\Big|_0^{1/2} = \frac{1}{2}\ln 3$

6. $L = \int_0^1 \sqrt{\left(\frac{1}{1+t^2}\right)^2 + \left(\frac{-t}{1+t^2}\right)^2}\, dt = \int_0^1 \sqrt{\frac{t^2+1}{(t^2+1)^2}}\, dt = \int_0^1 \frac{1}{\sqrt{t^2+1}}\, dt$

$\overset{t=\tan u}{=} \int_0^{\pi/4} \frac{1}{\sqrt{\tan^2 u + 1}} \sec^2 u\, du = \int_0^{\pi/4} \sec u\, du = \ln(\sec u + \tan u)\Big|_0^{\pi/4} = \ln(\sqrt{2}+1)$

7. $S = \int_{\sqrt{3}}^{2\sqrt{2}} 2\pi t\sqrt{t^2+1^2}\, dt \overset{u=t^2+1}{=} \int_4^9 \pi\sqrt{u}\, du = \frac{2}{3}\pi u^{3/2}\Big|_4^9 = \frac{2}{3}\pi(27-8) = \frac{38}{9}\pi$

8. $S = \int_{-3/4}^{0} (2\pi)\frac{2}{3}(1+t)^{3/2}\sqrt{[-(1-t)^{1/2}]^2 + [(1+t)^{1/2}]^2}\, dt = \frac{4\sqrt{2}\,\pi}{3}\int_{-3/4}^{0} (1+t)^{3/2}\, dt$

$= \frac{8\sqrt{2}\,\pi}{15}(1+t)^{5/2}\Big|_{-3/4}^{0} = \frac{8\sqrt{2}\,\pi}{15}\left(1 - \frac{1}{32}\right) = \frac{31}{60}\sqrt{2}\,\pi$

9. $S = \int_0^{\pi/2} 2\pi \sin t \cos t\sqrt{(2\sin t \cos t)^2 + (\cos^2 t - \sin^2 t)^2}\, dt$

$= 2\pi\int_0^{\pi/2} \sin t \cos t\sqrt{\sin^2 2t + \cos^2 2t}\, dt = 2\pi\int_0^{\pi/2} \sin t \cos t\, dt = \pi\sin^2 t\Big|_0^{\pi/2} = \pi$

10. $S = \int_1^{\sqrt[4]{3}} 2\pi t^2\sqrt{\left(\frac{2}{t}\right)^2 + (2t)^2}\, dt = 2\pi\int_1^{\sqrt[4]{3}} 2t\sqrt{1+t^4}\, dt$

$\overset{u=t^2}{=} 2\pi\int_1^{\sqrt{3}} \sqrt{1+u^2}\, du \overset{u=\tan v}{=} 2\pi\int_{\pi/4}^{\pi/3} \sec^3 v\, dv$

By (7) of Section 7.2,

$$S = 2\pi \left[\frac{1}{2}\sec v\,\tan v + \frac{1}{2}\ln|\sec v + \tan v|\right]\Bigg|_{\pi/4}^{\pi/3}$$

$$= \pi\left\{\left[2\sqrt{3} + \ln(2+\sqrt{3})\right] - \left[\sqrt{2} + \ln(\sqrt{2}+1)\right]\right\} = \pi\left[2\sqrt{3} - \sqrt{2} + \ln\frac{2+\sqrt{3}}{1+\sqrt{2}}\right].$$

11. a. By (12),

$$S = \int_\alpha^\beta 2\pi r \sin t\sqrt{(-r\sin t)^2 + (r\cos t)^2}\,dt = \int_\alpha^\beta 2\pi r\sin t\sqrt{r^2(\sin^2 t + \cos^2 t)}\,dt$$

$$= \int_\alpha^\beta 2\pi r^2 \sin t\,dt = -2\pi r^2\cos t\Big|_\alpha^\beta = 2\pi r^2(\cos\alpha - \cos\beta).$$

If $\alpha = 0$ and $\beta = \pi/4$, then $\beta - \alpha = \pi/4$ and $S = 2\pi r^2(1 - \sqrt{2}/2)$. If $\alpha = \pi/4$ and $\beta = \pi/2$, then $\beta - \alpha = \pi/4$ and $S = 2\pi r^2(\sqrt{2}/2 - 0)$. Since $1 - \sqrt{2}/2 \neq \sqrt{2}/2$, we see that S does not depend only on $\beta - \alpha$.

b. The results of parts (a) and (b) do not contradict the remark following Example 2 of Section 8.4. There $b - a$ referred to a difference of x values. Here $\beta - \alpha$ refers to a difference of t values, not x values.

12. a. By (4) and (5),

$$v = \frac{dL}{dt} = \sqrt{\left(\frac{dx}{dt}\right)^2 + \left(\frac{dy}{dt}\right)^2} = \sqrt{(-2\sin t)^2 + (3\cos t)^2} = \sqrt{4\sin^2 t + 9\cos^2 t}.$$

b. By (a), v is periodic with period π. Thus it suffices to find the extreme values of v on $[0, \pi]$. By (a),

$$\frac{dv}{dt} = \frac{1}{2\sqrt{4\sin^2 t + 9\cos^2 t}}(8\sin t\,\cos t + 9(2\cos t)(-\sin t)) = \frac{-5\cos t\,\sin t}{\sqrt{4\sin^2 t + 9\cos^2 t}}.$$

Thus $dv/dt = 0$ for t in $(0, \pi)$ only for $t = \pi/2$. Therefore the extreme values of v on $[0, \pi]$ can occur only for $t = 0$, $\pi/2$, or π. But $v(0) = 3$, $v(\pi/2) = 2$, and $v(\pi) = 3$. Thus the minimum velocity is 2 and the maximum velocity is 3. The velocity is minimum at the points $(0, 3)$ and $(0, -3)$ on the ellipse, and the velocity is maximum at the points $(2, 0)$ and $(-2, 0)$ on the ellipse.

13. a. By (2),

$$C_{ab} = \int_0^{2\pi} \sqrt{(-a\sin t)^2 + (b\cos t)^2}\,dt = \int_0^{2\pi}\sqrt{a^2\sin^2 t + b^2\cos^2 t}\,dt.$$

b. If $a = b > 0$, then by (a),

$$C_{ab} = \int_0^{2\pi}\sqrt{a^2\sin^2 t + a^2\cos^2 t}\,dt = \int_0^{2\pi} a\,dt = 2\pi a.$$

c. By (a),

$$\lim_{b\to 0+} C_{ab} = \lim_{b\to 0+} \int_0^{2\pi} \sqrt{a^2\sin^2 t + b^2\cos^2 t}\, dt = \int_0^{2\pi} \sqrt{a^2\sin^2 t}\, dt$$

$$= 2\int_0^{\pi} \sqrt{a^2\sin^2 t}\, dt = 2\int_0^{\pi} a\sin t\, dt = -2a\cos t\Big|_0^{\pi} = 4a.$$

14. a. By (12),

$$S = \int_0^{\pi} 2\pi b\sin t\sqrt{(-a\sin t)^2 + (b\cos t)^2}\, dt = \int_0^{\pi} 2\pi b\sin t\sqrt{a^2\sin^2 t + b^2\cos^2 t}\, dt$$

$$= \int_0^{\pi} 2\pi b\sin t\sqrt{a^2 + (b^2 - a^2)\cos^2 t}\, dt.$$

b. If $a = \sqrt{2}$ and $b = 2$, then by part (a) the surface area S is given by

$$S = \int_0^{\pi} 4\pi\sin t\sqrt{2 + 2\cos^2 t}\, dt \overset{u=\cos t}{=} \int_{-1}^{1} 4\pi\sqrt{2 + 2u^2}\, du$$

$$\overset{u=\tan\theta}{=} \int_{-\pi/4}^{\pi/4} 4\pi\sqrt{2}\sqrt{1+\tan^2\theta}\,\sec^2\theta\, d\theta = 4\pi\sqrt{2}\int_{-\pi/4}^{\pi/4} \sec^3\theta\, d\theta.$$

By (7) of Section 7.2,

$$S = 4\pi\sqrt{2}\left[\frac{1}{2}\sec\theta\,\tan\theta + \frac{1}{2}\ln|\sec\theta + \tan\theta|\right]\Bigg|_{-\pi/4}^{\pi/4}$$

$$= 4\pi\sqrt{2}\left[\left(\frac{1}{2}\sqrt{2} + \frac{1}{2}\ln(1+\sqrt{2})\right) - \left(-\frac{1}{2}\sqrt{2} + \frac{1}{2}\ln(-1+\sqrt{2})\right)\right]$$

$$= 4\pi\sqrt{2}\left[\sqrt{2} + \frac{1}{2}\ln(1+\sqrt{2}) - \frac{1}{2}\ln(-1+\sqrt{2})\right] = 8\pi + 4\pi\sqrt{2}\ln(1+\sqrt{2}).$$

15. a. $L = \displaystyle\int_0^{2\pi} \sqrt{(-3r\cos^2 t\,\sin t)^2 + (3r\sin^2 t\,\cos t)^2}\, dt = \int_0^{2\pi} \sqrt{9r^2\cos^2 t\,\sin^2 t\,(\cos^2 t + \sin^2 t)}\, dt$

$$= \int_0^{2\pi} 3r\sqrt{\cos^2 t\,\sin^2 t}\, dt = \int_0^{2\pi} 3r|\cos t\,\sin t|\, dt$$

$$= \int_0^{\pi/2} 3r\cos t\,\sin t\, dt + \int_{\pi/2}^{\pi} -3r\cos t\,\sin t\, dt + \int_{\pi}^{3\pi/2} 3r\cos t\,\sin t\, dt + \int_{3\pi/2}^{2\pi} -3r\cos t\,\sin t\, dt$$

$$= \frac{3}{2}r\sin^2 t\Big|_0^{\pi/2} - \frac{3}{2}r\sin^2 t\Big|_{\pi/2}^{\pi} + \frac{3}{2}r\sin^2 t\Big|_{\pi}^{3\pi/2} - \frac{3}{2}r\sin^2 t\Big|_{3\pi/2}^{2\pi} = 6r$$

b. From the parametric equations $x = r\cos^3 t$ and $y = r\sin^3 t$, we find that $x^{2/3} + y^{2/3} = r^{2/3}\cos^2 t + r^{2/3}\sin^2 t = r^{2/3}$.

c. $S = 2\int_0^{\pi/2} 2\pi r \sin^3 t \sqrt{(-3r\cos^2 t \sin t)^2 + (3r\sin^2 t \cos t)^2}\,dt$

$= 4\pi \int_0^{\pi/2} r\sin^3 t \sqrt{9r^2\cos^4 t \sin^2 t + 9r^2 \sin^4 t \cos^2 t}\,dt$

$= 12\pi r^2 \int_0^{\pi/2} \sin^3 t \sqrt{\cos^2 t \sin^2 t\,(\cos^2 t + \sin^2 t)}\,dt$

$= 12\pi r^2 \int_0^{\pi/2} \sin^4 t \cos t\,dt \overset{u=\sin t}{=} 12\pi r^2 \int_0^1 u^4\,du = 12\pi r^2 \left.\frac{u^5}{5}\right|_0^1 = \frac{12}{5}\pi r^2$

16. $S = \int_0^{\pi/2} 2\pi \sin^n t \sqrt{(-n\cos^{n-1} t \sin t)^2 + (n\sin^{n-1} t \cos t)^2}\,dt$

$= 2n\pi \int_0^{\pi/2} \sin^n t \sin t \cos t \sqrt{\cos^{2n-4} t + \sin^{2n-4} t}\,dt$

We can carry out the integration if $2n-4=0$ or 2, which means that $n=2$ or 3. (Exercise 15(c) uses $n=3$.)

17. a. By (10) with $v = \sqrt{2gr(\cos t_0 - \cos t)}$, $dx/dt = r(1-\cos t)$ and $dy/dt = r\sin t$, we have

$$\frac{dT}{dt} = \frac{\sqrt{(dx/dt)^2 + (dy/dt)^2}}{v} = \frac{\sqrt{r^2(1-\cos t)^2 + r^2\sin^2 t}}{\sqrt{2gr(\cos t_0 - \cos t)}} = \frac{\sqrt{r^2(2-2\cos t)}}{\sqrt{2gr(\cos t_0 - \cos t)}}.$$

Integrating from t_0 to π, we find that the time $T^*(t_0)$ it takes for the marble to reach bottom is given by

$$T^*(t_0) = \int_{t_0}^{\pi} \frac{dT}{dt}\,dt = \int_{t_0}^{\pi} \sqrt{\frac{r^2(2-2\cos t)}{2gr(\cos t_0 - \cos t)}}\,dt = \int_{t_0}^{\pi} \sqrt{\frac{r}{g}} \sqrt{\frac{1-\cos t}{\cos t_0 - \cos t}}\,dt.$$

Since $1-\cos t = 2\sin^2(t/2)$, $\cos t_0 = 2\cos^2(t_0/2) - 1$, and $\cos t = 2\cos^2(t/2) - 1$, it follows that

$$\sqrt{\frac{1-\cos t}{\cos t_0 - \cos t}} = \sqrt{\frac{2\sin^2(t/2)}{[2\cos^2(t_0/2)-1] - [2\cos^2(t/2)-1]}}$$

$$= \frac{\sin(t/2)}{\sqrt{\cos^2(t_0/2) - \cos^2(t/2)}} \quad \text{for } t_0 \le t \le \pi.$$

Therefore

$$T^*(t_0) = \sqrt{\frac{r}{g}} \int_{t_0}^{\pi} \frac{\sin(t/2)}{\sqrt{\cos^2(t_0/2) - \cos^2(t/2)}}\,dt.$$

b. Let $u = \cos(t/2)$, so that $du = -\frac{1}{2}\sin(t/2)\,dt$. By (a),

$$T^*(t_0) = \sqrt{\frac{r}{g}} \int_{t_0}^{\pi} \frac{\sin(t/2)}{\sqrt{\cos^2(t_0/2) - \cos^2(t/2)}}\,dt = \sqrt{\frac{r}{g}} \int_{\cos(t_0/2)}^{0} \frac{-2}{\sqrt{\cos^2(t_0/2) - u^2}}\,du$$

$$= -2\sqrt{\frac{r}{g}} \sin^{-1}\left[\frac{u}{\cos(t_0/2)}\right]\Bigg|_{\cos(t_0/2)}^{0} = -2\sqrt{\frac{r}{g}}\,(\sin^{-1} 0 - \sin^{-1} 1) = -2\sqrt{\frac{r}{g}}\left(0 - \frac{\pi}{2}\right) = \pi\sqrt{\frac{r}{g}}.$$

18. Recall that the positive y axis points downward. The line from the origin $(0,0)$ to the bottom point $(\pi r, 2r)$ is given parametrically by $x = rt$ and $y = (2r/\pi)t$ for $0 \le t \le \pi$. By (10),

$$\frac{dT}{dt} = \frac{\sqrt{(dx/dt)^2 + (dy/dt)^2}}{\sqrt{2gy}} = \frac{\sqrt{r^2 + (2r/\pi)^2}}{\sqrt{4grt/\pi}} = \sqrt{\frac{r}{g}}\,\frac{\sqrt{\pi^2+4}}{\sqrt{4\pi t}}.$$

By (7),

$$T_{st} = \int_0^\pi \frac{dT}{dt}\,dt = \int_0^\pi \sqrt{\frac{r}{g}}\,\frac{\sqrt{\pi^2+4}}{\sqrt{4\pi t}}\,dt = \sqrt{\frac{r}{g}}\,\frac{\sqrt{\pi^2+4}}{\sqrt{\pi}}\,\sqrt{t}\,\Big|_0^\pi = \sqrt{\frac{r}{g}}\,\sqrt{\pi^2+4}.$$

Since $\sqrt{\pi^2+4} > \sqrt{\pi^2} = \pi$, it follows that $T_{st} > \pi\sqrt{r/g} = T^*$.

10.3 Polar Coordinates

1. a. $x = 3\cos(\pi/4) = 3\sqrt{2}/2$; $y = 3\sin(\pi/4) = 3\sqrt{2}/2$; Cartesian coordinates: $(3\sqrt{2}/2, 3\sqrt{2}/2)$

   b. $x = -2\cos(-\pi/6) = -\sqrt{3}$; $y = -2\sin(-\pi/6) = 1$; Cartesian coordinates: $(-\sqrt{3}, 1)$

   c. $x = 3\cos(7\pi/3) = 3/2$; $y = 3\sin(7\pi/3) = 3\sqrt{3}/2$; Cartesian coordinates: $(3/2, 3\sqrt{3}/2)$

   d. $x = 5\cos 0 = 5$; $y = 5\sin 0 = 0$; Cartesian coordinates: $(5, 0)$

   e. $x = -2\cos(\pi/2) = 0$; $y = -2\sin(\pi/2) = -2$; Cartesian coordinates: $(0, -2)$

   f. $x = -2\cos(3\pi/2) = 0$; $y = -2\sin(3\pi/2) = 2$; Cartesian coordinates: $(0, 2)$

   g. $x = 4\cos(3\pi/4) = -2\sqrt{2}$; $y = 4\sin(3\pi/4) = 2\sqrt{2}$; Cartesian coordinates: $(-2\sqrt{2}, 2\sqrt{2})$

   h. $x = 0\cos(6\pi/7) = 0$; $y = 0\sin(6\pi/7) = 0$; Cartesian coordinates: $(0, 0)$

   i. $x = -1\cos(23\pi/3) = -1/2$; $y = -1\sin(23\pi/3) = \sqrt{3}/2$; Cartesian coordinates: $(-1/2, \sqrt{3}/2)$

   j. $x = -1\cos(-23\pi/3) = -1/2$; $y = -1\sin(-23\pi/3) = -\sqrt{3}/2$;
   Cartesian coordinates: $(-1/2, -\sqrt{3}/2)$

   k. $x = 1\cos(3\pi/2) = 0$; $y = 1\sin(3\pi/2) = -1$; Cartesian coordinates: $(0, -1)$

   l. $x = 3\cos(-5\pi/6) = -3\sqrt{3}/2$; $y = 3\sin(-5\pi/6) = -3/2$; Cartesian coordinates: $(-3\sqrt{3}/2, -3/2)$

2. a. $r = \sqrt{3^2+3^2} = 3\sqrt{2}$; $\tan\theta = 3/3 = 1$, so $\theta = \pi/4$; polar coordinates: $(3\sqrt{2}, \pi/4 + 2n\pi)$ and $(-3\sqrt{2}, 5\pi/4 + 2n\pi)$

   b. $r = \sqrt{4^2 + (-4)^2} = 4\sqrt{2}$; $\tan\theta = -4/4 = -1$, so $\theta = -\pi/4$; polar coordinates: $(4\sqrt{2}, -\pi/4 + 2n\pi)$ and $(-4\sqrt{2}, 3\pi/4 + 2n\pi)$

   c. $r = \sqrt{0^2 + 5^2} = 5$; since $x = 0$ and $y > 0$, we have $\theta = \pi/2$; polar coordinates: $(5, \pi/2 + 2n\pi)$ and $(-5, 3\pi/2 + 2n\pi)$

   d. $r = \sqrt{(-4)^2 + 0^2} = 4$; $\tan\theta = 0/(-4) = 0$, so $\theta = \pi$; polar coordinates: $(4, \pi + 2n\pi)$ and $(-4, 2n\pi)$

   e. $r = \sqrt{3^2 + (3\sqrt{3})^2} = \sqrt{36} = 6$; $\tan\theta = 3\sqrt{3}/3 = \sqrt{3}$, so $\theta = \pi/3$; polar coordinates: $(6, \pi/3 + 2n\pi)$ and $(-6, 4\pi/3 + 2n\pi)$

   f. $r = \sqrt{(-1/3)^2 + (\sqrt{3}/3)^2} = \sqrt{4/9} = 2/3$; $\tan\theta = (\sqrt{3}/3)/(-1/3) = -\sqrt{3}$, so $\theta = 2\pi/3$; polar coordinates: $(2/3, 2\pi/3 + 2n\pi)$ and $(-2/3, 5\pi/3 + 2n\pi)$

g. $r=\sqrt{(-3)^2+(\sqrt{3})^2}=\sqrt{12}=2\sqrt{3}$; $\tan\theta=\sqrt{3}/(-3)$, so $\theta=5\pi/6$; polar coordinates: $(2\sqrt{3}, 5\pi/6+2n\pi)$ and $(-2\sqrt{3}, 11\pi/6+2n\pi)$

h. $r=\sqrt{(-2\sqrt{3})^2+2^2}=\sqrt{16}=4$; $\tan\theta=2/(-2\sqrt{3})=-\sqrt{3}/3$, so $\theta=5\pi/6$; polar coordinates: $(4, 5\pi/6+2n\pi)$ and $(-4, 11\pi/6+2n\pi)$

i. polar coordinates: $(0,\theta)$, where θ is any angle

j. $r=\sqrt{(-5\sqrt{3})^2+(-5)^2}=10$; $\tan\theta=-5/(-5\sqrt{3})=\sqrt{3}/3$, so $\theta=7\pi/6$; polar coordinates: $(10, 7\pi/6+2n\pi)$ and $(-10, \pi/6+2n\pi)$

3. If $2x+3y=4$, then $2(r\cos\theta)+3(r\sin\theta)=4$, so $r=4/(2\cos\theta+3\sin\theta)$.

4. If $y^2=4x$, then $r^2\sin^2\theta=4(r\cos\theta)$, so $r=4(\cos\theta/\sin^2\theta)$.

5. If $x^2+9y^2=1$, then $r^2\cos^2\theta+9(r^2\sin^2\theta)=1$, so

$$r^2=\frac{1}{\cos^2\theta+9\sin^2\theta}=\frac{1}{8\sin^2\theta+1}, \quad \text{or} \quad r=\frac{1}{\sqrt{8\sin^2\theta+1}}.$$

6. If $9x^2+y^2=4y$, then $9(r^2\cos^2\theta)+r^2\sin^2\theta=4(r\sin\theta)$, so

$$r=\frac{4\sin\theta}{9\cos^2\theta+\sin^2\theta}=\frac{4\sin\theta}{8\cos^2\theta+1}.$$

7. If $(x^2+y^2)^2=x^2-y^2$, then $(r^2)^2=r^2\cos^2\theta-r^2\sin^2\theta$, so $r^4=r^2\cos 2\theta$, or $r^2=\cos 2\theta$.

8. If $x^2+y^2=2x$, then $r^2=2r\cos\theta$, so $r=2\cos\theta$.

9. If $x^2+y^2=4y$, then it follows that $r^2=4r\sin\theta$, so $r=4\sin\theta$.

10. If $y^2=x^3/(2-x)$, then

$$r^2\sin^2\theta=\frac{r^3\cos^3\theta}{2-r\cos\theta}$$

so $\sin^2\theta\,(2-r\cos\theta)=r\cos^3\theta$, or

$$r=\frac{2\sin^2\theta}{\sin^2\theta\,\cos\theta+\cos^3\theta}=\frac{2\sin^2\theta}{\cos\theta}.$$

11. If $y^2=x^2(3-x)/(1+x)$, then

$$r^2\sin^2\theta=\frac{r^2\cos^2\theta\,(3-r\cos\theta)}{1+r\cos\theta}$$

so $\sin^2\theta\,(1+r\cos\theta)=\cos^2\theta\,(3-r\cos\theta)$, or

$$r=\frac{3\cos^2\theta-\sin^2\theta}{\sin^2\theta\,\cos\theta+\cos^3\theta}=\frac{3\cos^2\theta-\sin^2\theta}{\cos\theta}.$$

12. If $r=5$, then $\sqrt{x^2+y^2}=5$, or $x^2+y^2=25$.

13. If $r = 3\cos\theta$, then $r^2 = 3r\cos\theta$, or $x^2 + y^2 = 3x$.

14. If $\tan\theta = 6$, then $\sin\theta = 6\cos\theta$, so $r\sin\theta = 6r\cos\theta$, or $y = 6x$.

15. If $\cot\theta = 3$, then $\cos\theta = 3\sin\theta$, so $r\cos\theta = 3r\sin\theta$, or $x = 3y$.

16. If $r\cot\theta = 3$, then $r \neq 0$, and $r\cos\theta = 3\sin\theta$, so $r(r\cos\theta) = 3r\sin\theta$, or $x\sqrt{x^2+y^2} = 3y$, for $(x, y) \neq (0, 0)$.

17. If $r = \sin 2\theta = 2\sin\theta\cos\theta$, then $r^3 = 2(r\sin\theta)(r\cos\theta)$, so $(x^2+y^2)^{3/2} = 2xy$, or $(x^2+y^2)^3 = 4x^2y^2$.

18. If $r = 2\sin\theta\tan\theta$, then $r\cos\theta = 2\sin^2\theta$, so $r^2(r\cos\theta) = 2(r\sin\theta)^2$, or $x(x^2+y^2) = 2y^2$.

19. If $r \neq 0$, the equation $r = 1 + \cos\theta$ is equivalent to the equation $r^2 = r + r\cos\theta$ since division by r is permissible. If $r = 0$ (which corresponds to the origin), then $r^2 = r + r\cos\theta$ is satisfied by (r, θ) for any θ, whereas $r = 1 + \cos\theta$ is satisfied by (r, π). Thus the origin is on the polar graph of both equations, so the polar graphs are the same.

20. Since $2 + \cos\theta \geq 2 - 1 > 0$, the equation $r = 2 + \cos\theta$ is not satisfied by $(0, \theta)$ for any θ, so the origin is not on the polar graph of $r = 2 + \cos\theta$. However, the equation $r^2 = 2r + r\cos\theta$ is satisfied by $(0, \theta)$ for any θ, so the origin is on the polar graph of $r^2 = 2r + r\cos\theta$. Thus the polar graphs are not the same.

21. $r = 5$

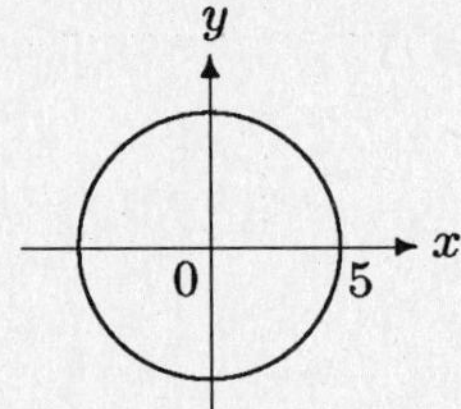

22. $r = -2$

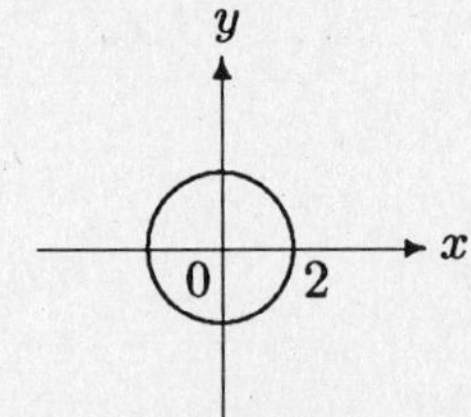

23. $r = 0$

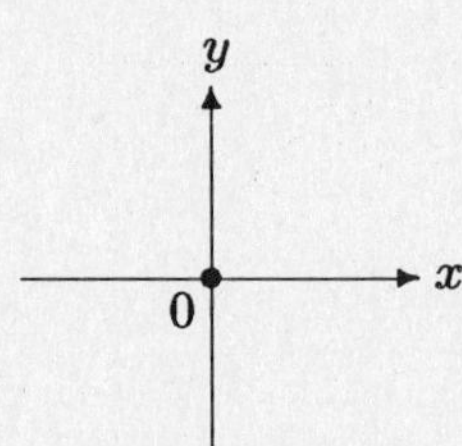

24. $\theta = 3\pi/2$

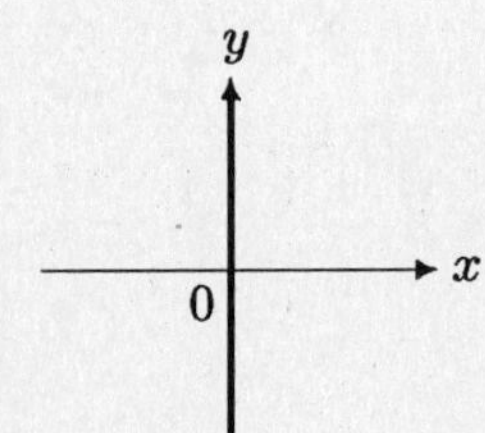

25. $\theta = -7\pi/6$

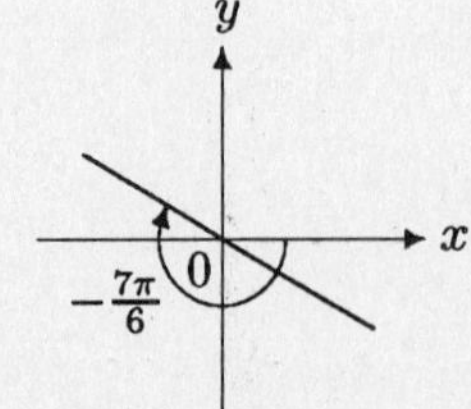

26. $|\theta| = \pi/3$

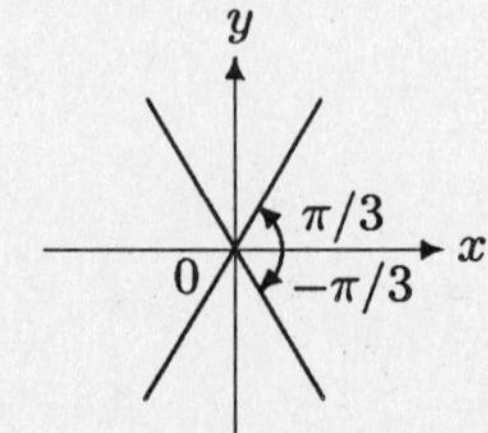

27. $r \sin\theta = 5$

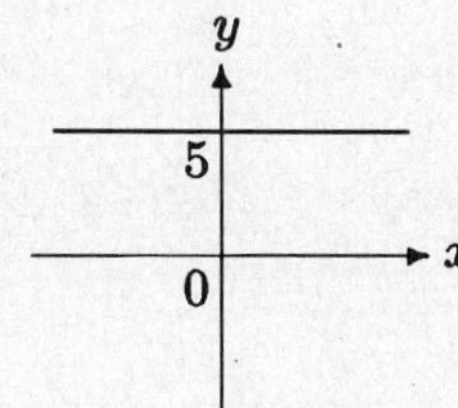

28. $r = 2\sin\theta$

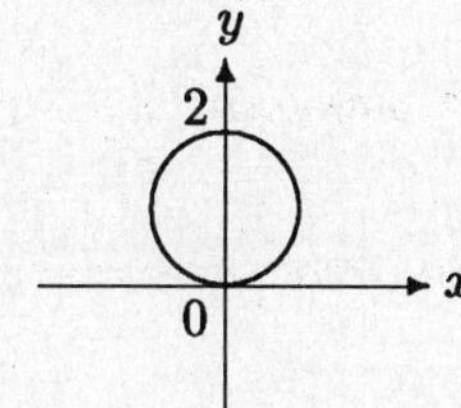

29. $r = -(3/2)\cos\theta$

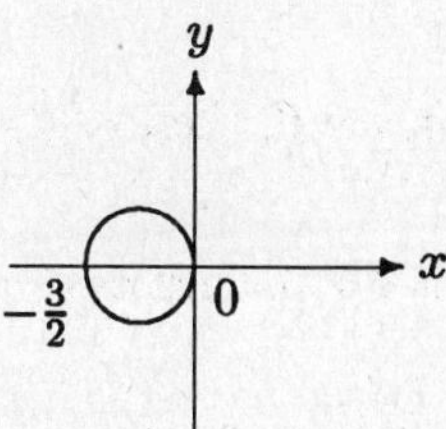

30. $r\sin(\theta - \pi/2) = 3$, or $r\cos\theta = -3$

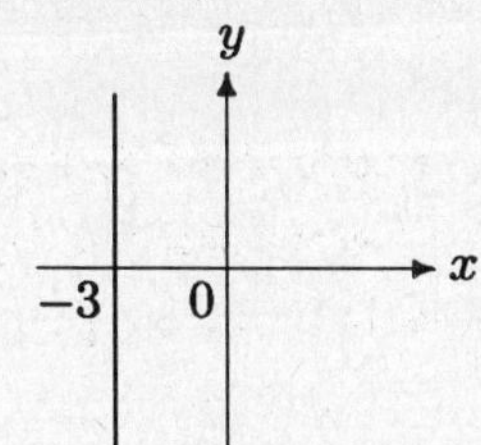

31. $r\cos(\theta - \pi/3) = 2$

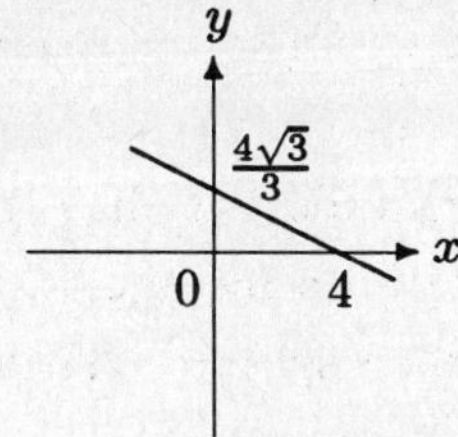

32. $r\cos(\theta + \pi/4) = -2$

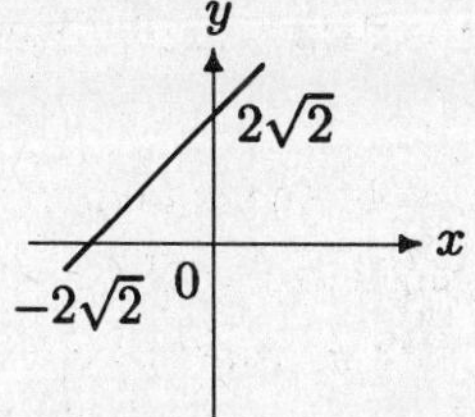

33. $r = 2\cot\theta\csc\theta$

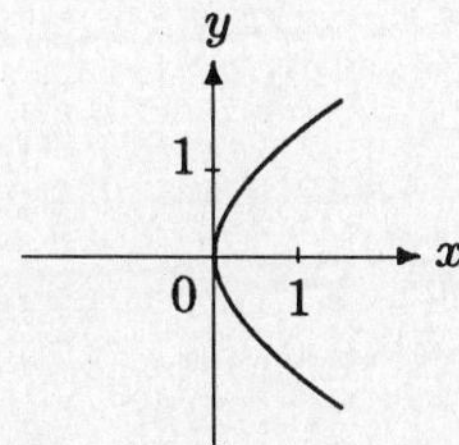

34. $r = -3\tan\theta\sec\theta$

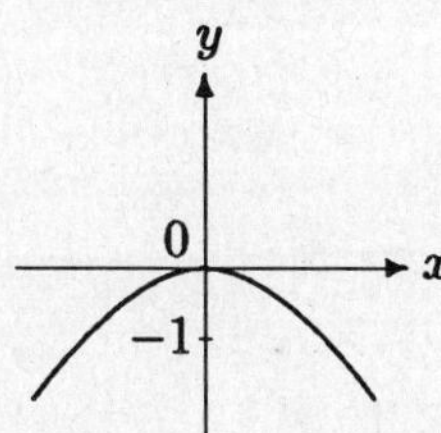

35. $r(\sin\theta + \cos\theta) = 1$

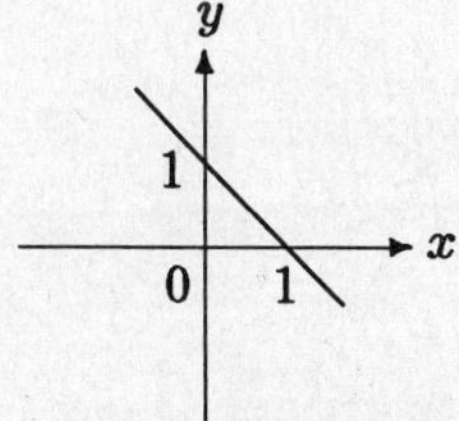

36. $r = 2/(3\cos\theta - 2\sin\theta)$

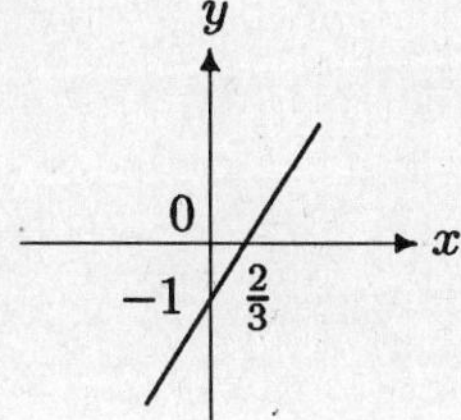

37. $r = 1 - \cos\theta$; symmetry with respect to the x axis

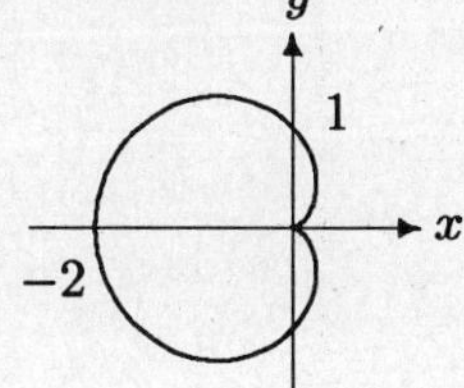

38. $r = 3(1 - \sin\theta)$; symmetry with respect to the y axis

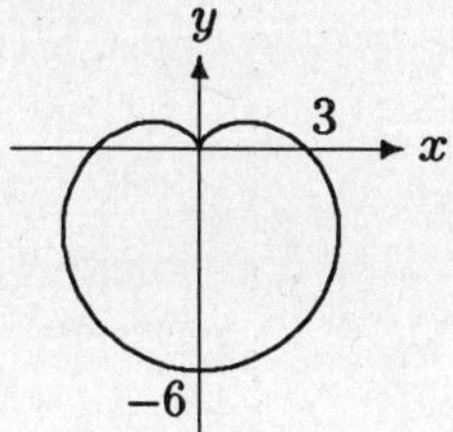

39. $r = 5(1 + \sin\theta)$; symmetry with respect to the y axis.

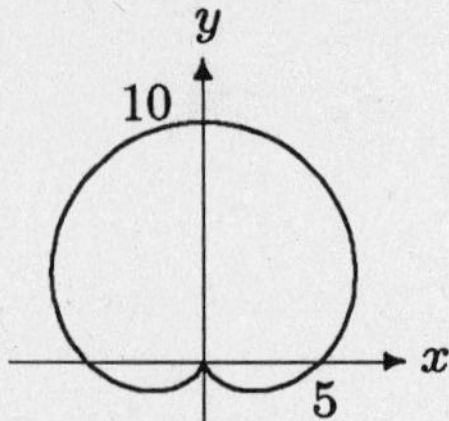

40. $r = 3\sin 2\theta$; symmetry with respect to both axes and origin.

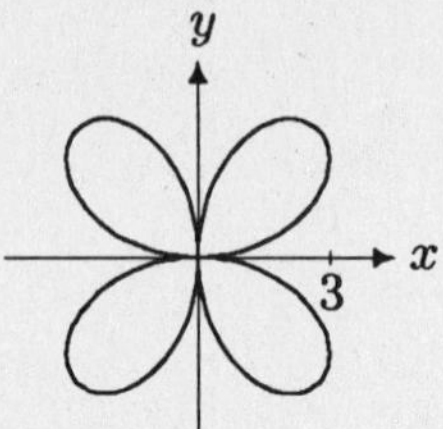

41. $r = -4\sin 3\theta$; symmetry with respect to the y axis.

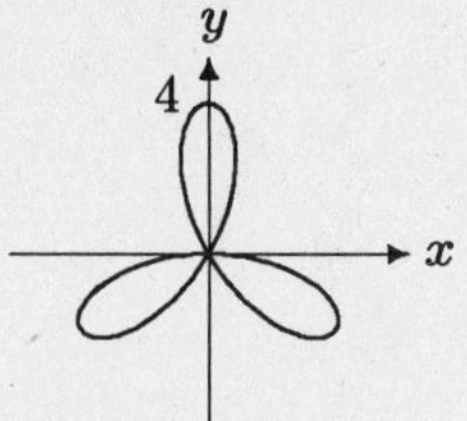

42. $r = -\sin 4\theta$; symmetry with respect to both axes and origin.

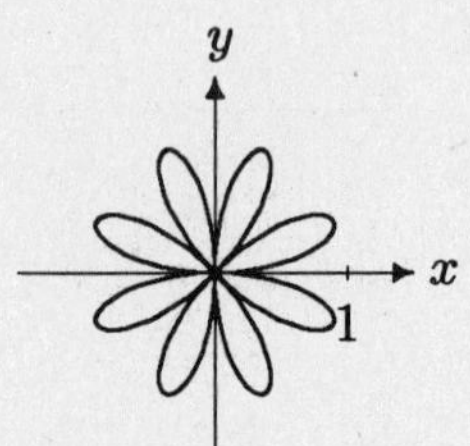

43. $r = 2\cos 6\theta$; symmetry with respect to both axes and origin.

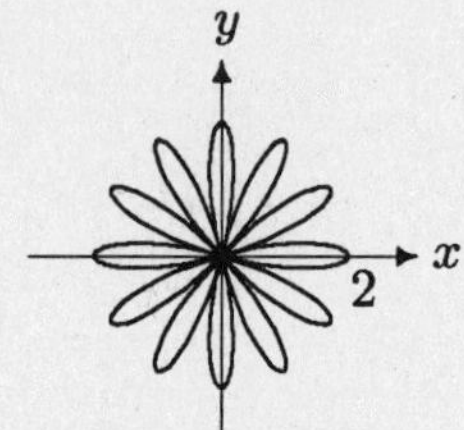

44. $r = \cos(\theta/2)$; symmetry with respect to both axes and origin (note if (r, θ) on graph then $(-r, \theta + 2\pi)$ on graph)

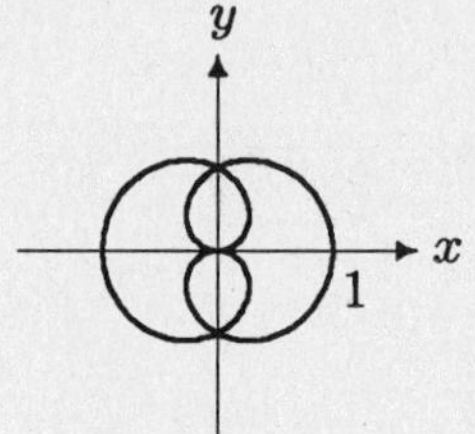

45. $r = \sin(\theta/2)$; symmetry with respect to both axes and origin (note if (r, θ) on graph then $(-r, \theta + 2\pi)$ on graph)

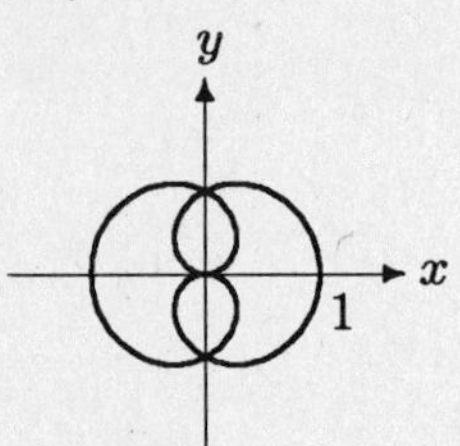

46. $r^2 = \sin\theta$; symmetry with respect to both axes and origin.

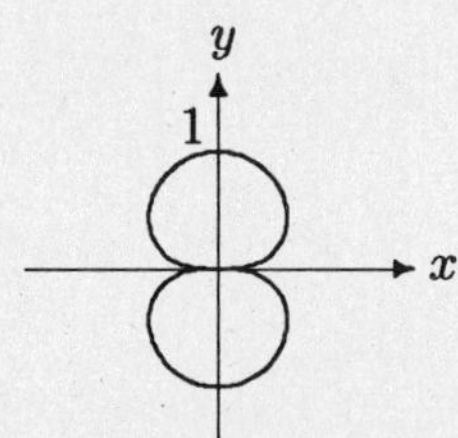

47. $r^2 = 25\cos\theta$; symmetry with respect to both axes and origin.

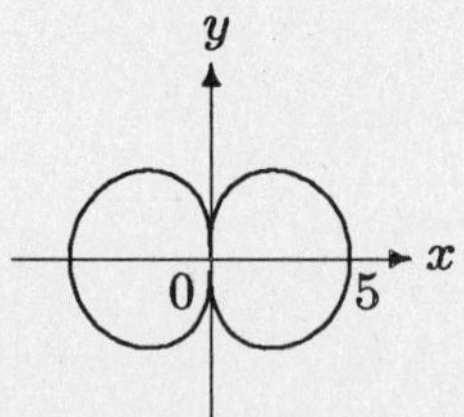

48. $r^2 = 9\sin 2\theta$; symmetry with respect to the origin.

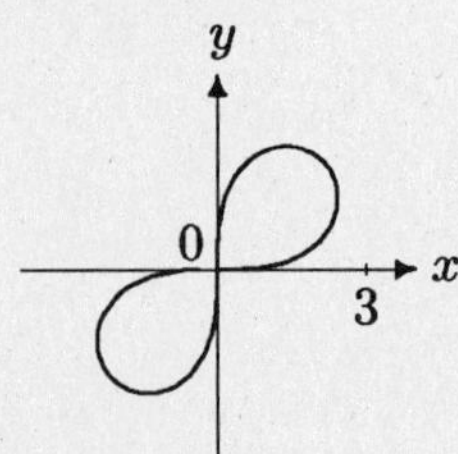

49. $r = 1 + 2\sin\theta$; symmetry with respect to the y axis.

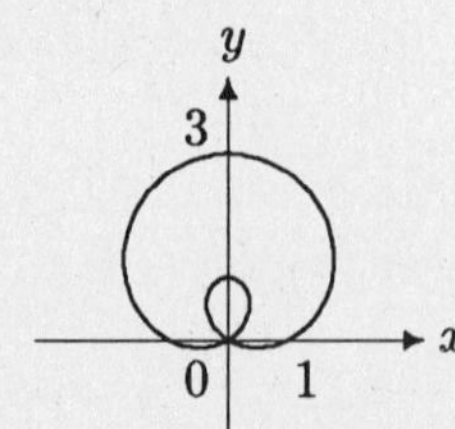

50. $r = 3\tan\theta$; symmetry with respect to both axes and origin.

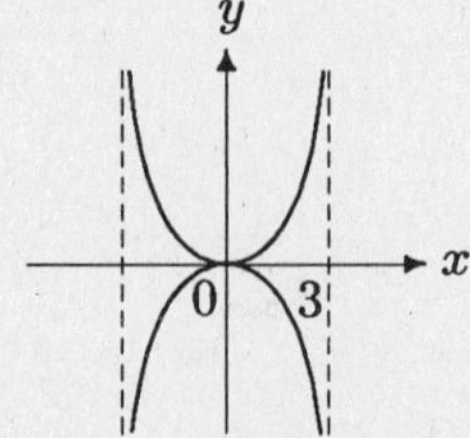

51. $r = e^{\theta/3}$; no symmetry with respect to either axis or origin.

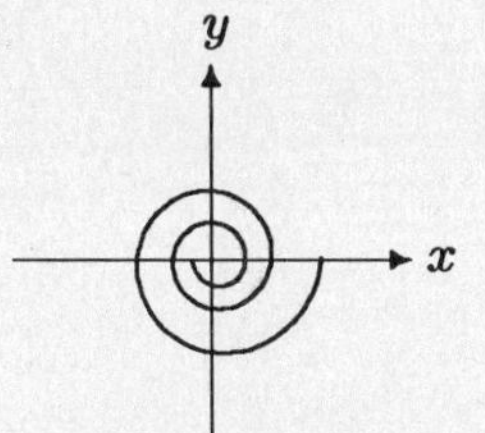

52. $r = \sin\theta + \cos\theta$, or $x^2 + y^2 = y + x$; a circle centered at $(\frac{1}{2}, \frac{1}{2})$ with radius $\sqrt{2}/2$; no symmetry with respect to either axis or origin.

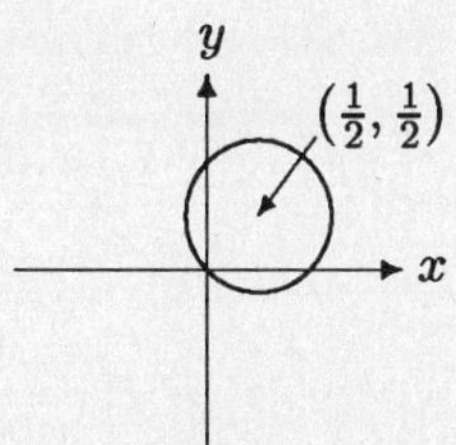

53. a. Since $\sin(-3\theta)\sin(-\theta) = -(\sin 3\theta)(-\sin\theta) = (\sin 3\theta)\sin\theta$, it follows that $(r, -\theta)$ is on the graph if (r, θ) is on the graph. Thus the graph is symmetric with respect to the x axis. Since $\sin 3(\pi - \theta) = \sin(3\pi - 3\theta) = \sin(\pi - 3\theta) = \sin 3\theta$ and since $\sin(\pi - \theta) = \sin\theta$, it follows that $(r, \pi - \theta)$ is on the graph if (r, θ) is on the graph. Thus the graph is symmetric with respect to the y axis. Symmetry with respect to the origin follows from symmetry with respect to both coordinate axes.

b. Since $\sin(-3\theta)\cos(-\theta) = -\sin(3\theta)\cos\theta$, it follows that $(-r, -\theta)$ is on the graph if (r, θ) is on the graph. Thus the graph is symmetric with respect to the y axis. Since $\sin 3(\pi - \theta) = \sin 3\theta$ by part (a) and since $\cos(\pi - \theta) = -\cos(-\theta) = -\cos\theta$, it follows that $(-r, \pi - \theta)$ is on the graph if (r, θ) is on the graph. Thus the graph is symmetric with respect to the x axis. Symmetry with respect to the origin follows from symmetry with respect to both axes.

c. Since $1 + \cos(-2\theta) + \cos(-3\theta) = 1 + \cos 2\theta + \cos 3\theta$, $(r, -\theta)$ is on the graph if (r, θ) is on the graph. Thus the graph is symmetric with respect to the x axis.

54. If n is odd, then small petals lie inside larger petals.

55. a. If n is even, there are $2n$ petals.

b. If n is odd, there are n petals.

56. If p and q are both odd, there are p petals. If either of p and q is even, there are $2p$ petals.

57. There are infinitely many petals.

58. b. The graph consists of n petals.

59. a. Suppose (r, θ) satisfies $r = 3(\cos\theta + 1)$. Then $3(\cos(\theta + \pi) - 1) = 3(-\cos\theta - 1) = -3(\cos\theta + 1) = -r$, so $(-r, \theta + \pi)$ satisfies the equation $r = 3(\cos\theta - 1)$. Conversely, if (r, θ) satisfies $r = 3(\cos\theta - 1)$, then $(-r, \theta + \pi)$ satisfies $r = 3(\cos\theta + 1)$. Since (r, θ) and $(-r, \theta + \pi)$ represent the same point, the graphs are the same.

b. Suppose (r, θ) satisfies $r = 2(\sin\theta + 1)$. Then $2(\sin(\theta + \pi) - 1) = 2(-\sin\theta - 1) = -2(\sin\theta + 1) = -r$, so $(-r, \theta + \pi)$ satisfies the equation $r = 2(\sin\theta - 1)$. Conversely, if (r, θ) satisfies $r = 2(\sin\theta - 1)$, then $(-r, \theta + \pi)$ satisfies $r = 2(\sin\theta + 1)$. Since (r, θ) and $(-r, \theta + \pi)$ represent the same point, the graphs are the same.

c. Since (r,θ) and $(r,\theta-2\pi)$ represent the same point, the graphs are the same.

60. $(1,0)$ satisfies $r=\frac{1}{2}(1+\cos\theta)$, and $(-1,\pi)$ satisfies $r^2=-\cos\theta$; the point $(1,0)$ in Cartesian coordinates is represented in polar coordinates by both $(1,0)$ and $(-1,\pi)$. Thus the graphs intersect at $(1,0)$. If (r,θ) is a set of polar coordinates for $(1,0)$ and if (r,θ) satisfies $r=\frac{1}{2}(1+\cos\theta)$, then $r\geq 0$, so that (r,θ) has the form $(1,2n\pi)$ for some integer n. But $(1,2n\pi)$ does not satisfy $r^2=-\cos\theta$. Thus no single set of polar coordinates for $(1,0)$ satisfies both equations.

61. Let (r,θ) be a point on the graph. Then

$$1=\sqrt{(r\cos\theta-1)^2+(r\sin\theta)^2}\,\sqrt{(r\cos\theta+1)^2+(r\sin\theta)^2}.$$

Squaring both sides, we obtain

$$1=(r^2-2r\cos\theta+1)\cdot(r^2+2r\cos\theta+1)=r^4-4r^2\cos^2\theta+2r^2+1$$

so that $r^2[r^2+2(1-2\cos^2\theta)]=0$. Thus either $r=0$ or $r^2=-2(1-2\cos^2\theta)=2\cos 2\theta$. Since $(0,\pi/4)$ satisfies the equation $r^2=2\cos 2\theta$, we may simply write $r^2=2\cos 2\theta$, even when $r=0$.

10.4 Length and Area in Polar Coordinates

1. By (2),

$$L=\int_{-\pi/2}^{\pi/2}\sqrt{(-2\sin\theta)^2+(2\cos\theta)^2}\,d\theta=\int_{-\pi/2}^{\pi/2}\sqrt{4(\sin^2\theta+\cos^2\theta)}\,d\theta=\int_{-\pi/2}^{\pi/2}2\,d\theta=2\pi.$$

2. By (2),

$$L=\int_0^{4\sqrt{2}}\sqrt{(2\theta)^2+(\theta^2)^2}\,d\theta=\int_0^{4\sqrt{2}}\sqrt{4\theta^2+\theta^4}\,d\theta=\int_0^{4\sqrt{2}}\theta\sqrt{4+\theta^2}\,d\theta$$

$$\overset{u=4+\theta^2}{=}\int_4^{36}\sqrt{u}\cdot\frac{1}{2}\,du=\frac{1}{3}u^{3/2}\Big|_4^{36}=\frac{1}{3}(216-8)=\frac{208}{3}.$$

3. By (2),

$$L=\int_0^{2\pi}\sqrt{(2\sin\theta)^2+(2-2\cos\theta)^2}\,d\theta=\int_0^{2\pi}\sqrt{4\sin^2\theta+4-8\cos\theta+4\cos^2\theta}\,d\theta$$

$$=\int_0^{2\pi}\sqrt{8-8\cos\theta}\,d\theta=2\int_0^{\pi}4\sqrt{\frac{1-\cos\theta}{2}}\,d\theta=8\int_0^{\pi}\sin\frac{\theta}{2}\,d\theta=-16\cos\frac{\theta}{2}\Big|_0^{\pi}=16.$$

4. By (2),

$$L=\int_0^{\pi}\sqrt{\left(\sin\frac{\theta}{2}\cos\frac{\theta}{2}\right)^2+\left(\sin^2\frac{\theta}{2}\right)^2}\,d\theta=\int_0^{\pi}\sqrt{\sin^2\frac{\theta}{2}\left(\cos^2\frac{\theta}{2}+\sin^2\frac{\theta}{2}\right)}\,d\theta$$

$$=\int_0^{\pi}\sin\frac{\theta}{2}\,d\theta=-2\cos\frac{\theta}{2}\Big|_0^{\pi}=4.$$

5. By (2),

$$L = \int_0^{2\pi} \sqrt{\left(\sin^2 \frac{\theta}{3} \cos \frac{\theta}{3}\right)^2 + \left(\sin^3 \frac{\theta}{3}\right)^2}\, d\theta = \int_0^{2\pi} \sqrt{\sin^4 \frac{\theta}{3} \left(\cos^2 \frac{\theta}{3} + \sin^2 \frac{\theta}{3}\right)}\, d\theta$$

$$= \int_0^{2\pi} \sin^2 \frac{\theta}{3}\, d\theta = \int_0^{2\pi} \left(\frac{1}{2} - \frac{1}{2}\cos \frac{2\theta}{3}\right) d\theta = \left(\frac{1}{2}\theta - \frac{3}{4}\sin \frac{2\theta}{3}\right)\Big|_0^{2\pi} = \pi + \frac{3\sqrt{3}}{8}.$$

6. By (2), $L = \int_{-\ln 3}^{0} \sqrt{(e^\theta)^2 + (e^\theta)^2}\, d\theta = \int_{-\ln 3}^{0} \sqrt{e^{2\theta} + e^{2\theta}}\, d\theta = \int_{-\ln 3}^{0} \sqrt{2}\, e^\theta\, d\theta = \sqrt{2}\, e^\theta \big|_{-\ln 3}^{0} = \sqrt{2}\,(1 - e^{-\ln 3}) = \sqrt{2}\,(1 - \frac{1}{3}) = \frac{2}{3}\sqrt{2}.$

7. $A = \int_0^{2\pi} (\frac{1}{2})\, 4^2\, d\theta = 8\theta\big|_0^{2\pi} = 16\pi$

8. $A = \int_0^{2\pi} \frac{1}{2}a^2\, d\theta = \frac{1}{2}a^2\theta\big|_0^{2\pi} = \pi a^2$

9. The entire region is obtained from $r = 3\sin\theta$ for $0 \le \theta \le \pi$; $A = \int_0^{\pi} (\frac{1}{2}) 9 \sin^2\theta\, d\theta = \frac{9}{2}(\frac{1}{2}\theta - \frac{1}{4}\sin 2\theta)\big|_0^{\pi} = \frac{9}{4}\pi$.

10. $A = \int_0^{\pi/3} (\frac{1}{2}) 9 \sin^2\theta\, d\theta = \frac{9}{2}\,(\frac{1}{2}\theta - \frac{1}{4}\sin 2\theta)\big|_0^{\pi/3} = \frac{3}{4}\pi - \frac{9}{16}\sqrt{3}.$

11. $A = \int_{\pi/2}^{3\pi/2} \frac{1}{2}(-2\cos\theta)^2\, d\theta = 2\int_{\pi/2}^{3\pi/2} \cos^2\theta\, d\theta = 2\,(\frac{1}{2}\theta + \frac{1}{4}\sin 2\theta)\big|_{\pi/2}^{3\pi/2} = \pi$

12. The four leaves have the same area. The area of one of them is given by $A_1 = \int_0^{\pi/2} \frac{1}{2}(9\sin 2\theta)^2\, d\theta = \frac{81}{2}\int_0^{\pi/2} \sin^2 2\theta\, d\theta = \frac{81}{2}\int_0^{\pi u/2} (\frac{1}{2} - \frac{1}{2}\cos 4\theta)\, d\theta = \frac{81}{2}\,(\frac{1}{2}\theta - \frac{1}{8}\sin 4\theta)\big|_0^{\pi/2} = \frac{81}{8}\pi$. Thus the total area $A = 4A_1 = \frac{81}{2}\pi$.

13. The region has the same area A as does the region described by $r = -9\cos 2\theta$ for $\pi/4 \le \theta \le \pi/2$. Now $A = \int_{\pi/4}^{\pi/2} \frac{1}{2}(-9\cos 2\theta)^2\, d\theta = \frac{81}{2}\int_{\pi/4}^{\pi/2} \cos^2 2\theta\, d\theta = \frac{81}{2}\int_{\pi/4}^{\pi/2} (\frac{1}{2} + \frac{1}{2}\cos 4\theta)\, d\theta = \frac{81}{2}\,(\frac{1}{2}\theta + \frac{1}{8}\sin 4\theta)\big|_{\pi/4}^{\pi/2} = \frac{81}{16}\pi$.

14. The three leaves have the same area. The area of one of them is given by $A_1 = \int_{-\pi/3}^{0} \frac{1}{2}(-4\sin 3\theta)^2\, d\theta = 8\int_{-\pi/3}^{0} \sin^2 3\theta\, d\theta = 8\int_{-\pi/3}^{0} (\frac{1}{2} - \frac{1}{2}\cos 6\theta)\, d\theta = 8\,(\frac{1}{2}\theta - \frac{1}{12}\sin 6\theta)\big|_{-\pi/3}^{0} = \frac{4}{3}\pi$.

15. The three leaves have the same area. The area of one of them is given by $A_1 = \int_{-\pi/6}^{\pi/6} \frac{1}{2}\left(\frac{1}{2}\cos 3\theta\right)^2 d\theta = \frac{1}{8}\int_{-\pi/6}^{\pi/6} \cos^2 3\theta\, d\theta = \frac{1}{8}\int_{-\pi/6}^{\pi/6} (\frac{1}{2} + \frac{1}{2}\cos 6\theta)\, d\theta = \frac{1}{8}\,(\frac{1}{2}\theta + \frac{1}{12}\sin 6\theta)\big|_{-\pi/6}^{\pi/6} = \frac{1}{48}\pi$. Thus the total area $A = 3A_1 = \pi/16$.

16. The eight leaves have the same area. The area of one of them is given by $A_1 = \int_0^{\pi/4} \frac{1}{2}(6\sin 4\theta)^2\, d\theta = 18\int_0^{\pi/4} \sin^2 4\theta\, d\theta = 18\int_0^{\pi/4} (\frac{1}{2} - \frac{1}{2}\cos 8\theta)\, d\theta = 18\,(\frac{1}{2}\theta - \frac{1}{16}\sin 8\theta)\big|_0^{\pi/4} = \frac{9}{4}\pi$. Thus the total area $A = 8A_1 = 18\pi$.

17. $A = \int_0^{2\pi} \frac{1}{2}(4)(1 - \sin\theta)^2\, d\theta = 2\int_0^{2\pi} (1 - 2\sin\theta + \sin^2\theta)\, d\theta = 2\int_0^{2\pi} (\frac{3}{2} - 2\sin\theta - \frac{1}{2}\cos 2\theta)\, d\theta$
$= 2\,(\frac{3}{2}\theta + 2\cos\theta - \frac{1}{4}\sin 2\theta)\big|_0^{2\pi} = 6\pi$

18. $A = \int_0^{2\pi} \frac{1}{2}(2 + 2\cos\theta)^2\, d\theta = 2\int_0^{2\pi} (1 + 2\cos\theta + \cos^2\theta)\, d\theta = 2\int_0^{2\pi} (\frac{3}{2} + 2\cos\theta + \frac{1}{2}\cos 2\theta)\, d\theta$
$= 2\,(\frac{3}{2}\theta + 2\sin\theta + \frac{1}{4}\sin 2\theta)\big|_0^{2\pi} = 6\pi$

19. $A = \int_0^{2\pi} \frac{1}{2}(4+3\cos\theta)^2\,d\theta = \frac{1}{2}\int_0^{2\pi}(16+24\cos\theta+9\cos^2\theta)\,d\theta = \frac{1}{2}\int_0^{2\pi}\left(\frac{41}{2}+24\cos\theta+\frac{9}{2}\cos 2\theta\right)\,d\theta$
$= \frac{1}{2}\left(\frac{41}{2}\theta + 24\sin\theta + \frac{9}{4}\sin 2\theta\right)\Big|_0^{2\pi} = \frac{41}{2}\pi$

20. The two leaves of the lemniscate have the same area. The area of one of them is given by $A_1 = \int_0^{\pi/2} \frac{1}{2}(\sqrt{9\sin 2\theta})^2\,d\theta = \frac{9}{2}\int_0^{\pi/2}\sin 2\theta\,d\theta = -\frac{9}{4}\cos 2\theta\Big|_0^{\pi/2} = \frac{9}{2}$. Thus the total area $A = 2A_1 = 9$.

21. The two leaves of the region have the same area. The area of one of them is given by

$$A_1 = \int_{-\pi/2}^{\pi/2}\frac{1}{2}(\sqrt{25\cos\theta})^2\,d\theta = \frac{25}{2}\int_{-\pi/2}^{\pi/2}\cos\theta\,d\theta = \frac{25}{2}\sin\theta\Big|_{-\pi/2}^{\pi/2} = 25.$$

Thus the total area $A = 2A_1 = 50$.

22. The two leaves of the region have the same area. The area of one of them is given by $A_1 = \int_{\pi/2}^{3\pi/2}\frac{1}{2}(\sqrt{-\cos\theta})^2\,d\theta = \frac{1}{2}\int_{\pi/2}^{3\pi/2}(-\cos\theta)\,d\theta = -\frac{1}{2}\sin\theta\Big|_{\pi/2}^{3\pi/2} = 1$. Thus the total area $A = 2A_1 = 2$.

23. $f(\theta) = 5,\ g(\theta) = 1;\ A = \int_0^{2\pi}\frac{1}{2}(5^2-1^2)\,d\theta = 12\theta\Big|_0^{2\pi} = 24\pi$

24. $f(\theta) = 5,\ g(\theta) = 2(1+\cos\theta);\ A = \int_0^{2\pi}\frac{1}{2}[5^2 - 4(1+\cos\theta)^2]\,d\theta = \frac{1}{2}\int_0^{2\pi}(21 - 8\cos\theta - 4\cos^2\theta)\,d\theta = \frac{1}{2}\int_0^{2\pi}(19 - 8\cos\theta - 2\cos 2\theta)\,d\theta = \frac{1}{2}(19\theta - 8\sin\theta - \sin 2\theta)\Big|_0^{2\pi} = 19\pi$

25. $f(\theta) = 1,\ g(\theta) = \left\{\begin{array}{ll}\sin\theta & \text{for } 0 \le \theta \le \pi \\ 0 & \text{for } \pi \le \theta \le 2\pi\end{array}\right\};$

$A = \int_0^{\pi}\frac{1}{2}(1^2 - \sin^2\theta)\,d\theta + \int_{\pi}^{2\pi}\frac{1}{2}(1^2)\,d\theta = \frac{1}{2}\left(\frac{1}{2}\theta + \frac{1}{4}\sin 2\theta\right)\Big|_0^{\pi} + \frac{1}{2}\theta\Big|_{\pi}^{2\pi} = \frac{1}{4}\pi + \frac{1}{2}\pi = \frac{3}{4}\pi.$

26. By symmetry, the area is 8 times the area of the region between the polar graphs of $r = \cos 2\theta$ and $r = 1$ for $0 \le \theta \le \pi/4$. Thus $A = 4\int_0^{\pi/4}(1^2 - \cos^2 2\theta)\,d\theta = 4\left(\theta - \frac{1}{2}\theta - \frac{1}{8}\sin 4\theta\right)\Big|_0^{\pi/4} = \frac{1}{2}\pi.$

27. $f(\theta) = 1,\ g(\theta) = \left\{\begin{array}{ll}\sqrt{\cos 2\theta} & \text{for } -\pi/4 \le \theta \le \pi/4 \text{ and } 3\pi/4 \le \theta \le 5\pi/4 \\ 0 & \text{for } \pi/4 \le \theta \le 3\pi/4 \text{ and } 5\pi/4 \le \theta \le 7\pi/4\end{array}\right\};$

$A = \int_{-\pi/4}^{\pi/4}\frac{1}{2}[1^2 - (\sqrt{\cos 2\theta})^2]\,d\theta + \int_{\pi/4}^{3\pi/4}\frac{1}{2}(1^2)\,d\theta + \int_{3\pi/4}^{5\pi/4}\frac{1}{2}[1^2 - (\sqrt{\cos 2\theta})^2]\,d\theta + \int_{5\pi/4}^{7\pi/4}\frac{1}{2}(1^2)\,d\theta$
$= \frac{1}{2}\int_{-\pi/4}^{\pi/4}(1 - \cos 2\theta)\,d\theta + \frac{1}{4}\pi + \frac{1}{2}\int_{3\pi/4}^{5\pi/4}(1 - \cos 2\theta)\,d\theta + \frac{1}{4}\pi$
$= \frac{1}{2}\left(\theta - \frac{1}{2}\sin 2\theta\right)\Big|_{-\pi/4}^{\pi/4} + \frac{1}{2}\left(\theta - \frac{1}{2}\sin 2\theta\right)\Big|_{3\pi/4}^{5\pi/4} + \frac{1}{2}\pi = \left(\frac{1}{4}\pi - \frac{1}{2}\right) + \left(\frac{\pi}{4} - \frac{1}{2}\right) + \frac{1}{2}\pi = \pi - 1$

28. $f(\theta) = 5(1+\cos\theta),\ g(\theta) = \left\{\begin{array}{ll}2\cos\theta & \text{for } -\pi/2 \le \theta \le \pi/2 \\ 0 & \text{for } \pi/2 \le \theta \le 3\pi/2\end{array}\right\};$

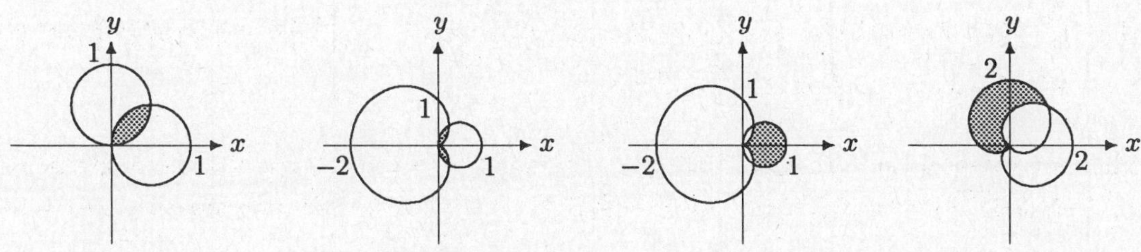

$$A = \int_{-\pi/2}^{\pi/2} \tfrac{1}{2}[25(1+\cos\theta)^2 - (2\cos\theta)^2]\,d\theta + \int_{\pi/2}^{3\pi/2} \tfrac{1}{2}(25)(1+\cos\theta)^2\,d\theta$$

$$= \tfrac{1}{2}\int_{-\pi/2}^{\pi/2}(25 + 50\cos\theta + 21\cos^2\theta)\,d\theta + \tfrac{25}{2}\int_{\pi/2}^{3\pi/2}(1+2\cos\theta+\cos^2\theta)\,d\theta$$

$$= \tfrac{1}{2}\int_{-\pi/2}^{\pi/2}\left(\tfrac{71}{2} + 50\cos\theta + \tfrac{21}{2}\cos 2\theta\right)d\theta + \tfrac{25}{2}\int_{\pi/2}^{3\pi/2}\left(\tfrac{3}{2} + 2\cos\theta + \tfrac{1}{2}\cos 2\theta\right)d\theta$$

$$= \tfrac{1}{2}\left(\tfrac{71}{2}\theta + 50\sin\theta + \tfrac{21}{4}\sin 2\theta\right)\Big|_{-\pi/2}^{\pi/2} + \tfrac{25}{2}\left(\tfrac{3}{2}\theta + 2\sin\theta + \tfrac{1}{4}\sin 2\theta\right)\Big|_{\pi/2}^{3\pi/2}$$

$$= \left(\tfrac{71}{4}\pi + 50\right) + \left(\tfrac{75}{4}\pi - 50\right) = \tfrac{73}{2}\pi$$

29. $f(\theta) = 2 + \cos\theta,\ g(\theta) = \left\{\begin{array}{ll} 0 & \text{for } -\pi/2 \le \theta \le \pi/2 \\ -\cos\theta & \text{for } \pi/2 \le \theta \le 3\pi/2 \end{array}\right\};$

$$A = \int_{\pi/2}^{\pi/2} \tfrac{1}{2}(2+\cos\theta)^2\,d\theta + \int_{\pi/2}^{3\pi/2} \tfrac{1}{2}[(2+\cos\theta)^2 - (-\cos\theta)^2]\,d\theta$$

$$= \tfrac{1}{2}\int_{-\pi/2}^{\pi/2}(4 + 4\cos\theta + \cos^2\theta)\,d\theta + \tfrac{1}{2}\int_{\pi/2}^{3\pi/2}(4 + 4\cos\theta)\,d\theta$$

$$= \tfrac{1}{2}\left(\tfrac{9}{2}\theta + 4\sin\theta + \tfrac{1}{4}\sin 2\theta\right)\Big|_{-\pi/2}^{\pi/2} + \tfrac{1}{2}(4\theta + 4\sin\theta)\Big|_{\pi/2}^{3\pi/2}$$

$$= \left(\tfrac{9}{4}\pi + 4\right) + (2\pi - 4) = \tfrac{17}{4}\pi$$

30. The two circles intersect for (r,θ) such that $r = 0$ or $\cos\theta = r = \sin\theta$, so that $\theta = \pi/4$. Thus $A = \int_0^{\pi/4} \frac{1}{2}\sin^2\theta\,d\theta + \int_{\pi/4}^{\pi/2} \frac{1}{2}\cos^2\theta\,d\theta = \frac{1}{4}\left(\theta - \frac{1}{2}\sin 2\theta\right)\Big|_0^{\pi/4} + \frac{1}{4}\left(\theta + \frac{1}{2}\sin 2\theta\right)\Big|_{\pi/4}^{\pi/2} = \frac{1}{8}\pi - \frac{1}{4}$.

31. The circle and the cardioid intersect for (r,θ) such that $r = 0$ or $\cos\theta = r = 1 - \cos\theta$, so that $\theta = -\pi/3$ or $\theta = \pi/3$. By symmetry we obtain $A = 2\left[\int_0^{\pi/3} \frac{1}{2}(1-\cos\theta)^2\,d\theta + \int_{\pi/3}^{\pi/2} \frac{1}{2}\cos^2\theta\,d\theta\right] = \int_0^{\pi/3}(1 - 2\cos\theta + \cos^2\theta)\,d\theta + \int_{\pi/3}^{\pi/2}\cos^2\theta\,d\theta = \left(\frac{3}{2}\theta - 2\sin\theta + \frac{1}{4}\sin 2\theta\right)\Big|_0^{\pi/3} + \left(\frac{1}{2}\theta + \frac{1}{4}\sin 2\theta\right)\Big|_{\pi/3}^{\pi/2} = \left(\frac{1}{2}\pi - \frac{7}{8}\sqrt{3}\right) + \left(\frac{1}{12}\pi - \frac{1}{8}\sqrt{3}\right) = \frac{7}{12}\pi - \sqrt{3}$.

32. The circle and the cardioid intersect for (r,θ) such that $r = 0$ or $\cos\theta = r = 1 - \cos\theta$, so that $\theta = -\pi/3$ or $\theta = \pi/3$. By symmetry we obtain $A = 2\int_0^{\pi/3} \frac{1}{2}[(\cos\theta)^2 - (1-\cos\theta)^2]\,d\theta = \int_0^{\pi/3}(2\cos\theta - 1)\,d\theta = (2\sin\theta - \theta)\Big|_0^{\pi/3} = \sqrt{3} - \frac{1}{3}\pi$.

33. The two cardioids intersect for (r,θ) such that $r = 0$ or $1 + \cos\theta = r = 1 + \sin\theta$, so that $\cos\theta = \sin\theta$, and thus $\theta = \pi/4$ or $\theta = 5\pi/4$. Thus $A = \int_{\pi/4}^{5\pi/4} \frac{1}{2}[(1+\sin\theta)^2 - (1+\cos\theta)^2]\,d\theta = \frac{1}{2}\int_{\pi/4}^{5\pi/4}(2\sin\theta + \sin^2\theta - 2\cos\theta - \cos^2\theta)\,d\theta = \frac{1}{2}\int_{\pi/4}^{5\pi/4}(2\sin\theta - 2\cos\theta - \cos 2\theta)\,d\theta = \frac{1}{2}\left(-2\cos\theta - 2\sin\theta - \frac{1}{2}\sin 2\theta\right)\Big|_{\pi/4}^{5\pi/4} = 2\sqrt{2}$.

34. The large loop is the graph of $r = 1 + 2\cos\theta$ for $-2\pi/3 \le \theta \le 2\pi/3$, while the small loop is the graph of $r = 1 + 2\cos\theta$ for $2\pi/3 \le \theta \le 4\pi/3$. Thus

$$A = \int_{-2\pi/3}^{2\pi/3} \frac{1}{2}(1 + 2\cos\theta)^2\,d\theta - \int_{2\pi/3}^{4\pi/3} \frac{1}{2}(1 + 2\cos\theta)^2\,d\theta$$

$$= \frac{1}{2}\int_{-2\pi/3}^{2\pi/3} (1 + 4\cos\theta + 4\cos^2\theta)\,d\theta - \frac{1}{2}\int_{2\pi/3}^{4\pi/3} (1 + 4\cos\theta + 4\cos^2\theta)\,d\theta$$

$$= \frac{1}{2}\int_{-2\pi/3}^{2\pi/3} (3 + 4\cos\theta + 2\cos 2\theta)\,d\theta - \frac{1}{2}\int_{2\pi/3}^{4\pi/3} (3 + 4\cos\theta + 2\cos 2\theta)\,d\theta$$

$$= \frac{1}{2}(3\theta + 4\sin\theta + \sin 2\theta)\Big|_{-2\pi/3}^{2\pi/3} - \frac{1}{2}(3\theta + 4\sin\theta + \sin 2\theta)\Big|_{2\pi/3}^{4\pi/3} = \left(2\pi + \frac{3}{2}\sqrt{3}\right) - \left(\pi - \frac{3}{2}\sqrt{3}\right) = \pi + 3\sqrt{3}.$$

35. a. Let $g = cf$. Then $g' = cf'$. By (2) the length of the graph of g is given by

$$L = \int_\alpha^\beta \sqrt{(g'(\theta))^2 + (g(\theta))^2}\,d\theta = \int_\alpha^\beta \sqrt{c^2(f'(\theta))^2 + c^2(f(\theta))^2}\,d\theta$$

$$= c\int_\alpha^\beta \sqrt{(f'(\theta))^2 + (f(\theta))^2}\,d\theta.$$

Thus the length L of the graph of f is also multiplied by c when f is multiplied by c.

b. Let $g = cf$. By (4), the area for g is given by

$$A = \int_\alpha^\beta \frac{1}{2}[g(\theta)]^2\,d\theta = \int_\alpha^\beta \frac{1}{2}c^2[f(\theta)]^2\,d\theta = c^2\int_\alpha^\beta \frac{1}{2}[f(\theta)]^2\,d\theta.$$

Thus the area A is multiplied by c^2 when f is multiplied by c.

36. a. If

$$y^2 = \frac{x^2(1+x)}{1-x}$$

then

$$r^2\sin^2\theta = \frac{r^2\cos^2\theta\,(1 + r\cos\theta)}{1 - r\cos\theta}$$

and for $r \ne 0$ this means that $\sin^2\theta\,(1 - r\cos\theta) = \cos^2\theta\,(1 + r\cos\theta)$, so that $r\cos\theta\,(\cos^2\theta + \sin^2\theta) = \sin^2\theta - \cos^2\theta$, or $r\cos\theta = 1 - 2\cos^2\theta$, or $r = \sec\theta - 2\cos\theta$. Now observe that if $x \ne 0$, then $(1+x)/(1-x) = y^2/x^2 \ge 0$, so that x can assume only the values in $[-1, 1]$, whereas y can assume any value. Since $x = r\cos\theta = 1 - 2\cos^2\theta$ and $y = x\tan\theta$, it follows that all the required values of x and y are assumed if θ assumes the values in $(-\pi/2, \pi/2)$.

b. The loop is the graph of $r = \sec\theta - 2\cos\theta$ for $-\pi/4 \le \theta \le \pi/4$, which has the same area as the region bounded by the graph of $r = 2\cos\theta - \sec\theta$ for $-\pi/4 \le \theta \le \pi/4$. Its area is given by

$$A = \int_{-\pi/4}^{\pi/4} \frac{1}{2}(2\cos\theta - \sec\theta)^2\,d\theta = \frac{1}{2}\int_{-\pi/4}^{\pi/4} (4\cos^2\theta - 4 + \sec^2\theta)\,d\theta$$

$$= \left[2\left(\frac{1}{2}\theta + \frac{1}{4}\sin 2\theta\right) - 2\theta + \frac{1}{2}\tan\theta\right]\Big|_{-\pi/4}^{\pi/4} = 2 - \frac{1}{2}\pi.$$

37. By (12) of Section 10.2 and (1) of this section, we have

$$S = \int_\alpha^\beta 2\pi f(\theta)\sin\theta\sqrt{[f'(\theta)\cos\theta - f(\theta)\sin\theta]^2 + [f'(\theta)\sin\theta + f(\theta)\cos\theta]^2}\,d\theta$$

$$= \int_\alpha^\beta 2\pi f(\theta)\sin\theta\sqrt{(f'(\theta))^2\cos^2\theta + (f(\theta))^2\sin^2\theta + (f'(\theta))^2\sin^2\theta + (f(\theta))^2\cos^2\theta\,d\theta}$$

$$= \int_\alpha^\beta 2\pi f(\theta)\sin\theta\sqrt{(f'(\theta))^2 + (f(\theta))^2}\,d\theta.$$

38. By (6),

$$S = \int_0^\pi 2\pi(1+\cos\theta)\sin\theta\sqrt{(-\sin\theta)^2 + (1+\cos\theta)^2}\,d\theta = \int_0^\pi 2\pi(1+\cos\theta)\sin\theta\sqrt{2+2\cos\theta}\,d\theta$$

$$= 2\sqrt{2}\,\pi\int_0^\pi (1+\cos\theta)^{3/2}\sin\theta\,d\theta = -\frac{4}{5}\sqrt{2}\,\pi(1+\cos\theta)^{5/2}\Big|_0^\pi = \frac{32}{5}\pi.$$

39. By (6),

$$S = \int_0^{\pi/4} 2\pi\sqrt{2\cos 2\theta}\,\sin\theta\sqrt{\left(\frac{-2\sin 2\theta}{\sqrt{2\cos 2\theta}}\right)^2 + (\sqrt{2\cos 2\theta})^2}\,d\theta$$

$$= \int_0^{\pi/4} 2\pi\sin\theta\sqrt{4\sin^2 2\theta + 4\cos^2 2\theta}\,d\theta = 4\pi\int_0^{\pi/4}\sin\theta\,d\theta = -4\pi\cos\theta\Big|_0^{\pi/4} = 2\pi(2-\sqrt{2}).$$

10.5 Conic Sections

1. $c = -2$; $y^2 = -8x$

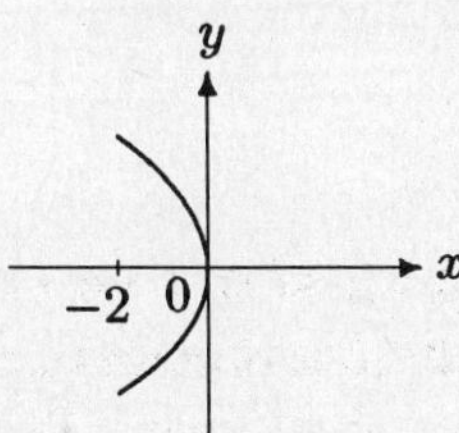

2. $c = -6$; $x^2 = -24y$

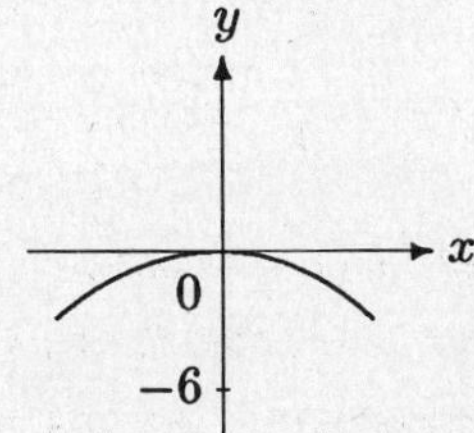

3. $c = 3$; $y^2 = 12(x-1)$

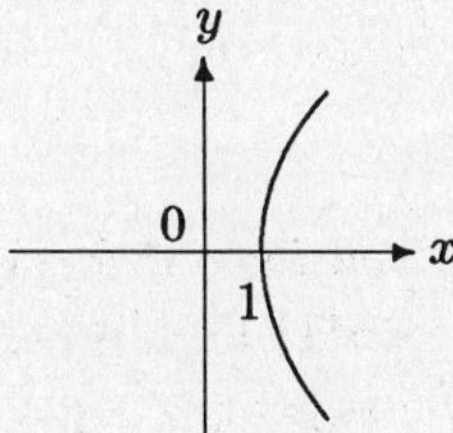

4. $c = 1$; $(x-3)^2 = 4(y-2)$

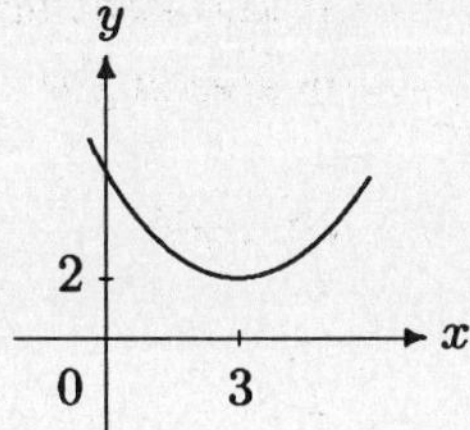

5. $y^2 = 4cx$ and $1^2 = 4c(-1)$, so $c = -\frac{1}{4}$; $y^2 = -x$.

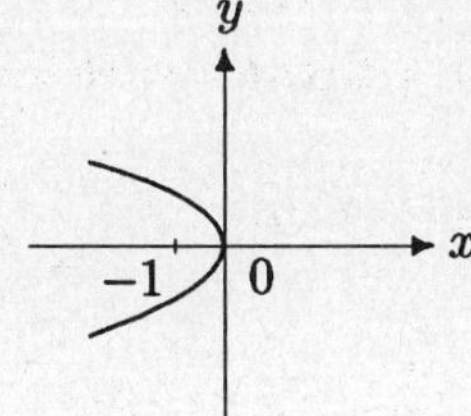

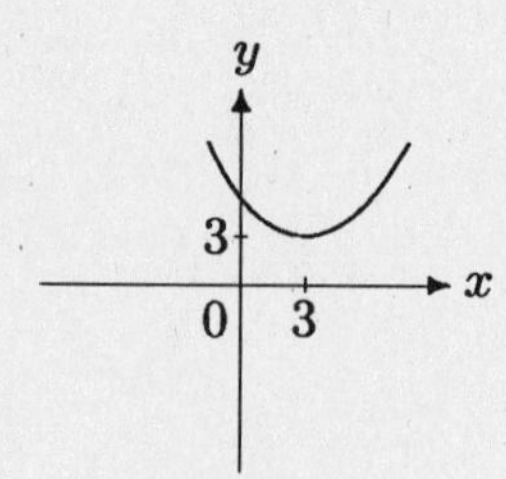

Exercise 6

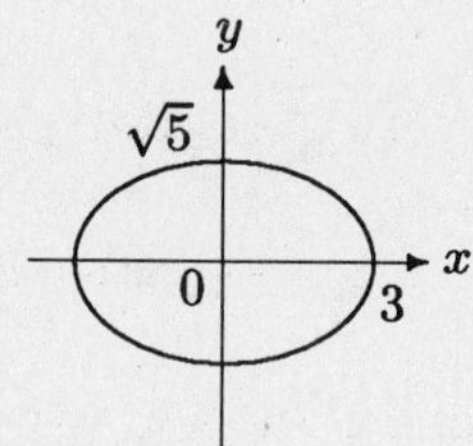

Exercise 7

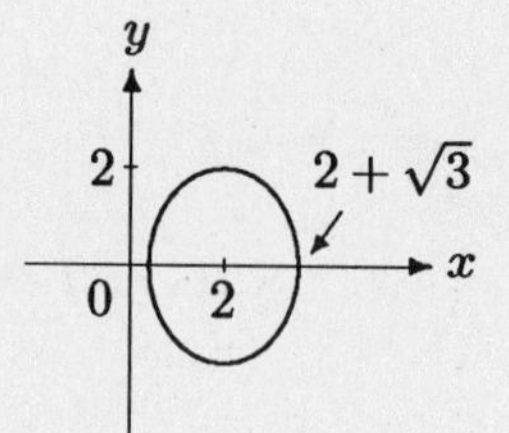

Exercise 8

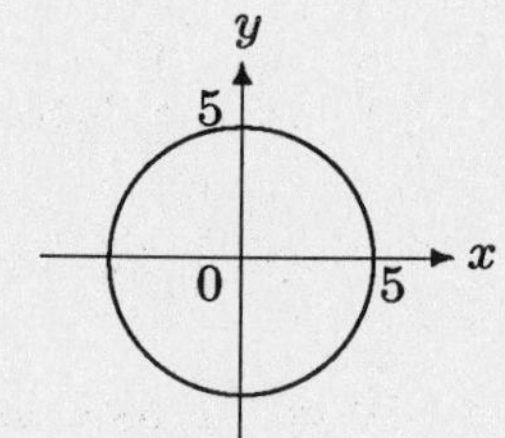

Exercise 9

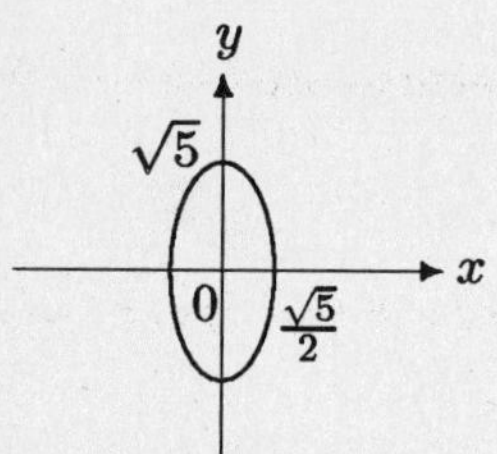

Exercise 10

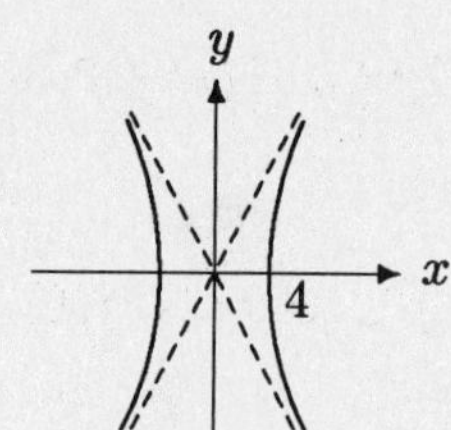

Exercise 11

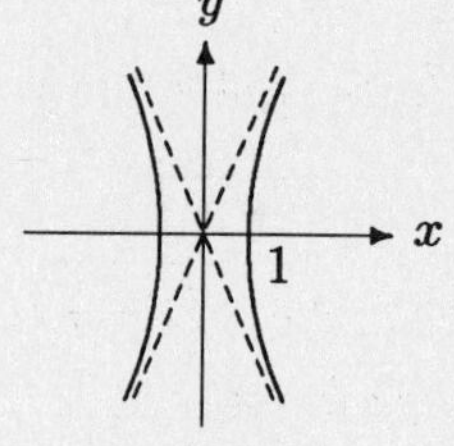

Exercise 12

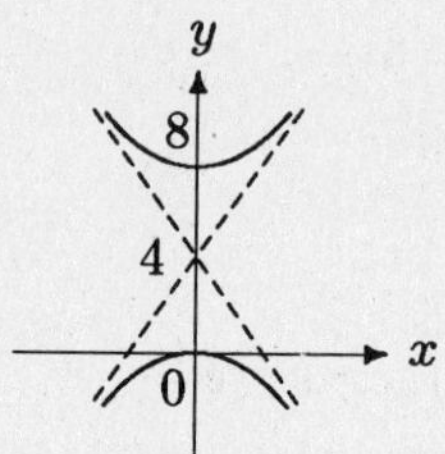

Exercise 13

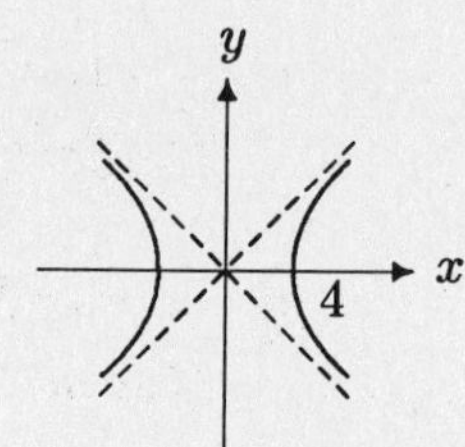

Exercise 14

6. $\sqrt{(x-3)^2+(y-4)^2} = |y-2|$; $(x-3)^2+(y-4)^2 = (y-2)^2$; $(x-3)^2+y^2-8y+16 = y^2-4y+4$; $(x-3)^2 = 4(y-3)$.

7. $a=3$, $c=2$, $b=\sqrt{5}$; $x^2/9+y^2/5=1$

8. center is $(2,0)$, $a=2$, $c=1$, $b=\sqrt{3}$; $(x-2)^2/3+y^2/4=1$

9. $a=5$; $x^2/25+y^2/b^2=1$. Since $(3,-4)$ lies on the ellipse, $\frac{9}{25}+16/b^2=1$, so $16/b^2=\frac{16}{25}$, or $b=5$. An equation of the ellipse is $x^2/25+y^2/25=1$, or $x^2+y^2=25$ (and is actually a circle).

10. Let an equation of the ellipse be $x^2/p^2+y^2/q^2=1$. Since $(-1,1)$ is on the ellipse, $1/p^2+1/q^2=1$. Since $(\frac{1}{2},-2)$ is on the ellipse, $1/4p^2+4/q^2=1$, so that $1/p^2=4-16/q^2$. Then $1-1/q^2=1/p^2=4-16/q^2$, so $3=15/q^2$. Thus $q=\sqrt{5}$, and consequently $p=\sqrt{5}/2$. The equation of the ellipse becomes $4x^2/5+y^2/5=1$.

11. $a=4$, $c=9$, $b=\sqrt{81-16}=\sqrt{65}$; $x^2/16-y^2/65=1$

12. $c=\sqrt{5}$; since $y=\pm 2x$ are the asymptotes, $b/a=2$, or $b=2a$; thus $5=c^2=a^2+(2a)^2=5a^2$, so $a=1$, $b=2$; $x^2-y^2/4=1$

13. The center is $(0,4)$, $c=5$; since $y=\frac{4}{3}x+4$ and $y=-\frac{4}{3}x+4$ are the asymptotes, $a/b=\frac{4}{3}$, or $a=\frac{4}{3}b$; thus $25=(\frac{4}{3}b)^2+b^2=25b^2/9$, so $b=3$, $a=4$; $(y-4)^2/16-x^2/9=1$.

14. $a=4$; since the asymptotes $y=(b/a)x$ and $y=-(b/a)x$ are perpendicular, it follows that

$$\frac{b}{a}=\frac{-1}{-b/a}=\frac{a}{b}$$

so that $a^2=b^2$, or $a=b$. Thus $b=4$, so that $x^2/16-y^2/16=1$.

15. $c = \frac{3}{4}$, focus is $(\frac{3}{4}, 0)$; vertex is $(0, 0)$; directrix is $x = -\frac{3}{4}$; axis is $y = 0$.

16. $c = -\frac{1}{8}$, focus is $(-\frac{1}{8}, 0)$; vertex is $(0, 0)$; directrix is $x = \frac{1}{8}$; axis is $y = 0$.

17. $c = \frac{1}{4}$, focus is $(1, -\frac{7}{4})$; vertex is $(1, -2)$; directrix is $y = -\frac{9}{4}$; axis is $x = 1$.

18. $c = 1$, focus is $(\frac{7}{4}, -3)$; vertex is $(\frac{3}{4}, -3)$; directrix is $x = -\frac{1}{4}$; axis is $y = -3$.

19. $a = 5$, $b = 3$, $c = \sqrt{25 - 9} = 4$; foci are $(0, -4)$ and $(0, 4)$; vertices are $(0, -5)$ and $(0, 5)$.

20. $a = 1/\sqrt{3}$, $b = \frac{1}{2}$, $c = \sqrt{\frac{1}{3} - \frac{1}{4}} = 1/\sqrt{12}$; foci are $(-1/\sqrt{12}, 0)$ and $(1/\sqrt{12}, 0)$; vertices are $(-1/\sqrt{3}, 0)$ and $(1/\sqrt{3}, 0)$.

21. $(x - 1)^2/\frac{1}{4} + y^2/1 = 1$; $a = 1$, $b = \frac{1}{2}$, $c = \sqrt{1 - \frac{1}{4}} = \sqrt{3}/2$; center is $(1, 0)$; foci are $(1, -\sqrt{3}/2)$ and $(1, \sqrt{3}/2)$; vertices are $(1, -1)$ and $(1, 1)$.

22. $(x + 1)^2/\frac{1}{25} + (y - 3)^2/1 = 1$; $a = 1$, $b = \frac{1}{5}$, $c = \sqrt{1 - \frac{1}{25}} = 2\sqrt{6}/5$; center is $(-1, 3)$; foci are $(-1, 3 - 2\sqrt{6}/5)$ and $(-1, 3 + 2\sqrt{6}/5)$; vertices are $(-1, 2)$ and $(-1, 4)$.

23. $a = 3$, $b = 4$, $c = 5$; foci are $(-5, 0)$ and $(5, 0)$; vertices are $(-3, 0)$ and $(3, 0)$; asymptotes are $y = \frac{4}{3}x$ and $y = -\frac{4}{3}x$.

24. $a = 1/\sqrt{5}$, $b = 2$, $c = \sqrt{\frac{21}{5}}$; foci are $(0, -\sqrt{\frac{21}{5}})$ and $(0, \sqrt{\frac{21}{5}})$; vertices are $(0, -1/\sqrt{5})$ and $(0, 1/\sqrt{5})$; asymptotes are $y = x/2\sqrt{5}$ and $y = -x/2\sqrt{5}$.

25. center is $(-3, -1)$; $a = 5$, $b = 12$, $c = \sqrt{25 + 144} = 13$; foci are $(-16, -1)$ and $(10, -1)$; vertices are $(-8, -1)$ and $(2, -1)$; asymptotes are $y + 1 = \frac{12}{5}(x + 3)$ and $y + 1 = -\frac{12}{5}(x + 3)$.

26. center is $(-2, 2)$; $a = 11 = b$, $c = \sqrt{121 + 121} = 11\sqrt{2}$; foci are $(-2, 2 - 11\sqrt{2})$ and $(-2, 2 + 11\sqrt{2})$; vertices are $(-2, -9)$ and $(-2, 13)$; asymptotes are $y - 2 = x + 2$ and $y - 2 = -x - 2$.

27. $0 = x^2 - 6x - 2y + 1 = (x^2 - 6x + 9) - 2y + 1 - 9 = (x - 3)^2 - 2(y + 4)$; $X = x - 3$, $Y = y + 4$; $X^2 = 2Y$; parabola with vertex $(3, -4)$, focus $(3, -\frac{7}{2})$, directrix $y = -\frac{9}{2}$.

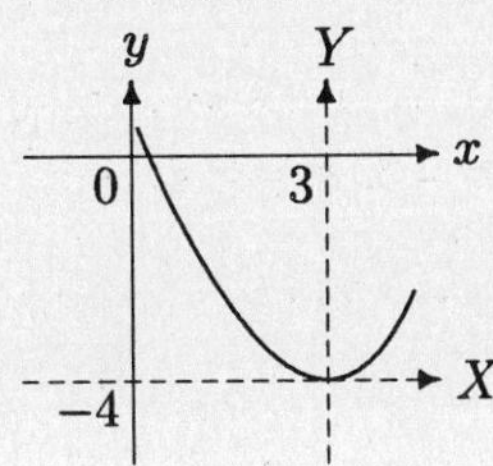

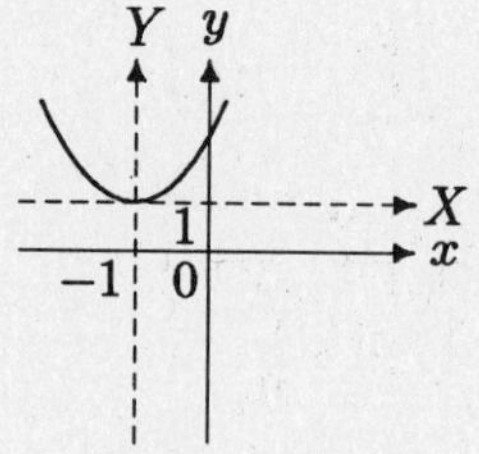

Exercise 28

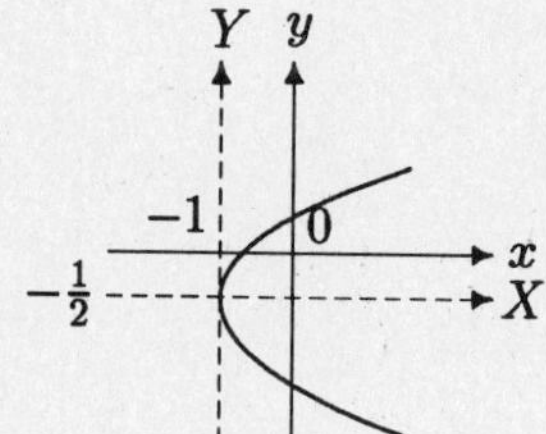

Exercise 29

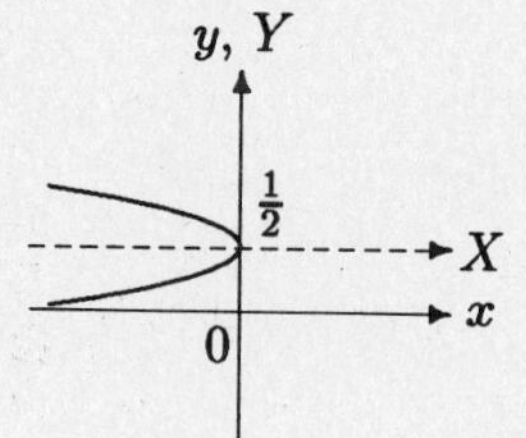

Exercise 30

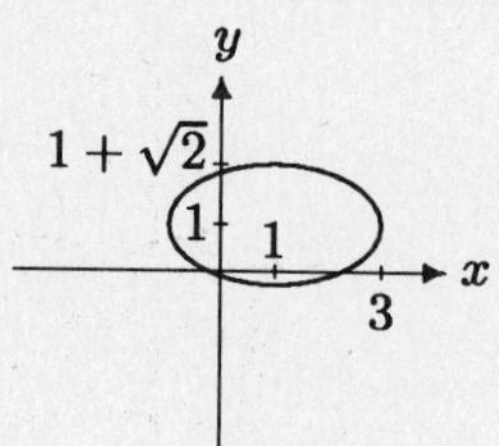

Exercise 31

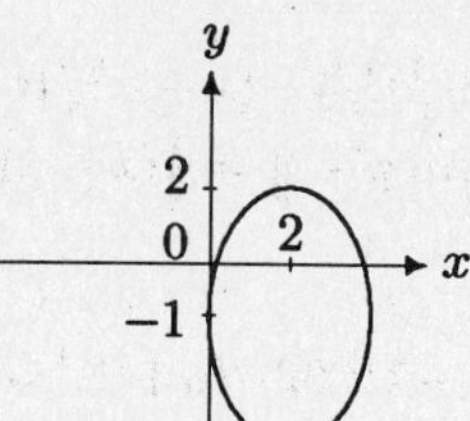

Exercise 32

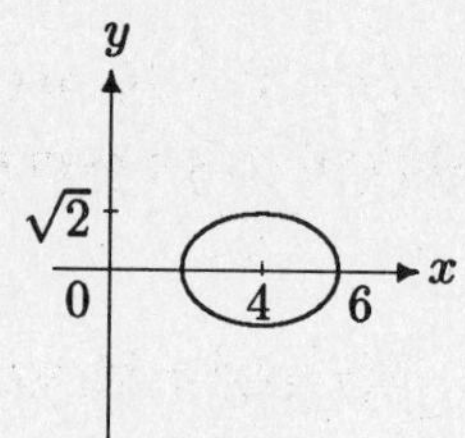

Exercise 33

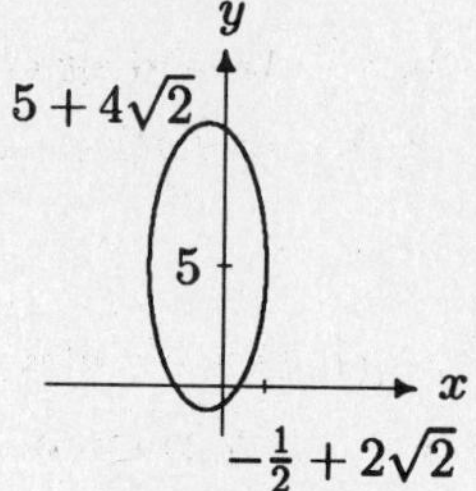

Exercise 34

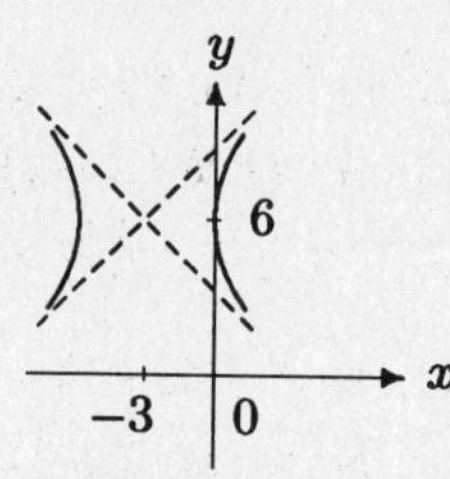

Exercise 35

28. $0 = 2x^2+4x-5y+7 = (2x^2+4x+2)-5y+7-2 = 2(x+1)^2-5(y-1)$; $X = x+1$, $Y = y-1$; $5Y = 2X^2$, or $X^2 = \frac{5}{2}Y$; parabola with vertex $(-1,1)$, focus $(-1,\frac{13}{8})$, directrix $y = \frac{3}{8}$.

29. $0 = 3y^2-5x+3y-\frac{17}{4} = (3y^2+3y+\frac{3}{4})-5x-\frac{17}{4}-\frac{3}{4} = 3(y+\frac{1}{2})^2-5(x+1)$; $X = x+1$, $Y = y+\frac{1}{2}$; $3Y^2 = 5X$, or $Y^2 = \frac{5}{3}X$; parabola with vertex $(-1,-\frac{1}{2})$, focus $(-\frac{7}{12},-\frac{1}{2})$, directrix $x = -\frac{17}{12}$.

30. $1 = -4y^2-x/2+4y = (-4y^2+4y-1)-x/2+1$, so that $x/2 = -4(y-\frac{1}{2})^2$; $X = x$, $Y = y-\frac{1}{2}$; $X = -8Y^2$, or $Y^2 = -\frac{1}{8}X$; parabola with vertex $(0,\frac{1}{2})$, focus $(-\frac{1}{2},\frac{1}{2})$, directrix $x = \frac{1}{2}$.

31. $x^2-2x+1+2(y^2-2y+1) = 4$, or $(x-1)^2+2(y-1)^2 = 4$, so that $(x-1)^2/4+(y-1)^2/2 = 1$; $a = 2$, $b = \sqrt{2}$, $c = \sqrt{4-2} = \sqrt{2}$; center is $(1,1)$; foci are $(1-\sqrt{2},1)$ and $(1+\sqrt{2},1)$; vertices are $(-1,1)$ and $(3,1)$.

32. $9(x^2-4x+4)+4(y^2+2y+1) = 36$, or $9(x-2)^2+4(y+1)^2 = 36$, so that $(x-2)^2/4+(y+1)^2/9 = 1$; $a = 3$, $b = 2$, $c = \sqrt{9-4} = \sqrt{5}$; center is $(2,-1)$, foci are $(2,-1-\sqrt{5})$ and $(2,-1+\sqrt{5})$; vertices are $(2,-4)$ and $(2,2)$.

33. $(x^2-8x+16)+2y^2 = -12+16 = 4$, or $(x-4)^2+2y^2 = 4$, so that $(x-4)^2/4+y^2/2 = 1$; $a = 2$, $b = \sqrt{2}$, $c = \sqrt{4-2} = \sqrt{2}$; center is $(4,0)$; foci are $(4-\sqrt{2},0)$ and $(4+\sqrt{2},0)$; vertices are $(2,0)$ and $(6,0)$.

34. $8(x^2+x+\frac{1}{4})+2(y^2-10y+25) = 12+2+50 = 64$, or $8(x+\frac{1}{2})^2+2(y-5)^2 = 64$, so that $(x+\frac{1}{2})^2/8+(y-5)^2/32 = 1$; $a = 4\sqrt{2}$, $b = 2\sqrt{2}$, $c = \sqrt{32-8} = 2\sqrt{6}$; center is $(-\frac{1}{2},5)$; foci are $(-\frac{1}{2},5-2\sqrt{6})$ and $(-\frac{1}{2},5+2\sqrt{6})$; vertices are $(-\frac{1}{2},5-4\sqrt{2})$ and $(-\frac{1}{2},5+4\sqrt{2})$.

35. $(x^2+6x+9)-(y^2-12y+36) = 9$, or $(x+3)^2-(y-6)^2 = 9$, so that $(x+3)^2/9-(y-6)^2/9 = 1$; $a = 3 = b$; center is $(-3,6)$; vertices are $(-6,6)$ and $(0,6)$; asymptotes are $y-6 = x+3$ and $y-6 = -(x+3)$.

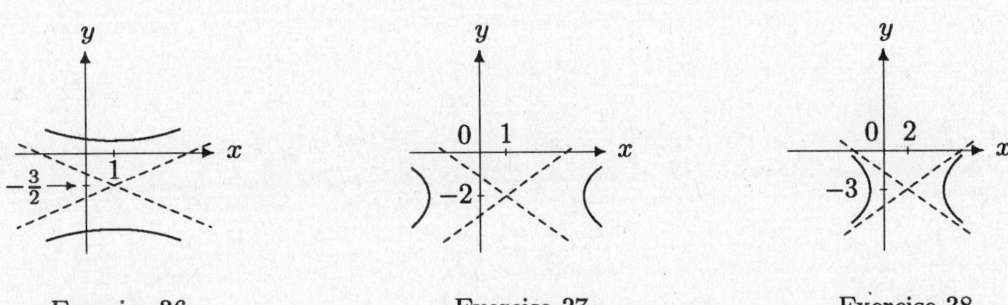

Exercise 36 Exercise 37 Exercise 38

36. $(x^2-2x+1)-4(y^2+3y+\frac{9}{4}) = -16$, or $4(y+\frac{3}{2})^2-(x-1)^2 = 16$, so that $(y+\frac{3}{2})^2/4-(x-1)^2/16 = 1$; center is $(1, -\frac{3}{2})$; $a = 2$, $b = 4$; vertices are $(1, -\frac{7}{2})$ and $(1, \frac{1}{2})$; asymptotes are $y + \frac{3}{2} = \frac{1}{2}(x-1)$ and $y + \frac{3}{2} = -\frac{1}{2}(x-1)$.

37. $4(x^2-2x+1)-9(y^2+4y+4) = 36$, or $4(x-1)^2-9(y+2)^2 = 36$, so that $(x-1)^2/9-(y+2)^2/4 = 1$; center is $(1, -2)$; $a = 3$, $b = 2$; vertices are $(-2, -2)$ and $(4, -2)$; asymptotes are $y+2 = \frac{2}{3}(x-1)$ and $y+2 = -\frac{2}{3}(x-1)$.

38. $4(x^2-4x+4)-9(y^2+6y+9) = 36$, or $4(x-2)^2-9(y+3)^2 = 36$, so that $(x-2)^2/9-(y+3)^2/4 = 1$; center is $(2, -3)$; $a = 3$, $b = 2$; vertices are $(-1, -3)$ and $(5, -3)$; asymptotes are $y+3 = \frac{2}{3}(x-2)$ and $y+3 = -\frac{2}{3}(x-2)$.

39. Since the parabola has vertex $(-1, 3)$ and a vertical axis, an equation of the parabola has the form $(x+1)^2 = 4c(y-3)$, for an appropriate nonzero constant c. Differentiating implicitly with respect to x, we obtain $2(x+1) = 4c(dy/dx)$. Since the parabola has slope 2 at $x = 1$, it follows that $2(1+1) = (4c)2$, so that $c = \frac{1}{2}$. Therefore the parabola is given by $(x+1)^2 = 4(\frac{1}{2})(y-3) = 2(y-3)$.

40. Since $y^2 = 4x$ for any point (x, y) on the parabola, the distance from (x, y) to $(1, 0)$ is $\sqrt{(x-1)^2+y^2} = \sqrt{(x-1)^2+4x}$. The distance is minimized for the same nonnegative value of x that the square of the distance is, so let $f(x) = (x-1)^2+4x$ for $x \geq 0$. Then $f'(x) = 2(x-1)+4 > 0$ for all $x \geq 0$. Thus $f(0)$ is the minimum value of f, so that $(0, 0)$ is the closest point to $(1, 0)$.

41. If the parabola has the form $x^2 = 4cy$ with $c > 0$, then the focus is $(0, c)$ and the endpoints of the latus rectum are $(2c, c)$ and $(-2c, c)$, and its length is $4c$. If $y^2 = 4cx$ with $c > 0$, then the endpoints of the latus rectum are $(c, 2c)$ and $(c, -2c)$, and its length is again $4c$.

42. The slope of the line $x + y = d$ is -1, and the slope of the parabola $x^2 = 2y$, or $y = x^2/2$, at $(x, x^2/2)$ is x. Thus if the line is tangential to the parabola, then $x = -1$, and $y = (-1)^2/2 = \frac{1}{2}$. Therefore $d = x+y = -1+\frac{1}{2} = -\frac{1}{2}$, and the point of tangency is $(-1, \frac{1}{2})$.

43. The slope of a line tangent to the parabola at a point $(a, a^2/2)$ is a, so an equation of the tangent line is $y - a^2/2 = a(x-a)$. If $(-1, -4)$ is on this line, then $-4-a^2/2 = a(-1-a)$, so that $a^2+2a-8 = 0$, and thus $a = -4$ or $a = 2$. Equations of the two lines tangent to the parabola are $y - 8 = -4(x+4)$ and $y - 2 = 2(x-2)$.

44. Since the ellipse is in standard position, it has an equation of the form $x^2/a^2+y^2/b^2=1$, for appropriate constants $a>0$ and $b>0$. Since the ellipse passes through $(0,2)$, it follows that $2^2/b^2=1$, so $b=2$. Thus $x^2/a^2+y^2/4=1$. By implicit differentiation, we obtain

$$\frac{2x}{a^2}+\frac{2y}{4}\frac{dy}{dx}=0, \quad \text{or} \quad \frac{y}{2}\frac{dy}{dx}=-\frac{2x}{a^2}.$$

By hypothesis, if $x=-2$ and $y>0$, then $dy/dx=1/\sqrt{2}$, so that $(y/2)(1/\sqrt{2})=-2(-2)/a^2$ and thus $y=8\sqrt{2}/a^2$. Then $x^2/a^2+y^2/b^2=1$ becomes

$$\frac{(-2)^2}{a^2}+\frac{(8\sqrt{2}/a^2)^2}{4}=1, \quad \text{or} \quad \frac{4}{a^2}+\frac{32}{a^4}=1.$$

It follows that $4a^2+32=a^4$, that is, $0=a^4-4a^2-32=(a^2-8)(a^2+4)$. Since $a>0$, this means that $a=2\sqrt{2}$. Consequently an equation of the ellipse is $x^2/8+y^2/4=1$.

45. Differentiating the equation $4x^2+y^2=8$ implicitly, we obtain $8x+2y(dy/dx)=0$, so that at (x_0,y_0), we have $dy/dx=-4x_0/y_0$. An equation of the line tangent at (x_0,y_0) is $y-y_0=(-4x_0/y_0)(x-x_0)$. This will be the line $2x+y=d$ if $2=4x_0/y_0$ and $d=y_0+4x_0^2/y_0$. Then $y_0=2x_0$. Since (x_0,y_0) is on the ellipse, $4x_0^2+(2x_0)^2=8$, so that $x_0=\pm 1$ and $y_0=\pm 2$. Then $d=4$ or $d=-4$, and the points of tangency are $(1,2)$ and $(-1,-2)$.

46. The slope of the line $2y-x=d$ is $\frac{1}{2}$. Differentiating the equation of the hyperbola implicitly, we obtain $12y(dy/dx)-6x=0$, so that $dy/dx=x/2y$. At (x_0,y_0) on the hyperbola, $dy/dx=x_0/(2y_0)$. If the given line is tangent to the hyperbola at (x_0,y_0), then $\frac{1}{2}=x_0/(2y_0)$, which means that $y_0=x_0$. Since (x_0,y_0) is on the hyperbola, we have $9=6x_0^2-3x_0^2=3x_0^2$, so that $x_0=\pm\sqrt{3}=y_0$. Then $d=2\sqrt{3}-\sqrt{3}=\sqrt{3}$ or $d=-2\sqrt{3}+\sqrt{3}=-\sqrt{3}$.

47. Let (x,y) be a point in the collection. Then $\sqrt{(x-3)^2+y^2}=\frac{1}{2}\sqrt{(x+3)^2+(y-y)^2}$, or $(x-3)^2+y^2=\frac{1}{4}(x+3)^2$. The equation becomes $3x^2-30x+27+4y^2=0$, or $3(x-5)^2+4y^2=48$, or $(x-5)^2/16+y^2/12=1$.

48. Let (x,y) be a point in the collection. Then $\sqrt{(x-3)^2+y^2}=2|x+3|$. Thus $(x-3)^2+y^2=4(x+3)^2$, or $3x^2+30x-y^2=-27$, so that $3(x^2+10x+25)-y^2=48$, or $(x+5)^2/16-y^2/48=1$. This is an equation of a hyperbola.

49. Let (x,y) be the vertex of the rectangle in the first quadrant, so that $y=b\sqrt{1-x^2/a^2}$. The area A of the rectangle is given by $A=4xy=4bx\sqrt{1-x^2/a^2}$, and

$$\frac{dA}{dx}=4b\sqrt{1-\frac{x^2}{a^2}}-\frac{4bx^2}{a^2}\left(1-\frac{x^2}{a^2}\right)^{-1/2}=\left(4b-\frac{8bx^2}{a^2}\right)\left(1-\frac{x^2}{a^2}\right)^{-1/2}.$$

Now $dA/dx=0$ for $4b-8bx^2/a^2=0$, or $x=(\sqrt{2}/2)a$, and $dA/dx>0$ if $0<x<a\sqrt{2}/2$, and $dA/dx<0$ if $a\sqrt{2}/2<x<a$. By (1) of Section 4.6 and the First Derivative Test, A is maximum if $x=a\sqrt{2}/2$. The vertices of the rectangle are $(\pm a\sqrt{2}/2, \pm b\sqrt{2}/2)$.

50. $0 = Ax^2 + Cy^2 + Dx + Ey + F = A\left(x^2 + \frac{D}{A}x + \frac{D^2}{4A^2}\right) + C\left(y^2 + \frac{E}{C}y + \frac{E^2}{4C^2}\right) + F - \frac{D^2}{4A} - \frac{E^2}{4C}$

$$= A\left(x + \frac{D}{2A}\right)^2 + C\left(y + \frac{E}{2C}\right)^2 - r, \quad \text{or} \quad A\left(x + \frac{D}{2A}\right)^2 + C\left(y + \frac{E}{2C}\right)^2 = r$$

a. If $r > 0$, then the equation describes an ellipse, since $AC > 0$.

b. If $r = 0$, then $A(x + D/2A)^2 + C(y + E/2C)^2 = 0$, and the graph is the point $(-D/2A, -E/2C)$.

c. If $r < 0$, then the graph consists of no points.

51. $0 = Ax^2 + Cy^2 + Dx + Ey + F = A\left(x^2 + \frac{D}{A}x + \frac{D^2}{4A^2}\right) + C\left(y^2 + \frac{E}{C}y + \frac{E^2}{4C^2}\right) + F - \frac{D^2}{4A} - \frac{E^2}{4C}$

$$= A\left(x + \frac{D}{2A}\right)^2 + C\left(y + \frac{E}{2C}\right)^2 - r, \quad \text{so that} \quad A\left(x + \frac{D}{2A}\right)^2 + C\left(y + \frac{E}{2C}\right)^2 = r.$$

a. If $r \neq 0$, then the graph of the equation is a hyperbola, since $AC < 0$.

b. If $r = 0$, then $(y + E/2C)^2 = -(A/C)(x + D/2A)^2$, which defines the two intersecting lines $y + E/2C = \pm\sqrt{-A/C}\,(x + D/2A)$.

52. Differentiating the equation $x^2/a^2 + y^2/b^2 = 1$ implicitly, we obtain $2x/a^2 + (2y/b^2)(dy/dx) = 0$, so that $dy/dx = -b^2x/(a^2y)$. At (x_0, y_0) we have $dy/dx = -b^2x_0/(a^2y_0)$. An equation of the tangent line is $y - y_0 = [-b^2x_0/(a^2y_0)](x - x_0)$. Multiplying both sides of this equation by y_0/b^2, we obtain

$$\frac{yy_0}{b^2} - \frac{y_0^2}{b^2} = -\frac{xx_0}{a^2} + \frac{x_0^2}{a^2}, \quad \text{and thus} \quad \frac{xx_0}{a^2} + \frac{yy_0}{b^2} = \frac{x_0^2}{a^2} + \frac{y_0^2}{b^2} = 1.$$

53. Differentiating the equation $x^2/a^2 - y^2/b^2 = 1$ implicitly, we obtain $2x/a^2 - (2y/b^2)(dy/dx) = 0$, so that $dy/dx = b^2x/(a^2y)$. At (x_0, y_0) we have $dy/dx = b^2x_0/(a^2y_0)$. An equation of the tangent line is $y - y_0 = [b^2x_0/(a^2y_0)](x - x_0)$. Multiplying both sides of this equation by y_0/b^2, we obtain

$$\frac{yy_0}{b^2} - \frac{y_0^2}{b^2} = \frac{xx_0}{a^2} - \frac{x_0^2}{a^2}, \quad \text{and thus} \quad \frac{xx_0}{a^2} - \frac{yy_0}{b^2} = \frac{x_0^2}{a^2} - \frac{y_0^2}{b^2} = 1.$$

54. Assume than an equation of the hyperbola is $x^2/a^2 - y^2/b^2 = 1$. Then the asymptotes are $y = (b/a)x$ and $y = -(b/a)x$. Any line parallel to but distinct from the line $y = (b/a)x$ has an equation of the form $y = (b/a)x + d$, where $d \neq 0$. If this line and the hyperbola intersect at (x, y), then

$$\frac{x^2}{a^2} - \frac{\left((b/a)x + d\right)^2}{b^2} = 1$$

so that $-(2dx/(ab)) - d^2/b^2 = 1$, or $x = -[a(b^2 + d^2)/(2bd)]$. Thus

$$y = \frac{b}{a}\left[-\frac{a(b^2 + d^2)}{2bd}\right] + d = d - \frac{b^2 + d^2}{2d}.$$

Thus the line intersects the hyperbola exactly once. Similar considerations apply to lines parallel to the other asymptote.

55. Let an equation of the ellipse be $x^2/a^2 + y^2/b^2 = 1$, and let $c = \sqrt{a^2 - b^2}$. The slope dy/dx of a line tangent to the ellipse is given by

$$\frac{2x}{a^2} + \frac{2y}{b^2}\frac{dy}{dx} = 0, \quad \text{or} \quad \frac{dy}{dx} = -\frac{2x}{a^2}\frac{b^2}{2y} = -\frac{b^2 x}{a^2 y}.$$

If the ray of light from $(c, 0)$ strikes the ellipse at (x_0, y_0), then the slope m_1 of the line from $(c, 0)$ to (x_0, y_0) is given by $m_1 = (y_0 - 0)/(x_0 - c) = y_0/(x_0 - c)$. Since $b^2x_0^2 + a^2y_0^2 = 1$, the tangent of the angle θ_1 from the tangent line to the ray is given by

$$\tan\theta_1 = \frac{m_1 - \dfrac{dy}{dx}}{1 + m_1\dfrac{dy}{dx}} = \frac{\dfrac{y_0}{x_0 - c} + \dfrac{b^2x_0}{a^2y_0}}{1 + \left(\dfrac{y_0}{x_0 - c}\right)\left(-\dfrac{b^2x_0}{a^2y_0}\right)}$$

$$= \frac{a^2y_0^2 + b^2x_0^2 - cb^2x_0}{a^2x_0y_0 - a^2cy_0 - b^2x_0y_0} = \frac{a^2b^2 - cb^2x_0}{c^2x_0y_0 - a^2cy_0} = -\frac{b^2}{cy_0}.$$

The slope m_2 of the line from $(-c, 0)$ to (x_0, y_0) is given by $m_2 = (y_0 - 0)/(x_0 + c) = y_0/(x_0 + c)$. The tangent of the angle θ_2 from that line to the tangent line is given by

$$\tan\theta_2 = \frac{\dfrac{dy}{dx} - m_2}{1 + \dfrac{dy}{dx}m_2} = \frac{-\dfrac{b^2x_0}{a^2y_0} - \dfrac{y_0}{x_0 + c}}{1 + \left(\dfrac{-b^2x_0}{a^2y_0}\right)\left(\dfrac{y_0}{x_0 + c}\right)}$$

$$= \frac{-b^2x_0^2 - b^2cx_0 - a^2y_0^2}{a^2x_0y_0 + a^2cy_0 - b^2x_0y_0} = \frac{-a^2b^2 - b^2cx_0}{c^2x_0y_0 + a^2cy_0} = \frac{-b^2}{cy_0}.$$

Since $\tan\theta_1 = \tan\theta_2$, we have $\theta_1 = \theta_2$, so that the reflected line passes through the second focus, $(-c, 0)$.

56. The path is symmetric about the vertical line which passes through its highest point, which is located at $(300, 200)$. Thus an equation of the parabola is $(x - 300)^2 = 4c(y - 200)$, where c is such that $(0, 0)$ lies on the parabola (as does (600,0)). Thus $(-300)^2 = 4c(-200)$, so that $c = 90{,}000/(-800) = -225/2$. The equation of the parabola becomes $(x - 300)^2 = -450(y - 200)$.

57. Since $a = 228$, $b = 227$, the lengths of the major and minor axes are 456 and 454, respectively, so the ratio is $\frac{456}{454} = \frac{228}{227}$.

58. $a \approx .1425$ and $b \approx .1205$, so that $c \approx \sqrt{(.1425)^2 - (.1205)^2} \approx .076066$. Then the distance from a vertex to the closest focus is approximately $.1425 - .076066 = .066434$ (miles).

59. Suppose Marian is at $(4400, 0)$ and Jack is at $(-4400, 0)$, which means that the distance between them is 8800. Let (x, y) be the point at which the lightning strikes. Then the distance the sound must travel to reach Jack is $\sqrt{(x + 4400)^2 + y^2}$, and the distance the sound must travel to reach Marian is $\sqrt{(x - 4400)^2 + y^2}$. Since sound travels at 1100 feet per second and since Marian hears the thunder 4 seconds before Jack by hypothesis, $x > 0$ and $\sqrt{(x + 4400)^2 + y^2} - \sqrt{(x - 4400)^2 + y^2} = 4 \cdot 1100 = 4400$.

By Definition 10.3 the collection of (x, y) satisfying this equation lies on a hyperbola. By our analysis of hyperbolas, along with the information in (13), the equation becomes

$$\frac{x^2}{a^2} - \frac{y^2}{b^2} = 1,$$

where $a = 2200$, $c = 4400$, and $b = 2200\sqrt{3}$, and where $x > 0$. Thus an equation for the location of the lightning is

$$\frac{x^2}{(2200)^2} - \frac{y^2}{3(2200)^2} = 1, \quad \text{for } x \geq 2200.$$

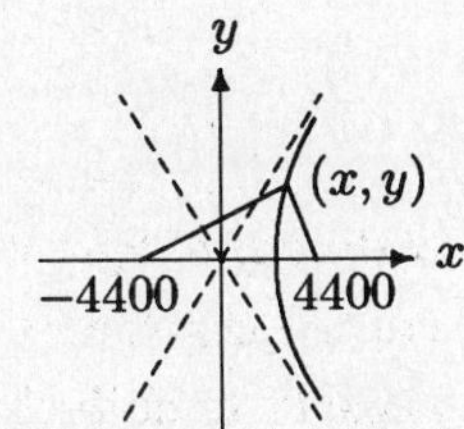

60. If Marian is at (4400, 0), Jack at (−4400, 0), and Bruce midway between Marian and Jack, we find that Bruce is at the origin. Since Bruce hears the thunder 1 second after Marian does, if (x, y) represents the point at which the lightning strikes, then

$$\sqrt{x^2 + y^2} - \sqrt{(x - 4400)^2 + y^2} = 1100$$

and this represents the equation $(x - 2200)^2/a^2 - y^2/b^2 = 1$, with $x > 2200$, and $a = \frac{1100}{2} = 550$. Since Marian and Bruce are at the foci, 4400 feet apart, $2c = 4400$, so that $c = 2200$. Thus $b = \sqrt{c^2 - a^2} = \sqrt{(2200)^2 - (550)^2} = 550\sqrt{15}$. Therefore the equation of the hyperbola becomes

$$\frac{(x - 2200)^2}{(550)^2} - \frac{y^2}{15(550)^2} = 1.$$

From the result of Exercise 59, along with the above equation, Marian hears the thunder 4 seconds before Jack and 1 second before Bruce only if the lightning strikes a point (x, y) satisfying

$$\frac{x^2}{(2200)^2} - \frac{y^2}{3(2200)^2} = 1 \quad \text{and} \quad \frac{(x - 2200)^2}{(550)^2} - \frac{y^2}{15(550)^2} = 1.$$

Solving for y^2 in the first equation yields $y^2 = 15(x - 2200)^2 - 15(550)^2$, and substituting in the first equation yields

$$\frac{x^2}{(2200)^2} - \frac{15(x - 2200)^2 - 15(550)^2}{3(2200)^2} = 1.$$

This equation reduces to $4x^2 - 5(4400)x + 9(550)^2 = 0$, so by the quadratic formula,

$$x = \frac{5500 \pm \sqrt{25(16)(275)^2 - 4(91)(275)^2}}{2} = 3575 \quad \text{or} \quad 1925.$$

Since x must be greater than 2200, it follows that $x = 3575$, and thus $y^2 = 15(3575 - 2200)^2 - 15(550)^2$, so that $y = \pm 825\sqrt{35}$. Consequently lightning strikes at $(3575, 825\sqrt{35})$ or at $(3575, -825\sqrt{35})$.

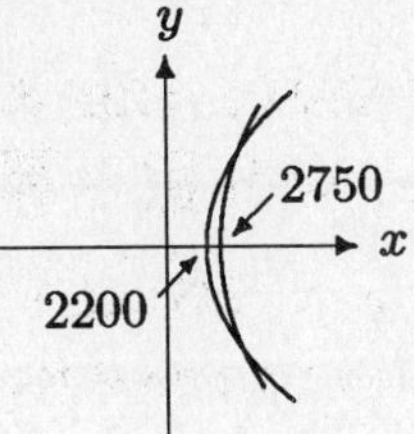

61. Let the vertex be (0, 0) and let the y axis be the axis of the parabola. Then an equation of the parabola is $x^2 = 4cy$, and by assumption, $(a/2, b)$ lies on the parabola. Thus $a^2/4 = 4cb$, so that $c = a^2/16b$, so that the equation becomes $x^2 = 4(a^2/16b)y = (a^2/4b)y$.

62. By Exercise 61 an equation of the parabola is $x^2 = (a^2/4b)y$. If $a = 3500$ and $b = 316$, then $x^2 = [(3500)^2/4(316)]y = (765{,}625/79)y$.

63. Let an equation of the cable be $x^2 = 4cy$. By hypothesis the cable makes an angle of $\pi/6$ with the support on the right, and hence an angle of $\pi/3$ with the ground. At that point $x/2c = dy/dx = \sqrt{3}$. The support lies on the line $x = \frac{1}{4}$, so that $\frac{1}{4}/2c = \sqrt{3}$, or $c = \sqrt{3}/24$, and thus $x^2 = 4(\sqrt{3}/24)y = (\sqrt{3}/6)y$. If the sag is b, then $(\frac{1}{4}, b)$ is on the parabola, so that $(\frac{1}{4})^2 = (\sqrt{3}/6)b$, or $b = \sqrt{3}/8 \approx 0.2165$ (miles).

10.6 Rotation of Axes

1. $A = 0 = C$, so $\theta = \pi/4$; the equation becomes

$$\left(\frac{\sqrt{2}}{2}X - \frac{\sqrt{2}}{2}Y\right)\left(\frac{\sqrt{2}}{2}X + \frac{\sqrt{2}}{2}Y\right) = -4 \quad \text{or} \quad \frac{Y^2}{8} - \frac{X^2}{8} = 1.$$

The conic section is a hyperbola.

2. $A = 1$, $B = \sqrt{3}$, $C = 0$; $\tan 2\theta = \sqrt{3}/(1-0) = \sqrt{3}$, so $\theta = \pi/6$; the equation becomes

$$\left(\frac{\sqrt{3}}{2}X - \frac{1}{2}Y\right)^2 + \sqrt{3}\left(\frac{\sqrt{3}}{2}X - \frac{1}{2}Y\right)\left(\frac{1}{2}X + \frac{\sqrt{3}}{2}Y\right) = 3, \quad \text{or} \quad \frac{X^2}{2} - \frac{Y^2}{6} = 1.$$

The conic section is a hyperbola.

3. $A = 1 = C$, so $\theta = \pi/4$; the equation becomes

$$\left(\frac{\sqrt{2}}{2}X - \frac{\sqrt{2}}{2}Y\right)^2 - \left(\frac{\sqrt{2}}{2}X - \frac{\sqrt{2}}{2}Y\right)\left(\frac{\sqrt{2}}{2}X + \frac{\sqrt{2}}{2}Y\right) + \left(\frac{\sqrt{2}}{2}X + \frac{\sqrt{2}}{2}Y\right)^2 = 2,$$

or $X^2/4 + 3Y^2/4 = 1$. The conic section is an ellipse.

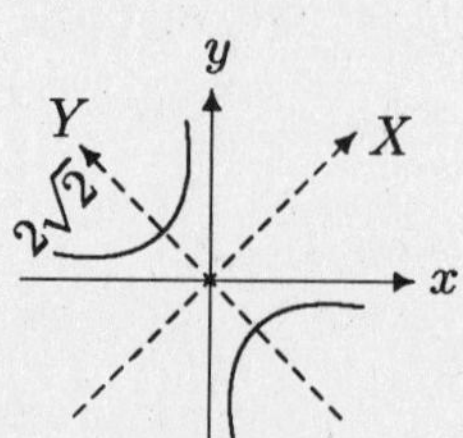

Exercise 1

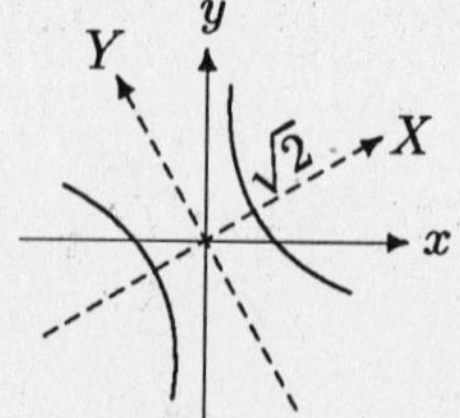

Exercise 2

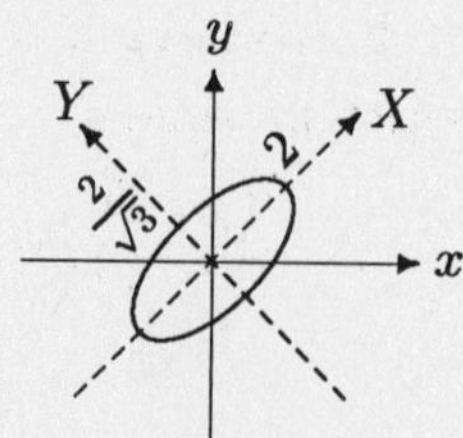

Exercise 3

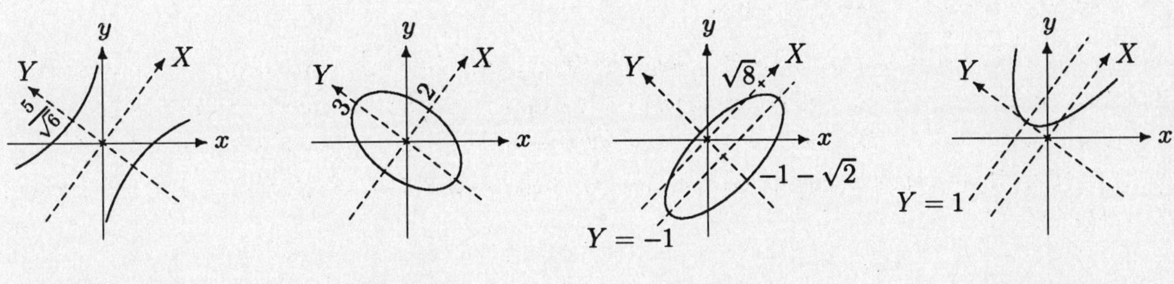

4. $A = 9$, $B = -24$, $C = 2$; $\tan 2\theta = -24/(9-2) = -\frac{24}{7}$; from Example 2, $\cos\theta = \frac{3}{5}$ and $\sin\theta = \frac{4}{5}$; the equation becomes

$$9\left(\frac{3}{5}X - \frac{4}{5}Y\right)^2 - 24\left(\frac{3}{5}X - \frac{4}{5}Y\right)\left(\frac{4}{5}X + \frac{3}{5}Y\right) + 2\left(\frac{4}{5}X + \frac{3}{5}Y\right)^2 - 75 = 0,$$

or $6Y^2/25 - 7X^2/75 = 1$. The conic section is a hyperbola.

5. $A = 145$, $B = 120$, $C = 180$, $\tan 2\theta = 120/(145-180) = -\frac{24}{7}$; from Example 2, $\cos\theta = \frac{3}{5}$ and $\sin\theta = \frac{4}{5}$; the equation becomes

$$145\left(\frac{3}{5}X - \frac{4}{5}Y\right)^2 + 120\left(\frac{3}{5}X - \frac{4}{5}Y\right)\left(\frac{4}{5}X + \frac{3}{5}Y\right) + 180\left(\frac{4}{5}X + \frac{3}{5}Y\right)^2 = 900,$$

or $X^2/4 + Y^2/9 = 1$. The conic section is an ellipse.

6. $A = 10 = C$, so $\theta = \pi/4$; the equation becomes

$$10\left(\frac{\sqrt{2}}{2}X - \frac{\sqrt{2}}{2}Y\right)^2 - 12\left(\frac{\sqrt{2}}{2}X - \frac{\sqrt{2}}{2}Y\right)\left(\frac{\sqrt{2}}{2}X + \frac{\sqrt{2}}{2}Y\right) + 10\left(\frac{\sqrt{2}}{2}X + \frac{\sqrt{2}}{2}Y\right)^2$$

$$-16\sqrt{2}\left(\frac{\sqrt{2}}{2}X - \frac{\sqrt{2}}{2}Y\right) + 16\sqrt{2}\left(\frac{\sqrt{2}}{2}X + \frac{\sqrt{2}}{2}Y\right) = 16,$$

or $4X^2 + 16Y^2 + 32Y = 16$, or $X^2/8 + (Y+1)^2/2 = 1$. The conic section is an ellipse.

7. $A = 16$, $B = -24$, $C = 9$; $\tan 2\theta = -24/(16-9) = -\frac{24}{7}$; from Example 2, $\cos\theta = \frac{3}{5}$ and $\sin\theta = \frac{4}{5}$; the equation becomes

$$16\left(\frac{3}{5}X - \frac{4}{5}Y\right)^2 - 24\left(\frac{3}{5}X - \frac{4}{5}Y\right)\left(\frac{4}{5}X + \frac{3}{5}Y\right) + 9\left(\frac{4}{5}X + \frac{3}{5}Y\right)^2$$

$$-5\left(\frac{3}{5}X - \frac{4}{5}Y\right) - 90\left(\frac{4}{5}X + \frac{3}{5}Y\right) + 25 = 0,$$

or $25Y^2 - 75X - 50Y + 25 = 0$, or $(Y-1)^2 = 3X$. The conic section is a parabola.

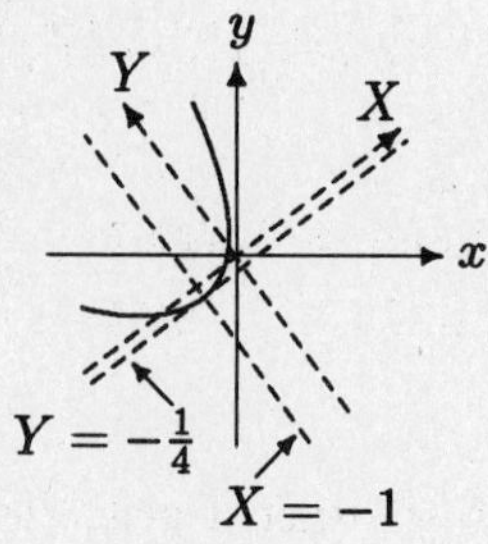

Exercise 8

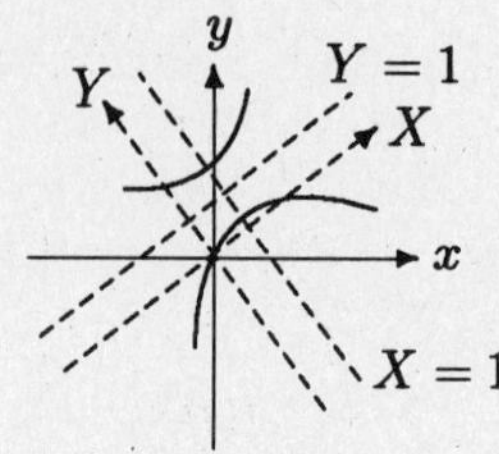

Exercise 9

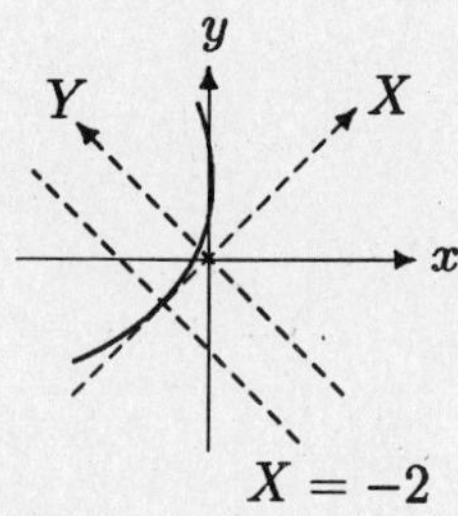

Exercise 10

8. $A = 16$, $B = 24$, $C = 9$; $\tan 2\theta = 24/(16-9) = \frac{24}{7}$; by the method of Example 2, $\cos 2\theta = \frac{7}{25}$, $\cos\theta = \frac{4}{5}$, and $\sin\theta = \frac{3}{5}$; the equation becomes

$$16\left(\frac{4}{5}X - \frac{3}{5}Y\right)^2 + 24\left(\frac{4}{5}X - \frac{3}{5}Y\right)\left(\frac{3}{5}X + \frac{4}{5}Y\right) + 9\left(\frac{3}{5}X + \frac{4}{5}Y\right)^2$$

$$+100\left(\frac{4}{5}X - \frac{3}{5}Y\right) - 50\left(\frac{3}{5}X + \frac{4}{5}Y\right) = 0,$$

or $25X^2 + 50X - 100Y = 0$, or $(X+1)^2 = 4(Y + \frac{1}{4})$. The conic section is a parabola.

9. $A = 2$, $B = -72$, $C = 23$; $\tan 2\theta = -72/(2-23) = \frac{24}{7}$; by the method of Example 2, $\cos 2\theta = \frac{7}{25}$, $\cos\theta = \frac{4}{5}$ and $\sin\theta = \frac{3}{5}$; the equation becomes

$$2\left(\frac{4}{5}X - \frac{3}{5}Y\right)^2 - 72\left(\frac{4}{5}X - \frac{3}{5}Y\right)\left(\frac{3}{5}X + \frac{4}{5}Y\right) + 23\left(\frac{3}{5}X + \frac{4}{5}Y\right)^2$$

$$+100\left(\frac{4}{5}X - \frac{3}{5}Y\right) - 50\left(\frac{3}{5}X + \frac{4}{5}Y\right) = 0,$$

or $-25X^2 + 50Y^2 + 50X - 100Y = 0$, or $2(Y-1)^2 - (X-1)^2 = 1$. The conic section is a hyperbola.

10. $A = 2 = C$, so $\theta = \pi/4$; the equation becomes

$$2\left(\frac{\sqrt{2}}{2}X - \frac{\sqrt{2}}{2}Y\right)^2 + 4\left(\frac{\sqrt{2}}{2}X - \frac{\sqrt{2}}{2}Y\right)\left(\frac{\sqrt{2}}{2}X + \frac{\sqrt{2}}{2}Y\right)$$

$$+2\left(\frac{\sqrt{2}}{2}X + \frac{\sqrt{2}}{2}Y\right)^2 + 28\sqrt{2}\left(\frac{\sqrt{2}}{2}X - \frac{\sqrt{2}}{2}Y\right) - 12\sqrt{2}\left(\frac{\sqrt{2}}{2}X + \frac{\sqrt{2}}{2}Y\right) + 16 = 0,$$

or $4X^2 + 16X - 40Y + 16 = 0$, or $(X+2)^2 = 10Y$. The conic section is a parabola.

11. $A = 9$, $B = -24$, $C = 2$; $\tan 2\theta = -24/(9-2) = -\frac{24}{7}$; from Example 2, $\cos\theta = \frac{3}{5}$ and $\sin\theta = \frac{4}{5}$; the equation becomes $9(\frac{3}{5}X - \frac{4}{5}Y)^2 - 24(\frac{3}{5}X - \frac{4}{5}Y)(\frac{4}{5}X + \frac{3}{5}Y) + 2(\frac{4}{5}X + \frac{3}{5}Y)^2 = 0$, or $18Y^2 = 7X^2$; the graph consists of two intersecting lines, $Y = \sqrt{\frac{7}{18}}\,X$ and $Y = -\sqrt{\frac{7}{18}}\,X$.

12. $A = 145$, $B = 120$, $C = 180$; $\tan 2\theta = 120/(145 - 180) = -\frac{24}{7}$; from Example 2, $\cos\theta = \frac{3}{5}$ and $\sin\theta = \frac{4}{5}$; the equation becomes $145(\frac{3}{5}X - \frac{4}{5}Y)^2 + 120(\frac{3}{5}X - \frac{4}{5}Y)(\frac{4}{5}X + \frac{3}{5}Y) + 180(\frac{4}{5}X + \frac{3}{5}Y)^2 = 0$, or $225X^2 + 100Y^2 = 0$; the graph is the point $(0,0)$.

13. $A = 145$, $B = 120$, $C = 180$; $\tan 2\theta = 120/(145 - 180) = -\frac{24}{7}$; from Example 2, $\cos\theta = \frac{3}{5}$ and $\sin\theta = \frac{4}{5}$; the equation becomes $145(\frac{3}{5}X - \frac{4}{5}Y)^2 + 120(\frac{3}{5}X - \frac{4}{5}Y)(\frac{4}{5}X + \frac{3}{5}Y) + 180(\frac{4}{5}X + \frac{3}{5}Y)^2 = -900$, or $225X^2 + 100Y^2 = -900$; no points on the graph.

14. Since $C = 0$, it follows that $B^2 - 4AC = B^2 - 0 = B^2 > 0$, so the graph is either degenerate or a hyperbola. If $\tan 2\theta = B/(A - C) = B$, the equation becomes

$$(\cos\theta\, X - \sin\theta\, Y)^2 + B(\cos\theta\, X - \sin\theta\, Y)(\sin\theta\, X + \cos\theta\, Y) = F$$

or

$$(\cos^2\theta + B\cos\theta\,\sin\theta)X^2 + (\sin^2\theta - B\sin\theta\,\cos\theta)Y^2 = F.$$

Since $0 < \theta < \pi/2$ and $B > 0$, we have $\cos^2\theta + B\cos\theta\,\sin\theta > 0$. Since $\tan 2\theta = B > 0$, we actually have $0 < \theta < \pi/4$, and thus

$$\sin^2\theta - B\sin\theta\,\cos\theta = \sin\theta\,\cos\theta\,(\tan\theta - B) = \sin\theta\,\cos\theta\,(\tan\theta - \tan 2\theta) < 0.$$

Thus the new equation has the form $aX^2 - bY^2 = F$, where $a > 0$ and $b > 0$. Thus the graph is a hyperbola if $F > 0$, and two intersecting lines if $F = 0$.

15. Since $A = 0 = C$, we have $\theta = \pi/4$. The equation becomes

$$B\left(\frac{\sqrt{2}}{2}X - \frac{\sqrt{2}}{2}Y\right)\left(\frac{\sqrt{2}}{2}X + \frac{\sqrt{2}}{2}Y\right) + D\left(\frac{\sqrt{2}}{2}X - \frac{\sqrt{2}}{2}Y\right) + E\left(\frac{\sqrt{2}}{2}X + \frac{\sqrt{2}}{2}Y\right) + F = 0$$

or

$$\frac{1}{2}B(X^2 - Y^2) + \frac{\sqrt{2}}{2}(D + E)X + \frac{\sqrt{2}}{2}(E - D)Y + F = 0.$$

When the squares are completed the equation will take the form $\frac{1}{2}B(X - a)^2 - \frac{1}{2}B(Y - b)^2 = c$. If $c \neq 0$, the graph is a hyperbola; if $c = 0$, the graph is two intersecting lines.

16. $A = 1 = C$, so $\theta = \pi/4$; the equation becomes

$$\left(\frac{\sqrt{2}}{2}X - \frac{\sqrt{2}}{2}Y\right)^2 + 2\left(\frac{\sqrt{2}}{2}X - \frac{\sqrt{2}}{2}Y\right)\left(\frac{\sqrt{2}}{2}X + \frac{\sqrt{2}}{2}Y\right) + \left(\frac{\sqrt{2}}{2}X + \frac{\sqrt{2}}{2}Y\right)^2$$
$$-\sqrt{2}\left(\frac{\sqrt{2}}{2}X - \frac{\sqrt{2}}{2}Y\right) + \sqrt{2}\left(\frac{\sqrt{2}}{2}X + \frac{\sqrt{2}}{2}Y\right) = 2$$

or $2X^2 + 2Y = 2$, so that $Y = 1 - X^2$. Since the line $y = x$ becomes the X axis in the XY coordinate system, in that system the region R becomes the region R' bounded by the X axis and the parabola $Y = 1 - X^2$. Thus D is the solid region obtained by revolving R' about the X axis. Since the parabola $Y = 1 - X^2$ and the X axis intersect for $X = -1$ and $X = 1$, it follows that

$$V = \pi\int_{-1}^{1}(1 - X^2)^2\,dX = \pi\int_{-1}^{1}(1 - 2X^2 + X^4)\,dX = \pi\left(X - \frac{2}{3}X^3 + \frac{1}{5}X^5\right)\Big|_{-1}^{1} = \frac{16\pi}{15}.$$

17. Let $B' = -2A\cos\theta\sin\theta + B(\cos^2\theta - \sin^2\theta) + 2C\cos\theta\sin\theta = B(\cos^2\theta - \sin^2\theta) - 2(A-C)\sin\theta\cos\theta$. From (6) and the equation preceding (6), we find that

$$A' = A\cos^2\theta + B\sin\theta\cos\theta + C\sin^2\theta$$

$$C' = A\sin^2\theta - B\sin\theta\cos\theta + C\cos^2\theta.$$

Therefore

$$\begin{aligned}(B')^2 - 4A'C' &= [B(\cos^2\theta - \sin^2\theta) - 2(A-C)\sin\theta\cos\theta]^2\\ &\quad -4(A\cos^2\theta + B\sin\theta\cos\theta + C\sin^2\theta)(A\sin^2\theta - B\sin\theta\cos\theta + C\cos^2\theta)\\ &= B^2(\cos^4\theta - 2\sin^2\theta\cos^2\theta + \sin^4\theta + 4\sin^2\theta\cos^2\theta)\\ &\quad -4AB(\sin\theta\cos^3\theta - \sin^3\theta\cos\theta - \sin\theta\cos^3\theta + \sin^3\theta\cos\theta)\\ &\quad +4BC((\sin\theta\cos^3\theta - \sin^3\theta\cos\theta - \sin\theta\cos^3\theta + \sin^3\theta\cos\theta)\\ &\quad +4A^2(\sin^2\theta\cos^2\theta - \sin^2\theta\cos^2\theta)\\ &\quad -4AC(2\sin^2\theta\cos^2\theta + \cos^4\theta + \sin^4\theta)\\ &\quad +4C^2(\sin^2\theta\cos^2\theta - \sin^2\theta\cos^2\theta)\\ &= B^2(\cos^2\theta + \sin^2\theta)^2 - 4AC(\cos^2\theta + \sin^2\theta)^2\\ &= B^2 - 4AC.\end{aligned}$$

But $B' = 0$ for the value of θ chosen in (8). Thus $B^2 - 4AC = -4A'C'$.

10.7 A Unified Description of Conic Sections

1. $c = \sqrt{25-9} = 4$; $e = \dfrac{4}{5}$

2. $c = \sqrt{64-49} = \sqrt{15}$; $e = \dfrac{\sqrt{15}}{8}$

3. $c = \sqrt{9+25} = \sqrt{34}$; $e = \dfrac{\sqrt{34}}{3}$

4. $c = \sqrt{25+9} = \sqrt{34}$; $e = \dfrac{\sqrt{34}}{5}$

5. $\dfrac{x^2}{2} + \dfrac{y^2}{8} = 1$; $c = \sqrt{8-2} = \sqrt{6}$; $e = \dfrac{\sqrt{6}}{\sqrt{8}} = \dfrac{\sqrt{3}}{2}$

6. $\dfrac{y^2}{2/3} - \dfrac{x^2}{4/3} = 1$; $c = \sqrt{\dfrac{2}{3} + \dfrac{4}{3}} = \sqrt{2}$; $e = \dfrac{\sqrt{2}}{\sqrt{2/3}} = \sqrt{3}$

7. $\dfrac{(x-3)^2}{2} + \dfrac{(y+3)^2}{8} = 1$; $c = \sqrt{8-2} = \sqrt{6}$; $e = \dfrac{\sqrt{6}}{\sqrt{8}} = \dfrac{\sqrt{3}}{2}$

8. $e = 1$ since the conic section is a parabola.

9. $\dfrac{(x-1)^2}{4}+\dfrac{(y-1)^2}{2}=1$; $c=\sqrt{4-2}=\sqrt{2}$; $e=\dfrac{\sqrt{2}}{2}$

10. $\dfrac{(x+2)^2}{16}-\dfrac{y^2}{4}=1$; $c=\sqrt{16+4}=2\sqrt{5}$; $e=\dfrac{2\sqrt{5}}{4}=\dfrac{\sqrt{5}}{2}$

11. $\dfrac{(x+1)^2}{9}-\dfrac{(y+2)^2}{49}=1$; $c=\sqrt{9+49}=\sqrt{58}$; $e=\dfrac{\sqrt{58}}{3}$

12. $e=1$ since the conic section is a parabola.

13. $c=9$, $e=\dfrac{3}{5}$, $a=\dfrac{9}{3/5}=15$, $b=\sqrt{225-81}=12$; $\dfrac{x^2}{225}+\dfrac{y^2}{144}=1$

14. $c=9$, $e=\dfrac{5}{3}$, $a=\dfrac{9}{5/3}=\dfrac{27}{5}$, $b=\sqrt{81-\left(\dfrac{27}{5}\right)^2}=\dfrac{36}{5}$; $\dfrac{25x^2}{729}-\dfrac{25y^2}{1296}=1$

15. $c=1$, $e=2$, $a=\dfrac{1}{2}$, $b=\sqrt{1-\dfrac{1}{4}}=\dfrac{\sqrt{3}}{2}$; $4y^2-\dfrac{4x^2}{3}=1$

16. $a=5$, $e=\dfrac{4}{5}$, $c=5\left(\dfrac{4}{5}\right)=4$, $b=\sqrt{25-16}=3$; $\dfrac{x^2}{25}+\dfrac{y^2}{9}=1$

17. $a=5$, $e=\dfrac{13}{5}$, $c=5\left(\dfrac{13}{5}\right)=13$, $b=\sqrt{169-25}=12$; $\dfrac{(y-5)^2}{25}-\dfrac{x^2}{144}=1$

18. $a=3$, $e=\dfrac{1}{2}$, $c=3\left(\dfrac{1}{2}\right)=\dfrac{3}{2}$, $b=\sqrt{9-\dfrac{9}{4}}=\dfrac{3\sqrt{3}}{2}$; $\dfrac{4(x+2)^2}{27}+\dfrac{(y-3)^2}{9}=1$

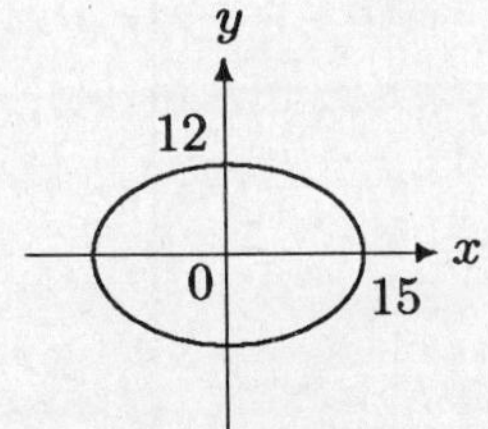

Exercise 13

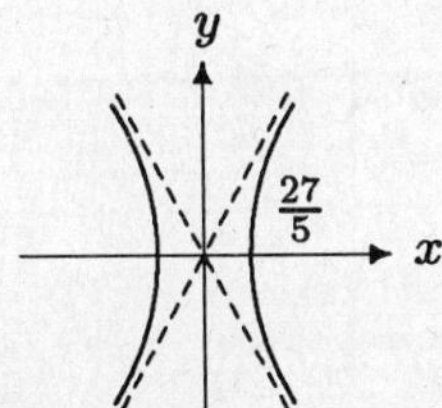

Exercise 14

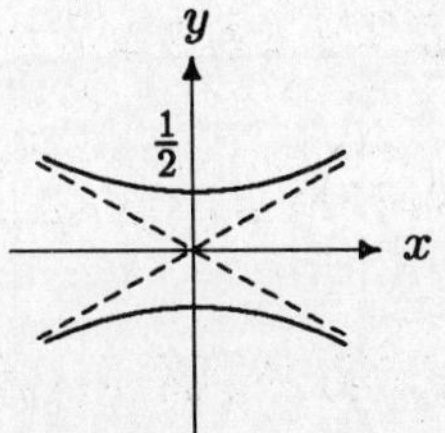

Exercise 15

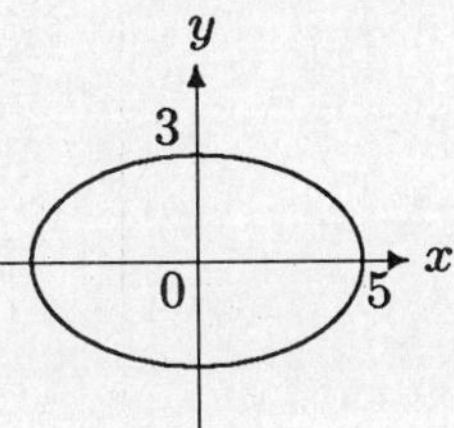

Exercise 16

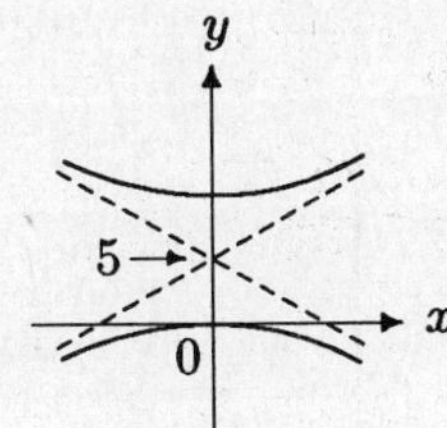

Exercise 17

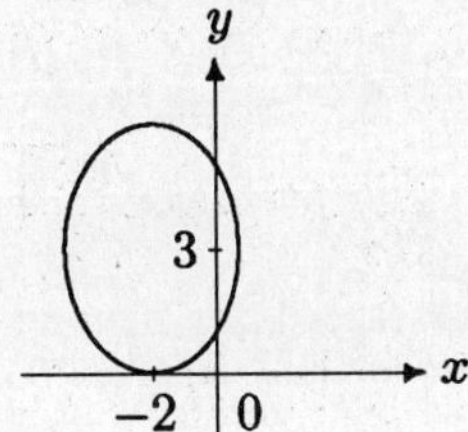

Exercise 18

19. Since $c = ae = a\sqrt{17}$, we have $b = \sqrt{17a^2 - a^2} = 4a$. Thus an equation of the hyperbola is either

$$\frac{x^2}{a^2} - \frac{y^2}{16a^2} = 1 \quad \text{or} \quad \frac{y^2}{a^2} - \frac{x^2}{16a^2} = 1.$$

Since the hyperbola passes through $(\sqrt{20}, 8)$, we find for the first of these equations that $20/a^2 - 64/16a^2 = 1$, or $a^2 = 16$, so that the equation becomes $x^2/16 - y^2/256 = 1$. For the second equation we find that $64/a^2 - 20/16a^2 = 1$, or $a^2 = \frac{251}{4}$, so that the equation becomes $4y^2/251 - x^2/1004 = 1$.

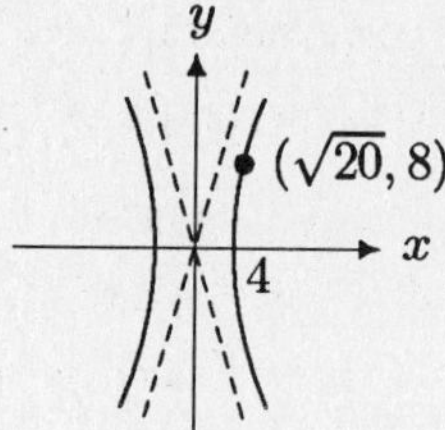

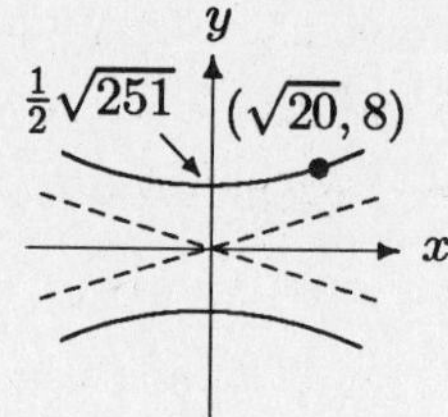

20. Since $c = ae = a\sqrt{3}/2$, we have $b = \sqrt{a^2 - \frac{3}{4}a^2} = a/2$. Thus an equation of the ellipse is either

$$\frac{x^2}{a^2} + \frac{4y^2}{a^2} = 1 \quad \text{or} \quad \frac{4x^2}{a^2} + \frac{y^2}{a^2} = 1.$$

Since the ellipse passes through $(-1, 1)$, we find for the first of these equations that $1/a^2 + 4/a^2 = 1$, or $a^2 = 5$, so that the equation becomes $x^2/5 + 4y^2/5 = 1$. For the second equation we find that $4/a^2 + 1/a^2 = 1$, or $a^2 = 5$, so that the equation becomes $4x^2/5 + y^2/5 = 1$.

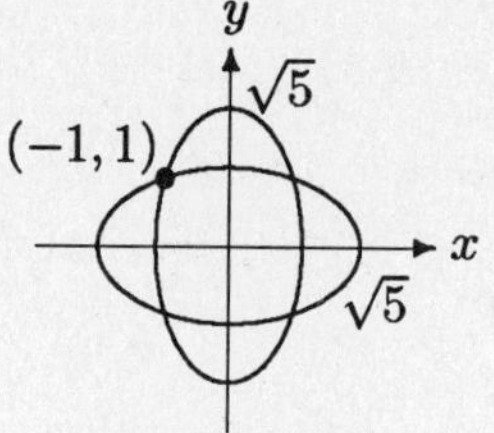

Exercise 20

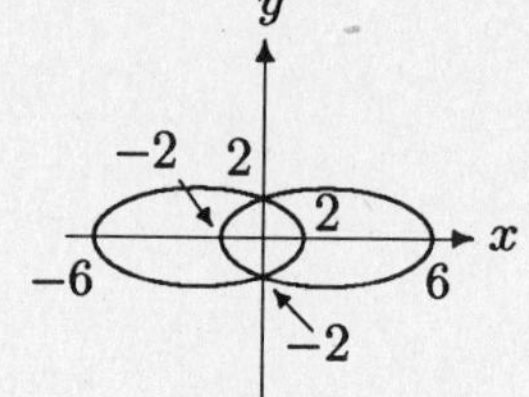

Exercise 21

21. Since $a = 4$ and $e = \frac{1}{2}$, we have $c = 4(\frac{1}{2}) = 2$. Thus $b = \sqrt{16 - 4} = 2\sqrt{3}$, and also the center is located at either $(2, 0)$ or $(-2, 0)$. Therefore an equation of the ellipse is either $(x-2)^2/16 + y^2/12 = 1$ or $(x+2)^2/16 + y^2/12 = 1$.

22. $e = \frac{1}{2}$, $k = 2$; ellipse with directrix $y = 2$

23. $e = 2$, $k = \frac{1}{2}$; hyperbola with directrix $x = -\frac{1}{2}$

24. $e = 1$, $k = 1$; parabola with directrix $y = -1$

25. $r = \dfrac{5}{1 - \frac{3}{5}\sin\theta}$; $e = \dfrac{3}{5}$, $k = \dfrac{25}{3}$; ellipse with directrix $y = -\dfrac{25}{3}$

26. $r = \dfrac{3}{1 - \frac{5}{3}\cos\theta}$; $e = \dfrac{5}{3}$, $k = \dfrac{9}{5}$; hyperbola with directrix $x = -\dfrac{9}{5}$

27. $r = \dfrac{\frac{1}{2}}{1-\cos\theta}$; $e = 1$, $k = \dfrac{1}{2}$; parabola with directrix $x = -\dfrac{1}{2}$

28. $r = \dfrac{3}{1-\frac{5}{4}\sin\theta}$; $e = \dfrac{5}{4}$, $k = \dfrac{12}{5}$; hyperbola with directrix $y = -\dfrac{12}{5}$

29. $e = 1$, $k = 3$; parabola with directrix $y = 3$

30. a. For the equation $r = \dfrac{1}{2+\cos\theta} = \dfrac{\frac{1}{2}}{1+\frac{1}{2}\cos\theta}$ we have $e = \frac{1}{2}$ and $k = 1$, so that the graph of the equation is an ellipse with focus $(0,0)$ and corresponding directrix $x = 1$. For the equation $r = 1/(1-\cos\theta)$, we have $e = 1$ and $k = 1$, so that the graph of the equation is a parabola with focus $(0,0)$ and corresponding directrix $x = -1$.

b. If $1/(2+\cos\theta) = r = 1/(1-\cos\theta)$, then $1-\cos\theta = 2+\cos\theta$, so that $\cos\theta = -\frac{1}{2}$. Thus $\theta = 2\pi/3$ or $\theta = 4\pi/3$, and $r = \frac{2}{3}$. The points of intersection are $(\frac{2}{3}, 2\pi/3)$ and $(\frac{2}{3}, 4\pi/3)$.

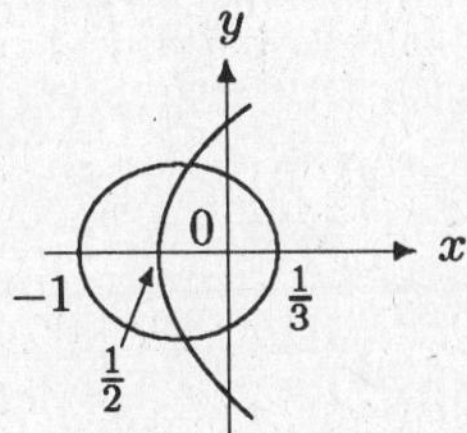

31. Since $e = .017$ and $a = \frac{299}{2}$, we have $c = (\frac{299}{2})(.017) = 2.5415$, and thus

$$b = \sqrt{\left(\frac{299}{2}\right)^2 - (2.5415)^2} \approx 149.48.$$

An approximate equation of the orbit is $x^2/(149.5)^2 + y^2/(149.48)^2 = 1$, if we place the x axis along the major axis and the origin at the center of the orbit.

32. A polar equation of the elliptical orbit of the earth is $r = ek/(1+e\cos\theta)$ if the origin is placed at the sun and the directrix corresponding to the focus at the origin has equation $x = k$ with $k > 0$. Then r represents the distance between the earth and the sun, and since $0 < e < 1$, r is minimum if the denominator is maximum, which occurs for $\theta = 0$. The minimum value of r is $ek/(1+e)$. To find an expression for k we notice from the discussion leading up to (4) that if a focus of an ellipse in standard position is $(c,0)$ then the corresponding directrix is $x = a/e$. Thus if a focus is $(0,0)$, then the directrix is $x = a/e - c$. Thus $k = a/e - c$, so that

$$\frac{ek}{1+e} = \frac{a-ce}{1+e} = \frac{a-ae^2}{1+e} = a(1-e).$$

From the information in the table, $a(1-e) \approx \frac{299}{2}(1-.017) = 146.96$ (million kilometers).

Chapter 10 Review

1.

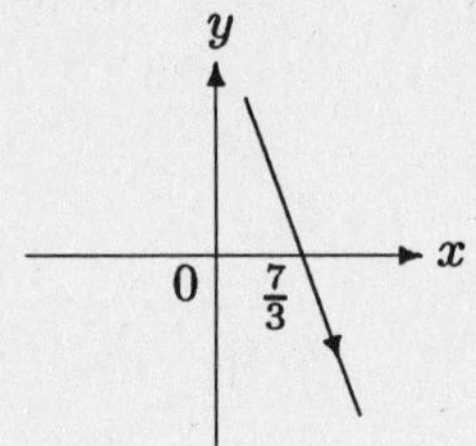

2.

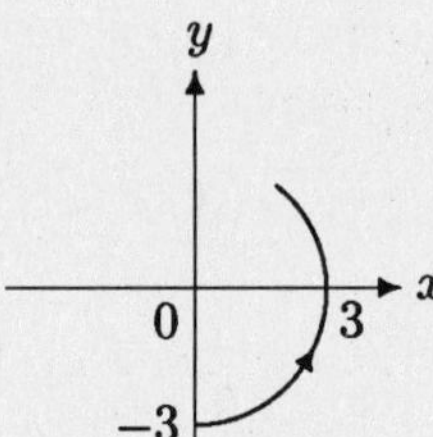

3. $L = \int_0^1 \sqrt{(\cosh 2t - 1)^2 + (2\sinh t)^2}\,dt = \int_0^1 \sqrt{(2\sinh^2 t)^2 + (2\sinh t)^2}\,dt = \int_0^1 \sqrt{4\sinh^4 t + 4\sinh^2 t}\,dt$

$= \int_0^1 2\sinh t\sqrt{\sinh^2 t + 1}\,dt = \int_0^1 2\sinh t\,\cosh t\,dt = \sinh^2 t\big|_0^1 = \sinh 1 = \frac{1}{2}(e - e^{-1})$

4. $L = \int_0^{\pi/2} \sqrt{(-\cos^2 t\,\sin t)^2 + (\sin t\,\cos t)^2}\,dt = \int_0^{\pi/2} \sqrt{\cos^4 t\,\sin^2 t + \sin^2 t\,\cos^2 t}\,dt$

$= \int_0^{\pi/2} \sin t\,\cos t\sqrt{\cos^2 t + 1}\,dt \overset{u=\cos^2 t+1}{=} \int_2^1 \sqrt{u}\left(-\frac{1}{2}\right) du$

$= -\frac{1}{2}\left(\frac{2}{3}u^{3/2}\right)\Big|_2^1 = -\frac{1}{3}(1 - 2\sqrt{2}) = \frac{1}{3}(2\sqrt{2} - 1)$

5. $S = \int_1^{\sqrt{3}} (2\pi)\frac{1}{2}\sqrt{(t^2)^2 + (t)^2}\,dt = 2\pi\int_1^{\sqrt{3}} \frac{1}{2}t^2\sqrt{t^4 + t^2}\,dt = 2\pi\int_1^{\sqrt{3}} \frac{1}{2}t^3\sqrt{t^2 + 1}\,dt$

$\overset{u=t^2+1}{=} 2\pi\int_2^4 \frac{1}{4}(u-1)\sqrt{u}\,du = \frac{1}{2}\pi\int_2^4 (u^{3/2} - u^{1/2})\,du = \frac{1}{2}\pi\left(\frac{2}{5}u^{5/2} - \frac{2}{3}u^{3/2}\right)\Big|_2^4$

$= \frac{1}{2}\pi\left(\frac{64}{5} - \frac{16}{3}\right) - \frac{1}{2}\pi\left(\frac{8}{5}\sqrt{2} - \frac{4}{3}\sqrt{2}\right) = \frac{1}{15}\pi(56 - 2\sqrt{2})$

6. $S = \int_0^{\pi/2} 2\pi e^t \sin t\sqrt{(e^t\cos t - e^t\sin t)^2 + (e^t\sin t + e^t\cos t)^2}\,dt$

$= 2\pi\int_0^{\pi/2} e^t\sin t\sqrt{2e^{2t}\cos^2 t + 2e^{2t}\sin^2 t}\,dt = 2\sqrt{2}\pi\int_0^{\pi/2} e^{2t}\sin t\,dt$

By Exercise 54(a) of Section 7.1, with $a = 2$, $b = 1$, and $x = t$, we have

$$S = 2\sqrt{2}\pi\left[\frac{e^{2t}}{5}(2\sin t - \cos t)\right]\Bigg|_0^{\pi/2} = 2\sqrt{2}\pi\left(\frac{2e^\pi}{5} + \frac{1}{5}\right) = \frac{2\sqrt{2}}{5}(2e^\pi + 1).$$

7. $r = \sin 5\theta$; symmetry with respect to y axis

8. $r = 2\cos\theta - 2$; symmetry with respect to the x axis

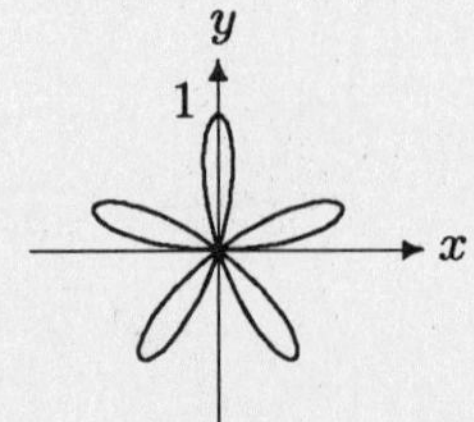

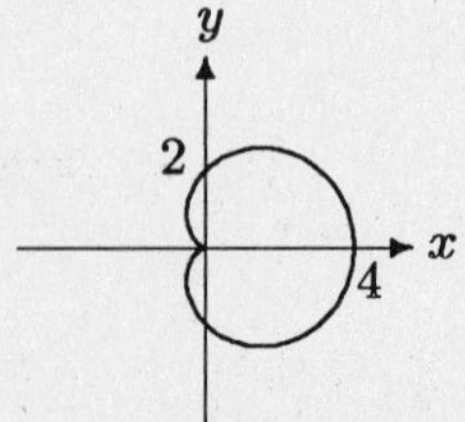

9. $r = \sqrt{3} - 2\sin\theta$; symmetry with respect to y axis

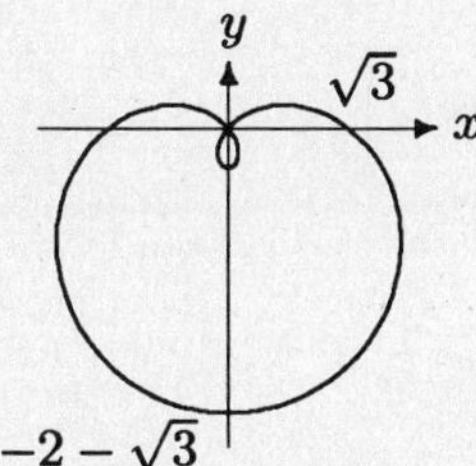

10. $r^2 = \frac{1}{4}\cos 2\theta$; symmetry with respect to both axes and origin

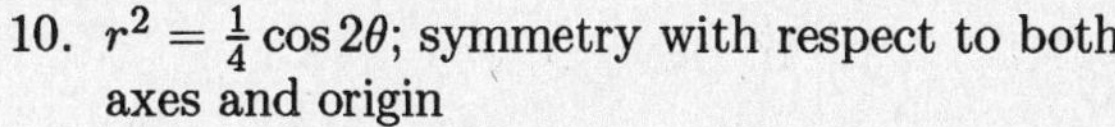

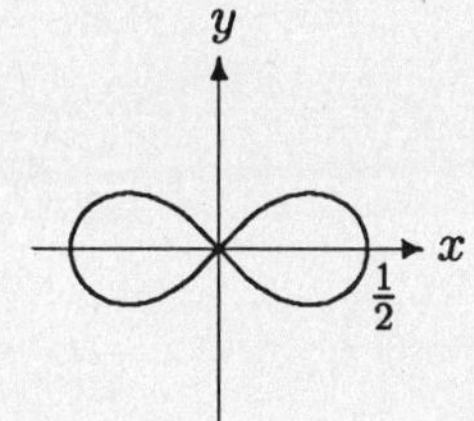

11. a. $r = 2\sin 2\theta$ and $r = 2\sin\theta$

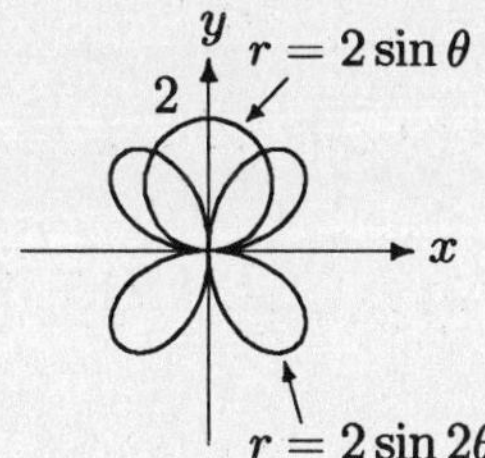

b. The graphs intersect for (r, θ) such that $2\sin 2\theta = r = 2\sin\theta$, which means $r = 0$ or $4\sin\theta\cos\theta = 2\sin\theta$, and thus $\theta = 0$, or $\theta = \pi$, or $\theta = \pi/3$ or $\theta = 5\pi/3$. In polar coordinates the points of intersection are the origin, $(\sqrt{3}, \pi/3)$ and $(-\sqrt{3}, 5\pi/3)$.

12. $$L = \int_0^\pi \sqrt{\cos^2\theta + (1+\sin\theta)^2}\,d\theta = \int_0^\pi \sqrt{2 + 2\sin\theta}\,d\theta = 2\int_0^\pi \sqrt{\frac{1+\cos(\pi/2-\theta)}{2}}\,d\theta$$
$$= 2\int_0^\pi \cos\left(\frac{\pi/2-\theta}{2}\right)d\theta = 2\int_0^\pi \cos\left(\frac{\pi}{4} - \frac{\theta}{2}\right)d\theta = -2\sin\left(\frac{\pi}{4} - \frac{\theta}{2}\right)\Big|_0^\pi$$
$$= -2\sin\left(-\frac{\pi}{4}\right) + 2\sin\frac{\pi}{4} = 2\sqrt{2}$$

13. The region enclosed by $r = 2\cos\theta$ is obtained from $r = 2\cos\theta$ for $-\pi/2 \le \theta \le \pi/2$. The region enclosed by $r = \sin\theta + \cos\theta$ is obtained from $r = \sin\theta + \cos\theta$ for $-\pi/4 \le \theta \le 3\pi/4$. The circles intersect for (r, θ) such that $2\cos\theta = r = \sin\theta + \cos\theta$, so that $\theta = \pi/4$. Thus

$$A = \int_{-\pi/4}^{\pi/4} \frac{1}{2}(\sin\theta + \cos\theta)^2\,d\theta + \int_{\pi/4}^{\pi/2} \frac{1}{2}(2\cos\theta)^2\,d\theta$$
$$= \frac{1}{2}\int_{-\pi/4}^{\pi/4}(1 + \sin 2\theta)\,d\theta + 2\int_{\pi/4}^{\pi/2}\cos^2\theta\,d\theta$$
$$= \frac{1}{2}\left(\theta - \frac{1}{2}\cos 2\theta\right)\Big|_{-\pi/4}^{\pi/4} + \left(\theta + \frac{1}{2}\sin 2\theta\right)\Big|_{\pi/4}^{\pi/2} = \frac{\pi}{2} - \frac{1}{2}.$$

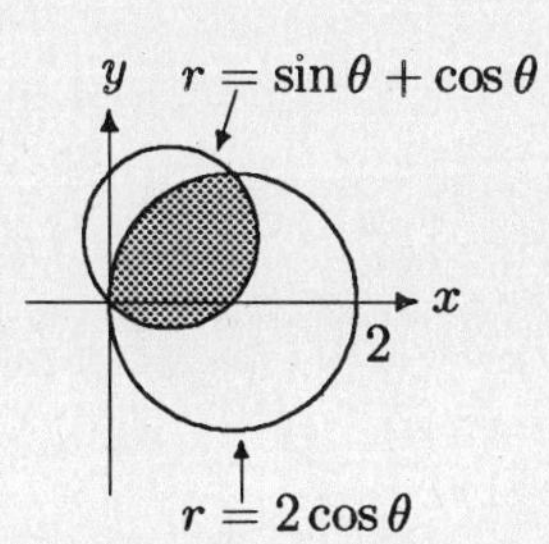

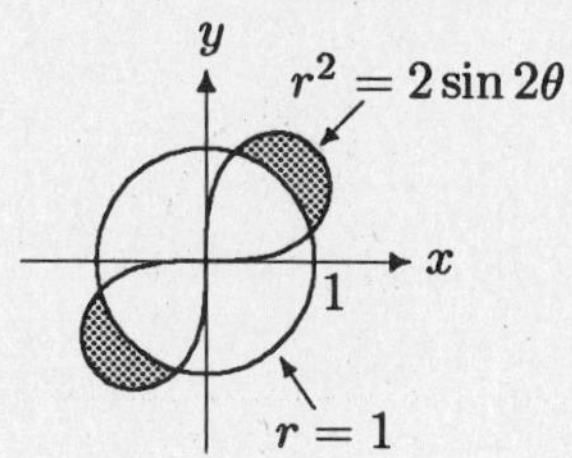

Exercise 14

14. The graphs intersect for (r, θ) such that $1 = r^2 = 2\sin 2\theta$, which means that $2\theta = \pi/6$ or $2\theta = 5\pi/6$, and thus $\theta = \pi/12$ or $5\pi/12$. The area of the portion of the region in the first quadrant is given by

$$A_1 = \int_{\pi/12}^{5\pi/12} \frac{1}{2}\left[(\sqrt{2\sin 2\theta})^2 - 1^2\right] d\theta = \frac{1}{2}\int_{\pi/12}^{5\pi/12} (2\sin 2\theta - 1)\, d\theta = \frac{1}{2}(-\cos 2\theta - \theta)\Big|_{\pi/12}^{5\pi/12} = \frac{1}{2}\sqrt{3} - \frac{\pi}{6}.$$

Thus the total area $A = 2A_1 = \sqrt{3} - \pi/3$.

15. The vertex is $(1, 4)$; $c = -4$; $(y-4)^2 = -16(x-1)$

16. The focus is $(-2, b)$ for an appropriate value of b. Since the directrix is $y = -10$ and the point $(6, -2)$ lies on the parabola, the definition of a parabola implies that $\sqrt{(-2-6)^2 + (b+2)^2} = |-2-(-10)| = 8$ so that $b = -2$. Therefore the focus is $(-2, -2)$, so that the vertex is $(-2, -6)$ and $c = 4$. Thus an equation of the parabola is $(x+2)^2 = 16(y+6)$.

17. $a = 2\sqrt{2}$; an equation of the ellipse is $x^2/b^2 + y^2/8 = 1$. Since $(1, \sqrt{6})$ is on the ellipse, we have $1/b^2 + \frac{6}{8} = 1$, so that $b = 2$. Consequently an equation of the ellipse becomes $x^2/4 + y^2/8 = 1$.

18. The center is $(1, -1)$; $a = 4$, $c = 2$, and $b = \sqrt{16-4} = 2\sqrt{3}$; $\dfrac{(x-1)^2}{12} + \dfrac{(y+1)^2}{16} = 1$

19. The center is $(-1, 2)$; $a = 2$; an equation of the hyperbola is $(x+1)^2/4 - (y-2)^2/b^2 = 1$. The asymptotes have equations $y - 2 = (b/2)(x+1)$ and $y - 2 = -(b/2)(x+1)$. Since the asymptotes are perpendicular, $b/2 = -1/(-b/2) = 2/b$ so that $b = 2$. The equation of the hyperbola becomes $(x+1)^2/4 - (y-2)^2/4 = 1$.

20. The center is $(2, -3)$; $c = 10$, and $b/a = \frac{4}{3}$; thus $a^2 = c^2 - b^2 = 100 - \frac{16}{9}a^2$, so that $a = 6$, $b = 8$. An equation of the hyperbola is $(x-2)^2/36 - (y+3)^2/64 = 1$.

21. The distance from the vertex to the directrix is 2. Since $e = 2$, the distance from the vertex to the focus is $2 \cdot 2 = 4$. Thus the focus corresponding to the vertex $(-2, 0)$ is $(2, 0)$. The center is $(p, 0)$, for an appropriate value of p. Then $2 = c/a = (2-p)/(-2-p)$, so that $p = -6$, and the center is $(-6, 0)$. Thus $a = 4$, $c = 8$, and $b = \sqrt{64-16} = 4\sqrt{3}$. Therefore an equation of the hyperbola is $(x+6)^2/16 - y^2/48 = 1$.

22. The center is $(0, -1)$; $e = \frac{1}{3}$, $c = 1$; thus $a = c/e = 3$, so that $b = \sqrt{9-1} = 2\sqrt{2}$. An equation of the ellipse is $x^2/8 + (y+1)^2/9 = 1$.

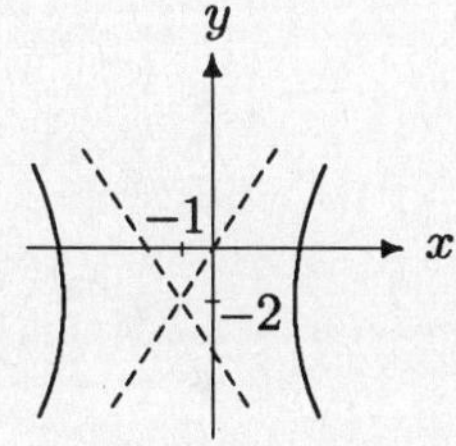

Exercise 23

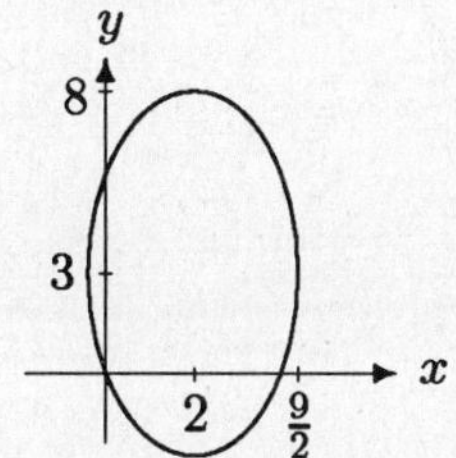

Exercise 24

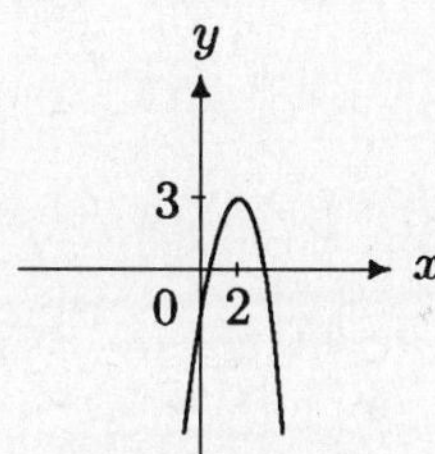

Exercise 25

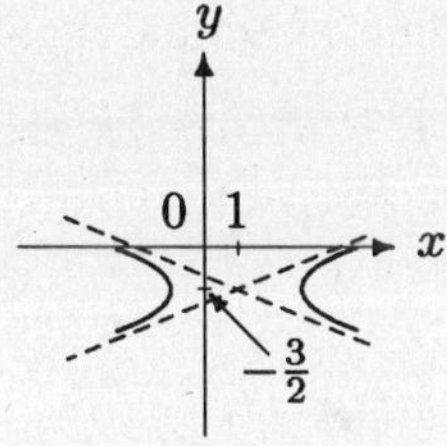

Exercise 26

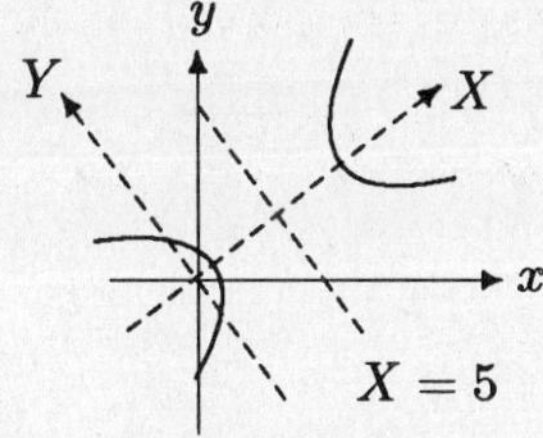

Exercise 27

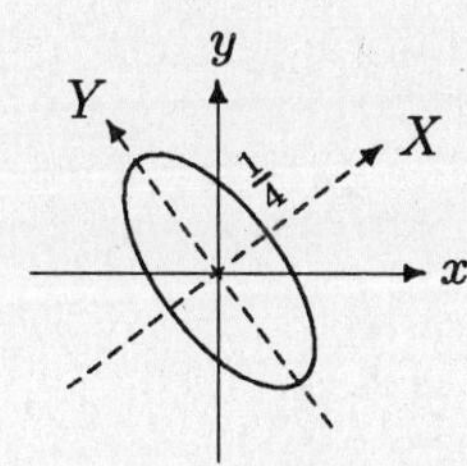

Exercise 28

23. $49(x^2+2x+1)-9(y^2+4y+4)=441$, or $49(x+1)^2-9(y+2)^2=441$, so that $(x+1)^2/9-(y+2)^2/49=1$.

24. $4(x^2-4x+4)+(y^2-6y+9)=25$, or $4(x-2)^2+(y-3)^2=25$, so that $4(x-2)^2/25+(y-3)^2/25=1$.

25. $9(x^2-4x+4)+5y-15=0$, so that $9(x-2)^2=-5(y-3)$.

26. $(x^2-2x+1)-4(y^2+3y+\frac{9}{4})=2$, or $(x-1)^2-4(y+\frac{3}{2})^2=2$, so that $(x-1)^2/2-2(y+\frac{3}{2})^2=1$.

27. $A=4$, $B=-24$, $C=11$; $\tan 2\theta=-24/(4-11)=\frac{24}{7}$; by the method of Example 2 in Section 10.6, $\cos 2\theta=\frac{7}{25}$, $\cos\theta=\frac{4}{5}$, and $\sin\theta=\frac{3}{5}$; the equation becomes $4(\frac{4}{5}X-\frac{3}{5}Y)^2-24(\frac{4}{5}X-\frac{3}{5}Y)(\frac{3}{5}X+\frac{4}{5}Y)+11(\frac{3}{5}X+\frac{4}{5}Y)^2+40(\frac{4}{5}X-\frac{3}{5}Y)+30(\frac{3}{5}X+\frac{4}{5}Y)-45=0$, or $-5X^2+50X+20Y^2-45=0$, or $(X-5)^2/16-Y^2/4=1$.

28. $A=73$, $B=72$, $C=52$; $\tan 2\theta=72/(73-52)=\frac{24}{7}$; by the method of Example 2 in Section 10.6, $\cos 2\theta=\frac{7}{25}$, $\cos\theta=\frac{4}{5}$ and $\sin\theta=\frac{3}{5}$; the equation becomes $73(\frac{4}{5}X-\frac{3}{5}Y)^2+72(\frac{4}{5}X-\frac{3}{5}Y)(\frac{3}{5}X+\frac{4}{5}Y)+52(\frac{3}{5}X+\frac{4}{5}Y)^2=25$, or $100X^2+25Y^2=25$. This is equivalent to $4X^2+Y^2=1$.

29. a. $\sqrt{(x-2)^2+(y-4)^2}=3|y|$, so that $(x-2)^2+(y-4)^2=9y^2$, or $(x-2)^2-8(y^2+y+\frac{1}{4})=-18$ or $4(y+\frac{1}{2})^2/9-(x-2)^2/18=1$.

b. $\sqrt{(x-2)^2+(y-4)^2}=|y|$, so that $(x-2)^2+(y-4)^2=y^2$, or $(x-2)^2-8(y-2)=0$, or $(x-2)^2=8(y-2)$.

c. $\sqrt{(x-2)^2+(y-4)^2}=\frac{1}{2}|y|$, so that $(x-2)^2+(y-4)^2=\frac{1}{4}y^2$, or $(x-2)^2+\frac{3}{4}(y^2-\frac{32}{3}y+\frac{256}{9})=\frac{16}{3}$, or $3(x-2)^2/16+9(y-16/3)^2/64=1$.

30. $e=4$, so the conic section is a hyperbola.

31. $r = \dfrac{\frac{3}{4}}{1 - \frac{1}{4}\cos\theta}$, so $e = \frac{1}{4}$, and hence the conic section is a ellipse.

32. Since $y^2 = -8x$ for any point (x, y) on the parabola, the distance from (x, y) to $(-10, 0)$ is

$$\sqrt{(x+10)^2 + y^2} = \sqrt{(x+10)^2 - 8x}.$$

The distance is minimized for the same nonpositive value of x that the square of the distance is, so let $f(x) = (x+10)^2 - 8x$ for $x \leq 0$. Then $f'(x) = 2(x+10) - 8 = 2x + 12$, and $f'(x) = 0$ if $x = -6$. Since $f'(x) < 0$ if $x < -6$ and $f'(x) > 0$ if $x > -6$, (1) of Section 4.6 and the First Derivative Test imply that $f(-6)$ is the minimum value of f on $(-\infty, 0]$, the domain of f. Thus $(-6, -4\sqrt{3})$ and $(-6, 4\sqrt{3})$ are the points on the parabola that are closest to the point $(-10, 0)$.

33. If $x^2 = 4cy$, then the slope of the line tangent to the parabola at $(x_0, x_0^2/4c)$ is $(dy/dx)|_{x=x_0} = x_0/2c$. An equation of the tangent line is $y - x_0^2/4c = (x_0/2c)(x - x_0)$. If the tangent line passes through (a, b), then $b - x_0^2/4c = (x_0/2c)(a - x_0)$, or $(1/4c)x_0^2 - (a/2c)x_0 + b = 0$. Solving for x_0, we find that

$$x_0 = \frac{a/2c \pm \sqrt{a^2/4c^2 - b/c}}{1/2c} = a \pm \sqrt{a^2 - 4bc}.$$

By assumption, $a^2 > |4cb|$, so that two such values of x_0 exist. Consequently equations of the tangent line are

$$y - \frac{(a + \sqrt{a^2 - 4bc})^2}{4c} = \frac{a + \sqrt{a^2 - 4bc}}{2c}(x - a - \sqrt{a^2 - 4bc})$$

and

$$y - \frac{(a - \sqrt{a^2 - 4bc})^2}{4c} = \frac{a - \sqrt{a^2 - 4bc}}{2c}(x - a + \sqrt{a^2 - 4bc}).$$

34. The focus divides the major axis into lines of length $a - c$ and $a + c$. Then

$$\sqrt{(a-c)(a+c)} = \sqrt{a^2 - c^2} = \sqrt{b^2} = b.$$

Thus the length b of the minor axis is the required geometric mean.

35. We have

$$x(-t) = \int_0^{-t} \cos\frac{\pi s^2}{2}\, ds \overset{u=-s}{=} \int_0^{t} \cos\frac{\pi u^2}{2}(-1)\, du = -x(t)$$

and

$$y(-t) = \int_0^{-t} \sin\frac{\pi s^2}{2}\, ds \overset{u=-s}{=} \int_0^{t} \sin\frac{\pi u^2}{2}(-1)\, du = -y(t).$$

Thus the spiral is symmetric with respect to the origin.

36. a. Since $r = 2\sin t$ is an equation of the circle, the coordinates (x_0, y) of A are given by $x_0 = r\cos t = 2\sin t\, \cos t$ and $y = r\sin t = 2\sin^2 t$. Since the line joining the origin and B makes an angle of t radians with respect to the positive x axis, the coordinates $(x, 2)$ of B satisfy $x = 2\cot t$. Thus the witch is given parametrically by $x = 2\cot t$ and $y = 2\sin^2 t$ for $0 < t < \pi$.

b. By part (a), $x^2 = 4\cot^2 t = 4(\csc^2 t - 1) = 4/\sin^2 t - 4 = 8/y - 4$. Therefore $8/y = x^2 + 4$, so that $y = 8/(x^2 + 4)$.

Cumulative Review(Chapters 1–9)

1. $\lim_{x\to\infty} \dfrac{x^2+1}{x\sqrt{3x^2+1}} = \lim_{x\to\infty} \dfrac{1+1/x^2}{\sqrt{3+1/x^2}} = \dfrac{1}{\sqrt{3}}$

2. Let $f(x) = \tan(\pi/4 - x)$. Then

$$\lim_{h\to 0} \frac{\tan(\pi/4-h)-1}{h} = \lim_{h\to 0} \frac{f(h)-f(0)}{h-0} = f'(0).$$

Since $f'(x) = [\sec^2(\pi/4-x)](-1) = -\sec^2(\pi/4-x)$, it follows that $f'(0) = -\sec^2(\pi/4) = -2$. Thus $\lim_{h\to 0}(\tan(\pi/4-h)-1)/h = -2$.

3. The conditions for applying l'Hôpital's Rule are met:

$$\lim_{x\to 0} \frac{1-\cos 4x}{3x^2} = \lim_{x\to 0} \frac{4\sin 4x}{6x} = \lim_{x\to 0} \frac{16\cos 4x}{6} = \frac{8}{3}.$$

4. $f'(x) = [-\sin(\ln x)](1/x) = -(1/x)\sin(\ln x)$

5. Notice that

$$f(x) = \int_{-x}^{x^2} \sin\sqrt{t^3+1}\,dt = \int_{-x}^{0} \sin\sqrt{t^3+1}\,dt + \int_{0}^{x^2} \sin\sqrt{t^3+1}\,dt.$$

Let $G(x) = \int_{-x}^{0} \sin\sqrt{t^3+1}\,dt$ and $H(x) = \int_0^{x^2} \sin\sqrt{t^3+1}\,dt$, so that $G(x) = -\int_0^{-x} \sin\sqrt{t^3+1}\,dt$. Then $G'(x) = [-\sin\sqrt{-x^3+1}](-1)$ and $H'(x) = (\sin\sqrt{x^6+1})(2x) = 2x\sin\sqrt{x^6+1}$. Therefore $f'(x) = G'(x) + H'(x) = \sin\sqrt{-x^3+1} + 2x\sin\sqrt{x^6+1}$.

6. The slope of the line l_z tangent to the unit circle $x^2+y^2=1$ at $(z, \sqrt{1-z^2})$ is $-z/\sqrt{1-z^2}$. Thus l_z is given by $(y-\sqrt{1-z^2})/(x-z) = -z/\sqrt{1-z^2}$, or equivalently, $y = -z(x-z)/\sqrt{1-z^2} + \sqrt{1-z^2} = (1-zx)/\sqrt{1-z^2}$. The x intercept of l_z occurs for $y=0$, which yields $1-zx=0$, that is, $x=1/z$. Now let $w =$ the x coordinate of $l_z = 1/z$. We are to find dw/dt when $w=2$, that is, $z=1/2$. By hypothesis, $dz/dt = 3$, so that $dw/dt = (dw/dz)(dz/dt) = (-1/z^2)(3)$. Therefore $(dw/dt)\big|_{z=1/2} = (-1/\frac{1}{4})(3) = -12$. Thus the x intercept is decreasing at the rate of 12 units per minute when the x intercept is 2.

7. a. Let x denote the horizontal distance between the person and the kite, and y the length of string let out. Then $x^2+30^2=y^2$. We want to find dx/dt when $y=50$. Now $(2x)(dx/dt) = (2y)(dy/dt)$. By hypothesis, $dy/dt = -4$, so that $dx/dt = (y/x)(dy/dt) = -4y/x$. Because the triangle is right-angled, when $y=50$ we have $x = \sqrt{(50)^2-(30)^2} = 40$. Therefore at the moment when $y=50$, we have $dx/dt = -4(50)/40 = -5$ (feet per second), so x is decreasing at 5 feet per second.

   b. Yes, because then $x=\sqrt{(45)^2-(30)^2}=15\sqrt{5}$, so that when $y=45$ we have $dx/dt = -4(45)/(15\sqrt{5}) = -12/\sqrt{5}$ (feet per second).

8. $f'(x) = \dfrac{(1/x)(x^n)-(\ln x)(nx^{n-1})}{x^{2n}} = \dfrac{x^{n-1}-nx^{n-1}\ln x}{x^{2n}} = \dfrac{1-n\ln x}{x^{n+1}}$,

so $f'(x) = 0$ if $1 - n\ln x = 0$, so that $\ln x = 1/n$, and thus $x = e^{1/n}$. Since

$$\lim_{x\to 0+} \frac{\ln x}{x^n} = -\infty \quad \text{and} \quad \lim_{x\to\infty} \frac{\ln x}{x^n} = 0$$

by l'Hôpital's Rule, and since

$$f(e^{1/n}) = \frac{\ln(e^{1/n})}{(e^{1/n})^n} = \frac{1/n}{e} = \frac{1}{ne} > 0$$

it follows that f is maximum at $e^{1/n}$.

9. $f'(x) = \cos x\cos(x-c) - \sin x\sin(x-c) = \cos[x + (x-c)] = \cos(2x-c)$, so that $f'(x) = 0$ if $\cos(2x-c) = 0$. Therefore $2x - c = \frac{1}{2}\pi + n\pi$, so that $x = \frac{1}{2}c + \frac{1}{4}\pi + \frac{1}{2}n\pi$ for some integer n. Since $f''(x) = -2\sin(2x-c)$, it follows that $f''(\frac{1}{2}c+\frac{1}{4}\pi+\frac{1}{2}n\pi) = -2\sin(c+\frac{1}{2}\pi+n\pi-c) = -2\sin(\frac{1}{2}\pi+n\pi)$, so that $f''(\frac{1}{2}c+\frac{1}{4}\pi+\frac{1}{2}n\pi) < 0$ if n is even. In that case, $f(\frac{1}{2}c+\frac{1}{4}\pi+\frac{1}{2}n\pi)$ is a relative maximum value. Since f has period π, $f(\frac{1}{2}c+\frac{1}{4}\pi)$ is the maximum value of f.

10. $f'(x) = e^{-2x}(1-2x)$; $f''(x) = 4e^{-2x}(x-1)$; relative maximum value is $f(\frac{1}{2}) = \frac{1}{2}e^{-1} = 1/(2e)$; increasing on $(-\infty, \frac{1}{2}]$ and decreasing on $[\frac{1}{2}, \infty)$; concave upward on $(1,\infty)$ and concave downward on $(-\infty, 1)$; inflection point is $(1, e^{-2})$; since $\lim_{x\to\infty} xe^{-2x} = \lim_{x\to\infty} x/e^{2x} = 0$ by l'Hôpital's Rule, the horizontal asymptote is $y = 0$.

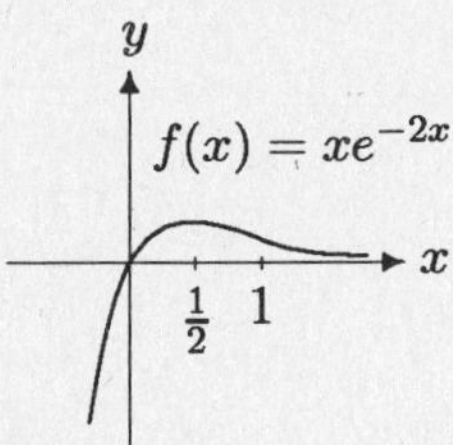

11. a. Let $f(x) = a^x$. Then $f'(x) = (\ln a)a^x$, so that $f'(0) = \ln a$. By the definition of the derivative, $f'(0) = \lim_{h\to 0}(f(h) - f(0))/(h-0) = \lim_{h\to 0}(a^h - 1)/h$. Thus $\lim_{h\to 0}(a^h-1)/h = \ln a$.

    b. Let $h = 1/n$. Then part (a) implies that $\ln a = \lim_{n\to\infty}(a^{1/n} - 1)/(1/n) = \lim_{n\to\infty} n(\sqrt[n]{a} - 1)$.

12. We will prove that f has an inverse by showing that if $x \neq z$, then $f(x) \neq f(z)$ (see (3) in Section 6.1). If $x \neq z$, then, since the exponential function is increasing, $e^{1/x} \neq e^{1/z}$, which means that

$$f(x) = \frac{1}{1+e^{1/x}} \neq \frac{1}{1+e^{1/z}} = f(z).$$

Thus f has an inverse. To find a formula for f^{-1}, let $y = f(x) = 1/(1+e^{1/x})$. Then $e^{1/x} = 1/y - 1$, so that $1/x = \ln(1/y - 1)$, and thus $x = 1/\ln(1/y-1)$. Therefore $f^{-1}(x) = 1/\ln(1/x - 1)$ for $0 < x < 1$ and $x \neq \frac{1}{2}$.

13. Let $u = 1 + 4x$, so that $du = 4\,dx$ and $36x = 9(u-1)$. If $x = 0$, then $u = 1$; if $x = \frac{3}{4}$, then $u = 4$. Thus

$$\int_0^{3/4} 36x\sqrt{1+4x}\,dx = \int_1^4 9(u-1)u^{1/2}\frac{1}{4}\,du = \frac{9}{4}\int_1^4 (u^{3/2} - u^{1/2})\,du$$

$$= \frac{9}{4}\left(\frac{2}{5}u^{5/2} - \frac{2}{3}u^{3/2}\right)\Big|_1^4 = \frac{9}{4}\left[\left(\frac{64}{5} - \frac{16}{3}\right) - \left(\frac{2}{5} - \frac{2}{3}\right)\right] = \frac{87}{5}.$$

14. $\displaystyle\int_0^{\pi/4} \frac{\tan x}{\sqrt{\sec x}}\,dx = \int_0^{\pi/4} \frac{\sin x}{\sqrt{\cos x}}\,dx = -2\sqrt{\cos x}\Big|_0^{\pi/4} = -2\sqrt{\cos(\pi/4)} + 2 = 2 - 2^{3/4}$

15. $u = x^2$, $dv = e^{2x}\,dx$; $du = 2x\,dx$, $v = \frac{1}{2}e^{2x}$; $\int x^2/e^{-2x}\,dx = \int x^2e^{2x}\,dx = \frac{1}{2}x^2e^{2x} - \int xe^{2x}\,dx$. For $\int xe^{2x}\,dx$, we let $u = x$, $dv = e^{2x}\,dx$; $du = dx$, $v = \frac{1}{2}e^{2x}$; $\int xe^{2x}\,dx = \frac{1}{2}xe^{2x} - \int \frac{1}{2}e^{2x}\,dx = \frac{1}{2}xe^{2x} - \frac{1}{4}e^{2x} + C_1$. Thus $\int x^2/e^{-2x}\,dx = \frac{1}{2}x^2e^{2x} - \frac{1}{2}xe^{2x} + \frac{1}{4}e^{2x} + C$.

16. $x = 2\sin u$, $dx = 2\cos u\,du$;

$$\int \frac{1}{(4-x^2)^{3/2}}\,dx = \int \frac{1}{(4-4\sin^2 u)^{3/2}}\,(2\cos u)\,du$$

$$= \int \frac{1}{8\cos^3 u}\,(2\cos u)\,du = \int \frac{1}{4}\sec^2 u\,du = \frac{1}{4}\tan u + C = \frac{x}{4\sqrt{4-x^2}} + C.$$

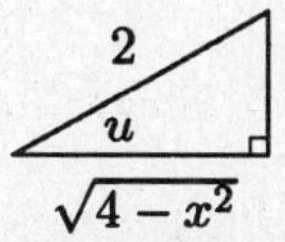

17. Since

$$\lim_{n\to\infty} \frac{(n+1)!/(1.4)^{n+1}}{n!/(1.4)^n} = \lim_{n\to\infty} \frac{n+1}{1.4} = \infty$$

the series diverges by the Ratio Test.

18. Since

$$\int_2^\infty \frac{1}{x(\ln x)^{3/2}}\,dx = \lim_{b\to\infty} \int_2^b \frac{1}{x(\ln x)^{3/2}}\,dx = \lim_{b\to\infty} -\frac{2}{(\ln x)^{1/2}}\Bigg|_2^b$$

$$= \lim_{b\to\infty} \left(-\frac{2}{(\ln b)^{3/2}} + \frac{2}{(\ln 2)^{1/2}}\right) = \frac{2}{(\ln 2)^{1/2}}$$

the series converges (absolutely).

19. Since

$$\lim_{n\to\infty} \left|\frac{5(n+1)^2x^{n+1}/[4^{(n+1)}((n+1)^3+2)]}{5n^2x^n/[4^n(n^3+2)]}\right| = \lim_{n\to\infty} \left(\frac{n+1}{n}\right)^2 \frac{1}{4}\,\frac{n^3+2}{(n+1)^3+2}\,|x| = \frac{1}{4}\,|x|$$

the series converges for $|x| < 4$ and diverges for $|x| > 4$. For $x = 4$, the series $\sum_{n=1}^\infty 5n^2/(n^3+2)$ diverges by comparison with the series $\sum_{n=1}^\infty 1/n$. For $x = -4$, the series $\sum_{n=1}^\infty 5n^2(-1)^n/(n^3+2)$ converges by the Alternating Series Test. Therefore the interval of convergence is $[-4, 4)$.

Chapter 11

Vectors, Lines and Planes

11.1 Cartesian Coordinates in Space

1. $|PQ| = \sqrt{(0-\sqrt{2})^2 + (1-0)^2 + (1-0)^2} = \sqrt{2+1+1} = 2$

2. $|PQ| = \sqrt{(3-2)^2 + (1-(-1))^2 + (0-(-2))^2} = \sqrt{1+4+4} = 3$

3. $|PQ| = \sqrt{(0-(-3))^2 + (8-4)^2 + (7-(-5))^2} = \sqrt{9+16+144} = 13$

4. $|PQ| = \sqrt{(4-4)^2 + (5-(-1))^2 + (11-3)^2} = \sqrt{0+36+64} = 10$

5. $|PQ| = \sqrt{(4-(-1))^2 + (2-3)^2 + (7-6)^2} = \sqrt{25+1+1} = 3\sqrt{3}$

6. $|PQ| = \sqrt{(\frac{1}{2}-1)^2 + (\frac{1}{2}\sqrt{2}-0)^2 + (0-(-\frac{1}{2}))^2} = \sqrt{\frac{1}{4}+\frac{1}{2}+\frac{1}{4}} = 1$

7. $$\begin{aligned} |PQ| &= \sqrt{(\sin x - 2\sin x)^2 + (2\cos x - \cos x)^2 + (0 - \tan x)^2} \\ &= \sqrt{\sin^2 x + \cos^2 x + \tan^2 x} = \sqrt{1+\tan^2 x} = |\sec x| \end{aligned}$$

8. $|PQ| = \sqrt{(0-e^x)^2 + (e^{-x}-0)^2 + (\sqrt{2}-2\sqrt{2})^2} = \sqrt{e^{2x}+e^{-2x}+2} = 2\cosh x$

9. Let $P=(3,0,2)$, $Q=(1,-1,5)$, and $R=(5,1,-1)$. Then
$$|PQ| = \sqrt{(1-3)^2+(-1-0)^2+(5-2)^2} = \sqrt{14}$$
and $|PR| = \sqrt{(5-3)^2+(1-0)^2+(-1-2)^2} = \sqrt{14}$. Thus P is equidistant from Q and R.

10. Let $P=(-1,1,2)$, $Q=(2,0,3)$, and $R=(3,4,5)$. The perimeter of the triangle is
$$\begin{aligned} |PQ|+|QR|+|RP| &= \sqrt{(2-(-1))^2+(0-1)^2+(3-2)^2} + \sqrt{(3-2)^2+(4-0)^2+(5-3)^2} \\ &\quad + \sqrt{(-1-3)^2+(1-4)^2+(2-5)^2} \\ &= \sqrt{11}+\sqrt{21}+\sqrt{34}. \end{aligned}$$

11. $(x-2)^2+(y-1)^2+(z+7)^2=25$

12. $(x+1)^2+y^2+(z-3)^2=2$

13. Completing the squares, we have $(x^2-2x+1)+(y^2-4y+4)+(z^2+6z+9)=-10+1+4+9$, or $(x-1)^2+(y-2)^2+(z+3)^2=4$, which is an equation of a sphere with center $(1,2,-3)$ and radius 2.

14. Completing the squares, we have $(x^2+6x+9)+(y^2+8y+16)+(z^2-4z+4)=9+16$, or $(x+3)^2+(y+4)^2+(z-2)^2=25$, which is an equation of a sphere with center $(-3,-4,2)$ and radius 5.

15. $x^2+(y+2)^2+(z+3)^2\le 36$

16. $(x-\frac{1}{2})^2+(y+1)^2\le 3$

17. $|PQ|=\sqrt{(2-1)^2+(1-(-1))^2+(-1-1)^2}=\sqrt{1+4+4}=3$;
$|RP|=\sqrt{1^2+(-1)^2+1^2}=\sqrt{3}$; $|RQ|=\sqrt{2^2+1^2+(-1)^2}=\sqrt{6}$.
Thus $|RP|^2+|RQ|^2=3+6=9=|PQ|^2$, so by the Pythagorean Theorem, the triangle is a right triangle.

18. $|PQ|=\sqrt{(2-3)^2+0^2+(-1-3)^2}=\sqrt{17}$;
$|PR|=\sqrt{(c-3)^2+1^2+(2-3)^2}=\sqrt{(c-3)^2+2}$;
$|QR|=\sqrt{(c-2)^2+1^2+(2-(-1))^2}=\sqrt{(c-2)^2+10}$.
Then $|PR|^2+|QR|^2=[(c-3)^2+2]+[(c-2)^2+10]=2c^2-10c+25$, so that $|PR|^2+|QR|^2=|PQ|^2$ if $2c^2-10c+25=17$, that is $c^2-5c+4=0$, so $c=1$ or 4.

19. If (x,y,z) is equidistant from $(2,1,0)$ and $(4,-1,-3)$, then $(x-2)^2+(y-1)^2+z^2=(x-4)^2+(y+1)^2+(z+3)^2$, so that $4x-4y-6z=21$.

20. If (x,y,z) is twice as far from $(0,0,0)$ as from $(-1,1,1)$, then $x^2+y^2+z^2=4[(x+1)^2+(y-1)^2+(z-1)^2]$, so that $3x^2+3y^2+3z^2+8x-8y-8z+12=0$, or $(x+\frac{4}{3})^2+(y-\frac{4}{3})^2+(z-\frac{4}{3})^2=\frac{4}{3}$. Thus the set of points is a sphere with center $(-\frac{4}{3},\frac{4}{3},\frac{4}{3})$.

21. Let $P=(x_0,y_0,z_0)$, $Q=(x_1,y_1,z_1)$ and $R=\left(\frac{1}{2}(x_0+x_1),\frac{1}{2}(y_0+y_1),\frac{1}{2}(z_0+z_1)\right)$. Then

$$\begin{aligned}|PR|^2&=\left[\frac{1}{2}(x_0+x_1)-x_0\right]^2+\left[\frac{1}{2}(y_0+y_1)-y_0\right]^2+\left[\frac{1}{2}(z_0+z_1)-z_0\right]^2\\&=\frac{1}{4}(x_1-x_0)^2+\frac{1}{4}(y_1-y_0)^2+\frac{1}{4}(z_1-z_0)^2\end{aligned}$$

and

$$\begin{aligned}|QR|^2&=\left[\frac{1}{2}(x_0+x_1)-x_1\right]^2+\left[\frac{1}{2}(y_0+y_1)-y_1\right]^2+\left[\frac{1}{2}(z_0+z_1)-z_1\right]^2\\&=\frac{1}{4}(x_0-x_1)^2+\frac{1}{4}(y_0-y_1)^2+\frac{1}{4}(z_0-z_1)^2.\end{aligned}$$

Thus $|PR|^2=|QR|^2$, so R is the midpoint of PQ.

22. By the result of Exercise 21, the midpoint is $\left(\frac{1}{2}(3-9), \frac{1}{2}(7+8), \frac{1}{2}(11+31)\right) = (-3, \frac{15}{2}, 21)$.

23. By the result of Exercise 21, the midpoint of the line segment joining $(2,-1,3)$ and $(4,1,7)$ is $(3,0,5)$, so the center of the sphere is $(3,0,5)$. The distance between $(2,-1,3)$ and $(3,0,5)$ is

$$\sqrt{(3-2)^2 + \left(0-(-1)\right)^2 + (5-3)^2} = \sqrt{1+1+4} = \sqrt{6},$$

so an equation of the sphere is $(x-3)^2 + y^2 + (z-5)^2 = 6$.

11.2 Vectors in Space

1. $\overrightarrow{PQ} = 3\mathbf{i} - 4\mathbf{j} + 10\mathbf{k}$

2. $\overrightarrow{PQ} = 2\mathbf{i} + 2\mathbf{j} + \mathbf{k}$

3. $\overrightarrow{PQ} = 3\mathbf{i} - 2\mathbf{j} + \sqrt{7}\,\mathbf{k}$

4. $\overrightarrow{PQ} = \sqrt{2}\,\mathbf{j} + \sqrt{3}\,\mathbf{k}$

5. $\mathbf{a} + \mathbf{b} = \mathbf{i} - 3\mathbf{j} + \mathbf{k}$; $\mathbf{a} - \mathbf{b} = 3\mathbf{i} - 7\mathbf{j} + 19\mathbf{k}$; $c\mathbf{a} = 4\mathbf{i} - 10\mathbf{j} + 20\mathbf{k}$

6. $\mathbf{a} + \mathbf{b} = \frac{3}{2}\mathbf{i} + \frac{1}{2}\mathbf{j} - 6\mathbf{k}$; $\mathbf{a} - \mathbf{b} = \frac{1}{2}\mathbf{i} + \frac{3}{2}\mathbf{j}$; $c\mathbf{a} = -\mathbf{i} - \mathbf{j} + 3\mathbf{k}$

7. $\mathbf{a} + \mathbf{b} = 2\mathbf{i} + \mathbf{j} + \mathbf{k}$; $\mathbf{a} - \mathbf{b} = 2\mathbf{i} - \mathbf{j} - \mathbf{k}$; $c\mathbf{a} = \frac{2}{3}\mathbf{i}$

8. $\mathbf{a} + \mathbf{b} = \mathbf{i} + \mathbf{k}$; $\mathbf{a} - \mathbf{b} = \mathbf{i} + 4\mathbf{j} - \mathbf{k}$; $c\mathbf{a} = \pi\mathbf{i} + 2\pi\mathbf{j}$

9. $\|\mathbf{a}\| = \sqrt{1^2 + (-1)^2 + 1^2} = \sqrt{3}$

10. $\|\mathbf{a}\| = \sqrt{2^2 + 1^2 + (-2)^2} = 3$

11. $\|\mathbf{b}\| = \sqrt{(-3)^2 + 4^2 + (-12)^2} = 13$

12. $\|\mathbf{b}\| = \sqrt{4^2 + (-8)^2 + 8^2} = 12$

13. $\|\mathbf{c}\| = \sqrt{(\sqrt{2})^2 + (-1)^2 + 1^2} = 2$

14. $\dfrac{\mathbf{a}}{\|\mathbf{a}\|} = \dfrac{\mathbf{a}}{\sqrt{3}} = \dfrac{1}{\sqrt{3}}\mathbf{i} + \dfrac{1}{\sqrt{3}}\mathbf{j} - \dfrac{1}{\sqrt{3}}\mathbf{k}$

15. $\dfrac{\mathbf{a}}{\|\mathbf{a}\|} = \dfrac{\mathbf{a}}{13} = -\dfrac{3}{13}\mathbf{i} + \dfrac{4}{13}\mathbf{j} - \dfrac{12}{13}\mathbf{k}$

16. $\dfrac{\mathbf{b}}{\|\mathbf{b}\|} = \dfrac{\mathbf{b}}{25} = \dfrac{7}{25}\mathbf{i} + \dfrac{12\sqrt{2}}{25}\mathbf{j} - \dfrac{12\sqrt{2}}{25}\mathbf{k}$

17. $\dfrac{\mathbf{b}}{\|\mathbf{b}\|} = \dfrac{\mathbf{b}}{\sqrt{13}} = \dfrac{2}{\sqrt{13}}\mathbf{i} - \dfrac{3}{\sqrt{13}}\mathbf{j}$

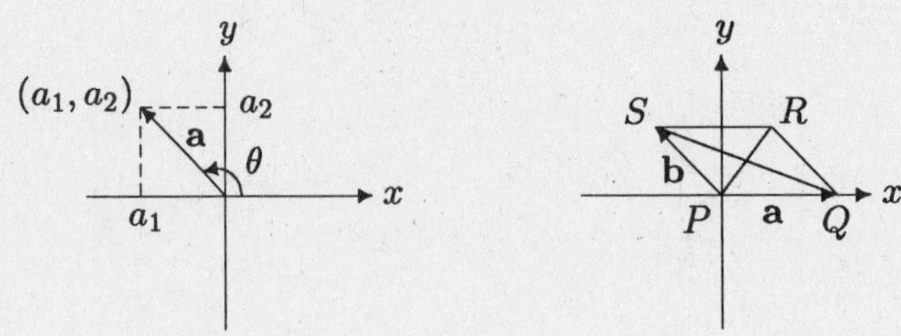

Exercise 23 Exercise 25

18. A unit vector $\mathbf{u}$ in the direction of $\mathbf{a}$ is given by

$$\mathbf{u} = \frac{\mathbf{a}}{\|\mathbf{a}\|} = \frac{\mathbf{i}+2\mathbf{j}-3\mathbf{k}}{\sqrt{1^2+2^2+(-3)^2}} = \frac{\mathbf{i}+2\mathbf{j}-3\mathbf{k}}{\sqrt{14}}.$$

Thus a vector $\mathbf{b}$ of length 5 in the direction opposite to $\mathbf{a}$ is given by $\mathbf{b} = -5\mathbf{u} = (-5/\sqrt{14})(\mathbf{i}+2\mathbf{j}-3\mathbf{k}) = (5/\sqrt{14})(-\mathbf{i}-2\mathbf{j}+3\mathbf{k})$.

19. $\|\mathbf{u}\|^2 = (\sqrt{1-b_1^2})^2 + (b_1\sqrt{1-b_2^2})^2 + (b_1 b_2)^2 = 1 - b_1^2 + b_1^2(1-b_2^2) + b_1^2 b_2^2 = 1$. Therefore $\mathbf{u}$ is a unit vector.

20. $\mathbf{F}_1 + \mathbf{F}_2 = (\sqrt{2}\,\mathbf{i} + \mathbf{j} - 4\mathbf{k}) + ((1-\sqrt{2})\mathbf{i} - 5\mathbf{j} - 4\mathbf{k}) = \mathbf{i} - 4\mathbf{j} - 8\mathbf{k}$.

21. $\mathbf{F}_1 + \mathbf{F}_2 = (10^{-3}\mathbf{i} + 0.12\mathbf{j} + 1.2 \times 10^4\mathbf{k}) + (3 \times 10^{-3}\mathbf{i} + 0.39\mathbf{j} - 5 \times 10^4\mathbf{k}) = 4 \times 10^{-3}\mathbf{i} + 0.51\mathbf{j} - 3.8 \times 10^4\mathbf{k}$

22. Let s be the length of the sides of the cube. Then $\overrightarrow{OB} + \overrightarrow{OD} + \overrightarrow{OF} = (s\mathbf{i} + s\mathbf{j}) + (s\mathbf{j} + s\mathbf{k}) + (s\mathbf{i} + s\mathbf{k}) = 2s\mathbf{i} + 2s\mathbf{j} + 2s\mathbf{k} = 2\overrightarrow{OG}$. Thus by Definition 12.4, $\overrightarrow{OB} + \overrightarrow{OD} + \overrightarrow{OF}$ is parallel to $\overrightarrow{OG}$.

23. a. If we place the vector $\mathbf{a}$ in the xy plane with its initial point at the origin and let its terminal point be (a_1, a_2), then $\mathbf{a} = a_1\mathbf{i} + a_2\mathbf{j}$. By the definition of $\cos\theta$ and $\sin\theta$, we have $\cos\theta = a_1/\|\mathbf{a}\|$ and $\sin\theta = a_2/\|\mathbf{a}\|$. Thus $\mathbf{a} = a_1\mathbf{i} + a_2\mathbf{j} = \|\mathbf{a}\|\,(\cos\theta\,\mathbf{i} + \sin\theta\,\mathbf{j})$.

    b. Let θ be the angle between the positive x axis and $\mathbf{u}$. Since $\|\mathbf{u}\| = 1$, it follows from part (a) that $\mathbf{u} = \cos\theta\,\mathbf{i} + \sin\theta\,\mathbf{j}$.

24. a. The vector $\overrightarrow{PQ} = \mathbf{b} - \mathbf{a}$ points from P to Q. Thus $\frac{1}{2}(\mathbf{b} - \mathbf{a})$ points from P to the midpoint of PQ. Since $\mathbf{a}$ points from the origin to P, it follows that $\mathbf{c} = \mathbf{a} + \frac{1}{2}(\mathbf{b} - \mathbf{a}) = \mathbf{a} + \frac{1}{2}\mathbf{b} - \frac{1}{2}\mathbf{a} = \frac{1}{2}(\mathbf{a} + \mathbf{b})$.

    b. By an argument similar to that in (a), we see that $\frac{2}{3}(\mathbf{b} - \mathbf{a})$ points from P to the point $\frac{2}{3}$ of the way from P to Q, so that $\mathbf{c} = \mathbf{a} + \frac{2}{3}(\mathbf{b} - \mathbf{a}) = \frac{1}{3}\mathbf{a} + \frac{2}{3}\mathbf{b}$.

25. Assume that the quadrilateral lies in the xy plane with P at the origin as in the figure, and let $\mathbf{a}$ and $\mathbf{b}$ be vectors along the two sides that contain the origin. Then $\mathbf{a} + \mathbf{b}$ and $\mathbf{a} - \mathbf{b}$ lie along the diagonals. Since the diagonals bisect each other, we have $\overrightarrow{SR} = \frac{1}{2}(\mathbf{a} - \mathbf{b}) + \frac{1}{2}(\mathbf{a} + \mathbf{b}) = \mathbf{a} = \overrightarrow{PQ}$ and $\overrightarrow{QR} = -\frac{1}{2}(\mathbf{a} - \mathbf{b}) + \frac{1}{2}(\mathbf{a} + \mathbf{b}) = \mathbf{b} = \overrightarrow{PS}$. Thus the opposite sides of the quadrilateral are parallel, so that the quadrilateral is a parallelogram.

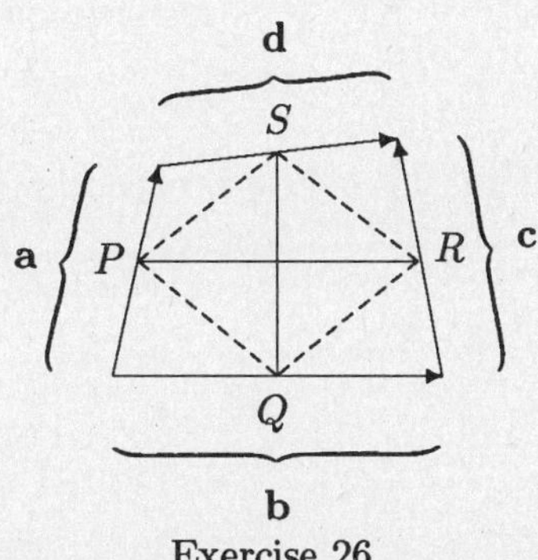

Exercise 26

26. Let P, Q, R, and S be the midpoints of the sides of the quadrilateral, and $\mathbf{a}$, $\mathbf{b}$, $\mathbf{c}$, and $\mathbf{d}$ the vectors corresponding to the four sides, as in the figure. Our first goal is to show that the vector from P to the midpoint of PR is the same as the vector from P to the midpoint of QS. To begin with, the vector from P to the midpoint of PR is $\frac{1}{2}\overrightarrow{PR} = \frac{1}{2}(-\frac{1}{2}\mathbf{a} + \mathbf{b} + \frac{1}{2}\mathbf{c}) = -\frac{1}{4}\mathbf{a} + \frac{1}{2}\mathbf{b} + \frac{1}{4}\mathbf{c}$. Next, the vector from Q to the midpoint of QS is $\frac{1}{2}(-\frac{1}{2}\mathbf{b} + \mathbf{a} + \frac{1}{2}\mathbf{d}) = -\frac{1}{4}\mathbf{b} + \frac{1}{2}\mathbf{a} + \frac{1}{4}\mathbf{d}$. Since $\mathbf{a} + \mathbf{d} = \mathbf{b} + \mathbf{c}$, this means that $\mathbf{d} = \mathbf{b} + \mathbf{c} - \mathbf{a}$, so that $-\frac{1}{4}\mathbf{b} + \frac{1}{2}\mathbf{a} + \frac{1}{4}\mathbf{d} = -\frac{1}{4}\mathbf{b} + \frac{1}{2}\mathbf{a} + \frac{1}{4}(\mathbf{b} + \mathbf{c} - \mathbf{a}) = \frac{1}{4}\mathbf{a} + \frac{1}{4}\mathbf{c}$. Thus the vector from P to the midpoint of QS is $-\frac{1}{2}\mathbf{a} + \frac{1}{2}\mathbf{b} + \frac{1}{2}\overrightarrow{QS} = -\frac{1}{2}\mathbf{a} + \frac{1}{2}\mathbf{b} + (\frac{1}{4}\mathbf{a} + \frac{1}{4}\mathbf{c}) = -\frac{1}{4}\mathbf{a} + \frac{1}{2}\mathbf{b} + \frac{1}{4}\mathbf{c}$, which is the same as the vector from P to the midpoint of PR. As a result, PR and QS bisect each other. By Exercise 25, the quadrilateral $PQRS$ is a parallelogram.

27. The force $\mathbf{F}_1$ exerted by the first child is given by $\mathbf{F}_1 = -20\mathbf{j}$, and the force $\mathbf{F}_2$ exerted by the second child is given by

$$\mathbf{F}_2 = 100\left(\cos\frac{\pi}{3}\,\mathbf{i} + \sin\frac{\pi}{3}\,\mathbf{j}\right) = 50(\mathbf{i} + \sqrt{3}\,\mathbf{j}).$$

If $\mathbf{F}$ is the force exerted by the third child, and θ the angle $\mathbf{F}$ makes with the positive x axis, then $\mathbf{F} = \|\mathbf{F}\|\ (\cos\theta\,\mathbf{i} + \sin\theta\,\mathbf{j})$. If the total force exerted on the ball is to be $\mathbf{0}$, then $\mathbf{F}_1 + \mathbf{F}_2 + \mathbf{F} = \mathbf{0}$, so that $-20\mathbf{j} + 50(\mathbf{i} + \sqrt{3}\,\mathbf{j}) + \|\mathbf{F}\|\ (\cos\theta\,\mathbf{i} + \sin\theta\,\mathbf{j}) = \mathbf{0}$. Combining coefficients of $\mathbf{i}$ and $\mathbf{j}$, we find that

$$50 + \|\mathbf{F}\|\cos\theta = 0 \quad\text{and}\quad -20 + 50\sqrt{3} + \|\mathbf{F}\|\sin\theta = 0$$

so that

$$\|\mathbf{F}\|\cos\theta = -50 \quad\text{and}\quad \|\mathbf{F}\|\sin\theta = 20 - 50\sqrt{3}.$$

Therefore

$$\tan\theta = \frac{\sin\theta}{\cos\theta} = \frac{20 - 50\sqrt{3}}{-50} = \sqrt{3} - \frac{2}{5}$$

and

$$\mathbf{F} = \|\mathbf{F}\|\ (\cos\theta\,\mathbf{i} + \sin\theta\,\mathbf{j}) = \|\mathbf{F}\|\cos\theta\,\mathbf{i} + \|\mathbf{F}\|\sin\theta\,\mathbf{j} = -50\mathbf{i} + (20 - 50\sqrt{3})\mathbf{j}.$$

28. Consider a coordinate system having its x axis along the line l. Let $\mathbf{F}_1$ be the force exerted by the tugboat at A and $\mathbf{F}_2$ the force exerted by the tugboat at B. Then

$$\mathbf{F}_1 = 1000\left(\cos\frac{\pi}{6}\,\mathbf{i} + \sin\frac{\pi}{6}\,\mathbf{j}\right) = 500(\sqrt{3}\,\mathbf{i} + \mathbf{j})$$

and

$$\mathbf{F}_2 = \|\mathbf{F}_2\| \left(\cos\frac{\pi}{4}\mathbf{i} - \sin\frac{\pi}{4}\mathbf{j}\right) = \frac{\|\mathbf{F}_2\|}{2}(\sqrt{2}\,\mathbf{i} - \sqrt{2}\,\mathbf{j}).$$

If the freighter is to move along l, then $\mathbf{F}_1 + \mathbf{F}_2 = c\mathbf{i}$ for some number c, so that

$$500(\sqrt{3}\,\mathbf{i} + \mathbf{j}) + \frac{\|\mathbf{F}_2\|}{2}(\sqrt{2}\,\mathbf{i} - \sqrt{2}\,\mathbf{j}) = c\mathbf{i}.$$

Equating the **j**-components of both sides, we find that $500 - (\|\mathbf{F}_2\|/2)\sqrt{2} = 0$, or $\|\mathbf{F}_2\| = 500\sqrt{2}$ (pounds).

29. Let $\mathbf{v}$ be the velocity of the airplane with respect to the ground, $\mathbf{v}_1$ the velocity of the airplane with respect to the air, and $\mathbf{v}_2$ the velocity of the air with respect to the ground. By the hint,

$$\mathbf{v} = \mathbf{v}_1 + \mathbf{v}_2 = 300\left(\cos\frac{\pi}{6}\mathbf{i} + \sin\frac{\pi}{6}\mathbf{j}\right) + 20\mathbf{j} = 150\sqrt{3}\,\mathbf{i} + 170\mathbf{j}.$$

Thus $\|\mathbf{v}\| = \sqrt{(150\sqrt{3})^2 + (170)^2} = \sqrt{96{,}400} \approx 310$ (miles per hour).

30. Consider a coordinate system with the positive y axis pointing north, in the direction the boat travels. Let $\mathbf{v}$ be the velocity of the boat with respect to the ground, $\mathbf{v}_1$ the velocity of the boat with respect to the air, and $\mathbf{v}_2$ the velocity of the air with respect to the ground. Then $\mathbf{v} = 8\mathbf{j}$, $\mathbf{v}_1 = c_1(\mathbf{i} - \mathbf{j})$, and $\mathbf{v}_2 = c_2\mathbf{i}$, for appropriate constants c_1 and c_2. By the hint to Exercise 29, $8\mathbf{j} = \mathbf{v} = \mathbf{v}_1 + \mathbf{v}_2 = c_1(\mathbf{i} - \mathbf{j}) + c_2\mathbf{i} = (c_1 + c_2)\mathbf{i} - c_1\mathbf{j}$. Equating coefficients of **i** and **j**, we find that $0 = c_1 + c_2$ and $8 = -c_1$, so that $c_1 = -8$ and $c_2 = 8$. Then the speed $\|\mathbf{v}_2\|$ of the wind is given by $\|\mathbf{v}_2\| = \|8\mathbf{i}\| = 8$ (miles per hour).

31. If we let $q_1 = 1.6 \times 10^{-19}$, $\mathbf{u}_1 = (-\mathbf{j} - \mathbf{k})/\sqrt{2}$, $r_1 = 10^{-11}\sqrt{2}$, $q_2 = -1.6 \times 10^{-19}$, $\mathbf{u}_2 = (-\mathbf{i} - \mathbf{j})/\sqrt{2}$, and $r_2 = 10^{-12}\sqrt{2}$, then

$$\mathbf{F} = \frac{q_1(1)}{4\pi\varepsilon_0 r_1^2}\mathbf{u}_1 + \frac{q_2(1)}{4\pi\varepsilon_0 r_2^2}\mathbf{u}_2 = \frac{1.6 \times 10^{-19}}{4\pi\varepsilon_0(2 \times 10^{-22})}\left(\frac{-\mathbf{j} - \mathbf{k}}{\sqrt{2}}\right) + \frac{-1.6 \times 10^{-19}}{4\pi\varepsilon_0(2 \times 10^{-24})}\left(\frac{-\mathbf{i} - \mathbf{j}}{\sqrt{2}}\right)$$

$$= \frac{100\sqrt{2}}{\pi\varepsilon_0}(-\mathbf{j} - \mathbf{k} + 100\mathbf{i} + 100\mathbf{j}) = \frac{100\sqrt{2}}{\pi\varepsilon_0}(100\mathbf{i} + 99\mathbf{j} - \mathbf{k}).$$

32. For the unit charge let $q = 1$ and $Q = (0, 10^{-11}, 0)$, for the proton let $q_1 = 1.6 \times 10^{-19}$ and $Q_1 = (3 \times 10^{-11}, 4 \times 10^{-11}, 0)$, and for the electron let $q_2 = -1.6 \times 10^{-19}$ and $Q_2 = (0, 0, 10^{-11})$. Then $r_1 = \|\overrightarrow{Q_1Q}\| = \sqrt{(3 \times 10^{-11})^2 + (3 \times 10^{-11})^2} = 3\sqrt{2} \times 10^{-11}$ and $r_2 = \|\overrightarrow{Q_2Q}\| = \sqrt{(10^{-11})^2 + (10^{-11})^2} = \sqrt{2} \times 10^{-11}$. Therefore

$$\mathbf{u}_1 = \frac{\overrightarrow{Q_1Q}}{\|\overrightarrow{Q_1Q}\|} = \frac{-3 \times 10^{-11}\mathbf{i} - 3 \times 10^{-11}\mathbf{j}}{3\sqrt{2} \times 10^{-11}} = -\frac{1}{\sqrt{2}}\mathbf{i} - \frac{1}{\sqrt{2}}\mathbf{j}$$

and

$$\mathbf{u}_2 = \frac{\overrightarrow{Q_2Q}}{\|\overrightarrow{Q_2Q}\|} = \frac{10^{-11}\mathbf{j} - 10^{-11}\mathbf{k}}{\sqrt{2} \times 10^{-11}} = \frac{1}{\sqrt{2}}\mathbf{j} - \frac{1}{\sqrt{2}}\mathbf{k}.$$

Then

$$\mathbf{F} = \frac{q_1 q}{4\pi\varepsilon_0 r_1^2}\mathbf{u}_1 + \frac{q_2 q}{4\pi\varepsilon_0 r_2^2}\mathbf{u}_2 = \frac{1.6\times 10^{-19}}{4\pi\varepsilon_0(18\times 10^{-22})}\left(-\frac{1}{\sqrt{2}}\mathbf{i} - \frac{1}{\sqrt{2}}\mathbf{j}\right) + \frac{-1.6\times 10^{-19}}{4\pi\varepsilon_0(2\times 10^{-22})}\left(\frac{1}{\sqrt{2}}\mathbf{j} - \frac{1}{\sqrt{2}}\mathbf{k}\right)$$

$$= \frac{200\sqrt{2}}{\pi\varepsilon_0}\left(-\frac{1}{18}\mathbf{i} - \frac{5}{9}\mathbf{j} + \frac{1}{2}\mathbf{k}\right).$$

33. Let $m = m_1 + m_2 + \cdots + m_n$. By writing the vectors in terms of the corresponding components, we find that

$$\begin{aligned}
m_1\overrightarrow{PP_1} + m_2\overrightarrow{PP_2} + \cdots + m_n\overrightarrow{PP_n} &= [m_1(x_1 - \bar{x})\mathbf{i} + m_1(y_1 - \bar{y})\mathbf{j}] \\
&\quad + [m_2(x_2 - \bar{x})\mathbf{i} + m_2(y_2 - \bar{y})\mathbf{j}] + \cdots \\
&\quad + [m_n(x_n - \bar{x})\mathbf{i} + m_n(y_n - \bar{y})\mathbf{j}] \\
&= [m_1(x_1 - \bar{x}) + m_2(x_2 - \bar{x}) + \cdots + m_n(x_n - \bar{x})]\mathbf{i} \\
&\quad + [m_1(y_1 - \bar{y}) + m_2(y_2 - \bar{y}) + \cdots + m_n(y_n - \bar{y})]\mathbf{j} \\
&= [(m_1x_1 + m_2x_2 + \cdots + m_nx_n) - (m_1 + m_2 + \cdots + m_n)\bar{x}]\mathbf{i} \\
&\quad + [(m_1y_1 + m_2y_2 + \cdots + m_ny_n) - (m_1 + m_2 + \cdots + m_n)\bar{y}]\mathbf{j} \\
&= [(m_1x_1 + m_2x_2 + \cdots + m_nx_n) - m\bar{x}]\mathbf{i} \\
&\quad + [(m_1y_1 + m_2y_2 + \cdots + m_ny_n) - m\bar{y}]\mathbf{j}
\end{aligned}$$

By (3) of Section 8.6, the coefficients of **i** and **j** are 0, so that $m_1\overrightarrow{PP_1} + m_2\overrightarrow{PP_2} + \cdots + m_n\overrightarrow{PP_n} = \mathbf{0}$.

34. a. Let $\mathbf{b} = b_1\mathbf{i} + b_2\mathbf{j} + b_3\mathbf{k}$. Since a ray and its reflection travel in a plane, we find that $b_1\mathbf{i} + b_2\mathbf{j}$ is parallel to $a_1\mathbf{i} + a_2\mathbf{j}$, so that $b_1 = ca_1$ and $b_2 = ca_2$ for an appropriate positive value of c. Since the angle of incidence θ and the angle of reflection are equal, and since **a** and **b** are unit vectors, $-a_3 = \sin\theta = b_3$. Thus $\mathbf{b} = ca_1\mathbf{i} + ca_2\mathbf{j} - a_3\mathbf{k}$. Since $\sqrt{c^2(a_1^2 + a_2^2) + a_3^2} = \|\mathbf{b}\| = 1 = \|\mathbf{a}\| = \sqrt{a_1^2 + a_2^2 + a_3^2}$, it follows that $c = 1$, so that $\mathbf{b} = a_1\mathbf{i} + a_2\mathbf{j} - a_3\mathbf{k}$.

b. Consider a coordinate system such that the mirrors correspond to the three coordinate planes, and assume that the ray is reflected first by the xy plane, then by the yz plane, and finally by the xz plane, in the first octant. If $a_1\mathbf{i} + a_2\mathbf{j} + a_3\mathbf{k}$ denotes the incident ray, then after reflection in the xy plane, the ray becomes $a_1\mathbf{i} + a_2\mathbf{j} - a_3\mathbf{k}$ by part (a). After reflection in the yz plane, this ray becomes $a_1\mathbf{i} - a_2\mathbf{j} - a_3\mathbf{k}$, and after reflection in the xz plane this ray becomes $-a_1\mathbf{i} - a_2\mathbf{j} - a_3\mathbf{k}$, which is parallel to the original incident ray.

11.3 The Dot Product

1. $\mathbf{a}\cdot\mathbf{b} = (1)(2) + (1)(-3) + (-1)(4) = -5$; $\cos\theta = \dfrac{\mathbf{a}\cdot\mathbf{b}}{\|\mathbf{a}\|\,\|\mathbf{b}\|} = \dfrac{-5}{\sqrt{3}\sqrt{29}} = \dfrac{-5}{\sqrt{87}}$

2. $\mathbf{a}\cdot\mathbf{b} = (\frac{1}{2})(2) + (\frac{1}{3})(-2) + (-2)(1) = -\frac{5}{3}$; $\cos\theta = \dfrac{\mathbf{a}\cdot\mathbf{b}}{\|\mathbf{a}\|\,\|\mathbf{b}\|} = \dfrac{-\frac{5}{3}}{(\sqrt{157}/6)3} = \dfrac{-10}{3\sqrt{157}}$

3. $\mathbf{a}\cdot\mathbf{b} = (\sqrt{2})(-\sqrt{2}) + (4)(-\sqrt{3}) + (\sqrt{3})(2) = -2 - 2\sqrt{3}$; $\cos\theta = \dfrac{\mathbf{a}\cdot\mathbf{b}}{\|\mathbf{a}\|\,\|\mathbf{b}\|} = \dfrac{-2-2\sqrt{3}}{\sqrt{21}\cdot 3} = -\dfrac{2(1+\sqrt{3})}{3\sqrt{21}}$

4. $\mathbf{a}\cdot\mathbf{b} = 4(-\frac{1}{2}) + (-2)(-1) + (0)(\sqrt{3}) = 0$; $\cos\theta = \dfrac{\mathbf{a}\cdot\mathbf{b}}{\|\mathbf{a}\|\,\|\mathbf{b}\|} = 0$

5. Let $\mathbf{a} = \sqrt{6}\,\mathbf{i} + \mathbf{j} - \mathbf{k}$ and $\mathbf{b} = \mathbf{i}$, and let θ be the angle between $\mathbf{a}$ and $\mathbf{b}$. Then

$$\cos\theta = \frac{\mathbf{a}\cdot\mathbf{b}}{\|\mathbf{a}\|\,\|\mathbf{b}\|} = \frac{\sqrt{6}}{\sqrt{8}\sqrt{1}} = \sqrt{\frac{3}{4}} = \frac{1}{2}\sqrt{3}, \quad \text{so} \quad \theta = \frac{\pi}{6}.$$

6. $\mathbf{a}\cdot\mathbf{b} = (1)(0) + (0)(1) = 0$; they are perpendicular.

7. $\mathbf{a}\cdot\mathbf{b} = (\sqrt{2})(-1) + (3)(\sqrt{2}) + (1)(5) = 2\sqrt{2} + 5 \neq 0$; they are not perpendicular.

8. $\overrightarrow{PQ} = -\mathbf{i} + 3\mathbf{j}$ and $\overrightarrow{PR} = -5\mathbf{i} + \mathbf{j}$, so $\overrightarrow{PQ}\cdot\overrightarrow{PR} = (-1)(-5) + (3)(1) = 8 \neq 0$. Thus $\overrightarrow{PQ}$ and $\overrightarrow{PR}$ are not perpendicular.

9. $\overrightarrow{PQ} = 3\mathbf{i} - 3\mathbf{j} + \mathbf{k}$ and $\overrightarrow{PR} = -2\mathbf{j} - 6\mathbf{k}$, so $\overrightarrow{PQ}\cdot\overrightarrow{PR} = (3)(0) + (-3)(-2) + (1)(-6) = 0$. Thus $\overrightarrow{PQ}$ and $\overrightarrow{PR}$ are perpendicular.

10. Since $(2\mathbf{i}+\mathbf{j}-\mathbf{k})\cdot(3\mathbf{i}+7\mathbf{j}+13\mathbf{k}) = 6+7-13 = 0$, $(2\mathbf{i}+\mathbf{j}-\mathbf{k})\cdot(20\mathbf{i}-29\mathbf{j}+11\mathbf{k}) = 40-29-11 = 0$, and $(3\mathbf{i}+7\mathbf{j}+13\mathbf{k})\cdot(20\mathbf{i}-29\mathbf{j}+11\mathbf{k}) = 60 - 203 + 143 = 0$, the three vectors are mutually perpendicular.

11. $\mathbf{pr}_{\mathbf{a}}\mathbf{b} = \dfrac{\mathbf{a}\cdot\mathbf{b}}{\|\mathbf{a}\|^2}\mathbf{a} = \dfrac{2}{9}(2\mathbf{i} - \mathbf{j} + 2\mathbf{k}) = \dfrac{4}{9}\mathbf{i} - \dfrac{2}{9}\mathbf{j} + \dfrac{4}{9}\mathbf{k}$

12. $\mathbf{pr}_{\mathbf{a}}\mathbf{b} = \dfrac{\mathbf{a}\cdot\mathbf{b}}{\|\mathbf{a}\|^2}\mathbf{a} = \dfrac{4\sqrt{3}-8}{16}(\sqrt{3}\,\mathbf{i} + 2\mathbf{j} - 3\mathbf{k}) = \dfrac{\sqrt{3}-2}{4}(\sqrt{3}\,\mathbf{i} + 2\mathbf{j} - 3\mathbf{k})$

13. $\overrightarrow{PQ} = -3\mathbf{i}$ and $\overrightarrow{PR} = -5\mathbf{i} + 4\mathbf{j}$, so $\overrightarrow{PQ}\cdot\overrightarrow{PR} = (-3)(-5) + (0)(4) = 15$ and $\|\overrightarrow{PQ}\|^2 = (-3)^2 + 0^2 = 9$. Thus

$$\mathbf{pr}_{\overrightarrow{PQ}}\overrightarrow{PR} = \left(\frac{\overrightarrow{PQ}\cdot\overrightarrow{PR}}{\|\overrightarrow{PQ}\|^2}\right)\overrightarrow{PQ} = \frac{15}{9}(-3\mathbf{i}) = -5\mathbf{i}.$$

14. $\overrightarrow{PQ} = -2\mathbf{i} - 2\mathbf{j} - 2\mathbf{k}$ and $\overrightarrow{PR} = -\mathbf{j} - 3\mathbf{k}$, so $\overrightarrow{PQ}\cdot\overrightarrow{PR} = (-2)(0) + (-2)(-1) + (-2)(-3) = 8$ and $\|\overrightarrow{PQ}\|^2 = (-2)^2 + (-2)^2 + (-2)^2 = 12$. Thus

$$\mathbf{pr}_{\overrightarrow{PQ}}\overrightarrow{PR} = \left(\frac{\overrightarrow{PQ}\cdot\overrightarrow{PR}}{\|\overrightarrow{PQ}\|^2}\right)\overrightarrow{PQ} = \frac{8}{12}(-2\mathbf{i} - 2\mathbf{j} - 2\mathbf{k}) = -\frac{4}{3}(\mathbf{i} + \mathbf{j} + \mathbf{k}).$$

15. $\mathbf{a}\cdot\mathbf{a}' = 0 + 2 - 2 = 0$. Thus $\mathbf{a}$ and $\mathbf{a}'$ are perpendicular.

$$\mathbf{pr}_{\mathbf{a}}\mathbf{b} = \frac{\mathbf{a}\cdot\mathbf{b}}{\|\mathbf{a}\|^2}\mathbf{a} = \frac{18}{6}\mathbf{a} = 3\mathbf{a} = 3(\mathbf{i} + 2\mathbf{j} - \mathbf{k})$$

$$\mathbf{pr}_{\mathbf{a}'}\mathbf{b} = \mathbf{b} - \mathbf{pr}_{\mathbf{a}}\mathbf{b} = 3\mathbf{i} + \mathbf{j} - 13\mathbf{k} - 3(\mathbf{i} + 2\mathbf{j} - \mathbf{k}) = -5\mathbf{j} - 10\mathbf{k} = -5\mathbf{a}'$$

Thus $\mathbf{b} = 3\mathbf{a} - 5\mathbf{a}'$.

16. $\mathbf{a}\cdot\mathbf{a}' = 2-3+1 = 0$. Thus $\mathbf{a}$ and $\mathbf{a}'$ are perpendicular.

$$\mathbf{pr_a b} = \frac{\mathbf{a}\cdot\mathbf{b}}{\|\mathbf{a}\|^2}\mathbf{a} = \frac{-6}{3}\mathbf{a} = -2\mathbf{a} = -2(\mathbf{i}+\mathbf{j}-\mathbf{k})$$

$$\mathbf{pr_{a'} b} = \mathbf{b} - \mathbf{pr_a b} = -5\mathbf{j}+\mathbf{k}+2(\mathbf{i}+\mathbf{j}-\mathbf{k}) = 2\mathbf{i}-3\mathbf{j}-\mathbf{k} = \mathbf{a}'$$

Thus $\mathbf{b} = -2\mathbf{a}+\mathbf{a}'$.

17. $\mathbf{a}\cdot\mathbf{a}' = 4-24+20 = 0$. Thus $\mathbf{a}$ and $\mathbf{a}'$ are perpendicular.

$$\mathbf{pr_a b} = \frac{\mathbf{a}\cdot\mathbf{b}}{\|\mathbf{a}\|^2}\mathbf{a} = \frac{-45}{45}\mathbf{a} = -\mathbf{a} = -(2\mathbf{i}-4\mathbf{j}+5\mathbf{k})$$

$$\mathbf{pr_{a'} b} = \mathbf{b} - \mathbf{pr_a b} = \mathbf{i}+13\mathbf{j}+\mathbf{k}+(2\mathbf{i}-4\mathbf{j}+5\mathbf{k}) = 3\mathbf{i}+9\mathbf{j}+6\mathbf{k} = \frac{3}{2}\mathbf{a}'$$

Thus $\mathbf{b} = -\mathbf{a}+\frac{3}{2}\mathbf{a}'$.

18. a. Let $P = (2,3,4)$, $Q = (3,5,5)$, and $R = (1,3,11)$. Then $\overrightarrow{PQ} = \mathbf{i}+2\mathbf{j}+\mathbf{k}$, $\overrightarrow{PR} = -\mathbf{i}+7\mathbf{k}$, and $\overrightarrow{QR} = -2\mathbf{i}-2\mathbf{j}+6\mathbf{k}$. Since $\overrightarrow{PQ}\cdot\overrightarrow{QR} = (1)(-2)+(2)(-2)+(1)(6) = 0$, $\overrightarrow{PQ}$ and $\overrightarrow{QR}$ are perpendicular. Therefore triangle PQR is a right triangle.

    b. Let $P = (0,-1,2)$, $Q = (1,4,-2)$, and $R = (5,0,1)$. Then $\overrightarrow{PQ} = \mathbf{i}+5\mathbf{j}-4\mathbf{k}$, $\overrightarrow{PR} = 5\mathbf{i}+\mathbf{j}-\mathbf{k}$, and $\overrightarrow{QR} = 4\mathbf{i}-4\mathbf{j}+3\mathbf{k}$. Since $\overrightarrow{PQ}\cdot\overrightarrow{PR} = (1)(5)+(5)(1)+(-4)(-1) = 14$, $\overrightarrow{PQ}\cdot\overrightarrow{QR} = (1)(4)+(5)(-4)+(-4)(3) = -28$, $\overrightarrow{QR}\cdot\overrightarrow{PR} = (4)(5)+(-4)(1)+(3)(-1) = 13$, no two of $\overrightarrow{PQ}$, $\overrightarrow{PR}$, and $\overrightarrow{QR}$ are perpendicular. Therefore triangle PQR is not a right triangle.

19. Let $\mathbf{a} = \mathbf{i}$, $\mathbf{b} = \mathbf{j}$, and $\mathbf{c} = \mathbf{k}$. Then $\mathbf{a}\cdot\mathbf{b} = 0 = \mathbf{a}\cdot\mathbf{c}$, but $\mathbf{b} \neq \mathbf{c}$.

20. $\mathbf{a}\cdot\mathbf{a} = (a_1)(a_1)+(a_2)(a_2)+(a_3)(a_3) = a_1^2+a_2^2+a_3^2 = \|\mathbf{a}\|^2$.

21. $\mathbf{a}\cdot\mathbf{b} = (a_1)(b_1)+(a_2)(b_2)+(a_3)(b_3) = (b_1)(a_1)+(b_2)(a_2)+(b_3)(a_3) = \mathbf{b}\cdot\mathbf{a}$.

22. a.
$$\begin{aligned}\mathbf{a}\cdot(\mathbf{b}+\mathbf{c}) &= \mathbf{a}\cdot[(b_1+c_1)\mathbf{i}+(b_2+c_2)\mathbf{j}+(b_3+c_3)\mathbf{k}]\\ &= a_1(b_1+c_1)+a_2(b_2+c_2)+a_3(b_3+c_3)\\ &= (a_1b_1+a_2b_2+a_3b_3)+(a_1c_1+a_2c_2+a_3c_3)\\ &= \mathbf{a}\cdot\mathbf{b}+\mathbf{a}\cdot\mathbf{c}\end{aligned}$$

    b. If $\mathbf{a}$ is perpendicular to $\mathbf{b}$ and $\mathbf{c}$, then $\mathbf{a}\cdot\mathbf{b} = 0 = \mathbf{a}\cdot\mathbf{c}$, so that by (a), $\mathbf{a}\cdot(\mathbf{b}+\mathbf{c}) = \mathbf{a}\cdot\mathbf{b}+\mathbf{a}\cdot\mathbf{c} = 0+0 = 0$, which implies that $\mathbf{a}$ is perpendicular to $\mathbf{b}+\mathbf{c}$.

    c. Using the properties of the dot product, we have

$$(\|\mathbf{b}\|\,\mathbf{a}+\|\mathbf{a}\|\,\mathbf{b})\cdot\ \|\mathbf{b}\|\,\mathbf{a}-\|\mathbf{a}\|\,\mathbf{b}) = \|\mathbf{b}\|^2\,\mathbf{a}\cdot\mathbf{a}+\|\mathbf{a}\|\,\|\mathbf{b}\|\,\mathbf{b}\cdot\mathbf{a}-\|\mathbf{b}\|\,\|\mathbf{a}\|\,\mathbf{a}\cdot\mathbf{b}-\|\mathbf{a}\|^2\,\mathbf{b}\cdot\mathbf{b}$$

$$= \|\mathbf{b}\|^2\,\|\mathbf{a}\|^2-\|\mathbf{a}\|^2\,\|\mathbf{b}\|^2 = 0.$$

    Therefore $\|\mathbf{b}\|\,\mathbf{a}+\|\mathbf{a}\|\,\mathbf{b}$ and $\|\mathbf{b}\|\,\mathbf{a}-\|\mathbf{a}\|\,\mathbf{b}$ are perpendicular if they are not zero.

23. a. $\mathbf{a}\cdot\mathbf{b} = \|\mathbf{a}\|\,\|\mathbf{b}\|\cos\theta = \cos\theta$ is maximum if $\theta = 0$.

b. $\mathbf{a}\cdot\mathbf{b} = \|\mathbf{a}\|\,\|\mathbf{b}\|\cos\theta = \cos\theta$ is minimum if $\theta = \pi$.

c. $|\mathbf{a}\cdot\mathbf{b}| = \|\mathbf{a}\|\,\|\mathbf{b}\|\,|\cos\theta| = |\cos\theta|$ is minimum if $\theta = \pi/2$.

24. a. $|\mathbf{a}\cdot\mathbf{b}| = \|\mathbf{a}\|\,\|\mathbf{b}\|\,|\cos\theta| \le \|\mathbf{a}\|\,\|\mathbf{b}\|$

b. By part (a), $(a_1b_1 + a_2b_2 + a_3b_3)^2 = (\mathbf{a}\cdot\mathbf{b})^2 = |\mathbf{a}\cdot\mathbf{b}|^2 \le \|\mathbf{a}\|^2\,\|\mathbf{b}\|^2 = (a_1^2 + a_2^2 + a_3^2)(b_1^2 + b_2^2 + b_3^2)$

c. Taking $b_1 = b_2 = b_3 = 1$ in part (b), we have $(a_1 + a_2 + a_3)^2 \le 3(a_1^2 + a_2^2 + a_3^2)$, so that

$$\left(\frac{a_1 + a_2 + a_3}{3}\right)^2 \le \frac{a_1^2 + a_2^2 + a_3^2}{3}.$$

25. a. $$\begin{aligned}\|\mathbf{a}+\mathbf{b}\|^2 &= (\mathbf{a}+\mathbf{b})\cdot(\mathbf{a}+\mathbf{b}) = \mathbf{a}\cdot(\mathbf{a}+\mathbf{b}) + \mathbf{b}\cdot(\mathbf{a}+\mathbf{b})\\ &= \mathbf{a}\cdot\mathbf{a} + \mathbf{a}\cdot\mathbf{b} + \mathbf{b}\cdot\mathbf{a} + \mathbf{b}\cdot\mathbf{b} = \|\mathbf{a}\|^2 + 2\mathbf{a}\cdot\mathbf{b} + \|\mathbf{b}\|^2\end{aligned}$$

b. By part (a), $\|\mathbf{a}+\mathbf{b}\|^2 = \|\mathbf{a}\|^2 + \|\mathbf{b}\|^2$ if and only if $2\mathbf{a}\cdot\mathbf{b} = 0$, that is, **a** and **b** are perpendicular.

c. By Exercise 24(a), $\mathbf{a}\cdot\mathbf{b} \le |\mathbf{a}\cdot\mathbf{b}| \le \|\mathbf{a}\|\,\|\mathbf{b}\|$. Using this and part (a) of this exercise, we have $\|\mathbf{a}+\mathbf{b}\|^2 = \|\mathbf{a}\|^2 + 2\mathbf{a}\cdot\mathbf{b} + \|\mathbf{b}\|^2 \le \|\mathbf{a}\|^2 + 2\,\|\mathbf{a}\|\,\|\mathbf{b}\| + \|\mathbf{b}\|^2 = (\|\mathbf{a}\| + \|\mathbf{b}\|)^2$. Taking square roots, we find that $\|\mathbf{a}+\mathbf{b}\| \le \|\mathbf{a}\| + \|\mathbf{b}\|$.

26. $\|\overrightarrow{PQ}\| = \|\overrightarrow{PR} + \overrightarrow{RQ}\| \le \|\overrightarrow{PR}\| + \|\overrightarrow{RQ}\|$

27. a. $$\begin{aligned}\|\mathbf{a}+\mathbf{b}\|^2 + \|\mathbf{a}-\mathbf{b}\|^2 &= (\mathbf{a}+\mathbf{b})\cdot(\mathbf{a}+\mathbf{b}) + (\mathbf{a}-\mathbf{b})\cdot(\mathbf{a}-\mathbf{b})\\ &= (\mathbf{a}\cdot\mathbf{a}+\mathbf{a}\cdot\mathbf{b}+\mathbf{b}\cdot\mathbf{a}+\mathbf{b}\cdot\mathbf{b}) + (\mathbf{a}\cdot\mathbf{a}-\mathbf{a}\cdot\mathbf{b}-\mathbf{b}\cdot\mathbf{a}+\mathbf{b}\cdot\mathbf{b}\\ &= 2(\mathbf{a}\cdot\mathbf{a}) + 2(\mathbf{b}\cdot\mathbf{b}) = 2\,\|\mathbf{a}\|^2 + 2\,\|\mathbf{b}\|^2\end{aligned}$$

b. $$\begin{aligned}\|\mathbf{a}+\mathbf{b}\|^2 - \|\mathbf{a}-\mathbf{b}\|^2 &= (\mathbf{a}+\mathbf{b})\cdot(\mathbf{a}+\mathbf{b}) - (\mathbf{a}-\mathbf{b})\cdot(\mathbf{a}-\mathbf{b})\\ &= \mathbf{a}\cdot\mathbf{a}+\mathbf{a}\cdot\mathbf{b}+\mathbf{b}\cdot\mathbf{a}+\mathbf{b}\cdot\mathbf{b}-\mathbf{a}\cdot\mathbf{a}+\mathbf{a}\cdot\mathbf{b}+\mathbf{b}\cdot\mathbf{a}-\mathbf{b}\cdot\mathbf{b}\\ &= 2(\mathbf{a}\cdot\mathbf{b}) + 2(\mathbf{b}\cdot\mathbf{a}) = 4\mathbf{a}\cdot\mathbf{b}\end{aligned}$$

c. Let **a** and **b** be vectors along two adjacent sides of the parallelogram, as in Figure 11.36. If the diagonals have equal length, then $\|\mathbf{a}+\mathbf{b}\| = \|\mathbf{a}-\mathbf{b}\|$, so that by part (b), $\mathbf{a}\cdot\mathbf{b} = 0$. Thus the sides are perpendicular, which means that the parallelogram is a rectangle. Conversely, if the parallelogram is a rectangle, then **a** and **b** are perpendicular, so that $\mathbf{a}\cdot\mathbf{b} = 0$, and thus by part (b), $\|\mathbf{a}+\mathbf{b}\|^2 - \|\mathbf{a}-\mathbf{b}\|^2 = 0$, or $\|\mathbf{a}+\mathbf{b}\|^2 = \|\mathbf{a}-\mathbf{b}\|^2$. This means that the diagonals have equal length.

28. If **a** and **b** are vectors along two adjacent sides of the rhombus, then $\mathbf{a}+\mathbf{b}$ and $\mathbf{a}-\mathbf{b}$ lie along the diagonals, and by hypothesis $\|\mathbf{a}\| = \|\mathbf{b}\|$. Thus

$$(\mathbf{a}+\mathbf{b})\cdot(\mathbf{a}-\mathbf{b}) = \mathbf{a}\cdot\mathbf{a} - \mathbf{a}\cdot\mathbf{b} + \mathbf{b}\cdot\mathbf{a} - \mathbf{b}\cdot\mathbf{b} = \|\mathbf{a}\|^2 - \|\mathbf{b}\|^2 = 0$$

which means that the diagonals are perpendicular.

29. Let the cube be placed so its center is the origin, its faces are parallel to the coordinate planes, and its edges have length $2r$. Let $\mathbf{a}$ and $\mathbf{b}$ be as in the figure, so $\mathbf{a} = r\mathbf{i}+r\mathbf{j}+r\mathbf{k}$ and $\mathbf{b} = r\mathbf{i}+r\mathbf{j}-r\mathbf{k}$. If θ is the angle between $\mathbf{a}$ and $\mathbf{b}$, then

$$\cos\theta = \frac{\mathbf{a}\cdot\mathbf{b}}{\|\mathbf{a}\|\,\|\mathbf{b}\|} = \frac{r^2+r^2-r^2}{(r\sqrt{3})(r\sqrt{3})} = \frac{1}{3}$$

so $\theta \approx 1.231$ (radians), or approximately $70.53°$.

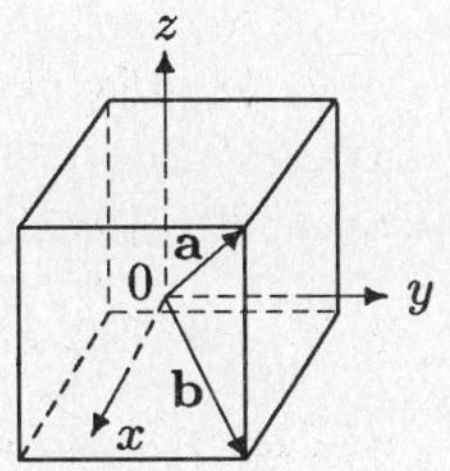

30. Let the parallelepiped be placed so its center is the origin, its faces are parallel to the coordinate planes, and one vertex is $(\frac{1}{2}, \frac{1}{2}, \frac{1}{2}c)$. Let $\mathbf{a}$ and $\mathbf{b}$ be as in the figure, so $\mathbf{a} = \frac{1}{2}\mathbf{i}+\frac{1}{2}\mathbf{j}-\frac{1}{2}c\mathbf{k}$ and $\mathbf{b} = \frac{1}{2}\mathbf{i}-\frac{1}{2}\mathbf{j}-\frac{1}{2}c\mathbf{k}$. If θ is the angle between $\mathbf{a}$ and $\mathbf{b}$, then

$$\cos\theta = \frac{\frac{1}{4}-\frac{1}{4}+\frac{1}{2}c^2}{(\frac{1}{2}\sqrt{2+c^2})(\frac{1}{2}\sqrt{2+c^2})} = \frac{2c^2}{2+c^2}.$$

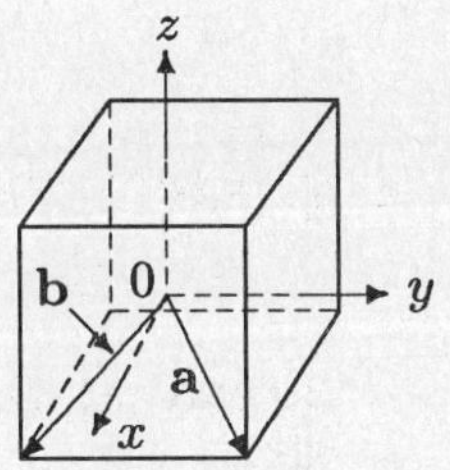

Thus $2c^2/(2+c^2) = \cos\pi/3 = \frac{1}{2}$ yields $4c^2 = 2+c^2$, so $c = \frac{2}{3}\sqrt{3}$.

31. Let θ be the angle between $\mathbf{a}$ and $\mathbf{c}$, and ϕ the angle between $\mathbf{c}$ and $\mathbf{b}$. If $\mathbf{c} \neq \mathbf{0}$, then

$$\cos\theta = \frac{\mathbf{a}\cdot\mathbf{c}}{\|\mathbf{a}\|\,\|\mathbf{c}\|} = \frac{\mathbf{a}\cdot(\|\mathbf{b}\|\mathbf{a}+\|\mathbf{a}\|\mathbf{b})}{\|\mathbf{a}\|\,\|\mathbf{c}\|} = \frac{\|\mathbf{b}\|\mathbf{a}\cdot\mathbf{a}+\|\mathbf{a}\|\mathbf{a}\cdot\mathbf{b}}{\|\mathbf{a}\|\,\|\mathbf{c}\|}$$

$$= \frac{\|\mathbf{b}\|\,\|\mathbf{a}\|^2+\|\mathbf{a}\|\,\mathbf{a}\cdot\mathbf{b}}{\|\mathbf{a}\|\,\|\mathbf{c}\|} = \frac{\|\mathbf{b}\|\,\|\mathbf{a}\|+\mathbf{a}\cdot\mathbf{b}}{\|\mathbf{c}\|}$$

and

$$\cos\phi = \frac{\mathbf{c}\cdot\mathbf{b}}{\|\mathbf{c}\|\|\mathbf{b}\|} = \frac{(\|\mathbf{b}\|\,\mathbf{a}+\|\mathbf{a}\|\,\mathbf{b})\cdot\mathbf{b}}{\|\mathbf{c}\|\,\|\mathbf{b}\|} = \frac{\|\mathbf{b}\|\mathbf{a}\cdot\mathbf{b}+\|\mathbf{a}\|\mathbf{b}\cdot\mathbf{b}}{\|\mathbf{c}\|\,\|\mathbf{b}\|}$$

$$= \frac{\|\mathbf{b}\|\,\mathbf{a}\cdot\mathbf{b}+\|\mathbf{a}\|\,\|\mathbf{b}\|^2}{\|\mathbf{c}\|\,\|\mathbf{b}\|} = \frac{\mathbf{a}\cdot\mathbf{b}+\|\mathbf{a}\|\,\|\mathbf{b}\|}{\|\mathbf{c}\|}.$$

Thus $\cos\theta = \cos\phi$. Since $0 \le \theta \le \pi$ and $0 \le \phi \le \pi$, this means that $\theta = \phi$. Thus $\mathbf{c}$ bisects the angle formed by $\mathbf{a}$ and $\mathbf{b}$.

32. Assume that the sled travels along the x axis from $P = (0,0)$ to $Q = (100,0)$, and the force $\mathbf{F}$ acts in the xy plane with the positive y axis pointing upward. It follows that

$$\overrightarrow{PQ} = 100\mathbf{i} \quad\text{and}\quad \mathbf{F} = 5\left(\cos\frac{\pi}{4}\,\mathbf{i}+\sin\frac{\pi}{4}\,\mathbf{j}\right) = \frac{5}{2}\sqrt{2}\,(\mathbf{i}+\mathbf{j}).$$

Consequently $W = \mathbf{F}\cdot\overrightarrow{PQ} = (\frac{5}{2}\sqrt{2})100 = 250\sqrt{2}$ (foot-pounds).

33. Using the same terminology as that in Example 7, we find that

$$\overrightarrow{PQ} = 500\mathbf{i} \quad\text{and}\quad \mathbf{F} = 100\left(\cos\frac{\pi}{6}\,\mathbf{i}+\sin\frac{\pi}{6}\,\mathbf{j}\right) = 50\sqrt{3}\,\mathbf{i}+50\mathbf{j}.$$

Therefore $W = \mathbf{F}\cdot\overrightarrow{PQ} = (50\sqrt{3})500 = 25{,}000\sqrt{3}$ (foot-pounds).

34. Consider a coordinate system with the origin at the base of the ramp, as in the figure. Then

$$\overrightarrow{PQ} = 15\left(\cos\frac{\pi}{6}\,\mathbf{i} + \sin\frac{\pi}{6}\,\mathbf{j}\right) = \frac{15}{2}(\sqrt{3}\,\mathbf{i} + \mathbf{j})$$

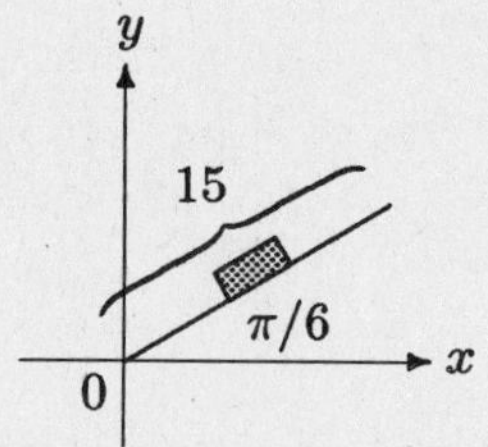

and $\mathbf{F} = 20\mathbf{i}$. Thus

$$W = \mathbf{F}\cdot\overrightarrow{PQ} = 20(\frac{15}{2}\sqrt{3}) = 150\sqrt{3} \text{ (foot-pounds).}$$

11.4 The Cross Product and Triple Products

1. $\mathbf{a}\times\mathbf{b} = \begin{vmatrix} \mathbf{i} & \mathbf{j} & \mathbf{k} \\ 1 & 1 & 0 \\ 0 & 1 & 1 \end{vmatrix} = \mathbf{i} - \mathbf{j} + \mathbf{k}$

   Thus $\mathbf{c}\cdot(\mathbf{a}\times\mathbf{b}) = (-1)(1) + (-3)(-1) + (4)(1) = 6.$

2. $\mathbf{a}\times\mathbf{b} = \begin{vmatrix} \mathbf{i} & \mathbf{j} & \mathbf{k} \\ 1 & 1 & 1 \\ 1 & 0 & -1 \end{vmatrix} = -\mathbf{i} + 2\mathbf{j} - \mathbf{k}$

   Thus $\mathbf{c}\cdot(\mathbf{a}\times\mathbf{b}) = (1)(-1) + (1)(2) + (-1)(-1) = 2.$

3. $\mathbf{a}\times\mathbf{b} = \begin{vmatrix} \mathbf{i} & \mathbf{j} & \mathbf{k} \\ 2 & 3 & -1 \\ -1 & 4 & 5 \end{vmatrix} = 19\mathbf{i} - 9\mathbf{j} + 11\mathbf{k}$

   Thus $\mathbf{c}\cdot(\mathbf{a}\times\mathbf{b}) = (2)(19) + (3)(-9) + (4)(11) = 55.$

4. $\mathbf{a}\times\mathbf{b} = \begin{vmatrix} \mathbf{i} & \mathbf{j} & \mathbf{k} \\ 3 & 4 & 12 \\ 3 & 4 & -12 \end{vmatrix} = -96\mathbf{i} + 72\mathbf{j}$

   Thus $\mathbf{c}\cdot(\mathbf{a}\times\mathbf{b}) = (\frac{1}{8})(-96) + (-\frac{1}{12})(72) + (\frac{1}{16})(0) = -18.$

5. $\mathbf{a}\times\mathbf{b} = \begin{vmatrix} \mathbf{i} & \mathbf{j} & \mathbf{k} \\ 3 & 4 & 12 \\ 3 & 4 & 12 \end{vmatrix} = 0\mathbf{i} + 0\mathbf{j} + 0\mathbf{k}$

   Thus $\mathbf{c}\cdot(\mathbf{a}\times\mathbf{b}) = (1)(0) + (1)(0) + (0)(0) = 0.$

6. $\sin\theta = \dfrac{\|\mathbf{a}\times\mathbf{b}\|}{\|\mathbf{a}\|\,\|\mathbf{b}\|} = \dfrac{\sqrt{(-96)^2 + (72)^2}}{\sqrt{3^2+4^2+12^2}\,\sqrt{3^2+4^2+(-12)^2}} = \dfrac{120}{(13)(13)} = \dfrac{120}{169}$

7. $$\begin{aligned}\mathbf{a}\times\mathbf{b} &= (a_2b_3 - a_3b_2)\mathbf{i} + (a_3b_1 - a_1b_3)\mathbf{j} + (a_1b_2 - a_2b_1)\mathbf{k} \\ &= -(b_2a_3 - b_3a_2)\mathbf{i} - (b_3a_1 - b_1a_3)\mathbf{j} - (b_1a_2 - b_2a_1)\mathbf{k} = -\mathbf{b}\times\mathbf{a}\end{aligned}$$

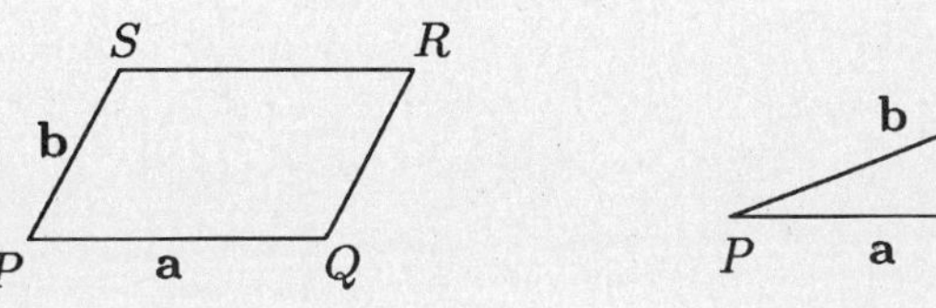

Exercise 12 Exercise 13

8. $$\begin{aligned}\mathbf{a}\times(\mathbf{b}+\mathbf{c}) &= [a_2(b_3+c_3)-a_3(b_2+c_2)]\mathbf{i}+[a_3(b_1+c_1)-a_1(b_3+c_3)]\mathbf{j}+[a_1(b_2+c_2)-a_2(b_1+c_1)]\mathbf{k}\\ &= [(a_2b_3-a_3b_2)+(a_2c_3-a_3c_2)]\mathbf{i}+[(a_3b_1-a_1b_3)+(a_3c_1-a_1c_3)]\mathbf{j}\\ &\quad +[(a_1b_2-a_2b_1)+(a_1c_2-a_2c_1)]\mathbf{k}\\ &= [(a_2b_3-a_3b_2)\mathbf{i}+(a_3b_1-a_1b_3)\mathbf{j}+(a_1b_2-a_2b_1)\mathbf{k}]\\ &\quad +[(a_2c_3-a_3c_2)\mathbf{i}+(a_3c_1-a_1c_3)\mathbf{j}+(a_1c_2-a_2c_1)\mathbf{k}]\\ &= \mathbf{a}\times\mathbf{b}+\mathbf{a}\times\mathbf{c}\end{aligned}$$

9. $\mathbf{0}=\mathbf{a}\times\mathbf{0}=\mathbf{a}\times(\mathbf{a}+\mathbf{b}+\mathbf{c})=(\mathbf{a}\times\mathbf{a})+(\mathbf{a}\times\mathbf{b})+(\mathbf{a}\times\mathbf{c})=(\mathbf{a}\times\mathbf{b})+(\mathbf{a}\times\mathbf{c})$. Thus $\mathbf{a}\times\mathbf{b}=-(\mathbf{a}\times\mathbf{c})=\mathbf{c}\times\mathbf{a}$ by Exercise 7. Similarly, $\mathbf{0}=\mathbf{b}\times\mathbf{0}=\mathbf{b}\times(\mathbf{a}+\mathbf{b}+\mathbf{c})=(\mathbf{b}\times\mathbf{a})+(\mathbf{b}\times\mathbf{b})+(\mathbf{b}\times\mathbf{c})=(\mathbf{b}\times\mathbf{a})+(\mathbf{b}\times\mathbf{c})$. Thus $\mathbf{b}\times\mathbf{c}=-(\mathbf{b}\times\mathbf{a})=\mathbf{a}\times\mathbf{b}$ by Exercise 7.

10. By Theorem 11.10(a), the cross product $(\mathbf{i}-3\mathbf{j}+2\mathbf{k})\times(-2\mathbf{i}+\mathbf{j}-5\mathbf{k})$ is such a vector. This cross product is
$$\begin{vmatrix}\mathbf{i} & \mathbf{j} & \mathbf{k}\\ 1 & -3 & 2\\ -2 & 1 & -5\end{vmatrix}=13\mathbf{i}+\mathbf{j}-5\mathbf{k}.$$

11. Let $P=(2,-3,4)$, $Q=(1,1,-1)$, and $R=(4,-1,-1)$. If $\mathbf{a}=\overrightarrow{OP}=2\mathbf{i}-3\mathbf{j}+4\mathbf{k}$, $\mathbf{b}=\overrightarrow{OQ}=\mathbf{i}+\mathbf{j}-\mathbf{k}$, and $\mathbf{c}=\overrightarrow{OR}=4\mathbf{i}-\mathbf{j}-\mathbf{k}$, then the volume is $|\mathbf{a}\cdot(\mathbf{b}\times\mathbf{c})|$. Since
$$\mathbf{a}\cdot(\mathbf{b}\times\mathbf{c})=\begin{vmatrix}2 & -3 & 4\\ 1 & 1 & -1\\ 4 & -1 & -1\end{vmatrix}=(-2+12-4)-(16+3+2)=-15$$
the volume is 15.

12. Let $\mathbf{a}=\overrightarrow{PQ}$ and $\mathbf{b}=\overrightarrow{PS}$. By (2) the area of parallelogram $PQRS$ is $\|\mathbf{a}\times\mathbf{b}\|=\|\overrightarrow{PQ}\times\overrightarrow{PS}\|$. Similarly, the area equals $\|\overrightarrow{PQ}\times\overrightarrow{QR}\|$, $\|\overrightarrow{SR}\times\overrightarrow{PS}\|$, and $\|\overrightarrow{SR}\times\overrightarrow{QR}\|$.

13. Let $\mathbf{a}=\overrightarrow{PQ}$ and $\mathbf{b}=\overrightarrow{PR}$. As we observed in the text, the area of triangle PQR is $\frac{1}{2}\|\mathbf{a}\times\mathbf{b}\|=\frac{1}{2}\|\overrightarrow{PQ}\times\overrightarrow{PR}\|$. Similarly, the area equals $\frac{1}{2}\|\overrightarrow{PQ}\times\overrightarrow{QR}\|$ and $\frac{1}{2}\|\overrightarrow{PR}\times\overrightarrow{QR}\|$.

14. Let $\mathbf{a}=\mathbf{i}$, $\mathbf{b}=2\mathbf{i}$, and $\mathbf{c}=3\mathbf{i}$. Then $\mathbf{a}\times\mathbf{b}=\mathbf{0}=\mathbf{a}\times\mathbf{c}$, but $\mathbf{b}\neq\mathbf{c}$.

15. We have $\mathbf{a}\cdot(\mathbf{b}-\mathbf{c})=\mathbf{a}\cdot\mathbf{b}-\mathbf{a}\cdot\mathbf{c}=0$ and $\mathbf{a}\times(\mathbf{b}-\mathbf{c})=\mathbf{a}\times\mathbf{b}-\mathbf{a}\times\mathbf{c}=\mathbf{0}$. If $\mathbf{b}$ and $\mathbf{c}$ were not equal, then $\mathbf{b}-\mathbf{c}$ would be nonzero and it would follow from the preceding calculations and the fact that $\mathbf{a}\neq\mathbf{0}$ that $\mathbf{a}$ is both perpendicular to and parallel to $\mathbf{b}-\mathbf{c}$, which is impossible. Thus it does follow that $\mathbf{b}=\mathbf{c}$.

16. If $\mathbf{a} = \mathbf{0}$ or $\mathbf{b} = \mathbf{0}$, the equation is trivially valid. Otherwise

$$\|\mathbf{a}\times\mathbf{b}\|^2 = \|\mathbf{a}\|^2\|\mathbf{b}\|^2\sin^2\theta = \|\mathbf{a}\|^2\|\mathbf{b}\|^2(1-\cos^2\theta) = \|\mathbf{a}\|^2\|\mathbf{b}\|^2 - (\|\mathbf{a}\|\|\mathbf{b}\|\cos\theta)^2 = \|\mathbf{a}\|^2\|\mathbf{b}\|^2 - (\mathbf{a}\cdot\mathbf{b})^2.$$

17. $\mathbf{b}\times\mathbf{c} = \begin{vmatrix} \mathbf{i} & \mathbf{j} & \mathbf{k} \\ 1/2 & 1 & -1 \\ 4 & -5 & 6 \end{vmatrix} = \mathbf{i} - 7\mathbf{j} - \frac{13}{2}\mathbf{k}$

$$\mathbf{a}\times(\mathbf{b}\times\mathbf{c}) = \begin{vmatrix} \mathbf{i} & \mathbf{j} & \mathbf{k} \\ 2 & -3 & 4 \\ 1 & -7 & -13/2 \end{vmatrix} = \frac{95}{2}\mathbf{i} + 17\mathbf{j} - 11\mathbf{k}$$

$$\mathbf{a}\times(\mathbf{b}\times\mathbf{c}) = \mathbf{b}(\mathbf{a}\cdot\mathbf{c}) - \mathbf{c}(\mathbf{a}\cdot\mathbf{b}) = 47\mathbf{b} + 6\mathbf{c} = \frac{95}{2}\mathbf{i} + 17\mathbf{j} - 11\mathbf{k}$$

18. $\mathbf{b}\times\mathbf{c} = \begin{vmatrix} \mathbf{i} & \mathbf{j} & \mathbf{k} \\ 3 & -7 & 2 \\ 2 & -5 & 0 \end{vmatrix} = 10\mathbf{i} + 4\mathbf{j} - \mathbf{k}$

$$\mathbf{a}\times(\mathbf{b}\times\mathbf{c}) = \begin{vmatrix} \mathbf{i} & \mathbf{j} & \mathbf{k} \\ 1 & -4 & 2 \\ 10 & 4 & -1 \end{vmatrix} = -4\mathbf{i} + 21\mathbf{j} + 44\mathbf{k}$$

$$\mathbf{a}\times(\mathbf{b}\times\mathbf{c}) = \mathbf{b}(\mathbf{a}\cdot\mathbf{c}) - \mathbf{c}(\mathbf{a}\cdot\mathbf{b}) = 22\mathbf{b} - 35\mathbf{c} = -4\mathbf{i} + 21\mathbf{j} + 44\mathbf{k}$$

19. If $\mathbf{u}\times\mathbf{a}$, $\mathbf{u}$ and $\mathbf{b}$ replace $\mathbf{a}$, $\mathbf{b}$, and $\mathbf{c}$ in (3), then

$$(\mathbf{u}\times\mathbf{a})\cdot(\mathbf{u}\times\mathbf{b}) = [(\mathbf{u}\times\mathbf{a})\times\mathbf{u}]\cdot\mathbf{b} = -[\mathbf{u}\times(\mathbf{u}\times\mathbf{a})]\cdot\mathbf{b}.$$

If $\mathbf{u}$ and $\mathbf{a}$ are perpendicular, then by (8), with $\mathbf{u}$ replacing $\mathbf{a}$ and $\mathbf{a}$ replacing $\mathbf{c}$, we find that $\mathbf{u}\times(\mathbf{u}\times\mathbf{a}) = -\|\mathbf{u}\|^2\mathbf{a}$, so $(\mathbf{u}\times\mathbf{a})\cdot(\mathbf{u}\times\mathbf{b}) = -[-\|\mathbf{u}\|^2\mathbf{a}]\cdot\mathbf{b} = \|\mathbf{u}\|^2(\mathbf{a}\cdot\mathbf{b})$. Similarly, the formula holds if $\mathbf{u}$ and $\mathbf{b}$ are perpendicular, since $(\mathbf{u}\times\mathbf{a})\cdot(\mathbf{u}\times\mathbf{b}) = (\mathbf{u}\times\mathbf{b})\cdot(\mathbf{u}\times\mathbf{a})$ and $\mathbf{a}\cdot\mathbf{b} = \mathbf{b}\cdot\mathbf{a}$.

20. Since $\mathbf{b}\times\mathbf{c} = (b_2c_3 - b_3c_2)\mathbf{i} + (b_3c_1 - b_1c_3)\mathbf{j} + (b_1c_2 - b_2c_1)\mathbf{k}$, we have

$$\begin{aligned}
\mathbf{a}\times(\mathbf{b}\times\mathbf{c}) &= [a_2(b_1c_2 - b_2c_1) - a_3(b_3c_1 - b_1c_3)]\mathbf{i} \\
&\quad + [a_3(b_2c_3 - b_3c_2) - a_1(b_1c_2 - b_2c_1)]\mathbf{j} \\
&\quad + [a_1(b_3c_1 - b_1c_3) - a_2(b_2c_3 - b_3c_2)]\mathbf{k} \\
&= [(a_1c_1 + a_2c_2 + a_3c_3)b_1 - (a_1b_1 + a_2b_2 + a_3b_3)c_1]\mathbf{i} \\
&\quad + [(a_1c_1 + a_2c_2 + a_3c_3)b_2 - (a_1b_1 + a_2b_2 + a_3b_3)c_2]\mathbf{j} \\
&\quad + [(a_1c_1 + a_2c_2 + a_3c_3)b_3 - (a_1b_1 + a_2b_2 + a_3b_3)c_3]\mathbf{k} \\
&= [(\mathbf{a}\cdot\mathbf{c})b_1 - (\mathbf{a}\cdot\mathbf{b})c_1]\mathbf{i} + [(\mathbf{a}\cdot\mathbf{c})b_2 - (\mathbf{a}\cdot\mathbf{b})c_2]\mathbf{j} + [(\mathbf{a}\cdot\mathbf{c})b_3 - (\mathbf{a}\cdot\mathbf{b})c_3]\mathbf{k} \\
&= (\mathbf{a}\cdot\mathbf{c})\mathbf{b} - (\mathbf{a}\cdot\mathbf{b})\mathbf{c} \\
&= \mathbf{b}(\mathbf{a}\cdot\mathbf{c}) - \mathbf{c}(\mathbf{a}\cdot\mathbf{b})
\end{aligned}$$

21. a. By the *bac* − *cab* rule,

$$\begin{aligned}&\mathbf{a}\times(\mathbf{b}\times\mathbf{c})+\mathbf{b}\times(\mathbf{c}\times\mathbf{a})+\mathbf{c}\times(\mathbf{a}\times\mathbf{b})\\&=[\mathbf{b}(\mathbf{a}\cdot\mathbf{c})-\mathbf{c}(\mathbf{a}\cdot\mathbf{b})]+[\mathbf{c}(\mathbf{b}\cdot\mathbf{a})-\mathbf{a}(\mathbf{b}\cdot\mathbf{c})]+[\mathbf{a}(\mathbf{c}\cdot\mathbf{b})-\mathbf{b}(\mathbf{c}\cdot\mathbf{a})]\\&=\mathbf{b}(\mathbf{a}\cdot\mathbf{c}-\mathbf{c}\cdot\mathbf{a})+\mathbf{c}(-\mathbf{a}\cdot\mathbf{b}+\mathbf{b}\cdot\mathbf{a})+\mathbf{a}(-\mathbf{b}\cdot\mathbf{c}+\mathbf{c}\cdot\mathbf{b})=\mathbf{0}.\end{aligned}$$

b. $\mathbf{a}\times(\mathbf{b}\times\mathbf{c})=(\mathbf{a}\times\mathbf{b})\times\mathbf{c}$ if and only if $\mathbf{a}\times(\mathbf{b}\times\mathbf{c})-(\mathbf{a}\times\mathbf{b})\times\mathbf{c}=\mathbf{0}$ if and only if $\mathbf{a}\times(\mathbf{b}\times\mathbf{c})+\mathbf{c}\times(\mathbf{a}\times\mathbf{b})=\mathbf{0}$. By part (a), this equation holds if and only if $\mathbf{b}\times(\mathbf{c}\times\mathbf{a})=\mathbf{0}$.

22. Using the *bac* − *cab* rule, we have

$$(\mathbf{a}\times\mathbf{b})\times\mathbf{c}=-\mathbf{c}\times(\mathbf{a}\times\mathbf{b})=-[\mathbf{a}(\mathbf{c}\cdot\mathbf{b})-\mathbf{b}(\mathbf{c}\cdot\mathbf{a})]=(\mathbf{a}\cdot\mathbf{c})\mathbf{b}-(\mathbf{b}\cdot\mathbf{c})\mathbf{a}.$$

23. We use the coordinate system shown in Figure 11.41, with the stapler in the yz plane. Let P be the origin, and Q the point at the end of the stapler at which the force $\mathbf{F}$ is applied. Then

$$\overrightarrow{PQ}=\frac{3}{2}\left(\cos\frac{\pi}{6}\mathbf{j}+\sin\frac{\pi}{6}\mathbf{k}\right)=\frac{3}{2}\left(\frac{\sqrt{3}}{2}\mathbf{j}+\frac{1}{2}\mathbf{k}\right)=\frac{3}{4}(\sqrt{3}\mathbf{j}+\mathbf{k})\quad\text{and}\quad\mathbf{F}=-32\mathbf{k}.$$

Thus $\mathbf{M}=\overrightarrow{PQ}\times\mathbf{F}=-24\sqrt{3}\,\mathbf{i}$.

24. Using the coordinate system shown in the figure, we have

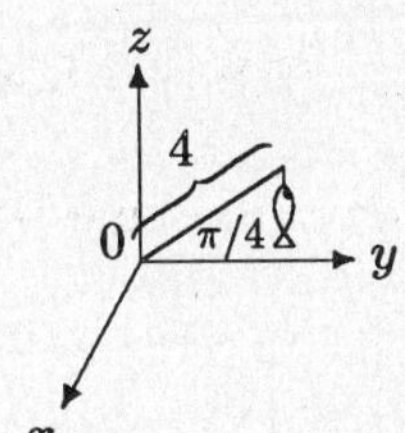

$$\overrightarrow{PQ}=4\left(\cos\frac{\pi}{4}\mathbf{j}+\sin\frac{\pi}{4}\mathbf{k}\right)=4\left(\frac{\sqrt{2}}{2}\mathbf{j}+\frac{\sqrt{2}}{2}\mathbf{k}\right)=2\sqrt{2}\,(\mathbf{j}+\mathbf{k})$$

and $\mathbf{F}=-5\mathbf{k}$. Thus $\mathbf{M}=\overrightarrow{PQ}\times\mathbf{F}=-10\sqrt{2}\,\mathbf{i}$.

11.5 Lines in Space

1. $\mathbf{r}_0=-2\mathbf{i}+\mathbf{j}$, so that a vector equation of the line is $\mathbf{r}=(-2+3t)\mathbf{i}+(1-t)\mathbf{j}+5t\mathbf{k}$, and thus parametric equations are $x=-2+3t$, $y=1-t$, $z=5t$; $a=3$, $b=-1$, $c=5$, so that symmetric equations of the line are $(x+2)/3=(y-1)/(-1)=z/5$.

2. $\mathbf{r}_0=\mathbf{0}$, so that a vector equation of the line is $\mathbf{r}=11t\mathbf{i}-13t\mathbf{j}-15t\mathbf{k}$, and thus parametric equations are $x=11t$, $y=-13t$, $z=-15t$; $a=11$, $b=-13$, $c=-15$, so that symmetric equations of the line are $x/11=y/(-13)=z/(-15)$.

3. $\mathbf{r}_0=3\mathbf{i}+4\mathbf{j}+5\mathbf{k}$, so that a vector equation of the line is $\mathbf{r}=(3+\frac{1}{2}t)\mathbf{i}+(4-\frac{1}{3}t)\mathbf{j}+(5+\frac{1}{6}t)\mathbf{k}$, and thus parametric equations are $x=3+\frac{1}{2}t$, $y=4-\frac{1}{3}t$, $z=5+\frac{1}{6}t$; $a=\frac{1}{2}$, $b=-\frac{1}{3}$, $c=\frac{1}{6}$, so that symmetric equations of the line are $(x-3)/\frac{1}{2}=(y-4)/(-\frac{1}{3})=(z-5)/\frac{1}{6}$.

4. $\mathbf{r}_0=-3\mathbf{i}+6\mathbf{j}+2\mathbf{k}$, so that a vector equation of the line is $\mathbf{r}=(-3+t)\mathbf{i}+(6-t)\mathbf{j}+2\mathbf{k}$, and thus parametric equations are $x=-3+t$, $y=6-t$, $z=2$; $a=1$, $b=-1$, $c=0$, so that symmetric equations of the line are $(x+3)/1=(y-6)/(-1)$ and $z=2$.

5. $\mathbf{r}_0 = 2\mathbf{i} + 5\mathbf{k}$, so that a vector equation of the line is $\mathbf{r} = 2\mathbf{i} + 2t\mathbf{j} + (5 + 3t)\mathbf{k}$, and thus parametric equations are $x = 2$, $y = 2t$, $z = 5 + 3t$; $a = 0$, $b = 2$, $c = 3$, so that symmetric equations of the line are $x = 2$ and $y/2 = (z - 5)/3$.

6. $\mathbf{r}_0 = 7\mathbf{i} - \mathbf{j} + 2\mathbf{k}$, so that a vector equation of the line is $\mathbf{r} = 7\mathbf{i} - \mathbf{j} + (2 + t)\mathbf{k}$, and thus parametric equations are $x = 7$, $y = -1$, $z = 2 + t$; $a = 0 = b$, $c = 1$, so that symmetric equations of the line are $x = 7$ and $y = -1$.

7. $\mathbf{r}_0 = 4\mathbf{i} + 2\mathbf{j} - \mathbf{k}$, so that a vector equation of the line is $\mathbf{r} = 4\mathbf{i} + (2 + t)\mathbf{j} - \mathbf{k}$, and thus parametric equations of the line are $x = 4$, $y = 2 + t$, $z = -1$; $a = 0 = c$, $b = 1$, so that symmetric equations of the line are $x = 4$ and $z = -1$.

8. $x_0 = 3$, $y_0 = -1$, $z_0 = 2$, $a = 4$, $b = 2$, $c = 1$, so that parametric equations for the line are $x = 3 + 4t$, $y = -1 + 2t$, $z = 2 + t$.

9. $x_0 = -1$, $y_0 = 1$, $z_0 = 0$, $a = -2 - (-1) = -1$, $b = 5 - 1 = 4$, $c = 7 - 0 = 7$, so that parametric equations for the line are $x = -1 - t$, $y = 1 + 4t$, $z = 7t$.

10. $x_0 = -1$, $y_0 = 1$, $z_0 = 0$, $a = -1 - (-1) = 0$, $b = 5 - 1 = 4$, $c = 7 - 0 = 7$, so that parametric equations for the line are $x = -1$, $y = 1 + 4t$, $z = 7t$.

11. $x_0 = -1$, $y_0 = 1$, $z_0 = 0$, $a = 0$, $b = 0$, $c = 7$, so that symmetric equations for the line are $x = -1$ and $y = 1$.

12. The line through $(1, 7, 5)$ and $(3, 2, -1)$ is parallel to $\mathbf{L}_1$, where

$$\mathbf{L}_1 = (3 - 1)\mathbf{i} + (2 - 7)\mathbf{j} + (-1 - 5)\mathbf{k} = 2\mathbf{i} - 5\mathbf{j} - 6\mathbf{k}.$$

The line through $(2, -2, 5)$ and $(-2, 8, 17)$ is parallel to $\mathbf{L}_2$, where

$$\mathbf{L}_2 = (-2 - 2)\mathbf{i} + (8 + 2)\mathbf{j} + (17 - 5)\mathbf{k} = -4\mathbf{i} + 10\mathbf{j} + 12\mathbf{k}.$$

Now $\mathbf{L}_1$ and $\mathbf{L}_2$ are parallel since $\mathbf{L}_2 = -2\mathbf{L}_1$. Thus the two lines are parallel.

13. The line through $(2, -1, 3)$ and $(0, 7, 9)$ is parallel to $\mathbf{L}_1$, where

$$\mathbf{L}_1 = (0 - 2)\mathbf{i} + (7 + 1)\mathbf{j} + (9 - 3)\mathbf{k} = -2\mathbf{i} + 8\mathbf{j} + 6\mathbf{k}.$$

The line through $(-1, 0, 4)$ and $(2, 3, 1)$ is parallel to $\mathbf{L}_2$, where

$$\mathbf{L}_2 = (2 + 1)\mathbf{i} + (3 - 0)\mathbf{j} + (1 - 4)\mathbf{k} = 3\mathbf{i} + 3\mathbf{j} - 3\mathbf{k}.$$

Since $\mathbf{L}_1 \cdot \mathbf{L}_2 = (-2)(3) + (8)(3) + (6)(-3) = 0$, $\mathbf{L}_1$ and $\mathbf{L}_2$ are perpendicular. Consequently the two lines are perpendicular.

14. The line through $(5, 7, 9)$ and $(4, 11, 9)$ is parallel to $\mathbf{L}_1$, where

$$\mathbf{L}_1 = (4 - 5)\mathbf{i} + (11 - 7)\mathbf{j} + (9 - 9)\mathbf{k} = -\mathbf{i} + 4\mathbf{j}.$$

The line with equations $(x - 1)/(-3) = (y - 2)/12$, $z = 5$ is parallel to $\mathbf{L}_2$, where $\mathbf{L}_2 = -3\mathbf{i} + 12\mathbf{j}$. Since $\mathbf{L}_2 = 3\mathbf{L}_1$, the two lines are parallel.

15. The line through $(0,0,5)$ and $(1,-1,4)$ is parallel to $\mathbf{L}_1$, where

$$\mathbf{L}_1 = (1-0)\mathbf{i} + (-1-0)\mathbf{j} + (4-5)\mathbf{k} = \mathbf{i} - \mathbf{j} - \mathbf{k}.$$

The line with equation $x/7 = (y-3)/4 = (z+9)/3$ is parallel to $\mathbf{L}_2$, where $\mathbf{L}_2 = 7\mathbf{i} + 4\mathbf{j} + 3\mathbf{k}$. Since $\mathbf{L}_1 \cdot \mathbf{L}_2 = (1)(7) + (-1)(4) + (-1)(3) = 0$, $\mathbf{L}_1$ and $\mathbf{L}_2$ are perpendicular. Consequently the two lines are perpendicular.

16. By (3), the parametric equations have the form $x = x_0 + at$, $y = y_0 + bt$, $z = z_0 + ct$. Since P_1 corresponds to $t = 0$ and P_2 corresponds to $t = 1$, we have

$$-1 = x_0 + a \cdot 0, \qquad -2 = y_0 + b \cdot 0, \qquad -3 = z_0 + c \cdot 0$$

$$2 = x_0 + a, \qquad -1 = y_0 + b, \qquad 0 = z_0 + c$$

Thus $x_0 = -1$, $y_0 = -2$, $z_0 = -3$, so $a = 2 - x_0 = 3$, $b = -1 - y_0 = 1$, $c = -z_0 = 3$. Thus the parametric equations are $x = -1 + 3t$, $y = -2 + t$, $z = -3 + 3t$.

17. By (3), the parametric equations have the form $x = x_0 + at$, $y = y_0 + bt$, $z = z_0 + ct$. Since P_1 corresponds to $t = 0$ and P_2 corresponds to $t = 2$, we have

$$-1 = x_0 + a \cdot 0, \qquad -2 = y_0 + b \cdot 0, \qquad -3 = z_0 + c \cdot 0$$

$$2 = x_0 + 2a, \qquad -1 = y_0 + 2b, \qquad 0 = z_0 + 2c$$

Thus $x_0 = -1$, $y_0 = -2$, $z_0 = -3$, so that $a = \frac{1}{2}(2 - x_0) = \frac{3}{2}$, $b = \frac{1}{2}(-1 - y_0) = \frac{1}{2}$, $c = -\frac{1}{2}z_0 = \frac{3}{2}$. Thus the parametric equations are $x = -1 + \frac{3}{2}t$, $y = -2 + \frac{1}{2}t$, $z = -3 + \frac{3}{2}t$.

18. By (3), the parametric equations have the form $x = x_0 + at$, $y = y_0 + bt$, $z = z_0 + ct$. Since P_1 corresponds to $t = -1$ and P_2 corresponds to $t = 4$, we have

$$-1 = x_0 - a, \qquad -2 = y_0 - b, \qquad -3 = z_0 - c$$

$$2 = x_0 + 4a, \qquad -1 = y_0 + 4b, \qquad 0 = z_0 + 4c$$

Subtracting the equations vertically, we find that $a = \frac{3}{5}$, $b = \frac{1}{5}$, $c = \frac{3}{5}$, so that $x_0 = -1 + a = -\frac{2}{5}$, $y_0 = -2 + b = -\frac{9}{5}$, $z_0 = -3 + c = -\frac{12}{5}$. Thus the parametric equations are $x = -\frac{2}{5} + \frac{3}{5}t$, $y = -\frac{9}{5} + \frac{1}{5}t$, $z = -\frac{12}{5} + \frac{3}{5}t$.

19. The point $P_0 = (1,-2,-1)$ is on the line, and the line is parallel to $\mathbf{i} - 2\mathbf{j} + 3\mathbf{k}$. If $P_1 = (5,0,-4)$, then P_1 is not on the line, and $\overrightarrow{P_0P_1} = 4\mathbf{i} + 2\mathbf{j} - 3\mathbf{k}$, so by (5) the distance D is given by

$$D = \frac{\|(\mathbf{i} - 2\mathbf{j} + 3\mathbf{k}) \times (4\mathbf{i} + 2\mathbf{j} - 3\mathbf{k})\|}{\sqrt{1^2 + (-2)^2 + 3^2}} = \frac{\|15\mathbf{j} + 10\mathbf{k}\|}{\sqrt{14}} = 5\sqrt{\frac{13}{14}}.$$

20. The point $P_0 = (-2,0,1)$ is on the line, and the line is parallel to $\mathbf{j} + \mathbf{k}$. If $P_1 = (2,1,0)$, then P_1 is not on the line, and $\overrightarrow{P_0P_1} = 4\mathbf{i} + \mathbf{j} - \mathbf{k}$, so by (5) the distance D is given by

$$D = \frac{\|(\mathbf{j} + \mathbf{k}) \times (4\mathbf{i} + \mathbf{j} - \mathbf{k})\|}{\sqrt{1^2 + 1^2}} = \frac{\|-2\mathbf{i} + 4\mathbf{j} - 4\mathbf{k}\|}{\sqrt{2}} = 3\sqrt{2}.$$

21. The line has a vector equation $\mathbf{r} = (-3+2t)\mathbf{i} + (-3-3t)\mathbf{j} + (3+5t)\mathbf{k}$, and if $P_1 = (0,0,0)$, then P_1 is not on the line. Let $P_0 = (-3,-3,3)$, and let $\mathbf{L} = 2\mathbf{i} - 3\mathbf{j} + 5\mathbf{k}$, so that $\mathbf{r}$ and $\mathbf{L}$ are parallel. Then $\overrightarrow{P_0P_1} = 3\mathbf{i} + 3\mathbf{j} - 3\mathbf{k}$, and by (5) the distance D from P_1 to the given line is given by

$$D = \frac{\|(2\mathbf{i} - 3\mathbf{j} + 5\mathbf{k}) \times (3\mathbf{i} + 3\mathbf{j} - 3\mathbf{k})\|}{\sqrt{2^2 + (-3)^2 + 5^2}} = \frac{3\|-2\mathbf{i} + 7\mathbf{j} + 5\mathbf{k}\|}{\sqrt{38}} = 3\sqrt{\frac{39}{19}}.$$

22. $P = (-1,-1,0)$ is on the line $x - 2y = 1$; $Q = (\frac{3}{2}, 0, 0)$ is on the line $2x - 4y = 3$; $\mathbf{L} = \mathbf{i} + \frac{1}{2}\mathbf{j}$ is parallel to the line $x - 2y = 1$. Thus

$$D = \frac{\|\mathbf{L} \times \overrightarrow{PQ}\|}{\|\mathbf{L}\|} = \frac{\|(\mathbf{i} + \frac{1}{2}\mathbf{j}) \times (\frac{5}{2}\mathbf{i} + \mathbf{j})\|}{\|\mathbf{i} + \frac{1}{2}\mathbf{j}\|} = \frac{\|-\frac{1}{4}\mathbf{k}\|}{\sqrt{5}/2} = \frac{1}{10}\sqrt{5}.$$

23. $P = (1,-1,2)$ is on the first line; $Q = (0,2,3)$ is on the second line; $\mathbf{L} = 2\mathbf{i} - \mathbf{j} - 2\mathbf{k}$ is parallel to the first line. Thus

$$D = \frac{\|\mathbf{L} \times \overrightarrow{PQ}\|}{\|\mathbf{L}\|} = \frac{\|(2\mathbf{i} - \mathbf{j} - 2\mathbf{k}) \times (-\mathbf{i} + 3\mathbf{j} + \mathbf{k})\|}{\|2\mathbf{i} - \mathbf{j} - 2\mathbf{k}\|} = \frac{\|5\mathbf{i} + 5\mathbf{k}\|}{3} = \frac{5}{3}\sqrt{2}.$$

24. $\sqrt{(x-x)^2 + (y-0)^2 + (z-0)^2} = 3$, or $y^2 + z^2 = 9$.

25. $\sqrt{(x-0)^2 + (y-y)^2 + (z-0)^2} = \sqrt{2}$, or $x^2 + z^2 = 2$.

26. Let $P_1 = (x,y,z)$ be on the cylinder, and let $\mathbf{L} = \mathbf{i} + \mathbf{j} + \mathbf{k}$, so that $\mathbf{L}$ is parallel to the axis of the cylinder. Using Theorem 11.12 with $P_0 = (0,0,0)$ we find that the distance D from P_1 to the axis of the cylinder is 5 if

$$5 = D = \frac{\|(\mathbf{i} + \mathbf{j} + \mathbf{k}) \times (x\mathbf{i} + y\mathbf{j} + z\mathbf{k})\|}{\sqrt{1^2 + 1^2 + 1^2}}$$

$$= \frac{\|(z-y)\mathbf{i} + (x-z)\mathbf{j} + (y-x)\mathbf{k}\|}{\sqrt{3}} = \frac{\sqrt{(z-y)^2 + (x-z)^2 + (y-x)^2}}{\sqrt{3}}$$

so that $(z-y)^2 + (x-z)^2 + (y-x)^2 = 75$.

27. The line through $(1,4,2)$ and $(4,-3,-5)$ is parallel to $3\mathbf{i} - 7\mathbf{j} - 7\mathbf{k}$, and the line through $(1,4,2)$ and $(-5,-10,-8)$ is parallel to $-6\mathbf{i} - 14\mathbf{j} - 10\mathbf{k}$. Since these two vectors are not parallel, the three points do not lie on the same line.

28. The points $(2,5,7)$ and $(0,3,2)$ lie on a line parallel to $-2\mathbf{i} - 2\mathbf{j} - 5\mathbf{k}$, and thus parametric equations of the line are $x = 2 - 2t$, $y = 5 - 2t$, $z = 7 - 5t$. If $(x,y,1)$ is to be on the line, then $1 = 7 - 5t$, so that $t = \frac{6}{5}$. Therefore $x = 2 - 2(\frac{6}{5}) = -\frac{2}{5}$ and $y = 5 - 2(\frac{6}{5}) = \frac{13}{5}$.

29. Notice that $\mathbf{a} - \mathbf{b}$ lies on l, so is parallel to $\mathbf{L}$. Thus $\mathbf{L} \times (\mathbf{a} - \mathbf{b}) = \mathbf{0}$. Since $\mathbf{0} = \mathbf{L} \times (\mathbf{a} - \mathbf{b}) = (\mathbf{L} \times \mathbf{a}) - (\mathbf{L} \times \mathbf{b})$, it follows that $\mathbf{L} \times \mathbf{a} = \mathbf{L} \times \mathbf{b}$.

11.6 Planes in Space

1. $x_0 = -1$, $y_0 = 2$, $z_0 = 3$, $a = -4$, $b = 15$, $c = -\frac{1}{2}$; $-4(x+1) + 15(y-2) - \frac{1}{2}(z-3) = 0$, or $8x - 30y + z = -65$.

2. $x_0 = \pi$, $y_0 = 0$, $z_0 = -\pi$, $a = 2$, $b = 3$, $c = -4$; $2(x-\pi) + 3(y-0) - 4(z+\pi) = 0$, or $2x + 3y - 4z = 6\pi$.

3. $x_0 = 9$, $y_0 = 17$, $z_0 = -7$, $a = 2$, $b = 0$, $c = -3$; $2(x-9) + 0(y-17) - 3(z+7) = 0$, or $2x - 3z = 39$.

4. $x_0 = -1$, $y_0 = -1$, $z_0 = -1$, $a = 1/\sqrt{2} = b$, $c = -1/\sqrt{2}$;
$(1/\sqrt{2})(x+1) + (1/\sqrt{2})(y+1) - (1/\sqrt{2})(z+1) = 0$, or $x + y - z = -1$.

5. $x_0 = 2$, $y_0 = 3$, $z_0 = -5$, $a = 0$, $b = 1$, $c = 0$; $0(x-2) + 1(y-3) + 0(z+5) = 0$, or $y = 3$.

6. Let $P_0 = (2,-1,4)$, $P_1 = (5,3,5)$, and $P_2 = (2,4,3)$. Then $\overrightarrow{P_0P_1} = 3\mathbf{i} + 4\mathbf{j} + \mathbf{k}$ and $\overrightarrow{P_0P_2} = 5\mathbf{j} - \mathbf{k}$. Since $\overrightarrow{P_0P_1}$ and $\overrightarrow{P_0P_2}$ are not parallel, P_0, P_1 and P_2 determine a plane, and the normal $\mathbf{N}$ we take is given by $\mathbf{N} = \overrightarrow{P_0P_1} \times \overrightarrow{P_0P_2} = (3\mathbf{i} + 4\mathbf{j} + \mathbf{k}) \times (5\mathbf{j} - \mathbf{k}) = -9\mathbf{i} + 3\mathbf{j} + 15\mathbf{k}$. An equation of the plane is $-9(x-2) + 3(y+1) + 15(z-4) = 0$, or $-9x + 3y + 15z = 39$.

7. The point $P_0 = (-2,-1,-5)$ is on the line, and hence on the plane. Let $P_1 = (1,-1,2)$, so that $\overrightarrow{P_0P_1} = 3\mathbf{i} + 7\mathbf{k}$. The vector $\mathbf{i} + \mathbf{j} + 2\mathbf{k}$ is parallel to the line but not parallel to $\overrightarrow{P_0P_1}$. For a normal to the plane we take
$$\mathbf{N} = \overrightarrow{P_0P_1} \times (\mathbf{i} + \mathbf{j} + 2\mathbf{k}) = (3\mathbf{i} + 7\mathbf{k}) \times (\mathbf{i} + \mathbf{j} + 2\mathbf{k}) = -7\mathbf{i} + \mathbf{j} + 3\mathbf{k}.$$
An equation of the plane is $-7(x+2) + 1(y+1) + 3(z+5) = 0$, or $7x - y - 3z = 2$.

8. Let $P_0 = (1,-1,5)$ and $P_1 = (-3,4,0)$, so that P_0 and P_1 are on the plane. Then $\overrightarrow{P_0P_1} = -4\mathbf{i} + 5\mathbf{j} - 5\mathbf{k}$ and $3\mathbf{i} + 2\mathbf{j} + 4\mathbf{k}$ are not parallel. Thus a normal to the plane is given by $\mathbf{N} = \overrightarrow{P_0P_1} \times (3\mathbf{i} + 2\mathbf{j} + 4\mathbf{k}) = (-4\mathbf{i} + 5\mathbf{j} - 5\mathbf{k}) \times (3\mathbf{i} + 2\mathbf{j} + 4\mathbf{k}) = 30\mathbf{i} + \mathbf{j} - 23\mathbf{k}$. An equation of the plane is $30(x-1) + 1(y+1) - 23(z-5) = 0$, or $30x + y - 23z = -86$.

9. A normal to the plane is given by $\mathbf{N} = 2\mathbf{i} + 5\mathbf{j} + 9\mathbf{k}$, so an equation of the plane is $2(x-2) + 5(y - \frac{1}{2}) + 9(z - \frac{1}{3}) = 0$, or $4x + 10y + 18z = 19$.

10. The line is parallel to $2\mathbf{i} - 3\mathbf{j} + 4\mathbf{k}$, and thus parametric equations for the line are $x = 2 + 2t$, $y = -1 - 3t$, $z = 4t$.

11. a. The line l is perpendicular to the vectors $2\mathbf{i} - 3\mathbf{j} + 4\mathbf{k}$ and $\mathbf{i} - \mathbf{k}$, which are normal to the two planes. Thus l is parallel to $(2\mathbf{i} - 3\mathbf{j} + 4\mathbf{k}) \times (\mathbf{i} - \mathbf{k}) = 3\mathbf{i} + 6\mathbf{j} + 3\mathbf{k}$ and hence to $\mathbf{i} + 2\mathbf{j} + \mathbf{k}$. Since $(1,0,0)$ is on the intersection of the two planes, a vector equation of l is $\mathbf{r} = \mathbf{i} + t(\mathbf{i} + 2\mathbf{j} + \mathbf{k}) = (1+t)\mathbf{i} + 2t\mathbf{j} + t\mathbf{k}$.

    b. A normal to the plane is given by $\mathbf{N} = \mathbf{i} + 2\mathbf{j} + \mathbf{k}$, so that an equation of the plane is $1(x+9) + 2(y-12) + 1(z-14) = 0$, or $x + 2y + z = 29$.

12. a. From the equations for l we find that $(x+1)/2 = -z$, so that $x = -2z - 1$ and $(y+3)/3 = -z$, so that $y = -3z - 3$. Substituting for x and y in the equation for $\mathcal{P}$, we obtain $3(-2z-1) - 2(-3z-3) + 4z = -1$, so that $z = -1$. Therefore $x = -2(-1) - 1 = 1$ and $y = -3(-1) - 3 = 0$, so that $P_0 = (1, 0, -1)$.

    b. A normal for the plane is given by $\mathbf{N} = 2\mathbf{i} + 3\mathbf{j} - \mathbf{k}$, so that an equation for the plane is $2(x-1) + 3(y-0) - 1(z+1) = 0$, or $2x + 3y - z = 3$.

    c. Since the vector $3\mathbf{i} - 2\mathbf{j} + 4\mathbf{k}$ is parallel to any line perpendicular to the plane, and since the desired line passes through $P_0 = (1, 0, -1)$, symmetric equations of the line are $(x-1)/3 = y/(-2) = (z+1)/4$.

13. The point $P_1 = (3, -1, 4)$ is not on the plane, whereas $P_0 = (0, 0, 5)$ is on the plane. Then $\overrightarrow{P_0P_1} = 3\mathbf{i} - \mathbf{j} - \mathbf{k}$. If $\mathbf{N} = 2\mathbf{i} - \mathbf{j} + \mathbf{k}$, then $\mathbf{N}$ is normal to the plane, and by Theorem 12.13 the distance D from P_1 to the plane is given by

$$D = \frac{|\mathbf{N} \cdot \overrightarrow{P_0P_1}|}{\|\mathbf{N}\|} = \frac{|(2\mathbf{i} - \mathbf{j} + \mathbf{k}) \cdot (3\mathbf{i} - \mathbf{j} - \mathbf{k})|}{\sqrt{2^2 + (-1)^2 + 1^2}} = \frac{6}{\sqrt{6}} = \sqrt{6}.$$

14. The point $P_1 = (2, 0, -4)$ is not on the plane, whereas $P_0 = (2, 0, \frac{1}{4})$ is on the plane. Then $\overrightarrow{P_0P_1} = -\frac{17}{4}\mathbf{k}$. If $\mathbf{N} = \mathbf{i} + 2\mathbf{j} + 4\mathbf{k}$, then $\mathbf{N}$ is normal to the plane, and by Theorem 11.13 the distance D from P_1 to the plane is given by

$$D = \frac{|\mathbf{N} \cdot \overrightarrow{P_0P_1}|}{\|\mathbf{N}\|} = \frac{|(\mathbf{i} + 2\mathbf{j} + 4\mathbf{k}) \cdot (-\frac{17}{4}\mathbf{k})|}{\sqrt{1^2 + 2^2 + 4^2}} = \frac{17}{\sqrt{21}} = \frac{17}{21}\sqrt{21}.$$

15. If the plane passes through the origin, then $d = 0$, so that the distance from the origin to the plane and the number $|d|/\sqrt{a^2 + b^2 + c^2}$ are both 0. If the plane does not pass through the origin, let $P_1 = (0, 0, 0)$. Also assume that $c \neq 0$, and let $P_0 = (0, 0, d/c)$, so that P_0 is on the plane. By Theorem 11.13, the distance D from P_1 to the plane is given by

$$D = \frac{|(a\mathbf{i} + b\mathbf{j} + c\mathbf{k}) \cdot \overrightarrow{P_0P_1}|}{\sqrt{a^2 + b^2 + c^2}} = \frac{|(a\mathbf{i} + b\mathbf{j} + c\mathbf{k}) \cdot ((d/c)\mathbf{k})|}{\sqrt{a^2 + b^2 + c^2}} = \frac{|d|}{\sqrt{a^2 + b^2 + c^2}}.$$

The same result follows if $a \neq 0$, or if $b \neq 0$.

16. The planes are perpendicular if and only if their normals, $a_1\mathbf{i} + b_1\mathbf{j} + c_1\mathbf{k}$ and $a_2\mathbf{i} + b_2\mathbf{j} + c_2\mathbf{k}$, are perpendicular, which happens if and only if

$$a_1a_2 + b_1b_2 + c_1c_2 = (a_1\mathbf{i} + b_1\mathbf{j} + c_1\mathbf{k}) \cdot (a_2\mathbf{i} + b_2\mathbf{j} + c_2\mathbf{k}) = 0.$$

17. Let (x, y, z) be on the plane. Then

$$\sqrt{(x-3)^2 + (y-1)^2 + (z-5)^2} = \sqrt{(x-5)^2 + (y+1)^2 + (z-3)^2}.$$

Squaring both sides, we obtain $(x-3)^2 + (y-1)^2 + (z-5)^2 = (x-5)^2 + (y+1)^2 + (z-3)^2$. Simplifying, we obtain $x - y - z = 0$.

18. 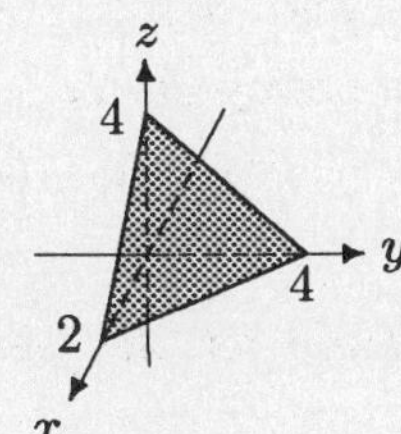

$2x + y + z = 4$

19. 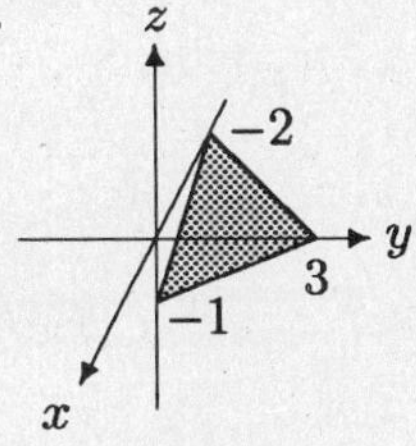

$-\frac{1}{2}x + \frac{1}{3}y - z = 1$

20. 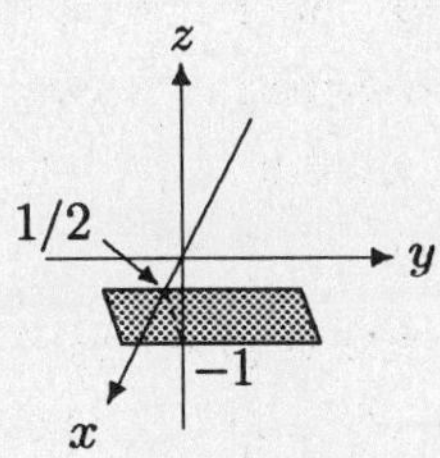

$2x - z = 1$

21. 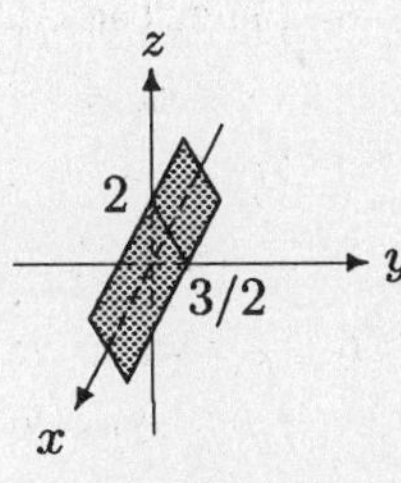

$4y + 3z = 6$

22. The vector $a\mathbf{i} - b\mathbf{j}$ lies along the line joining $(a,0,0)$ and $(0,b,0)$, and the vector $b\mathbf{j} - c\mathbf{k}$ lies along the line joining $(0,b,0)$ and $(0,0,c)$. Thus $\mathbf{N} = (a\mathbf{i} - b\mathbf{j}) \times (b\mathbf{j} - c\mathbf{k}) = bc\mathbf{i} + ac\mathbf{j} + ab\mathbf{k}$ is normal to the plane containing $(a,0,0)$, $(0,b,0)$, and $(0,0,c)$. Thus an equation of the plane is $bc(x-a) + acy + abz = 0$, or $bcx + acy + abz = abc$, or $x/a + y/b + z/c = 1$.

23. Let $P_0 = (2,3,2)$, $P_1 = (1,-1,-3)$, and $P_2 = (1,0,-1)$. Then $\overrightarrow{P_0P_1} = -\mathbf{i} - 4\mathbf{j} - 5\mathbf{k}$ and $\overrightarrow{P_0P_2} = -\mathbf{i} - 3\mathbf{j} - 3\mathbf{k}$. Thus a normal $\mathbf{N}$ to the plane containing the three points is given by

$$\mathbf{N} = \overrightarrow{P_0P_1} \times \overrightarrow{P_0P_2} = (-\mathbf{i} - 4\mathbf{j} - 5\mathbf{k}) \times (-\mathbf{i} - 3\mathbf{j} - 3\mathbf{k}) = -3\mathbf{i} + 2\mathbf{j} - \mathbf{k}.$$

Therefore an equation of the plane is $-3(x-2) + 2(y-3) - 1(z-2) = 0$, or $3x - 2y + z = 2$. Since $3 \cdot 5 - 2 \cdot 9 + 5 = 2$, the fourth point $(5,9,5)$ lies on the plane, so that all four given points lie on the same plane.

24. Let $t = (x-1)/2 = (y+1)/3 = (z+5)/7$, so that $x = 1 + 2t$, $y = -1 + 3t$, and $z = -5 + 7t$. Let $P_1 = (1+2t, -1+3t, -5+7t)$ and $P_0 = (1,-3,0)$, so that P_1 is not on the plane (unless $t = -3$) and P_0 is on the plane, and $\overrightarrow{P_0P_1} = 2t\mathbf{i} + (2+3t)\mathbf{j} + (-5+7t)\mathbf{k}$. The normal $\mathbf{N}$ to the plane is given by $\mathbf{N} = 2\mathbf{i} + 2\mathbf{j} - \mathbf{k}$. By Theorem 12.13 the distance from P_1 to the plane is given by

$$D = \frac{|\mathbf{N} \cdot \overrightarrow{P_0P_1}|}{\|\mathbf{N}\|} = \frac{|(2\mathbf{i} + 2\mathbf{j} - \mathbf{k}) \cdot [2t\mathbf{i} + (2+3t)\mathbf{j} + (-5+7t)\mathbf{k}]|}{\sqrt{2^2 + 2^2 + (-1)^2}} = \frac{|3t+9|}{3} = |t+3|.$$

Now $D = 3$ if $|t+3| = 3$, which means $t = 0$ or $t = -6$. If $t = 0$, then $P_1 = (1,-1,-5)$ and if $t = -6$, then $P_1 = (-11,-19,-47)$. These two points are both distance 3 from the plane.

25. Since $(\mathbf{a} \times \mathbf{b}) \times (\mathbf{c} \times \mathbf{d})$ is perpendicular to $(\mathbf{a} \times \mathbf{b})$ and $(\mathbf{c} \times \mathbf{d})$, which are normal to $\mathcal{P}_1$ and $\mathcal{P}_2$ respectively, $(\mathbf{a} \times \mathbf{b}) \times (\mathbf{c} \times \mathbf{d})$ is parallel to all vectors that lie in both $\mathcal{P}_1$ and $\mathcal{P}_2$, and thus is parallel to the intersection of $\mathcal{P}_1$ and $\mathcal{P}_2$.

26. Normals of the planes in (a) – (d) are $\mathbf{i} + 2\mathbf{j} - 3\mathbf{k}$, $15\mathbf{i} - 9\mathbf{j} + \mathbf{k}$, $-2\mathbf{i} - 4\mathbf{j} + 6\mathbf{k}$, and $5\mathbf{i} - 3\mathbf{j} + \frac{1}{3}\mathbf{k}$, respectively. Since the first and third, and the second and fourth are multiples of each other, the planes in (a) and (c) are parallel, and the planes in (b) and (d) are parallel. Since the equation in (c) can be obtained from the one in (a) by multiplying by -2 and rearranging, the planes in (a) and (c) are identical.

27. Normals of the planes in (a) – (d) are $\mathbf{i} + \mathbf{j} - \mathbf{k}$, $\mathbf{i} - \mathbf{j}$, $\mathbf{j} - \mathbf{k}$, and $\mathbf{i} + \mathbf{j}$. Since none of these is a multiple of another, no two planes are identical or parallel. Since $(\mathbf{i} + \mathbf{j} - \mathbf{k}) \cdot (\mathbf{i} - \mathbf{j}) = 0$ and $(\mathbf{i} - \mathbf{j}) \cdot (\mathbf{i} + \mathbf{j}) = 0$, the planes in (a) and (b) are perpendicular, as are the planes in (b) and (d).

28. a. The vector $\mathbf{k}$ is normal to the xy plane, so an equation of the plane is $1(z-3)=0$, or $z=3$.

    b. The vector $\mathbf{i}$ is normal to the plane, so an equation of the plane is $1(x+1)=0$, or $x=-1$.

    c. The vector $\mathbf{j}$ is normal to the plane, so an equation of the plane is $1(y-2)=0$, or $y=2$.

29. a. The vector $\mathbf{i}$ is normal to the plane, so an equation of the plane is $1(x+4)=0$, or $x=-4$.

    b. The vector $\mathbf{j}$ is normal to the plane, so an equation of the plane is $1(y+5)=0$, or $y=-5$.

    c. The vector $\mathbf{k}$ is normal to the plane, so an equation of the plane is $1(z+3)=0$, or $z=-3$.

30. The points $(-2,1,4)$ and $(0,3,1)$ determine the vector $2\mathbf{i}+2\mathbf{j}-3\mathbf{k}$, and $(2\mathbf{i}+2\mathbf{j}-3\mathbf{k})\times(2\mathbf{i}-4\mathbf{j}+6\mathbf{k}) = -18\mathbf{j}-12\mathbf{k}$. Thus an equation of the plane is $0(x+2)-18(y-1)-12(z-4)=0$, or $18y+12z=-66$.

31. From the first and second equations, $x=1-y$ and $z=2-y$. Substituting in the third equation, we find that $3=x+z=(1-y)+(2-y)=3-2y$, so that $y=0$. Thus $x=1$ and $z=2$. The point of intersection is $(1,0,2)$.

32. From the first and third equations, $2-y=x-z=y$, so that $y=1$. Then the first and second equations become $x-z=1$ and $-x-z=1$, so that $1+z=x=-1-z$. Thus $z=-1$, so that $x=0$. The point is $(0,1,-1)$.

33. Adding the first and second equations, we obtain $3x=-1$, so that $x=-\frac{1}{3}$. The second equation becomes $3y+z=-\frac{5}{3}$. Subtracting the third equation from this equation, we obtain $y=-\frac{11}{6}$. Therefore $z=\frac{23}{6}$. The point is $(-\frac{1}{3},-\frac{11}{6},\frac{23}{6})$.

34. Since the third equation can be obtained from the first equation by multiplying by $\frac{1}{2}$, the two corresponding planes are identical. Multiplying the second equation by 2 and adding it to the third, we obtain $3x-5z=6$, so that $z=(3x-6)/5$. Multiplying the second equation by 3 and subtracting the third equation from it, we obtain $2x-5y-4=0$, so that $y=(2x-4)/5$. If $x=t$, then the points of intersection form a line having the parametric equations $x=t$, $y=-\frac{4}{5}+\frac{2}{5}t$, $z=-\frac{6}{5}+\frac{3}{5}t$.

35. The two planes are parallel. Let $P_0=(0,0,2)$ and $P_1=(0,0,\frac{1}{3})$, which are on the first and second planes, respectively. Then $\overrightarrow{P_0P_1}=-\frac{5}{3}\mathbf{k}$, and a normal $\mathbf{N}$ to either plane is given by $\mathbf{N}=\mathbf{i}-\mathbf{j}+\mathbf{k}$. By Theorem 11.13, the distance D is given by

$$D=\frac{|\mathbf{N}\cdot\overrightarrow{P_0P_1}|}{\|\mathbf{N}\|}=\frac{\frac{5}{3}}{\sqrt{1^2+(-1)^2+1^2}}=\frac{5\sqrt{3}}{9}.$$

36. The two planes are parallel. Let $P_0=(0,4,0)$ and $P_1=(0,-1,1)$, which are on the first and second planes, respectively. Then $\overrightarrow{P_0P_1}=-5\mathbf{j}+\mathbf{k}$ and a normal $\mathbf{N}$ to either plane is given by $\mathbf{N}=\mathbf{j}-2\mathbf{k}$. By Theorem 11.13, the distance D is given by

$$D=\frac{|\mathbf{N}\cdot\overrightarrow{P_0P_1}|}{\|\mathbf{N}\|}=\frac{7}{\sqrt{1^2+(-2)^2}}=\frac{7\sqrt{5}}{5}.$$

37. The two planes are parallel. Let $P_0 = (\frac{5}{2}, 0, 0)$ and $P_1 = (-\frac{1}{4}, 0, 0)$, which are on the first and second planes, respectively. Then $\overrightarrow{P_0P_1} = -\frac{11}{4}\mathbf{i}$, and a normal $\mathbf{N}$ to either plane is given by $\mathbf{N} = 2\mathbf{i} - 3\mathbf{j} + 4\mathbf{k}$. By Theorem 11.13,

$$D = \frac{|\mathbf{N}\cdot\overrightarrow{P_0P_1}|}{\|\mathbf{N}\|} = \frac{\frac{11}{2}}{\sqrt{2^2 + (-3)^2 + 4^2}} = \frac{11}{58}\sqrt{29}.$$

38. The vectors $\mathbf{N}_1 = 2\mathbf{i} - \mathbf{j} + \mathbf{k}$ and $\mathbf{N}_2 = \mathbf{i} + \mathbf{j} + 3\mathbf{k}$ are normal to the first and second planes, respectively. Thus

$$\cos\theta = \frac{\mathbf{N}_1\cdot\mathbf{N}_2}{\|\mathbf{N}_1\|\|\mathbf{N}_2\|} = \frac{4}{\sqrt{6}\sqrt{11}} = \frac{2}{33}\sqrt{66}$$

so $\theta \approx 1.056$ radians, or $\theta \approx 60.50°$.

39. The vectors $\mathbf{N}_1 = \mathbf{j} - \mathbf{k}$ and $\mathbf{N}_2 = 4\mathbf{i} - \mathbf{j} - 2\mathbf{k}$ are normal to the first and second planes, respectively. Thus

$$\cos\theta = \frac{\mathbf{N}_1\cdot\mathbf{N}_2}{\|\mathbf{N}_1\|\|\mathbf{N}_2\|} = \frac{1}{\sqrt{2}\sqrt{21}} = \frac{1}{42}\sqrt{42}$$

so that $\theta \approx 1.416$ radians, or $\theta \approx 81.12°$.

40. The vectors $\mathbf{N}_1 = \mathbf{i} + 2\mathbf{j} - 3\mathbf{k}$ and $\mathbf{N}_2 = 2\mathbf{i} - 4\mathbf{j} - 6\mathbf{k}$ are normal to the first and second planes, respectively. Thus

$$\cos\theta = \frac{\mathbf{N}_1\cdot\mathbf{N}_2}{\|\mathbf{N}_1\|\|\mathbf{N}_2\|} = \frac{12}{\sqrt{14}\sqrt{56}} = \frac{3}{7}$$

so $\theta \approx 1.128$ radians, or $\theta \approx 64.62°$.

41. The given information implies that the two planes intersect in a line l. Since $\mathbf{N}_1 \times \mathbf{N}_2$ is perpendicular to both $\mathbf{N}_1$ and $\mathbf{N}_2$, it follows that $\mathbf{N}_1 \times \mathbf{N}_2$ is parallel to l. We know that P lies on l if and only if $\overrightarrow{PP_0}$ is parallel to any vector $\mathbf{L}$ that is parallel to l. Thus P lies in the intersection of the two planes if and only if $\overrightarrow{PP_0}$ is parallel to $\mathbf{N}_1 \times \mathbf{N}_2$. By Corollary 11.11 this is equivalent to the condition $(\mathbf{N}_1 \times \mathbf{N}_2) \times \overrightarrow{PP_0} = \mathbf{0}$.

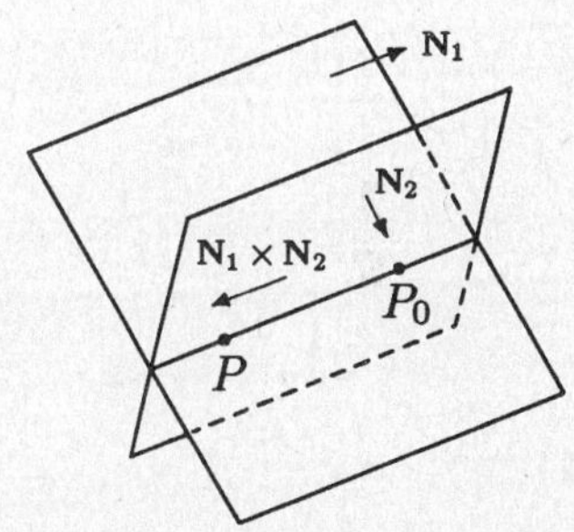

Chapter 11 Review

1. $2\mathbf{a} + \mathbf{b} - 3\mathbf{c} = 5\mathbf{i} - 10\mathbf{j} + 11\mathbf{k}$; $\mathbf{a} \times \mathbf{b} = \begin{vmatrix} \mathbf{i} & \mathbf{j} & \mathbf{k} \\ 2 & -3 & 1 \\ 1 & -1 & 0 \end{vmatrix} = \mathbf{i} + \mathbf{j} + \mathbf{k}$;

$\mathbf{c}\cdot(\mathbf{a} \times \mathbf{b}) = (\mathbf{j} - 3\mathbf{k})\cdot(\mathbf{i} + \mathbf{j} + \mathbf{k}) = -2$;

$\mathbf{a} \times (\mathbf{b} \times \mathbf{c}) = \mathbf{b}(\mathbf{a}\cdot\mathbf{c}) - \mathbf{c}(\mathbf{a}\cdot\mathbf{b}) = -6\mathbf{b} - 5\mathbf{c} = -6\mathbf{i} + \mathbf{j} + 15\mathbf{k}$

2. $2\mathbf{a} + \mathbf{b} - 3\mathbf{c} = 9\mathbf{j} - 8\mathbf{k}$; $\mathbf{a} \times \mathbf{b} = \begin{vmatrix} \mathbf{i} & \mathbf{j} & \mathbf{k} \\ \frac{1}{2} & -1 & 2 \\ 2 & -4 & 6 \end{vmatrix} = 2\mathbf{i} + \mathbf{j}$;

$\mathbf{c}\cdot(\mathbf{a} \times \mathbf{b}) = (\mathbf{i} - 5\mathbf{j} + 6\mathbf{k})\cdot(2\mathbf{i} + \mathbf{j}) = -3$;

$\mathbf{a} \times (\mathbf{b} \times \mathbf{c}) = \mathbf{b}(\mathbf{a}\cdot\mathbf{c}) - \mathbf{c}(\mathbf{a}\cdot\mathbf{b}) = \frac{35}{2}\mathbf{b} - 17\mathbf{c} = 18\mathbf{i} + 15\mathbf{j} + 3\mathbf{k}$

3. $2\mathbf{a}+\mathbf{b}-3\mathbf{c} = 11\mathbf{i}-9\mathbf{j}+6\mathbf{k}$; $\mathbf{a}\times\mathbf{b} = \begin{vmatrix} \mathbf{i} & \mathbf{j} & \mathbf{k} \\ 3 & -2 & 1 \\ 5 & -2 & 1 \end{vmatrix} = 2\mathbf{j}+4\mathbf{k}$;

$\mathbf{c}\cdot(\mathbf{a}\times\mathbf{b}) = (\mathbf{j}-\mathbf{k})\cdot(2\mathbf{j}+4\mathbf{k}) = -2$;

$\mathbf{a}\times(\mathbf{b}\times\mathbf{c}) = \mathbf{b}(\mathbf{a}\cdot\mathbf{c}) - \mathbf{c}(\mathbf{a}\cdot\mathbf{b}) = -3\mathbf{b}-20\mathbf{c} = -15\mathbf{i}-14\mathbf{j}+17\mathbf{k}$

4. $\cos\theta = \dfrac{(3\mathbf{i}-4\mathbf{j}+12\mathbf{k})\cdot(\mathbf{i}-\mathbf{k})}{\|3\mathbf{i}-4\mathbf{j}+12\mathbf{k}\|\,\|\mathbf{i}-\mathbf{k}\|} = \dfrac{-9}{13\sqrt{2}}$

5. Let $Q = (b_1, b_2, b_3)$. Then $\overrightarrow{PQ} = (b_1-1)\mathbf{i} + (b_2+2)\mathbf{j} + (b_3-3)\mathbf{k}$, so that $\overrightarrow{PQ} = \mathbf{a}$ if $b_1 - 1 = 2$, $b_2+2=-2$, $b_3-3=1$, that is, if $b_1 = 3$, $b_2 = -4$, $b_3 = 4$. Thus $Q = (3,-4,4)$.

6. a. $\mathbf{a}\cdot\mathbf{b} = (2)(5)+(-3)(3)+(5)(-7) = -34$

   b. $\mathbf{a}\times\mathbf{b} = \begin{vmatrix} \mathbf{i} & \mathbf{j} & \mathbf{k} \\ 2 & -3 & 5 \\ 5 & 3 & -7 \end{vmatrix} = 6\mathbf{i}+39\mathbf{j}+21\mathbf{k}$

   c. $\mathbf{pr_a b} = \dfrac{\mathbf{a}\cdot\mathbf{b}}{\|\mathbf{a}\|^2}\mathbf{a} = \dfrac{-34}{38}(2\mathbf{i}-3\mathbf{j}+5\mathbf{k}) = -\dfrac{34}{19}\mathbf{i}+\dfrac{51}{19}\mathbf{j}-\dfrac{85}{19}\mathbf{k}$

7. Let $\mathbf{b} = 2\mathbf{i}-\mathbf{j}-\mathbf{k}$, $\mathbf{a} = 2\mathbf{j}+\mathbf{k}$, and $\mathbf{a}' = -20\mathbf{i}-2\mathbf{j}+4\mathbf{k}$. Note that $\mathbf{a}\cdot\mathbf{a}' = -4+4 = 0$, so that $\mathbf{a}$ and $\mathbf{a}'$ are perpendicular. Next,

$$\mathbf{pr_a b} = \frac{\mathbf{a}\cdot\mathbf{b}}{\|\mathbf{a}\|^2}\mathbf{a} = -\frac{3}{5}\mathbf{a} = -\frac{3}{5}(2\mathbf{j}+\mathbf{k})$$

$$\mathbf{pr_{a'} b} = \mathbf{b} - \mathbf{pr_a b} = 2\mathbf{i}-\mathbf{j}-\mathbf{k}+\frac{3}{5}(2\mathbf{j}+\mathbf{k}) = 2\mathbf{i}+\frac{1}{5}\mathbf{j}-\frac{2}{5}\mathbf{k} = -\frac{1}{10}\mathbf{a}'.$$

Thus $\mathbf{b} = -\frac{3}{5}\mathbf{a} - \frac{1}{10}\mathbf{a}'$.

8. Let $P = (1,1,1)$, $Q = (2,3,5)$, and $R = (-1,3,1)$. The area of the triangle with vertices P, Q, and R is $\frac{1}{2}\|\overrightarrow{PQ}\times\overrightarrow{PR}\|$. Since $\overrightarrow{PQ} = \mathbf{i}+2\mathbf{j}+4\mathbf{k}$ and $\overrightarrow{PR} = -2\mathbf{i}+2\mathbf{j}$, it follows that

$$\overrightarrow{PQ}\times\overrightarrow{PR} = \begin{vmatrix} \mathbf{i} & \mathbf{j} & \mathbf{k} \\ 1 & 2 & 4 \\ -2 & 2 & 0 \end{vmatrix} = -8\mathbf{i}-8\mathbf{j}+6\mathbf{k}.$$

Thus the area is $\frac{1}{2}\|\overrightarrow{PQ}\times\overrightarrow{PR}\| = \frac{1}{2}\sqrt{164} = \sqrt{41}$.

9. If $P_0 = (\frac{1}{2}, \frac{1}{3}, 0)$, $P_1 = (1,1,-1)$, and $P_2 = (-2,-3,5)$, then $\overrightarrow{P_0P_1} = \frac{1}{2}\mathbf{i}+\frac{2}{3}\mathbf{j}-\mathbf{k}$, whereas $\overrightarrow{P_1P_2} = -3\mathbf{i}-4\mathbf{j}+6\mathbf{k}$. Thus $-6\overrightarrow{P_0P_1} = \overrightarrow{P_1P_2}$, so that the three points are collinear. Symmetric equations of the line are $(x-1)/-3 = (y-1)/-4 = (z+1)/6$.

10. a. $\overrightarrow{PQ} = (4-2)\mathbf{i}+(3-5)\mathbf{j}+(8-(-7))\mathbf{k} = 2\mathbf{i}-2\mathbf{j}+15\mathbf{k}$

   b. $\|\overrightarrow{PQ}\| = \sqrt{2^2+(-2)^2+(15)^2} = \sqrt{233}$

   c. i. $\mathbf{r}_0 = \overrightarrow{OP} = 2\mathbf{i}+5\mathbf{j}-7\mathbf{k}$ and $\mathbf{L} = \overrightarrow{PQ} = 2\mathbf{i}-2\mathbf{j}+15\mathbf{k}$, so that a vector equation of l is $\mathbf{r} = 2\mathbf{i}+5\mathbf{j}-7\mathbf{k}+t(2\mathbf{i}-2\mathbf{j}+15\mathbf{k}) = (2+2t)\mathbf{i}+(5-2t)\mathbf{j}+(-7+15t)\mathbf{k}$.

ii. $x_0 = 2$, $y_0 = 5$, $z_0 = -7$, $a = 2$, $b = -2$, $c = 15$, so parametric equations of l are $x = 2 + 2t$, $y = 5 - 2t$, $z = -7 + 15t$.

iii. $x_0 = 2$, $y_0 = 5$, $z_0 = -7$, $a = 2$, $b = -2$, $c = 15$, so symmetric equations of l are $(x-2)/2 = (y-5)/-2 = (z+7)/15$.

11. The line is parallel to $2\mathbf{i} - 3\mathbf{j} + 4\mathbf{k}$, which is normal to the plane. Since $\mathbf{r}_0 = -3\mathbf{i} - 3\mathbf{j} + \mathbf{k}$, a vector equation of the line is $\mathbf{r} = (-3+2t)\mathbf{i} + (-3-3t)\mathbf{j} + (1+4t)\mathbf{k}$.

12. Using (1) of Section 11.6 with $a = 2$, $b = 1$, $c = -1$ and $x_0 = -1$, $y_0 = 3$, $z_0 = 2$, we have $2(x+1) + 1(y-3) + (-1)(z-2) = 0$, or $2x + y - z = -1$.

13. Let $P_0 = (-1,1,1)$, $P_1 = (0,2,1)$, and $P_2 = (0,0,\frac{3}{2})$. Then $\overrightarrow{P_0P_1} = \mathbf{i} + \mathbf{j}$ and $\overrightarrow{P_0P_2} = \mathbf{i} - \mathbf{j} + \frac{1}{2}\mathbf{k}$. Thus a normal $\mathbf{N}$ to the plane containing the three points is given by

$$\mathbf{N} = \overrightarrow{P_0P_1} \times \overrightarrow{P_0P_2} = \frac{1}{2}\mathbf{i} - \frac{1}{2}\mathbf{j} - 2\mathbf{k}.$$

Therefore an equation of the plane is $\frac{1}{2}(x+1) - \frac{1}{2}(y-1) - 2(z-1) = 0$, or $\frac{1}{2}x - \frac{1}{2}y - 2z = -3$. Since $\frac{1}{2}(13) - \frac{1}{2}(-1) - 2(5) = -3$, the fourth point $(13,-1,5)$ lies on the plane, so that all four points lie on the same plane.

14. Let $P_0 = (1,0,-1)$, $P_1 = (-5,3,2)$, and $P_2 = (2,-1,4)$. Then $\overrightarrow{P_0P_1} = -6\mathbf{i} + 3\mathbf{j} + 3\mathbf{k}$ and $\overrightarrow{P_0P_2} = \mathbf{i} - \mathbf{j} + 5\mathbf{k}$. Thus a normal $\mathbf{N}$ to the plane containing the three points is given by

$$\mathbf{N} = \overrightarrow{P_0P_1} \times \overrightarrow{P_0P_2} = 18\mathbf{i} + 33\mathbf{j} + 3\mathbf{k}.$$

Therefore an equation of the plane is $18(x-1) + 33(y-0) + 3(z+1) = 0$, or $6x + 11y + z = 5$.

15. Since a normal $\mathbf{N}$ of the plane is perpendicular to the z axis, $\mathbf{N} = a\mathbf{i} + b\mathbf{j}$ for appropriate choices of a and b. Thus an equation of the plane is $a(x-3) + b(y+1) + 0(z-5) = 0$, or $ax + by = 3a - b$. Since $(7,9,4)$ is on the plane, $7a + 9b = 3a - b$, so that $4a = -10b$, or $a = -\frac{5}{2}b$. Therefore an equation of the plane is $-\frac{5}{2}bx + by = -\frac{15}{2}b - b$, or $5x - 2y = 17$.

16. The line is parallel to $7\mathbf{i} + 9\mathbf{j} + 45\mathbf{k}$, and the vector $9\mathbf{i} - 2\mathbf{j} - \mathbf{k}$ is perpendicular to the plane. Since $(7\mathbf{i} + 9\mathbf{j} + 45\mathbf{k}) \cdot (9\mathbf{i} - 2\mathbf{j} - \mathbf{k}) = 0$, these two vectors are perpendicular, so that the line and the plane are parallel.

17. The point $P_1 = (1,-2,5)$ is not on the plane, whereas $P_0 = (1,-2,0)$ is on the plane. Then $\overrightarrow{P_0P_1} = 5\mathbf{k}$. If $\mathbf{N} = 3\mathbf{i} - 4\mathbf{j} + 12\mathbf{k}$, then $\mathbf{N}$ is normal to the plane, and the distance D from P_1 to the plane is given by

$$D = \frac{|\mathbf{N} \cdot \overrightarrow{P_0P_1}|}{\|\mathbf{N}\|} = \frac{|(3\mathbf{i} - 4\mathbf{j} + 12\mathbf{k}) \cdot (5\mathbf{k})|}{\sqrt{3^2 + (-4)^2 + (12)^2}} = \frac{60}{13}.$$

18. The point $P_1 = (1,-2,5)$ is not on the line, and the line is parallel to $\mathbf{L} = 3\mathbf{i} - 4\mathbf{j} + 12\mathbf{k}$. The point $P_0 = (1,-2,0)$ is on the line, and $\overrightarrow{P_0P_1} = 5\mathbf{k}$. Therefore the distance D from P_1 to the line is given by

$$D = \frac{\|\mathbf{L} \times \overrightarrow{P_0P_1}\|}{\|L\|} = \frac{\|(3\mathbf{i} - 4\mathbf{j} + 12\mathbf{k}) \times (5\mathbf{k})\|}{\sqrt{3^2 + (-4)^2 + (12)^2}} = \frac{\|-20\mathbf{i} - 15\mathbf{j}\|}{13} = \frac{25}{13}.$$

19. a. Letting $y = 4$ and $z = 1$ in the first equation, we obtain $3x - 4 + 1 = 2$, or $x = \frac{5}{3}$. Thus the three planes have the point $(\frac{5}{3}, 4, 1)$ in common.

    b. If (x, y, z) is on the first two planes, then $2x + y - 2z - 1 = 0 = 3x + y - z - 2$, so that $-z = x - 1$, or $x = 1 - z$. If (x, y, z) is on the first and third planes, then $2x + y - 2z - 1 = 0 = 2x - 2y + 2z$, so that $3y - 1 = 4z$, or $y = (4z + 1)/3$. Thus if (x, y, z) is on all three planes, then $0 = x - y + z = (1 - z) - ((4z + 1)/3) + z$, so that $z = \frac{1}{2}$. Thus $x = \frac{1}{2}$ and $y = 1$. Thus the planes have the point $(\frac{1}{2}, 1, \frac{1}{2})$ in common.

    c. If (x, y, z) is on the first two planes, then $2x - 11y + 6z + 2 = 0 = 2x - 3y + 2z - 2$, or $z + 1 = 2y$. If (x, y, z) is on the first and third planes, then $2x - 11y + 6z + 2 = 0 = 2x - 9y + 5z + 1$, or $z + 1 = 2y$. Thus $z = 2y - 1$. Substituting $z = 2y - 1$ into the equation $2x - 3y + 2z = 2$, we obtain $2x - 3y + 2(2y - 1) = 2$, or $2x + y = 4$. Thus $x = -\frac{1}{2}y + 2$. If we let $y = t$, then $x = 2 - \frac{1}{2}t$, $y = t$, $z = -1 + 2t$ are parametric equations of the line common to the three planes.

20. Symmetric equations of the line are $(x - a)/a = (y - b)/b = (z - c)/c$. If we substitute 0 for x, y, and z in these equations, then the equations become $-1 = -1 = -1$. Thus $(0, 0, 0)$ lies on the line.

21. An equation of the required plane is $a(x - a) + b(y - b) + c(z - c) = 0$, or $ax + by + cz = a^2 + b^2 + c^2$.

22. $\mathbf{L} = 3\mathbf{i} + 2\mathbf{j} + 6\mathbf{k}$ is parallel to l, and $\mathbf{N} = 2\mathbf{i} - 3\mathbf{j} + 4\mathbf{k}$ is perpendicular to $\mathcal{P}_0$ and $\mathcal{P}_1$.

    a. If l did not intersect $\mathcal{P}_0$ and $\mathcal{P}_1$, then $\mathbf{L}$ would be perpendicular to $\mathbf{N}$. But $\mathbf{L} \cdot \mathbf{N} = (3)(2) + (2)(-3) + (6)(4) = 24 \neq 0$. Therefore $\mathbf{L}$ and $\mathbf{N}$ are not perpendicular, so l intersects both $\mathcal{P}_0$ and $\mathcal{P}_1$.

    b. The points $P_0 = (1, 0, 0)$ and $P_1 = (3, 0, 0)$ are on the planes $\mathcal{P}_0$ and $\mathcal{P}_1$, respectively. Since the planes $\mathcal{P}_0$ and $\mathcal{P}_1$ are parallel, the distance between $\mathcal{P}_0$ and $\mathcal{P}_1$ equals the distance D between the point P_0 and the plane $\mathcal{P}_1$, which by (3) of Section 11.6 is given by

$$D = \frac{|\mathbf{N} \cdot \overrightarrow{P_0P_1}|}{\|\mathbf{N}\|} = \frac{|(2\mathbf{i} - 3\mathbf{j} + 4\mathbf{k}) \cdot (2\mathbf{i})|}{\sqrt{2^2 + (-3)^2 + 4^2}} = \frac{4}{29}\sqrt{29}.$$

    If θ is the angle between $\overrightarrow{Q_0Q_1}$ and $\mathbf{N}$, or equivalently, between $\mathbf{L}$ and $\mathbf{N}$, then

$$|\overrightarrow{Q_0Q_1}| = \left|\frac{D}{\cos\theta}\right| = \frac{D}{\left|\dfrac{\mathbf{L} \cdot \mathbf{N}}{\|\mathbf{L}\|\,\|\mathbf{N}\|}\right|} = \frac{\frac{4}{29}\sqrt{29}}{\dfrac{24}{\sqrt{49}\sqrt{29}}} = \frac{7}{6}.$$

23. Using the notation in the figure, we have $\mathbf{a} = \mathbf{c} + \mathbf{d}$, $\mathbf{b} = -\mathbf{c} + \mathbf{d}$, and $\|\mathbf{c}\| = \|\mathbf{d}\| = r$, the radius of the circle. Thus

$$\mathbf{a} \cdot \mathbf{b} = (\mathbf{c} + \mathbf{d}) \cdot (-\mathbf{c} + \mathbf{d}) = -\mathbf{c} \cdot \mathbf{c} + \mathbf{c} \cdot \mathbf{d} - \mathbf{c} \cdot \mathbf{d} + \mathbf{d} \cdot \mathbf{d} = \|\mathbf{d}\|^2 - \|\mathbf{c}\|^2 = 0$$

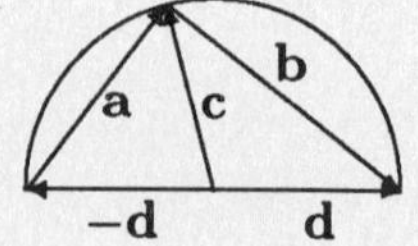

so $\mathbf{a}$ and $\mathbf{b}$ are perpendicular. Therefore every angle inscribed in a semicircle is a right angle.

24. Let the triangle have vertices P, Q, and R, and the vectors **a**, **b**, and **c** point from the vertices to the midpoints of the opposite sides, as in the figure. Then $\mathbf{a} = \overrightarrow{PR} + \frac{1}{2}\overrightarrow{RQ}$, $\mathbf{b} = \overrightarrow{QP} + \frac{1}{2}\overrightarrow{PR}$, and $\mathbf{c} = \overrightarrow{RQ} + \frac{1}{2}\overrightarrow{QP}$, so that

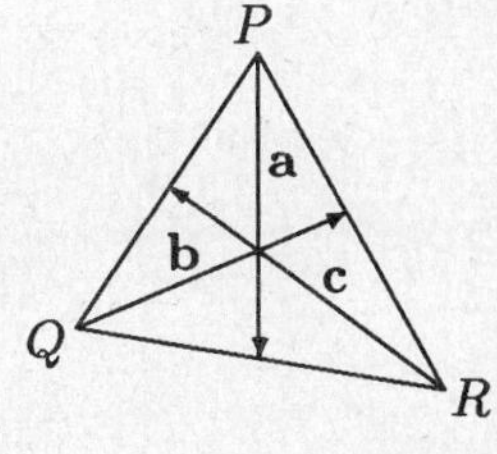

$$\mathbf{a}+\mathbf{b}+\mathbf{c} = (\overrightarrow{PR} + \frac{1}{2}\overrightarrow{RQ}) + (\overrightarrow{QP} + \frac{1}{2}\overrightarrow{PR}) + (\overrightarrow{RQ} + \frac{1}{2}\overrightarrow{QP})$$

$$= \frac{3}{2}\overrightarrow{PR} + \frac{3}{2}\overrightarrow{RQ} + \frac{3}{2}\overrightarrow{QP} = \frac{3}{2}\overrightarrow{PP} = \mathbf{0}.$$

25. a. Since $\mathbf{a}\cdot\mathbf{c} = \mathbf{b}\cdot\mathbf{c}$ for all **c**, we let $\mathbf{c} = \mathbf{a}-\mathbf{b}$ and find that $\|\mathbf{a}-\mathbf{b}\|^2 = (\mathbf{a}-\mathbf{b})\cdot(\mathbf{a}-\mathbf{b}) = (\mathbf{a}-\mathbf{b})\cdot\mathbf{c} = \mathbf{a}\cdot\mathbf{c} - \mathbf{b}\cdot\mathbf{c} = 0$. Thus $\mathbf{a}-\mathbf{b} = \mathbf{0}$, so that $\mathbf{a} = \mathbf{b}$.

b. If $\mathbf{a} \neq \mathbf{b}$, then $\mathbf{a}-\mathbf{b} \neq 0$, so we let **c** be a nonzero vector perpendicular to $\mathbf{a}-\mathbf{b}$. It follows that $\mathbf{0} = (\mathbf{a}\times\mathbf{c}) - (\mathbf{b}\times\mathbf{c}) = (\mathbf{a}-\mathbf{b})\times\mathbf{c}$. Therefore $\|\mathbf{a}-\mathbf{b}\|\,\|\mathbf{c}\| = 0$, which is impossible since $\|\mathbf{a}-\mathbf{b}\| \neq 0$ and $\|\mathbf{c}\| \neq 0$. Thus $\mathbf{a} = \mathbf{b}$.

26. Let $c = -(\mathbf{a}\cdot\mathbf{b})/\|\mathbf{b}\|^2$. Then

$$\|\mathbf{a}+c\mathbf{b}\|^2 = (\mathbf{a}+c\mathbf{b})\cdot(\mathbf{a}+c\mathbf{b}) = \mathbf{a}\cdot\mathbf{a} + 2c\mathbf{a}\cdot\mathbf{b} + c^2\mathbf{b}\cdot\mathbf{b}$$

$$= \|\mathbf{a}\|^2 - \frac{2(\mathbf{a}\cdot\mathbf{b})^2}{\|\mathbf{b}\|^2} + \frac{(\mathbf{a}\cdot\mathbf{b})^2}{\|\mathbf{b}\|^4}\|\mathbf{b}\|^2 = \|\mathbf{a}\|^2 - \frac{(\mathbf{a}\cdot\mathbf{b})^2}{\|\mathbf{b}\|^2}.$$

Therefore $\|\mathbf{a}\| \leq \|\mathbf{a}+c\mathbf{b}\|$ for every number c only if $(\mathbf{a}\cdot\mathbf{b})^2/\|\mathbf{b}\|^2 = 0$, that is, if $\mathbf{a}\cdot\mathbf{b} = 0$, or **a** and **b** are perpendicular. Conversely, if **a** and **b** are perpendicular, then for any number c,

$$\|\mathbf{a}\|^2 \leq \|\mathbf{a}\|^2 + c^2\|\mathbf{b}\|^2 = \mathbf{a}\cdot\mathbf{a} + 2c\mathbf{a}\cdot\mathbf{b} + c^2\mathbf{b}\cdot\mathbf{b} = \|\mathbf{a}+c\mathbf{b}\|^2,$$

so that $\|\mathbf{a}\| \leq \|\mathbf{a}+c\mathbf{b}\|$ for all numbers c.

27. Letting $\mathbf{a} = \cos x\,\mathbf{i} + \sin x\,\mathbf{j}$ and $\mathbf{b} = \cos y\,\mathbf{i} - \sin y\,\mathbf{j}$, we find that $\mathbf{a}\cdot\mathbf{b} = \cos x\cos y - \sin x\sin y$. But by the definitions of **a** and **b**, the angle between **a** and **b** is $x+y$, (see figure), so that $\mathbf{a}\cdot\mathbf{b} = \|\mathbf{a}\|\,\|\mathbf{b}\|\cos(x+y) = \cos(x+y)$. Thus

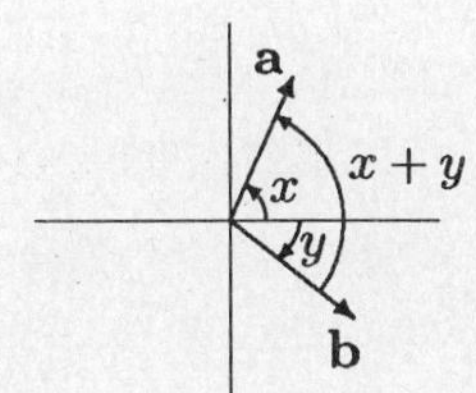

$$\cos(x+y) = \cos x\,\cos y - \sin x\,\sin y.$$

28. a.
$$\begin{aligned}\|\mathbf{a}+\mathbf{b}\|^2\|\mathbf{a}-\mathbf{b}\|^2 &= [(\mathbf{a}+\mathbf{b})\cdot(\mathbf{a}+\mathbf{b})][(\mathbf{a}-\mathbf{b})\cdot(\mathbf{a}-\mathbf{b})]\\ &= [\|\mathbf{a}\|^2 + 2\mathbf{a}\cdot\mathbf{b} + \|\mathbf{b}\|^2]\cdot[\|\mathbf{a}\|^2 - 2\mathbf{a}\cdot\mathbf{b} + \|\mathbf{b}\|^2]\\ &= (\|\mathbf{a}\|^4 + 2\|\mathbf{a}\|^2\|\mathbf{b}\|^2 + \|\mathbf{b}\|^4) - 4(\mathbf{a}\cdot\mathbf{b})^2\\ &= (\|\mathbf{a}\|^2 + \|\mathbf{b}\|^2)^2 - 4(\mathbf{a}\cdot\mathbf{b})^2\end{aligned}$$

b. Since $-4(\mathbf{a}\cdot\mathbf{b})^2 \leq 0$, we infer that $\|\mathbf{a}+\mathbf{b}\|^2\|\mathbf{a}-\mathbf{b}\|^2 \leq (\|\mathbf{a}\|^2 + \|\mathbf{b}\|^2)^2$, so that $\|\mathbf{a}+\mathbf{b}\|\,\|\mathbf{a}-\mathbf{b}\| \leq \|\mathbf{a}\|^2 + \|\mathbf{b}\|^2$.

29. Using the fact that **a**, **b**, and **c** are pairwise perpendicular, we have

$$\|\mathbf{d}\|^2 = \mathbf{d}\cdot\mathbf{d} = (a\mathbf{a}+b\mathbf{b}+c\mathbf{c})\cdot(a\mathbf{a}+b\mathbf{b}+c\mathbf{c}) = a^2(\mathbf{a}\cdot\mathbf{a})+b^2(\mathbf{b}\cdot\mathbf{b})+c^2(\mathbf{c}\cdot\mathbf{c}).$$

Since **a**, **b**, and **c** are unit vectors, $\mathbf{a}\cdot\mathbf{a} = \mathbf{b}\cdot\mathbf{b} = \mathbf{c}\cdot\mathbf{c} = 1$, so that $a^2(\mathbf{a}\cdot\mathbf{a})+b^2(\mathbf{b}\cdot\mathbf{b})+c^2(\mathbf{c}\cdot\mathbf{c}) = a^2+b^2+c^2$, and thus $\|\mathbf{d}\| = \sqrt{a^2+b^2+c^2}$.

30. Let **r**, **s** be as in the figure. Then $\mathbf{s} = \cos\phi\,\mathbf{k}$ since **s** is parallel to the z axis and $\|\mathbf{u}\| = 1$. Next, **r** has length $\sin\phi$ since $\|\mathbf{u}\| = 1$. Since **r** is in the xy plane, makes the angle θ with the positive x axis, and has length $\sin\phi$, it follows that $\mathbf{r} = (\sin\phi)(\cos\theta\,\mathbf{i}+\sin\theta\,\mathbf{j}) = \sin\phi\,\cos\theta\,\mathbf{i}+\sin\phi\,\sin\theta\,\mathbf{j}$. Therefore $\mathbf{u} = \mathbf{r}+\mathbf{s} = \cos\theta\,\sin\phi\,\mathbf{i}+\sin\theta\,\sin\phi\,\mathbf{j}+\cos\phi\,\mathbf{k}$.

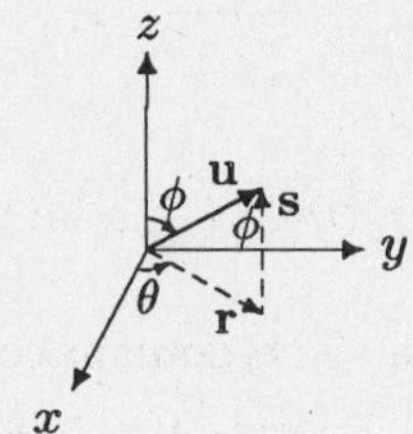

31. Consider a coordinate system with the forces applied at the origin, the 500 pound force $\mathbf{F}_1$ along the positive x axis and the 300 pound force along the line at an angle of $\pi/3$ with the positive x axis. Then $\mathbf{F}_1 = 500\mathbf{i}$ and $\mathbf{F}_2 = 300(\cos(\pi/3)\,\mathbf{i}+\sin(\pi/3)\,\mathbf{j}) = 150\mathbf{i}+150\sqrt{3}\,\mathbf{j}$. Thus the resultant force $\mathbf{F} = \mathbf{F}_1+\mathbf{F}_2 = 500\mathbf{i}+(150\mathbf{i}+150\sqrt{3}\mathbf{j}) = 650\mathbf{i}+150\sqrt{3}\mathbf{j}$. Therefore the magnitude of **F** is given by $\|\mathbf{F}\| = \sqrt{(650)^2+(150)^2(3)} = 700$ (pounds). For the cosine of the angle θ between **F** and $\mathbf{F}_1$ we obtain

$$\cos\theta = \frac{\mathbf{F}\cdot\mathbf{F}_1}{\|\mathbf{F}\|\,\|\mathbf{F}_1\|} = \frac{650\cdot 500}{700\cdot 500} = \frac{13}{14}.$$

32. a. Let $\mathbf{F}_1$ and $\mathbf{F}_2$ be the forces pointing downward and upward, respectively. Then $\mathbf{F}_1 = 5(\cos\theta\,\mathbf{i}-\sin\theta\,\mathbf{j})$ and $\mathbf{F}_2 = 5(\cos\theta\,\mathbf{i}+\sin\theta\,\mathbf{j})$. We must choose θ so that $\mathbf{F}_1+\mathbf{F}_2 = 5\mathbf{i}$. But $\mathbf{F}_1+\mathbf{F}_2 = 5(\cos\theta\,\mathbf{i}-\sin\theta\,\mathbf{j})+5(\cos\theta\,\mathbf{i}+\sin\theta\,\mathbf{j}) = 10\cos\theta\,\mathbf{i}$, so that $\mathbf{F}_1+\mathbf{F}_2 = 5\mathbf{i}$ if and only if $10\cos\theta = 5$, or $\cos\theta = \frac{1}{2}$. Thus $\theta = \pi/3$.

    b. We proceed as in part (a), but now we need $\mathbf{F}_1+\mathbf{F}_2 = 6\mathbf{i}$. Thus we need $10\cos\theta = 6$, or $\cos\theta = 0.6$. By calculator, $\theta \approx 0.927295218$ radian ($\approx 53°$)

33. Consider a coordinate system with the river flowing in the direction of the negative x axis and the motorboat traveling with increasing values of y. Let $\mathbf{v}_1$ be the velocity of the motorboat with respect to the water, and $\mathbf{v}_2$ the velocity of the river, so that $\mathbf{v}_1+\mathbf{v}_2$ is the velocity of the motorboat with respect to the ground. Notice that $\mathbf{v}_2 = -5\mathbf{i}$ and $\mathbf{v}_1 = 10(\cos\theta\,\mathbf{i}+\sin\theta\,\mathbf{j})$, with θ to be chosen so that $\mathbf{v}_1+\mathbf{v}_2 = c\mathbf{j}$ for an appropriate positive value of c. But $\mathbf{v}_1+\mathbf{v}_2 = 10(\cos\theta\,\mathbf{i}+\sin\theta\,\mathbf{j})-5\mathbf{i} = (10\cos\theta-5)\mathbf{i}+10\sin\theta\,\mathbf{j}$, so that $10\cos\theta-5 = 0$ and $10\sin\theta = c > 0$ if $\theta = \pi/3$. Thus the boat should be pointed at an angle of $\pi/3$ with respect to the shore. Also $\mathbf{v}_1+\mathbf{v}_2 = 10\sin(\pi/3)\,\mathbf{j} = 5\sqrt{3}\,\mathbf{j}$. Therefore the $\frac{1}{2}$ mile width of the river is traveled at a speed of $5\sqrt{3}$ miles per hour in $1/(10\sqrt{3})$ hours, or approximately 3.46410 minutes.

34. Let **v** be the velocity of the jet with respect to the ground, $\mathbf{v}_1$ the velocity of the jet with respect to the air, and $\mathbf{v}_2$ the velocity of the air (jet stream). Then $\mathbf{v} = \mathbf{v}_1+\mathbf{v}_2 = 500\mathbf{j}+100\mathbf{i}$. The ground speed of the jet is $\|\mathbf{v}\|$ and $\|\mathbf{v}\| = \sqrt{500^2+100^2} = 100\sqrt{26} \approx 509.902$ miles per hour.

35. If we let $q_1 = 3.2 \times 10^{-19}$, $\mathbf{u}_1 = -\mathbf{i}$, $r_1 = 10^{-12}$, $q_2 = -6.4 \times 10^{-19}$, $\mathbf{u}_2 = -\mathbf{j}$, $r_2 = 2 \times 10^{-12}$, $q_3 = 4.8 \times 10^{-19}$, $\mathbf{u}_3 = -\mathbf{k}$, and $r_3 = 3 \times 10^{-12}$, then

$$\mathbf{F} = \frac{q_1(1)}{4\pi\varepsilon_0 r_1^2}\mathbf{u}_1 + \frac{q_2(1)}{4\pi\varepsilon_0 r_2^2}\mathbf{u}_2 + \frac{q_3(1)}{4\pi\varepsilon_0 r_3^2}\mathbf{u}_3$$

$$= \frac{3.2 \times 10^{-19}}{4\pi\varepsilon_0 10^{-24}}(-\mathbf{i}) + \frac{-6.4 \times 10^{-19}}{4\pi\varepsilon_0(4 \times 10^{-24})}(-\mathbf{j}) + \frac{4.8 \times 10^{-19}}{4\pi\varepsilon_0(9 \times 10^{-24})}(-\mathbf{k}) = \frac{10^4}{\pi\varepsilon_0}\left(-8\mathbf{i} + 4\mathbf{j} - \frac{4}{3}\mathbf{k}\right).$$

Cumulative Review(Chapters 1–10)

1. a. The domain consists of all x such that $(1-2x)/(1-3x) \geq 0$, or $\frac{2}{3}[(x-\frac{1}{2})/(x-\frac{1}{3})] \geq 0$. This occurs if $x \geq \frac{1}{2}$ and $x > \frac{1}{3}$, or if $x \leq \frac{1}{2}$ and $x < \frac{1}{3}$. Thus the domain is the union of $(-\infty, \frac{1}{3})$ and $[\frac{1}{2}, \infty)$.

   b. $\lim_{x\to-\infty} f(x) = \lim_{x\to-\infty}\sqrt{\dfrac{1-2x}{1-3x}} = \lim_{x\to-\infty}\sqrt{\dfrac{1/x-2}{1/x-3}} = \sqrt{\dfrac{0-2}{0-3}} = \sqrt{\dfrac{2}{3}}$

2. The conditions for applying l'Hôpital's Rule three times are met;

$$\lim_{x\to0+} x(\ln x)^3 = \lim_{x\to0+}\frac{(\ln x)^3}{1/x} = \lim_{x\to0+}\frac{3(\ln x)^2(1/x)}{-1/x^2} = \lim_{x\to0+}\frac{3(\ln x)^2}{-1/x}$$

$$= \lim_{x\to0+}\frac{6(\ln x)(1/x)}{1/x^2} = \lim_{x\to0+}\frac{6\ln x}{1/x} = \lim_{x\to0+}\frac{6/x}{-1/x^2} = \lim_{x\to0+}(-6x) = 0$$

3. $\lim_{x\to\infty} x^{\tan(1/x)} = \lim_{x\to\infty} e^{\tan(1/x)\ln x} = e^{\lim_{x\to\infty}\ln x/\cot(1/x)}$

By l'Hôpital's Rule,

$$\lim_{x\to\infty}\frac{\ln x}{\cot(1/x)} = \lim_{x\to\infty}\frac{1/x}{[-\csc^2(1/x)](-1/x^2)} = \lim_{x\to\infty}\sin\frac{1}{x}\,\frac{\sin(1/x)}{1/x} = 0\cdot 1 = 0.$$

Thus

$$\lim_{x\to\infty} x^{\tan(1/x)} = e^{\lim_{x\to\infty}\ln x/\cot(1/x)} = e^0 = 1.$$

4. $f'(x) = \dfrac{-2(1+3x)-3(1-2x)}{(1+3x)^2} = \dfrac{-5}{(1+3x)^2} = -20$

if $(1+3x)^2 = \frac{1}{4}$, or $1+3x = -\frac{1}{2}$ or $1+3x = \frac{1}{2}$, which means that $x = -\frac{1}{2}$ or $x = -\frac{1}{6}$.

5. a. $f'(x) = \dfrac{1}{(\pi/2)+\tan^{-1}x}\,\dfrac{1}{x^2+1} > 0$ for all x.

   Therefore f is increasing, so f^{-1} exists. The domain of f^{-1} = the range of f. Since the range of $\tan^{-1}x$ is $(-\pi/2, \pi/2)$, it follows that the range of $\pi/2+\tan^{-1}x$ is $(0,\pi)$ and the range of $\ln(\pi/2+\tan^{-1}x)$ is $(-\infty, \ln\pi)$. Thus the domain of f^{-1} is $(-\infty, \ln\pi)$. The range of f^{-1} = the domain of $f = (-\infty, \infty)$.

b. $(f^{-1})'(\ln \pi/3) = 1/f'(a)$ for the value of a in $(-\infty, \infty)$ such that $f(a) = \ln \pi/3$, or by the definition of f, $\ln(\pi/2 + \tan^{-1} a) = \ln \pi/3$. This means that $\pi/2 + \tan^{-1} a = \pi/3$, so that $\tan^{-1} a = -\pi/6$ and hence $a = -\sqrt{3}/3$. Thus

$$(f^{-1})'\left(\ln\frac{\pi}{3}\right) = \frac{1}{f'(-\sqrt{3}/3)} = \frac{1}{\dfrac{1}{\pi/2+\tan^{-1}(-\sqrt{3}/3)}\,\dfrac{1}{(-\sqrt{3}/3)^2+1}} = \left(\frac{\pi}{2}-\frac{\pi}{6}\right)\left(\frac{1}{3}+1\right) = \frac{4\pi}{9}.$$

c. $y = f^{-1}(x)$ if and only if $x = f(y) = \ln(\pi/2 + \tan^{-1} y)$ if and only if $e^x = \pi/2 + \tan^{-1} y$ if and only if $\tan^{-1} y = e^x - \pi/2$ if and only if $y = \tan(e^x - \pi/2)$. Therefore $f^{-1}(x) = \tan(e^x - \pi/2)$ for $x < \ln \pi$.

6. $\dfrac{dy}{dx} = \cos x$, so $\left.\dfrac{dy}{dx}\right|_{x=\pi/4} = \cos\dfrac{\pi}{4} = \dfrac{\sqrt{2}}{2}$; slope of normal line $= \dfrac{-1}{\sqrt{2}/2} = -\sqrt{2}$;

equation of normal line: $y - \dfrac{\sqrt{2}}{2} = -\sqrt{2}\left(x - \dfrac{\pi}{4}\right)$.

7. a. $\dfrac{dy}{dx} = \dfrac{dy}{dt}\,\dfrac{1}{dx/dt} = \dfrac{\sin t}{1-\cos t}$; $\cos t = 1 - y$ and $0 < t < \pi$, so $\sin t = \sqrt{1-\cos^2 t} = \sqrt{1-(1-y)^2} = \sqrt{2y-y^2}$; thus

$$\frac{dy}{dx} = \frac{\sin t}{1-\cos t} = \frac{\sqrt{2y-y^2}}{y}.$$

b. Since $\cos t = 1 - y$, we have $t = \cos^{-1}(1-y)$ for $0 < t < \pi$. Thus by part (a), $x = t - \sin t = \cos^{-1}(1-y) - \sqrt{2y-y^2}$.

c. By differentiating the equation for x in part (b) implicitly with respect to x, we obtain

$$1 = \frac{-1}{\sqrt{1-(1-y)^2}}\left(-\frac{dy}{dx}\right) - \frac{1}{2\sqrt{2y-y^2}}(2-2y)\frac{dy}{dx}$$

or

$$1 = \frac{1}{\sqrt{2y-y^2}}\frac{dy}{dx} - \frac{1-y}{\sqrt{2y-y^2}}\frac{dy}{dx}, \quad \text{so} \quad \frac{dy}{dx} = \frac{\sqrt{2y-y^2}}{y}.$$

8. Let $t = 0$ when the ball is dropped. Then the height h of the ball at time t is given by $h = 96 - 16t^2$, so the horizontal distance from the pole to the shadow is $x = h \cot 30° = (96 - 16t^2)\sqrt{3}$. Thus $dx/dt = -32\sqrt{3}\,t$.

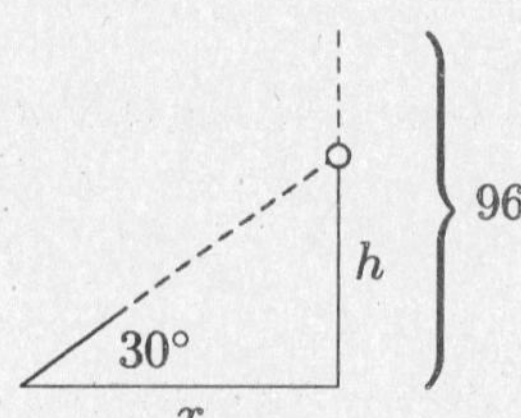

a. Note that $t = 1$ after 1 second, so at that moment, $dx/dt = -32\sqrt{3}$, and the shadow is moving at the rate of $32\sqrt{3}$ feet per second.

b. Since $h = 96 - 16t^2$, $h = 0$ if $96 - 16t^2 = 0$, or $t^2 = 6$, or $t = \sqrt{6}$; $(dx/dt)\big|_{t=\sqrt{6}} = -32\sqrt{3}\,\sqrt{6} = -96\sqrt{2}$. Thus the shadow is moving at the rate of $96\sqrt{2}$ feet per second when the ball hits the ground.

9. $f'(x) = 5(x^2 - 5)(x^2 - 1)$; $f''(x) = 20x(x^2 - 3)$;

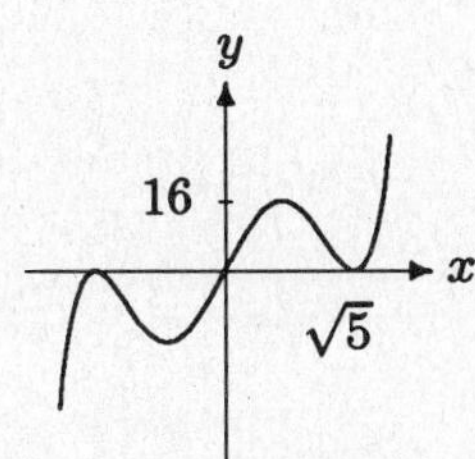

relative maximum values are $f(-\sqrt{5}) = 0$ and $f(1) = 16$; relative minimum values are $f(-1) = -16$ and $f(\sqrt{5}) = 0$; increasing on $(-\infty, -\sqrt{5}]$, $[-1, 1]$, and $[\sqrt{5}, \infty)$; decreasing on $[-\sqrt{5}, -1]$ and $[1, \sqrt{5}]$; concave upward on $(-\sqrt{3}, 0)$ and $(\sqrt{3}, \infty)$, and concave downward on $(-\infty, -\sqrt{3})$ and $(0, \sqrt{3})$; inflection points are $(-\sqrt{3}, -4\sqrt{3})$, $(0, 0)$, and $(\sqrt{3}, 4\sqrt{3})$; symmetric with respect to the origin.

10. Let x denote the length of the legs of the triangle, and y the length of the side of the rectangle. We must maximize the area of the window. Since the perimeter is 16, we have $2y + 2x + \sqrt{2}\,x = 16$, so that $y = 8 - (1 + 1/\sqrt{2})x$. The area A is given by

$$A = \frac{1}{2}x^2 + \sqrt{2}\,xy = \frac{1}{2}x^2 + \sqrt{2}\,x\left[8 - \left(1 + \frac{1}{\sqrt{2}}\right)x\right] = 8\sqrt{2}x - \left(\sqrt{2} + \frac{1}{2}\right)x^2.$$

Thus $A'(x) = 8\sqrt{2} - (2\sqrt{2} + 1)x$, so that $A'(x) = 0$ if $x = 8\sqrt{2}/(2\sqrt{2} + 1)$. Since $A''(x) = -2\sqrt{2} - 1 < 0$ for $x > 0$, A is maximum for $x = 8\sqrt{2}/(2\sqrt{2} + 1)$. Then

$$y = 8 - \left(1 + \frac{1}{\sqrt{2}}\right)\left(\frac{8\sqrt{2}}{2\sqrt{2} + 1}\right) = 8 - \frac{8\sqrt{2} + 8}{2\sqrt{2} + 1} = \frac{8\sqrt{2}}{2\sqrt{2} + 1} = x.$$

Therefore the maximum amount of light enters the window if the length of the legs of the triangle equals the length of the vertical sides of the rectangle.

11. The graph of f and the line $y = \frac{5}{2}$ intersect at (x, y) if $x + 1/x = \frac{5}{2}$, or $2x^2 - 5x + 2 = 0$, or $(2x - 1)(x - 2) = 0$, or $x = \frac{1}{2}$ or $x = 2$. Since $x + 1/x \le \frac{5}{2}$ for $1 \le x \le 2$ and $x + 1/x \ge \frac{5}{2}$ for $2 \le x \le 3$, the area A is given by

$$A = \int_1^2 \left[\frac{5}{2} - \left(x + \frac{1}{x}\right)\right] dx + \int_2^3 \left[\left(x + \frac{1}{x}\right) - \frac{5}{2}\right] dx$$

$$= \left(\frac{5}{2}x - \frac{1}{2}x^2 - \ln x\right)\Big|_1^2 + \left(\frac{1}{2}x^2 + \ln x - \frac{5}{2}x\right)\Big|_2^3 = (1 - \ln 2) + (\ln 3 - \ln 2) = 1 + \ln\frac{3}{4}.$$

12. Let $u = 1/t$, so that $du = -(1/t^2)\,dt$. Then

$$\int \frac{1}{t^2}\csc\frac{1}{t}\tan^2\frac{1}{t}\,dt = \int -\csc u\tan^2 u\,du = \int -\frac{\sin u}{\cos^2 u}\,du.$$

Let $v = \cos u$, so that $dv = -\sin u\,du$. Then

$$\int -\frac{\sin u}{\cos^2 u}\,du = \int \frac{1}{v^2}\,dv = -\frac{1}{v} + C = -\frac{1}{\cos u} + C = -\sec u + C.$$

Thus

$$\int \frac{1}{t^2}\csc\frac{1}{t}\tan^2\frac{1}{t}\,dt = -\sec u + C = -\sec\frac{1}{t} + C.$$

13. $\dfrac{x^3}{x^2-x+1} = x+1-\dfrac{1}{x^2-x+1} = x+1-\dfrac{1}{(x-\frac{1}{2})^2+\frac{3}{4}}$

Thus

$$\int \frac{x^3}{x^2-x+1}\,dx = \int \left[x+1-\frac{1}{(x-\frac{1}{2})^2+\frac{3}{4}}\right]dx$$

$$= \frac{1}{2}x^2+x-\frac{2}{\sqrt{3}}\tan^{-1}\left[\frac{2}{\sqrt{3}}\left(x-\frac{1}{2}\right)\right]+C = \frac{1}{2}x^2+x-\frac{2}{\sqrt{3}}\tan^{-1}\frac{2x-1}{\sqrt{3}}+C.$$

14. Let $x = (1/\sqrt{2})\sec u$, so that $dx = (1/\sqrt{2})\sec u\,\tan u\,du$. Then

$$\int \frac{1}{x^6\sqrt{2x^2-1}}\,dx = \int \frac{1}{\frac{1}{8}\sec^6 u\,\tan u}\,\frac{1}{\sqrt{2}}\sec u\,\tan u\,du = \int \frac{8}{\sqrt{2}\sec^5 u}\,du$$

$$= \int 4\sqrt{2}\cos^5 u\,du = \int 4\sqrt{2}(1-\sin^2 u)^2\cos u\,du.$$

Let $v = \sin u$, so that $dv = \cos u\,du$. Then

$$\int 4\sqrt{2}(1-\sin^2 u)^2\cos u\,du = \int 4\sqrt{2}(1-v^2)^2\,dv = 4\sqrt{2}\int (1-2v^2+v^4)\,dv$$

$$= 4\sqrt{2}\left(v-\frac{2}{3}v^3+\frac{1}{5}v^5\right)+C = 4\sqrt{2}\left(\sin u-\frac{2}{3}\sin^3 u+\frac{1}{5}\sin^5 u\right)+C.$$

From the figure,

$$\sin u = \frac{\sqrt{2x^2-1}}{\sqrt{2}\,x} = \sqrt{\frac{2x^2-1}{2x^2}} = \sqrt{1-\frac{1}{2x^2}}$$

so that

$$\int \frac{1}{x^6\sqrt{2x^2-1}}\,dx = 4\sqrt{2}\left(\sin u-\frac{2}{3}\sin^3 u+\frac{1}{5}\sin^5 u\right)+C$$

$$= 4\sqrt{2}\left[\sqrt{1-\frac{1}{2x^2}}-\frac{2}{3}\left(\sqrt{1-\frac{1}{2x^2}}\right)^3+\frac{1}{5}\left(\sqrt{1-\frac{1}{2x^2}}\right)^5\right]+C$$

$$= 4\sqrt{2}\left(1-\frac{1}{2x^2}\right)^{1/2}-\frac{8}{3}\sqrt{2}\left(1-\frac{1}{2x^2}\right)^{3/2}+\frac{4}{5}\sqrt{2}\left(1-\frac{1}{2x^2}\right)^{5/2}+C.$$

15. Let $u = -3x^2$, so that $du = -6x\,dx$. If $x = 2$, then $u = -12$, and if $x = b$, then $u = -3b^2$. Thus

$$\int_2^\infty xe^{-3x^2}\,dx = \lim_{b\to\infty}\int_2^b xe^{-3x^2}\,dx = \lim_{b\to\infty}\int_{-12}^{-3b^2} e^u\left(-\frac{1}{6}\right)du$$

$$= \lim_{b\to\infty}\left(-\frac{1}{6}e^u\right)\Big|_{-12}^{-3b^2} = \lim_{b\to\infty}\frac{1}{6}(e^{-12}-e^{-3b^2}) = \frac{1}{6}e^{-12}.$$

16. $V = \displaystyle\int_0^3 2\pi x f(x)\,dx = \int_0^3 2\pi\frac{x^3}{\sqrt{x^2+9}}\,dx$

Let $u = x^2 + 9$, so that $du = 2x\,dx$ and $x^2 = u - 9$. If $x = 0$, then $u = 9$, and if $x = 3$, then $u = 18$. Thus

$$V = \int_0^3 2\pi \frac{x^3}{\sqrt{x^2+9}}\,dx = \pi \int_0^3 \frac{x^2}{\sqrt{x^2+9}}\,2x\,dx = \pi \int_9^{18} \frac{u-9}{\sqrt{u}}\,du = \pi \int_9^{18} (u^{1/2} - 9u^{-1/2})\,du$$

$$= \left(\frac{2}{3}u^{3/2} - 18u^{1/2}\right)\Bigg|_9^{18} = \pi\left[\left(\frac{2}{3}(18)^{3/2} - 18(18)^{1/2}\right) - \left(\frac{2}{3}\cdot 27 - 18\cdot 3\right)\right] = 18\pi(2-\sqrt{2}).$$

17. $L = \displaystyle\int_{-1}^{1} \sqrt{(-e^{-t}\sin 2t + 2e^{-t}\cos 2t)^2 + (-e^{-t}\cos 2t - 2e^{-t}\sin 2t)^2}\,dt$

$= \displaystyle\int_{-1}^{1} e^{-t}\sqrt{\sin^2 2t - 4\sin 2t\,\cos 2t + 4\cos^2 2t + \cos^2 2t + 4\cos 2t\,\sin 2t + 4\sin^2 2t}\,dt$

$= \displaystyle\int_{-1}^{1} e^{-t}\sqrt{5}\,dt = -\sqrt{5}\,e^{-t}\Big|_{-1}^{1} = \sqrt{5}(e - e^{-1})$

18. The cardioids intersect at (r, θ) if $r = 0$ or $1 + \cos\theta = r = 1 - \cos\theta$, that is, $\cos\theta = 0$, so that $\theta = \pi/2$ or $\theta = 3\pi/2$. Using symmetry with respect to both axes, we find that

$$A = 4\int_0^{\pi/2} \frac{1}{2}(1-\cos\theta)^2\,d\theta = 2\int_0^{\pi/2} (1 - 2\cos\theta + \cos^2\theta)\,d\theta$$

$$= 2\int_0^{\pi/2} \left(1 - 2\cos\theta + \frac{1}{2} + \frac{1}{2}\cos 2\theta\right)d\theta$$

$$= 2\left(\frac{3}{2}\theta - 2\sin\theta + \frac{1}{4}\sin 2\theta\right)\Bigg|_0^{\pi/2} = \frac{3\pi}{2} - 4.$$

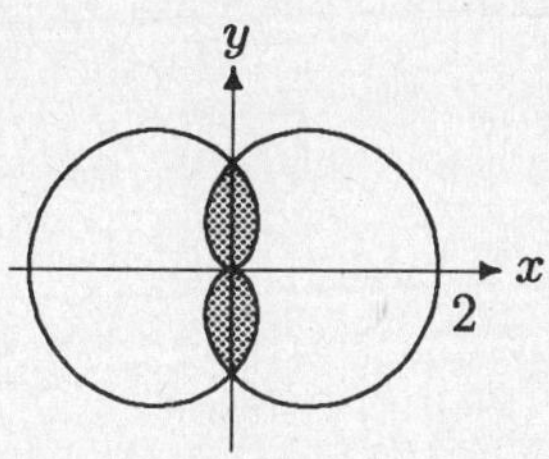

19. For any c,

$$\lim_{n\to\infty} (\sqrt{n+c} - \sqrt{n}) = \lim_{n\to\infty} \frac{(\sqrt{n+c} - \sqrt{n})(\sqrt{n+c} + \sqrt{n})}{\sqrt{n+c} + \sqrt{n}}$$

$$= \lim_{n\to\infty} \frac{n+c-n}{\sqrt{n+c}+\sqrt{n}} = \lim_{n\to\infty} \frac{c}{\sqrt{n+c}+\sqrt{n}} = 0.$$

Thus the limit exists for all c.

20. Since $\dfrac{4}{n(n+2)} = \dfrac{2}{n} - \dfrac{2}{n+2}$, the series is a telescoping series, and

$$\sum_{n=1}^{\infty} \frac{4}{n(n+2)} = \sum_{n=1}^{\infty} \left(\frac{2}{n} - \frac{2}{n+2}\right) = \left(\frac{2}{1} - \frac{2}{3}\right) + \left(\frac{2}{2} - \frac{2}{4}\right) + \left(\frac{2}{3} - \frac{2}{5}\right) + \left(\frac{2}{4} - \frac{2}{6}\right) + \cdots = 2 + 1 = 3.$$

21. Since

$$\lim_{n\to\infty} \frac{n^2}{\sqrt{n^4+2}} = \lim_{n\to\infty} \frac{1}{\sqrt{1+2/n^4}} = 1$$

$\lim_{n\to\infty} (-1)^n n^2/\sqrt{n^4+2}$ does not exist. By Corollary 9.9 the given series diverges.

22. Let $a_n = [2 \cdot 4 \cdot 6 \cdots (2n-2)(2n)]/n^n$. Then

$$\frac{a_{n+1}}{a_n} = \frac{2 \cdot 4 \cdot 6 \cdots (2n)(2n+2)}{2 \cdot 4 \cdot 6 \cdots (2n-2)(2n)} \cdot \frac{n^n}{(n+1)^{n+1}} = \frac{(2n+2)n^n}{(n+1)^{n+1}} = \frac{2n^n}{(n+1)^n} = \frac{2}{(1+1/n)^n}.$$

Thus

$$\lim_{n\to\infty} \frac{a_{n+1}}{a_n} = \lim_{n\to\infty} \frac{2}{(1+1/n)^n} = \frac{2}{e} < 1$$

so the given series converges by the Ratio Test. Since the series is a positive series, it converges absolutely.

23. By Theorem 9.28 and the uniqueness of Taylor series, the Taylor series for $\int_0^x f(t)\,dt$ is

$$\sum_{n=1}^{\infty} \int_0^x \frac{t^n}{n+2}\,dt = \sum_{n=1}^{\infty} \frac{x^{n+1}}{(n+1)(n+2)}.$$

For $x \neq 0$,

$$\lim_{n\to\infty} \frac{|x^{n+2}|/[(n+2)(n+3)]}{|x^{n+1}|/[(n+1)(n+2)]} = \lim_{n\to\infty} \frac{n+1}{n+3}|x| = |x|.$$

By the Generalized Ratio Test, the series $\sum_{n=1}^{\infty} x^{n+1}/[(n+1)(n+2)]$ converges for $|x| < 1$ and diverges for $|x| > 1$. For $x = 1$ the series becomes $\sum_{n=1}^{\infty} 1/[(n+1)(n+2)]$, which converges by comparison with the p series $\sum_{n=1}^{\infty} 1/n^2$. For $x = -1$ the series becomes $\sum_{n=1}^{\infty} (-1)^n\, 1/[(n+1)(n+2)]$, which converges by the Alternating Series Test. Consequently the interval of convergence of $\sum_{n=1}^{\infty} x^{n+1}/[(n+1)(n+2)]$ is $[-1, 1]$.

Chapter 12

Vector-Valued Functions

12.1 Definitions and Examples

1. domain: $(-\infty, \infty)$; $f_1(t) = t$, $f_2(t) = t^2$, $f_3(t) = t^3$

2. domain: $[-1, 1]$; $f_1(t) = \sqrt{t+1}$, $f_2(t) = \sqrt{1-t}$, $f_3(t) = 1$

3. $\tanh t$ is defined for all t; domain: union of $(-\infty, -2)$, and $(-2, 2)$ and $(2, \infty)$; $f_1(t) = \tanh t$, $f_2(t) = 0$, $f_3(t) = -1/(t^2 - 4)$

4. $\mathbf{F}(t) = \left(\frac{1}{t}\ln t - e^{-5t}\cot t\right)\mathbf{i} + \left[(4-t^2)\cot t - \frac{1}{t}(t^2-1)\right]\mathbf{j} + [e^{-5t}(t^2-1) - (4-t^2)\ln t]\mathbf{k}$

   Thus the domain consists of all intervals of the form $(n\pi, (n+1)\pi)$ for any nonnegative integer n. Also

   $$f_1(t) = \frac{1}{t}\ln t - e^{-5t}\cot t, \quad f_2(t) = (4-t^2)\cot t - \frac{1}{t}(t^2-1), \quad \text{and} \quad f_3(t) = e^{-5t}(t^2-1) - (4-t^2)\ln t.$$

5. $\mathbf{F}(t) = 2\sqrt{t}\,\mathbf{i} - 2t^{3/2}\mathbf{j} - (t^3+1)\mathbf{k}$. Thus the domain is $[0, \infty)$. Also $f_1(t) = 2\sqrt{t}$, $f_2(t) = -2t^{3/2}$, and $f_3(t) = -(t^3+1)$.

6. $(\mathbf{F} - \mathbf{G})(t) = (2t - e^t)\mathbf{i} + (t^2 - e^{-t})\mathbf{j} + (-\ln t - 2t)\mathbf{k}$. Thus the domain is $(0, \infty)$. Also $f_1(t) = 2t - e^t$, $f_2(t) = t^2 - e^{-t}$, and $f_3(t) = -\ln t - 2t$.

7. $(2\mathbf{F} - 3\mathbf{G})(t) = (2t - 3\cos t)\mathbf{i} + (2t^2 - 3\sin t)\mathbf{j} + (2t^3 - 3)\mathbf{k}$. Thus the domain is $(-\infty, \infty)$. Also $f_1(t) = 2t - 3\cos t$, $f_2(t) = 2t^2 - 3\sin t$, and $f_3(t) = 2t^3 - 3$.

8. $(\mathbf{F} \times \mathbf{G})(t) = (t^2 - t^3\sin t)\mathbf{i} + (t^3\cos t - t)\mathbf{j} + (t\sin t - t^2\cos t)\mathbf{k}$. Thus the domain is $(-\infty, \infty)$. Also $f_1(t) = t^2 - t^3\sin t$, $f_2(t) = t^3\cos t - t$, and $f_3(t) = t\sin t - t^2\cos t$.

9. $(\mathbf{F} \times \mathbf{G})(t) = \frac{1}{\sqrt{t}}(1 - \cos t)\mathbf{i} - \frac{1}{\sqrt{t}}(t - \sin t)\mathbf{j} - t(t - \sin t)\mathbf{k}$. Thus the domain is $(0, \infty)$. Also $f_1(t) = (1/\sqrt{t})(1 - \cos t)$, $f_2(t) = -(1/\sqrt{t})(t - \sin t)$, and $f_3(t) = -t(t - \sin t)$.

10. $(f\mathbf{F})(t) = \sqrt{t}\ln t\,\mathbf{i} - 4\sqrt{t}\,e^{2t}\,\mathbf{j} + (\sqrt{t}\sqrt{t-1}/t)\,\mathbf{k}$. Thus the domain is $[1, \infty)$. Also $f_1(t) = \sqrt{t}\ln t$, $f_2(t) = -4\sqrt{t}\,e^{2t}$, and $f_3(t) = \sqrt{t-1}/\sqrt{t}$.

11. $(\mathbf{F} \circ g)(t) = \cos t^{1/3}\mathbf{i} + \sin t^{1/3}\mathbf{j} + \sqrt{t^{1/3}+2}\,\mathbf{k}$. Thus the domain consists of all t for which $t^{1/3} + 2 \geq 0$, and hence is $[-8, \infty)$. Also $f_1(t) = \cos t^{1/3}$, $f_2(t) = \sin t^{1/3}$, and $f_3(t) = \sqrt{t^{1/3}+2}$.

12. $(\mathbf{F} \circ g)(t) = e^{-2\ln t}\mathbf{i} + e^{(\ln t)^2}\mathbf{j} + (\ln t)^3\mathbf{k} = \dfrac{1}{t^2}\mathbf{i} + e^{(\ln t)^2}\mathbf{j} + (\ln t)^3\mathbf{k}$. Thus the domain is $(0, \infty)$. Also $f_1(t) = 1/t^2$, $f_2(t) = e^{(\ln t)^2}$, and $f_3(t) = (\ln t)^3$.

13.

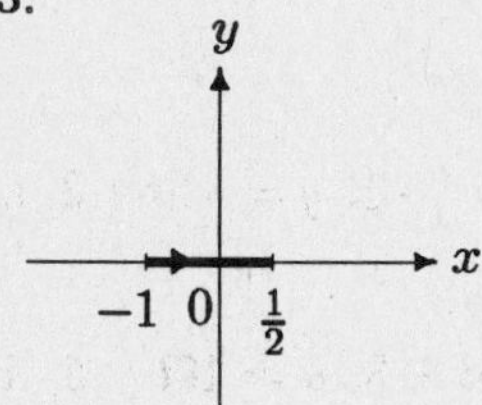

14.

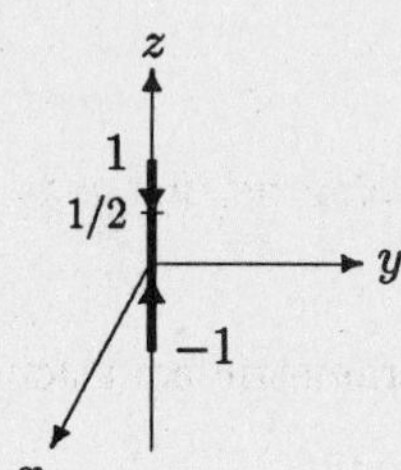

15.

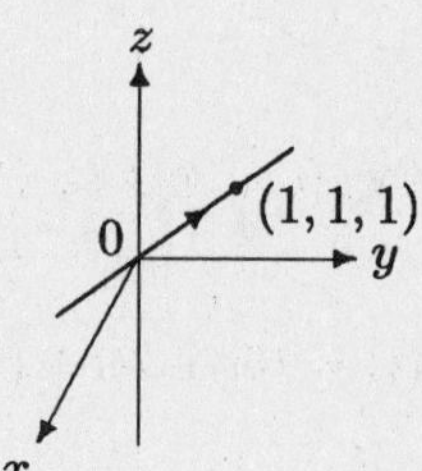

16.

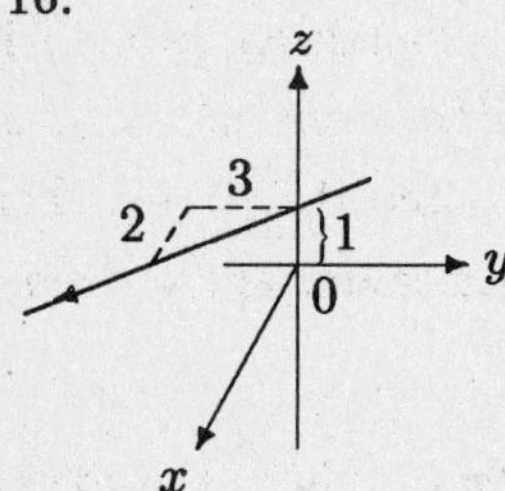

17.

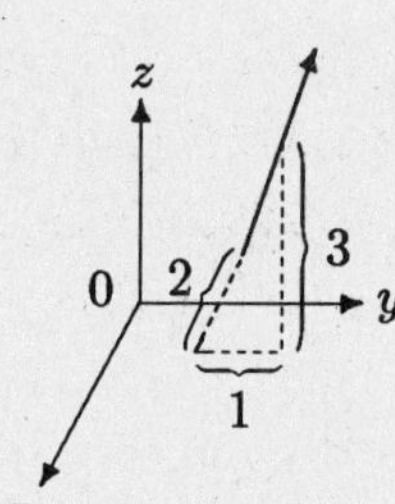

18.

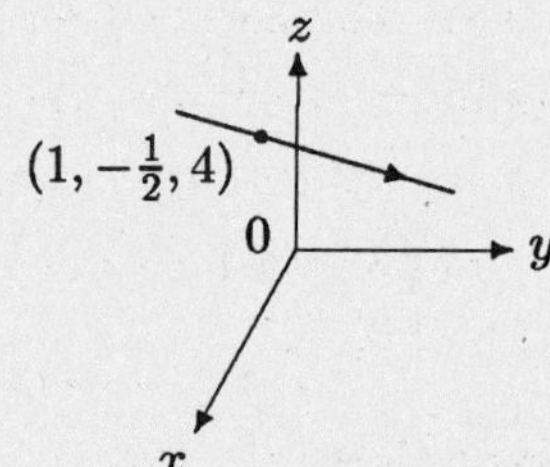

19.

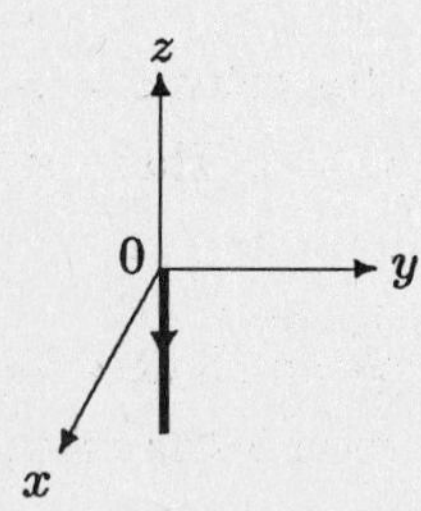

20.

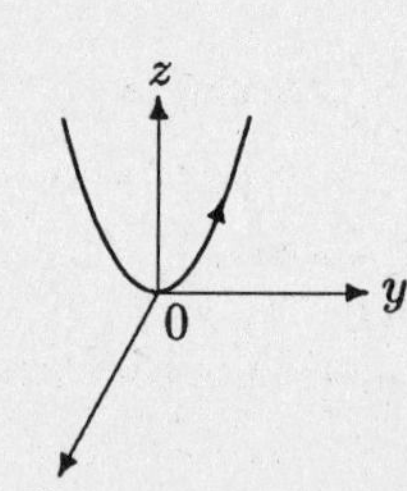

21.

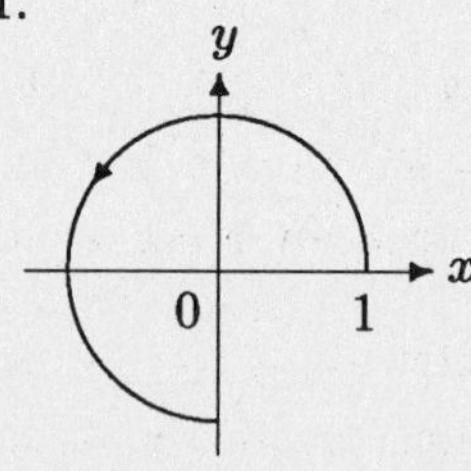

22.

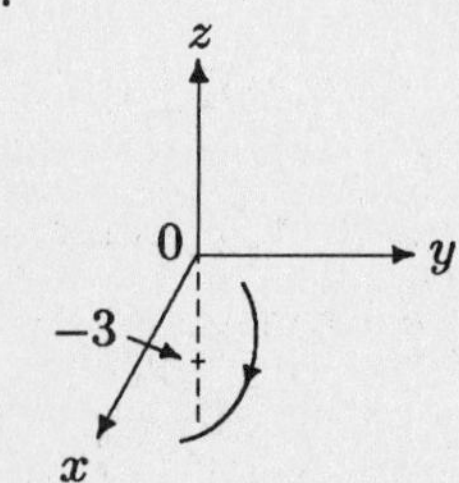

23.

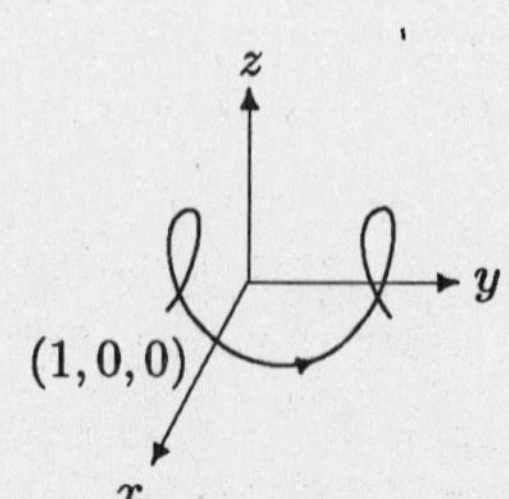

24.

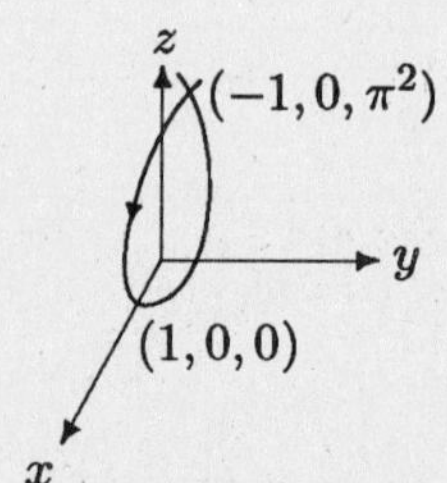

25.

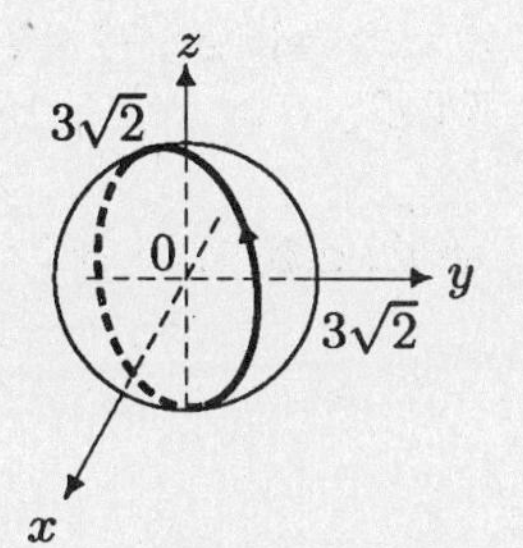

26.

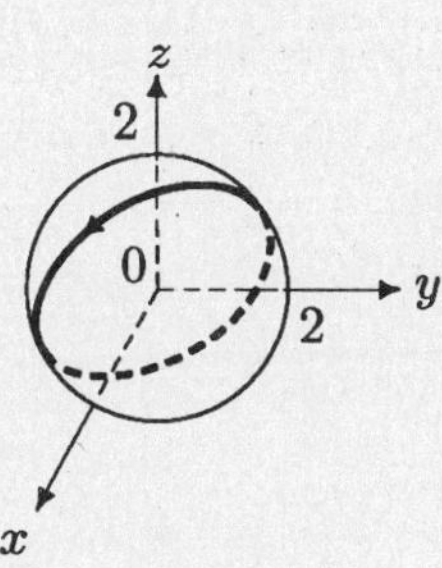

31. a. $(\mathbf{F}-\mathbf{G})(t) = (t-1)\mathbf{i} + (-2t+3)\mathbf{j} - 4t\mathbf{k}$, so parametric equations are $x = t-1$, $y = -2t+3$, and $z = -4t$.

b. $(\mathbf{F}+3\mathbf{G})(t) = (5t+3)\mathbf{i} + (10t-5)\mathbf{j}$, so parametric equations are $x = 5t+3$, $y = 10t-5$, and $z = 0$.

c. $(\mathbf{F}\circ g)(t) = 2\cos t\,\mathbf{i} + (\cos t + 1)\,\mathbf{j} - 3\cos t\,\mathbf{k}$. Then $x = 2\cos t$, $y = \cos t + 1$, and $z = -3\cos t$ for all real t, which yields the line segment parametrized by $x = 2t$, $y = t+1$, $z = -3t$ for $-1 \le t \le 1$.

32. If (x,y,z) is on the curve, then $x = t\cos\pi t$, $y = t\sin\pi t$, and $z = t$. If in addition (x,y,z) is on the cylinder $x^2+y^2 = 4$, then $(t\cos\pi t)^2 + (t\sin\pi t)^2 = 4$, so that $t^2(\cos^2\pi t + \sin^2\pi t) = 4$, or $t^2 = 4$, or $t = \pm 2$. If $t = 2$, then $(x,y,z) = (2\cos 2\pi, 2\sin 2\pi, 2) = (2,0,2)$, and if $t = -2$, then $(x,y,z) = (-2\cos(-2\pi), -2\sin(-2\pi), -2) = (-2,0,-2)$. The points of intersection are therefore $(2,0,2)$ and $(-2,0,-2)$

33. If (x,y,z) is on the curve, then $x = \cos\pi t$, $y = \sin\pi t$, and $z = t$. If in addition (x,y,z) is on the sphere $x^2+y^2+z^2 = 10$, then $(\cos\pi t)^2 + (\sin\pi t)^2 + t^2 = 10$, so that $t^2 = 9$, and thus $t = \pm 3$. If $t = 3$, then $(x,y,z) = (\cos 3\pi, \sin 3\pi, 3) = (-1,0,3)$, and if $t = -3$, then $(x,y,z) = (\cos(-3\pi), \sin(-3\pi), -3) = (-1,0,-3)$. The points of intersection are therefore $(-1,0,3)$ and $(-1,0,-3)$.

34. Since $x = \cos t$, $y = \sin t$, and $z = a\cos t + b\sin t$ for $0 \le t \le 2\pi$, the curve lies in the plane $z = ax+by$. Also $x^2+y^2 = \cos^2 t + \sin^2 t = 1$, so the curve lies on the circular cylinder $x^2+y^2 = 1$. Thus the curve lies in the intersection of a plane and a circular cylinder.

35. $\mathbf{F}(t)$ can be written $\mathbf{a}+\mathbf{b}$, where $\mathbf{a}$ describes the motion of the center of the circle and $\mathbf{b}$ describes the motion of P around the center. As in Example 7, $\mathbf{a} = rt\mathbf{i} + r\mathbf{j}$. Also, if C is the center of the circle, then t represents the number of radians through which $\overrightarrow{CP}$ has rotated since time 0. At that time $\overrightarrow{CP}$ makes an angle of $(3\pi/2 - t)$ radians with the positive x axis, so $\mathbf{b} = \overrightarrow{CP} = b\cos(3\pi/2 - t)\mathbf{i} + b\sin(3\pi/2 - t)\mathbf{j} = -b\sin t\,\mathbf{i} - b\cos t\,\mathbf{j}$. Consequently

$$\mathbf{F}(t) = \mathbf{a}+\mathbf{b} = (rt\mathbf{i} + r\mathbf{j}) + (-b\sin t\,\mathbf{i} - b\cos t\,\mathbf{j}) = (rt - b\sin t)\mathbf{i} + (r - b\cos t)\mathbf{j}.$$

36. a. After t units of time, the point that starts at $(b,0)$ occupies the position at P. We have $\mathbf{F}(t) = \overrightarrow{OP} = \overrightarrow{OC} + \overrightarrow{CP}$. Because the large circle has radius b and the small circle has radius r, it follows that

$$\overrightarrow{OC} = \frac{b-r}{b}\overrightarrow{OQ} = \frac{b-r}{b}(b\cos t\,\mathbf{i} + b\sin t\,\mathbf{j}) = (b-r)\cos t\,\mathbf{i} + (b-r)\sin t\,\mathbf{j}.$$

To determine $\overrightarrow{CP}$ we observe that after t units of time, P has traveled bt units, so the arc on the r-circle is also bt. Since the arc length $bt = -r\theta$, where θ is the angle through which $\overrightarrow{CP}$ has turned, it follows that $\theta = -(b/r)t$. With respect to the positive x axis, $\overrightarrow{CP}$ has traveled through $(-b/r)t + t$ radians. Therefore

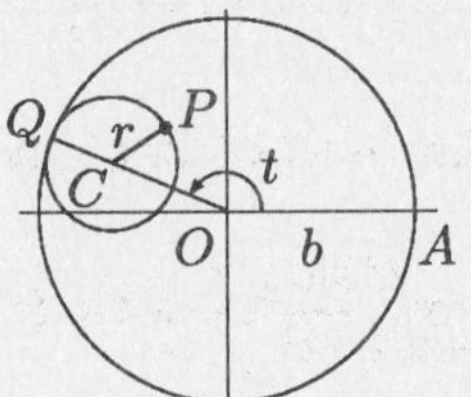

$$\overrightarrow{CP} = r\cos\left(-\frac{b}{r}t + t\right)\mathbf{i} + r\sin\left(-\frac{b}{r}t + t\right)\mathbf{j}$$

$$= r\cos\left(\frac{b-r}{r}t\right)\mathbf{i} - r\sin\left(\frac{b-r}{r}t\right)\mathbf{j}.$$

Consequently

$$\mathbf{F} = \overrightarrow{OC} + \overrightarrow{CP} = \left[(b-r)\cos t + r\cos\left(\frac{b-r}{r}\right)t\right]\mathbf{i} + \left[(b-r)\sin t - r\sin\left(\frac{b-r}{r}\right)t\right]\mathbf{j}.$$

b. If $b = 2r$, then $\mathbf{F} = (r\cos t + r\cos t)\mathbf{i} + (r\sin t - r\sin t)\mathbf{j} = 2\cos t\,\mathbf{i}$. Thus the motion is linear.

c. If $b = nr$, then the number of cusps is n.

37. $\mathbf{F}(t)$ can be written $\mathbf{a}+\mathbf{b}$, where $\mathbf{a}$ describes the motion of the center C of the circle and $\mathbf{b}$ describes the motion of P around the center. First of all, $\mathbf{a} = (r+b)\cos t\,\mathbf{i} + (r+b)\sin t\,\mathbf{j}$. The number t represents the number of radians through which $\overrightarrow{OC}$ has rotated since time 0. Notice that an angle of t radians on the fixed circle corresponds to an arc of length rt, which in turn corresponds to an arc of length rt on the rolling circle. If the corresponding angle on the rolling circle has α radians, then the arc has length $b\alpha$, so that $b\alpha = rt$, or $\alpha = (r/b)t$. Thus by time t the angle OCP has $(r/b)t$ radians, so that $\overrightarrow{CP}$ makes an angle of $(r/b)t + t$ radians with the line parallel to the negative x axis, and hence an angle of $\pi + (r/b)t + t$ radians with a line parallel to the positive x axis. Therefore

$$\mathbf{b} = \overrightarrow{CP} = b\cos\left(\pi + \frac{r}{b}t + t\right)\mathbf{i} + b\sin\left(\pi + \frac{r}{b}t + t\right)\mathbf{j} = -b\cos\left(\frac{r}{b}t + t\right)\mathbf{i} - b\sin\left(\frac{r}{b}t + t\right)\mathbf{j}.$$

Consequently

$$\mathbf{F}(t) = \mathbf{a} + \mathbf{b} = [(r+b)\cos t\,\mathbf{i} + (r+b)\sin t\,\mathbf{j}] + \left[-b\cos\left(\frac{r}{b}t + t\right)\mathbf{i} - b\sin\left(\frac{r}{b}t + t\right)\mathbf{j}\right]$$

$$= \left[(r+b)\cos t - b\cos\left(\frac{r+b}{b}t\right)\right]\mathbf{i} + \left[(r+b)\sin t - b\sin\left(\frac{r+b}{b}t\right)\right]\mathbf{j}.$$

38. Place the coordinate system so that the axis of the cylinder is the z axis, and the base of the staircase lies on the positive x axis. Let $0 \le t \le 2\pi$, and let $\mathbf{F}(t)$ be the vector from the origin to the point on the staircase whose $\mathbf{i}$ and $\mathbf{j}$ components are $50\cos t$ and $50\sin t$, respectively. Then $\mathbf{F}(t) = 50\cos t\,\mathbf{i} + 50\sin t\,\mathbf{j} + at\,\mathbf{k}$, for $0 \le t \le 2\pi$, where a is chosen so that one revolution yields a height of 200 feet, that is, $a(2\pi) = 200$. This means that $a = 200/2\pi = 100/\pi$, so that $\mathbf{F}(t) = 50\cos t\,\mathbf{i} + 50\sin t\,\mathbf{j} + (100/\pi)t\,\mathbf{k}$ for $0 \le t \le 2\pi$.

12.2 Limits and Continuity of Vector-Valued Functions

1. $\lim_{t\to 4}(\mathbf{i}-\mathbf{j}+\mathbf{k}) = \mathbf{i}-\mathbf{j}+\mathbf{k}$

2. $\lim_{t\to -1}(3\mathbf{i}+t\mathbf{j}+t^5\mathbf{k}) = \left(\lim_{t\to -1} 3\right)\mathbf{i}+\left(\lim_{t\to -1} t\right)\mathbf{j}+\left(\lim_{t\to -1} t^5\right)\mathbf{k} = 3\mathbf{i}-\mathbf{j}-\mathbf{k}$

3. $\lim_{t\to\pi}(\tan t\,\mathbf{i}+3t\,\mathbf{j}-4\mathbf{k}) = \left(\lim_{t\to\pi}\tan t\right)\mathbf{i}+\left(\lim_{t\to\pi} 3t\right)\mathbf{j}+\left(\lim_{t\to\pi}(-4)\right)\mathbf{k} = 0\mathbf{i}+3\pi\mathbf{j}-4\mathbf{k} = 3\pi\mathbf{j}-4\mathbf{k}$

4. $\lim_{t\to 0}\left(\frac{\sin t}{t}\mathbf{i}+e^t\mathbf{j}+(t+\sqrt{2})\mathbf{k}\right) = \left(\lim_{t\to 0}\frac{\sin t}{t}\right)\mathbf{i}+\left(\lim_{t\to 0} e^t\right)\mathbf{j}+\left(\lim_{t\to 0}(t+\sqrt{2})\right)\mathbf{k} = \mathbf{i}+\mathbf{j}+\sqrt{2}\,\mathbf{k}$

5. $$\begin{aligned}\lim_{t\to 2^-}\mathbf{F}(t) &= \lim_{t\to 2^-}(5\mathbf{i}-\sqrt{2t^2+2t+4}\,\mathbf{j}+e^{-(t-2)}\mathbf{k})\\ &= \left(\lim_{t\to 2^-} 5\right)\mathbf{i}+\left(\lim_{t\to 2^-} -\sqrt{2t^2+2t+4}\right)\mathbf{j}+\left(\lim_{t\to 2^-} e^{-(t-2)}\right)\mathbf{k} = 5\mathbf{i}-4\mathbf{j}+\mathbf{k}\end{aligned}$$

   and

   $$\lim_{t\to 2^+}\mathbf{F}(t) = \lim_{t\to 2^+}(t^2+1)\mathbf{i}+(4-t^3)\mathbf{j}+\mathbf{k} = \left(\lim_{t\to 2^+}(t^2+1)\right)\mathbf{i}+\left(\lim_{t\to 2^+}(4-t^3)\right)\mathbf{j}+\left(\lim_{t\to 2^+} 1\right)\mathbf{k} = 5\mathbf{i}-4\mathbf{j}+\mathbf{k}.$$

   Since $\lim_{t\to 2^-}\mathbf{F}(t) = \lim_{t\to 2^+}\mathbf{F}(t) = 5\mathbf{i}-4\mathbf{j}+\mathbf{k}$, it follows that $\lim_{t\to 2}\mathbf{F}(t)$ exists and that $\lim_{t\to 2}\mathbf{F}(t) = 5\mathbf{i}-4\mathbf{j}+\mathbf{k}$.

6. $\lim_{t\to 0}\mathbf{F}(t) = \lim_{t\to 0}(t\mathbf{i}+e^{-1/t^2}\mathbf{j}+t^2\mathbf{k}) = 0\mathbf{i}+0\mathbf{j}+0\mathbf{k} = \mathbf{0}$

7. $\lim_{t\to 0}(\mathbf{F}-\mathbf{G})(t) = \lim_{t\to 0}\left[(e^{-1/t^2}+\pi)\mathbf{i}+\left(\cos t-\frac{1+\cos t}{t}\right)\mathbf{j}+t^3\mathbf{k}\right]$

   Since $\lim_{t\to 0}(1+\cos t)/t$ and hence $\lim_{t\to 0}(\cos t-(1+\cos t)/t)$ does not exist, Theorem 12.4 implies that $\lim_{t\to 0}(\mathbf{F}-\mathbf{G})(t)$ does not exist.

8. $\lim_{t\to 1}(\mathbf{F}\cdot\mathbf{G})(t) = \lim_{t\to 1}[\mathbf{F}(t)\cdot\mathbf{G}(t)] = \lim_{t\to 1}\left[(t^2+1)\frac{\sin(t-1)}{t-1}-1-\sqrt{t^2+1}\cos\pi t\right]$

   Since

   $$\lim_{t\to 1}\frac{\sin(t-1)}{t-1} = \lim_{u\to 0}\frac{\sin u}{u} = 1$$

   we find that $\lim_{t\to 1}(\mathbf{F}\cdot\mathbf{G})(t) = 2-1+\sqrt{2} = 1+\sqrt{2}$.

9. $$\begin{aligned}&\lim_{t\to 3}\left(\frac{t^2-5t+6}{t-3}\mathbf{i}+\frac{t^2-2t-3}{t-3}\mathbf{j}+\frac{t^2+4t-21}{t-3}\mathbf{k}\right) = \lim_{t\to 3}[(t-2)\mathbf{i}+(t+1)\mathbf{j}+(t+7)\mathbf{k}]\\ &= \left(\lim_{t\to 3}(t-2)\right)\mathbf{i}+\left(\lim_{t\to 3}(t+1)\right)\mathbf{j}+\left(\lim_{t\to 3}(t+7)\right)\mathbf{k} = \mathbf{i}+4\mathbf{j}+10\mathbf{k}\end{aligned}$$

10. Since $\lim_{t\to 1}(t^2+1)/(t-1)$ does not exist, the given limit does not exist, by virtue of Theorem 12.4.

11. a. Let $\mathbf{F}$ be defined at each point in some open interval (t_0, t_1). A vector $\mathbf{L}$ is the limit of $\mathbf{F}(t)$ as t approaches t_0 from the right if for every $\varepsilon > 0$ there is a number $\delta > 0$ such that

    $$\text{if } 0 < t-t_0 < \delta, \quad \text{then } \|\mathbf{F}(t)-\mathbf{L}\| < \varepsilon.$$

In this case we write $\lim_{t \to t_0^+} \mathbf{F}(t) = \mathbf{L}$. To prove that such limits can be computed componentwise, we can use the statement and proof of Theorem 12.4, with "$\lim_{t \to t_0}$" replaced by "$\lim_{t \to t_0^+}$", and "$0 < |t - t_0| < \delta$" replaced by "$0 < t - t_0 < \delta$".

b. Let $\mathbf{F}$ be defined at each point in some open interval (t_1, t_0) A vector $\mathbf{L}$ is the limit of $\mathbf{F}(t)$ as t approaches t_0 from the left if for every $\varepsilon > 0$ there is a number $\delta > 0$ such that

$$\text{if} \quad -\delta < t - t_0 < 0, \quad \text{then } \|\mathbf{F}(t) - \mathbf{L}\| < \varepsilon.$$

In this case we write $\lim_{t \to t_0^-} \mathbf{F}(t) = \mathbf{L}$. To prove that such limits can be computed componentwise, use the statement and proof of Theorem 12.4, with "$\lim_{t \to t_0}$" replaced by "$\lim_{t \to t_0^-}$", and "$0 < |t - t_0| < \delta$" replaced by "$-\delta < t - t_0 < 0$".

12. a. Since $\displaystyle\lim_{t \to 0^+} \frac{-\ln t}{t}$ does not exist, neither does the given limit.

b. $\displaystyle\lim_{t \to 1^+} [e^{1/(1-t)}\,\mathbf{i} + \sqrt{t-1}\,\mathbf{j} + \ln t\,\mathbf{k}] = \left(\lim_{t \to 1^+} e^{1/(1-t)}\right)\mathbf{i} + \left(\lim_{t \to 1^+} \sqrt{t-1}\right)\mathbf{j} + \left(\lim_{t \to 1^+} \ln t\right)\mathbf{k}$

$= 0\mathbf{i} + 0\mathbf{j} + 0\mathbf{k} = \mathbf{0}$.

c. $\displaystyle\lim_{t \to 1^-} [\sqrt{1-t}\,\mathbf{i} - (1-t)\ln(1-t)\,\mathbf{j}] = \left(\lim_{t \to 1^-} \sqrt{1-t}\right)\mathbf{i} + \left(\lim_{t \to 1^-} -(1-t)\ln(1-t)\right)\mathbf{j}$

Since

$$\lim_{t \to 1^-} (1-t)\ln(1-t) = \lim_{u \to 0^+} u \ln u = \lim_{t \to 0^+} \frac{\ln u}{1/u} = \lim_{t \to 0^+} \frac{1/u}{-1/u^2} = \lim_{u \to 0^+} (-u) = 0$$

by l'Hôpital's Rule, we find that $(\lim_{t \to 1^-} \sqrt{1-t})\mathbf{i} + (\lim_{t \to 1^-} -(1-t)\ln(1-t))\mathbf{j} = 0\mathbf{i} + 0\mathbf{j} = \mathbf{0}$. Thus $\lim_{t \to 1^-} (\sqrt{1-t}\,\mathbf{i} - (1-t)\ln(1-t)\mathbf{j}) = \mathbf{0}$.

13. a. Let $\mathbf{F}$ be defined at each point in an interval of the form (t_0, ∞). A vector $\mathbf{L}$ is the limit of $\mathbf{F}(t)$ as t approaches ∞ if for every $\varepsilon > 0$ there is a number M such that

$$\text{if} \quad t > M, \quad \text{then } \|\mathbf{F}(t) - \mathbf{L}\| < \varepsilon.$$

In this case we write $\lim_{t \to \infty} \mathbf{F}(t) = \mathbf{L}$. To prove that such limits can be computed componentwise, use the statement and proof of Theorem 12.4, with "$\lim_{t \to t_0}$" replaced by "$\lim_{t \to \infty}$", "$\delta > 0$" by "M", and "$0 < |t - t_0| < \delta$" by "$t > M$".

b. $\displaystyle\lim_{t \to \infty} \left(\frac{1}{t}\mathbf{i} + \frac{t-1}{t+1}\mathbf{j} + \frac{\sin t^3}{t^2}\mathbf{k}\right) = \left(\lim_{t \to \infty} \frac{1}{t}\right)\mathbf{i} + \left(\lim_{t \to \infty} \frac{t-1}{t+1}\right)\mathbf{j} + \left(\lim_{t \to \infty} \frac{\sin t^3}{t^2}\right)\mathbf{k}$

Since $|(\sin t^3)/t^2| \le 1/t^2$, we have $\lim_{t \to \infty} (\sin t^3)/t^2 = 0$. Thus

$$\left(\lim_{t \to \infty} \frac{1}{t}\right)\mathbf{i} + \left(\lim_{t \to \infty} \frac{t-1}{t+1}\right)\mathbf{j} + \left(\lim_{t \to \infty} \frac{\sin t^3}{t^2}\right)\mathbf{k} = 0\mathbf{i} + \mathbf{j} + 0\mathbf{k} = \mathbf{j}.$$

14. a. By Theorem 12.5(a), $\lim_{t \to t_0} (\mathbf{F} + \mathbf{G})(t) = \lim_{t \to t_0} \mathbf{F}(t) + \lim_{t \to t_0} \mathbf{G}(t) = \mathbf{F}(t_0) + \mathbf{G}(t_0) = (\mathbf{F} + \mathbf{G})(t_0)$, so that $\mathbf{F} + \mathbf{G}$ is continuous at t_0.

b. By Theorem 12.5(c) with $f(t) = c$ for all t,

$$\lim_{t\to t_0}(c\mathbf{F})(t) = \lim_{t\to t_0} c \cdot \lim_{t\to t_0}\mathbf{F}(t) = c\big(\mathbf{F}(t_0)\big) = (c\mathbf{F})(t_0),$$

so that $c\mathbf{F}$ is continuous at t_0.

c. Let f_1, f_2, and f_3 be the component functions of $\mathbf{F}$. Then

$$\|\mathbf{F}(t)\| = \sqrt{\big(f_1(t)\big)^2 + \big(f_2(t)\big)^2 + \big(f_3(t)\big)^2}.$$

Since f_1, f_2, and f_3 are continuous at t_0 by Theorem 12.7, and since the square root function is continuous on $(0, \infty)$, it follows that $\|\mathbf{F}\|$ is continuous at t_0.

d. By Theorem 12.5(d),

$$\lim_{t\to t_0}(\mathbf{F}\cdot\mathbf{G})(t) = \lim_{t\to t_0}\mathbf{F}(t)\cdot \lim_{t\to t_0}\mathbf{G}(t) = \mathbf{F}(t_0)\cdot\mathbf{G}(t_0) = (\mathbf{F}\cdot\mathbf{G})(t_0),$$

so that $\mathbf{F}\cdot\mathbf{G}$ is continuous at t_0.

e. By Theorem 12.5(e),

$$\lim_{t\to t_0}(\mathbf{F}\times\mathbf{G})(t) = \lim_{t\to t_0}\mathbf{F}(t)\times \lim_{t\to t_0}\mathbf{G}(t) = \mathbf{F}(t_0)\times\mathbf{G}(t_0) = (\mathbf{F}\times\mathbf{G})(t_0),$$

so that $\mathbf{F}\times\mathbf{G}$ is continuous at t_0.

12.3 Derivatives and Integrals of Vector-Valued Functions

1. $\mathbf{F}'(t) = \mathbf{j} + 5t^4\mathbf{k}$

2. $\mathbf{F}'(t) = (2t+1)\mathbf{j} - \mathbf{k}$

3. $\mathbf{F}'(t) = \frac{3}{2}(1+t)^{1/2}\mathbf{i} + \frac{3}{2}(1-t)^{1/2}\mathbf{j} + \frac{3}{2}\mathbf{k}$

4. $\mathbf{F}'(t) = (2t\cos t - t^2\sin t)\mathbf{i} + (3t^2\sin t + t^3\cos t)\mathbf{j} + 4t^3\mathbf{k}$

5. $\mathbf{F}'(t) = \sec^2 t\,\mathbf{i} + \sec t\,\tan t\,\mathbf{k}$

6. $\mathbf{F}'(t) = (e^t\cos t - e^t\sin t)\mathbf{i} - (e^t\sin t + e^t\cos t)\mathbf{k}$

7. $\mathbf{F}'(t) = \sinh t\,\mathbf{i} + \cosh t\,\mathbf{j} - \dfrac{1}{2\sqrt{t}}\mathbf{k}$

8. $\mathbf{F}'(t) = \dfrac{4}{\sqrt{1-16t^2}}\mathbf{i} - \dfrac{6}{1+(2t-1)^2}\mathbf{j} + \dfrac{14}{t}\mathbf{k}$

9. $(4\mathbf{F} - 2\mathbf{G})(t) = (8\sec t - 6t)\mathbf{i} + (2t^2 - 12)\mathbf{j} + 12\csc t\,\mathbf{k}$, so that $(4\mathbf{F} - 2\mathbf{G})'(t) = (8\sec t\,\tan t - 6)\mathbf{i} + 4t\mathbf{j} - 12\csc t\,\cot t\,\mathbf{k}$

10. $(\mathbf{F}\cdot\mathbf{G})(t) = 6t\sec t + 3t^2 - 4\csc^2 t$; $(\mathbf{F}\cdot\mathbf{G})'(t) = (6\sec t + 6t\sec t\,\tan t) + 6t + 8\csc^2 t\,\cot t$

11. $(\mathbf{F}\times\mathbf{G})(t) = -3\ln t\,\mathbf{i} - 2\sec t\,\ln t\,\mathbf{j}$; $(\mathbf{F}\times\mathbf{G})'(t) = \dfrac{-3}{t}\mathbf{i} - \left(2\sec t\,\tan t\,\ln t + \dfrac{2}{t}\sec t\right)\mathbf{j}$

12. $(\mathbf{F}\cdot\mathbf{G})(t) = 3 + e^{-t}$ for $t \neq 0$; $(\mathbf{F}\cdot\mathbf{G})'(t) = -e^{-t}$ for $t \neq 0$

13. $(\mathbf{F}\times\mathbf{G})(t) = \left(t - \dfrac{3}{t}e^{-t}\right)\mathbf{k}$; $(\mathbf{F}\times\mathbf{G})'(t) = \left(1 + \dfrac{3}{t^2}e^{-t} + \dfrac{3}{t}e^{-t}\right)\mathbf{k}$

14. $(\mathbf{F}\cdot\mathbf{G})(t) = \dfrac{4t+8t^3}{(1+t^2)^3} - \dfrac{4t+8t^3}{(1+t^2)^3} = 0$; $(\mathbf{F}\cdot\mathbf{G})'(t) = 0$

15. $(\mathbf{F}\circ g)'(t) = \mathbf{F}'(g(t))g'(t) = \left(\dfrac{1}{\sqrt{t}}\mathbf{i} - 8e^{2\sqrt{t}}\mathbf{j} + \dfrac{1}{(\sqrt{t})^2}\mathbf{k}\right)\dfrac{1}{2\sqrt{t}} = \dfrac{1}{2t}\mathbf{i} - \dfrac{4e^{2\sqrt{t}}}{\sqrt{t}}\mathbf{j} + \dfrac{1}{2}t^{-3/2}\mathbf{k}$

16. $(\mathbf{F}\circ g)'(t) = \mathbf{F}'(g(t))g'(t) = \left(3\cos^2 t\,\mathbf{i} - \sqrt{3}\mathbf{j} - \dfrac{2}{\cos^3 t}\mathbf{k}\right)(-\sin t) = -3\sin t\cos^2 t\,\mathbf{i} + \sqrt{3}\sin t\,\mathbf{j} + 2\sin t\sec^3 t\,\mathbf{k}$

17. $\displaystyle\int\left(t^2\mathbf{i} - (3t-1)\mathbf{j} - \frac{1}{t^3}\mathbf{k}\right)dt = \frac{t^3}{3}\mathbf{i} - \left(\frac{3}{2}t^2 - t\right)\mathbf{j} + \frac{1}{2t^2}\mathbf{k} + \mathbf{C}$

18. By parts we find that $\int t\cos t\,dt = t\sin t - \int \sin t\,dt = t\sin t + \cos t + C$ and $\int t\sin t\,dt = -t\cos t + \int \cos t\,dt = -t\cos t + \sin t + C$. Thus

$$\int (t\cos t\,\mathbf{i} + t\sin t\,\mathbf{j} + 3t^4\mathbf{k})\,dt = (t\sin t + \cos t)\mathbf{i} + (-t\cos t + \sin t)\mathbf{j} + \frac{3}{5}t^5\mathbf{k} + \mathbf{C}.$$

19. $\int_0^1 (e^t\mathbf{i} + e^{-t}\mathbf{j} + 2t\mathbf{k})\,dt = e^t\big|_0^1\mathbf{i} - e^{-t}\big|_0^1\mathbf{j} + t^2\big|_0^1\mathbf{k} = (e-1)\mathbf{i} + (1-e^{-1})\mathbf{j} + \mathbf{k}$

20. $\int_0^1 (\cosh t\,\mathbf{i} + \sinh t\,\mathbf{j} + \mathbf{k})\,dt = \sinh t\big|_0^1\mathbf{i} + \cosh t\big|_0^1\mathbf{j} + t\big|_0^1\mathbf{k} = (\sinh 1)\mathbf{i} + (\cosh 1 - 1)\mathbf{j} + \mathbf{k}$

21. $\int_{-1}^1 [(1+t)^{3/2}\mathbf{i} + (1-t)^{3/2}\mathbf{j}]\,dt = \frac{2}{5}(1+t)^{5/2}\big|_{-1}^1\mathbf{i} - \frac{2}{5}(1-t)^{5/2}\big|_{-1}^1\mathbf{j} = \frac{8}{5}\sqrt{2}\,(\mathbf{i}+\mathbf{j})$

22. $\mathbf{v}(t) = 3\mathbf{i} + 2\mathbf{j} - 32\mathbf{k}$, $\|\mathbf{v}(t)\| = \sqrt{9+4+(-32t)^2} = \sqrt{13+1024t^2}$, $\mathbf{a}(t) = -32\mathbf{k}$

23. $\mathbf{v}(t) = -\sin t\,\mathbf{i} + \cos t\,\mathbf{j} - 32\mathbf{k}$,
$\|\mathbf{v}(t)\| = \sqrt{(-\sin t)^2 + \cos^2 t + (-32t)^2} = \sqrt{1+1024t^2}$,
$\mathbf{a}(t) = -\cos t\,\mathbf{i} - \sin t\,\mathbf{j} - 32\mathbf{k}$

24. $\mathbf{v}(t) = -e^{-t}\mathbf{i} - e^{-t}\mathbf{j}$, $\|\mathbf{v}(t)\| = \sqrt{(-e^{-t})^2 + (-e^{-t})^2} = e^{-t}\sqrt{2}$, $\mathbf{a}(t) = e^{-t}\mathbf{i} + e^{-t}\mathbf{j}$

25. $\mathbf{v}(t) = 2\mathbf{i} + 2t\mathbf{j} + \dfrac{1}{t}\mathbf{k}$, $\|\mathbf{v}(t)\| = \sqrt{4 + 4t^2 + \dfrac{1}{t^2}} = \dfrac{2t^2+1}{t}$, $\mathbf{a}(t) = 2\mathbf{j} - \dfrac{1}{t^2}\mathbf{k}$

26. $\mathbf{v}(t) = \sinh t\,\mathbf{i} + \cosh t\,\mathbf{j} + \mathbf{k}$,
$\|\mathbf{v}(t)\| = \sqrt{\sinh^2 t + \cosh^2 t + 1} = \sqrt{2\cosh^2 t} = \sqrt{2}\cosh t$,
$\mathbf{a}(t) = \cosh t\,\mathbf{i} + \sinh t\,\mathbf{j}$

27. $\mathbf{v}(t) = (e^t\sin t + e^t\cos t)\mathbf{i} + (e^t\cos t - e^t\sin t)\mathbf{j} + e^t\mathbf{k}$,
$\|\mathbf{v}(t)\| = \sqrt{(e^{2t}\sin^2 t + 2e^{2t}\sin t\cos t + e^{2t}\cos^2 t) + (e^{2t}\cos^2 t - 2e^{2t}\sin t\cos t + e^{2t}\sin^2 t) + e^{2t}} = e^t\sqrt{3}$,
$\mathbf{a}(t) = 2e^t\cos t\,\mathbf{i} - 2e^t\sin t\,\mathbf{j} + e^t\mathbf{k}$

28. $\mathbf{v}(t) = \int \mathbf{a}(t)\,dt = \int -32\mathbf{k}\,dt = -32t\,\mathbf{k} + \mathbf{C}$;
$\mathbf{r}(t) = \int \mathbf{v}(t)\,dt = \int(-32t\,\mathbf{k} + \mathbf{C})\,dt = -16t^2\,\mathbf{k} + \mathbf{C}t + \mathbf{C}_1$.
Since $\mathbf{v}(0) = \mathbf{v}_0 = \mathbf{0}$, we have $\mathbf{C} = \mathbf{0}$, so that $\mathbf{v}(t) = -32t\,\mathbf{k}$. Since $\mathbf{r}(0) = \mathbf{r}_0 = \mathbf{0}$, we have $\mathbf{C}_1 = \mathbf{0}$, so that $\mathbf{r}(t) = -16t^2\,\mathbf{k}$. Finally, $\|\mathbf{v}(t)\| = 32|t|$.

29. $\mathbf{v}(t) = \int \mathbf{a}(t)\,dt = \int -32\mathbf{k}\,dt = -32t\,\mathbf{k} + \mathbf{C}$;
$\mathbf{r}(t) = \int \mathbf{v}(t)\,dt = \int(-32t\,\mathbf{k} + \mathbf{C})\,dt = -16t^2\mathbf{k} + \mathbf{C}t + \mathbf{C}_1$.
Since $\mathbf{v}(0) = \mathbf{v}_0 = \mathbf{i} + \mathbf{j}$, we have $\mathbf{C} = \mathbf{i} + \mathbf{j}$, so that $\mathbf{v}(t) = \mathbf{i} + \mathbf{j} - 32t\mathbf{k}$. Since $\mathbf{r}(0) = \mathbf{r}_0 = \mathbf{0}$, we have $\mathbf{C}_1 = \mathbf{0}$, so that $\mathbf{r}(t) = t\mathbf{i} + t\mathbf{j} - 16t^2\mathbf{k}$. Finally, $\|\mathbf{v}(t)\| = \sqrt{1 + 1 + (-32t)^2} = \sqrt{2 + 1024t^2}$.

30. As in Exercise 28, $\mathbf{v}(t) = -32t\mathbf{k} + \mathbf{C}$ and $\mathbf{r}(t) = -16t^2\mathbf{k} + \mathbf{C}t + \mathbf{C}_1$. Since $\mathbf{v}(0) = \mathbf{v}_0 = 3\mathbf{i} - 2\mathbf{j} + \mathbf{k}$, we have $\mathbf{C} = 3\mathbf{i} - 2\mathbf{j} + \mathbf{k}$, so that $\mathbf{v}(t) = 3\mathbf{i} - 2\mathbf{j} + (1 - 32t)\mathbf{k}$. Since $\mathbf{r}(0) = \mathbf{r}_0 = 5\mathbf{j} + 2\mathbf{k}$, we have $\mathbf{C}_1 = 5\mathbf{j} + 2\mathbf{k}$, so that $\mathbf{r}(t) = -16t^2\mathbf{k} + (3\mathbf{i} - 2\mathbf{j} + \mathbf{k})t + 5\mathbf{j} + 2\mathbf{k} = 3t\mathbf{i} + (5 - 2t)\mathbf{j} + (2 + t - 16t^2)\mathbf{k}$. Finally,

$$\|\mathbf{v}(t)\| = \sqrt{9 + 4 + (1 - 64t + 1024t^2)} = \sqrt{14 - 64t + 1024t^2}.$$

31. $\mathbf{v}(t) = \int \mathbf{a}(t)\,dt = \int(-\cos t\,\mathbf{i} - \sin t\,\mathbf{j})\,dt = -\sin t\,\mathbf{i} + \cos t\,\mathbf{j} + \mathbf{C}$;
$\mathbf{r}(t) = \int \mathbf{v}(t)\,dt = \int(-\sin t\,\mathbf{i} + \cos t\,\mathbf{j} + \mathbf{C})\,dt = \cos t\,\mathbf{i} + \sin t\,\mathbf{j} + \mathbf{C}t + \mathbf{C}_1$.
Since $\mathbf{v}(0) = \mathbf{v}_0 = \mathbf{k}$, we have $\mathbf{k} = -\sin 0\,\mathbf{i} + \cos 0\,\mathbf{j} + \mathbf{C} = \mathbf{j} + \mathbf{C}$, so that $\mathbf{C} = \mathbf{k} - \mathbf{j}$, and thus $\mathbf{v}(t) = -\sin t\,\mathbf{i} + (\cos t - 1)\mathbf{j} + \mathbf{k}$. Since $\mathbf{r}(0) = \mathbf{r}_0 = \mathbf{i}$, we have $\mathbf{i} = \cos 0\,\mathbf{i} + \sin 0\,\mathbf{j} + (\mathbf{k} - \mathbf{j})0 + \mathbf{C}_1 = \mathbf{i} + \mathbf{C}_1$, so that $\mathbf{C}_1 = \mathbf{0}$, and thus $\mathbf{r}(t) = \cos t\,\mathbf{i} + \sin t\,\mathbf{j} + t(\mathbf{k} - \mathbf{j}) = \cos t\,\mathbf{i} + (\sin t - t)\mathbf{j} + t\mathbf{k}$. Finally, $\|\mathbf{v}(t)\| = \sqrt{\sin^2 t + (\cos t - 1)^2 + 1} = \sqrt{3 - 2\cos t}$.

32. $\mathbf{v}(t) = \int \mathbf{a}(t)\,dt = \int(e^t\mathbf{i} + e^{-t}\mathbf{j})\,dt = e^t\mathbf{i} - e^{-t}\mathbf{j} + \mathbf{C}$;
$\mathbf{r}(t) = \int \mathbf{v}(t)\,dt = \int(e^t\mathbf{i} - e^{-t}\mathbf{j} + \mathbf{C})\,dt = e^t\mathbf{i} + e^{-t}\mathbf{j} + \mathbf{C}t + \mathbf{C}_1$.
Since $\mathbf{v}(0) = \mathbf{v}_0 = \mathbf{i} - \mathbf{j} + \sqrt{2}\,\mathbf{k}$, we have $\mathbf{i} - \mathbf{j} + \sqrt{2}\,\mathbf{k} = e^0\mathbf{i} - e^{-0}\mathbf{j} + \mathbf{C} = \mathbf{i} - \mathbf{j} + \mathbf{C}$, so that $\mathbf{C} = \sqrt{2}\,\mathbf{k}$, and thus $\mathbf{v}(t) = e^t\mathbf{i} - e^{-t}\mathbf{j} + \sqrt{2}\,\mathbf{k}$. Since $\mathbf{r}(0) = \mathbf{r}_0 = \mathbf{i} + \mathbf{j}$, we have $\mathbf{i} + \mathbf{j} = e^0\mathbf{i} + e^{-0}\mathbf{j} + \sqrt{2}\,(0)\mathbf{k} + \mathbf{C}_1 = \mathbf{i} + \mathbf{j} + \mathbf{C}_1$, so that $\mathbf{C}_1 = \mathbf{0}$, and thus $\mathbf{r}(t) = e^t\mathbf{i} + e^{-t}\mathbf{j} + t(\sqrt{2}\,\mathbf{k}) + \mathbf{0} = e^t\mathbf{i} + e^{-t}\mathbf{j} + \sqrt{2}\,t\,\mathbf{k}$. Finally, $\|\mathbf{v}(t)\| = \sqrt{e^{2t} + e^{-2t} + 2} = e^t + e^{-t}$.

33. $\mathbf{F}(t) = \left(\int_0^t u\tan u^3\,du\right)\mathbf{i} + \left(\int_0^t \cos e^u\,du\right)\mathbf{j} + \left(\int_0^t e^{(u^2)}\,du\right)\mathbf{k}$, and thus $\mathbf{F}'(t) = t\tan t^3\,\mathbf{i} + \cos e^t\,\mathbf{j} + e^{(t^2)}\,\mathbf{k}$.

34. $\mathbf{G}(t) = \left(\int_0^{t^2} \cos u\,du\right)\mathbf{i} + \left(\int_0^{t^2} e^{-(u^2)}\,du\right)\mathbf{j} + \left(\int_0^{t^2} \tan u\,du\right)\mathbf{k}$, so that $\mathbf{G}'(t) = (\cos t^2)(2t)\mathbf{i} + (e^{-t^4})(2t)\mathbf{j} + (\tan t^2)(2t)\mathbf{k}$.

35. $\|\mathbf{F}(t)\| = \sqrt{\dfrac{16t^2}{(1+4t^2)^2} + \dfrac{1 - 8t^2 + 16t^4}{(1+4t^2)^2}} = \sqrt{\dfrac{(1+4t^2)^2}{(1+4t^2)^2}} = 1$, so that by Corollary 12.11, $\mathbf{F}(t) \cdot \mathbf{F}'(t) = 0$ for all t.

36. $\mathbf{F}'(t) = -\sin t\,\mathbf{i} + \cos t\,\mathbf{j}$ and $\dfrac{\mathbf{F}(\pi) - \mathbf{F}(0)}{\pi - 0} = \dfrac{-\mathbf{i} - \mathbf{i}}{\pi - 0} = \dfrac{-2}{\pi}\mathbf{i}$.

Now $\mathbf{F}'(\pi/2) = -\mathbf{i}$, so that $\mathbf{F}(\pi/2)$ is parallel to $[\mathbf{F}(\pi) - \mathbf{F}(0)]/(\pi - 0)$. But for any other value of t in $(0, \pi)$ the $\mathbf{j}$ component of $\mathbf{F}'(t)$ is nonzero, and hence $\mathbf{F}(t) \neq [\mathbf{F}(\pi) - \mathbf{F}(0)]/(\pi - 0)$. Consequently there is no value of t in $(0, \pi)$ such that $\mathbf{F}(t) = [\mathbf{F}(\pi) - \mathbf{F}(0)]/(\pi - 0)$.

37. $\mathbf{F}'(t) = \cos t\,\mathbf{i} + \sin t\,\mathbf{j}$ and $\mathbf{F}''(t) = -\sin t\,\mathbf{i} + \cos t\,\mathbf{j} = -\mathbf{F}(t)$. Since $\|\mathbf{F}(t)\| = \|\mathbf{F}''(t)\| = 1$, it follows that $\mathbf{F}(t)$ and $\mathbf{F}''(t)$ are parallel but have opposite, and hence dissimilar, directions, for all t.

38. $\mathbf{F}'(t) = -2e^{-2t}\mathbf{i} + 2e^{2t}\mathbf{k}$ and $\mathbf{F}''(t) = 4e^{-2t}\mathbf{i} + 4e^{2t}\mathbf{k} = 4\mathbf{F}(t)$. Since $\|\mathbf{F}(t)\| = \sqrt{e^{-4t} + e^{4t}} \neq 0$, it follows that $\mathbf{F}(t)$ and $\mathbf{F}''(t)$ are not only parallel but have the same direction for all t.

39. By Theorem 12.10(e), $\dfrac{d}{dt}(\mathbf{F} \times \mathbf{F}')(t) = [\mathbf{F}'(t) \times \mathbf{F}'(t)] + [\mathbf{F}(t) \times \mathbf{F}''(t)] = \mathbf{F}(t) \times \mathbf{F}''(t)$.

40. If $\mathbf{F}(t)$ is parallel to $\mathbf{F}''(t)$ for all t, then there is a constant c such that $\mathbf{F}''(t) = c\mathbf{F}(t)$ for all t. Then by Exercise 39 and properties of cross products, $(d/dt)(\mathbf{F} \times \mathbf{F}')(t) = \mathbf{F}(t) \times \mathbf{F}''(t) = c(\mathbf{F}(t) \times \mathbf{F}(t)) = \mathbf{0}$, so that by integration, $(\mathbf{F} \times \mathbf{F}')(t) = \mathbf{C}$ for some constant vector $\mathbf{C}$.

41. a. $\mathbf{r}(t) = \cos t\,\mathbf{i} + \sin t\,\mathbf{j} + t\,\mathbf{k}$, so that $\mathbf{v}(t) = -\sin t\,\mathbf{i} + \cos t\,\mathbf{j} + \mathbf{k}$, $\|\mathbf{r}(t)\| = \sqrt{(\cos t)^2 + (\sin t)^2 + t^2} = \sqrt{1 + t^2}$, and $\|\mathbf{v}(t)\| = \sqrt{(-\sin t)^2 + (\cos t)^2 + 1^2} = \sqrt{2}$. Thus

$$\cos\theta(t) = \frac{\mathbf{r}(t) \cdot \mathbf{v}(t)}{\|\mathbf{r}(t)\|\,\|\mathbf{v}(t)\|} = \frac{(\cos t)(-\sin t) + (\sin t)(\cos t) + (t)(1)}{\sqrt{1+t^2}\,\sqrt{2}} = \frac{t}{\sqrt{2(1+t^2)}}.$$

Since $0 \leq \theta(t) \leq \pi$, it follows that

$$\theta(t) = \cos^{-1}\frac{t}{\sqrt{2(1+t^2)}}.$$

b. By part (a), $\theta(0) = \cos^{-1} 0 = \pi/2$.

c. By part (a),

$$\theta(\pi/2) = \cos^{-1}\frac{\pi/2}{\sqrt{2(1+\pi^2/4)}} \approx 0.9316761004 \text{ radians}.$$

42. By using Theorem 12.10(d) and then Theorem 12.10(e), we find that

$$\begin{aligned}\frac{d}{dt}[\mathbf{F} \cdot (\mathbf{G} \times \mathbf{H})] &= \frac{d\mathbf{F}}{dt} \cdot (\mathbf{G} \times \mathbf{H}) + \mathbf{F} \cdot \frac{d}{dt}(\mathbf{G} \times \mathbf{H}) \\ &= \frac{d\mathbf{F}}{dt} \cdot (\mathbf{G} \times \mathbf{H}) + \mathbf{F} \cdot \left[\left(\frac{d\mathbf{G}}{dt} \times \mathbf{H}\right) + \left(\mathbf{G} \times \frac{d\mathbf{H}}{dt}\right)\right] \\ &= \frac{d\mathbf{F}}{dt} \cdot (\mathbf{G} \times \mathbf{H}) + \mathbf{F} \cdot \left(\frac{d\mathbf{G}}{dt} \times \mathbf{H}\right) + \mathbf{F} \cdot \left(\mathbf{G} \times \frac{d\mathbf{H}}{dt}\right)\end{aligned}$$

43. Let $\mathbf{F}(t) = \mathbf{v}(t)$, so that $\mathbf{F}'(t) = \mathbf{a}(t)$. Since the speed is constant, we have $\|\mathbf{F}(t)\| = \|\mathbf{v}(t)\| = c$, for some constant c. By Corollary 12.11, $\mathbf{v} \cdot \mathbf{a}(t) = \mathbf{F}(t) \cdot \mathbf{F}'(t) = 0$. Therefore the acceleration vector is perpendicular to the velocity vector.

44. By the Chain Rule, $\dfrac{d}{dt}\|\mathbf{v}\|^2 = 2\|\mathbf{v}\|\dfrac{d}{dt}\|\mathbf{v}\|$. By the version of the Product Rule for scalar products,

$$\frac{d}{dt}(\mathbf{v} \cdot \mathbf{v}) = \left(\frac{d}{dt}\mathbf{v}\right) \cdot \mathbf{v} + \mathbf{v} \cdot \left(\frac{d}{dt}\mathbf{v}\right) = \mathbf{a} \cdot \mathbf{v} + \mathbf{v} \cdot \mathbf{a} = 2\,\mathbf{v} \cdot \mathbf{a}.$$

Since $\|\mathbf{v}\|^2 = \mathbf{v} \cdot \mathbf{v}$, it follows that

$$2\|\mathbf{v}\|\frac{d}{dt}\|\mathbf{v}\| = 2\,\mathbf{v} \cdot \mathbf{a} \quad \text{or} \quad \|\mathbf{v}\|\frac{d}{dt}\|\mathbf{v}\| = \mathbf{v} \cdot \mathbf{a}.$$

45. Let $K_1(t)$ and $K_2(t)$ be the kinetic energies of the mass at any time t during its first and second journeys, respectively. By Example 10, the first time the position is given by $\mathbf{r}_1(t) = (-16t^2 + 96)\mathbf{k}$, so that $\mathbf{r}_1(\sqrt{6}) = \mathbf{0}$, and thus the ball hits the ground when $t = \sqrt{6}$. Since $\mathbf{v}_1(t) = -32t\mathbf{k}$, and $K_1(t) = \frac{1}{2}m\|\mathbf{v}_1(t)\|^2$, we therefore have $K_1(\sqrt{6}) = \frac{1}{2}m\left|-32(\sqrt{6})\right|^2 = 3072m$. The second time the position is given by $\mathbf{r}_2(t) = (-16t^2 - 80t + 96)\mathbf{k} = -16(t^2 + 5t - 6)\mathbf{k} = -16(t+6)(t-1)\mathbf{k}$, so that $\mathbf{r}_2(1) = \mathbf{0}$, and thus the ball hits the ground when $t = 1$. Since $\mathbf{v}_2(t) = (-32t - 80)\mathbf{k}$, and $K_2(t) = \frac{1}{2}m\,\|\mathbf{v}_2(t)\|^2$, we have $K_2(1) = \frac{1}{2}m\,|-32-80|^2 = 6272m$. Consequently $K_2(1) - K_1(\sqrt{6}) = 6272m - 3072m = 3200m$, and this is how much larger the kinetic energy is at impact the second time.

46. Since $K(t) = \frac{1}{2}m\,\|\mathbf{v}(t)\|^2$ (see Exercise 45), the Chain Rule implies that

$$K'(t) = m\,\|\mathbf{v}(t)\|\,\frac{d}{dt}\|\mathbf{v}(t)\|\,.$$

By Exercise 44 it follows that $K'(t) = m\mathbf{v}(t)\cdot\mathbf{a}(t) = \big(m\mathbf{a}(t)\big)\cdot\mathbf{v}(t)$, so by (9), $K'(t) = \mathbf{F}(t)\cdot\mathbf{v}(t)$.

47. a. Initial position: $\mathbf{r}_0 = \mathbf{0}$; velocity: $\mathbf{v}(t) = 90\sqrt{2}\,\mathbf{i} + 90\sqrt{2}\,\mathbf{j} + (64 - 32t)\mathbf{k}$; initial velocity: $\mathbf{v}_0 = 90\sqrt{2}\,\mathbf{i} + 90\sqrt{2}\,\mathbf{j} + 64\mathbf{k}$

b. $\mathbf{r}(4) = 360\sqrt{2}\,\mathbf{i} + 360\sqrt{2}\,\mathbf{j} + 0\mathbf{k}$, so the height is 0 when $t = 4$; distance from initial position: $\|\mathbf{r}(4) - \mathbf{r}(0)\| = \|360\sqrt{2}\,\mathbf{i} + 360\sqrt{2}\,\mathbf{j}\| = 720$ (feet).

48. By Example 10 with $g = 32$, we have $\mathbf{r}(t) = -16t^2\mathbf{k} + t\mathbf{v}_0 + \mathbf{r}_0$. By hypothesis, $\mathbf{v}_0 = 2\mathbf{i} + 3\mathbf{k}$ and $\mathbf{r}_0 = \mathbf{k}$. Thus $\mathbf{r}(t) = -16t^2\mathbf{k} + t(2\mathbf{i} + 3\mathbf{k}) + \mathbf{k} = 2t\mathbf{i} + (1 + 3t - 16t^2)\mathbf{k}$.

49. a. We choose a coordinate system so that the base of the container lies on the xy plane, with the origin as in the figure. By Example 10, the position of a water droplet t seconds after it leaves the container is given by $\mathbf{r}(t) = -\frac{1}{2}gt^2\mathbf{k} + t\mathbf{v}_0 + \mathbf{r}_0$. By assumption, $\mathbf{v}_0 = \sqrt{2gh}\,\mathbf{j}$ and $\mathbf{r}_0 = (H-h)\mathbf{k}$. Thus $\mathbf{r}(t) = -\frac{1}{2}gt^2\mathbf{k} + \sqrt{2gh}\,t\mathbf{j} + (H-h)\mathbf{k} = \sqrt{2gh}\,t\mathbf{j} + [(H-h) - \frac{1}{2}gt^2]\mathbf{k}$ until the droplet hits the floor.

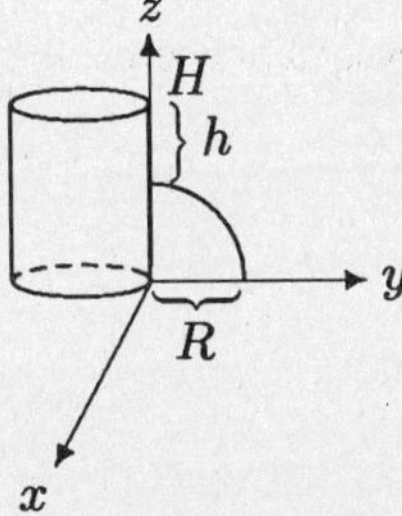

b. When a given droplet hits the floor, the $\mathbf{k}$ component of $\mathbf{r}$ is 0, so $[(H-h) - \frac{1}{2}gt^2] = 0$, and thus $t = \sqrt{2(H-h)/g}$. Then R, which is the $\mathbf{j}$ component of $\mathbf{r}$ at that instant, is given by $R = \sqrt{2gh}\,\sqrt{2(H-h)/g} = 2\sqrt{h(H-h)}$. Now R is maximized for the same value of h as R_1, where $R_1 = R^2$. Since $R_1(h) = 4h(H-h)$ and $R_1'(h) = 4H - 8h$, we find that $R_1'(h) = 0$ if $h = \frac{1}{2}H$. Since $R_1''(h) = -8 < 0$, it follows that R_1, and hence R, is maximized if $h = H/2$.

c. If $h = H/2$, then $R = 2\sqrt{(H/2)(H - H/2)} = 2(H/2) = H$.

50. Place the coordinate system so that the floor represents the xy plane and the ball rolls on a line directly above the negative x axis towards the edge, located at the point $(0, 0, 2.6)$. Then by Example 10, the position of the ball t seconds after it leaves the table is given by $\mathbf{r}(t) = -16t^2\mathbf{k} + t\mathbf{v}_0 + \mathbf{r}_0$. By assumption, $\mathbf{v}_0 = 2\mathbf{i}$ and $\mathbf{r}_0 = 2.6\mathbf{k}$. Thus $\mathbf{r}(t) = -16t^2\mathbf{k} + 2t\mathbf{i} + 2.6\mathbf{k} = 2t\mathbf{i} + (2.6 - 16t^2)\mathbf{k}$.

a. The **k** component of $\mathbf{r}(t)$ is 0 if $2.6 = 16t^2$, or $t = \sqrt{2.6}/4 \approx .40$. Thus the ball hits the floor after approximately .40 seconds.

b. $\mathbf{v}(t) = 2\mathbf{i} - 32t\mathbf{k}$, so that

$$\left\|\mathbf{v}\left(\frac{\sqrt{2.6}}{4}\right)\right\| = \left\|2\mathbf{i} - 32\left(\frac{\sqrt{2.6}}{4}\right)\mathbf{k}\right\| = \sqrt{4+166.4} = \sqrt{170.4} \approx 13\,(\text{feet per second}).$$

51. Taking the radius of the earth to be 3960 miles, so the radius of the satellite's orbit is $3960+500 = 4460$ (miles), we use the comments following (7) to deduce the speed v_0 of the satellite:

$$v_0 = \sqrt{\frac{C}{r_0}} = \sqrt{\frac{32(3960)^2(5280)^2}{(4460)(5280)}} \approx 24{,}400\,(\text{feet per second})$$

or approximately 16,600 miles per hour.

52. By the hint, $2\pi v_0 =$ the circumference $= 24(3600)v_0$. By (7) we have $r_0 = C/v_0^2$, so that

$$\frac{24(3600)v_0}{2\pi} = r_0 = \frac{C}{v_0^2}, \quad \text{so} \quad v_0^3 = \frac{2\pi C}{24(3600)} = \frac{2\pi(32)(3960)^2(5280)^2}{24(3600)}.$$

Therefore $v_0 \approx 10{,}057.53$ (feet per second), or approximately 6857.41 miles per hour. Then

$$r_0 = \frac{(24)(3600)v_0}{2\pi} \approx 138{,}300{,}965.1\,(\text{feet})$$

or approximately 26,193.4 miles. (It follows that such a communications satellite circles the earth at approximately $26{,}193 - 3960 = 22{,}233$ miles above the surface of the earth.)

53. The bobsled moves $60(\frac{5280}{3600})$ feet per second, so by (5),

$$\|\mathbf{a}(t)\| = \frac{v_0^2}{r} = \frac{[60(\frac{5280}{3600})]^2}{100} = 77.44\,(\text{feet per second per second}).$$

54. a. By (5), $\|\mathbf{a}(t)\| = \dfrac{[(2.5)\times 10^5]^2}{1} = 6.25 \times 10^{10}$ (kilometers per second per second).

b. By (5), $\|\mathbf{a}(t)\| = \dfrac{[(2.9)\times 10^5]^2}{1} = 8.41 \times 10^{10}$ (kilometers per second per second).

55. Set up a coordinate system with origin at the nozzle of the gun, as in the diagram. Let time $t = 0$ correspond to the instant at which the target is released. Let (d, h) be the coordinates of the target at that time, and let $\mathbf{v}(0) = v_2\,\mathbf{j} + v_3\,\mathbf{k}$ be the initial velocity of the projectile. By the solution of Example 10, the position $\mathbf{r}_1(t)$ of the projectile and the position $\mathbf{r}_2(t)$ of the target at any time $t \geq 0$ (until either hits the ground) are given by

$$\mathbf{r}_1(t) = -\frac{1}{2}gt^2\mathbf{k} + (v_2\,\mathbf{j} + v_3\,\mathbf{k})t = v_2 t\,\mathbf{j} + \left(v_3 t - \frac{1}{2}gt^2\right)\mathbf{k}$$

and

$$\mathbf{r}_2(t) = -\frac{1}{2}gt^2\,\mathbf{k} + d\,\mathbf{j} + h\,\mathbf{k} = d\,\mathbf{j} + \left(h - \frac{1}{2}gt^2\right)\mathbf{k}.$$

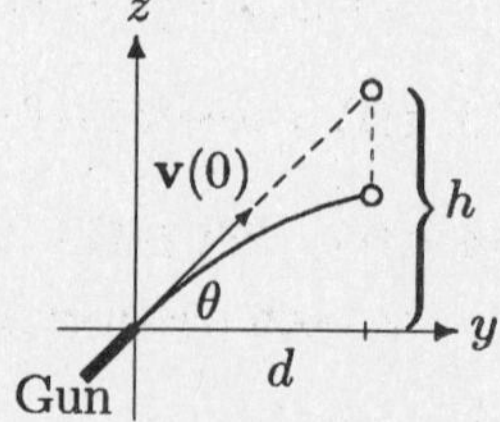

The projectile hits the target if $\mathbf{r}_1(t) = \mathbf{r}_2(t)$ for some value of t, that is,

$$v_2 t\,\mathbf{j} + \left(v_3 t - \frac{1}{2}gt^2\right)\mathbf{k} = d\,\mathbf{j} + \left(h - \frac{1}{2}gt^2\right)\mathbf{k}.$$

This is equivalent to $v_2 t = d$ and $v_3 t = h$. From the diagram, $\tan\theta = h/d = v_3/v_2$. Thus the projectile hits the target at time $t = d/v_2 = h/v_3$ unless either hits the ground before that time.

12.4 Space Curves and Their Lengths

1. $\mathbf{r}'(t) = \mathbf{i} + 2t\mathbf{j} + 3t^2\mathbf{k}$; $\mathbf{r}'$ is continuous and is never $\mathbf{0}$, so $\mathbf{r}$ is smooth.

2. $\mathbf{r}'(t) = \mathbf{i} + \mathbf{j} + \mathbf{k}$; $\mathbf{r}'$ is constant and nonzero, so $\mathbf{r}$ is smooth.

3. $\mathbf{r}'(t) = \begin{cases} -\mathbf{i} + \mathbf{j} + \mathbf{k} & \text{for } t < 0 \\ \mathbf{i} + \mathbf{j} + \mathbf{k} & \text{for } t > 0 \end{cases}$

   so $\mathbf{r}'$ is continuous and nonzero on $(-\infty, 0)$ and on $(0, \infty)$. Since the one-sided derivatives at 0 are $-\mathbf{i} + \mathbf{j} + \mathbf{k}$ and $\mathbf{i} + \mathbf{j} + \mathbf{k}$ respectively, we conclude that $\mathbf{r}$ is piecewise smooth but not smooth.

4. $\mathbf{r}'(t) = \frac{2}{3}t^{-1/3}\mathbf{i} + \mathbf{j} + 2t\mathbf{k}$. Since the one-sided derivatives at 0 do not exist, $\mathbf{r}$ is neither smooth nor piecewise smooth.

5. $\mathbf{r}'(t) = \frac{3}{2}(1+t)^{1/2}\mathbf{i} - \frac{3}{2}(1-t)^{1/2}\mathbf{j} + \frac{3}{2}\mathbf{k}$ for $-1 < t < 1$, and the appropriate one-sided derivatives exist at -1 and 1. Since $\mathbf{r}'$ is continuous and nonzero on $[-1, 1]$, $\mathbf{r}$ is smooth.

6. $\mathbf{r}'(t) = \cos t\,\mathbf{i} - \sin t\,\mathbf{j} + 2t\,\mathbf{k}$, and $\|\mathbf{r}'(t)\| = \sqrt{\cos^2 t + \sin^2 t + 4t^2} = \sqrt{1 + 4t^2} > 0$ for all t. Thus $\mathbf{r}'$ is continuous and nonzero, so $\mathbf{r}$ is smooth.

7. $\mathbf{r}'(t) = -2\cos t\,\sin t\,\mathbf{i} + 2\sin t\,\cos t\,\mathbf{j} + 2t\,\mathbf{k}$; $\mathbf{r}$ is continuous and $\mathbf{r}'(t) = \mathbf{0}$ only if $t = 0$. Thus $\mathbf{r}$ is piecewise smooth.

8. $\mathbf{r}'(t) = e^t\mathbf{i} - e^{-t}\mathbf{j} + 2\mathbf{k}$; $\mathbf{r}'$ is continuous and is never zero, so $\mathbf{r}$ is smooth.

9. $\mathbf{r}'(t) = (e^t - 1)\mathbf{i} + 2t\,\mathbf{j} + 3t^2\,\mathbf{k}$; $\mathbf{r}'$ is continuous and $\mathbf{r}'(t) = \mathbf{0}$ only if $t = 0$. Thus $\mathbf{r}$ is piecewise smooth.

10. $\mathbf{r}'(t) = 2\mathbf{i} + 2t\,\mathbf{j} + (1/t)\mathbf{k}$; $\mathbf{r}'$ is continuous on $(0, \infty)$ and is never zero, so $\mathbf{r}$ is smooth.

11. The line segment is parallel to $7\mathbf{i} - 2\mathbf{j} + 4\mathbf{k}$ and starts at $(-3, 2, 1)$. Thus a parametrization is $\mathbf{r}(t) = (-3 + 7t)\mathbf{i} + (2 - 2t)\mathbf{j} + (1 + 4t)\mathbf{k}$ for $0 \le t \le 1$, and $\mathbf{r}$ is smooth.

12. The line segment is parallel to $6\mathbf{i} - \frac{5}{2}\mathbf{j}$ and starts at $(0, 3, -2)$. Thus a parametrization is $\mathbf{r}(t) = 6t\,\mathbf{i} + (3 - \frac{5}{2}t)\mathbf{j} - 2\mathbf{k}$ for $0 \le t \le 1$, and $\mathbf{r}$ is smooth.

13. $\mathbf{r}(t) = 6\cos t\,\mathbf{i} + 6\sin t\,\mathbf{j}$ for $0 \le t \le 2\pi$ is one such smooth parametrization.

14. $\mathbf{r}(t) = (2\mathbf{i} + 4\mathbf{j} - \mathbf{k}) + \frac{5}{2}(\cos t\,\mathbf{i} + \sin t\,\mathbf{j}) = (2 + \frac{5}{2}\cos t)\mathbf{i} + (4 + \frac{5}{2}\sin t)\mathbf{j} - \mathbf{k}$ for $0 \le t \le 2\pi$ is one such smooth parametrization.

15. $\mathbf{r}(t) = \cos t\,\mathbf{i} + \sin t\,\mathbf{j}$ for $0 \le t \le \pi$ is one such smooth parametrization.

16. $\mathbf{r}(t) = \cos t\,\mathbf{i} - \sin t\,\mathbf{j}$ for $0 \le t \le \pi/2$ is one such smooth parametrization.

17. Notice that the quarter circle in the xy plane that extends from $(\sqrt{2}/2, \sqrt{2}/2)$ to $(\sqrt{2}/2, -\sqrt{2}/2)$ corresponds to the quarter circle from $(1, \pi/4)$ to $(1, -\pi/4)$ in polar coordinates. This leads us to $\mathbf{r}(t) = \cos t\,\mathbf{i} - \sin t\,\mathbf{j} + 4\mathbf{k}$ for $-\pi/4 \le t \le \pi/4$, which is smooth.

18. $\mathbf{r}(t) = t\,\mathbf{i} + (t^2 + 1)\mathbf{j}$ is one such smooth parametrization.

19. $\mathbf{r}(t) = t\,\mathbf{i} + \tan t\,\mathbf{j}$ for $0 \le t \le \pi/4$ is one such smooth parametrization.

20. $\mathbf{r}(t) = t\,\mathbf{i} + (t^5 - t^2 + 5)\mathbf{j}$ for $-1 \le t \le 0$ is one such smooth parametrization.

21. $L = \int_0^{2\pi} \sqrt{[3\cos^2 t\,(-\sin t)]^2 + [3\sin^2 t \cos t]^2}\,dt$

$= \int_0^{2\pi} 3|\sin t\, \cos t|\,dt = 12\int_0^{2\pi} \sin t\, \cos t\,dt = 6\sin^2 t\big|_0^{2\pi} = 6$

22. $L = \int_1^2 \sqrt{4 + 4t^2 + 1/t^2}\,dt = \int_1^2 (2t + 1/t)\,dt = (t^2 + \ln t)\big|_1^2 = 3 + \ln 2$

23. $L = \int_{-1}^1 \sqrt{\frac{1}{4}(1+t) + \frac{1}{4}(1-t) + \frac{1}{4}}\,dt = \int_{-1}^1 \frac{1}{2}\sqrt{3}\,dt = \frac{1}{2}\sqrt{3}\,t\big|_{-1}^1 = \sqrt{3}$

24. $L = \int_0^1 \sqrt{\sinh^2 t + \cosh^2 t + 1}\,dt = \int_0^1 \sqrt{2\cosh^2 t}\,dt$

$= \sqrt{2}\int_0^1 \cosh t\,dt = \sqrt{2}\,\sinh t\big|_0^1 = \sqrt{2}\,\sinh 1 = \frac{\sqrt{2}}{2}(e - e^{-1})$

25. $L = \int_0^1 \sqrt{e^{2t} + e^{-2t} + 2}\,dt = \int_0^1 \sqrt{(e^t + e^{-t})^2}\,dt = \int_0^1 (e^t + e^{-t})\,dt = (e^t - e^{-t})\big|_0^1 = e - e^{-1}$

26. $L = \int_0^{20/3} \sqrt{\sin^2 t + \cos^2 t + \frac{9}{4}t}\,dt = \int_0^{20/3} \sqrt{1 + \frac{9}{4}t}\,dt = \frac{8}{27}(1 + \frac{9}{4}t)^{3/2}\big|_0^{20/3} = \frac{56}{3}$

27. $L = \int_1^{\sqrt{8}} \sqrt{[36t^2(t^2-1)] + 36t^2 + 36t^2}\,dt = \int_1^{\sqrt{8}} 6\sqrt{t^4 + t^2}\,dt$

$= \int_1^{\sqrt{8}} 6t\sqrt{t^2+1}\,dt = 2(t^2+1)^{3/2}\big|_1^{\sqrt{8}} = 54 - 4\sqrt{2}$

28. $L = \int_0^1 \sqrt{(9 - 18t^2 + 9t^4) + 36t^2 + (9 + 18t^2 + 9t^4)}\,dt$

$= \int_0^1 \sqrt{18(1 + 2t^2 + t^4)}\,dt = \int_0^1 3\sqrt{2}(1+t^2)\,dt = 3\sqrt{2}\,(t + t^3/3)\big|_0^1 = 4\sqrt{2}$

29. $\dfrac{ds}{dt} = \sqrt{4\cos^2 2t + 4\sin^2 2t + t} = \sqrt{4+t}$

30. $\dfrac{ds}{dt} = \sqrt{t^4 + 2t^2 + 1} = t^2 + 1$

31. $\dfrac{ds}{dt} = \sqrt{(\cos t - t\sin t)^2 + (\sin t + t\cos t)^2 + 1} = \sqrt{\cos^2 t + \sin^2 t + t^2(\sin^2 t + \cos^2 t) + 1} = \sqrt{2 + t^2}$

32. $\dfrac{ds}{dt} = \sqrt{4 + 4t^2 + t^4} = 2 + t^2$

33. $\dfrac{ds}{dt} = \sqrt{(1 - \cos t)^2 + \sin^2 t + 1} = \sqrt{3 - 2\cos t}$

34. $L = \int_{-1}^{1} \sqrt{\cos^2 t + \sin^2 t + t^4}\, dt = \int_{-1}^{1} \sqrt{1+t^4}\, dt$. By Simpson's Rule with $n = 10$, $L \approx 2.178854037$.

35. $L = \int_0^2 \sqrt{4\sin^2 2t + 4\cos^2 2t + 4t^3}\, dt = 2\int_0^2 \sqrt{1+t^3}\, dt$. By Simpson's Rule with $n = 10$, $L \approx 6.482559337$.

36. $L = \int_{-1}^{1} \sqrt{1+4t^2+9t^4}\, dt$. By Simpson's Rule with $n = 10$, $L \approx 3.726041989$.

37. $L = \int_0^1 \sqrt{t^2+t^4+t^6}\, dt$. By Simpson's Rule with $n = 10$, $L \approx 0.668455969$.

38. $s(t) = \int_0^t \sqrt{(x'(u))^2 + (y'(u))^2}\, du = \int_0^t \sqrt{r^2(1-\cos u)^2 + r^2\sin^2 u}\, du$

$= \int_0^t r\sqrt{1 - 2\cos u + \cos^2 u + \sin^2 u}\, du = \int_0^t r\sqrt{2 - 2\cos u}\, du$

$= \int_0^t r\sqrt{4\sin^2(u/2)}\, du = \int_0^t 2r\sin(u/2)\, du = -4r\cos(u/2)\big|_0^t = 4r(1-\cos(t/2))$ for $0 \le t \le 2\pi$

39. $s(t) = \int_0^t \sqrt{(x'(u))^2 + (y'(u))^2 + (z'(u))^2}\, du = \int_0^t \sqrt{2^2 + \cos^2 u + \sin^2 u}\, du = \int_0^t \sqrt{5}\, du = \sqrt{5}\, t$

40. Since $s(a) = 0$, we have $s(t) = s(t) - s(a) = \int_a^t \|\mathbf{r}'(u)\| du$. If $\|\mathbf{r}'(u)\| = 1$ for all u in I, then $s(t) = \int_a^t 1\, du = t - a$. Conversely, if $s(t) = t - a$, then $t - a = \int_a^t \|\mathbf{r}'(u)\| du$, so that $1 = \|\mathbf{r}'(t)\|$ for all t in I.

41. $\|\mathbf{r}(t)\| = \sqrt{\dfrac{(1-t^2)^2}{(1+t^2)^2} + \dfrac{4t^2}{(1+t^2)^2}} = 1$ for all t, so $\mathbf{r}$ parametrizes a portion of the circle $x^2 + y^2 = 1$. Let $f_1(t)$ denote the $\mathbf{i}$ component of $\mathbf{r}$. Since $f_1(0) = 1$ and $\lim_{t\to-\infty} f_1(t) = \lim_{t\to\infty} f_1(t) = -1$, we conclude from the Intermediate Value Theorem that f_1 takes all values in the interval $(-1, 1]$. Since the $\mathbf{j}$ component of $\mathbf{r}$ is positive for $t > 0$ and negative for $t < 0$, it follows that $\mathbf{r}$ parametrizes all the points on the circle between $(1,0)$ and $(-1,0)$. Finally, $(-1,0)$ is not included in the parametrization since $(1-t^2)/(1+t^2) \ne -1$ for all t and hence $\mathbf{r}(t) \ne -\mathbf{i}$ for all t.

42. Since $\left(\dfrac{t^2+1}{t^2-1}\right)^2 - \left(\dfrac{2t}{t^2-1}\right)^2 = \dfrac{(t^2-1)^2}{(t^2-1)^2} = 1$ for all $t \ne \pm 1$, it follows that $\mathbf{r}$ parametrizes a portion of the hyperbola $x^2 - y^2 = 1$. Notice that $\mathbf{r}(0) = -\mathbf{i}$, $\lim_{t\to-\infty} \mathbf{r}(t) = \mathbf{i}$, $\lim_{t\to\infty} \mathbf{r}(t) = \mathbf{i}$, $\lim_{t\to-1^-} \|\mathbf{r}(t)\| = \lim_{t\to-1^+} \|\mathbf{r}(t)\| = \lim_{t\to 1^-} \|\mathbf{r}(t)\| = \lim_{t\to 1^+} \|\mathbf{r}(t)\| = \infty$. Also, the $\mathbf{i}$ component of $\mathbf{r}(t)$ is positive if and only if $|t| > 1$, and the $\mathbf{j}$ component of $\mathbf{r}(t)$ is positive if and only if $-1 < t < 0$. or $t > 1$. These observations, along with 4 applications of the Intermediate Value Theorem (one for each quadrant), imply that $\mathbf{r}$ parametrizes all points on the hyperbola $x^2 - y^2 = 1$ except $(1,0)$, which is not included because $(t^2+1)/(t^2-1) \ne 1$ for all t, and hence $\mathbf{r}(t) \ne \mathbf{i}$ for all t. The figure indicates which portions of the hyperbola are parametrized for various values of t.

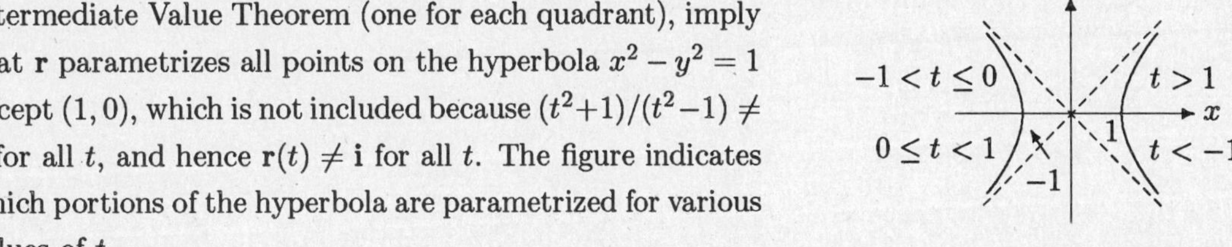

43. a. Assume that the radius of the circle is $r > 0$. Then $n = 8$ and $d = 2r$. Thus $\pi n d/8 = [\pi(8)(2r)]/8 = 2\pi r =$ circumference L of the circle.

b. $n = 18$, $d = \frac{1}{3}$, so $L \approx [\pi(18)(\frac{1}{3})]/8 = 3\pi/4$.

44. Since the helix has radius 10^{-8} centimeters and each turn results in a climb of 3.4×10^{-8} centimeters, it follows that one turn of the helix is parametrized by $\mathbf{r}(t) = 10^{-8}\cos t\,\mathbf{i} + 10^{-8}\sin t\,\mathbf{j} + 3.4\times10^{-8}t/2\pi\,\mathbf{k}$ for $0 \le t \le 2\pi$. Therefore the length L of one complete turn of the helix is given by

$$L = \int_0^{2\pi} \sqrt{(-10^{-8}\sin t)^2 + (10^{-8}\cos t)^2 + (3.4\times10^{-8}/2\pi)^2}\,dt$$

$$= \int_0^{2\pi} 10^{-8}\sqrt{\sin^2 t + \cos^2 t + (3.4/2\pi)^2}\,dt = \int_0^{2\pi} 10^{-8}\sqrt{1+(3.4/2\pi)^2}\,dt = 2\pi\sqrt{1+(3.4/2\pi)^2}\,10^{-8}.$$

Since there are approximately 2.9×10^8 turns, the total length of each helix in a DNA molecule is approximately $(2.9\times10^8)(2\pi\sqrt{1+(3.4/2\pi)^2}\,10^{-8}) \approx 20.7$ centimeters.

12.5 Tangents and Normals to Curves

1. $\mathbf{r}'(t) = 2t\mathbf{i} + 2\mathbf{j}$; $\|\mathbf{r}'(t)\| = \sqrt{(2t)^2+2^2} = 2\sqrt{t^2+1}$;

$$\mathbf{T}(t) = \frac{\mathbf{r}'(t)}{\|\mathbf{r}'(t)\|} = \frac{2t\mathbf{i}+2\mathbf{j}}{2\sqrt{t^2+1}} = \frac{t}{\sqrt{t^2+1}}\mathbf{i} + \frac{1}{\sqrt{t^2+1}}\mathbf{j};$$

$$\mathbf{T}'(t) = \frac{\sqrt{t^2+1} - t^2/\sqrt{t^2+1}}{t^2+1}\mathbf{i} - \frac{t}{(t^2+1)^{3/2}}\mathbf{j} = \frac{1}{(t^2+1)^{3/2}}\mathbf{i} - \frac{t}{(t^2+1)^{3/2}}\mathbf{j};$$

$$\|\mathbf{T}'(t)\| = \sqrt{\frac{1}{(t^2+1)^3} + \frac{t^2}{(t^2+1)^3}} = \frac{1}{t^2+1}; \mathbf{N}(t) = \frac{\mathbf{T}'(t)}{\|\mathbf{T}'(t)\|} = \frac{1}{\sqrt{t^2+1}}\mathbf{i} - \frac{t}{\sqrt{t^2+1}}\mathbf{j}$$

2. $\mathbf{r}'(t) = 3\cos^2 t\,(-\sin t)\mathbf{i} + 3\sin^2 t\,\cos t\,\mathbf{j} = -3\sin t\,\cos^2 t\,\mathbf{i} + 3\sin^2 t\,\cos t\,\mathbf{j}$;

$$\|\mathbf{r}'(t)\| = 3\sin t\,\cos t\sqrt{(-\cos t)^2 + (\sin t)^2} = 3\sin t\,\cos t;$$

$$\mathbf{T}(t) = \frac{\mathbf{r}'(t)}{\|\mathbf{r}'(t)\|} = -\cos t\,\mathbf{i} + \sin t\,\mathbf{j}; \mathbf{T}'(t) = \sin t\,\mathbf{i} + \cos t\,\mathbf{j};$$

$$\|\mathbf{T}'(t)\| = \sqrt{\sin^2 t + \cos^2 t} = 1; \mathbf{N}(t) = \frac{\mathbf{T}'(t)}{\|\mathbf{T}'(t)\|} = \sin t\,\mathbf{i} + \cos t\,\mathbf{j}$$

3. $\mathbf{r}'(t) = -\sin t\,\mathbf{i} - \sin t\,\mathbf{j} + \sqrt{2}\cos t\,\mathbf{k}$; $\|\mathbf{r}'(t)\| = \sqrt{(-\sin t)^2 + (-\sin t)^2 + (\sqrt{2}\cos t)^2} = \sqrt{2}$;

$$\mathbf{T}(t) = \frac{\mathbf{r}'(t)}{\|\mathbf{r}'(t)\|} = -\frac{\sin t}{\sqrt{2}}\mathbf{i} - \frac{\sin t}{\sqrt{2}}\mathbf{j} + \cos t\,\mathbf{k}; \mathbf{T}'(t) = -\frac{\cos t}{\sqrt{2}}\mathbf{i} - \frac{\cos t}{\sqrt{2}}\mathbf{j} - \sin t\,\mathbf{k};$$

$$\|\mathbf{T}'(t)\| = \sqrt{\left(\frac{-\cos t}{\sqrt{2}}\right)^2 + \left(\frac{-\cos t}{\sqrt{2}}\right)^2 + (-\sin t)^2} = 1;$$

$$\mathbf{N}(t) = \frac{\mathbf{T}'(t)}{\|\mathbf{T}'(t)\|} = -\frac{\cos t}{\sqrt{2}}\mathbf{i} - \frac{\cos t}{\sqrt{2}}\mathbf{j} - \sin t\,\mathbf{k}$$

4. $\mathbf{r}'(t) = \frac{1}{2}(1+t)^{1/2}\mathbf{i} - \frac{1}{2}(1-t)^{1/2}\mathbf{j} + \frac{\sqrt{2}}{2}\mathbf{k}$; $\|\mathbf{r}'(t)\| = \frac{1}{2}\sqrt{(1+t)+(1-t)+2} = 1$;

$$\mathbf{T}(t)=\frac{\mathbf{r}'(t)}{\|\mathbf{r}'(t)\|}=\frac{1}{2}(1+t)^{1/2}\,\mathbf{i}-\frac{1}{2}(1-t)^{1/2}\,\mathbf{j}+\frac{\sqrt{2}}{2}\,\mathbf{k};\ \mathbf{T}'(t)=\frac{1}{4}(1+t)^{-1/2}\,\mathbf{i}+\frac{1}{4}(1-t)^{-1/2}\,\mathbf{j};$$

$$\|\mathbf{T}'(t)\|=\frac{1}{4}\sqrt{(1+t)^{-1}+(1-t)^{-1}}=\frac{1}{4}\sqrt{\frac{1-t+1+t}{(1+t)(1-t)}}=\frac{1}{4}\sqrt{\frac{2}{1-t^2}};$$

$$\mathbf{N}(t)=\frac{\mathbf{T}'(t)}{\|\mathbf{T}'(t)\|}=\sqrt{\frac{1-t}{2}}\,\mathbf{i}+\sqrt{\frac{1+t}{2}}\,\mathbf{j}$$

5. $\mathbf{r}'(t)=2\mathbf{i}+2t\mathbf{j}+t^2\mathbf{k};\ \|\mathbf{r}'(t)\|=\sqrt{2^2+(2t)^2+(t^2)^2}=\sqrt{4+4t^2+t^4}=2+t^2;$

$$\mathbf{T}(t)=\frac{\mathbf{r}'(t)}{\|\mathbf{r}'(t)\|}=\frac{2}{2+t^2}\,\mathbf{i}+\frac{2t}{2+t^2}\,\mathbf{j}+\frac{t^2}{2+t^2}\,\mathbf{k};$$

$$\mathbf{T}'(t)=\frac{-4t}{(2+t^2)^2}\,\mathbf{i}+\frac{2(2+t^2)-4t^2}{(2+t^2)^2}\,\mathbf{j}+\frac{2t(2+t^2)-2t^3}{(2+t^2)^2}\,\mathbf{k}=\frac{-4t}{(2+t^2)^2}\,\mathbf{i}+\frac{4-2t^2}{(2+t^2)^2}\,\mathbf{j}+\frac{4t}{(2+t^2)^2}\,\mathbf{k};$$

$$\|\mathbf{T}'(t)\|=\frac{1}{(2+t^2)^2}\sqrt{(-4t)^2+(4-2t^2)^2+(4t)^2}=\frac{1}{(2+t^2)^2}\sqrt{16+16t^2+4t^4}=\frac{2}{2+t^2};$$

$$\mathbf{N}(t)=\frac{\mathbf{T}'(t)}{\|\mathbf{T}'(t)\|}=\frac{-2t}{2+t^2}\,\mathbf{i}+\frac{2-t^2}{2+t^2}\,\mathbf{j}+\frac{2t}{2+t^2}\,\mathbf{k}$$

6. $\mathbf{r}'(t)=-\frac{4}{5}\sin t\,\mathbf{i}-\cos t\,\mathbf{j}+\frac{3}{5}\sin t\,\mathbf{k};$

$$\|\mathbf{r}'(t)\|=\sqrt{(\tfrac{-4}{5}\sin t)^2+(-\cos t)^2+(\tfrac{3}{5}\sin t)^2}=\sqrt{\sin^2 t+\cos^2 t}=1;$$

$$\mathbf{T}(t)=\frac{\mathbf{r}'(t)}{\|\mathbf{r}'(t)\|}=-\tfrac{4}{5}\sin t\,\mathbf{i}-\cos t\,\mathbf{j}+\tfrac{3}{5}\sin t\,\mathbf{k};$$

$$\mathbf{T}'(t)=-\tfrac{4}{5}\cos t\,\mathbf{i}+\sin t\,\mathbf{j}+\tfrac{3}{5}\cos t\,\mathbf{k};$$

$$\|\mathbf{T}'(t)\|=\sqrt{(-\tfrac{4}{5}\cos t)^2+\sin^2 t+(\tfrac{3}{5}\cos t)^2}=\sqrt{\cos^2 t+\sin^2 t}=1;$$

$$\mathbf{N}(t)=\frac{\mathbf{T}'(t)}{\|\mathbf{T}'(t)\|}=-\tfrac{4}{5}\cos t\,\mathbf{i}+\sin t\,\mathbf{j}+\tfrac{3}{5}\cos t\,\mathbf{k}$$

7. $\mathbf{r}'(t)=e^t\mathbf{i}-e^{-t}\mathbf{j}+\sqrt{2}\,\mathbf{k};\ \|\mathbf{r}'(t)\|=\sqrt{e^{2t}+e^{-2t}+2}=e^t+e^{-t};$

$$\mathbf{T}(t)=\frac{\mathbf{r}'(t)}{\|\mathbf{r}'(t)\|}=\frac{e^t}{e^t+e^{-t}}\,\mathbf{i}-\frac{e^{-t}}{e^t+e^{-t}}\,\mathbf{j}+\frac{\sqrt{2}}{e^t+e^{-t}}\,\mathbf{k};$$

$$\mathbf{T}'(t)=\frac{e^t(e^t+e^{-t})-e^t(e^t-e^{-t})}{(e^t+e^{-t})^2}\,\mathbf{i}-\frac{-e^{-t}(e^t+e^{-t})-e^{-t}(e^t-e^{-t})}{(e^r+e^{-t})^2}\,\mathbf{j}-\frac{\sqrt{2}\,(e^t-e^{-t})}{(e^t+e^{-t})^2}\,\mathbf{k}$$

$$=\frac{2}{(e^t+e^{-t})^2}\,\mathbf{i}+\frac{2}{(e^t+e^{-t})^2}\,\mathbf{j}-\frac{\sqrt{2}\,(e^t-e^{-t})}{(e^t+e^{-t})^2}\,\mathbf{k};$$

$$\|\mathbf{T}'(t)\|=\frac{1}{(e^t+e^{-t})^2}\sqrt{2^2+2^2+[\sqrt{2}\,(e^{-t}-e^t)]^2}=\frac{\sqrt{2e^{-2t}+4+2e^{2t}}}{(e^t+e^{-t})^2}=\frac{\sqrt{2}}{e^t+e^{-t}};$$

$$\mathbf{N}(t)=\frac{\mathbf{T}'(t)}{\|\mathbf{T}'(t)\|}=\frac{\sqrt{2}}{e^t+e^{-t}}\,\mathbf{i}+\frac{\sqrt{2}}{e^t+e^{-t}}\,\mathbf{j}-\frac{e^t-e^{-t}}{e^t+e^{-t}}\,\mathbf{k}$$

8. $\mathbf{r}'(t) = \sinh t\,\mathbf{i} + \cosh t\,\mathbf{j} + \mathbf{k}$; $\|\mathbf{r}'(t)\| = \sqrt{\sinh^2 t + \cosh^2 t + 1} = \sqrt{2\cosh^2 t} = \sqrt{2}\cosh t$;

$$\mathbf{T}(t) = \frac{\mathbf{r}'(t)}{\|\mathbf{r}'(t)\|} = \frac{\sinh t}{\sqrt{2}\cosh t}\mathbf{i} + \frac{1}{\sqrt{2}}\mathbf{j} + \frac{1}{\sqrt{2}\cosh t}\mathbf{k} = \frac{1}{\sqrt{2}}\tanh t\,\mathbf{i} + \frac{1}{\sqrt{2}}\mathbf{j} + \frac{1}{\sqrt{2}}\operatorname{sech} t\,\mathbf{k};$$

$$\mathbf{T}'(t) = \frac{1}{\sqrt{2}}\operatorname{sech}^2 t\,\mathbf{i} - \frac{1}{\sqrt{2}}\operatorname{sech} t\tanh t\,\mathbf{k};$$

$$\|\mathbf{T}'(t)\| = \frac{1}{\sqrt{2}}\sqrt{\operatorname{sech}^4 t + \operatorname{sech}^2 t\tanh^2 t} = \frac{1}{\sqrt{2}}\operatorname{sech} t\sqrt{\operatorname{sech}^2 t + \tanh^2 t} = \frac{1}{\sqrt{2}}\operatorname{sech} t;$$

$$\mathbf{N}(t) = \frac{\mathbf{T}'(t)}{\|\mathbf{T}'(t)\|} = \operatorname{sech} t\,\mathbf{i} - \tanh t\,\mathbf{k}$$

9. $\mathbf{r}'(t) = 2\mathbf{i} + 2t\mathbf{j} + \frac{1}{t}\mathbf{k}$; $\|\mathbf{r}'(t)\| = \sqrt{2^2 + (2t)^2 + \left(\frac{1}{t}\right)^2} = \sqrt{4t^2 + 4 + \frac{1}{t^2}} = 2t + \frac{1}{t} = \frac{2t^2+1}{t}$;

$$\mathbf{T}(t) = \frac{\mathbf{r}'(t)}{\|\mathbf{r}'(t)\|} = \frac{2t}{2t^2+1}\mathbf{i} + \frac{2t^2}{2t^2+1}\mathbf{j} + \frac{1}{2t^2+1}\mathbf{k};$$

$$\begin{aligned}\mathbf{T}'(t) &= \frac{2(2t^2+1) - 2t(4t)}{(2t^2+1)^2}\mathbf{i} + \frac{4t(2t^2+1) - 2t^2(4t)}{(2t^2+1)^2}\mathbf{j} - \frac{4t}{(2t^2+1)^2}\mathbf{k}\\ &= \frac{2-4t^2}{(2t^2+1)^2}\mathbf{i} + \frac{4t}{(2t^2+1)^2}\mathbf{j} - \frac{4t}{(2t^2+1)^2}\mathbf{k};\end{aligned}$$

$$\|\mathbf{T}'(t)\| = \frac{1}{(2t^2+1)^2}\sqrt{(2-4t^2)^2 + (4t)^2 + (-4t)^2} = \frac{\sqrt{16t^4 + 16t^2 + 4}}{(2t^2+1)^2} = \frac{2}{2t^2+1};$$

$$\mathbf{N}(t) = \frac{\mathbf{T}'(t)}{\|\mathbf{T}'(t)\|} = \frac{1-2t^2}{2t^2+1}\mathbf{i} + \frac{2t}{2t^2+1}\mathbf{j} - \frac{2t}{2t^2+1}\mathbf{k}$$

10. $\mathbf{r}'(t) = 9t^{7/2}\mathbf{i} + \frac{9}{2}\sqrt{2}\,t^2\mathbf{j} + \frac{9}{2}\sqrt{2}\,t^2\mathbf{k}$;

$$\|\mathbf{r}'(t)\| = 9\sqrt{(t^{7/2})^2 + \left(\frac{\sqrt{2}}{2}t^2\right)^2 + \left(\frac{\sqrt{2}}{2}t^2\right)^2} = 9\sqrt{t^7 + t^4} = 9t^2\sqrt{t^3+1};$$

$$\mathbf{T}(t) = \frac{\mathbf{r}'(t)}{\|\mathbf{r}'(t)\|} = \frac{t^{3/2}}{\sqrt{t^3+1}}\mathbf{i} + \frac{\sqrt{2}}{2\sqrt{t^3+1}}\mathbf{j} + \frac{\sqrt{2}}{2\sqrt{t^3+1}}\mathbf{k};$$

$$\begin{aligned}\mathbf{T}'(t) &= \frac{\frac{3}{2}t^{1/2}\sqrt{t^3+1} - t^{3/2}(\frac{1}{2})(t^3+1)^{-1/2}(3t^2)}{t^3+1}\mathbf{i} - \frac{3\sqrt{2}\,t^2}{4}(t^3+1)^{-3/2}\mathbf{j} - \frac{3\sqrt{2}\,t^2}{4}(t^3+1)^{-3/2}\mathbf{k}\\ &= \frac{3t^{1/2}}{2(t^3+1)^{3/2}}\mathbf{i} - \frac{3\sqrt{2}\,t^2}{4(t^3+1)^{3/2}}\mathbf{j} - \frac{3\sqrt{2}\,t^2}{4(t^3+1)^{3/2}}\mathbf{k};\end{aligned}$$

$$\|\mathbf{T}'(t)\| = \frac{3}{2(t^3+1)^{3/2}}\sqrt{(t^{1/2})^2 + \left(-\frac{\sqrt{2}\,t^2}{2}\right)^2 + \left(-\frac{\sqrt{2}\,t^2}{2}\right)^2} = \frac{3t^{1/2}}{2(t^3+1)};$$

$$\mathbf{N}(t) = \frac{\mathbf{T}'(t)}{\|\mathbf{T}'(t)\|} = \frac{1}{(t^3+1)^{1/2}}\mathbf{i} - \frac{\sqrt{2}\,t^{3/2}}{2(t^3+1)^{1/2}}\mathbf{j} - \frac{\sqrt{2}\,t^{3/2}}{2(t^3+1)^{1/2}}\mathbf{k}$$

11. $\mathbf{v} = r(1-\cos t)\mathbf{i} + r\sin t\,\mathbf{j}$; $\|\mathbf{v}\| = \sqrt{r^2(1-\cos t)^2 + r^2\sin^2 t} = \sqrt{2r^2(1-\cos t)}$;

$$a_{\mathrm{T}} = \frac{d\,\|\mathbf{v}\|}{dt} = \frac{r^2\sin t}{\sqrt{2r^2(1-\cos t)}};\ \mathbf{a} = \frac{d\mathbf{v}}{dt} = r\sin t\,\mathbf{i} + r\cos t\,\mathbf{j};$$

$$\|\mathbf{a}\|^2 = r^2\sin^2 t + r^2\cos^2 t = r^2;$$

$$a_{\mathrm{N}} = \sqrt{\|\mathbf{a}\|^2 - a_{\mathrm{T}}^2} = \sqrt{r^2 - \frac{r^4\sin^2 t}{2r^2(1-\cos t)}} = \sqrt{r^2 - \frac{r^2(1-\cos^2 t)}{2(1-\cos t)}} = \frac{|r|}{\sqrt{2}}\sqrt{1-\cos t}$$

12. $\mathbf{v} = -2\sin t\,\mathbf{i} + 3\cos t\,\mathbf{j}$; $\|\mathbf{v}\| = \sqrt{4\sin^2 t + 9\cos^2 t} = \sqrt{4+5\cos^2 t}$;

$$a_{\mathrm{T}} = \frac{d\,\|\mathbf{v}\|}{dt} = \frac{-5\cos t\,\sin t}{\sqrt{4+5\cos^2 t}};\ \mathbf{a} = -2\cos t\,\mathbf{i} - 3\sin t\,\mathbf{j};$$

$$\|\mathbf{a}\|^2 = 4\cos^2 t + 9\sin^2 t = 4 + 5\sin^2 t;$$

$$a_{\mathrm{N}} = \sqrt{\|\mathbf{a}\|^2 - a_{\mathrm{T}}^2} = \sqrt{4+5\sin^2 t - \frac{25\cos^2 t\,\sin^2 t}{4+5\cos^2 t}} = \sqrt{\frac{16+20(\cos^2 t+\sin^2 t)}{4+5\cos^2 t}} = \frac{6}{\sqrt{4+5\cos^2 t}}$$

13. $\mathbf{v} = 2\mathbf{i} + 2t\mathbf{j} + t^2\mathbf{k}$; $\|\mathbf{v}\| = \sqrt{4+4t^2+t^4} = 2+t^2$; $a_{\mathrm{T}} = \dfrac{d\,\|\mathbf{v}\|}{dt} = 2t$;

$$\mathbf{a} = 2\mathbf{j} + 2t\mathbf{k};\ \|\mathbf{a}\|^2 = 4(1+t^2);\ a_{\mathrm{N}} = \sqrt{\|\mathbf{a}\|^2 - a_{\mathrm{T}}^2} = \sqrt{4(1+t^2)-4t^2} = 2$$

14. $\mathbf{v} = -\frac{4}{5}\sin t\,\mathbf{i} - \cos t\,\mathbf{j} + \frac{3}{5}\sin t\,\mathbf{k}$; $\|\mathbf{v}\| = \sqrt{\frac{16}{25}\sin^2 t + \cos^2 t + \frac{9}{25}\sin^2 t} = 1$;

$$a_{\mathrm{T}} = \frac{d\,\|\mathbf{v}\|}{dt} = 0;\ \mathbf{a} = -\tfrac{4}{5}\cos t\,\mathbf{i} + \sin t\,\mathbf{j} + \tfrac{3}{5}\cos t\,\mathbf{k};$$

$$\|\mathbf{a}\|^2 = \tfrac{16}{25}\cos^2 t + \sin^2 t + \tfrac{9}{25}\cos^2 t = 1;\ a_{\mathrm{N}} = \sqrt{\|\mathbf{a}\|^2 - a_{\mathrm{T}}^2} = \sqrt{1-0} = 1$$

15. $\mathbf{v} = e^t\mathbf{i} - e^{-t}\mathbf{j} + \sqrt{2}\,\mathbf{k}$; $\|\mathbf{v}\| = \sqrt{e^{2t}+e^{-2t}+2} = e^t + e^{-t}$; $a_{\mathrm{T}} = \dfrac{d\,\|\mathbf{v}\|}{dt} = e^t - e^{-t}$;

$$\mathbf{a} = e^t\mathbf{i} + e^{-t}\mathbf{j};\ \|\mathbf{a}\|^2 = e^{2t} + e^{-2t};\ a_{\mathrm{N}} = \sqrt{\|\mathbf{a}\|^2 - a_{\mathrm{T}}^2} = \sqrt{(e^{2t}+e^{-2t}) - (e^t - e^{-t})^2} = \sqrt{2}$$

16. $\mathbf{r}(t) = -2\mathbf{i} + (-2+3\cos t)\mathbf{j} - (1+3\sin t)\mathbf{k}$ for $0 \le t \le 2\pi$

17. $\mathbf{r}(t) = -4\sin t\,\mathbf{j} + 4\cos t\,\mathbf{k}$ for $0 \le t \le 2\pi$

18. $$\mathbf{r}(t) = \begin{cases} t\mathbf{i} & \text{for } 0 \le t \le 1 \\ \cos\frac{\pi}{2}(t-1)\,\mathbf{i} + \sin\frac{\pi}{2}(t-1)\,\mathbf{j} & \text{for } 1 \le t \le 2 \\ (3-t)\mathbf{j} & \text{for } 2 \le t \le 3 \end{cases}$$

19. $$\mathbf{r}(t) = \begin{cases} t\mathbf{i} + t^2\mathbf{j} & \text{for } 0 \le t \le 1 \\ (2-t)\mathbf{i} + (2-t)\mathbf{j} & \text{for } 1 \le t \le 2 \end{cases}$$

20. $$\mathbf{r}(t) = \begin{cases} 4(1-t)\mathbf{i} + 3t\mathbf{j} & \text{for } 0 \le t \le 1 \\ 3(2-t)\mathbf{j} + 5(t-1)\mathbf{k} & \text{for } 1 \le t \le 2 \\ 4(t-2)\mathbf{i} + 5(3-t)\mathbf{k} & \text{for } 2 \le t \le 3 \end{cases}$$

21. $\mathbf{r}(t) = \begin{cases} (t+1)\mathbf{i} & \text{for } 0 \le t \le 1 \\ 2\cos\frac{\pi}{2}(t-1)\,\mathbf{i} + 2\sin\frac{\pi}{2}(t-1)\,\mathbf{j} & \text{for } 1 \le t \le 2 \\ (4-t)\mathbf{j} & \text{for } 2 \le t \le 3 \\ \sin\frac{\pi}{2}(t-3)\,\mathbf{i} + \cos\frac{\pi}{2}(t-3)\,\mathbf{j} & \text{for } 3 \le t \le 4 \end{cases}$

22. Since $\mathbf{r}_1(0) = \mathbf{j} = \mathbf{r}_2(0)$, the two curves intersect at $(0,1,0)$. Since $\mathbf{r}_1'(t) = (t+1)\mathbf{i} + \mathbf{j} - \mathbf{k}$ and $\mathbf{r}_2'(t) = \cos t\,\mathbf{i} + e^t\mathbf{j} - \sec^2 t\,\mathbf{k}$, we have $\mathbf{r}_1'(0) = \mathbf{i}+\mathbf{j}-\mathbf{k}$ and $\mathbf{r}_2'(0) = \mathbf{i}+\mathbf{j}-\mathbf{k}$, so that the vectors tangent to the two curves at $(0,1,0)$ are parallel.

23. Since $\mathbf{r}_1(t) = \mathbf{i} + 2\mathbf{j} + \mathbf{k} = \mathbf{r}_2(-1)$, the two curves intersect at $(1,2,1)$. Since $\mathbf{r}_1'(t) = \mathbf{i} + 2\mathbf{j} + 2t\mathbf{k}$ and $\mathbf{r}_2'(t) = 2t\mathbf{i} - \mathbf{j} - 2t\mathbf{k}$, we have $\mathbf{r}_1'(1) = \mathbf{i}+2\mathbf{j}+2\mathbf{k}$ and $\mathbf{r}_2'(-1) = -2\mathbf{i}-\mathbf{j}+2\mathbf{k}$. Thus $\mathbf{T}_1(1) = \frac{1}{3}(\mathbf{i}+2\mathbf{j}+2\mathbf{k})$ and $\mathbf{T}_2(-1) = \frac{1}{3}(-2\mathbf{i} - \mathbf{j} + 2\mathbf{k})$, so that $\mathbf{T}_1(1)\cdot\mathbf{T}_2(-1) = \frac{1}{9}(-2-2+4) = 0$. Thus the two tangent vectors are perpendicular.

24. $\dfrac{d}{dt}\left(\|\mathbf{v}\|^2\right) = \dfrac{d}{dt}(\mathbf{v}\cdot\mathbf{v}) = \dfrac{d\mathbf{v}}{dt}\cdot\mathbf{v} + \mathbf{v}\cdot\dfrac{d\mathbf{v}}{dt} = 2\mathbf{v}\cdot\mathbf{a} = 0$, so that $\|\mathbf{v}\|^2$, and hence $\|\mathbf{v}\|$, is constant.

25. Since $a_\mathbf{T} = d\,\|\mathbf{v}\|\,/dt$, it follows from Theorem 4.6 that $a_\mathbf{T} = 0$ only if $\|\mathbf{v}\|$ is constant.

26. Let $\mathbf{r}$ be a smooth parametrization of a curve lying on the sphere. Then $\|\mathbf{r}\| = c$ for some constant c, so that by Corollary 12.11, $\mathbf{r}\cdot\dfrac{d\mathbf{r}}{dt} = 0$. Since $\mathbf{T} = \dfrac{d\mathbf{r}/dt}{\|d\mathbf{r}/dt\|}$, it follows that $\mathbf{r}\cdot\mathbf{T} = \dfrac{1}{\|d\mathbf{r}/dt\|}\left(\mathbf{r}\cdot\dfrac{d\mathbf{r}}{dt}\right) = 0$, so that $\mathbf{r}$ and $\mathbf{T}$ are perpendicular.

27. Let $\mathbf{r}(t) = t\,\mathbf{i} + \sin t\,\mathbf{j}$. Then $d\mathbf{r}/dt = \mathbf{i} + \cos t\,\mathbf{j}$ and $\|d\mathbf{r}/dt\| = \sqrt{1+\cos^2 t}$. Therefore

$$\mathbf{T}(t) = \frac{1}{\sqrt{1+\cos^2 t}}\,\mathbf{i} + \frac{\cos t}{\sqrt{1+\cos^2 t}}\,\mathbf{j}.$$

Thus

$$\mathbf{T}'(t) = \frac{\sin t\,\cos t}{(1+\cos^2 t)^{3/2}}\,\mathbf{i} - \frac{\sin t}{(1+\cos^2 t)^{3/2}}\,\mathbf{j}.$$

But $\mathbf{T}'(t) = \mathbf{0}$ if $t = n\pi$, so $\mathbf{N}(n\pi)$ fails to exist, for all integers n.

28. $\dfrac{d\mathbf{r}}{dt} = x'(t)\mathbf{i} + y'(t)\mathbf{j}$ and $\left\|\dfrac{d\mathbf{r}}{dt}\right\| = \sqrt{\left(x'(t)\right)^2 + \left(y'(t)\right)^2}$, so

$$\mathbf{T}(t) = \frac{x'(t)}{\sqrt{\left(x'(t)\right)^2 + \left(y'(t)\right)^2}}\,\mathbf{i} + \frac{y'(t)}{\sqrt{\left(x'(t)\right)^2 + \left(y'(t)\right)^2}}\,\mathbf{j}.$$

29. By (3), (4), and (7),

$$(\mathbf{v}\cdot\mathbf{v})\,\mathbf{a} - (\mathbf{v}\cdot\mathbf{a})\,\mathbf{v} = \|\mathbf{v}\|^2\left(\frac{\mathbf{v}\cdot\mathbf{a}}{\|\mathbf{v}\|}\,\mathbf{T} + \frac{\|\mathbf{v}\times\mathbf{a}\|}{\|\mathbf{v}\|}\,\mathbf{N}\right) - (\mathbf{v}\cdot\mathbf{a})\,\|\mathbf{v}\|\,\mathbf{T} = \|\mathbf{v}\|\,\|\mathbf{v}\times\mathbf{a}\|\,\mathbf{N}.$$

Using the fact that $\mathbf{N}$ is a unit vector, and dividing each side of the previous equation by its length, we conclude that

$$\mathbf{N} = \frac{(\mathbf{v}\cdot\mathbf{v})\mathbf{a} - (\mathbf{v}\cdot\mathbf{a})\mathbf{v}}{\|(\mathbf{v}\cdot\mathbf{v})\mathbf{a} - (\mathbf{v}\cdot\mathbf{a})\mathbf{v}\|}.$$

30. $\mathbf{r}(t) = 2\cos t\,\mathbf{i} + 2\sin t\,\mathbf{j} + 3t\,\mathbf{k}$; $\mathbf{v}(t) = -2\sin t\,\mathbf{i} + 2\cos t\,\mathbf{j} + 3\mathbf{k}$; $\mathbf{a}(t) = -2\cos t\,\mathbf{i} - 2\sin t\,\mathbf{j}$. Thus

$$\mathbf{v}(t) \times \mathbf{a}(t) = \begin{vmatrix} \mathbf{i} & \mathbf{j} & \mathbf{k} \\ -2\sin t & 2\cos t & 3 \\ -2\cos t & -2\sin t & 0 \end{vmatrix} = 6\sin t\,\mathbf{i} - 6\cos t\,\mathbf{j} + 4\,\mathbf{k}$$

and

$$\|\mathbf{v}(t) \times \mathbf{a}(t)\| = \sqrt{(6\sin t)^2 + (-6\cos t)^2 + 4^2} = \sqrt{6^2 + 4^2} = \sqrt{52}.$$

By (8),

$$\mathbf{B} = \frac{\mathbf{v} \times \mathbf{a}}{\|\mathbf{v} \times \mathbf{a}\|} = \frac{1}{\sqrt{52}}(6\sin t\,\mathbf{i} - 6\cos t\,\mathbf{j} + 4\mathbf{k}) = \frac{1}{\sqrt{13}}(3\sin t\,\mathbf{i} - 3\cos t\,\mathbf{j} + 2\mathbf{k}).$$

31. a. By (3) and (4),

$$\mathbf{v} \times \mathbf{a} = \|\mathbf{v}\|\,\mathbf{T} \times \left(\frac{d\|\mathbf{v}\|}{dt}\mathbf{T} + \|\mathbf{v}\|\left\|\frac{d\mathbf{T}}{dt}\right\|\mathbf{N}\right) = \|\mathbf{v}\|^2\left\|\frac{d\mathbf{T}}{dt}\right\|\mathbf{T} \times \mathbf{N}.$$

Therefore $\mathbf{v} \times \mathbf{a}$ and $\mathbf{T} \times \mathbf{N}$ point in the same direction.

b. It follows from (a) that $\mathbf{B} = \mathbf{T} \times \mathbf{N} = c\mathbf{v} \times \mathbf{a}$, where $c > 0$. Since $\mathbf{B}$ is a unit vector, we have $1 = \|\mathbf{B}\| = c\|\mathbf{v} \times \mathbf{a}\|$, so that $c = 1/\|\mathbf{v} \times \mathbf{a}\|$. Thus

$$\mathbf{B} = c\mathbf{v} \times \mathbf{a} = \frac{\mathbf{v} \times \mathbf{a}}{\|\mathbf{v} \times \mathbf{a}\|}.$$

32. By (6) in Section 11.4, $\mathbf{N}(t) \times \mathbf{B}(t) = \mathbf{N}(t) \times (\mathbf{T}(t) \times \mathbf{N}(t)) = (\mathbf{N}(t) \cdot \mathbf{N}(t))\mathbf{T}(t) - (\mathbf{N}(t) \cdot \mathbf{T}(t))\mathbf{N}(t) = \mathbf{T}(t)$, since $\mathbf{N}(t)$ is a unit vector and $\mathbf{N}(t)$ and $\mathbf{T}(t)$ are perpendicular.

33. a. From (9) and (10), $\tan\theta = \dfrac{\|\mathbf{F}_n\|\sin\theta}{\|\mathbf{F}_n\|\cos\theta} = \dfrac{mv_R^2/\rho}{mg} = \dfrac{v_R^2}{\rho g}$, so that $v_R^2 = \rho g \tan\theta$.

b. $v_R = \sqrt{\rho g \tan\theta} = \sqrt{500(32)\tan(\pi/12)} \approx 65.5$ (feet per second), or 44.6 (miles per hour).

c. If ρ' and $v_{R'}$ are the new radius and rated speed, respectively, then $v_{R'} = 2v_R$ if $\sqrt{\rho' g \tan\theta} = 2\sqrt{\rho g \tan\theta} = \sqrt{4\rho g \tan\theta}$, so that $\rho' = 4\rho$. Since $\rho = 500$, it follows that if $\rho' = 2000$ (feet), then the rated speed will be doubled.

12.6 Curvature

1. From Exercise 1 in Section 12.5, $\kappa(t) = \dfrac{\|\mathbf{T}'(t)\|}{\|\mathbf{r}'(t)\|} = \dfrac{1/(t^2+1)}{2\sqrt{t^2+1}} = \dfrac{1}{2(t^2+1)^{3/2}}$.

2. From Exercise 2 in Section 12.5, $\kappa(t) = \dfrac{\|\mathbf{T}'(t)\|}{\|\mathbf{r}'(t)\|} = \dfrac{1}{3\sin t\,\cos t}$.

3. From Exercise 3 in Section 12.5, $\kappa(t) = \dfrac{\|\mathbf{T}'(t)\|}{\|\mathbf{r}'(t)\|} = \dfrac{1}{\sqrt{2}}$.

4. From Exercise 4 in Section 12.5, $\kappa(t) = \dfrac{\|\mathbf{T}'(t)\|}{\|\mathbf{r}'(t)\|} = \dfrac{1}{4}\sqrt{\dfrac{2}{1-t^2}}$.

5. From Exercise 5 in Section 12.5, $\kappa(t) = \dfrac{\|\mathbf{T}'(t)\|}{\|\mathbf{r}'(t)\|} = \dfrac{2/(2+t^2)}{2+t^2} = \dfrac{2}{(2+t^2)^2}$.

6. From Exercise 6 in Section 12.5, $\kappa(t) = \dfrac{\|\mathbf{T}'(t)\|}{\|\mathbf{r}'(t)\|} = 1$.

7. From Exercise 7 in Section 12.5, $\kappa(t) = \dfrac{\|\mathbf{T}'(t)\|}{\|\mathbf{r}'(t)\|} = \dfrac{\sqrt{2}/(e^t+e^{-t})}{e^t+e^{-t}} = \dfrac{\sqrt{2}}{(e^t+e^{-t})^2}$.

8. From Exercise 8 in Section 12.5, $\kappa(t) = \dfrac{\|\mathbf{T}'(t)\|}{\|\mathbf{r}'(t)\|} = \dfrac{(\operatorname{sech} t)/\sqrt{2}}{\sqrt{2}\cosh t} = \dfrac{1}{2\cosh^2 t}$.

9. From Exercise 9 in Section 12.5, $\kappa(t) = \dfrac{\|\mathbf{T}'(t)\|}{\|\mathbf{r}'(t)\|} = \dfrac{2/(2t^2+1)}{(2t^2+1)/t} = \dfrac{2t}{(2t^2+1)^2}$.

10. From Exercise 10 in Section 12.5, $\kappa(t) = \dfrac{\|\mathbf{T}'(t)\|}{\|\mathbf{r}'(t)\|} = \dfrac{3t^{1/2}/[2(t^3+1)]}{9t^2\sqrt{t^3+1}} = \dfrac{1}{6t^{3/2}(t^3+1)^{3/2}}$.

11. $\mathbf{v} = \dfrac{d\mathbf{r}}{dt} = 2\mathbf{i} + 2t\mathbf{j}$; $\|\mathbf{v}\| = \sqrt{2^2+(2t)^2} = 2\sqrt{1+t^2}$; $\mathbf{a} = \dfrac{d\mathbf{v}}{dt} = 2\mathbf{j}$; $\mathbf{v}\times\mathbf{a} = \begin{vmatrix} \mathbf{i} & \mathbf{j} & \mathbf{k} \\ 2 & 2t & 0 \\ 0 & 2 & 0 \end{vmatrix} = 4\mathbf{k}$;

$\|\mathbf{v}\times\mathbf{a}\| = 4$; $\kappa = \dfrac{\|\mathbf{v}\times\mathbf{a}\|}{\|\mathbf{v}\|^3} = \dfrac{4}{(2\sqrt{1+t^2})^3} = \dfrac{1}{2(1+t^2)^{3/2}}$

12. $\mathbf{v} = \dfrac{d\mathbf{r}}{dt} = (\cos t - t\sin t)\mathbf{i} + (\sin t + t\cos t)\mathbf{j}$;

$$\begin{aligned}\|\mathbf{v}\| &= \sqrt{(\cos t - t\sin t)^2 + (\sin t + t\cos t)^2} \\ &= \sqrt{\cos^2 t - 2t\cos t\,\sin t + t^2\sin^2 t + \sin^2 t + 2t\sin t\,\cos t + t^2\cos^2 t} = \sqrt{1+t^2};\end{aligned}$$

$\mathbf{a} = \dfrac{d\mathbf{v}}{dt} = (-\sin t - \sin t - t\cos t)\mathbf{i} + (\cos t + \cos t - t\sin t)\mathbf{j} = -2(\sin t + t\cos t)\mathbf{i} + (2\cos t - t\sin t)\mathbf{j}$;

$$\mathbf{v}\times\mathbf{a} = \begin{vmatrix} \mathbf{i} & \mathbf{j} & \mathbf{k} \\ \cos t - t\sin t & \sin t + t\cos t & 0 \\ -(2\sin t + t\cos t) & 2\cos t - t\sin t & 0 \end{vmatrix} = (2+t^2)\mathbf{k};\ \kappa = \frac{\|\mathbf{v}\times\mathbf{a}\|}{\|\mathbf{v}\|^3} = \frac{2+t^2}{(1+t^2)^{3/2}}$$

13. $\mathbf{v} = \dfrac{d\mathbf{r}}{dt} = e^t(\sin t + \cos t)\mathbf{i} + e^t(\cos t - \sin t)\mathbf{j} + \mathbf{k}$;

$$\begin{aligned}\|\mathbf{v}\| &= \sqrt{e^{2t}(\sin t + \cos t)^2 + e^{2t}(\cos t - \sin t)^2 + 1} \\ &= \sqrt{e^{2t}(\sin^2 t + 2\sin t\,\cos t + \cos^2 t + \cos^2 t - 2\cos t\sin t + \sin^2 t) + 1} = \sqrt{2e^{2t}+1};\end{aligned}$$

$\mathbf{a} = \dfrac{d\mathbf{v}}{dt} = [e^t(\sin t + \cos t) + e^t(\cos t - \sin t)]\mathbf{i} + [e^t(\cos t - \sin t) + e^t(-\sin t - \cos t)]\mathbf{j} = 2e^t\cos t\,\mathbf{i} - 2e^t\sin t\,\mathbf{j}$;

$$\mathbf{v}\times\mathbf{a} = \begin{vmatrix} \mathbf{i} & \mathbf{j} & \mathbf{k} \\ e^t(\sin t + \cos t) & e^t(\cos t - \sin t) & 1 \\ 2e^t\cos t & -2e^t\sin t & 0 \end{vmatrix} = 2e^t\sin t\,\mathbf{i} + 2e^t\cos t\,\mathbf{j} - 2e^{2t}\mathbf{k};$$

$\|\mathbf{v}\times\mathbf{a}\| = 2e^t\sqrt{\sin^2 t + \cos^2 t + (-e^t)^2} = 2e^t\sqrt{1+e^{2t}}$; $\kappa = \dfrac{\|\mathbf{v}\times\mathbf{a}\|}{\|\mathbf{v}\|^3} = \dfrac{2e^t(1+e^{2t})^{1/2}}{(2e^{2t}+1)^{3/2}}$

14. $\mathbf{v} = \dfrac{d\mathbf{r}}{dt} = t(t^2-1)^{1/2}\mathbf{i} + \dfrac{\sqrt{2}}{2}t\mathbf{j} + \dfrac{\sqrt{2}}{2}t\mathbf{k}$; $\|\mathbf{v}\| = \sqrt{t^2(t^2-1)+\frac{1}{2}t^2+\frac{1}{2}t^2} = t^2$;

$$\mathbf{a} = \left[(t^2-1)^{1/2} + \frac{t^2}{(t^2-1)^{1/2}}\right]\mathbf{i} + \frac{\sqrt{2}}{2}\mathbf{j} + \frac{\sqrt{2}}{2}\mathbf{k} = \frac{2t^2-1}{(t^2-1)^{1/2}}\mathbf{i} + \frac{\sqrt{2}}{2}\mathbf{j} + \frac{\sqrt{2}}{2}\mathbf{k};$$

$$\mathbf{v}\times\mathbf{a} = \begin{vmatrix} \mathbf{i} & \mathbf{j} & \mathbf{k} \\ t(t^2-1)^{1/2} & \frac{\sqrt{2}}{2}t & \frac{\sqrt{2}}{2}t \\ \frac{2t^2-1}{(t^2-1)^{1/2}} & \frac{\sqrt{2}}{2} & \frac{\sqrt{2}}{2} \end{vmatrix} = \frac{\sqrt{2}t^3}{2(t^2-1)^{1/2}}\mathbf{j} - \frac{\sqrt{2}t^3}{2(t^2-1)^{1/2}}\mathbf{k};$$

$$\|\mathbf{v}\times\mathbf{a}\| = \frac{|t^3|}{(t^2-1)^{1/2}};\ \kappa = \frac{\|\mathbf{v}\times\mathbf{a}\|}{\|\mathbf{v}\|^3} = \frac{|t^3|\,/(t^2-1)^{1/2}}{t^6} = \frac{1}{|t^3|\,(t^2-1)^{1/2}}$$

15. $\mathbf{v} = \dfrac{d\mathbf{r}}{dt} = \cos t\,\mathbf{i} - \sin t\,\mathbf{j} + t^{1/2}\mathbf{k}$; $\|\mathbf{v}\| = \sqrt{\cos^2 t + \sin^2 t + t} = \sqrt{1+t}$;

$$\mathbf{a} = \frac{d\mathbf{v}}{dt} = -\sin t\,\mathbf{i} - \cos t\,\mathbf{j} + \tfrac{1}{2}t^{-1/2}\mathbf{k};$$

$$\mathbf{v}\times\mathbf{a} = \begin{vmatrix} \mathbf{i} & \mathbf{j} & \mathbf{k} \\ \cos t & -\sin t & t^{1/2} \\ -\sin t & -\cos t & \frac{1}{2}t^{-1/2} \end{vmatrix} = \left(-\tfrac{1}{2}t^{-1/2}\sin t + t^{1/2}\cos t\right)\mathbf{i} + \left(-t^{1/2}\sin t - \tfrac{1}{2}t^{-1/2}\cos t\right)\mathbf{j} - \mathbf{k};$$

$$\begin{aligned}\|\mathbf{v}\times\mathbf{a}\| &= \sqrt{(-\tfrac{1}{2}t^{-1/2}\sin t + t^{1/2}\cos t)^2 + (-t^{1/2}\sin t - \tfrac{1}{2}t^{-1/2}\cos t)^2 + 1} \\ &= \sqrt{\tfrac{1}{4}t^{-1}\sin^2 t - \sin t\,\cos t + t\cos^2 t + t\sin^2 t + \sin t\,\cos t + \tfrac{1}{4}t^{-1}\cos^2 t + 1} \\ &= \sqrt{\tfrac{1}{4}t^{-1} + 1 + t} = \sqrt{\frac{1+4t+4t^2}{4t}} = \frac{2t+1}{2\sqrt{t}};\end{aligned}$$

$$\kappa = \frac{\|\mathbf{v}\times\mathbf{a}\|}{\|\mathbf{v}\|^3} = \frac{(2t+1)/(2\sqrt{t})}{(\sqrt{1+t})^3} = \frac{2t+1}{2\sqrt{t}\,(1+t)^{3/2}}$$

16. $x = 2\cos t$, $\dfrac{dx}{dt} = -2\sin t$, $\dfrac{d^2x}{dt^2} = -2\cos t$; $y = 3\sin t$, $\dfrac{dy}{dt} = 3\cos t$, $\dfrac{d^2y}{dt^2} = -3\sin t$;

$$\kappa = \frac{\left|\dfrac{dx}{dt}\dfrac{d^2y}{dt^2} - \dfrac{d^2x}{dt^2}\dfrac{dy}{dt}\right|}{\left[\left(\dfrac{dx}{dt}\right)^2 + \left(\dfrac{dy}{dt}\right)^2\right]^{3/2}} = \frac{|6\sin^2 t + 6\cos^2 t|}{(4\sin^2 t + 9\cos^2 t)^{3/2}} = \frac{6}{(4\sin^2 t + 9\cos^2 t)^{3/2}}$$

$$= \frac{6}{(4+5\cos^2 t)^{3/2}};$$

for $t_0 = 0$, $\kappa = 6/9^{3/2} = \frac{2}{9}$, so that $\rho = 1/\kappa = \frac{9}{2}$.

17. By the solution of Exercise 16, $\kappa = 6/(4+5\cos^2 t)^{3/2}$; for $t_0 = \pi/2$, $\kappa = 6/4^{3/2} = \frac{3}{4}$, so that $\rho = 1/\kappa = \frac{4}{3}$.

18. $x = 2\cosh t$, $\dfrac{dx}{dt} = 2\sinh t$, $\dfrac{d^2x}{dt^2} = 2\cosh t$; $y = 3\sinh t$, $\dfrac{dy}{dt} = 3\cosh t$, $\dfrac{d^2y}{dt^2} = 3\sinh t$;

$$\kappa = \frac{\left|\frac{dx}{dt}\frac{d^2y}{dt^2} - \frac{d^2x}{dt^2}\frac{dy}{dt}\right|}{\left[\left(\frac{dx}{dt}\right)^2 + \left(\frac{dy}{dt}\right)^2\right]^{3/2}} = \frac{|6\sinh^2 t - 6\cosh^2 t|}{(4\sinh^2 t + 9\cosh^2 t)^{3/2}} = \frac{6}{(4\sinh^2 t + 9\cosh^2 t)^{3/2}};$$

for $t_0 = 0$, $\kappa = 6/9^{3/2} = \frac{2}{9}$, so that $\rho = 1/\kappa = \frac{9}{2}$.

19. $x = t$, $\dfrac{dx}{dt} = 1$, $\dfrac{d^2x}{dt^2} = 0$; $y = \dfrac{1}{3}t^3$, $\dfrac{dy}{dt} = t^2$, $\dfrac{d^2y}{dt^2} = 2t$;

$$\kappa = \frac{\left|\frac{dx}{dt}\frac{d^2y}{dt^2} - \frac{d^2x}{dt^2}\frac{dy}{dt}\right|}{\left[\left(\frac{dx}{dt}\right)^2 + \left(\frac{dy}{dt}\right)^2\right]^{3/2}} = \frac{2|t|}{(1+t^4)^{3/2}};\ \text{for } t_0 = 1,\ \kappa = \frac{2}{2^{3/2}} = \frac{1}{\sqrt{2}},\ \text{so that } \rho = \frac{1}{\kappa} = \sqrt{2}.$$

20. $\dfrac{dy}{dx} = \cos x$, $\dfrac{d^2y}{dx^2} = -\sin x$; $\kappa = \dfrac{|d^2y/dx^2|}{[1 + (dy/dx)^2]^{3/2}} = \dfrac{\sin x}{(1 + \cos^2 x)^{3/2}}$

21. $\dfrac{dy}{dx} = \dfrac{1}{x}$, $\dfrac{d^2y}{dx^2} = -\dfrac{1}{x^2}$; $\kappa = \dfrac{|d^2y/dx^2|}{[1 + (dy/dx)^2]^{3/2}} = \dfrac{1/x^2}{(1 + 1/x^2)^{3/2}} = \dfrac{x}{(1 + x^2)^{3/2}}$

22. $\dfrac{dy}{dx} = \dfrac{1}{3}x^{-2/3}$, $\dfrac{d^2y}{dx^2} = -\dfrac{2}{9}x^{-5/3}$;

$$\kappa = \frac{|d^2y/dx^2|}{[1 + (dy/dx)^2]^{3/2}} = \frac{\frac{2}{9}x^{-5/3}}{(1 + \frac{1}{9}x^{-4/3})^{3/2}} = \frac{6x^{1/3}}{(9x^{4/3} + 1)^{3/2}}$$

23. $\dfrac{dy}{dx} = -\dfrac{1}{x^2}$, $\dfrac{d^2y}{dx^2} = \dfrac{2}{x^3}$; $\kappa = \dfrac{|d^2y/dx^2|}{[1 + (dy/dx)^2]^{3/2}} = \dfrac{-2/x^3}{(1 + 1/x^4)^{3/2}} = \dfrac{-2x^3}{(1 + x^4)^{3/2}}$

24. $x = 3\cos t$, $\dfrac{dx}{dt} = -3\sin t$, $\dfrac{d^2x}{dt^2} = -3\cos t$; $y = 2\sin t$, $\dfrac{dy}{dt} = 2\cos t$, $\dfrac{d^2y}{dt^2} = -2\sin t$;

$$\kappa = \frac{\left|\frac{dx}{dt}\frac{d^2y}{dt^2} - \frac{d^2x}{dt^2}\frac{dy}{dt}\right|}{\left[\left(\frac{dx}{dt}\right)^2 + \left(\frac{dy}{dt}\right)^2\right]^{3/2}} = \frac{|6\sin^2 t + 6\cos^2 t|}{(9\sin^2 t + 4\cos^2 t)^{3/2}} = \frac{6}{(4 + 5\sin^2 t)^{3/2}}$$

Evidently the curvature is maximum when the denominator is smallest (namely for $\sin t = 0$), and is minimum when the denominator is largest (namely for $\sin t = \pm 1$). Since $\sin t = 0$ if $t = 0$ or $t = \pi$, and $\sin t = \pm 1$ if $t = \pi/2$ or $-\pi/2$, it follows that the curvature is maximum at the points $(3\cos 0, 2\sin 0) = (3, 0)$ and $(3\cos\pi, 2\sin\pi) = (-3, 0)$, and is minimum at the points $(3\cos(\pi/2), 2\sin(\pi/2)) = (0, 2)$ and $(3\cos(-\pi/2), 2\sin(-\pi/2)) = (0, -2)$.

25. $\dfrac{dy}{dx} = e^x = \dfrac{d^2y}{dx^2}$; $\kappa = \dfrac{|d^2y/dx^2|}{[1 + (dy/dx)^2]^{3/2}} = \dfrac{e^x}{(1 + e^{2x})^{3/2}}$;

$$\frac{d\kappa}{dx} = \frac{e^x(1 + e^{2x})^{3/2} - e^x(\frac{3}{2})(1 + e^{2x})^{1/2}(2e^{2x})}{(1 + e^{2x})^3} = \frac{e^x - 2e^{3x}}{(1 + e^{2x})^{5/2}} = \frac{e^x(1 - 2e^{2x})}{(1 + e^{2x})^{5/2}}$$

$d\kappa/dx = 0$ if $1 - 2e^{2x} = 0$, or $x = -\frac{1}{2}\ln 2$. Since $d\kappa/dx > 0$ for $x < -\frac{1}{2}\ln 2$, and $d\kappa/dx < 0$ for $x > -\frac{1}{2}\ln 2$, κ is maximum at $(-\frac{1}{2}\ln 2, \sqrt{2}/2)$.

26. a. $\displaystyle\lim_{x\to-1^-} \frac{f(x)-f(-1)}{x+1} = \lim_{x\to-1^-} \frac{-x-1}{x+1} = -1;$

$$\lim_{x\to-1^+} \frac{f(x)-f(-1)}{x+1} = \lim_{x\to-1^+} \frac{(-\frac{1}{8}x^4 + \frac{3}{4}x^2 + \frac{3}{8}) - 1}{x+1} = \lim_{x\to-1^+} (-\frac{1}{2}x^3 + \frac{3}{2}x) = -1$$

by l'Hôpital's Rule. Thus $f'(-1) = -1$. Similarly, $f'(1) = 1$. Also, $f'(x) = -1$ for $x < -1$, $f'(x) = g'(x) = -\frac{1}{2}x^3 + \frac{3}{2}x$ for $|x| < 1$ and $f'(x) = 1$ for $x > 1$. Next,

$$\lim_{x\to-1^-} \frac{f'(x)-f'(-1)}{x+1} = \lim_{x\to-1^-} \frac{-1+1}{x+1} = 0$$

and

$$\lim_{x\to-1^+} \frac{f'(x)-f'(-1)}{x+1} = \lim_{x\to-1^+} \frac{-\frac{1}{2}x^3 + \frac{3}{2}x + 1}{x+1} = \lim_{x\to-1^+} (-\frac{3}{2}x^2 + \frac{3}{2}) = 0$$

by l'Hôpital's Rule. Thus $f''(-1) = 0$. Similarly, $f''(1) = 0$. Also, $f''(x) = 0$ for $x < -1$, $f''(x) = g''(x) = -\frac{3}{2}x^2 + \frac{3}{2}$ for $|x| < 1$. Since $\lim_{x\to-1^+} f''(x) = 0 = \lim_{x\to1^-} f''(x)$, it follows that f'' is continuous on $(-\infty, \infty)$. By (5) the curvature of f is also continuous on $(-\infty, \infty)$.

b. Let $g(x) = ax^3 + bx^2 + cx + d$, with $a \neq 0$. Then $g'(x) = 3ax^2 + 2bx + c$ and $g''(x) = 6ax + 2b$. Since $g''(x) = 0$ only for $x = -b/3a$, it follows that

$$\lim_{x\to-1^+} \kappa(x) = \lim_{x\to-1^+} \frac{|g''(x)|}{\left[1 + (g'(x))^2\right]^{3/2}} \neq 0 \quad \text{or} \quad \lim_{x\to1^-} \kappa(x) = \lim_{x\to1^-} \frac{|g''(x)|}{\left[1 + (g'(x))^2\right]^{3/2}} \neq 0.$$

But $\lim_{x\to-1^-} \kappa(x) = 0 = \lim_{x\to1^+} \kappa(x)$ from the definition of f, so κ cannot be continuous at both -1 and 1 simultaneously.

27. $\mathbf{v} = -\sin t\,\mathbf{i} + \cos t\,\mathbf{j} + \mathbf{k}$; $\|\mathbf{v}\| = \sqrt{\sin^2 t + \cos^2 t + 1} = \sqrt{2}$;

$$\mathbf{a} = -\cos t\,\mathbf{i} - \sin t\,\mathbf{j};\ \mathbf{v}\times\mathbf{a} = \begin{vmatrix} \mathbf{i} & \mathbf{j} & \mathbf{k} \\ -\sin t & \cos t & 1 \\ -\cos t & -\sin t & 0 \end{vmatrix} = \sin t\,\mathbf{i} - \cos t\,\mathbf{j} + \mathbf{k};$$

$$\|\mathbf{v}\times\mathbf{a}\| = \sqrt{\sin^2 t + \cos^2 t + 1} = \sqrt{2};\ \kappa = \frac{\|\mathbf{v}\times\mathbf{a}\|}{\|\mathbf{v}\|^3} = \frac{\sqrt{2}}{(\sqrt{2})^3} = \frac{1}{2}$$

28. Since $d^2y/dx^2 = 0$ at any point of inflection, (5) implies that $\kappa = 0$ at any point of inflection.

29. a. By Definition 12.19, $\|d\mathbf{T}/dt\| = \kappa\|d\mathbf{r}/dt\| = \kappa\|\mathbf{v}\|$, so that by (5) of Section 12.5,

$$a_{\mathbf{N}} = \|\mathbf{v}\|\,\|d\mathbf{T}/dt\| = \kappa\,\|\mathbf{v}\|^2\,.$$

b. Since the graph of the sine function has an inflection point at $(\pi, 0)$, Exercise 28 implies that $\kappa = 0$ at $(\pi, 0)$. Thus by part (a), $a_{\mathbf{N}} = 0$ at $(\pi, 0)$.

30. $x = f(\theta)\cos\theta$, $\dfrac{dx}{d\theta} = f'(\theta)\cos\theta - f(\theta)\sin\theta$; $\dfrac{d^2x}{d\theta^2} = f''(\theta)\cos\theta - 2f'(\theta)\sin\theta - f(\theta)\cos\theta$;

$$y = f(\theta)\sin\theta,\ \frac{dy}{d\theta} = f'(\theta)\sin\theta + f(\theta)\cos\theta;\ \frac{d^2y}{d\theta^2} = f''(\theta)\sin\theta + 2f'(\theta)\cos\theta - f(\theta)\sin\theta;$$

$$\kappa = \frac{\left|\dfrac{dx}{d\theta}\dfrac{d^2y}{d\theta^2} - \dfrac{d^2x}{d\theta^2}\dfrac{dy}{d\theta}\right|}{\left[\left(\dfrac{dx}{d\theta}\right)^2 + \left(\dfrac{dy}{d\theta}\right)^2\right]^{3/2}}$$

$$= \frac{|2[f'(\theta)]^2(\cos^2\theta + \sin^2\theta) - f(\theta)f''(\theta)(\sin^2\theta + \cos^2\theta) + [f(\theta)]^2(\sin^2\theta + \cos^2\theta)|}{[(f'(\theta))^2(\cos^2\theta + \sin^2\theta) + (f(\theta))^2(\sin^2\theta + \cos^2\theta)]^{3/2}}$$

$$= \frac{|2[f'(\theta)]^2 - f(\theta)f''(\theta) + [f(\theta)]^2|}{[(f'(\theta))^2 + (f(\theta))^2]^{3/2}}$$

31. By Exercise 30,

$$\kappa(\theta) = \frac{|2(3\cos 3\theta)^2 - \sin 3\theta(-9\sin 3\theta) + \sin^2 3\theta|}{[(3\cos 3\theta)^2 + \sin^2 3\theta]^{3/2}} = \frac{18\cos^2 3\theta + 10\sin^2 3\theta}{(9\cos^2 3\theta + \sin^2 3\theta)^{3/2}} = \frac{8\cos^2 3\theta + 10}{(8\cos^2 3\theta + 1)^{3/2}}.$$

32. By Exercise 30,

$$\kappa(\theta) = \frac{|2\sin^2\theta - (1-\cos\theta)\cos\theta + (1-\cos\theta)^2|}{[\sin^2\theta + (1-\cos\theta)^2]^{3/2}} = \frac{3(1-\cos\theta)}{[2(1-\cos\theta)]^{3/2}} = \frac{3\sqrt{2}}{4(1-\cos\theta)^{1/2}}.$$

33. a. $\theta'(t) = \kappa(t)$; $\mathbf{v} = \cos\theta(t)\,\mathbf{i} + \sin\theta(t)\,\mathbf{j}$; $\|\mathbf{v}\| = \sqrt{\cos^2\theta(t) + \sin^2\theta(t)} = 1$;

$\mathbf{a} = (-\sin\theta(t))\theta'(t)\,\mathbf{i} + (\cos\theta(t))\theta'(t)\,\mathbf{j} = -\kappa(t)\sin\theta(t)\,\mathbf{i} + \kappa(t)\cos\theta(t)\,\mathbf{j}$;

$$\mathbf{v}\times\mathbf{a} = \begin{vmatrix} \mathbf{i} & \mathbf{j} & \mathbf{k} \\ \cos\theta(t) & \sin\theta(t) & 0 \\ -\kappa(t)\sin\theta(t) & \kappa(t)\cos\theta(t) & 0 \end{vmatrix} = \kappa(t)\mathbf{k};$$

$\|\mathbf{v}\times\mathbf{a}\| = \kappa(t)$. Thus the curvature is $\|\mathbf{v}\times\mathbf{a}\| / \|\mathbf{v}\|^3 = \kappa(t)$.

b. Taking $a = 0$ in part (a), we find that $\theta(t) = \int_0^t (1/\sqrt{1-u^2})\,du = \sin^{-1} t$, so that

$$\int_0^t \cos\theta(u)\,du = \int_0^t \cos(\sin^{-1} u)\,du = \int_0^t \sqrt{1-u^2}\,du$$

$$\overset{u=\sin w}{=} \int_0^{\sin^{-1} t} \sqrt{1-\sin^2 w}\,\cos w\,dw = \int_0^{\sin^{-1} t} \cos^2 w\,dw$$

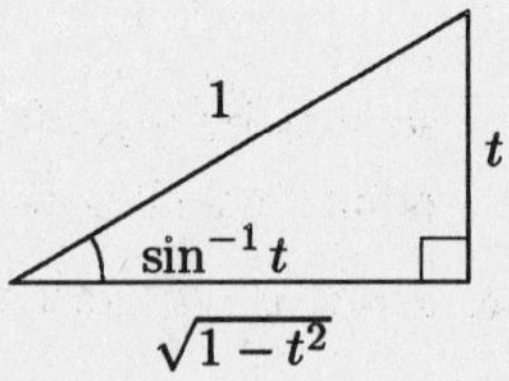

$$= \int_0^{\sin^{-1} t} \left(\frac{1}{2} + \frac{1}{2}\cos 2w\right) dw = \left(\frac{1}{2}w + \frac{1}{4}\sin 2w\right)\Big|_0^{\sin^{-1} t}$$

$$= \frac{1}{2}\sin^{-1} t + \frac{1}{2}\sin(\sin^{-1} t)\cos(\sin^{-1} t) = \frac{1}{2}\sin^{-1} t + \frac{t}{2}\sqrt{1-t^2};$$

$$\int_0^t \sin\theta(u)\,du = \int_0^t \sin(\sin^{-1} u)\,du = \int_0^t u\,du = \frac{1}{2}t^2.$$

Thus the desired parametrization is

$$\mathbf{r}(t) = \left(\frac{1}{2}\sin^{-1} t + \frac{t}{2}\sqrt{1-t^2}\right)\mathbf{i} + \frac{1}{2}t^2\mathbf{j} \quad \text{for} \quad -1 < t < 1.$$

c. Taking $a = 0$ in part (a), we find that $\theta(t) = \int_0^t (1/(1+u^2))\,du = \tan^{-1} t$, so that

$$\int_0^t \cos\theta(u)\,du = \int_0^t \cos(\tan^{-1} u)\,du = \int_0^t \frac{1}{\sqrt{1+u^2}}\,du$$

$$\overset{u=\tan w}{=} \int_0^{\tan^{-1} t} \frac{1}{\sqrt{1+\tan^2 w}} \sec^2 w\,dw = \int_0^{\sin^{-1} t} \sec w\,dw$$

$$= \ln|\sec w + \tan w|\Big|_0^{\tan^{-1} t} = \ln|\sec(\tan^{-1} t) + \tan(\tan^{-1} t)|$$

$$= \ln(t + \sqrt{1+t^2});$$

$$\int_0^t \sin\theta(u)\,du = \int_0^t \sin(\tan^{-1} u)\,du = \int_0^t \frac{u}{\sqrt{1+u^2}}\,du = \sqrt{1+u^2}\Big|_0^t = \sqrt{1+t^2} - 1.$$

Thus the desired parametrization is $\mathbf{r}(t) = \ln(t + \sqrt{1+t^2})\,\mathbf{i} + (\sqrt{1+t^2} - 1)\,\mathbf{j}$.

34. In each of the parametrizations, $y = 0$ for $t < 0$, so that $\kappa(t) = 0$ by (4). Thus $\lim_{t\to 0^-} \kappa(t) = 0$ in each case.

a. $x = t$, $y = t^2$ for $t > 0$. From (4),

$$\kappa(t) = \frac{|(1)(2) - 0(2t)|}{[1^2 + (2t)^2]^{3/2}} = \frac{2}{(1+4t^2)^{3/2}}$$

so that $\lim_{t\to 0^+} \kappa(t) = 2/(1+0)^{3/2} = 2$. Thus the curvature is discontinuous at 0, and hence the function cannot trace out a railroad track.

b. $x = t$, $y = t^{7/3}$ for $t > 0$. From (4),

$$\kappa(t) = \frac{\left|(1)(\frac{28}{9}t^{1/3}) - (0)(\frac{7}{3}t^{4/3})\right|}{[1^2 + (\frac{7}{3}t^{4/3})^2]^{3/2}} = \frac{\frac{28}{9}t^{1/3}}{[1 + \frac{49}{9}t^{8/3}]^{3/2}}$$

so that $\lim_{t\to 0^+} \kappa(t) = 0$. Also

$$\left.\frac{dx}{dt}\right|_{t=0} = 1, \quad \left.\frac{d^2x}{dt^2}\right|_{t=0} = 0 = \left.\frac{dy}{dt}\right|_{t=0} = \left.\frac{d^2y}{dt^2}\right|_{t=0}$$

so that by (4), $\kappa(0) = |1\cdot 0 - 0\cdot 0|/(1^2 + 0^2)^{3/2} = 0$. Thus the curvature is continuous at each point, including at 0, and hence the function could trace out a railroad track.

c. $x = t$, $y = t^3$ for $t > 0$. From (4),

$$\kappa(t) = \frac{|(1)(6t) - (0)(3t^2)|}{[1^2 + (3t^2)^2]^{3/2}} = \frac{6t}{(1+9t^4)^{3/2}}$$

so that $\lim_{t\to 0^+} \kappa(t) = 0$. Also

$$\left.\frac{dx}{dt}\right|_{t=0} = 1, \quad \left.\frac{d^2x}{dt^2}\right|_{t=0} = 0 = \left.\frac{dy}{dt}\right|_{t=0} = \left.\frac{d^2y}{dt^2}\right|_{t=0}$$

so that by (4), $\kappa(0) = |1\cdot 0 - 0\cdot 0|/(1^2 + 0^2)^{3/2} = 0$. Thus the curvature is continuous at each point, including at 0, and hence the function could trace out a railroad track.

35. $a_{\mathbf{T}} = d\|\mathbf{v}\|/dt = (0-81)/(9-0) = -9$. Since $\|\mathbf{v}(0)\| = 81$ and $d\|\mathbf{v}\|/dt = -9$, we have $\|\mathbf{v}\| = 81 - 9t$. Since the radius of the circle is 729, it follows that $\kappa = 1/\rho = \frac{1}{729}$, so that by Exercise 29(a), $a_{\mathbf{N}} = \kappa\|\mathbf{v}\|^2 = \frac{1}{729}(81-9t)^2 = (9-t)^2/9$. Thus $\|\mathbf{a}\| = \sqrt{a_{\mathbf{T}}^2 + a_{\mathbf{N}}^2} = \sqrt{81 + (9-t)^4/81}$.

36. $\mathbf{F} = \mathbf{F}_1 + \mathbf{F}_2 = -2\mathbf{k} - 2\mathbf{j} + 2\sqrt{3}\,\mathbf{k} = -2\mathbf{j} + 2(\sqrt{3}-1)\mathbf{k}$, so that $\mathbf{a} = \mathbf{F}/m = 16\mathbf{F} = -32\mathbf{j} + 32(\sqrt{3}-1)\mathbf{k}$. Since the path of the ball is circular, it follows from Example 3 of Section 12.5 that the normal vector points along the string toward the point of attachment. Thus $\mathbf{N} = \cos(2\pi/3)\,\mathbf{j} + \sin(2\pi/3)\,\mathbf{k} = -\frac{1}{2}\mathbf{j} + (\sqrt{3}/2)\mathbf{k}$. Then $a_{\mathbf{N}} = \mathbf{a}\cdot\mathbf{N} = (-32)(-\frac{1}{2}) + 32(\sqrt{3}-1)\sqrt{3}/2 = 16 + 16(\sqrt{3}-1)\sqrt{3} = 64 - 16\sqrt{3}$. By Exercise 29(a),

$$\|\mathbf{v}\| = \sqrt{a_{\mathbf{N}}/\kappa} = \sqrt{\frac{64-16\sqrt{3}}{1/3}} = 4\sqrt{12 - 3\sqrt{3}} \approx 10.43 \text{ (feet per second).}$$

12.7 Kepler's Laws of Motion

1. a. Since $\mathbf{u}$ is a unit vector, $\mathbf{u}$ and $d\mathbf{u}/dt$ are perpendicular by Corollary 12.11. Thus by (6),

$$p = \|p\mathbf{k}\| = \left\|r^2\left(\mathbf{u} \times \frac{d\mathbf{u}}{dt}\right)\right\| = r^2\,\|\mathbf{u}\|\left\|\frac{d\mathbf{u}}{dt}\right\|\sin\frac{\pi}{2} = r^2\left\|\frac{d\mathbf{u}}{dt}\right\|.$$

   b. Since $dr/dt = 0$ when r is minimum, (5) implies that $d\mathbf{r}/dt = r(d\mathbf{u}/dt)$ when r is minimum.

   c. Since r_0 is the minimum value of r, and v_0 is the corresponding speed, it follows from (a) and (b) that

$$p = r_0^2\left\|\frac{d\mathbf{u}}{dt}\right\| = r_0\left\|r_0\frac{d\mathbf{u}}{dt}\right\| = r_0\left\|\frac{d\mathbf{r}}{dt}\right\| = r_0 v_0.$$

2. a. From (11) and Exercise 1(c) we find that $r = \dfrac{p^2}{GM + w\cos\theta} = \dfrac{r_0^2 v_0^2}{GM + w\cos\theta}$.

   b. From the solution of part (a) we see that r is minimum when $\cos\theta$ is maximum, that is, when $\cos\theta = 1$, or $\theta = 0$. Since the minimum value of r is r_0, we have $r_0 = r_0^2 v_0^2/(GM + w)$, so that $r_0 = (GM + w)/v_0^2$.

   c. If the orbit is elliptical, then by (14), $GM > w$. It then follows from the solution of part (a) that r is maximum when $\cos\theta$ is minimum, that is, when $\cos\theta = -1$, or $\theta = \pi$.

3. If the orbit is circular, then r is constant, so that $r = r_0$. From (13) and Exercise 1(c) we have $r_0^2 = p^4/G^2M^2 = r_0^4 v_0^4/G^2M^2$. Solving for v_0, we find that $v_0 = \sqrt{GM/r_0}$.

4. From Exercise 3, $v_0 = \sqrt{\dfrac{GM}{r_0}} = \sqrt{\dfrac{1.237 \times 10^{12}}{5000}} \approx 15{,}729.0$ (miles per hour).

5. By (23), $T = \sqrt{\dfrac{4\pi^2 a^3}{GM}} = \sqrt{\dfrac{4\pi^2(5000)^3}{1.237 \times 10^{12}}} \approx 1.99733$ (hours).

6. For a circular orbit we have $r = a = r_0$. From (23) we have

$$a = \sqrt[3]{\frac{GMT^2}{4\pi^2}} = \sqrt[3]{\frac{1.237 \times 10^{12} \times (23.9344)^2}{4\pi^2}} \approx 26{,}182.9 \text{ (miles).}$$

Thus the distance of the satellite from the surface of the earth is approximately 26,182.9 − 3960 = 22,222.9 (miles). By Exercise 3, the velocity is given by

$$v_0 = \sqrt{\frac{GM}{r_0}} = \sqrt{\frac{1.237 \times 10^{12}}{26{,}182.9}} \approx 6{,}873.47 \text{ (miles per hour).}$$

7. By (22),

$$c = \sqrt{a^2 - b^2} = \sqrt{\frac{p^4G^2M^2}{(G^2M^2 - w^2)^2} - \frac{p^4}{G^2M^2 - w^2}} = \sqrt{\frac{G^2M^2}{G^2M^2 - w^2} - 1}\,\frac{p^2}{\sqrt{G^2M^2 - w^2}}$$

$$= \frac{w}{\sqrt{G^2M^2 - w^2}}\,\frac{p^2}{\sqrt{G^2M^2 - w^2}} = \frac{wp^2}{G^2M^2 - w^2}.$$

Since c is the distance from the center of the ellipse to either focus and since the center is

$$(-wp^2/(G^2M^2 - w^2), 0)$$

by (21), it follows that one focus is the origin, where the sun is located.

8. By Exercise 2(b), $r = r_0$ when $\theta = 0$. Thus by Exercise 2(a), $r_0 = r_0^2v_0^2/(GM + w)$. Solving for w, we find that $w = r_0v_0^2 - GM$.

9. a. Since $d\mathbf{r}/dt$ is perpendicular to $\mathbf{k}$, (9) implies that

$$\|GM\mathbf{u} + \mathbf{w}_1\| = \left\|\frac{d\mathbf{r}}{dt} \times p\mathbf{k}\right\| = p\left\|\frac{d\mathbf{r}}{dt}\right\| \|\mathbf{k}\| \sin\frac{\pi}{2} = p\left\|\frac{d\mathbf{r}}{dt}\right\|.$$

This $\|d\mathbf{r}/dt\| = (1/p)\|GM\mathbf{u} + \mathbf{w}_1\|$.

b. Since $\mathbf{w}_1 = w\mathbf{i}$ and $\mathbf{u} = \cos\theta\,\mathbf{i} + \sin\theta\,\mathbf{j}$, we have

$$\|GM\mathbf{u} + \mathbf{w}_1\| = \|(GM\cos\theta + w)\mathbf{i} + GM\sin\theta\,\mathbf{j}\|$$

$$= \sqrt{(GM\cos\theta + w)^2 + G^2M^2\sin^2\theta} = \sqrt{G^2M^2 + w^2 + 2GMw\cos\theta}.$$

Thus $\|GM\mathbf{u} + \mathbf{w}_1\|$ is maximum when $\cos\theta = 1$, or $\theta = 0$, and the maximum value is $GM + w$. By Exercises 9(a), 8, and 1(c) we find that the maximum speed is

$$\frac{GM + w}{p} = \frac{r_0v_0^2}{p} = \frac{r_0v_0^2}{r_0v_0} = v_0.$$

10. a. $b = \sqrt{a^2 - c^2} = \sqrt{a^2 - a^2e^2} = a\sqrt{1 - e^2} \approx 92{,}955{,}821\sqrt{1 - (.016732)^2} \approx 92{,}942{,}808$ (miles)
By (20),

$$p = \frac{2ab}{T} \cdot \frac{2(92{,}955{,}821)(92{,}942{,}808)}{24(365.256)} \approx 6.19247 \times 10^{12} \text{ (miles squared per hour).}$$

b. $r_0 = a - c = a - ae = a(1 - e) \approx 92{,}955{,}821(1 - .016732) \approx 91{,}400{,}484$ (miles)

c. By Exercise 1(c) and the preceding results,

$$v_0 = \frac{p}{r_0} \approx \frac{6.19247 \times 10^{12}}{91{,}400{,}484} \approx 67{,}751.0 \text{ (miles per hour).}$$

d. By (23) the mass M of the sun is given by

$$M = \frac{4\pi^2 a^3}{GT^2} \approx \frac{4\pi^2(92{,}955{,}821)^3}{3.024 \times 10^{-12}[24(365.256)]^2} \approx 1.36455 \times 10^{29} \text{ (slugs).}$$

11. a. We have $a - c = r_0 = 100 + 3960 = 4060$ and $2a = 3100 + 100 + 2(3960) = 11{,}120$, so that $a = 5560$ and $c = 5560 - 4060 = 1500$. Thus

$$b = \sqrt{a^2 - c^2} = \sqrt{5560^2 - 1500^2} \approx 5353.84.$$

By equations (20) and (23) we have

$$p = \frac{2\pi ab}{T} = 2\pi ab\sqrt{\frac{GM}{4\pi^2 a^3}} = b\sqrt{\frac{GM}{a}} \approx 5353.84\sqrt{\frac{1.237 \times 10^{12}}{5560}} \approx 7.98570 \times 10^7.$$

By Exercise 1(c),

$$v_0 = \frac{p}{r_0} \approx \frac{7.98570 \times 10^7}{4060} \approx 19{,}669.2 \text{ (miles per hour).}$$

b. By Exercise 8, $w = r_0 v_0^2 - GM \approx 4060(19{,}669.2)^2 - 1.237 \times 10^{12} \approx 3.33722 \times 10^{11}$. At aphelion $\mathbf{u} = -\mathbf{i}$, so that $\|GM\mathbf{u} + \mathbf{w}_1\| = \|-GM\mathbf{i} + w\mathbf{i}\| = GM - w$. Thus, by Exercise 9(a) the minimum velocity is given by

$$\left\|\frac{d\mathbf{r}}{dt}\right\| = \frac{1}{p}\,\|GM\mathbf{u} + \mathbf{w}_1\| = \frac{GM - w}{p}$$

$$\approx \frac{1.237 \times 10^{12} - 3.33722 \times 10^{11}}{7.98570 \times 10^7} \approx 11{,}311.2 \text{ (miles per hour).}$$

12. a. By Exercise 1(c), $p = r_0 v_0 = (100 + 3960)(20{,}000) = 8.12 \times 10^7$, and by Exercise 8, $w = r_0 v_0^2 - GM = (4060)(20{,}000)^2 - 1.237 \times 10^2 = 3.87 \times 10^{11}$. Thus equation (14) becomes

$$[(1.237\times10^{12})^2 - (3.87\times10^{11})^2]x^2 + 2(3.87\times10^{11})(8.12\times10^7)^2 x + (1.237\times10^{12})^2 y^2 = (8.12\times10^7)^4$$

or approximately $(1.38 \times 10^{24})x^2 + (5.10 \times 10^{27})x + (1.53 \times 10^{24})y^2 = 4.35 \times 10^{31}$.

b. By Exercise 2(c), $\cos\theta = -1$ at apogee. Thus by Exercise 2(a) and the values of $r_0 v_0$ and w found in part (a) of this exercise,

$$r = \frac{r_0^2 v_0^2}{GM - w} \approx \frac{(8.12 \times 10^7)^2}{1.237 \times 10^{12} - 3.87 \times 10^{11}} \approx 7756.99$$

at apogee. Thus the distance from apogee to the surface of the earth is approximately $7756.99 - 3960 = 3796.99$ (miles).

c. By (23) and the values of p and w found in part (a) of this exercise,

$$T = \frac{2\pi p^3 GM}{(G^2M^2 - w^2)^{3/2}} \approx \frac{2\pi(8.12 \times 10^7)^3(1.237 \times 10^{12})}{[(1.237 \times 10^{12})^2 - (3.87 \times 10^{11})^2]^{3/2}} \approx 2.56573 \text{ (hours)}.$$

13. Since $GM = w$ for a parabolic orbit, it follows from Exercise 8 that $GM = w = r_0v_0^2 - GM$, so that $v_0 = \sqrt{2GM/r_0}$.

14. $v_0 = \sqrt{2gr_0} = \sqrt{2(7.855 \times 10^4)(100 + 3960)} \approx 25{,}255.2$ (miles per hour).

15. Let F_e be the magnitude of the gravitational force exerted by the earth on the spacecraft, F_m the magnitude of the gravitational force exerted by the moon on the spacecraft, m the mass of the spacecraft, and M_m the mass of the moon. By Newton's Law of Gravitation,

$$\frac{F_e}{F_m} = \frac{GM_em/(240{,}000 - 4080)^2}{GM_mm/(4080)^2} = \frac{(4080)^2}{(M_m/M_e)(235{,}920)^2} \approx \frac{(4080)^2}{(.0123)(235{,}920)^2} \approx .024316.$$

16. Let M_m be the mass of the moon and M_e the mass of the earth. Then

$$GM_m = GM_e \cdot \frac{M_m}{M_e} \approx (1.237 \times 10^{12})(.0123) = 1.52151 \times 10^{10}.$$

a. By Exercise 3, $v_0 = \sqrt{\dfrac{GM_m}{r_0}} \approx \sqrt{\dfrac{1.52151 \times 10^{10}}{1200}} \approx 3560.79$ (miles per hour).

b. By Exercise 13, $v_0 = \sqrt{\dfrac{2GM_m}{r_0}} \approx \sqrt{\dfrac{2(1.52151 \times 10^{10})}{1200}} \approx 5035.72$ (miles per hour).

17. By (23),

$$a^3 = \frac{GMT^2}{4\pi^2} \approx \frac{(1.323 \times 10^{26})(75.6)^2}{4\pi^2},$$

so that $a \approx 2.68 \times 10^9$ (kilometers). Since $2a$ is the length of the major axis, which is the sum of the distance of the closest approach and the distance of farthest retreat of the comet, it follows that the distance of farthest retreat is $2 \times 2.68 \times 10^9 - 5.31 \times 10^7 \approx 5.31 \times 10^9$ kilometers.

18. $\mathbf{L}'(t) = \dfrac{d}{dt}(\mathbf{r} \times m\mathbf{v}) = \dfrac{d}{dt}\left(\mathbf{r} \times m\dfrac{d\mathbf{r}}{dt}\right) = m\dfrac{d}{dt}\left(\mathbf{r} \times \dfrac{d\mathbf{r}}{dt}\right)$. Thus by (3), $\mathbf{L}'(t) = \mathbf{0}$.

19. a. When the planet makes one revolution in a circular orbit about the sun, it travels a distance of $2\pi r$ at a constant speed v, and the length of time required is T. Thus $2\pi r = vT$, or $T = 2\pi r/v$.

b. By (24), (25), and (26) in that order, $\|\mathbf{F}\| = \dfrac{mv^2}{r} = \dfrac{m}{r}\left(\dfrac{4\pi^2r^2}{T^2}\right) = \dfrac{m}{r}\left(\dfrac{4\pi^2r^2}{cr^3}\right) = \dfrac{4\pi^2}{c}\dfrac{m}{r^2}$.

Chapter 12 Review

1.

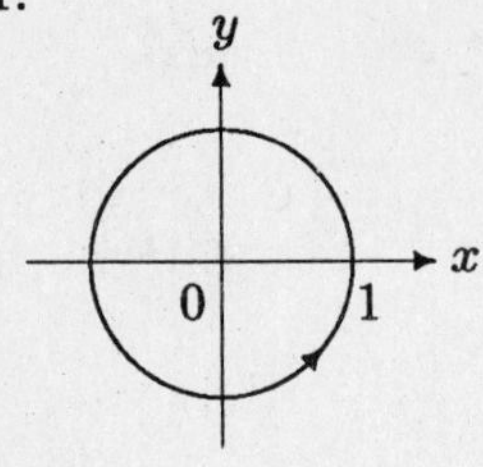

2.

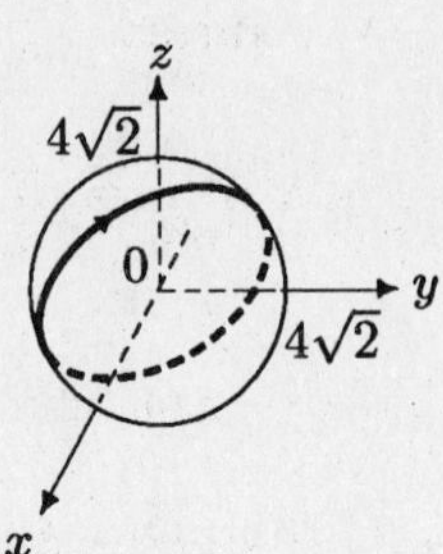

3. $(\mathbf{F}\times\mathbf{G})(t) = \begin{vmatrix} \mathbf{i} & \mathbf{j} & \mathbf{k} \\ t & 1 & 0 \\ 0 & 1 & t \end{vmatrix} = t\mathbf{i} - t^2\mathbf{j} + t\mathbf{k}$

$[(\mathbf{F}\times\mathbf{G})\times\mathbf{H}](t) = \begin{vmatrix} \mathbf{i} & \mathbf{j} & \mathbf{k} \\ t & -t^2 & t \\ 0 & t & 0 \end{vmatrix} = -t^2\mathbf{i} + t^2\mathbf{k}$

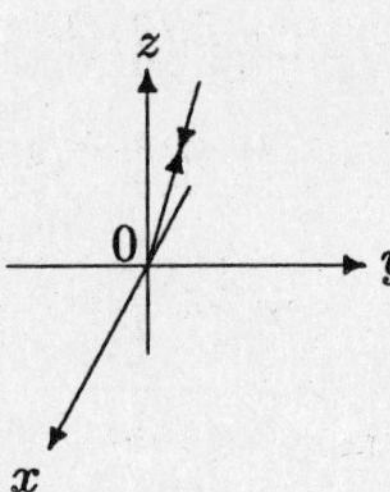

4. a. $(\mathbf{F}\cdot\mathbf{G})(t) = te^t - t^2e^{-t} + 1;$

$(\mathbf{F}\cdot\mathbf{G})'(t) = e^t + te^t + 2te^{-t} - t^2e^{-t} = (1+t)e^t + (2t - t^2)e^{-t}$

b. $(\mathbf{F}\times\mathbf{G})(t) = \begin{vmatrix} \mathbf{i} & \mathbf{j} & \mathbf{k} \\ e^t & t^2 & e^{-t} \\ t & e^{-t} & e^t \end{vmatrix} = (t^2e^t - e^{-2t})\mathbf{i} + (te^{-t} - e^{2t})\mathbf{j} + (1 - t^3)\mathbf{k};$

$(\mathbf{F}\times\mathbf{G})'(t) = (2te^t + t^2e^t + 2e^{-2t})\mathbf{i} + (e^{-t} - te^{-t} - 2e^{2t})\mathbf{j} - 3t^2\mathbf{k}$

5. a. $(\mathbf{F}\cdot\mathbf{G})(t) = t^3$; $(\mathbf{F}\cdot\mathbf{G})'(t) = 3t^2$

b. $(\mathbf{F}\times\mathbf{G})(t) = \begin{vmatrix} \mathbf{i} & \mathbf{j} & \mathbf{k} \\ \frac{1}{t} & t & 0 \\ 0 & t^2 & \frac{-1}{t^2} \end{vmatrix} = \frac{-1}{t}\mathbf{i} + \frac{1}{t^3}\mathbf{j} + t\,\mathbf{k}$; $(\mathbf{F}\times\mathbf{G})'(t) = \frac{1}{t^2}\mathbf{i} - \frac{3}{t^4}\mathbf{j} + \mathbf{k}$

6. $(\mathbf{F}\circ g)'(t) = \mathbf{F}'(g(t))g'(t) = \left[\frac{1}{e^{2t}}\mathbf{i} + (\ln e^{2t} + 1)\mathbf{j} - \frac{1}{e^{2t}}\mathbf{k}\right](2e^{2t}) = 2\mathbf{i} + 2e^{2t}(2t+1)\mathbf{j} - 2\mathbf{k}$

7. $\int\left(\tan 2\pi t\,\mathbf{i} + \sec^2 2\pi t\,\mathbf{j} + \frac{4}{1+t^2}\mathbf{k}\right)dt = \left(\int \tan 2\pi t\,dt\right)\mathbf{i} + \left(\int \sec^2 2\pi t\,dt\right)\mathbf{j} + \left(\int \frac{4}{1+t^2}\,dt\right)\mathbf{k}$

$= -\frac{1}{2\pi}\ln|\cos 2\pi t|\,\mathbf{i} + \frac{1}{2\pi}\tan 2\pi t\,\mathbf{j} + 4\tan^{-1} t\,\mathbf{k} + \mathbf{C}$

8. $\|\mathbf{F}(t)\| = \sqrt{\frac{4t^2}{(1+t^2)^2} + \frac{(1-t^2)^2}{(1+t^2)^2}} = \sqrt{\frac{1+2t^2+t^4}{(1+t^2)^2}} = 1$

so that by Corollary 12.11, $\mathbf{F}(t)\cdot\mathbf{F}'(t) = 0$. Since $\mathbf{F}(t) \neq \mathbf{0}$ for all t, it follows that $\mathbf{F}$ is perpendicular to $\mathbf{F}'$.

9. a. $L = \int_0^{3\pi} \sqrt{(e^t\cos t - e^t\sin t)^2 + (e^t\sin t + e^t\cos t)^2}\,dt = \int_0^{3\pi} e^t\sqrt{2}\,dt = e^t\sqrt{2}\Big|_0^{3\pi} = \sqrt{2}\,(e^{3\pi} - 1)$

b. As in part (a) but with the limits of integration altered,

$$L = \int_{-2\pi}^{1} e^t\sqrt{2}\,dt = e^t\sqrt{2}\Big|_{-2\pi}^{1} = \sqrt{2}\,(e - e^{-2\pi}).$$

10. $\mathbf{r} = e^t\mathbf{i} + \ln(\sec e^t)\mathbf{j}$; $\mathbf{v} = e^t\mathbf{i} + \dfrac{(\sec e^t\ \tan e^t)e^t}{\sec e^t}\mathbf{j} = e^t\mathbf{i} + e^t\tan e^t\,\mathbf{j}$;

$\|\mathbf{v}\| = e^t\sqrt{1+\tan^2 e^t} = e^t|\sec e^t|$; at time 0, $\|\mathbf{v}\| = e^0|\sec e^0| = \sec 1$.

11. $\mathbf{r} = [(\frac{3}{2}t)^{2/3} - 1]\mathbf{i} + \frac{2}{3}[(\frac{3}{2}t)^{2/3} - 1]^{3/2}\mathbf{j}$;

$\mathbf{v} = \frac{2}{3}(\frac{3}{2}t)^{-1/3}(\frac{3}{2})\mathbf{i} + [(\frac{3}{2}t)^{2/3} - 1]^{1/2}(\frac{2}{3})(\frac{3}{2}t)^{-1/3}(\frac{3}{2})\mathbf{j} = (\frac{3}{2}t)^{-1/3}\mathbf{i} + [(\frac{3}{2}t)^{2/3} - 1]^{1/2}(\frac{3}{2}t)^{-1/3}\mathbf{j}$;

$\|\mathbf{v}\| = (\frac{3}{2}t)^{-1/3}\sqrt{1 + [(\frac{3}{2}t)^{2/3} - 1]} = (\frac{3}{2}t)^{-1/3}(\frac{3}{2}t)^{1/3} = 1$

12. $\mathbf{r}(0) = 0\mathbf{i} + 0\mathbf{j} = \mathbf{0}$, so that the Folium of Descartes passes through the origin.

$$\mathbf{r}'(t) = \frac{3(1+t^3) - 3t(3t^2)}{(1+t^3)^2}\mathbf{i} + \frac{6t(1+t^3) - 3t^2(3t^2)}{(1+t^3)^2}\mathbf{j} = \frac{3(1-2t^3)}{(1+t^3)^2}\mathbf{i} + \frac{3t(2-t^3)}{(1+t^3)^2}\mathbf{j}$$

$\mathbf{r}'(0) = 3\mathbf{i}$; $\mathbf{T}(0) = \mathbf{r}'(0)/\|\mathbf{r}'(0)\| = \mathbf{i}$, so that $\mathbf{T}(0)$ is parallel to the x axis.

13. $\mathbf{v} = (3 - 3t^2)\mathbf{i} + 6t\mathbf{j} + (3 + 3t^2)\mathbf{k}$;

$\|\mathbf{v}\| = \sqrt{(3-3t^2)^2 + (6t)^2 + (3+3t^2)} = \sqrt{18 + 36t^2 + 18t^4} = 3\sqrt{2}\,(1+t^2)$;

$\mathbf{a} = -6t\mathbf{i} + 6\mathbf{j} + 6t\mathbf{k}$;

$$\mathbf{v}\times\mathbf{a} = \begin{vmatrix} \mathbf{i} & \mathbf{j} & \mathbf{k} \\ 3-3t^2 & 6t & 3+3t^2 \\ -6t & 6 & 6t \end{vmatrix} = 18(t^2-1)\mathbf{i} - 36t\mathbf{j} + 18(t^2+1)\mathbf{k}$$

$\|\mathbf{v}\times\mathbf{a}\| = 18\sqrt{(t^2-1)^2 + (-2t)^2 + (t^2+1)^2} = 18\sqrt{2t^4 + 4t^2 + 2} = 18\sqrt{2}\,(t^2+1)$;

$$\kappa = \frac{\|\mathbf{v}\times\mathbf{a}\|}{\|\mathbf{v}\|^3} = \frac{18\sqrt{2}\,(t^2+1)}{[3\sqrt{2}\,(1+t^2)]^3} = \frac{1}{3(1+t^2)^2}$$

14. $\mathbf{v} = \mathbf{i} + \sinh t\,\mathbf{j}$; $\|\mathbf{v}\| = \sqrt{1+\sinh^2 t} = \cosh t$; $\mathbf{a} = \cosh t\,\mathbf{j}$; $\mathbf{v}\times\mathbf{a} = \cosh t\,\mathbf{k}$;

$\|\mathbf{v}\times\mathbf{a}\| = \cosh t$; $\kappa = \dfrac{\|\mathbf{v}\times\mathbf{a}\|}{\|\mathbf{v}\|^3} = \dfrac{\cosh t}{\cosh^3 t} = \dfrac{1}{\cosh^2 t}$

15. a. $y = \dfrac{1}{x}$, $\dfrac{dy}{dx} = -\dfrac{1}{x^2}$, $\dfrac{d^2y}{dx^2} = \dfrac{2}{x^3}$; $\kappa = \dfrac{|d^2y/dx^2|}{[1+(dy/dx)^2]^{3/2}} = \dfrac{2/x^3}{(1+1/x^4)^{1/2}} = \dfrac{2x^3}{(x^4+1)^{3/2}}$

b. $\dfrac{d\kappa}{dx} = \dfrac{6x^2(x^4+1)^{3/2} - 2x^3(\frac{3}{2})(x^4+1)^{1/2}(4x^3)}{(x^4+1)^3} = \dfrac{6x^2(1-x^4)}{(x^4+1)^{5/2}}$

Since $d\kappa/dx > 0$ for $x < 1$ and $d\kappa/dx < 0$ for $x > 1$, it follows from (1) of Section 4.6 and the First Derivative Test that κ is maximum for $x = 1$. Thus the maximum value of κ is $\kappa(1) = 2/2^{3/2} = \sqrt{2}/2$.

c. Using the value of κ at $(1,1)$ from part (b), we have $\rho(1) = 1/\kappa(1) = \sqrt{2}$. Thus the radius of curvature at $(1,1)$ is $\sqrt{2}$.

16. a. $\mathbf{r}'(t) = \mathbf{i} + \sqrt{2}\,t^{1/2}\,\mathbf{j} + t\,\mathbf{k}$, and since $\|\mathbf{r}'(t)\| = \sqrt{1 + 2t + t^2} = 1 + t$ for $t > 0$, the curve is smooth.

b. $L = \displaystyle\int_0^1 \|\mathbf{r}'(t)\|\; dt = \int_0^1 (1+t)\,dt = \left(t + \frac{t^2}{2}\right)\Big|_0^1 = \frac{3}{2}$

c. $\mathbf{v}(t) = \mathbf{r}'(t) = \mathbf{i} + \sqrt{2}\,t^{1/2}\,\mathbf{j} + t\mathbf{k}$; $\|\mathbf{v}(t)\| = \|\mathbf{r}'(t)\| = 1 + t$; $\mathbf{a}(t) = \frac{1}{2}\sqrt{2}\,t^{-1/2}\,\mathbf{j} + \mathbf{k}$

d. $a_{\mathbf{T}} = \dfrac{d\,\|\mathbf{v}\|}{dt} = \dfrac{d}{dt}(1+t) = 1$; $a_{\mathbf{N}} = \sqrt{\|\mathbf{a}(t)\|^2 - a_{\mathbf{T}}^2} = \sqrt{\left(\dfrac{1}{2t} + 1\right) - 1} = \dfrac{1}{\sqrt{2t}}$

e. $$\mathbf{v} \times \mathbf{a} = \begin{vmatrix} \mathbf{i} & \mathbf{j} & \mathbf{k} \\ 1 & \sqrt{2}\,t^{1/2} & t \\ 0 & \frac{1}{2}\sqrt{2}\,t^{-1/2} & 1 \end{vmatrix} = \tfrac{1}{2}\sqrt{2}\,t^{1/2}\,\mathbf{i} - \mathbf{j} + \tfrac{1}{2}\sqrt{2}\,t^{-1/2}\,\mathbf{k}$$

Thus $\|\mathbf{v} \times \mathbf{a}\| = \sqrt{\frac{1}{2}t + 1 + \frac{1}{2}t^{-1}} = (1/\sqrt{2})(t^{1/2} + t^{-1/2})$. Since $\|\mathbf{v}\|^3 = (1+t)^3$, it follows that

$$\kappa(t) = \frac{\|\mathbf{v} \times \mathbf{a}\|}{\|\mathbf{v}\|^3} = \frac{(1/\sqrt{2})(t^{1/2} + t^{-1/2})}{(1+t)^3} = \frac{1}{\sqrt{2t}\,(1+t)^2}.$$

17. $\mathbf{v} = e^t(\cos t - \sin t)\mathbf{i} + e^t(\sin t + \cos t)\mathbf{j} + e^t\mathbf{k}$;

$\mathbf{a} = e^t(\cos t - \sin t - \sin t - \cos t)\mathbf{i} + e^t(\sin t + \cos t + \cos t - \sin t)\mathbf{j} + e^t\mathbf{k} = -2e^t \sin t\,\mathbf{i} + 2e^t \cos t\,\mathbf{j} + e^t\,\mathbf{k}$;

$\|\mathbf{v}\| = \sqrt{e^{2t}(\cos t - \sin t)^2 + e^{2t}(\sin t + \cos t)^2 + e^{2t}} = e^t\sqrt{3}$

$$\mathbf{v} \times \mathbf{a} = \begin{vmatrix} \mathbf{i} & \mathbf{j} & \mathbf{k} \\ e^t(\cos t - \sin t) & e^t(\sin t + \cos t) & e^t \\ -2e^t \sin t & 2e^t \cos t & e^t \end{vmatrix} = e^{2t}(\sin t - \cos t)\mathbf{i} - e^{2t}(\sin t + \cos t)\mathbf{j} + 2e^{2t}\mathbf{k};$$

$\|\mathbf{v} \times \mathbf{a}\| = e^{2t}\sqrt{(\sin t - \cos t)^2 + (\sin t + \cos t)^2 + 2^2} = e^{2t}\sqrt{6}$

$\kappa = \dfrac{\|\mathbf{v} \times \mathbf{a}\|}{\|\mathbf{v}\|^3} = \dfrac{e^{2t}\sqrt{6}}{(e^t\sqrt{3})^3} = \dfrac{\sqrt{2}}{3e^t}$; $\rho = \dfrac{1}{\kappa} = \dfrac{3\sqrt{2}\,e^t}{2}$

18. $\mathbf{r}'(t) = 2e^{2t}\mathbf{i} + 2\sqrt{2}\,e^t\mathbf{j} + 2\mathbf{k}$;

$\|\mathbf{r}'(t)\| = \sqrt{(2e^{2t})^2 + (2\sqrt{2}\,e^t)^2 + 2^2} = 2\sqrt{e^{4t} + 2e^{2t} + 1} = 2(e^{2t} + 1)$;

$\mathbf{T}(t) = \dfrac{\mathbf{r}'(t)}{\|\mathbf{r}'(t)\|} = \dfrac{e^{2t}}{e^{2t}+1}\mathbf{i} + \dfrac{\sqrt{2}\,e^t}{e^{2t}+1}\mathbf{j} + \dfrac{1}{e^{2t}+1}\mathbf{k}$;

$$\mathbf{T}'(t) = \frac{2e^{2t}(e^{2t}+1) - e^{2t}(2e^{2t})}{(e^{2t}+1)^2}\,\mathbf{i} + \frac{\sqrt{2}\,e^t(e^{2t}+1) - \sqrt{2}\,e^t(2e^{2t})}{(e^{2t}+1)^2}\,\mathbf{j} - \frac{2e^{2t}}{(e^{2t}+1)^2}\,\mathbf{k}$$

$$= \frac{2e^{2t}}{(e^{2t}+1)^2}\,\mathbf{i} + \frac{\sqrt{2}\,(-e^{3t}+e^t)}{(e^{2t}+1)^2}\,\mathbf{j} - \frac{2e^{2t}}{(e^{2t}+1)^2}\,\mathbf{k};$$

$$\|\mathbf{T}'(t)\| = \frac{e^t}{(e^{2t}+1)^2}\sqrt{(2e^t)^2 + \left(\sqrt{2}\,(-e^{2t}+1)\right)^2 + (-2e^t)^2} = \frac{e^t}{(e^{2t}+1)^2}\sqrt{2e^{4t}+4e^{2t}+2} = \frac{\sqrt{2}\,e^t}{e^{2t}+1};$$

$$\mathbf{N}(t) = \frac{\mathbf{T}'(t)}{\|\mathbf{T}'(t)\|} = \frac{\sqrt{2}\,e^t}{e^{2t}+1}\,\mathbf{i} + \frac{1-e^{2t}}{e^{2t}+1}\,\mathbf{j} - \frac{\sqrt{2}\,e^t}{e^{2t}+1}\,\mathbf{k};$$

$$\kappa(t) = \frac{\|\mathbf{T}'(t)\|}{\|\mathbf{r}'(t)\|} = \frac{\sqrt{2}\,e^t/(e^{2t}+1)}{2(e^{2t}+1)} = \frac{\sqrt{2}\,e^t}{2(e^{2t}+1)^2}$$

19. $\mathbf{r}'(t) = (1-\cos t)\mathbf{i} + \sin t\,\mathbf{j} + 2\cos\frac{t}{2}\,\mathbf{k};$

$$\|\mathbf{r}'(t)\| = \sqrt{(1-\cos t)^2 + \sin^2 t + 4\cos^2\frac{t}{2}} = \sqrt{1 - 2\cos t + \cos^2 t + \sin^2 t + 4\cos^2\frac{t}{2}}$$

$$= \sqrt{2 - 2\cos t + 2 + 2\cos t} = 2;$$

$$\mathbf{T}(t) = \frac{\mathbf{r}'(t)}{\|\mathbf{r}'(t)\|} = \frac{1}{2}(1-\cos t)\mathbf{i} + \frac{1}{2}\sin t\,\mathbf{j} + \cos\frac{t}{2}\,\mathbf{k};$$

$$\mathbf{T}'(t) = \frac{1}{2}\sin t\,\mathbf{i} + \frac{1}{2}\cos t\,\mathbf{j} - \frac{1}{2}\sin\frac{t}{2}\,\mathbf{k};$$

$$\|\mathbf{T}'(t)\| = \frac{1}{2}\sqrt{\sin^2 t + \cos^2 t + \sin^2\frac{t}{2}} = \frac{1}{2}\sqrt{1 + \sin^2\frac{t}{2}} = \frac{1}{2}\sqrt{\frac{3}{2} - \frac{1}{2}\cos t} = \frac{\sqrt{2}}{4}\sqrt{3-\cos t};$$

$$\mathbf{N}(t) = \frac{\mathbf{T}'(t)}{\|\mathbf{T}'(t)\|} = \frac{\sqrt{2}\,\sin t}{\sqrt{3-\cos t}}\,\mathbf{i} + \frac{\sqrt{2}\,\cos t}{\sqrt{3-\cos t}}\,\mathbf{j} - \frac{\sqrt{2}\,\sin(t/2)}{\sqrt{3-\cos t}}\,\mathbf{k};$$

$$\kappa(t) = \frac{\|\mathbf{T}'(t)\|}{\|\mathbf{r}'(t)\|} = \frac{\sqrt{2}}{8}\sqrt{3-\cos t}$$

20. $\mathbf{r}'(t) = \cos t\,\mathbf{i} + \left[-\sin t + \dfrac{(\sec^2(t/2))\frac{1}{2}}{\tan(t/2)}\right]\mathbf{j} = \cos t\,\mathbf{i} + \left(-\sin t + \dfrac{1}{2\sin(t/2)\,\cos(t/2)}\right)\mathbf{j}$

$$= \cos t\,\mathbf{i} + \left(-\sin t + \frac{1}{\sin t}\right)\mathbf{j} = \cos t\,\mathbf{i} + \left(\frac{-\sin^2 t + 1}{\sin t}\right)\mathbf{j} = \cos t\,\mathbf{i} + \frac{\cos^2 t}{\sin t}\,\mathbf{j}$$

$$= \cos t\,\mathbf{i} + \cos t\,\cot t\,\mathbf{j}$$

Thus if $0 < t < \pi$ and $t \neq \pi/2$, then an equation of the line tangent at $\left(\sin t, \cos t + \ln(\tan(t/2))\right)$ is

$$y - \cos t - \ln\left(\tan\frac{t}{2}\right) = \frac{\cos t\,\cot t}{\cos t}(x - \sin t) = (\cot t)(x - \sin t).$$

This line intersects the y axis at the point $(0, y_0)$ for which $y_0 - \cos t - \ln(\tan(t/2)) = (\cot t)(0 - \sin t) = -\cos t$, so that $y_0 = \ln(\tan(t/2))$. Thus the distance from the point $\left(0, \ln(\tan(t/2))\right)$ of intersection with the y axis to the point $\left(\sin t, \cos t + \ln(\tan(t/2))\right)$ is

$$\sqrt{(\sin t - 0)^2 + \left[\cos t + \ln\left(\tan\frac{t}{2}\right) - \ln\left(\tan\frac{t}{2}\right)\right]^2} = \sqrt{\sin^2 t + \cos^2 t} = 1.$$

21. Since $\|\mathbf{v}\| = 1$ and $\mathbf{a} = d\mathbf{v}/dt$, it follows from Corollary 12.11 that $\mathbf{v}\cdot\mathbf{a} = \mathbf{v}\cdot d\mathbf{v}/dt = 0$. Since $\|\mathbf{v}\| = \|\mathbf{a}\| = 1$, we conclude that $\mathbf{v}$ and $\mathbf{a}$ are perpendicular. Thus $\|\mathbf{v}\times\mathbf{a}\| = \|\mathbf{v}\|\,\|\mathbf{a}\|\sin(\pi/2) = 1$, so that $\kappa = \|\mathbf{v}\times\mathbf{a}\|/\|\mathbf{v}\|^3 = 1$.

Cumulative Review(Chapters 1–11)

1. $\lim_{x\to -3^+} \frac{1}{|x-3|} = \frac{1}{6}$ and $\lim_{x\to -3^+} \frac{1}{x+3} = \infty$; $\lim_{x\to -3^+} \left(\frac{1}{x+3} - \frac{1}{|x-3|}\right) = \infty$.

2. $\lim_{x\to 0^+} (\cos x)^{1/x^2} = \lim_{x\to 0^+} e^{(1/x^2)\ln(\cos x)} = e^{\lim_{x\to 0^+}(1/x^2)\ln(\cos x)}$

   By l'Hôpital's Rule,

$$\lim_{x\to 0^+} \frac{\ln(\cos x)}{x^2} = \lim_{x\to 0^+} \frac{(1/\cos x)(-\sin x)}{2x} = \lim_{x\to 0^+} \left(-\frac{1}{2}\right)\left(\frac{1}{\cos x}\right)\left(\frac{\sin x}{x}\right) = \left(-\frac{1}{2}\right)(1)(1) = -\frac{1}{2}.$$

   Thus $\lim_{x\to 0^+} (\cos x)^{1/x^2} = e^{-1/2}$.

3. For $x = 0$, $\lim_{y\to 0} \frac{x^2 - y^3}{x^2 + y^2} = \lim_{y\to 0}\left(-\frac{y^3}{y^2}\right) = \lim_{y\to 0}(-y) = 0$.

   For $x \neq 0$, $\lim_{y\to 0} \frac{x^2 - y^3}{x^2 + y^2} = \frac{x^2 - 0^3}{x^2 + 0^2} = 1$.

4. a. By l'Hôpital's Rule,

$$\lim_{x\to 0} f(x) = \lim_{x\to 0} \frac{\sin x^2}{x} = \lim_{x\to 0} \frac{(\cos x^2)(2x)}{1} = (\cos 0)(0) = 0 = f(0)$$

   so f is continuous at 0.

   b. Let $y = x^2$, so that y approaches 0 when x approaches 0. Then

$$\lim_{x\to 0} \frac{f(x) - f(0)}{x - 0} = \lim_{x\to 0} \frac{(\sin x^2)/x - 0}{x - 0} = \lim_{x\to 0} \frac{\sin x^2}{x^2} = \lim_{y\to 0} \frac{\sin y}{y} = 1.$$

   Consequently f is differentiable at 0, and $f'(0) = 1$.

5. $f'(x) = \dfrac{1}{\sqrt{1 - ((\sin x)/5)^2}}\left(\dfrac{\cos x}{5}\right) = \dfrac{\cos x}{\sqrt{25 - \sin^2 x}}$

6. Differentiating the equation implicitly, we find that $x/2 + (y/8)(dy/dx) = 0$, so $dy/dx = -4x/y$. The tangent at (x, y) has slope 1 if $dy/dx = 1$, which occurs if $y = -4x$. Then $x^2/4 + (-4x)^2/16 = 1$, or $5x^2/x = 1$, so $x = -2\sqrt{5}/5$ or $x = 2\sqrt{5}/5$. If $x = -2\sqrt{5}/5$, then $y = -4(-2\sqrt{5}/5) = 8\sqrt{5}/5$, and if $x = 2\sqrt{5}/5$, then $y = -4(2\sqrt{5}/5) = -8\sqrt{5}/5$. Thus the tangents at $(-2\sqrt{5}/5, 8\sqrt{5}/5)$ and $(2\sqrt{5}/5, -8\sqrt{5}/5)$ both have slope 1.

7. Rewriting the given equation, we obtain $x^3 - 2y^3 = 6x^2 + 6y^2$. By implicit differentiation, $3x^2 - 6y^2(dy/dx) = 12x + 12y(dy/dx)$. The tangent is horizontal at (x, y) provided that $dy/dx = 0$, which means that $3x^2 = 12x$, and thus $x = 0$ or $x = 4$. If $x = 0$, then $y \neq 0$ since $(x^3 - 2y^3)/(x^2 + y^2) = 6$, and therefore the equation $x^3 - 2y^3 = 6x^2 + 6y^2$ becomes $-2y = 6$, so that $y = -3$. If $x = 4$, then the equation becomes $64 - 2y^3 = 96 + 6y^2$, or $y^3 + 3y^2 + 16 = 0$, or $(y + 4)(y^2 - y + 4) = 0$, so $y = -4$. Therefore the tangent line is horizontal at $(0, -3)$ and $(4, -4)$.

8. Let $f(x) = \sqrt{x}$, $a = 64$, and $h = -1$. Then $f'(x) = 1/(2\sqrt{x})$ and thus $\sqrt{63} = f(a+h) \approx f(a) + f'(a)h = \sqrt{64} + [1/(2\sqrt{64})](-1) = 8 - \frac{1}{16} = \frac{127}{16}$.

9. At t hours after noon, the train traveling 60 miles per hour is $100 - 60t$ miles from the junction, and the other train is $120 - 80t$ miles from the junction. If D is the distance between the two trains, then by the Law of Cosines, $D^2 = (120 - 80t)^2 + (100 - 60t)^2 - 2(120 - 80t)(100 - 60t)\cos(\pi/3)$, so by implicit differentiation, we find that

$$2D\frac{dD}{dt} = 2(120 - 80t)(-80) + 2(100 - 60t)(-60) + 80(100 - 60t) + 60(120 - 80t).$$

At 1 p.m., $t = 1$, so $D^2 = 40^2 + 40^2 - 2(40)(40)\frac{1}{2} = 40^2$, and thus $D = 40$. Therefore $80(dD/dt) = 2(40)(-80) + 2(40)(-60) + 80(40) + 60(40)$, which yields $dD/dt = -70$. Thus at 1 p.m. the trains are approaching each other at the rate of 70 miles per hour.

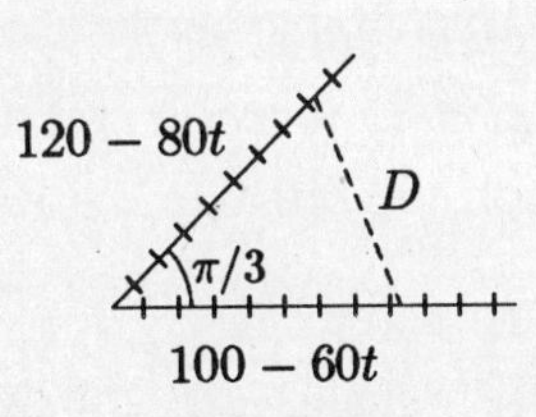

Exercise 9

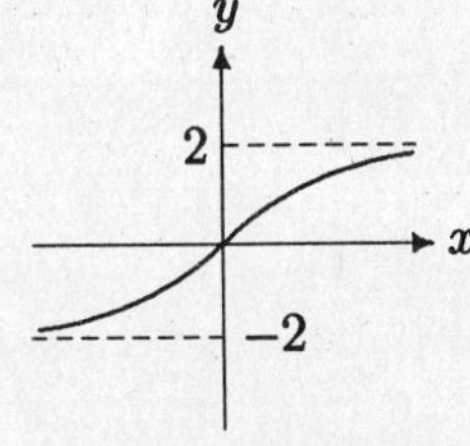

Exercise 10

10. $f'(x) = \dfrac{8}{(x^2 + 4)^{3/2}}$; $f''(x) = \dfrac{-24x}{(x^2 + 4)^{5/2}}$;

increasing on $(-\infty, \infty)$; concave upward on $(-\infty, 0)$ and concave downward on $(0, \infty)$; inflection point is $(0, 0)$; symmetry with respect to the origin.

11. Using the notation in the diagram, we have $2x + y - 3 = 77$, or $y = 80 - 2x$. Thus the area A is given by $A = xy = x(80 - 2x) = 80x - 2x^2$. Therefore $A'(x) = 80 - 4x$, and $A'(x) = 0$ for $x = 20$. Since $A''(x) = -4 < 0$, it follows from (1) in Section 4.6 and the Second Derivative Test that A is maximum for $x = 20$. Then $y = 80 - 2(20) = 40$. Thus the fence should be 20 feet long perpendicular

to the house, and 40 feet long parallel to the house. If the gate is to be placed on one of the sides perpendicular to the house, as in the second diagram, we find that $x + (x - 3) + y = 77$, so that once again $y = 80 - 2x$, which yields the same dimensions as before.

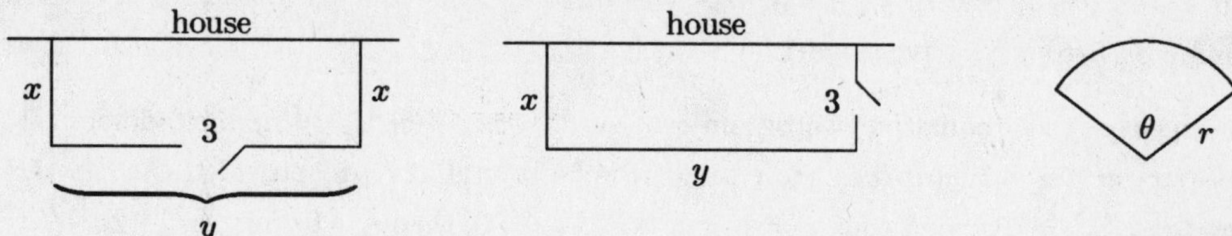

Exercise 11 Exercise 12

12. Let r and θ be as in the diagram. Since the perimeter is 10 centimeters, we have $2r + r\theta = 10$, so $\theta = (10-2r)/r = (10/r) - 2$. Thus the area A is given by $A = \frac{1}{2}r^2\theta = (\frac{1}{2}r^2)(10/r - 2) = 5r - r^2$. Then $A'(r) = 5 - 2r$, and $A'(r) = 0$ for $r = \frac{5}{2}$. Since $A''(r) = -2 < 0$, it follows from (1) in Section 4.6 and the Second Derivative Test that A is maximum for $r = \frac{5}{2}$. The corresponding value of θ is $\frac{10}{5/2} - 2 = 2$.

13. Let $f(t)$ be the amount of the substance remaining after t years. Then $f(t) = f(0)e^{kt}$ for some k, and we need to find the half-life h, which is $-(1/k)\ln 2$. Now by hypothesis, $f(5) = .9f(0)$. Thus $.9f(0) = f(5) = f(0)e^{k5}$, so $e^{5k} = .9$, or $5k = \ln .9$, or $k = \frac{1}{5}\ln .9$. Then $\frac{1}{2}f(0) = f(h) = f(0)e^{kh}$, so $\frac{1}{2} = e^{kh}$, or $kh = \ln\frac{1}{2} = -\ln 2$, or $h = -(1/k)\ln 2 = -5(\ln 2/\ln .9) \approx 32.8941$. Thus the half-life is approximately 32.8941 years.

14. Let $t = \sqrt{x}$, so that $dt = \dfrac{1}{2\sqrt{x}}\,dx$;

$$\int \sqrt{x}\cos\sqrt{x}\,dx = \int (\sqrt{x})^2(\cos\sqrt{x})\frac{1}{\sqrt{x}}\,dx = \int t^2(\cos t)2\,dt = \int 2t^2\cos t\,dt.$$

For $\int 2t^2\cos t\,dt$ we integrate by parts, with $u = 2t^2$, $dv = \cos t\,dt$, $du = 4t\,dt$, and $v = \sin t$; $\int 2t^2\cos t\,dt = 2t^2\sin t - \int 4t\sin t\,dt$. For $\int 4t\sin t\,dt$ we integrate by parts, with $u = 4t$, $dv = \sin t\,dt$, $du = 4\,dt$, and $v = -\cos t$; $\int 4t\sin t\,dt = -4t\cos t + \int 4\cos t\,dt = -4t\cos t + 4\sin t + C$. Thus $\int\sqrt{x}\cos\sqrt{x}\,dx = \int 2t^2\cos t\,dt = 2t^2\sin t + 4t\cos t - 4\sin t + C_1 = 2x\sin\sqrt{x} + 4\sqrt{x}\cos\sqrt{x} - 4\sin\sqrt{x} + C_1$.

15. $\dfrac{x}{(x+2)(x^2+6)} = \dfrac{A}{x+2} + \dfrac{Bx+C}{x^2+6}$; $x = A(x^2+6) + (Bx+C)(x+2)$;

$A + B = 0$, $2B + C = 1$, $6A + 2C = 0$; $A = -\frac{1}{5}$, $B = \frac{1}{5}$, $C = \frac{3}{5}$;

$$\int \frac{x}{(x+2)(x^2+6)}\,dx = \int\left(\frac{-1}{5(x+2)} + \frac{x+3}{5(x^2+6)}\right)dx$$
$$= -\frac{1}{5}\int\frac{1}{x+2}\,dx + \frac{1}{5}\int\frac{x}{x^2+6}\,dx + \frac{3}{5}\int\frac{1}{x^2+6}\,dx$$
$$= -\frac{1}{5}\ln|x+2| + \frac{1}{10}\ln(x^2+6) + \frac{3}{5\sqrt{6}}\tan^{-1}\frac{x}{\sqrt{6}} + C$$

16. Let $u = 3t - 2$, so that $du = 3\,dt$ and $t = \frac{1}{3}(u+2)$;

$$\int 27t^2\sqrt{3t-2}\,dt = \int 27\left[\frac{1}{3}(u+2)\right]^2\sqrt{u}\,\frac{1}{3}\,du = \int (u+2)^2\sqrt{u}\,du = \int (u^{5/2} + 4u^{3/2} + 4u^{1/2})\,du$$

$$= \frac{2}{7}u^{7/2} + \frac{8}{5}u^{5/2} + \frac{8}{3}u^{3/2} + C = \frac{2}{7}(3t-2)^{7/2} + \frac{8}{5}(3t-2)^{5/2} + \frac{8}{3}(3t-2)^{3/2} + C.$$

17. Let $u = \sqrt{x}$, so that $du = \dfrac{1}{2\sqrt{x}}\,dx$. If $x = b$, then $u = \sqrt{b}$, and if $x = \pi^2/4$, then $u = \pi/2$. Thus

$$\int_0^{\pi^2/4} \frac{\cos\sqrt{x}}{\sqrt{x}}\,dx = \lim_{b\to 0+} \int_b^{\pi^2/4} \frac{\cos\sqrt{x}}{\sqrt{x}}\,dx = \lim_{b\to 0+} \int_{\sqrt{b}}^{\pi/2} (\cos u)2\,du$$

$$= \lim_{b\to 0+} 2\int_{\sqrt{b}}^{\pi/2} \cos u\,du = \lim_{b\to 0+} 2\sin u\Big|_{\sqrt{b}}^{\pi/2} = \lim_{b\to 0+} (2 - \sin\sqrt{b}) = 2.$$

Thus the integral converges and its value is 2.

18. The hypotenuse of the cross-sectional triangle at x has length $\sqrt{1-x^2}$, and since the triangle is isosceles and right, each leg has length $(1/\sqrt{2})\sqrt{1-x^2}$. Thus the area $A(x)$ of the triangle is

$$\frac{1}{2}\left(\frac{1}{\sqrt{2}}\sqrt{1-x^2}\right)\left(\frac{1}{\sqrt{2}}\sqrt{1-x^2}\right) = \frac{1}{4}(1-x^2).$$

Therefore

$$V = \int_{-1}^{1} A(x)\,dx = \int_{-1}^{1} \frac{1}{4}(1-x^2)\,dx = \frac{1}{4}\left(x - \frac{1}{3}x^3\right)\Big|_{-1}^{1} = \frac{1}{3}.$$

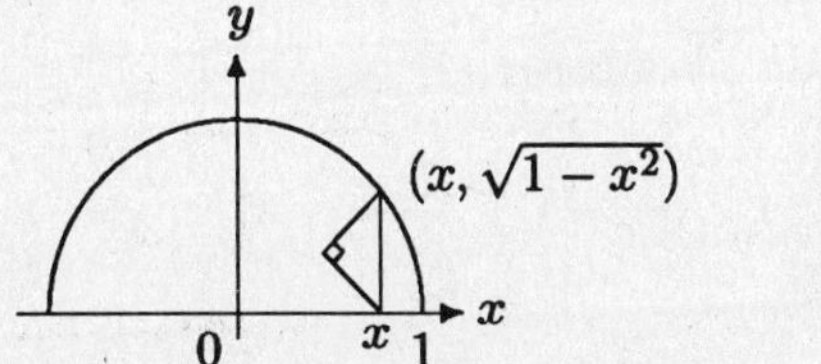

19. From the diagram, $r(x)/(10-x) = \frac{5}{10} = \frac{1}{2}$, so that $r(x) = (10-x)/2$ and therefore $A(x) = \pi[r(x)]^2 = (\pi/4)(10-x)^2$. Since a particle of water x feet from the bottom is to be raised $13 - x$ feet, we find that

$$W = 62.5\int_0^4 (13-x)\left[\frac{\pi}{4}(10-x)^2\right]dx$$

$$= \frac{62.5\pi}{4}\int_0^4 (-x^3 + 33x^2 - 360x + 1300)\,dx$$

$$= \frac{62.5\pi}{4}\left(-\frac{1}{4}x^4 + 11x^3 - 180x^2 + 1300x\right)\Big|_0^4$$

$$= 46{,}250\pi \text{ (foot-pounds)}.$$

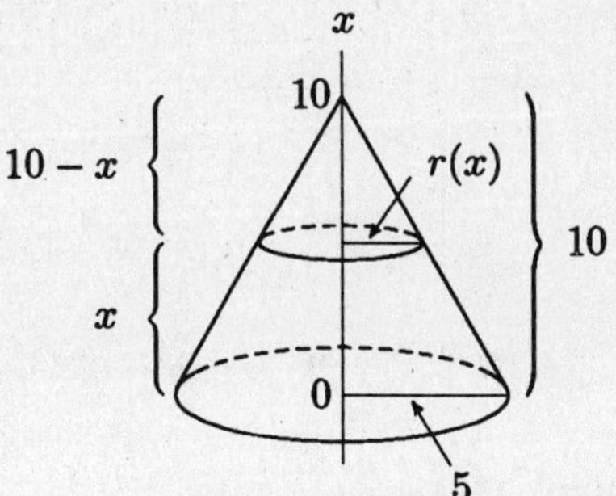

20. $L = \int_1^3 \sqrt{1+[f'(x)]^2}\,dx = \int_1^3 \sqrt{1+\left(\frac{1}{2}x - \frac{1}{2x}\right)^2}\,dx = \int_1^3 \sqrt{\frac{1}{4}x^2 + \frac{1}{2} + \frac{1}{4x^2}}\,dx$

$$= \int_1^3 \sqrt{\left(\frac{1}{2}x + \frac{1}{2x}\right)^2}\,dx = \int_1^3 \left(\frac{1}{2}x + \frac{1}{2x}\right)dx = \left(\frac{1}{4}x^2 + \frac{1}{2}\ln x\right)\Big|_1^3 = 2 + \frac{1}{2}\ln 3$$

21. Since $(-1)^n n/(n+1) > 0$ for n even and $(-1)^n n/(n+1) < 0$ for n odd, the only possible limit is 0. But $\lim_{n\to\infty} |(-1)^n n/(n+1)| = \lim_{n\to\infty} n/(n+1) = 1$, so the sequence cannot approach 0. Thus $\lim_{n\to\infty}(-1)^n n/(n+1)$ does not exist, so the given sequence diverges.

22. The conditions for applying l'Hôpital's Rule twice are met;

$$\lim_{x\to\infty} \frac{\sinh x}{x^2} = \lim_{x\to\infty} \frac{\cosh x}{2x} = \lim_{x\to\infty} \frac{\sinh x}{2} = \infty.$$

Thus $\lim_{x\to\infty}(\sinh n)/n^2 = \infty$, so the given series diverges by the nth term test.

23. $$\lim_{n\to\infty} \frac{\dfrac{(n+1)^{n+1}}{3^{n+1}(n+1)!}}{n^n/(3^n n!)} = \lim_{n\to\infty} \frac{(n+1)^{n+1}}{n^n} \frac{3^n n!}{3^{n+1}(n+1)!} = \lim_{n\to\infty} \frac{(n+1)^{n+1}}{3n^n(n+1)} = \lim_{n\to\infty} \frac{(n+1)^n}{3n^n}$$

$$= \lim_{n\to\infty} \frac{1}{3}\left(1+\frac{1}{n}\right)^n = \frac{e}{3} < 1$$

By the Ratio Test the series converges. Since the terms are positive, the series converges absolutely.

24. For $x \neq 0$, the given series is a geometric series with ratio $(3/4^2)x^2$. Thus the series converges for $\frac{3}{16}x^2 < 1$ and diverges otherwise. Thus the interval of convergence is $(-4/\sqrt{3}, 4/\sqrt{3})$.

25. $f(x) = -\dfrac{2x}{(1+x^2)^2} = \dfrac{d}{dx}\left(\dfrac{1}{1+x^2}\right) = \dfrac{d}{dx}\left(\sum_{n=0}^{\infty}(-1)^n x^{2n}\right) = \sum_{n=1}^{\infty}(-1)^n(2n)x^{2n-1}$

Since

$$\lim_{n\to\infty}\left|\frac{(-1)^{n+1}(2n+2)x^{2n+1}}{(-1)^n(2n)x^{2n-1}}\right| = \lim_{n\to\infty}\frac{(2n+2)}{2n}|x^2| = |x^2|$$

the radius of convergence of the series is 1. For $x = 1$ the series becomes $\sum_{n=1}^{\infty}(-1)^n 2n$, which diverges; for $x = -1$ the series becomes $-\sum_{n=0}^{\infty}(-1)^n(2n)$, which also diverges. Thus the interval of convergence of $\sum_{n=1}^{\infty}(-1)^n(2n)x^{2n-1}$ is $(-1, 1)$.

26. The vector $2\mathbf{i} - 4\mathbf{j} + \mathbf{k}$ is parallel to the given line. Thus $\mathbf{v}$ is to be perpendicular to $\mathbf{a} = 2\mathbf{i} - 4\mathbf{j} + \mathbf{k}$ and $\mathbf{b} = 2\mathbf{i} - 3\mathbf{j} - \mathbf{k}$. Since

$$\begin{vmatrix} \mathbf{i} & \mathbf{j} & \mathbf{k} \\ 2 & -4 & 1 \\ 2 & -3 & -1 \end{vmatrix} = [4-(-3)]\mathbf{i} + [2-(-2)]\mathbf{j} + [-6-(-8)]\mathbf{k} = 7\mathbf{i} + 4\mathbf{j} + 2\mathbf{k}$$

the vector $7\mathbf{i} + 4\mathbf{j} + 2\mathbf{k}$ is perpendicular to $\mathbf{a}$ and $\mathbf{b}$. Since $\|7\mathbf{i} + 4\mathbf{j} + 2\mathbf{k}\| = \sqrt{49+16+4} = \sqrt{69}$, the vector $\mathbf{v} = -(7/\sqrt{69})\mathbf{i} - (4/\sqrt{69})\mathbf{j} - (2/\sqrt{69})\mathbf{k}$ is the unit vector with negative $\mathbf{k}$ component that is perpendicular to $\mathbf{a}$ and $\mathbf{b}$.

27. Let P_1, P_2, and P_3 be the points $(1,-1,2)$, $(2,3,-1)$, and $(0,2,0)$, respectively. Then $\overrightarrow{P_1P_2} = \mathbf{i}+4\mathbf{j}-3\mathbf{k}$ and $\overrightarrow{P_1P_3} = -\mathbf{i}+3\mathbf{j}-2\mathbf{k}$, so that

$$\overrightarrow{P_1P_2} \times \overrightarrow{P_1P_3} = \begin{vmatrix} \mathbf{i} & \mathbf{j} & \mathbf{k} \\ 1 & 4 & -3 \\ -1 & 3 & -2 \end{vmatrix} = [-8-(-9)]\mathbf{i} + [3-(-2)]\mathbf{j} + [3-(-4)]\mathbf{k} = \mathbf{i}+5\mathbf{j}+7\mathbf{k}.$$

Since $\overrightarrow{P_1P_2} \times \overrightarrow{P_1P_3}$ is perpendicular to the plane, and $(1,-1,2)$ lies on the plane, an equation of the plane is $1(x-1)+5(y+1)+7(z-2)=0$, or $x+5y+7z=10$.

Appendix

1. The least upper bound is 1; the greatest lower bound is -1.

2. The least upper bound is 100; the greatest lower bound is $\frac{1}{2}$.

3. The least upper bound is π; the greatest lower bound is 0.

4. The least upper bound is $\sqrt{2}$; the greatest lower bound is -9.9.

5. The least upper bound is 5; the greatest lower bound is 0.

6. The least upper bound is 4; the greatest lower bound is -1.

7. The least upper bound is 1; the greatest lower bound is 0.

8. The least upper bound is $\frac{1}{3}$; the greatest lower bound is $\frac{3}{10}$.

9. Assume that the set S of positive integers has an upper bound. By the Least Upper Bound Axiom S would then have a least upper bound M. For any number n in S, $n+1$ is in S, so that by the definition of M, we have $n+1 \leq M$. Thus $n \leq M-1$, and consequently $M-1$ is an upper bound of S. This contradicts the property of M that M is the least upper bound. Therefore S has no upper bopund.

10. a. Assume that S had an upper bound. By the Least Upper Bound Axiom S would then have a least upper bound M. For any positive number na in S, $(n+1)a$ is in S, so that by the definition of M, we have $na + a = (n+1)a \leq M$. Thus $na \leq M - a$, and it follows that $M - a$ is an upper bound, and since $a > 0$ we deduce that M is not the least upper bound of S. Therefore S has no least upper bound.

    b. By part (a), b is not an upper bound of S, since S has no upper bounds. But this means that there is an element na in S such that $na > b$.

11. Let S be a set that is bounded below, and let T be the set of all numbers of the form $-s$, for s in S. Since S is bounded below, T is bounded above, so by the Least Upper Bound Axiom, there is a least upper bound M for T. If s is in S, then $-s$ is in T, so $-s \leq M$, and thus $s \geq -M$. Consequently $-M$ is a lower bound of S. If N is any lower bound of S, then $-N$ is an upper bound of T, so $-N \geq M$ since M is the least upper bound of T. Therefore $N \leq -M$. Thus $-M$ is the greatest lower bound of S.

12. Since $1/n > 1/(n+1) > 0$ for all n, Theorem A.27 implies that $\{1/n\}_{n=1}^{\infty}$ converges to a number L, and $1/n \geq L \geq 0$ for all n. If $L \neq 0$, then $n \leq 1/L$ for all n, which contradicts Exercise 9. Thus $L = 0$, and therefore $\lim_{n\to\infty} 1/n = 0$.

13. Let $\varepsilon = 1$, and δ be any positive number less than 1. If $x = \delta$ and $y = \frac{1}{2}\delta$, then

$$|x - y| = \frac{1}{2}\delta < \delta, \quad \text{and} \quad \left|\frac{1}{x} - \frac{1}{y}\right| = \left|\frac{1}{\delta} - \frac{2}{\delta}\right| = \frac{1}{\delta} > 1 = \varepsilon.$$

Thus $1/x$ is not uniformly continuous on $(0, 1)$.